Gregory Pederzani
28 Front St.
Nashua, N.H.

INTERNATIONAL SERIES IN PHYSICS

F. K. RICHTMYER, Consulting Editor

ATOMS, MOLECULES AND QUANTA

INTERNATIONAL SERIES IN PHYSICS

F. K. RICHTMYER, *Consulting Editor*

ATOMS, MOLECULES AND QUANTA

BY

ARTHUR EDWARD RUARK, Ph.D.

Professor of Physics at the University of Pittsburgh

AND

HAROLD CLAYTON UREY, Ph.D.

Associate Professor of Chemistry at Columbia University

First Edition
Sixth Impression

McGRAW-HILL BOOK COMPANY, Inc.

NEW YORK AND LONDON

1930

TO MY PARENTS AND GRANDPARENTS

A. E. R.

TO MY MOTHER

H. C. U.

PREFACE

This book was written with a double purpose. It is intended to serve the needs of those who approach the fascinating study of atomic and molecular structure for the first time, and portions of it are therefore written in full and simple style for these newcomers. It also seeks to furnish workers in the field with an up-to-date account of the laws of quantum theory and with a general account of the important experimental researches in the field. Parts of the book have been used by one of us as the basis of lectures to graduate students of chemistry at the Johns Hopkins University.

We believe that the conception of a planetary atom, governed by ordinary mechanics, will remain a useful qualitative tool for many years, whatever the theoretical developments may be. To appreciate the new mechanics and to use it effectively, one must first acquire an understanding of classical mechanics, with which the older quantum dynamics is identical except for the addition of the quantizing conditions. In fact, the classical kinetic and potential energies serve as the starting point for the new quantum mechanics. It is for this reason that the first part of this volume presents the approximate mechanical models of atoms and molecules and copious experimental facts, while the new mechanics is reserved for later chapters.

Orbital models are probably the nearest approach to an adequate description of atomic systems which can be secured in terms of our ordinary mechanical concepts. At the present time an earnest effort is being made to lay aside models and to focus attention on the connections between purely experimental quantities. We are in sympathy with this effort. It helps to emphasize the enduring quality of experimental facts, independent of the form in which they are expressed. On the other hand, a very large number of physicists and chemists do not wish to eliminate models from their methods of thought, nor to rely entirely on mathematical connections between their observations. In the past these models have consisted of particles moving on selected orbits, and now they consist largely of the more useful waves and nodes of the Schrödinger theory. It is only human nature to construct a new picture of a hidden mechanism as soon as an old one is discarded.

Chapters I to XIV inclusive are concerned mainly with the history and the chief experimental facts of the quantum theory and with the progress of atomic and molecular structure prior to the introduction of the new mechanics. Certain auxiliary subjects, such as Hamiltonian dynamics, are also developed early in the book. In these chapters we have sought to attain clarity at any cost. The reader is repeatedly reminded that the theories set forth are only a first approximation to the true state of affairs, and references are given to later chapters where the subject matter is treated by the new mechanics.

In Chaps. XV to XX we develop the fundamental ideas of quantum mechanics, while Chap. XXI gives an account of the wave properties of material bodies. It is a disappointment to us not to have been able to include chapters on quantum phenomena within the nucleus, and on the new statistics. Both of these subjects were omitted for lack of space.

We hope that the reader of this volume will experience a pleasure akin to that which we have enjoyed while recording the wealth of experimental data now available on the structure of the atom and the striking correlation of much of this data by the new mechanics.

A. E. RUARK.
H. C. UREY.

PITTSBURGH, PA.,
NEW YORK, N. Y.,
January, 1930.

ACKNOWLEDGEMENTS

We have received much helpful cooperation in the preparation of this volume. The many reprints which we have received have been a very distinct help and we take this opportunity to express our thanks for them. We have had the cooperation of Dr. Richard Vollrath in the preparation of Chap. XIV. Professor R. T. Birge has been most kind in keeping us informed in regard to his values for the fundamental constants. We are indebted to him and to Prof. R. S. Mulliken for reading Chap. XII. Professor E. E. Witmer has given us valuable suggestions on parts of Chap. XIX, and Prof. G. Breit has kindly reviewed the latter part of the book. Our especial thanks are due to Dr. Ferdinand G. Brickwedde of the Bureau of Standards, who has read the entire manuscript with critical care and has contributed much to its improvement. Dr. R. H. Crist has helped extensively with the reading of proof.

Our wives, Frieda Daum Urey and Grace Hazen Ruark, have aided in the revision of the manuscript and in proofreading, and we wish to acknowledge our indebtedness to them for this help and for constant encouragement throughout the preparation of the volume.

We wish to thank H. D. Babcock, M. S. Blackett, H. Byck, L. F. Curtiss, C. J. Davisson and L. H. Germer, J. S. Foster, F. A. Jenkins, C. C. Kiess, S. Kikuchi, R. M. Langer and Miss G. K. Walker, F. L. Mohler, C. V. Raman, B. B. Weatherby, C. T. R. Wilson, and R. W. Wood, who have kindly supplied us with original photographs. The University of Chicago Press and many authors and publishing houses have kindly granted permission for the reproduction of figures.

We have had the opportunity of seeing in manuscript form the first book of this series, "Quantum Mechanics," by Condon and Morse. It gives greater detail on many wave mechanical problems than is given in this volume and reference is made to it for these problems.

The manuscript was prepared while one author was associated with the Chemistry Department of Johns Hopkins University and he takes this opportunity to express his indebtedness to that university and to his colleagues there, especially Profs. R. W. Wood and K. Herzfeld. The other author began his portion of the work while at the Bureau of Standards; it was continued while he was a member of the Sheffield faculty at Yale, and later at the Mellon Institute. He has profited greatly from friendly discussions with Drs. G. Breit, P. D. Foote, C. C. Kiess, W. F. Meggers, and F. L. Mohler; with his colleagues at Sloane Laboratory, especially Prof. Leigh Page; and with Drs. Nicholas Rashevsky, E. Hutchisson, and J. J. Weigle of the University of Pittsburgh.

CONTENTS

CHAPTER XII

CHAPTER XV

CHAPTER XVI

CHAPTER XVII

CHAPTER XVIII

CHAPTER XIX

CHAPTER XX

CHAPTER XXI

APPENDICES

ATOMS, MOLECULES, AND QUANTA

CHAPTER I

INTRODUCTORY

1. THE NATURE OF ATOMIC THEORY

Once, when the famous Boltzmann had concluded a lecture on atoms and molecules, the equally famous Mach arose and said, in effect, "You do not know that molecules exist." Boltzmann replied, "I *know* that there are molecules." Mach answered, "You *do not*," and so the debate ended. Today, the most ardent lover of modern atomic theory would side with Mach, but he would add, "I know that the hypotheses I use about the nature of the atom and the light it emits give me a deeper understanding of the behavior of gross matter in my experiments. They help me to predict the existence of phenomena which otherwise would remain shrouded in mystery." Today, no physicist worthy of the name would claim that we have certain knowledge of the path of an electron in the atom even in the simplest case, provided we mean by certain knowledge the kind of understanding we gain from our everyday sight and sound perceptions; but he would claim that we possess today a set of very ingenious and reasonable statements and equations dealing with atomic behavior.

If we put our confidence in these fundamental laws of atomic dynamics, they enable us to calculate accurately the observable quantities character-istic of each type of atom or molecule—the frequencies of light it can emit, the relative intensities of the lines in its spectrum, its behavior when it collides with electrons or other atoms, its reaction in the presence of light or X-rays, and its behavior in electric or magnetic fields. These remarks will suffice to make our position clear. Wherever definite statements of a theoretical character are made in this book, the reader must keep in mind the situation we have just outlined.

2. THE PERIODIC SYSTEM AND THE ATOMIC NUMBER

We begin our study of atomic structure by calling attention to certain important regularities in connection with the periodic classification of the elements, as shown in Table 1, which is a modernized version of the Mendeléeff table. Several anomalies in the periodic system were noted

1

by Mendeléeff himself; the eighth group of elements consisting of three groups of triads does not fit well into the table; the rare earths have no satisfactory position in the table at all; and finally, certain elements, A and K, Te and I, Co and Ni, would be placed in the wrong groups if the arrangement according to atomic weight were strictly adhered to. Moreover, the vacant spaces in Group VIII might be taken to indicate the existence of yet undiscovered elements for these positions. All these imperfections, except that of inversion of order, are eliminated in a table suggested by Bagley and improved by Julius Thomsen, and now of especial interest because it is most nearly in accord with the

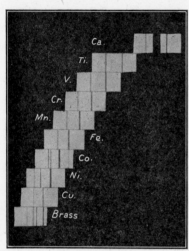

FIG. 1.—The X-ray spectra. (*After Moseley.*)

modern theory of atoms. This table (Chap. IX, Fig. 1) is almost self-explanatory. The successive periods are not of equal length, but consist of 2, 8, 8, 18, 18, 32, and an incomplete period of 6 elements, respectively. Similar elements are joined by lines as far as possible though this cannot be done in all cases. For example, the similar valency of Cu, Ag, and Au, and K, Rb, and Cs cannot be shown. In general, it is less convenient to refer to this table than to the Mendeléeff table; but the former does show that a greater symmetry exists than is indicated by the latter, and gives spaces for the iron, palladium and platinum metals, and also the rare-earth elements. It has no vacant spaces like those in the VIII group of the Mendeléeff arrangement. The inverted order of A and K, Te and I, Co and Ni, when arranged according to increasing atomic weights indicates in itself that atomic weight is not the fundamental property with respect to which the remaining properties are periodic.

The study of the X-ray spectra of the elements by Moseley (1913) showed that the X-ray wave lengths characteristic of the elements vary in a continuous manner from element to element as arranged in the periodic table. Figure 1 shows photographs of the X-ray emission spectra of several elements as given by Moseley. It will be seen that Fe, Co, and Ni have an order fixed by the X-ray spectra exactly the same as that given by a study of their chemical properties and not that required by the order of increasing atomic weights. Now, if the elements are numbered in the order in which they occur in Table 1, that is, in the order determined by their X-ray spectra, the integer belonging to each element is called its "atomic number." The usefulness of such a numeration

TABLE 1.—PERIODIC SYSTEM OF THE ELEMENTS[1]

Period	Group I a	Group I b	Group II a	Group II b	Group III a	Group III b	Group IV a	Group IV b	Group V a	Group V b	Group VI a	Group VI b	Group VII a	Group VII b	Group VIII a	Group VIII b
I	1 H 1.0078															2 He 4.002
II	3 Li 6.940		4 Be 9.02			5 B 10.82		6 C 12.000		7 N 14.008		8 O 16.000		9 F 19.00			10 Ne 20.183
III	11 Na 22.997		12 Mg 24.32			13 Al 26.97		14 Si 28.06		15 P 31.02		16 S 32.06		17 Cl 35.457			18 A 39.94
IV	19 K 39.10		20 Ca 40.07		21 Sc 45.10		22 Ti 47.90		23 V 50.96		24 Cr 52.01		25 Mn 54.93		26 Fe 55.84 27 Co 58.94 28 Ni 58.69	
		29 Cu 63.57		30 Zn 65.38		31 Ga 69.72		32 Ge 72.60		33 As 74.96		34 Se 79.2		35 Br 79.916		36 Kr 82.9
V	37 Rb 85.44		38 Sr 87.63		39 Y 88.92		40 Zr 91.22		41 Cb 93.1		42 Mo 96.0		43		44 Ru 101.7 45 Rh 102.91 46 Pd 106.7	
		47 Ag 107.880		48 Cd 112.41		49 In 114.8		50 Sn 118.70		51 Sb 121.77		52 Te 127.5		53 I 126.932		54 Xe 130.2
VI	55 Cs 132.81		56 Ba 137.36		57 to 71 Rare earths[2]		72 Hf 178.6		73 Ta 181.5		74 W 184.0		75 Re 188.7		76 Os 190.8 77 Ir 193.1 78 Pt 195.23	
		79 Au 197.2		80 Hg 200.61		81 Tl 204.39		82 Pb 207.22		83 Bi 209.00		84 Po 210		85		86 Rn 222
VII	87		88 Ra 225.97		89 Ac		90 Th 232.12		91 Pa		92 U 238.14					

[1] The atomic weights are those given by BAXTER (*J. A. C. S.* **51**, 647 (1929)) except Po.

[2] Rare Earths

| VI 57–71 | 57 La 138.90 | 58 Ce 140.13 | 59 Pr 140.92 | 60 Nd 144.27 | 61 Il ..... | 62 Sm 150.43 | 63 Eu 152.0 | 64 Gd 157.26 | 65 Tb 159.2 | 66 Dy 162.46 | 67 Ho 163.5 | 68 Er 167.64 | 69 Tm 169.4 | 70 Yb 173.6 | 71 Lu 175.0 |

was first pointed out by Rydberg. He numbered the elements beginning
with 3 for hydrogen, assuming that two unknown elements preceded
hydrogen. Moseley's work indicated, and Bohr's theory of atoms has
shown conclusively, that this is not correct. The atomic numbers at
present accepted are those given in Table 1. Rydberg pointed out that
the atomic numbers of the inert gases obey the following regularity.
Consider the series

$$Z = 2(1^2 + 2^2 + 2^2 + 3^2 + 3^2 + 4^2 + \cdots),$$

in which Z is the atomic number. If the series is broken after any
member, we obtain the atomic number of an inert gas. The successive
terms give the number of elements in the periods of the Thomsen periodic
table. The reason for this is explained in Chap. IX.

The simple but all important physical meaning of the atomic number
is this: The element in the Zth place of the periodic table consists of a
positive nucleus endowed with the electric charge $+Ze$, together with
Z electrons, each having the charge $-e$. The quantity $-e$ is called the
electronic charge and is equal to $-4.77 \cdot 10^{-10}$ electrostatic units. And
now we encounter the question of the arrangement and motion of these
parts.

3. VALENCY AND STATIC MODELS OF THE ATOM

It is natural to suppose that valence is connected with the number
of loosely bound electrons in the atom. Thus, one would be inclined to
say that the inert gases represent very stable configurations, that the
alkali metals have one loosely bound electron, the alkaline earths 2, and
so on. On the other hand, if the atom lacks one electron of the number
required to complete an inert gas configuration, we have a monovalent
electronegative element (a halogen), while a divalent electronegative
element would require two electrons to form the inert gas configuration.

In aqueous solution, atoms standing near the inert gases in the periodic
table tend to lose or gain electrons until the positive or negative ions
thus formed resemble the nearest inert gas. Similarly, the stability of
the electron configurations of Ni, Pd, and Pt explains the existence of
monovalent ions of the elements following them, Cu, Ag, and Au.

It is in accord with our present views to assume that the so-called
"outside shell" (or "ring" or "layer") of a rare gas atom (other than
helium) has 8 electrons. In 1904, Abegg emphasized the importance
of the number 8 in the periodic table of the elements. He regarded this
as the number of points on the atom which could be occupied by electrons.
In the same year, Sir J. J. Thomson proposed a theory in which electrons,
assumed to be small compared to the size of an atom, were embedded in a
sphere of uniformly distributed positive electricity of the same order of
magnitude as the atoms themselves. He found that the electrons in
such a sphere, considered as lying in a plane, for simplicity, would arrange

themselves into stable configurations of concentric rings, and noted the application of this to the periodic law.   Though the actual numbers which he secured for the populations of successive rings did not follow the Rydberg formula, at all, this model led him to suggest the above views in regard to valence.   Though he considered only the arrangement of electrons in a plane because of its mathematical simplicity, he recognized of course that the electrons would distribute themselves in concentric shells.   The model is no longer tenable, simply because we have others which are in much better agreement with experimental data. In 1916, G. N. Lewis and Kossel elaborated the views of Abegg and Thomson in regard to the periodic law and polar valencies.   Lewis proposed a static model of the atom and limited his discussion to the first two short periods of 8 atoms, while Kossel accepted a dynamic model proposed by Bohr and also considered the polar valencies of the atoms of the long periods.   Langmuir (1919) extended the Lewis theory to the long periods.

The stability of the organic compounds generally, and the existence of stereoisomers and optical isomers, prejudice chemists in favor of static models of atoms, for it seems difficult to believe that such great stability is underlaid with a highly mobile dynamical system of electrons. Though static models have been somewhat satisfactory for the qualitative explanation of chemical valence, it must be admitted that they have yielded few quantitative results.   The postulates thus far stated for such theories do not lead to exact mathematical treatments and quantitative checks against experimental data.   Thus, they tend to become so flexible that they can explain qualitatively any new results but are quite unable to stimulate new experiments.   Practically all advances have been made by the consideration of dynamical models, and, in particular, the models proposed by Bohr which have held the center of the field from 1913 to 1925.   In the latter year, an improved system of atomic mechanics was introduced, and it became apparent that the Bohr model is a first approximation to the models suggested by the new theory.   We must emphasize, however, that it is an *excellent* approximation—so excellent, in fact, that we shall study it to the exclusion of all others in the first portion of this book, reserving later chapters for consideration of refinements introduced by the new mechanics, which cannot be appreciated without a knowledge of what went before.   Similarly, before we can properly study the Bohr atom we must address ourselves to the currents of thought which brought it into being— the development of the electromagnetic theory of light and the rise of the quantum theory.

4. THE ELECTROMAGNETIC THEORY OF LIGHT.   MOTION WITHIN THE ATOM

In 1864, Maxwell proposed the electromagnetic theory of light, which first showed a relation between light and electromagnetic phenomena in general. The theory showed (see Appendix VIII) that an accelerated electric charge would radiate electromagnetic waves and that these would travel through space with a velocity equal to the ratio of the electromagnetic to the electrostatic units of charge. This ratio is equal to the velocity of light and, immediately, it appeared probable that light consists of such electromagnetic waves. Since that time, a vast amount of experimental evidence has accumulated in favor of the theory as applied to gross matter. In the atomic realm, too, it has had striking triumphs, though we know today that modifications are necessary in this domain.

The simplest electromagnetic model of a light source is the variable electric doublet, composed of two equally and oppositely charged particles

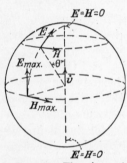

FIG. 2.—Electric and magnetic forces in the field of a doublet.

held together by an elastic force, so that they oscillate with respect to each other with simple harmonic motion. Maxwell's theory of light requires that such an oscillator should emit unifrequentic radiation with the following properties at distances large compared with the size of the oscillator and the wave length. The surface of any individual wave front is very nearly a sphere moving out from the oscillator with a constant velocity. If the poles of the sphere are defined as the points at which it is pierced by the prolongation of the doublet axis (Fig. 2), then the amplitude of the wave is zero at the poles and a maximum at the equator. The wave consists in a variation of electric intensity accompanied by a variation of magnetic intensity; the two intensity vectors are perpendicular to each other and to the direction in which the wave is moving. The electric force is always in the meridian, while the magnetic force is in the direction of the lines of latitude.

Thomson's model of an atom having but one electron imbedded in a sphere of positive electricity of equal charge would behave like such an oscillator. The force acting on the electron would be proportional to its distance from the center of the sphere, provided the positive charge distribution is not altered by the presence of the electron. The electron would oscillate in a straight line through the center of the sphere. If the damping forces are so small that they do not change the motion appreciably during a time which is large compared with the period of an oscillation, then, during such an interval, its distance x from the center at an instant t is

$$x = a \cos 2\pi\omega t. \qquad (1)$$

In the light waves emitted by such an oscillator the electric and magnetic intensities vary according to the law of simple harmonic motion with frequency ω, that is, the light is monochromatic.

If the charges comprising the doublet are not held by a force varying directly as the displacement, the motion will not obey equation (1). For many simple force laws, however, it will be periodic. If the motion of the particle contains the frequencies ω, 2ω, . . . , *i.e.*, a fundamental frequency and its overtones, then the wave of light emitted also contains these frequencies and the spectrum emitted by the doublet would be as shown in Fig. 3. Such a spectrum is obtained from radio circuits. Certain molecules yield a similar spectrum in the infra-red. If several independent frequencies are present in the motion of a charged particle, or, if there are several oscillating charges, the displacement of the electrical center of gravity of the charges, and also the light waves emitted, will contain frequencies of the type,

$$0 \quad \omega \quad 2\omega \quad 3\omega \quad 4\omega$$

FIG. 3.

$$\tau_1\omega_1 + \tau_2\omega_2 + \cdots + \tau_n\omega_n, \tag{2}$$

where ω_1 . . . ω_n are the fundamental frequencies of the system; τ_1 . . . τ_n are any whole numbers from $-\infty$ to $+\infty$, except that they cannot all be zero, and the summation must be positive. Such is the complex spectrum predicted by Maxwell's theory for atoms containing many electrons. One other point is essential; the frequencies depend, in general, on the energy of the vibrating system and so, as the system loses energy, these frequencies change. Thus, instead of a spectrum consisting of only a few frequencies, we should predict, on the basis of electromagnetic theory, that more or less continuous spectra would be emitted. True enough, the light emitted by liquids and solids when heated or when excited to luminosity by radiation, by the impact of electrically charged particles, or in other ways, consists of a continuous range of wave lengths, and the emission of monochromatic light from such bodies is a rather special, but by no means infrequent phenomenon. The emitting atoms in liquids and solids, however, are disturbed by the atoms near them. We should expect that the light from gases and vapors at low pressure would be truly characteristic of isolated atoms. Such light consists of many sharply defined wave lengths (atomic line spectra and molecular band spectra) and the emission of a continuous spectrum is to be considered as an accessory phenomenon. All lines of evidence point to the conclusion that atomic spectra are not of the type which are predicted by classical mechanics and electromagnetics.

5. THE LIMITATIONS OF CLASSICAL MECHANICS AND ELECTRODYNAMICS

We know that gases do not emit light spontaneously, as required by Maxwell's theory for any system of charged particles subject to accelerations. Further, the frequencies emitted when gases are excited electrically do not agree with equation (2), so that the simple model on which this expression is based cannot be correct, in spite of its proved capacity for explaining many of the electromagnetic and optical properties of material media. The interesting generalization which has emerged from the study of spectra is this: To each atom or molecule can be assigned a number of frequencies called "spectral terms," say $\nu_1, \ldots$ $\nu_n \ldots$, such that the actual frequencies ν_{nm} in the light emitted are always *differences* of these terms, that is,

$$\nu_{nm} = \nu_n - \nu_m. \tag{3}$$

This fundamental truth is known as the "Ritz combination principle." Equation (3) suggests at once that the frequencies of the atomic motion are $\nu_1 \ldots$, and that for some reason the frequencies of the radiation are only the beat (or heterodyne) frequencies between them. However, the values of the ν_{nm}'s, obtained experimentally, are radically different from those belonging to any gross physical system of point charges, or rigid charged bodies, which are of the type of equation (2), if the system is multiply periodic. This is a troublesome situation. (The type of system which *does* have such frequencies is discussed in Chap. XV, *ff.*)

The discovery of the negative electron and the proof that it is a constituent of all atoms was followed closely by the discovery of radio-active phenomena. The development of this latter subject, especially in the hands of Rutherford and his associates, showed that the positive charge within an atom is concentrated in a region very small compared to the size of the atom deduced from kinetic gas theory, and indicated that the atom must be similar to a miniature solar system; but, if ordinary mechanics and electrodynamics were applied, such an atom would show an instability at variance with the facts, quite apart from the question of radiation losses. The favorite illustration is a comparison with the way in which the solar system would behave if it were to pass near a cold star. The initial state of the system could be chosen in any way we wish. All mechanical constants of the system would be changed, and their new values would depend on the exact nature of the encounter· But *all evidence indicates that an atom can have only a discrete set of energy values,*

$$E_1, E_2, \cdots E_n \cdots$$

When an atom suffers a collision (see Chaps. III and XIII), it emerges from the encounter with its internal energy equal to some one of these values; and quite generally, whenever a transient disturbance of any kind affects the atom, it is left either in its original state of energy or in one of the other states in the sequence. This is only one illustration of the failure of our customary mechanical ideas in dealing with the atom. More evidence of this failure is obtained from a study of heat capacities at low temperatures, and from the distribution of energy in the black-body spectrum.

6. THE EQUIPARTITION LAW AND HEAT CAPACITIES

According to the kinetic theory of gases, the average kinetic energy of a gas molecule at the absolute temperature T is

$$\overline{\frac{1}{2}m(v_x^2 + v_y^2 + v_z^2)} = \frac{3}{2}\frac{RT}{N} = \frac{3}{2}kT.$$

R is the gas constant per mole; k is Boltzmann's constant—that is, the gas constant for one molecule ($1.37 \cdot 10^{-16}$ ergs per degree Centigrade)—and N is Avogadro's number. The mass of the molecule is m and v_x, v_y, v_z are the components of its velocity in the directions of the X-, Y-, and Z-axes, respectively. The bar over the expression on the left indicates an average value. Thus, the kinetic energy of the molecule is the sum of three terms each representing the kinetic energy contributed by its motion in the direction of one axis. From considerations of symmetry, it is evident that in a body of gas containing many molecules the mean values of these three terms are equal to each other and equal to one third of the total mean kinetic energy, so that

$$\frac{\overline{mv_x^2}}{2} = \frac{\overline{mv_y^2}}{2} = \frac{\overline{mv_z^2}}{2} = \frac{kT}{2},$$

that is, the mean translational kinetic energy is equal to $kT/2$ for each degree of freedom.

The heat capacity of a gas at constant volume is defined to be the rate of increase of the energy of the gas with respect to temperature, i.e., $(\partial E/\partial T)_v$ and this is $Nk/2 = R/2$ per mole for each degree of freedom of the molecule. Then for a gas composed of molecules which do not rotate and whose parts do not vibrate with respect to each other, the heat capacity per mole at constant volume should be $3R/2$. Furthermore, in the case of an ideal gas, the molar heat capacity at constant pressure exceeds that at constant volume by R, and so should be equal to $5R/2$. These deductions have been verified for monatomic gases and, therefore, we may conclude that the motions of the particles which compose the atoms are not affected by temperature to an appreciable extent over the entire range in which measurements have been made, so that there is no contribution to the heat capacity due to changes in the internal energy of the atom. This is strong evidence that internal energy cannot be taken up continuously by the particles of the atom. There is a similar effect in the case of molecules. Let the state of a molecule be defined by giving the values of a number of coordinates $q_1 \ldots q_n$. If the variation of the coordinate q_n gives rise only to a squared term of the form $\frac{1}{2}C_n\dot{q}_n^2$ in the kinetic energy, C_n being independent of q_n, then we can prove by the methods of statistical mechanics that the average of this term is $kT/2$. Thus, the average contribution of such a term to the kinetic energy is the same, regardless of the precise nature of the coordinate q. This is called the "equipartition theorem." Now, the number of degrees of freedom of a molecule is equal to three times the number of particles it contains. Thus, if we count the atoms composing a molecule as particles (disregarding the electrons for the moment), the number of degrees of freedom of a molecule having n atoms is equal to $3n$, and we should expect the heat capacity associated with the kinetic energy of all the particles to be $3nR/2$ per mole. If potential energy is associated with any of these degrees of freedom, which is generally the case, the heat capacity will be greater than $3nR/2$ and, therefore, this is only a minimum value.

This consequence of the law of equipartition of energy is not obeyed even approximately as we can easily see by considering a diatomic gas. The two atoms have six degrees of freedom so that its minimum heat capacity at constant volume should be $3R$. But the ordinary diatomic gases, such as H_2, O_2, N_2, etc., have heat capacities nearly equal to $5R/2$ at ordinary temperatures. Why does this discrepancy exist? Boltzmann assumed that the molecule rotates in space but that the two atoms do not vibrate with respect to each other. There are three degrees of freedom associated with the translation of the molecule as a whole and two degrees associated with its rotation. The energy of such a molecule is entirely kinetic. Its mean energy is therefore $5kT/2$ according to Boltzmann's assumption and the heat capacity $5R/2$ per mole, in agreement with experiment. But it should be noted that ordinary mechanics does not explain the "freezing up" of the vibrational motion.

In the case of solid bodies, each atom has three degrees of freedom and is bound to an equilibrium position by a force which varies directly as the displacement in the case of small vibrations. With this law of force the mean kinetic energy is equal to the mean potential energy, so that the mean total energy will be equal to twice $3kT/2$, and, therefore, the heat capacity per mole will be $3R$ or 5.96 calories. This is Boltzmann's explanation of the law of DuLong and Petit, discovered empirically. This law holds approximately for many substances at ordinary temperatures but it does not hold for the lighter elements, as, for example, carbon where the deviation is large; nor does it hold for any substance at low temperatures.

The law of equipartition of energy requires that the heat capacity be constant for all temperatures, at least if the energy is entirely kinetic. This prediction also is not true, for the heat capacities of all solid bodies approach zero as the temperature approaches absolute zero. Moreover, the heat capacity of hydrogen gas decreases very markedly below room temperatures and reaches a constant value of $3R/2$ at about 35° absolute. Here again, we are dealing with "frozen" degrees of freedom. Another difficulty is that the electrons and nuclei of the individual atoms do not contribute to the specific heat.

The equipartition law is derived by the use of Newton's laws of mechanics and the assumptions of statistical mechanics. We are driven to the same conclusion which was reached in the last paragraph, that classical mechanics cannot be applied without modification to the motions inside atoms and molecules.

7. BLACK-BODY RADIATION

The theory of electromagnetic radiation and the theorem of equipartition of energy lead to the following conclusions in regard to the light energy radiated from a black body, *i.e.*, a body which absorbs all light falling on it, neither reflecting nor transmitting any of this light. If the energy lying between the wave lengths λ and $\lambda + d\lambda$, emitted from unit area of a black body in unit time is $s_\lambda d\lambda$, then we have

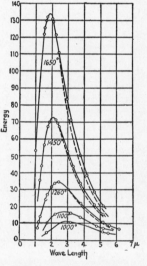

$$s_\lambda d\lambda = \frac{2\pi c k T d\lambda}{\lambda^4}, \qquad (4)$$

c being the velocity of light.

This is the Rayleigh-Jeans radiation law. The energy carried by all wave lengths from 0 to ∞ is

$$s = \int_0^\infty s_\lambda d\lambda = 2\pi c k T \int_0^\infty \lambda^{-4} d\lambda. \qquad (5)$$

At all temperatures, the first equation requires that the energy radiated per unit range of wave length shall approach an infinite value as the wave length decreases (see Chap. III, Sec. **1**, however). The second equation states that the total energy radiated per unit time and unit surface should be infinite. Both conclusions are obviously wrong. Lummer and Pringsheim

Fig. 4.—Wave-length distribution of black-body radiation.

(1897-1899) measured the distribution of energy in black-body radiation with respect to wave length and temperature. Their results are shown graphically in Fig. 4. The most recent measurements are those of Rubens and Michel.[1] The experimental results follow the Rayleigh-Jeans formula at long wave lengths but depart very decidedly from it at shorter wave lengths. Stefan (1879) discovered empirically that the total energy radiated from a black body at temperature T follows the law

$$s = \sigma T^4, \qquad (6)$$

where σ is known as "Stefan's constant." Boltzmann subsequently deduced this law by thermodynamical reasoning. Thus, the total energy emitted must be finite at all temperatures, and not infinite as given by the Rayleigh-Jeans law.

[1] *Berl. Akad. Ber.*, p. 590 (1921).

The invalidity of equation (4) is the crucial phenomenon which led Planck to introduce the quantum theory. The theory deals with processes in which energy is interchanged by atomic systems in definite parcels, instead of continuously, and it takes its name from this circumstance. The word quantum comes from Latin *quantus*, meaning how much. It signifies a fixed amount of any manifold or extent.

8. INTRODUCTION AND EARLY DEVELOPMENT OF QUANTUM THEORY

The above examples of the failure of our usual laws have one common feature—the systems dealt with are in rapid oscillatory motion, and the discrepancies between theory and experiment are pronounced at high frequencies but become small at low frequencies. The laws of electrodynamics can be used with confidence at radio frequencies, but they cannot account for the characteristics of light waves as emitted by atoms and in particular for the absence of overtones in the light. Anomalies of heat capacity behave in the same way. Carbon atoms in diamond vibrate with a high frequency because of their low mass and the firmness with which they are held in place, while copper atoms vibrate with a low frequency because of high mass and weak binding. Finally, the classical formula for black-body radiation holds for low frequencies of light but not for high. This calls attention to a useful condition which the true laws of atomic dynamics must satisfy. They must merge into the older laws when applied to large masses or low frequencies.

The first step toward an appropriate modification of classical theory was a startling hypothesis of Planck (1900) which yielded the correct law of distribution of black-body radiation. He assumed:

1. A black body contains simple harmonic oscillators like those described in Sec. **4**, vibrating with all possible frequencies.

2. The frequency emitted by an oscillator is the same as its motional frequency.

3. The emission (or absorption) occurs during very rapid changes in the amplitude of the oscillator, taking place at intervals. Between these transitions the amplitude remains constant, so that no radiation is emitted or absorbed.

4. An oscillator emitting a given frequency ν can exchange energy with the radiation field only in units called quanta, having the magnitude $h\nu$, where h is a constant named after its discoverer.

Planck's constant $\equiv h = 6.547 \cdot 10^{-27}$ erg seconds.

The essential novelty lies in assumptions (3) and (4). Postponing proofs to Chap. III, we may state that these assumptions lead to the distribution law,

$$s_\lambda = \frac{2\pi c}{\lambda^4} \frac{ch}{\lambda} \frac{1}{e^{\frac{ch}{kT\lambda}} - 1},$$

instead of equation (5), and this gives for the Stefan-Boltzmann law,

$$s = \int s_\lambda d\lambda = \frac{2\pi^5 k^4}{15 c^2 h^3} \cdot T^4.$$

Both equations agree with the facts within the limits of experimental error.

Einstein (1907) used Planck's assumptions to derive an expression for the heat capacity of a solid body, assuming that the oscillators are the atoms composing the body. The mean energy of an atom with three vibrational degrees of freedom is found to be

$$\overline{E} = \frac{3h\nu}{e^{\frac{h\nu}{kT}} - 1},$$

instead of $3kT$ and the heat capacity per mole at constant volume will be

$$C_v = \left(\frac{\partial \overline{E}}{\partial T}\right)_v = 3R\left(\frac{h\nu}{kT}\right)^2 \frac{e^{\frac{h\nu}{kT}}}{\left(e^{\frac{h\nu}{kT}} - 1\right)^2}.$$

The weakness of this theory lies in the assumption that the actual solid body can be represented by a group of oscillators having only *one* frequency, which must be determined by comparison with experimental data. However, when suitable values of ν obtained in this manner are substituted in the formula for C_v, it gives fairly good agreement with the experimental heat capacities for a number of elements. For low frequencies and high temperatures, C_v approaches the value $3R$ required by DuLong and Petit's law, but for high frequencies or low temperatures the heat capacity is lower than $3R$. In 1912, Debye published a theory of the specific heats of the elements in a solid state, in which the atomic oscillators can possess all frequencies up to a certain maximum, ν_{max}.[1] We may note here that the agreement with experiment leaves little to be desired.

Another important step, in the early development of the theory, was Einstein's explanation of the photoelectric effect—the ejection of electrons from a metal surface by light or by X-rays. For a given surface illuminated with monochromatic light of frequency ν, the maximum kinetic energy of the electrons, $mv^2/2$, is not a function of the light intensity, but a straight-line function of the frequency. The physical basis of this was recognized by Einstein, and can be expressed by the equation

$$\frac{mv^2}{2} = h\nu - P.$$

The significance is, that P is the work required to separate the electron from the metal surface. An amount of energy $h\nu$ is expended on each

[1] See for example, EUCKEN, JETTE, and LAMER, "Principles of Physical Chemistry," McGraw-Hill Book Company, Inc., New York (1924).

electron in separating it from the surface and in giving it kinetic energy. This shows that assumption (4) above, originally stated for fictitious linear oscillators, can be extended to cover the present case.

The experimental facts in regard to the photoelectric effect also led Einstein to his hypothesis of unidirectional light quanta, or photons. Experiments showed that the photo-effect begins at once when a weak beam of X-rays falls on a metal plate. However, the energy density in some of the beams actually used was such that several hours would have to elapse before an amount of energy equal to $h\nu$ could fall on the area of one of the atoms in the surface, provided that the energy is spread uniformly over a spherical wave front. To explain this discrepancy, Einstein assumed that the quantum of energy $h\nu$ emitted by a single atom is not propagated in the form of a spherical wave, but passes out in a single direction. There is no lateral spreading and the whole quantum can be absorbed by another atom, however far it may have traveled. The experimental evidence at our command today favors this hypothesis. How it can be reconciled with the usual electrodynamic theory of light will be explained in Chap. III, Sec. **13** and Chap. XV, Sec. **17**. Suffice it to say that the older theory can no longer be interpreted as it was before the advent of the new quantum mechanics. Thus, the photo-effect offers strong support for Planck's original assumptions, and the way was open for a broad and rational extension of those assumptions to atomic systems in general.

9. BOHR'S THEORY OF ATOMIC STRUCTURE

This extension was made by Bohr in 1913, following the work of J. W. Nicholson and of Arthur Haas (Chap. V, Sec. **2**) which was only partially successful. Bohr obtained a quantum theory of the spectrum of atomic hydrogen, based on the following postulates, which are more precisely stated and fully explained in Chap. III;

1. *Atomic systems exist only in a number of stationary states, separated from each other by finite energy differences so that any gain or loss of energy by the atom results in a complete transition from one stationary state to another;*

2. *Radiation emitted or absorbed by the system is monochromatic and its frequency ν_{nm} is determined by the relation*

$$\nu_{nm} = \frac{E_n - E_m}{h},$$

where E_n and E_m are the energies possessed by the atom in the nth and mth states, respectively.

It is an essential feature of Bohr's theory that the frequencies emitted by an atom are generally different from all the frequencies in its motion. And now we must make an assumption as to the laws of motion which govern the particles in the atom when it is not radiating. An excellent first approximation to the true state of affairs is obtained if we assume that these particles can be treated as point-charges and that they obey the ordinary laws of mechanics.　In many problems the nucleus can be considered at rest, while the electrons move around it like planets around a sun.　Let us discuss the hydrogen atom, which is the simplest of all, and the best understood.　It is the first element in the periodic system, and its atomic number Z is 1, that is, the atom has only one electron of charge $-e$ moving around a massive nucleus of charge $+e$.　We assume that the force between the two varies as the inverse square of the distance —the usual law of force in electrostatic problems.　Then the electron can move on an elliptical orbit with the nucleus at one focus of the ellipse, as illustrated in Fig. 4, Chap. IV.　It will suffice for our purpose here if we consider only the circular orbits.

If the electron could move on any orbit whatever, then, in a shift from one orbit to another, the atom could lose any amount of energy whatever, and by the second postulate above, an aggregate of such atoms would emit a continuous spectrum.　Since this is not the case, it is clear that the electron is *not* free to choose any path whatever.　It moves only on certain privileged paths, which obey a set of equations called the quantum conditions, not derivable from the ordinary laws of mechanics or electrodynamics (Chap. III, Sec. 8).　Such is the picture given by Planck and Bohr to explain the inherent stability of the atoms in general; the electrons move in certain configurations picked out by the aid of the quantum conditions, and are said to occupy *quantized orbits*.　When the atom is exposed to a transient disturbance of any kind, it either shifts to another stable quantized state, or returns to its original one after the disturbance has passed.　Results like these lead easily to the impression that natural phenomena are essentially *discontinuous;* but this is a question for philosophy.　The important point for the physicist is that *quantized atoms* show a behavior which is simple compared with what we might expect if classical mechanics were valid.　A world of atoms having the capacity to exist in all states of energy would be a world of chaos!

So strong was the evidence in favor of Bohr's theory, that, until about 1923, it was believed that his concepts would persist unaltered; but from that time on, it became increasingly apparent that the values of the energy predicted by the usual rules for picking out the orbits were not always quite correct.　Now this trouble might have been conquered by simply altering the laws which were used for picking out the actual orbits.　Many such attempts were made, but none were quite acceptable; the subject languished, and many bizarre papers were published.　Then, in 1925, the "way out" was discovered by Heisenberg.　That way consisted of a thorough generalization and revision of the laws of mechanics.　Independently, the same goal was reached by Schrödinger in

1926, following suggestions of de Broglie which date from 1923. The ideas involved are simple enough—illuminating in fact—but to appreciate them fully a more intimate knowledge of Bohr's theory is required. We shall give a more detailed account of the Heisenberg-Schrödinger mechanics beginning with Chap. XV, and the curious reader may turn to it now with profit; but here we begin a detailed study of atomic science as it was before 1925. For years to come, physicists will talk in the language of the Bohr theory and it will suggest new pathways to further knowledge.

REFERENCES

(All the following were published prior to the development of the new mechanics, and therefore are based on Bohr's theory. Texts on the new mechanics are listed at the end of Chap. XV.)

Recent Treatises:

SOMMERFELD, A., "Atombau und Spektrallinien," 4th ed., Vieweg, Braunschweig (1924). This is perhaps the best known reference work on atomic physics. The third edition was translated into English and there is also a French edition.

ANDRADE, E. N. DA C., "The Structure of the Atom," 3rd ed., Bell, London (1927). This is the most comprehensive treatise in English. Mathematics is much less prominent than in Sommerfeld. About one-fourth of the book deals with the study of the nucleus, and the other three-fourths with the extranuclear structure.

DARROW, K. K., "Introduction to Contemporary Physics," D. Van Nostrand Company, Inc., New York (1926). This book, intermediate between an advanced treatise and a popular account, is suitable for the educated layman or for the scientist who wishes to orient himself in the field of atomic structure.

PAULI, W., JR., "Quantentheorie," a part of Vol. 23 of the Geiger-Scheel Handbuch der Physik, Springer, Berlin (1926). This deals with the essential points of the mathematical theory, including both thermodynamic and statistical applications of quantum theory as well as the study of atomic structure proper. Molecular spectra are not discussed.

VAN VLECK, J. H., "Quantum Principles and Line Spectra," *Bull.* 54 of the National Research Council, Publication Office, National Research Council, Washington, D. C. (1926). The same remarks apply to this book as to PAULI's "Handbuch" article. It is out of print, but mimeographed copies can be obtained from the publishers.

REICHE, F., "The Quantum Theory," 2nd ed. E. P. Dutton and Co., New York.

BIRTWISTLE, G., "The Quantum Theory," The Cambridge University Press (1926).

GERLACH, W., "Matter, Electricity, Energy," translated from the 1926 German edition by F. J. FUCHS, D. van Nostrand Co., Inc. New York (1928). This is experimental in attitude and contains very little mathematics.

RICHTMYER, F. K., "Introduction to Modern Physics," McGraw-Hill Book Company, Inc., New York (1928).

Older Treatises:

FOOTE, P. D., and MOHLER, F. L. "The Origin of Spectra," The Chemical Catalog Co., New York (1922). It covers the excitation of spectra and the phenomena of energy interchange between electrons and atoms, principally from an experimental standpoint. It is out of print at present.

SILBERSTEIN, L., "Report on Quantum Theory of Spectra," Adam Hilger, London (1920).

BRILLOUIN, L., "La Theorie des Quanta et l'Atome de Bohr," Blanchard, Paris (1922).

LEWIS, W. C. McC., "Quantum Theory," forming Vol. 3 of "A System of Physical Chemistry," 2nd ed., Longmans Green and Co., New York (1919).

BERTHOUD, "The New Theories of Matter and the Atom," The Macmillan Company (1924).

CRANSTON, "The Structure of Matter," D. van Nostrand Co., Inc. (1924).

CHAPTER II

THE ELEMENTARY CONSTITUENTS OF ATOMS[1]

1. FARADAY'S LAW AND THE ATOMIC NATURE OF ELECTRICITY

In 1833, Faraday announced his laws of electrolysis, which are as follows: (1) The amount of material deposited at either electrode of a cell is proportional to the quantity of electricity which passes; (2) equal amounts of electricity deposit equal numbers of gram equivalents of different substances. In 1874, Stoney gave an address before the British Association, pointing out that it is almost a necessary consequence of this law and the atomic theory of matter that electricity should be atomic in character. Helmholtz emphasized the same fact in his Faraday lecture in 1881. To Stoney we owe the name "electron," which was first applied to the elementary unit of electricity of either sign, but now is limited to the negative unit, while the positive unit of equal magnitude is called a "proton."

Faraday's law does not prove that electricity is discontinuous but it makes this assumption very probable. If electricity is continuous, it seems very strange that all ions must become charged with equal amounts or with amounts which are in the ratio of simple integers. This appearance of simple integral numbers is just as valid an argument for the atomic character of electricity as it was for the atomic theory of matter as shown in the law of multiple proportions, but it is not a proof.

The elementary charge can be calculated from the amount of electricity required to deposit one gram-atom of a substance, the valence, and the number of atoms in a gram-atom. The quantity of electricity required to deposit a gram equivalent from an electrolyte is called the "faraday" and is equal to 96,489 ± 7 absolute coulombs or 9,648.9 ± 0.7 electromagnetic units. So, if e is the elementary unit of electricity and N is the Avogadro or Loschmidt number—the number of molecules in a gram-molecular weight,

$$e = \frac{9,648.9 \pm 0.7}{N} \text{ electromagnetic units.}$$

However, e can be determined directly with greater accuracy than N and so the value of the latter has been calculated by this equation with the use of the experimental value of e.

[1] The more elementary facts about electrons and positive nuclei are so widely known that our account of them will be brief. For detailed accounts we refer the reader to the general references given at the end of the chapter. Much of the present chapter will deal with accurate methods for studying these particles.

We do not know why all electrons have the same charge within the limits of experimental accuracy, but such is generally admitted to be the case. Nor do we know why the charge of the hydrogen nucleus is equal to the electronic charge, but of opposite sign. When these facts are accepted, however, we arrive at a *partial* understanding of the fact that other nuclei have charges which are multiples of the electronic charge. We believe these nuclei are composed of hydrogen nuclei and of electrons, and that the charges of these particles are not altered when they combine.

2. THE ISOLATION OF THE ELECTRON

Sir J. J. Thomson and his collaborators showed that gases become conducting when illuminated by X-rays and that positively and negatively charged ions are formed. Sir Wm. Crookes obtained more detailed information by a study of the conduction of electricity through gases at low pressures (0.01 mm. of mercury). When currents driven by high potentials pass through gases at low pressures, electrons are shot out from the cathode. Under suitable conditions their path through the evacuated space can be followed by the light emitted by the small amount of gas present and appears as a straight bright beam perpendicular to the cathode. They cause many objects on which they fall to phosphoresce and the point where they strike the glass wall of the bulb may be observed in this way. Such beams cast well-defined shadows of objects placed in their paths. They are deflected by electric and magnetic fields and the direction of deflection shows that they carry a negative charge, also they impart a negative charge to insulated objects on which they fall. The electrons of these beams are able to penetrate thin sheets of metal and can be led out of the discharge tube through an aluminium window as Lenard first showed. These fast electrons have the same properties regardless of the metal used for the cathode and of the kind or pressure of gas in the discharge tube. The evidence is conclusive that they are a common constituent of all matter.

3. RADIOACTIVE DISINTEGRATION

Certain elements of high atomic weight, as well as K and Rb, are unstable in the sense that they spontaneously change to elements of lower atomic weight with production of heat and with the emission of alpha, beta, and gamma rays. The alpha rays are helium nuclei, having a mass practically equal to that of the helium atom, and a positive charge, $+2e$. The beta rays are electrons, and the gamma rays are light quanta of very short wave length. These phenomena were first observed by Becquerel, in 1896, in compounds of uranium and are known as the "phenomena of radioactivity." In 1898, the Curies' succeeded in isolating the element radium and following this many new radioactive elements were discovered until at the present time about forty are known.   The average lives of these elements vary from about 10^{-11} seconds in the case of thorium C′ to $2.4 \cdot 10^{10}$ years in the case of thorium.

The study of radioactivity has followed two main courses: first, there has been the study of the disintegration phenomena, the radiations emitted, the laws of transformation of elements, and the properties of the radioactive elements themselves; and second, the radiations emitted have been found to serve as very powerful tools for the investigation of the structure of atoms in general and in fact have furnished the key for the solution of the atomic structure problem.   It is this latter study which is of interest here and, therefore, the properties of the alpha, beta, and gamma rays will be described quite briefly (see general references on radioactivity at end of chapter).

The alpha rays can be recognized experimentally in a number of ways. They ionize gases through which they pass, breaking the molecules up into positively and negatively charged bodies, and thus cause them to become electrically conducting.   For example, an electroscope is discharged if alpha rays pass through the gas about the leaves.   They blacken a photographic plate on which they fall and cause certain substances such as zinc sulfide to fluoresce.   If a fluorescent screen, on which a weak beam of alpha rays is falling, is viewed through a low power microscope, it is possible to observe faint but distinct star-like flashes of light which give very realistic evidence of a rain of particles on the screen.   They are deflected by electric and magnetic fields in the directions to be expected for rapidly moving positively charged particles. The rays are able to pass through a few centimeters of gas at atmospheric pressure, or through very thin foils of light metals before they are completely stopped.   The distance alpha particles penetrate into gases, known as the "range," is very nearly the same for all the particles from one radioactive element, and varies from 2.53 cm. of air at normal temperature and pressure in the case of uranium to 8.17 cm. for thorium C′.   The range varies inversely as the pressure, and directly as the temperature, and, therefore, each alpha particle is stopped by nearly the same number of collisions with molecules of the gas.

A simple calculation shows that a particle moving in a straight line through a gas at standard temperature and pressure would pass through thousands of molecules in each millimeter of its path if the molecules have the radii deduced from kinetic theory.   The alpha particle apparently does pass through molecules in this way and produces thousands of ions in each millimeter of path.   C. T. R. Wilson[1] used this fact in devising a method for making the paths of alpha particles visible.   If a gas saturated with water vapor is suddenly expanded, it becomes supersaturated.   Wilson's method consists in rapidly expanding, by means

[1] *Proc. Roy. Soc.* **87**, 277 (1912).

of a piston, air saturated with water vapor and at the same time shooting
alpha particles through it (Fig. 1).   The ions produced by each particle

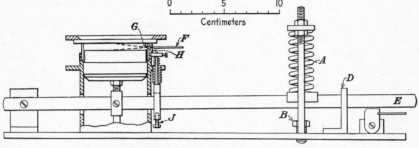

Fig. 1.—A Wilson cloud-track apparatus used by Blackett.

serve as nuclei for the condensation of water vapor from the supersaturated gas and, under proper illumination, an easily visible white line

(a)

(b)   (c)

Fig. 2.— (a) Paths of electrons ejected from atoms by X-rays.   (*After Wilson, Proc.
Roy. Soc.* **104**, 1 (1923).)   (b) α-ray tracks in helium.   (*After Blackett, Proc. Roy. Soc.* **107**,
360 (1924).)   The angle between the forked tracks is very close to 90°.   (c) α-ray tracks in
oxygen.   (*After Blackett, Proc. Roy. Soc.* **103**, 78 (1923).)

appears which can be photographed (Fig. 2).   For the most part, the
tracks are straight lines of nearly constant length, but, sometimes,
near the end of the track, a sharp break appears, just as though the

particle had collided with a heavy body. In a few cases the deflection is larger than 90°. Further, the track is sometimes branched, indicating that the atom struck has recoiled with enough energy to produce ions on its own account. Deflections of alpha particles through large angles are also observed when they fall on thin metal foil. Whatever be the cause of the deflection, the phenomenon is termed "scattering." The energy of the particle is used up in ionizing the molecules and it is finally neutralized by picking up electrons. The number of pairs of ions produced in a centimeter of path varies greatly with the velocity. In air, at 15°C. and 760 mm. pressure, the maximum value of about 71,000 ion pairs per centimeter is reached when the alpha particle has a velocity of about $8.3 \cdot 10^8$ cm. per second.

The beta rays also ionize gases, though not so intensely as alpha particles, affect the photographic plate, and cause substances on which they impinge to fluoresce. They are deflected by electric and magnetic fields in the directions to be expected for negatively charged particles. They can pass through thick layers of gases and through thin metal foils.

While alpha particles have paths of very nearly the same length so that a very sharp range is found, the absorption of beta rays by matter follows an exponential law just as in the case of cathode particles (Chap. II, Sec. 15) and they are half absorbed by a few hundredths cm. of aluminium. The paths of beta rays can be made visible by Wilson's method and are found to be much more tortuous than alpha-ray tracks and to have fewer droplets showing that fewer ions are formed. Beta rays are in fact identical with cathode particles except for their higher velocities, the fastest known being those of thorium C with a velocity equal to 0.999 times the velocity of light. For convenience we shall refer to either beta rays or cathode rays as fast electrons.

The gamma rays are the most penetrating radiations emitted by radioactive substances. They pass through long distances in air and even through many centimeters of metals such as lead. They are weak ionizers of gases, and affect the photographic plate. They are undeflected by electric and magnetic fields and generally behave like light of short wave length.

4. MOTION OF A CHARGED PARTICLE IN ELECTRIC AND MAGNETIC FIELDS

In order to investigate directly the charge, mass, and velocity of electrons and positive ions, we observe their motions through electric and magnetic fields combined in suitable ways. By definition, a particle with charge e in a steady electric field of intensity $\mathbf{E}$ is acted on by a force

$$\mathbf{f} = \mathbf{E}e,$$

so that **E** is the force per unit charge. Its potential energy at some point Q in the field is

$$V = -\int_\infty^Q f_s ds = -e\int_\infty^Q E_s ds = e\Phi.$$

Here the integral is taken along any path from ∞ to Q, and f_s is the component of **f** parallel to ds. Φ is the electrostatic potential at the point Q—the potential energy per unit charge.

The equation of energy for a charged particle moving in an electric field is

$$\frac{mv^2}{2} + \Phi e = E,$$

where E is the total energy.   Suppose the particle is initially at rest at a point where its potential energy is $\Phi_1 e$.   If it moves under the action of electric forces to another point with potential Φ_2, its kinetic energy at the latter point is

$$\frac{mv^2}{2} = e(\Phi_1 - \Phi_2). \tag{1}$$

Between two parallel condenser plates charged to a potential difference Φ, the uniform electric field has intensity $Y = \Phi/d$, if their distance apart is d, where d is very small compared to the dimensions of the plates.   Figure 3 shows such a pair of condenser plates, A and B.   Let a charge moving with a velocity v along the X-axis, parallel to the plates, enter the field at O, which is taken as the origin, and be deflected as indicated.   No force acts on the particle parallel to the X-axis, so its x-component of velocity remains unchanged,

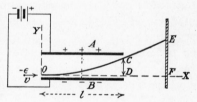

Fig. 3.—Deflection of a negative charge in an electric field.

and the distance traveled by the particle in time t is such that

$$x = vt. \tag{2}$$

The equation of motion for the y-coordinate is

$$\frac{md^2y}{dt^2} = Ye,$$

so

$$\frac{mdy}{dt} = Yet, \quad my = \frac{Yet^2}{2}, \tag{3}$$

the constants of integration being zero, since y and dy/dt are both zero at $t = 0$.   The elimination of t from equations (2) and (3) gives the equation of the path, which is parabolic between O and C.

$$y = Y\left(\frac{e}{m}\right)\frac{x^2}{2v^2}. \tag{4}$$

Beyond C the path is again a straight line CE with the equation

$$y = Y\left(\frac{e}{m}\right)\frac{l^2}{2v^2} + \left(\frac{Ye}{mv^2}\right)(x - l)l. \tag{4a}$$

At E, the particle can be detected by methods soon to be described, so the values of y and x for one point on the path are known. If v is known, all the quantities in equation $(4a)$, except e/m, can be measured and thus the value of e/m can be determined.

We now show how v can be determined from the deflection in a uniform magnetic field. The force exerted on the particle by a magnetic field **H** is

$$f = evH \sin (\mathbf{v}, \mathbf{H}) \tag{5}$$

where $\sin (\mathbf{v}, \mathbf{H})$ is the sine of the angle between **v** and **H**. In particular, if the particle moves at right angles to the lines of force, the force is Hev. It is always perpendicular to **v** and to **H**, and is directed in the sense in which a right-handed screw moves if so rotated that it brings the velocity vector **v** into coincidence with **H** (Fig. 4). Therefore, the magnetic force can alter the direction of the velocity but not its magnitude. If **v** and **H** are perpendicular to each other, the particle will move in a circle with a radius determined by the condition that the centrifugal force and the force exerted by the field shall be equal,

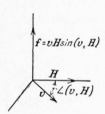

Fig. 4.—The force acting on a positive charge moving in a magnetic field.

$$Hev = \frac{mv^2}{r}. \tag{6}$$

Both H and r can be measured, giving us the value of e/mv. An experiment with the same particles, having the same initial velocity, in an electric field will yield e/mv^2, and so the values of both v and e/m can be obtained. By combining the effects of electric and magnetic fields upon moving charged particles, it is possible to determine the ratio e/m. If the force, due to a uniform electric field, is balanced by magnetic force, the particle moves in a straight line, as though both fields were absent, and the forces obey the equation,

$$Ye = Hev, \tag{7}$$

so that $v = Y/H$. The experimental method is to place the condenser plates of Fig. 3 between the poles of an electromagnet in such a way that the direction of **H** is perpendicular to **Y** and **v**, that is, perpendicular to the plane of the page. The values of Y and H are so chosen that they cause the particle to move along OX when both fields are acting; this gives us v. Now the electric field is removed, and the particle moves on a circle of radius r. Substituting v in equation (6), we have

$$\frac{e}{m} = \frac{Y}{H^2 r}. \tag{8}$$

The quantities on the right can all be measured. Again, the deflection in the electric field alone may be measured, and substituting $v = Y/H$ in equations (4) or (4a), we obtain e/m independently.

It is difficult to obtain high precision in measurements of this kind. The electric field is not uniform near the edges of the condenser plates, nor is the magnetic field near the edges of the pole pieces. The equations given are only approximate for these reasons and it is difficult to derive the equations for any given apparatus, or to determine them experimentally. Deflection experiments give values of e/m for cathode rays varying from about 1.71 to $1.85 \cdot 10^7$ e.m.u per gram. (e.m.u. means electromagnetic units.) The most probable value lies near $1.76 \cdot 10^7$.

5. THE DEPENDENCE OF e/m ON VELOCITY

Simple deflection experiments on beta particles give results agreeing closely enough with the above figures to leave little doubt that they are identical with cathode particles except for their higher velocities. However, some indications that the ratio e/m decreases with the velocity were secured from such determinations. The Lorentz theory of the electron, and also the theory of relativity, requires that the mass m of the electron shall vary with its velocity according to the equation,

$$m = \frac{m_0}{(1 - \beta^2)^{\frac{1}{2}}}, \quad \beta = \frac{v}{c}, \tag{9}$$

where m_0 is the mass of the electron at rest and c is the velocity of light. The mass m differs very slightly from m_0 except for values of v approaching the velocity of light, so that we are practically limited to the use of high-speed electrons in testing equation (9). Experiments by Kaufmann[1] showed definitely that e/m does vary with the velocity of the particles and that it probably approaches zero as v approaches c. His experimental method, due originally to J. J. Thomson, is shown diagrammatically in Fig. 5. S and N are the poles of an electromagnet and A and B the plates of a condenser arranged so that they can be charged to different potentials by a battery. A narrow beam of beta particles is aimed downward, normal to the paper at the point P. Below, a photographic plate is placed perpendicular to the direction of the beam of beta particles. The magnetic field displaces the particles toward the right while the electric field causes them to be displaced toward the positive plate. Assuming that the ratio e/m is constant, we can show from equations (4) and (6) that for small displacements the deflection in the Y-direction due to the electric field is

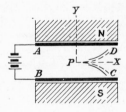

FIG. 5.—Kaufmann's apparatus for determining e/m.

$$y = \frac{a^2}{2} \frac{eY}{mv^2},$$

[1] *Ann. Physik.* **19,** 487 (1906). Final results.

where a is the length of the condenser plates, and that in the x direction, due to the magnetic field is, if x is small,

$$x = \frac{b^2}{2}\frac{eH}{mv},$$

where b is the length of path between the pole pieces. The particles fly some distance in a field-free space and then hit a photographic plate. The displacement y at the photographic plate is proportional to (e/m) (Y/v^2) and the displacement, x, to $(e/m)(H/v)$. Eliminating the velocity we have,

$$y = K\frac{Y}{H^2}\left(\frac{m}{e}\right)x^2 \tag{10}$$

where K is a constant depending on a, b, and other dimensions of the apparatus. Therefore, the particles fall at various points on a parabola through P as shown by the dotted line PD, depending on their velocities. Reversing the direction of the electric field causes them to fall along PC. Kaufmann found that the photographic plate was darkened along the solid curves. The shape of these curves indicates that the mass increases as the velocity increases and that it approaches a very great value as the velocity approaches that of light, but the experiment did not determine the exact way in which the mass changes with velocity.

The method of compensated rays, used by Bestelmeyer,[1] Bucherer[2] and others, is illustrated by Fig. 6. It makes use of electric and magnetic fields, perpendicular to each other and to the direction of the beam of electrons. The uniform magnetic field extends over the condenser plates and the space about them, and has a direction normal to the plane of the paper. Photoelectrons from the plate Pt, entering at the left with a velocity $v = Y/H$, move in a straight line through the region of the condenser plates C but electrons of all other velocities are deflected to one plate or the other. The emerging beam is then deflected by the magnetic field alone and follows one of the curves a or a'. The radius of this circular path is

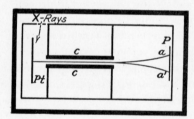

Fig. 6.—Compensated ray apparatus for measuring e/m.

$$r = \left(\frac{m}{e}\right)\frac{Y}{H^2}.$$

With the aid of a photographic plate P, r is determined, and so we obtain m/e. Knowing v and m/e, we can use equation (9) to calculate e/m_0. If equation (9) is correct, this should be a constant, whatever be the value of v. Table 1 shows the results of a number of Bucherer's deter-

[1] *Ann. Physik*, **22**, 429 (1907).
[2] *Ann. Physik*, **28**, 513 (1909).

minations of e/m_0. The constancy of this ratio is commonly interpreted as favorable to equation (9). It is desirable, however, that new determinations be made, using all the resources of modern high vacuum technique, because of the importance of equation (9).

TABLE 1

v/c	e/m_0 in Electromagnetic Units
0.3173	1.752×10^7
0.3787	1.761
0.4281	1.760
0.5154	1.763
0.6870	1.767

The ratio of charge to mass for the hydrogen ion is 9,580 e.m.u. per gram, from electrochemical data, so that the e/m ratio for the electron is about 1,847 times as great as that for the hydrogen ion.

In 1901, Rutherford attempted to determine the e/m ratio of alpha particles from their deflection in electric and magnetic fields and showed that they were deflected as though they carried a positive charge. Later, he deposited the radioactive elements resulting from the decay of radon on a fine wire; the active material is radium C. Since the alpha particles from any sample of radium C have the same velocities, masses, and charges, the effects of electric and magnetic fields were studied separately. The value of e/m is $4.82 \cdot 10^3$, about one-half the value for hydrogen. The discovery by Ramsay and Soddy that helium is produced when radium disintegrates showed that the alpha particle is a doubly charged helium atom, that is, simply a helium nucleus with an atomic weight of 4. We know today that these particles are emitted by the nucleus of the radium atom (atomic weight 226) when it disintegrates, leaving behind the nucleus of an atom of weight 222.

6. THE ELEMENTARY UNIT OF CHARGE

The first attempts to determine the elementary unit of charge e, following Stoney's estimate of $0.3 \cdot 10^{-10}$ e.s.u., were made by Townsend, J. J. Thomson, and H. A. Wilson. The methods of Townsend and Thomson are essentially the same. A charged cloud of water droplets is produced by expansion. The charge carried by the cloud is measured and its total mass is determined by absorbing the water and weighing it. The average radius of the droplets is determined by observing the rate of fall of the top surface of the cloud under gravity. According to Stokes' law,[1] the velocity of fall of a sphere of radius r through a viscous medium of density d_0 is

$$v = \frac{2gr^2(d - d_0)}{9\eta},$$ (11)

See LAMB, "Hydrodynamics," 5th ed. Sec. 337, Cambridge University Press.

where g is the acceleration of gravity, η the viscosity of the gas, and d the density of the sphere. In this way we obtain the average mass of a droplet, and therefore the number of droplets. Assuming that each one carries a single elementary charge, its value can be calculated from the total charge and the number of droplets. Townsend secured $3 \cdot 10^{-10}$ e.s.u. while Thomson obtained $6.5 \cdot 10^{-10}$ and $3.4 \cdot 10^{-10}$ e.s.u. in two sets of experiments. Since only the average mass of the droplet is determined and there is no way of knowing that each droplet carries one elementary unit of charge, the method cannot be expected to give precise results. Wilson modified this method by observing the rate of fall v_1 under gravity alone, and the rate v_2, under the combined forces of gravity and of an electric field. In this case, the condition for uniform fall is, by Stokes' law,

$$mg + Xe = 6\pi r\eta v_2, \tag{12a}$$

mg being the *apparent* weight of the drop in the medium of density d_0, while in the absence of the electric field,

$$mg = 6\pi r\eta v_1. \tag{12b}$$

We have also

$$m = \frac{4\pi r^3 D}{3}, \text{ where } D = d - d_0.$$

In these equations, the quantities observed are X, D, η, v_1 and v_2; m and r can be eliminated and

$$e = \frac{4\pi g(v_2 - v_1)v_1^{1/2}}{3XD^{1/2}}\left(\frac{9\eta}{2g}\right)^{3/2}. \tag{13}$$

The deviations for this method were large and the results of the same order of magnitude as before. In determining v_1 and v_2, it is necessary to assume that the size of the droplets is the same and the variations in the results indicate that this is not true.

The most exact determination of e is that of Millikan. In repeating Wilson's work he found that individual droplets could be kept in the field of a telescope for appreciable lengths of time. This made possible the elimination of many uncertainties, such as the assumption that each droplet has only one unit of charge and that they are of the same size. He observed drops of water, mercury, and oil, and found the oil drops most satisfactory. The electric fields used were higher than those used by Wilson and were mostly in a direction to oppose the force of gravity so that the condition for steady fall was

$$-mg + Xe = 6\pi r\eta v_2. \tag{14}$$

The particle moves upward or downward, depending on whether Xe is greater or less than mg. The special case in which $Xe = mg$ is known as the "balanced-drop method." Dividing equation (12b) by equation (14) and solving for e we obtain

$$e = \frac{mg(v_1 + v_2)}{Xv_1}. \qquad (15)$$

Millikan's apparatus is shown in Fig. 7.[1] An oil mist is produced by an atomizer; some of the drops fall through the opening in the upper condenser plate, and pick up charges from ions in the gas produced by a beam of X-rays. The particle selected for observation is viewed through

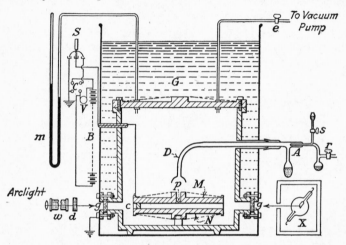

Fig. 7.—Millikan's apparatus for determining e. (*Reproduced by permission of the University of Chicago Press from "The Electron".*)

a telescope equipped with horizontal hair lines so that the time of fall between known levels can be determined. When a droplet has fallen below the bottom crosshair, an electric field is established between the condenser plates and the time of rise of the same particle is determined. In this way, one droplet can be observed for long periods of time.

The experiment can be best understood by considering the actual record of a droplet. The time required for it to fall a distance of 0.5222 cm. under gravity was 13.593 seconds, the average of 17 determinations varying only by amounts to be expected in stop-watch measurements. The times required for successive trips upward were 12.5, 12.4, 21.8, 34.8, 84.5, 85.5, 34.6, 34.8, 16.0, 34.8, 34.6, 21.9 seconds. After two trips, the time changed to 21.8 seconds, showing that a negative ion had been captured, since the particle was positive. The other changes also indicate the capture of ions, some positive and some negative. According to equation (15) the charge is proportional to $v_1 + v_2$, and, if the charges carried by the droplet are all multiples of a certain unit, this sum should always be an integral multiple of the value of $v_1 + v_2$ when the elementary charge is carried. Table 2, which is an abridgement of one given in Millikan's book "The Electron," shows that such is the case; $v_1 = 0.03743$ cm. per second.

[1] MILLIKAN, R. A. "The Electron," University of Chicago Press (1924).

TABLE 2

t	v_2	$v_1 + v_2$	n	$\Delta(v_1 + v_2)$	Δn
12.45	0.04196	0.07939	9.06		
				0.01806	−2.06
21.5	0.02390	0.06133	7.00		
				0.00885	. −1.01
34.7	0.01505	0.05248	5.99		
				0.00891	−1.01
85.0	0.006144	0.04357	4.98		

The column n gives the number of elementary charges carried by the droplet and Δn the number of charges gained by the droplet on successive trips. The experiment proves conclusively that the charge on the droplet is an integral multiple of an elementary unit and that the charge changes only by multiples of this unit.

The determination of the value of the charge requires the use of Stokes' law. It is given by equation (13) with the sign of v_1 changed, since the particle in Millikan's experiments *rises* against gravity when the field is applied. All the quantities in this modified equation can be determined by Millikan's method, observing one particle. The number of elementary charges on a droplet is obtained by the method just described and then the absolute value of the charge is obtained by determining all the unknowns in equation (13). However, Stokes' law applies only when the droplet is large compared to the mean distance between the molecules of the gas. Since the droplets used were very small, it was necessary to use a corrected form of Stokes' law,

$$v_1 = \frac{2}{9} \frac{gr^2 D}{\eta} \left(1 + A\frac{l}{r} \right), \tag{16}$$

where A is an empirical constant, and l the mean free path of the gas molecules. With this correction, consistent values for the elementary charge are obtained.

Millikan's value for e is $(1.591 \pm 0.002) \cdot 10^{-20}$ e.m.u. or $(4.770 \pm 0.005) \cdot 10^{-10}$ e.s.u. Together with the value of e/m_0 this permits a calculation of the mass of the electron,

$$m_0 = (8.994 \pm 0.014) \cdot 10^{-28} \text{ gram.}$$

Avogadro's number can be calculated from the relation

$$N = \frac{F}{e} = \frac{9{,}648.9}{1.591 \cdot 10^{-20}} = (6.064 \pm 0.006) \cdot 10^{23}.$$

The mass of any atom can be calculated from its atomic weight and Avogadro's number N. That of the hydrogen atom is

$$\frac{1.00777}{6.064 \cdot 10^{23}} = (1.6618 \pm 0.0017) \, 10^{-24} \text{ gram.}$$

The so-called radius of the electron can be calculated on the assumption that the mass is electromagnetic in origin. By this we mean, that the resistance to acceleration is supposed to be due entirely to the reaction of the electron's own electric and magnetic fields upon it, when it is subjected to a force. Further, it is supposed that the electron at rest is spherical, and that its charge is uniformly distributed on the surface of the sphere. The mass is given by

$$m_0 = \frac{2e^2}{3c^2a},$$ (17)

where a is the radius.[1] We find that $a = 1.69 \cdot 10^{-13}$ cm., a value 10^5 times smaller than atomic radii. On a similar basis, the radius of the hydrogen nucleus would be only $0.92 \cdot 10^{-16}$ cm., since it is much heavier than the electron. These values must not be taken too seriously. When the unsettled subject of models of the electron is discussed, it is customary, following Poincaré, to postulate a system of cohesional forces inside the electron, non-electromagnetic in character, but the existence of these forces makes doubtful the calculation of the radius referred to above. It seems probable, however, that in close collision with other entities the electron behaves more or less as a particle of radius $2 \cdot 10^{-13}$ would do. This is the only sense in which it has any meaning to speak of its size.

7. EARLY RESEARCHES ON ISOTOPES

Soddy and Fajans (1913) first pointed out that certain radioactive atoms having different masses and different radioactive properties should occupy the same position in the periodic system, and suggested that non-radioactive elements might consist of several atomic species having different atomic weights. Soddy called these species "isotopes." They stated that they would be chemically inseparable and further pointed out that lead from uranium minerals, produced as the end product of the radioactive decomposition of uranium, should have a lower atomic weight than lead obtained from the radioactive decomposition of thorium. The first of these statements explained the results of Boltwood,[2] Marckwald and Keetman,[3] and Auer von Welsbach[4] who showed that mesothorium and ionium cannot be separated chemically. Similarly, mesothorium and radium in the alkaline earth group and uranium I and II of the sixth group have been shown to be inseparable. The second statement was verified by careful determination of the atomic weight of lead from different sources as shown in Table 3. Table 4 gives data in regard to atomic weights and other physical properties, collected by T. W. Richards.

[1] See JEANS, "Electricity and Magnetism," p. 586, 4th ed.
[2] *Am. J. Sci.*, **22**, 537 (1906); **24**, 370 (1907).
[3] *Jahrbuch f. Radioaktivität*, **6**, 269 (1909).
[4] *Wien. Ber. iia*, **119**, 1011 (1910).

TABLE 3

Source	Atomic Weight
Ceylon thorite	207.77
Norwegian cleveite	206.08
Australian mixture	206.34
Carnotite	206.36
Pitchblend (Morogoro)	206.046
Norwegian thorite	207.9
Uranium lead (theoretical)	206
Thorium lead (theoretical)	208
Ordinary lead	207.20

TABLE 4

Property	Common lead A	Australian mixture B	Norwegian cleveite C	Percentage differences A − B	B − C
Atomic weight	207.19	206.34	206.08	0.42	0.54
Density	11.337	11.280	11.273	0.42	0.56
Atomic volume	18.277	18.278	18.281	0.01	0.02
Melting point	600.53	600.59	....	0.01	....
Solubility (nitrate)	37.281	37.130	....	0.41	....
Refractive index (nitrate)	1.7815	1.7814	....	0.01	....

It can be seen from Table 4 that the various samples described differ only in those properties which depend on atomic weight. This difference in atomic weight is due to the fact that the nuclei of the various isotopes of a given element have identical charges, but different masses. The configuration of the outer electrons depends only on the charge of the nucleus, aside from extremely minute effects due to its mass and possibly to a small magnetic moment.

8. THE SEPARATION OF ISOTOPES

In the case of the radioactive elements and the stable elements derived from them, such as uranium lead and thorium lead, nature furnishes us with pure atomic species, but, in the case of the non-radioactive elements which have several isotopes, we are always confronted with a mixture of constant proportions. Careful and extensive researches[1] have shown that the atomic weights of materials taken from widely separated sources on the earth's surface, from igneous rocks, from sedimentary rocks, and from the sea, are identical within the errors of measurement. Still more striking is the fact that the atomic weight of nickel from meteorites is the same as that of terrestrial nickel; the same is true for other elements investigated. On the basis of this work, Aston suggested that the evolution of the elements occurring when

[1] See Aston's "Isotopes," 2nd ed., pp. 141–142 for a detailed account.

the sun was in its youth "must have been such as to lead to a proportionality of isotopes of the same element which was constant from the start." The radioactive isotopes are an exception, for their disintegration alters the proportions in which they were present in former times.

The separation of the non-radioactive isotopes is a problem of considerable interest because of the information about the nucleus which could be obtained by transmutation experiments on a single isotope (Sec. **16**). Methods for separating isotopes can depend only on the difference in mass. Those which have been used with success are diffusion through porous walls, and evaporation at low pressures. Fractional distillation in the usual sense of the word cannot be used, for the boiling points of the various isotopes are too close together. The first method was used by Aston to show that neon can be separated into two fractions having different densities and by Harkins (using HCl) to produce samples of chlorine having different atomic weights. Stern and Volmer[1] have applied this method to show that H and O are pure elements. The evaporation method was used by Brönsted and Hevesy[2] and by Mulliken[3] to obtain partial separation of the Hg isotopes. The mercury was evaporated so slowly that the rate of diffusion of the atoms within the liquid was great enough to maintain approximately an equilibrium mixture of isotopes in the surface, and at such low pressures that the evaporated atoms could be caught on a surface cooled with liquid air before they collided with other atoms in the vapor phase. Under these conditions the rate of evaporation is inversely proportional to the square root of the mass and thus the lighter isotopes evaporate more rapidly, resulting in a slight fractionation. By repeating the process a number of times, extreme samples of mercury were secured having densities differing by 0.05 per cent, and combining weights differing by 0.1 of a unit. Other ingenious methods, described in detail in Aston's "Isotopes," depend on centrifuging, ionic migration, electrolysis (the discharge potentials being supposed slightly different for various isotopes), and fractional crystallization. These methods have not been successful. None of the methods so far mentioned can be used to separate isotopes in the pure state nor to show how many isotopes make up a given chemical element nor their individual masses. The study of the positively charged constituents of atoms, however, has made it possible to investigate the non-radioactive isotopes in detail, and the methods of separation described above provide confirmatory evidence.

[1] *Ann. Physik*, **59**, 225–238 (1919). Oxygen has three isotopes 16, 17, and 18, but the latter two are present in too small amounts to be detected by this means.

[2] *Phil. Mag.*, **43**, 31 (1922).

[3] *J. A. C. S.*, **44**, 2387 (1922); and **45**, 1592 (1923).

9. THE PARABOLA METHOD FOR STUDYING POSITIVE RAYS

In every discharge tube there are positively charged particles which move toward the cathode. The presence of such particles was first demonstrated by Goldstein by boring a small hole in the cathode (called by him a canal), and, thus, allowing these particles to stream into the space behind the cathode. Their track appears as a bright pencil of light, due not only to their own emission but also to that of the molecules which they strike. J. J. Thomson has summarized the results in this field in his "Rays of Positive Electricity" (see reference at end of chapter).

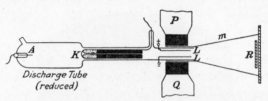

Fig. 8a.—J. J. Thomson's positive ray apparatus. *A* is the anode, *K* the cathode, *P* and *Q* the magnetic poles, *LL* the condenser, and *R* the photographic plate.

The principal experimental method used by Thomson (Fig. 8a) is nearly identical with that used by Kaufmann in his experiments on electrons. As in the experiments of Kaufmann (Sec. **5**), the particles will fall on curves which are approximately parabolas. The particles of high velocity are deflected only slightly and, therefore, fall nearer to the apex of the parabola, while those of lower velocity are deflected more, and so fall farther from the apex. If particles of all velocities were present, the curves would be complete, as shown at *OA* and *OB* in Fig. 8b. If the direction of the magnetic field is reversed, the particles will be deflected downward, as shown by the curves *OC* and *OD*. The directions of the electric and magnetic fields which deflect the particles to each of the four branches of the parabolas are shown by the arrows *E* and *H*. If negative particles are present, the positions at which they fall can be secured by reversing the directions of both *E* and *H* in the

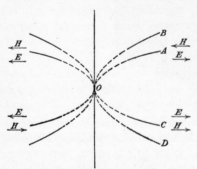

Fig. 8b.—Diagram of positive ray parabolas.

figure. Particles moving with "infinite" velocity would pass through *O*. Since the particles cannot have a velocity greater than that given to them by falling through the entire potential difference across the cathode ray tube, *i.e.*, between *A* and *K* in Fig. 8a, only incomplete parabolas will actually appear on the photographic plate, as in Fig. 9.

The deflection due to the electric field is inversely proportional to the kinetic energy of the particle and, therefore, will be the same for all particles which have the same charge and have fallen through the same potential, regardless of any difference in mass. The deflection due to the magnetic field is inversely proportional to the momentum of the particle, and, since the momentum is larger for heavier particles of the same kinetic energy, these will be deflected less than the lighter particles. Curve *OB* is produced by particles of larger mass than those which

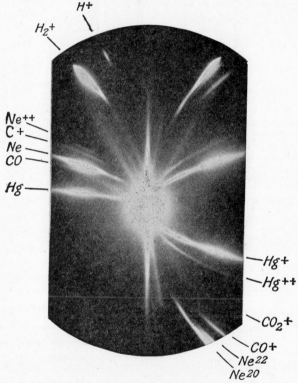

FIG. 9.—The parabolas of neon. (*After Thomson. Taken from Aston's "Isotopes" p.* 28.)

produce *OA*. From the shape of the curves it is possible to determine both the velocity of a particle falling on any point of the curves and also the ratio of charge to mass. The calculation is troublesome and, due to uncertainties in the distribution of the electric and magnetic fields, is not very precise. Experiments of this kind show definitely that the masses of particles carrying positive charges are of the same order of magnitude as the masses of the atoms, and that chemically pure elements may consist of a mixture of atoms of different masses. Figure 9 shows curves due to two isotopes of neon.

10. DEMPSTER'S METHOD

Dempster[1] has used the so-called magnetic spectrograph for studying positive particles and for determining the ratio of charge to mass. A diagram of his apparatus is shown in Fig. 10. The positive ions of charge ϵ are produced at A by causing electrons from a heated filament to fall on a salt of the element to be investigated. These fall through a small electric field and pass through the slit at C. Between C and S_1,

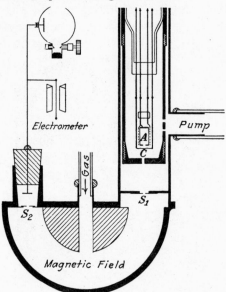

Fig. 10.—Dempster's apparatus for detecting isotopes.

there is a large electric field which causes the ions to pass through S_1 with a velocity

$$v = \left(\frac{2\Phi\epsilon}{M}\right)^{1/2}, \qquad (18)$$

where Φ is the potential difference between C and S_1. The apparatus below S_1 and S_2 is placed between the poles of an electromagnet so that the ions, after entering at S_1, move in a semicircle to S_2. The radius of the circle r, equal to half the distance between S_1 and S_2, depends on the magnetic field strength and velocity of the particle in the way given in equation (6), if m is replaced by M and e by ϵ. Eliminating the velocity from equations (6) and (18) we have

$$\frac{\epsilon}{M} = \frac{2\Phi}{H^2r^2}. \qquad (19)$$

The experimental procedure is usually to fix H at a convenient value and to vary Φ until the ions fall through S_2 and discharge the electrometer.

[1] *Phys. Rev.*, **11**, 316 (1918)

11. ASTON'S MASS SPECTROGRAPH

Aston[1] devised another arrangement of electric and magnetic fields (Fig. 11) which proved to be most convenient for the analysis of positive ions and has improved it until a very high precision in the determination of atomic masses is possible. A narrow beam of positive ions is selected from a source at the left by means of the slits S_1 and S_2. This beam passes between the charged plates P_1 and P_2 and is spread into a fan falling on D, the deflection depending on the charge and velocity of the ions. Only those ions will pass through the slit D which have charge and velocity such that they fulfill the relation

$$\theta v^2 = \frac{lE\epsilon}{M},\tag{20}$$

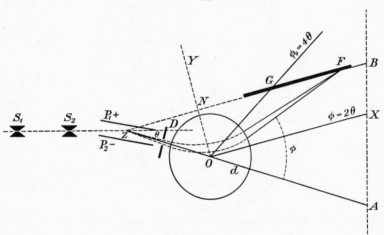

Fig. 11.—Aston's mass spectrograph.

where θ is the angle of deflection, which is always small and fixed by the position of D; v the velocity of the ions; l, the length of the path between the plates P_1 and P_2; and E, the electric intensity between these plates. These ions then pass between the poles of an electromagnet arranged so that it deflects them in the direction opposite to the deflection caused by the electric field. The angle of deflection φ can be obtained from equation (6) and for small deflections, is given by

$$\varphi v = \frac{\epsilon LH}{M},\tag{21}$$

L being the length of path in the magnetic field. Eliminating v from equations (20) and (21),

$$\varphi = LH\left(\frac{\theta}{lE}\right)^{1/2}\left(\frac{\epsilon}{M}\right)^{1/2}.$$

[1] *Phil. Mag.*, **38**, 709 (1919); also his book "Isotopes" (reference at end of chapter).

The great advantage of this method lies in the fact that ions having a certain value of ϵ/M but slightly different velocities due to the finite width of the slit D will nevertheless be focused on the same point of a photographic plate placed at GF, because an ion which is bent slightly less than the average by the electric field and has therefore a slightly higher velocity, is bent back proportionately less strongly by the magnetic field, while the opposite is the case for a strongly deflected slower ion. Therefore, the paths of slow and fast ions will intersect at some point. The locus of this point is found as follows:

By differentiating equation (20),

$$v^2 d\theta + 2\theta v dv = 0, \text{ or } \frac{d\theta}{\theta} = -\frac{2dv}{v},$$

and by differentiating equation (21),

$$v d\varphi + \varphi dv = 0, \text{ or } \frac{d\varphi}{\varphi} = -\frac{dv}{v}.$$

Therefore, $d\theta/\theta = 2d\varphi/\varphi$, an expression which is true for all values of the velocities. If $d\theta$ is the angle defined by the slit D, the width of the beam after traveling a distance equal to the total length of path will be $(b + r)d\theta$, neglecting the effect of the magnetic field, where b is the distance OZ and r is approximately OF. The effect of the magnetic field is to decrease this width by an amount $-rd\varphi$ and therefore the total width is

$$(b + r)d\theta - rd\varphi = bd\theta + r(d\theta - d\varphi) = d\theta\left(b + r\left(1 - \frac{\varphi}{2\theta}\right)\right).$$

If the rays are to be brought to a focus, this width must be zero and this will be true when

$$b + r\left(1 - \frac{\varphi}{2\theta}\right) = 0, \text{ or } \frac{r}{b} = \left(\frac{2\theta}{\varphi - 2\theta}\right). \tag{22}$$

This is the equation of a straight line GF making an angle θ with the original direction of the beam, in the sense opposite to the direction of deflection of the ions. Ions with the same ϵ/M but of slightly different velocities will fall on the same point on this line, as shown in Fig. 11, making it possible to secure very sharp images on the photographic plate. The theory as presented is not exact since the variations of the fields near the edges and the different paths traversed by the ions are not considered. By taking these into account, Aston has made this so-called mass spectrograph an instrument of high precision. He has studied the isotopes of a large number of elements, with the results shown in Table 5, which also includes the data of other investigators.

The nearly integral atomic weights of isotopes, the emission of alpha and beta particles by radioactive elements, and the artificial transmutation of elements with emission of protons (Sec. **16**) indicate that Prout's hypothesis was not far from correct; the nuclei of all atoms are probably constructed of protons and electrons, and it is likely that these particles form groups similar to the helium nucleus. Of course, the mere fact that alpha, beta, and hydrogen particles are emitted by nuclei does not prove their independent existence before the emission, but, with mental reservations, we shall speak as though such were the case. On this basis, we find the number of electrons in the nucleus as follows: The mass is almost entirely due to the protons, the number A of which is therefore nearly equal to the atomic weight. If there are N electrons, the nuclear charge will be

$$A - N = Z, \tag{23}$$

in terms of e as a unit.

12. REGULARITIES IN THE SYSTEM OF ISOTOPES

Table 5 abounds in interesting regularities, which must be accounted for by any successful theory of nuclear structure. We shall now review some of these regularities, basing our discussion, in part, on Chaps. IX and X of Aston's "Isotopes":

TABLE 5[1]

Element	Chemical atomic weight	Mass numbers of isotopes
H 1	1.0078	1
He 2	4.002	4
Li 3	6.940	7, 6
Be 4	9.02	9
B 5	10.82	11, 10
C 6	12.000	12, 13[4]
N 7	14.008	14, 15[5]
O 8	16.000	16, 18,[2] 17[2]
F 9	19.00	19
Ne 10	20.183	20, 22, 21[3]
Na 11	22.997	23
Mg 12	24.32	24, 25, 26
Al 13	26.97	27
Si 14	28.06	28, 29, 30
P 15	31.02	31
S 16	32.06	32, 33, 34
Cl 17	35.457	35, 37
A 18	39.94	40, 36
K 19	39.10	39, 41
Ca 20	40.07	40, 44
Sc 21	45.10	45
Ti 22	47.90	48
V 23	50.96	51
Cr 24	52.01	52
Mn 25	54.93	55
Fe 26	55.84	56, 54
Co 27	58.94	59
Ni 28	58.69	58, 60
Cu 29	63.57	63, 65
Zn 30	65.38	64, 66, 68, 67, 65; 70, 69
Ga 31	69.72	69, 71
Ge 32	72.60	74, 72, 70, 73, 75, 76, 71, 77
As 33	74.96	75
Se 34	79.2	80, 78, 76, 82, 77, 74
Br 35	79.916	79, 81
Kr 36	82.9	84, 86, 82, 83, 80, 78
Rb 37	85.44	85, 87
Sr 38	87.63	88, 86

[1] See Aston, *Proc. Roy. Soc.*, **115**, 487 (1927) and references there given; *Nature*, **122**, 167 and 345 (1928).   The istopes are given in the order of decreasing abundance.
[2] Giauque and Johnston, *Nature* (1929); *J. A. C. S.* (1929).
[3] Hogness and Kvalnes, *Nature*, **122**, 441 (1928).
[4] King and Birge, *Nature*, **124**, 127 (1929); *Phys. Rev.*, **34**, 376 (1929).
[5] Naudé, *Phys. Rev.*, **34**, 1498 (1929).

TABLE. 5.—(Continued).

Element	Chemical atomic weight	Mass numbers of isotopes
Y 39...............	88.92	89
Zr 40...............	91.22	90, 94, 92, (96)
Ag 47...............	107.880	107, 109
Cd 48...............	112.41	114, 112, 110, 113, 111, 116
In 49...............	114.8	115
Sn 50...............	118.70	120, 118, 116, 124, 119, 117, 122, 121, 112, 114, 115
Sb 51...............	121.77	121, 123
Te 52...............	127.5	128, 130, 126
I 53...............	126.932	127
Xe 54...............	130.2	129, 132, 131, 134, 136, 128, 130, 126, 124
Cs 55...............	132.81	133
Ba 56...............	137.36	138
La 57...............	138.90	139
Ce 58...............	140.13	140, 142
Pr 59...............	140.92	141
Nd 60...............	144.27	142, 144, 146, (145)
Hg 80...............	200.61	202, 200, 199, 198, 201, 204
Pb 82...............	207.22	208, 206, 207, (209), (203), (204)
Bi 83...............	209.00	209

1. Nuclei of even atomic number are more numerous than those of odd atomic number. Nuclei with mass numbers divisible by 4 are much more abundant than those with mass numbers not divisible by 4. Those containing even numbers of electrons are more numerous than those having odd numbers of electrons.

2. The atomic weights are generally very close to integers, on the scale O = 16, though definite divergences occur.

3. With the exception of hydrogen the atomic weight of a nucleus of charge Z is at least $2Z$, or, by equation (23), $N \geqq Z$. There is never less than one electron to every two protons, and the proportion of electrons rises as Z increases.

4. The number of isotopes of one element and their range of mass numbers are both rather small.

5. Elements of odd atomic number never have more than two isotopes, and the mass numbers of these usually differ by 2.

6. Isobars, that is, nuclei with the same weight but different charges, are comparatively rare.

13. DISTRIBUTION AND ABUNDANCE OF ISOTOPES

There are several interesting points in regard to the distribution of isotopes, first pointed out by Harkins. The total number of elements listed in Table 5 is 57, 29 of even and 28 of odd atomic number. There are 108 isotopes of even atomic number, but only 38 of odd atomic number. The isotopes having an even number of electrons within the nucleus, as calculated from equation (23), exceed those having an odd number of electrons in the ratio 115:31. The number of isotopes for the four possible combinations of these factors are as follows:

Even Z	Even Z	Odd Z	Odd Z
Even N	Odd N	Even N	Odd N
80	28	35	3

Harkins[1] has pointed out that the first 29 elements of the periodic system compose 99.85 per cent of the lithosphere, 99.98 per cent of the stone meteorites and 100 per cent of the iron meteorites, and that the even-numbered elements are far more abundant than the odd.   Figure 12a is a diagram by Harkins, showing the percentages by weight (this is equivalent to the percentage of protons) of the elements in the stone meteorites.   It will be noted that in every case, the even-numbered element is more abundant by weight than either of the odd-numbered

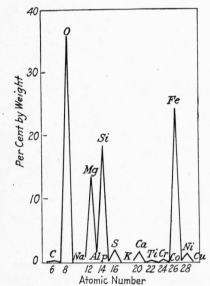

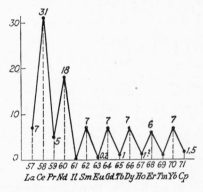

FIG. 12a.—Proportion by weight of elements in the stone meteorites. (*After Harkins.*)

FIG. 12b.—The relative abundance of the rare earths. (*After Goldsmidt and Thomassen.*)   The numbers indicate the relative abundance of atoms, yttrium being taken as 100.

elements preceding and following it.   Perhaps the most striking illustration of this type of variation is the relative abundance of the rare earths as shown in Fig. 12b, from the work of Goldsmidt and Thomassen.[2] Moreover, the five most abundant elements (either by weight or in number of atoms), O, Mg, Si, S, and Fe, make up nearly 96 per cent of the total number of atoms in these meteorites and, if we take account of the relative numbers of isotopes in these elements, we find that 90.6 per cent of the total number of nuclei have mass numbers divisible by 4, namely, O^{16}, Mg^{24}, Si^{28}, S^{32}, Fe^{56}.*

[1] HARKINS, W. D., *J. A. C. S.*, **39**, 856, 870 (1917); *Phil. Mag.*, **42**, 305 (1921). Harkins also classified isotopes into the four groups given above.

[2] *Videnskabs. Skrift.* I, *Math. naturw. Kl.*, **4** (1924).

* HARKINS, *Phil. Mag.*, **42**, 305 (1921).

As a first hypothesis we may assume that the more abundant atomic species are also the more stable, though this is not necessarily true. An instance is the fact ascertained by Biltz and Ziegert[1] that the less abundant isotope 41 of potassium is responsible for its radioactivity. They compared the radioactivity of ordinary potassium with that of a sample in which the isotope 41 had been increased 4.8 per cent, finding a difference in activity of 4.2 ± 0.8 per cent.

14. PRECISION MEASUREMENTS OF NUCLEAR WEIGHTS

The latest instrument constructed by Aston[2] is capable of an accuracy of one ten thousandth unit in the atomic weight scale, and by its use he has shown that very few nuclei have exactly integral mass numbers. The value, 16.0000, is assigned arbitrarily as the atomic weight of the oxygen atom. In this work, the mass of the planetary electrons carried by the ions must be taken into account, for the "atomic weight" of the electron is

$$W \text{ (electron)} = 0.000546. \tag{24}$$

The atomic weights which have been accurately determined with the new spectrograph are listed in Table 6, together with the packing fraction,

TABLE 6

Atom	Atomic weight	Packing fraction $\times 10^4$	Prob-able error $\times 10^4$	Atom	Atomic weight	Packing fraction $\times 10^4$	Prob-able error $\times 10^4$
H..........	1.00778	77.8	1.5	Cl³⁷........	36.980	−5.0	1.5
He..........	4.00216	5.4	1	A⁴⁰.........	39.971	−7.2	1
Li⁶.........	6.012	20.0	3	As..........	74.934	−8.8	1.5
Li⁷.........	7.012	17.0	3	Kr⁷⁸........	77.926	−9.4	2
B¹⁰.........	10.0135	13.5	1.5	Br⁷⁹........	78.929	−9.0	1.5
B¹¹.........	11.0110	10.0	1.5	Kr⁸⁰........	79.926	−9.1	2
C..........	12.0036	3.0	1	Br⁸¹........	80.926	−8.6	1.5
N..........	14.008	5.7	2	Kr⁸²........	81.927	−8.8	1.5
O..........	16	0.0	...	Kr⁸³........	82.927	−8.7	1.5
F..........	19.0000	0.0	1	Kr⁸⁴	83.928	−8.5	1.5
Ne²⁰........	20.0004	0.2	1	Kr⁸⁶........	85.929	−8.2	1.5
Ne²²........	(22.0048	2.2	?)	Sn¹²⁰........	119.912	−7.3	2
P..........	30.9825	−5.6	1.5	I...........	126.932	−5.3	2
Cl³⁵........	34.983	−4.8	1.5	Xe¹³⁴.......	133.929	−5.3	2
A³⁶........	35.976	−6.6	1.5	Hg²⁰⁰.......	200.016	+0.8	2

[1] *Physik. Z.*, **29**, 197 (1928).
[2] *Proc. Roy. Soc.*, **115**, 487 (1927).

which is defined as the difference between the atomic weight W and the number of protons A divided by the number of protons:

$$\text{Packing fraction} = \frac{(W - A)}{A}.$$

The data on lithium are those of Costa,[1] as recalculated by Aston.

The difference between the packing fraction of hydrogen and that of any other element is the decrease in mass of 1 gram-molecule of hydrogen nuclei when they are combined to form atoms of that element, assuming that heavier elements are compounds of protons and electrons. This decrease in mass is a measure of the loss of energy in the synthesis of atomic nuclei, for according to the relativity theory the mass M and energy E are connected by the equation

$$E = c^2 M,$$

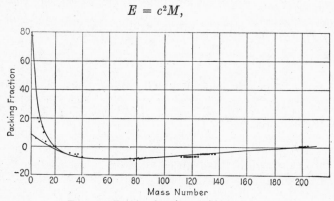

FIG. 13.—Packing fractions.   (*After Aston.*)

where c is the velocity of light. It is now quite generally believed that such syntheses are going on in stars, and it has been suggested that the energy given up forms the highly penetrating radiation which comes to the earth from outside sources. The greater the energy loss which occurs in the formation of a nucleus, the more stable we expect it to be. Unfortunately, the limit of experimental error of the packing fraction is so large that it is not quite possible to compare the stability of nuclei, as determined in this way, with their relative abundance except perhaps in the case of boron and less certainly in the case of lithium. B^{10} and Li^6 have odd Z and odd N, whereas B^{11} and Li^7 have odd Z even N, and are more abundant than the lighter isotopes, as shown by the chemical atomic weights. Therefore, we expect that B^{10} and Li^6 should be less stable than B^{11} and Li^7, respectively, both because they are representatives of an infrequent type of nucleus and because they are the less abundant isotopes. This is indeed the case, for the boron isotopes, B^{10} and B^{11}, have the packing fractions $13.5 \pm 1.5 \times 10^{-4}$ and $10.0 \pm$

---

[1] *Ann. Physique*, **4**, 426 (1925).

1.5×10^{-4}, respectively, and the limit of error is not as great as the difference between them. The packing fractions of the isotopes of lithium also agree with the conclusion that Li^6 is the less stable isotope, but the probable limit of error is as great as the difference between them. The method of determining the atomic weights of isotopes, however, is such that the difference in atomic weights is probably much more precise than their absolute values, and, therefore, we can be quite certain that the packing fractions of the lithium isotopes confirm the conclusions in regard to stability drawn from their relative abundance in nature. Figure 13 shows a plot of packing fractions against atomic number. The abundant even-numbered elements below neon are characterized by smaller values than the odd-numbered elements, which indicates, in a statistical way, that the former are more stable. Beck[1] has constructed a classification of isotopes somewhat similar to the periodic table of the elements, which brings out many interesting regularities.

15. METHODS OF STUDYING THE NUCLEUS

Up to this point we have assumed the existence of atomic nuclei carrying most of the mass of the atom. We shall now consider the proofs for this assumption and the experimental methods for studying other properties of the positively charged constituents of atoms. The investigation of the nucleus depends on the detailed study of the scattering of alpha particles and high-speed electrons when passing through a gas or a thin metal foil, and on the determination of wave lengths and intensities of gamma rays. Alpha particles move with velocities varying from $0.0456c$ to $0.0688c$, depending on the radioactive element emitting them, while fast electrons are available with velocities up to $0.957c$. The energy of the alpha particles ranges from $6.2 \cdot 10^{-6}$ to $1.41 \cdot 10^{-5}$ ergs. That of the fastest beta rays is smaller, namely, $2.1 \cdot 10^{-6}$ ergs. As mentioned previously, the introduction of matter, either as a gas or a thin metal foil across the path of a beam of alpha rays or electrons, causes it to become diffuse. The particles are scattered mostly through small angles (up to $3°$) though a few are scattered through very large angles ($90°$ and greater). Lenard[2] has shown that the absorption of electrons by matter is due mainly to their removal from the beam by scattering through large angles and that the intensity I of the beam after passing through a layer of matter x cm. thick is

$$I = I_0 e^{-ax}, \tag{25}$$

where I_0 is the original intensity; a is called the absorption coefficient and depends on the velocity of the electrons. It becomes smaller as the velocity increases and is approximately proportional to the density of the

[1] Z. Physik, **47**, 407 and **50**, 548 (1928).
[2] Ann. Physik, **81**, 94 (1926) and earlier papers.

substance D, or what is the same thing, to the number of atoms passed through times their atomic weight. Lenard gives a table showing the variation of a/D with the velocity of the fast electrons. According to kinetic theory, if a number of particles be fired into a layer of stationary "billiard ball" atoms x cm. thick, arranged at random, with a total cross-sectional area of all the atoms in unit volume equal to a, the fraction of the particles emerging will be e^{-ax}; a is therefore a measure of the total projected area of all the particles in 1 cc. of the absorbing substance and the variation in a as seen in the table means that the effective area of these particles decreases as the velocity of the fast electrons increases. The value of a/D for particles with a velocity equal to $0.9c$ is 6 g^{-1} cm.^{2} and therefore for nitrogen gas at standard temperature and pressure a is $6 \cdot 0.00125$, or 0.0075 cm.^{2}; but using the radius $1.9 \cdot 10^{-8}$ cm. obtained from kinetic theory of gases, the total projected area per cm.^{3} should be about $3 \cdot 10^4$ cm.^{2}, so that the effective cross-section of a molecule of nitrogen for fast electrons of velocity 0.90 of that of light is only $2.5 \cdot 10^{-7}$ of its effective cross-section for collisions with other molecules of nitrogen. The ratio of the effective radii for the two cases is $5 \cdot 10^{-4}$.

VARIATION OF ABSORPTION COEFFICIENT WITH VELOCITY

$\beta = v/c$	a/D g.$^{-1}$ cm.^{2}	$\beta = v/c$	a/D g.$^{-1}$ cm.^{2}
0.90	6	0.10	8.0×10^5
0.80	13	0.08	14×10^5
0.70	29	0.06	25×10^5
0.60	83	0.04	58×10^5
0.50	2.2×10^2	0.03	86×10^5
0.40	7.4×10^2	0.02	130×10^5
0.30	29×10^2	0.01	180×10^5
0.20	360×10^2		

To explain this discrepancy Lenard assumed that atoms were composed of electric doublets which he called "dynamids," consisting of a positive and a negative electric charge bound closely together. When the experiments of Rutherford established the nuclear atom the assumption was made that the scattering of fast electrons is due to collisions with the nuclei and also the electrons within the atoms, and that those particles have effective radii small compared with the gas-kinetic radius of the atom.

To account exactly for the scattering of fast electrons is a much more difficult problem than that of the scattering of alpha particles, which we shall consider next. Since the flashes produced by individual alpha particles impinging on a phosphorescent screen can be observed, it is possible to study the distribution of scattered particles by simply counting the numbers scattered at various angles from the direction of the original beam. The scattering may occur in two ways: first, it may be the result of small deflections produced by collisions with many atoms, or second, it may be produced by a single large deflection due to a collision with one atom. The distribution of the scattered particles will be very different depending on which of these mechanisms is the correct one. The first alternative requires that the number scattered through a given angle shall be proportional to the square root of the thickness of the metal foil through which they pass, while the second requires that the number be proportional to the thickness. The following table[1] shows that the scattering is very nearly proportional to the thickness and, therefore, is decisively in favor of single scattering at the larger angles for most of the particles. The distribution of the particles scattered

Number of foils	Equivalent thickness in centimeters of air ($= T$)	Number of scintillations in a given direction ($= N$)	$\dfrac{N}{T}$
1	0.11	21.9	200
2	0.22	38.4	175
5	0.51	84.3	165
8	0.81	121.5	150
9	0.90	145	160

through small angles obeys the laws of probability and is compatible with the theory of multiple scattering. If the probability of scattering through a large angle is calculated from this distribution on the basis of multiple scattering, it is found that the number to be expected, theoretically, for an angle of 90°, say, is so small that the large angle scattering would never have been observed, and is, therefore, in disagreement with experiment. These two results are the starting point for Rutherford's argument that the scattering is due to single collisions with particles in the metal foils used.

As we have seen, Rutherford then assumed that the atom consists of a massive nucleus carrying all the positive charge and electrons of smaller mass at fairly large distances from the nucleus. Such an assumption is necessary in order to secure the large fields necessary to scatter alpha particles through a large angle. Let the charge on the alpha particle be $2e$, and that on the positive nucleus of an atom in the metal foil be Ze where Z is the atomic number and e the absolute value of the electronic charge, and let the particle move along the line PS (Fig. 14) when at a very large distance from the nucleus at K. The orbit of the particle is an hyperbola with K at one focus, possessing the equation

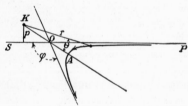

Fig. 14.—Scattering of an alpha particle by a heavy nucleus.

[1] Geiger and Marsden, *Phil. Mag.*, **25**, 615 (1913).

given in equation (29), Chap. IV.   Remembering that $e = 4.77 \cdot 10^{-10}$, we put $e_1 = 2e$, and $e_2 = Ze$, in equation (29), obtaining

$$r = \frac{-p_0^2/2\mu Ze^2}{1 - \epsilon \cos(\theta + \theta_0)}, \tag{26}$$

where

$$\epsilon^2 = 1 + \frac{E_0 p_0^2}{2\mu Z^2 e^4},$$

and p_0, E_0, are the initial angular momentum about K and the initial energy, respectively.   We can use the mass of the nucleus M in place of the reduced mass μ and regard the struck nucleus as remaining stationary if we limit ourselves to collisions of alpha particles with heavy atoms as we shall do at present.   In order that θ shall be the angle between KA and r, as shown in Fig. 14, θ_0 must equal 0.   For $r = \infty$, $\theta = $ angle POA.   Then from equation (26),

$$\frac{1}{\epsilon} = \cos(POA)$$

or,

$$\tan(POA) = \left(\frac{p_0}{2Ze^2}\right)\left(\frac{2E_0}{M}\right)^{1/2}.$$

Now $2E_0/M = v^2$ and $p_0 = Mvp$, if v is the initial velocity, and p the perpendicular distance from the line PS to K.   Further, the angle φ is the angle of deflection and it follows that

$$\cot\left(\frac{\varphi}{2}\right) = \frac{Mv^2 p}{2Ze^2}. \tag{27}$$

This determines the angle of deflection in terms of the original velocity of the alpha particle, the mass M, the charges on the nucleus and alpha particle, and the perpendicular distance p.

The deflected particles are usually observed on a screen placed perpendicular to the direction of the scattered beam, as shown in Fig. 15. S is the source of alpha particles, F the scattering foil, P the phosphorescent screen, and M the microscope used in the observations.   The number of scattered

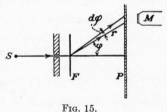

FIG. 15.

particles is expressed in terms of the number falling on unit area perpendicular to the direction of scattering.   Supposing that Q particles fall on the foil, this number, dN_φ/dA, falling between the scattering angles, φ and $\varphi + d\varphi$, is,

$$\frac{dN_\varphi}{dA} = Qnt\, \frac{Z^2 e^4}{M^2 v^4} \frac{\csc^4(\varphi/2)}{r^2}, \tag{28}$$

where n is the number of atoms per unit volume, t the foil thickness, and r the distance from the atom to the point where the alpha particle hits the screen.

To prove this, we shall modify slightly the treatment in Andrade's "Structure of the Atom," page 22. Since matter is extremely open in its structure, the overlapping of the spheres of action of the nuclei need not be considered. The number of nuclei per unit area of the foil is nt, so the area belonging to one nucleus is $1/nt$. The chance that a particle passes at a distance between p and $p + dp$ from a nucleus is

$$\frac{2\pi p dp}{(1/nt)},$$

and when Q particles hit the foil, the number satisfying this criterion is

$$Qnt \cdot 2\pi p dp.$$

After being scattered, these particles will lie in an angular range between φ and $\varphi + d\varphi$, and from equation (27),

$$dp = \frac{Ze^2}{Mv^2} \operatorname{cosec}^2\left(\frac{\varphi}{2}\right) d\varphi.$$

Substituting this in the preceding equation, the number between φ and $\varphi + d\varphi$ is found to be

$$4\pi Qnt\left(\frac{Z^2 e^4}{M^2 v^4}\right) \cot\left(\frac{\varphi}{2}\right) \operatorname{cosec}^2\left(\frac{\varphi}{2}\right) d\varphi.$$

The area covered by these on a screen perpendicular to r will be $2\pi r^2 \sin \varphi d\varphi = 4\pi r^2 \sin (\varphi/2) \cos (\varphi/2) d\varphi$, and the number per unit area will be the value given in equation (28).

If the total number of particles falling on the foil Q is counted, it is possible to determine the absolute charge on the nucleus since all other quantities in equation (28) are measurable. Geiger and Marsden showed that when p is not too small, equation (28) is verified within the limits of experimental error and so have proved the nuclear atom to be in accord with their experiments. Chadwick, using equation (28), has determined the charges on the nuclei of Cu, Ag, and Pt and found that Z for these elements is 29.3, 46.3, and 77.4, while their atomic numbers are 29, 47, and 78, respectively, showing that the atomic number is the number of positive units of charge on the nucleus.

The alpha particle will approach nearest to the atomic nucleus if it is fired directly at it so that $p = 0$. It will come to rest at some distance b where the potential energy is equal to the total kinetic energy of the particle when at a large distance from the nucleus. Then, if the inverse square law holds true,

$$\frac{2Ze^2}{b} = \frac{Mv^2}{2}; \text{ or } b = \frac{4Ze^2}{Mv^2}. \tag{29}$$

If equation (28) holds for scattering through angles close to 180°, we must conclude that the inverse square law of force holds down to distances as small as b. It has no very definite meaning to speak of the radius of the nucleus, but if we define the nuclear radius as the distance at which the inverse square law of force breaks down, then scattering experiments give us a means of estimating this quantity. The value of b for the gold nucleus ($Z = 79$) and the alpha particles of radium C, which have a velocity of $0.064c$, is $3 \cdot 10^{-12}$ cm. from equation (29). The distribution of scattered particles predicted by equation (28) holds true for gold up to angles of 150°; for this angle the alpha particle must approach within about $3 \cdot 10^{-12}$ cm. so that this distance is an upper limit for the radius of the gold nucleus. Similar experiments in which hydrogen is bombarded with fast alpha particles show however that the inverse square law no longer holds at distances of about $3 \cdot 10^{-13}$ cm.

16. THE DISRUPTION OF THE ATOMIC NUCLEUS

In collisions between alpha particles and atoms of high atomic weight, it is permissible to regard the struck nucleus as remaining stationary. This cannot be done when we consider collisions between alpha particles and nuclei with masses of the same order of magnitude. Figure 16 shows the paths of an alpha particle and a light nucleus during a collision. Let the masses be m and M, respectively, and the initial and final velocities of the alpha particle be v_0 and v_1, while the final velocity of the nucleus is u. After impact, let the alpha particle move at an angle φ and the nucleus at an angle θ with the original direction of the particle. The laws of conservation of momentum and energy require that

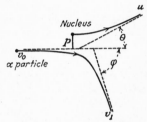

FIG. 16.—The scattering of an alpha particle by a light nucleus.

$$mv_0 = mv_1 \cos \varphi + Mu \cos \theta,$$
$$0 = -mv_1 \sin \varphi + Mu \sin \theta,$$
$$mv_0{}^2 = mv_1{}^2 + Mu^2,$$

$$u = 2v_0 \frac{m}{m + M} \cos \theta, \qquad \tan \varphi = \frac{M \sin 2\theta}{m - M \cos 2\theta}. \qquad (30)$$

For the hydrogen nucleus $M = m/4$, and

$$u_\mathrm{H} = 1.6v_0 \cos \theta, \qquad (31)$$

while for He,

$$u_\mathrm{He} = v_0 \cos \theta, \qquad \tan \varphi = \cot \theta. \qquad (32)$$

This shows that for scattering by He, $\varphi + \theta = \pi/2$. Branched tracks of alpha particles in helium gas photographed by Wilson's method are found to have an angle of 90° between them. The angle θ can be calculated only if the law of force is known. Assuming that the inverse square law holds, it can be shown that

$$\tan \theta = \frac{pv_0{}^2 \, mM}{2Ze^2(m + M)}.$$

The velocity of the hydrogen nucleus can be calculated as a function of p and, just as in the case of the scattering from heavy atoms, the probability of the hydrogen nucleus being shot out at any angle θ can be calculated.

Experiments designed to test whether the scattering obeys the formulas derived on the assumption of the inverse square law of force have been carried out by Rutherford,[1] and Chadwick and Bieler.[2] The conclusion is that the inverse square law holds down to about $2.4 \cdot 10^{-13}$ cm. for collisions between hydrogen nuclei and alpha particles. If p is smaller than this amount, many more hydrogen nuclei are thrown forward than the theory predicts.

The range R of a positively charged particle such as a hydrogen nucleus or an alpha particle has been shown experimentally to be proportional to the third power of the velocity of the particle and Bohr[3] has deduced a theory showing that to a first approximation the range is proportional to its mass and inversely proportional to the square of its charge. If the collision between the alpha particle and the hydrogen nucleus is head on, so that θ of equation (32) is zero, $v_H = 1.6v_0$, and

$$\frac{R_H}{R_{He}} = \frac{v_H{}^3 Z_{He}{}^2 M_H}{v_{He}{}^3 Z_H{}^2 M_{He}} = 4.1.$$

Therefore, the range of a high-speed hydrogen nucleus produced by an alpha particle with a range of 31 cm. in hydrogen would be 127 cm. The more exact theory makes this range somewhat less, about 117 cm. The range of such a high-speed hydrogen nucleus in air is about one-fourth of this, or 29 cm. This is the maximum range possible for if $\theta > 0$, u_H will be less than $1.6v_0$ and the range will be less than this value. The maximum range of any other fast nucleus of higher mass than hydrogen produced by collision with an alpha particle will be less than this as can be seen from equation (30). If any particles having a range greater than 29 cm. of air are produced by bombarding a substance with alpha particles of radium C, they must be ejected from the atomic nuclei.[4] Rutherford first showed that such long-range particles exist and Rutherford and Chadwick have shown that they are produced from a number of elements and that they are deflected by magnetic fields to a degree expected for hydrogen nuclei. Furthermore, these high-speed particles are ejected backward as well as forward with respect to the direction of the bombarding nuclei.

Certainly in the case of some elements, part of the energy of the high-speed H particles must be supplied from the internal energy of the nucleus. Kirsch and Petterson and their co-workers have extended the study to other elements and have devised methods for detecting H-particles of smaller range. In this way they have shown that other elements are disintegrated, but with the ejection of slower H-particles.

[1] *Phil. Mag.*, **37**, 537 (1919).

[2] *Ibid.*, **42**, 923 (1921).

[3] *Phil. Mag.*, **25**, 10 (1913); **30**, 581 (1915).

[4] See Handbuch der Physik, **22**, 146–178, for complete references to the literature on this subject.

Moreover there are indications that alpha particles unite with nitrogen atoms when they are bombarded by alpha particles of radium *C*.

Table 7 gives the list of elements[1] which are reported to be disintegrated by bombardment with alpha particles, together with the packing

TABLE 7

	Atomic number	Packing fraction $\times 10^4$	Range of particles in centimeters of air		
			Forward	Backward	Observer
Li..................	3	20, 17	..	..	1
Be..................	4	....	..	..	2
B...................	5	13.5, 10	58	38	3
C...................	6	3	..	..	4
N...................	7	5.7	40	18	3
O...................	8	0	..	..	5
F...................	9	0	65	48	3
Ne..................	10	0.2	..	..	3
Na..................	11	....	58	36	3
Mg..................	12	....	..	..	2
Al..................	13	....	90	67	3
Si..................	14	....	..	..	2
P...................	15	−5.6	65	49	3
S...................	16	....	..	..	3
Cl..................	17	−4.8, −5.0	..	..	3
K...................	18	....	..	..	3
A...................	19	−6.6, −7.2	..	..	3
Ti..................	22	....	..	..	2
Cr..................	24	....	..	..	2
Fe..................	26	....	..	..	2
Cu..................	29	....	..	..	2
Se..................	34	....	..	..	2
Br..................	35	....	..	..	2
Zr..................	40	....	..	..	2
Sn..................	50	−7.3	..	..	2
Te..................	52	....	..	..	2
I...................	53	−5.3	..	..	2

[1] KARA-MICHAILOVA, E., Hand. d. Physik, **22**, 166.

[2] KIRSCH, G., and H. PETTERSON, *Mitt. Ra.-Inst.* **167**; *Wiener Ber.* (IIa) **133**, 235 (1924); *Mitt. Ra.-Inst.* **176**a and **180**; *Wiener Ber.* (IIa) **134**, (1925).

[3] RUTHERFORD, E., and J. CHADWICK, *Proc. Roy. Soc.*, **36**, 417 (1924); *Phil. Mag.* **42**, 809 (1921); **44**, 417 (1922).

[4] PETTERSON, H., *Mitt. Ra.-Inst.* **173**; *Wiener Ber.* (IIa) **133**, 573 (1924).

[5] KIRSCH, G., *Mitt Ra.-Inst.* **169**, *Wiener Ber.* (IIa) **133**, 461.

[1] These elements are quite certainly disintegrated but there is some disagreement between workers in this field as to the ratio of the number of disintegrated atoms to alpha particles. This has been critically discussed by BOTHE, *Naturwis.*, **16**, 204 (1928).

fractions, and the forward and backward ranges determined by Rutherford and Chadwick.

The energy relations involved in these disintegrations have been considered by Rutherford and Chadwick. In the case of the elements P, Al, and F the energy of the H-particle is greater than that of the alpha particle causing the disintegration so that the internal nuclear energy must supply part of the energy. Until the nature of the nuclear fragments is known and until the packing fractions of all light elements are determined, it is impossible to say anything with certainty in regard to the energy balance in these disintegration processes. Even the question of whether the nuclei are disintegrated or the alpha particle combines with one nuclear fragment to form an atom of higher atomic weight is uncertain, though this seems probable in view of experiments of the type illustrated in Fig. 2.[1]

REFERENCES

CROWTHER, J. A., "Ions, Electrons, and Ionizing Radiations," Longmans, Green and Co., New York (1919).

KOVARIK and McKEEHAN, "Radioactivity," *Bull.* 51, Nat. Res. Council, Washington (1925).

HEVESY and PANETH, "Radioactivity," translated by R. W. Lawson, Oxford University Press (1926).

ST. MEYER and E. VON SCHWEIDLER, "Radioaktivitat," 2nd ed., Teubner, Berlin (1927).

THOMSON, J. J., "Rays of Positive Electricity," 2nd ed., Longmans, Green and Co., New York (1921).

ASTON, F. W., "Isotopes," 2nd ed., Arnold, London (1924).

ANDRADE, E. N. DA C., "Structure of the Atom," 3rd ed., Bell, London.

RUTHERFORD, E., "Radioactive Substances," Cambridge University Press (1913).

"Handbuch der Physik," Vols. 22 and 24, Springer, Berlin (1927).

MILLIKAN, R. A., "The Electron," Chicago University Press (1916).

KOHLRAUSCH, K. W. F., "Radioactivität," Vol. 15 of the Wien-Harms "Handbuch der Experimentalphysik," Akademische Verlagsgesellschaft, Leipzig (1929).

[1] BLACKETT, *Proc. Roy. Soc.* **103,** 78 (1923); HARKINS, *Z. Physik,* **50,** 97 (1928).

CHAPTER III

THE FOUNDATIONS OF THE QUANTUM THEORY AND THEIR EXPERIMENTAL JUSTIFICATION

1. BLACK-BODY RADIATION

It is curious but true that the detailed study of a single experimental law led Planck to propose the quantum theory. That law describes the way in which the radiation from a so-called black body, having wave lengths between λ and $\lambda + d\lambda$, depends on wave length and on temperature. By a black body, we mean a hypothetical body which absorbs all incident radiation, transmitting and reflecting none. While no such object exists in nature, the radiation which it would emit is very closely approximated by that emerging from a very small hole in the wall of a uniformly heated hollow body. Such a hollow body is often called a "black body," or sometimes a "hohlraum." Interest in the radiation emitted by a black body has grown steadily since Kirchhoff discovered a law, named after him, which will now be explained. Let $S_\lambda d\lambda$ be the rate of emission of radiation with wave lengths between λ and $\lambda + d\lambda$, from unit surface of a given body, at a certain temperature. Let A_λ be the coefficient of absorption for rays of the same wave length falling on the body. Then the law states that,

At a given temperature, S_λ/A_λ is a constant, s_λ, independent of the nature of the body.

(This law, as well as the other laws of radiation stated here, is proved in Planck's "Wärmestrahlung," referred to at the end of this chapter.) Now when $A_\lambda = 1$ (perfect absorber), $S_\lambda = s_\lambda$, so that $s_\lambda \, d\lambda$ is the rate of emission from unit surface of a black body. Kirchhoff's law shows, therefore, that the rate of emission from a black body depends only on the wave length considered and the temperature but not on any property of the black body itself.

It can be shown that at temperature T, s_λ is identical with the radiation which passes in a given sense through an imaginary unit surface drawn inside a hollow enclosure with walls at temperature T. The radiation at any point inside such an enclosure is quite independent of the nature and shape of the walls, and the streams of radiation in all directions are equal. Further, the condition of the radiation at all points inside the enclosure is identical. In particular the energy per

53

unit volume of the radiation in the range $d\lambda$ is uniform, and is denoted by

$$\rho_\lambda d\lambda.$$

It is a matter of mere geometry and integration to show that

$$\rho_\lambda = \frac{4\pi s_\lambda}{c}, \tag{1}$$

where c is the velocity of light in vacuum.

Thus, it is immaterial whether we use ρ_λ or s_λ in our calculations and we choose to use the former. By the aid of classical thermodynamics, together with the value of the radiation pressure in terms of energy density, we can deduce *Wien's displacement law* that

$$\rho_\lambda = c_1\lambda^{-5}f(\lambda T), \tag{2}$$

where c_1 is a constant and $f(\lambda T)$ an arbitrary function. ρ may also be written in the form $c_1T^5F(\lambda T)$, where

$$F(\lambda T) = \frac{f(\lambda T)}{\lambda^5 T^5}.$$

From this, we can deduce the Stefan-Boltzmann law by integration, without knowing the form of f. The total energy density carried by radiation of all wave lengths is

$$\rho = \int_0^\infty \rho_\lambda d\lambda = c_1T^4 \int_0^\infty F(\lambda T)d(\lambda T) = aT^4, \tag{3}$$

a being constant.

This is as far as we can go in determining ρ_λ by the aid of general principles. To proceed further, we must study the equilibrium of radiation with some form of absorbing and emitting matter. The type of matter we deal with is of no consequence, provided it is endowed with certain characteristics which are common to all species of atoms or molecules, and provided that *every* wave length can be absorbed and emitted by a reasonable number of the particles. For this reason, Planck discussed a very simple case—a collection of harmonic oscillators having all possible frequencies. His treatment is quite long, so we shall give another proof of the radiation law, due to Jeans and explained in his "Kinetic Theory of Gases," fourth edition. The underlying idea is to break up the radiation field into monochromatic wave trains; to find the number of trains which have wave lengths between λ and $\lambda + d\lambda$; and to determine the energy carried by each wave train when a steady state is reached by applying thermodynamic criteria which must be satisfied in the equilibrium condition. Consider a cube of unit volume having perfectly reflecting walls, with one corner at the origin, containing plane electromagnetic waves moving parallel and antiparallel to the X-axis, but not in any other direction. Suppose these waves are plane polarized, with electric force parallel to the Y-axis. A boundary condition is imposed by the fact that the walls are perfect reflectors; namely, the tangential components of the electric and magnetic force must be

zero. If this were not true, radiation would penetrate the walls. Therefore, at the planes $x = 0$ and $x = 1$, the electric and magnetic forces
vanish. In the ideal case considered, equilibrium has been attained,
and the field of radiation must be composed of stationary monochromatic
waves. As a function of x and t, the electric force is of the type

$$E_y = \sum_m A_m \sin m\pi x \cos (\pi mct - \alpha_m), \qquad (4)$$

where nothing is known, as yet, about the amplitude constants and phase
constants, A_m and α_m. The slowest mode of vibration is represented by
the standing wave shown at 1 in Fig. 1, where the ordinates represent the
values of the electric vector. It is composed
of two sine vibrations of wave length 2, one
passing to the right and the other to the left.
Similarly, in the other cases shown, the wave
lengths of the sine vibrations which form the
stationary waves are $\frac{2}{2}$, $\frac{2}{3}$, etc. Each
stationary wave, that is, each term in the
expression for the electric force, is called a
"mode of vibration." Although the decomposition of the force into sinusoidal constituents is a purely mathematical process, we
are at liberty to consider each monochromatic
standing wave train as an entity possessing
energy, momentum, and other physical
characteristics. The justification lies in the

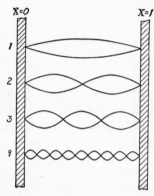

FIG. 1.—Standing waves in a
hollow enclosure.

fact that the time average of the energy of the whole system is composed
of a sum of terms, one of which is contributed by each wave train.

The electromagnetic energy density at a given point is $(E^2 + H^2)/8\pi$, H being
the magnetic force. The time averages of the two terms are equal so the energy is
the average of $E^2/4\pi$. E^2 contains square terms of the type $A_m{}^2 \sin^2 m\pi x \cos^2$
$(\pi mct - \alpha_m)$, and also cross-product terms. The time average of each cross-product
term is zero, and the average of $\cos^2 (\pi mct - \alpha_m)$ is $\frac{1}{2}$ so the total energy density is
equal to

$$\tfrac{1}{2}\Sigma A_m{}^2 \sin^2 m\pi x.$$

From this, the energy of the whole cube can be obtained by volume integration.

We need to know how many modes of vibration have their wave
lengths in the range between two fixed wave lengths, λ_2 and λ_1, where
$\lambda_1 > \lambda_2$. Because we know from experiment that in practical cases
most of the energy density will reside in wave lengths short compared
with 1 cm., we limit our investigation to large values of m. Suppose
that in the sequence of possible wave lengths, $\dfrac{2}{m-1}, \dfrac{2}{m}, \dfrac{2}{m+1}, \cdots$, the
term $2/m_1$ is the first value smaller than λ_1 and $2/(m_2 - 1)$ is the last

value larger than λ_2. That is, excluding cases where λ_1 and λ_2 are equal to some of the allowed wave lengths,

$$\frac{2}{m_1 - 1} > \lambda_1 > \frac{2}{m_1} > \cdots > \frac{2}{m_2 - 1} > \lambda_2 > \frac{2}{m_2}.$$

Then the number of modes of vibration with wave length greater than or equal to λ_2 and less than λ_1 is obviously $m_2 - m_1$. Now,

$$m_2 - m_1 \cong \frac{2}{\lambda_2} - \frac{2}{\lambda_1} = \frac{2(\lambda_1 - \lambda_2)}{\lambda_1 \lambda_2}.$$

If λ_1 and λ_2 differ by a very small quantity $d\lambda$, then the number is

$$\frac{2 d\lambda}{\lambda^2}.$$

If we take into account the vibrations in which the electrical force is parallel to the z-axis, the number must be doubled. This quantity is referred to as the *number of vibrations per unit length* in the wave length range $d\lambda$, for the reason that if the enclosure is expanded to a length of l cm. parallel to the x-axis, it can contain l times as many stationary vibrations in the range $d\lambda$. The typical wave train is given by the expression $A_m \sin (m\pi x/l) \cos (m\pi ct/l - \alpha_m)$.

We pass now to the three-dimensional analogue of this calculation and consider the waves which pass in all directions inside a vessel of volume V. When a wave train is reflected at the walls its direction is changed, and all in all the situation is very complicated. However, it will always be mathematically possible to break the waves up into monochromatic trains and to determine the number for which the wave length lies in the range $d\lambda$. This number is found to be proportional to the volume of the enclosure so it is reasonable to speak of the number per unit volume just as we spoke of the number per unit length above. It is found[1] to be

$$8\pi\lambda^{-4}d\lambda. \tag{5}$$

The amplitudes of the modes of vibration vary in an irregular way, so the energy associated with each one is also variable from wave train to wave train. However, the *average* energy of each wave train can be obtained by the methods of statistical mechanics. As mentioned in Chap. I, Sec. **6,** the average kinetic energy associated with a squared term $C_n \dot{q}_n{}^2/2$ in the kinetic energy of any dynamical system is $kT/2$. In classical electrodynamics a monochromatic wave train may be considered as a dynamical system having kinetic energy $H^2/8\pi$ and potential energy $E^2/8\pi$ per unit volume, so the time averages of its potential and kinetic energies are equal, whatever the amplitude A_m may be. If we consider many such wave trains with different amplitudes, the mean energy of a single train, obtained by averaging the square of the amplitude of the

[1] JEANS, *loc. cit.*

electric force, will therefore be kT.   Multiplying this by the number of
modes in the range $d\lambda$, we obtain the radiation density,

$$\rho_\lambda d\lambda = 8\pi kT\lambda^{-4}d\lambda. \tag{6}$$

This is called the Rayleigh-Jeans distribution law, after its discoverers.[1]
Although it agrees quite well with experiment in the region of large
wave lengths and high temperatures, in other words, for large values of
λT, it breaks down for small values of λT.   Of course, it cannot be used
when dealing with wave lengths of the same magnitude as the dimensions
of the hollow enclosure, since the approximations involved in deriving
equation (5) are then unjustifiable.   As to the situation at very small
wave lengths, it is often stated that the Rayleigh-Jeans law predicts an
unlimited accumulation of energy in this region, and so it does, because
of the factor λ^{-4}.   So far as we know, there is no lower limit to the
possible wave length of radiation, and, therefore, no upper limit for
ρ_λ as λ decreases.   The trouble is that in this region the average energy
of a wave train is not kT (see equation (9)).   Also, the use of a perfectly
reflecting enclosure in our proof is an unjustified abstraction.   In
actuality, the wave trains owe their existence to the matter in the walls
or in the enclosure itself.   Now, the molecules which can absorb and
emit high frequencies must be characterized by large internal forces,
and it may occur that such molecules do not exist in sufficient numbers
to justify a continuous statistical analysis in discussing the mean energy
of a molecule or of a wave train.   The breakdown of the formula at
wave lengths large enough so that these considerations do not apply
is sufficient, however, to show that something is wrong with the assumptions used in our proof.   The experimental evidence as to this breakdown
was described in Chap. I and is conclusive.

2. PLANCK'S DISTRIBUTION LAW

The preceding paragraphs give a sufficient description of the difficulties into which we fall by applying classical theory to derive the
distribution law of black-body radiation.   Planck was led by an ingenious
argument to the assumption that the energy of a linear oscillator can
assume only the discrete values

$$0, h\nu, 2h\nu, \cdots nh\nu, \cdots .$$

Let us apply this idea to the modes of vibration of the Hohlraum, considering each mode as a linear oscillator.   The assumption that the
energy of each mode can take only the values $nh\nu$ invalidates the result
that the average energy associated with each wave train is kT.   Now,
when we are dealing with an aggregate of quantized systems, the following extension of Boltzmann's law holds true.   If the possible energies of a

[1] Rayleigh, *Phil. Mag.*, **49**, 539 (1900); Jeans, *ibid*. **17**, 239 (1909).

quantized system are $E_1, E_2 \ldots$, then the numbers of atoms in these energy states are proportional to

$$p_1 e^{-E_1/kT}, \, p_2 e^{-E_2/kT}, \quad \ldots \, , \quad p_n e^{-E_n/kT}, \quad \ldots . \tag{7}$$

The quantity p_n is a number called the *a priori* probability of the state. Generally, it is equal to the number of possible states of motion of the system in which it has the energy E_n. In the case of the oscillator, each energy state corresponds to one definite state of motion, so all the p_n's equal one. Now let the number of oscillators, *i.e.*, modes of vibration, in the state of lowest energy be N_0. From equation (7), the total number will be

$$N = N_0 + N_0 e^{-h\nu/kT} + \cdots + N_0 e^{-nh\nu/kT} + \cdots ,$$

since $E_2 - E_1 = E_3 - E_2 = \cdots = h\nu$. The energy of the modes carrying n quanta is

$$nh\nu \, N_0 e^{-nh\nu/kT} ,$$

the total energy is

$$\sum_{n=0}^{n=\infty} nh\nu N_0 e^{-nh\nu/kT} ,$$

and so the average energy of one mode will be

$$\overline{E} = \frac{\Sigma nh\nu \cdot N_0 e^{-nh\nu/kT}}{\Sigma N_0 e^{-nh\nu/kT}} = h\nu \frac{\Sigma n e^{-nx}}{\Sigma e^{-nx}}, \; (n = 0 \cdots \infty), \tag{8}$$

where we have written $x = h\nu/kT$.

The denominator is a geometric series and is equal to $1/(1 - e^{-x})$. The numerator is the derivative of the denominator with its sign changed, that is, $e^{-x}/(1 - e^{-x})^2$. Therefore,

$$\overline{E} = \frac{h\nu}{e^x - 1} = \frac{h\nu}{e^{h\nu/kT} - 1}. \tag{9}$$

To obtain Planck's distribution law, we need only multiply $\overline{E}$ by the total number of modes of vibration having frequencies between ν and $\nu + d\nu$, secured from equation (5) by substituting $\lambda = c/\nu$. We get, for the energy density between these frequencies,

$$\rho_\nu d\nu = \rho_\lambda d\lambda = \frac{8\pi \nu^2 d\nu}{c^3} \overline{E} = \frac{8\pi h\nu^3 d\nu}{c^3} \frac{1}{e^{h\nu/kT} - 1} = \frac{8\pi hcd\lambda}{\lambda^5} \frac{1}{e^{hc/\lambda kT} - 1}. \tag{10}$$

The energy density per unit frequency range ρ_ν is not the same as ρ_λ, for $d\nu = -cd\lambda/\lambda^2$. It is quite customary to write ρ_λ in the form

$$\rho_\lambda = c_1 \lambda^{-5} \frac{1}{e^{c_2/\lambda T} - 1}. \tag{11}$$

The value of c_1, calculated from the universal constants involved, is $4.93 \cdot 10^{-15}$ if λ and $d\lambda$ are in centimeters, and $4 \cdot 93 \cdot 10^{25}$ if they are in Ångström units. The value of c_2 in c.g.s. units is 1.432 cm. degrees, as calculated from the universal constants. This is in excellent agreement with the experimental value of Coblentz.[1] There is some

[1] Bureau Standards, *Bull.* **15**, 529 (1920).

confusion as to the definition of c_2. Often it is given as 14,320, with the implication that λ is to be expressed in microns, which is the usual procedure in experimental papers on this subject.

It is important to examine the form assumed by ρ_ν for long wave lengths or high temperatures, perhaps, it is better to say, the region of high values of λT. In this domain, $e^{h\nu/kT} - 1$ approximates to $h\nu/kT$ and $\bar{E}$ is nearly equal to the value kT derived from the equipartition theorem. This carries with it the validity of the Rayleigh-Jeans law in this region, in agreement with experimental results. The physical basis for the asymptotic approach of Planck's law to the classical distribution is easily seen. When we deal with large wave lengths, the step $h\nu$ between adjacent energy levels is small, and conditions must approach those characteristic of systems with their energies distributed continuously. Likewise, at high temperatures, the ratio of $h\nu$ to the average energy of a mode of vibration is smaller, and the effects introduced by the discrete character of the possible energy values are less prominent. The reader can easily show that Planck's law approaches the Rayleigh-Jeans law if h approaches zero. Now let us consider the form assumed by Planck's law when the expression $e^{h\nu/kT}$ in the denominator is large compared with unity—that is, when λT is small. It becomes

$$\rho_\nu = \frac{8\pi h\nu^3}{c^3} e^{-h\nu/kT}, \rho_\lambda = 8\pi hc\lambda^{-5} e^{-hc/\lambda kT} = c_1\lambda^{-5} e^{-c_2/\lambda T},$$

which is Wien's law.[1]

This approximation is an excellent one throughout the visible region, up to very high temperatures; for example, if $\lambda = 6,000\text{Å}$ and $T = 3,000°\text{K}$, $e^{c_2/\lambda T}$ is about 2,200; under these conditions the difference between the two laws is below the limits of present day errors of measurement. It is useful to have an appreciation of the energy distribution which is the basis of Wien's law. If the energy step $h\nu$ is large and T is small, then the number of molecules in the second quantized level is small compared with the number in the level of zero energy and the number in all higher levels can be neglected entirely. The average energy is approximately

$$\frac{h\nu e^{-h\nu/kT}}{1 + e^{-h\nu/kT}},$$

or $h\nu e^{-h\nu/kT}$, since the second term in the denominator is negligible. Multiplying this by the number of modes of vibration between ν and $\nu + d\nu$, we get Wien's law.

3. STEFAN'S LAW

The total energy density of black-body radiation is given by

$$\rho = \int_0^\infty \rho_\nu d\nu = \frac{8\pi h}{c^3}\left(\frac{kT}{h}\right)^4 \int_0^\infty \frac{(h\nu/kT)^3\, d(h\nu/kT)}{e^{h\nu/kT} - 1}.$$

[1] *Ann. Physik*, **58**, 662 (1896).

Expanding by actual division, we have

$$\frac{1}{(e^x - 1)} = \frac{1}{e^x(1 - e^{-x})} = e^{-x} + e^{-2x} + \cdots$$

and integrating by parts, term by term, we find that

$$\int_0^\infty (e^{-x} + e^{-2x} + \cdots)x^3 dx = 6\left(1 + \frac{1}{2^4} + \cdots + \frac{1}{n^4} \cdots \right) = \frac{\pi^4}{15}$$

Therefore,

$$\rho = aT^4, \text{ where } a = \frac{8\pi^5 k^4}{15h^3 c^3}. \tag{12}$$

The total radiation per second from unit surface of a black body is $c\rho/4$. Thus, the constant in Stefan's law takes the value $ac/4$, that is, if the total radiation is σT^4, then

$$\sigma = \frac{2\pi^5 k^4}{15 c^2 h^3} = (5.714 \pm 0.006)10^{-5}, \tag{13}$$

in c.g.s. units. The experimental values obtained for σ show a disquieting range of variation.[1] A reasonable mean value is $5.74 \cdot 10^{-5}$ in absolute c.g.s. units, while we obtain $5.71 \cdot 10^{-5}$ from equation (13), using the values of the universal constants given in the appendix. The latter value agrees with that of Coblentz (loc. cit.).

Differentiating Planck's law, with respect to λ, holding T constant, and setting the result equal to zero, we find the condition which determines $\lambda_{max}T$. Writing $x = h\nu/kT$ as before, it is $(1 - x_{max}/5)e^{x_{max}} = 1 \cdot$ By trial, the only real root of this equation is 4.9651, whence

$$\lambda_{max}T = \frac{hc}{4.9651\,k} = 0.2884 \text{ cm. degrees.}$$

The value of $\lambda_{max}T$ found by Lummer and Pringsheim[2] was 0.294 cm. degrees.

4. EINSTEIN'S DERIVATION OF PLANCK'S DISTRIBUTION LAW

The above proof of Planck's law may be criticized because it depends on the use of classical theory in getting the number of modes of vibration per unit wave-length interval, and upon non-classical assumptions in getting the average energy of each mode. Einstein[3] has given a proof which depends only on the most general assumptions of the quantum theory, of thermodynamics, and of statistical mechanics. Following his original treatment, we consider the entities in a black-body enclosure which give rise to the constituent $\rho_\nu d\nu$ of the radiation. Let us suppose, for simplicity, that they are atoms existing only in discrete energy states. Consider two quantized states of energies E_1 and E_2, where

[1] See Planck, "Wärmestrahlung," 5th ed., p. 64.
[2] Verh. d. Deutsch. physik. Ges. **2**, 176 (1900).
[3] Verh. d. Deutsch. physik. Ges. **18**, 318 (1916); Physik. Z., **18**, 121 (1917).

$E_2 > E_1$, having *a priori* probabilities p_1 and p_2. In the Hohlraum at temperature T, the numbers of atoms in these states are

$$n_1 = n_0 p_1 e^{-\frac{E_1}{kT}} \text{ and } n_2 = n_0 p_2 e^{-\frac{E_2}{kT}},$$

where n_0 is the number of atoms which would be in a state of zero energy having unit statistical weight. We *postulate*, that there is a probability

$$A_{21} dt$$

that in time dt, an atom in state 2 will pass spontaneously to state 1 with the emission of light. A_{21} corresponds to the existence of the radiation loss from an accelerated electron in classical theory. We define a probability

$$B_{12} \rho_\nu dt$$

that an atom in state 1 will pass to state 2 in time dt by absorption of radiation in the neighborhood of the frequency ν. B_{12} is supposed to contain a factor which depends on the width $\Delta\nu$ of the range of frequencies which are capable of carrying the atoms from the lower state to the upper state. Other frequencies are not supposed to affect the atom in state 1. There is also a probability,

$$B_{21} \rho_\nu dt,$$

that an atom in state 2 will pass to state 1 in time dt because of the presence of radiation of frequency ν. The quantities B_{12} and B_{21} are called the coefficients of positive and negative absorption ("positive und negative Einstrahlung"). The introduction of the coefficient B_{21} corresponds to the fact that on the classical theory the rate of emission of an atom may be increased when radiation falls on it with appropriate phase relations. (Example: Left-handed circularly polarized light falls on a right-handed circular rotator, opposing its rotation, so that the deceleration of the rotator is greater than that due to the damping forces of its own field, and its rate of radiation is increased.)

When thermal equilibrium is attained, the number of transitions from state 2 to state 1 must be equal to the number of transitions from state 1 to state 2. That is,

$$n_2(A_{21} + B_{21}\, \rho_\nu) = n_1 B_{12}\, \rho_\nu, \tag{14}$$

or

$$p_2 e^{-\frac{E_2}{kT}}(A_{21} + B_{21}\, \rho_\nu) = p_1 e^{-\frac{E_1}{kT}} B_{12}\, \rho_\nu. \tag{15}$$

Now at very high temperatures, ρ_ν varies directly with T. Wien's displacement law requires that

$$\rho_\nu = \alpha \nu^3 f\!\left(\frac{\nu}{T}\right) = \alpha T^3 F\!\left(\frac{\nu}{T}\right).$$

The variation of F at high temperature for a fixed finite ν is the same as its variation with ν when ν is small compared with a fixed finite value of T. The Rayleigh-Jeans law shows that in the region of small ν/T, F is proportional to ν^2/T^2 and ρ_ν varies directly with T. Therefore, at very high temperatures, A_{21} may be neglected in comparison with $B_{21}\rho_\nu$ and equation (15) reduces to the form,

$$p_2 B_{21} = p_1 B_{12}. \tag{16}$$

From equations (15) and (16) we see that

$$\rho_\nu = \frac{A_{21}/B_{21}}{e^{\frac{E_2 - E_1}{kT}} - 1}. \tag{17}$$

But Wien's displacement law, equation (2), shows that we must put

$$\frac{A_{21}}{B_{21}} = \alpha \nu^3, \tag{18}$$

$$E_2 - E_1 = h\nu, \tag{19}$$

and therefore,

$$\rho_\nu = \frac{\alpha \nu^3}{e^{\frac{h\nu}{kT}} - 1}. \tag{20}$$

At the present stage, h and α appear only as constants of proportionality which must be evaluated by experiments, or by an appeal to limiting cases where more complete information can be obtained. In the region of small ν/T, the Rayleigh-Jeans formula holds true, and

$$\rho_\nu = \frac{8\pi \nu^2 kT}{c^3},$$

so that we must have

$$\alpha = \frac{8\pi h}{c^3}.$$

The important point is, we have here a proof of Planck's law and of $\Delta E = h\nu$, depending on the first and second laws of thermodynamics, Boltzmann's distribution law, the hypothesis of detailed balance between the absorption and emission processes, the existence of quantized states, Wien's displacement law, and the validity of the Rayleigh-Jeans formula for small ν/T. All of these underlying relations are extremely well founded. The reasoning is essentially an application of the law of mass action to the equilibrium,

$$\text{excited atom} \rightleftarrows \text{atom} + \text{quantum}.$$

$B_{12}\rho_\nu$ and $A_{21} + B_{21}\rho_\nu$ are proportional to the velocity coefficients of the two opposing reactions, so that the equilibrium constant is the ratio of these quantities. The emissions corresponding to the term $B_{21}\rho_\nu$ are "catalyzed" by the incoming quanta which cause them, for these quanta are simply scattered and therefore lose no energy.

Einstein's proof of Planck's law does not depend on the hypothesis of unidirectional quanta, since no mention of the nature of radiation is made in the above demonstration. However, in another section of his 1917 paper, he showed that if the quanta are unidirectional, the pressure they exert on molecules which absorb or emit them will just suffice to maintain the average translational energy at the value $3kT/2$, predicted by statistical mechanics. This result is misinterpreted frequently, and is supposed to be a proof that the average energy cannot be maintained at this value by any other type of quantum. The truth is that the best evidence for the existence of unidirectional quanta comes from other fields of investigation, such as the photoelectric effect, now to be discussed, and the experiments described in Secs. **13, 14,** and **15.**

5. THE PHOTOELECTRIC EFFECT AND THE INVERSE PHOTOELECTRIC EFFECT

The ejection of electrons when light, X-rays, or gamma rays fall on a substance is a phenomenon which is by no means confined to metals; but in the case of ordinary light it is much more prominent and easily studied for metals than for non-conductors. It is often thought of as a surface effect, although radiation can also free electrons from their usual positions in the interior of non-conducting substances. The essential facts are these:

1. For every substance there is a wave length called the "photoelectric threshold" above which no emission occurs. This is large for electropositive elements and decreases as the element becomes more electronegative. However, the threshold value depends on the state of the surface as regards crystal structure, adsorbed gas, etc., and the results of different investigators may vary by large amounts. For the alkali metals, the threshold lies in the visible; for most other metals and for solid non-metals it is in the ultra-violet. Some typical values[1] are as follows: Li, $5,200 - 5,260$ A.; Na, $5,830 - 6,850$; K, $6,120 - 10,000$; Fe, $2,870 - 3,150$; Ni, $2.700 - 3,030$; Zn, $3,020 - 4,010$; Rb, $> 10,000$; Cs, $> 10,000$; W, $2,300 - 2,735$; Pt, $1,850 - 3,020$.

2. The electrons emerge with all velocities from zero up to a maximum value v, such that

$$\frac{mv^2}{2} = h\nu - h\nu_0, \tag{21}$$

where ν_0 is the frequency corresponding to the threshold wave length. The reason is that $h\nu_0$ is the minimum work required to bring an electron through the surface. If the electron comes from a deeper layer of atoms, the velocity will be smaller, since work must be done to bring it to the surface.

---

[1] Taken from GUDDEN, "Lichtelektrische Erscheinungen", Springer, Berlin (1928).

3. The photoelectric current is proportional to the intensity of the light over a range of as much as one-million fold.

4. In a general way, photoelectric efficiency is small. Several hundred absorbed quanta are required to eject one electron from many metal surfaces.

5. The effect begins within $3 \cdot 10^{-9}$ second after the light strikes the surface, as Lawrence and Beams[1] have shown. This is an upper limit to the possible lag.

The validity of equation (21) is closely connected with the existence of light quanta of energy $h\nu$. Careful tests of this equation have been made by Millikan[2] in the region of ordinary light, using Na, K, and Li surfaces prepared in vacuum. The method is to determine the back electromotive force Φ between the sensitive surface and a receiving electrode, connected to a quadrant electrometer, which is just sufficient to prevent the fastest photoelectrons from reaching this electrode and causing a deflection of the electrometer. If there were no contact potential between the alkali metal surface and the receiver, the work which would have to be done on each electron to reduce its velocity to zero should be

$$\Phi e = \frac{mv^2}{2} = h\nu - h\nu_0, \tag{22}$$

where Φ and e are measured in electrostatic units. But, if a contact potential Φ_c accelerates the electron a greater stopping potential Φ_s must be applied, such that

$$(\Phi_s - \Phi_c)e = h\nu - h\nu_0. \tag{23}$$

Of course, Φ_c may be either positive or negative. Since Φ_c is unknown, this equation cannot be used to test equation (21) directly, but, if the stopping voltages are determined for a number of different wave lengths, the curve showing Φ_s as a function of ν should be a straight line and its slope should be h/e. Since e is known, this offers a method of determining h. Millikan's data lie very accurately on a straight line, and yield the result $h = 6.56 \cdot 10^{-27}$.

In the X-ray region, the law of equation (21) is also closely verified. Here the term $h\nu$ is very large compared with the energy required to remove an electron from the surface, and the term $h\nu_0$ is often left out of consideration. In this region, however, the best way of proving that a quantum has the energy $h\nu$ consists in a study of the *inverse photoelectric effect*. If a fast-moving electron is stopped by the metal target of an X-ray tube, part or all of its energy may be changed into radiation. This radiation is called the "Bremsstrahlung" (literally, deceleration radiation) or "continuous radiation." Assuming that

[1] *Phys. Rev.*, **32**, 478 (1928).
[2] *Phys. Rev.*, **7**, 362 (1916). See also his book "The Electron," referred to at the end of Chap. II.

all the energy of an electron can be transformed into a single quantum, the maximum frequency which that quantum can possess will be given by

$$\Phi e = h\nu_{max}, \tag{24}$$

which is called the equation of Duane and Hunt.[1] As a matter of fact the continuous X-ray spectrum excited by electrons falling through a potential Φ has a sharp limit on the side of short wave lengths. Duane and his collaborators[2] have used equation (24) to measure h, finding the value $6.556 \cdot 10^{-27}$. In conclusion, all the experiments described support the expression $h\nu$ for the energy of a quantum of frequency ν. While the accuracy of measurement of h is in no case very great, the evidence favors the belief that h is really a constant over the whole range from the infra-red to the shortest gamma rays.

6. BOHR'S FUNDAMENTAL POSTULATES

We come now to the two fundamental postulates which Bohr used in working out his theory of the hydrogen atom and which he enunciated as the basis for studying the structure of all atoms. Each postulate arose from careful consideration of experimental data. He was confronted by evidence that the hydrogen atom contains a single electron revolving around a positive nucleus, and that both electron and nucleus are surrounded by inverse square force fields. But also, the hydrogen atom gives a spectrum of well-defined lines and the question arises, how can any atom so constituted produce a line spectrum? We saw in Chap. I, Sec. 4, that a line spectrum can be produced by an atomic model made up of independent harmonic oscillators, for the frequency of such an oscillator does not depend on its amplitude and will not change as the motion dies away. But under the inverse square law, if the laws of gross electrodynamics apply, the loss of energy due to radiation will cause the electron to spiral into the nucleus, in contradiction with the high degree of permanence so characteristic of matter in general. As the orbit becomes smaller, the frequency should increase and a broad band of wave lengths should be emitted.

It must not be thought that this disagrees with the result that a stable elliptic orbit is pursued by a particle moving under the inverse square law. In the derivation of this law (Chap. IV, Sec. 6), forces due to radiation are not taken into account. In treatises on electricity (such as Richardson's "Electron Theory of Matter," p. 266) it is shown that a charge which is subjected to an acceleration $\ddot{x}$ experiences a force $2e^2\ddot{x}/3c^3$, which is generally so directed as to retard its motion. This is the so-called radiation force and is independent of the charge distribution and the nature of the motion, so long as dx/dt is not too close

---

[1] *Phys. Rev.*, **6**, 166 (1917).

[2] BLAKE and DUANE, *Phys. Rev.*, **10**, 625 (1917); DUANE, PALMER, and CHI-SUN-YEH, *J. O. S. A.*, **5**, 376 (1921).

to c.   Now the computation which shows the existence of this force depends on the validity of the laws of mechanics and of electrodynamics, as well as the expression (Appendix VIII) for the force on a charge in terms of the electric and magnetic field strengths which act upon it. Bohr saw fit to question this computation, because of the experimental truth that atoms *do* exist in stable states without radiation and that they *do* emit sharp spectral lines.   The result is the first fundamental postulate of the quantum theory of atomic structure, a rational generalization of Planck's assumption that his oscillators could have only certain discrete amounts of energy.

1. *Among the conceivable states of motion of the parts of an isolated atom there is a set of stationary states in which the atom can remain a finite time without radiating.   When in these states, the atom possesses a stability unexplainable on the basis of classical mechanics and electrodynamics, of such a sort that every spontaneous change from a stationary state of motion results in a transition to another stationary state.*

The words, "stationary state," do not imply that the particles of the atom are at rest.   By "stationary" is meant that the motion of the particles is periodic, the energy of the system being constant.   These conditions of the atom are often called "steady states" or "quantized states," or "energy levels," just as in the case of the Planck oscillators.

Bohr's second assumption deals with the emission of radiation and is a generalization of Planck's assumption in regard to emission by linear oscillators:

2. *The emission of radiation by an atom or a molecule occurs during a transition from a stationary state of energy E_2 to another having a lower energy E_1.   The quantum emitted can be absorbed completely by a similar atom, in the stationary state of energy E_1, and raises it to the state of energy E_2.   In its interaction with spectroscopic instruments the quantum behaves as though it consisted of a nearly monochromatic wave train whose wave length λ is given by the relation*

$$\epsilon = E_2 - E_1 = \frac{hc}{\lambda} = h\nu. \tag{25}$$

The absorption of radiation by an atom or molecule occurs during a transition from a stationary state of energy E_1 to another having a higher energy E_2.   The frequency of the absorbed radiation is given by equation (25).

In postulate 1, the word "spontaneous" is an essential one.   If an atom is temporarily exposed to light of a wave length which it cannot absorb, its state of motion is altered, but after the disturbance has passed it returns to its original scheme of orbital motion.   Even in this case the stationary state is a *different* one, if we agree to consider the velocity of the atom as a necessary datum in describing the stationary state.   It must be emphasized that E_1 and E_2 include the kinetic energy of translation.   When an atom initially at rest absorbs a quantum, it recoils, for the quantum carries momentum as well as energy.   The energy of the quantum is divided between giving the atom kinetic energy of translation, and increasing its internal energy.

These postulates are well constructed and have stood the test of time, for they are the expression of experimental truths and do not depend in any way on the detailed structure of the atom or the nature of radiation. They enable us to treat many questions without any reference to a detailed mechanism of the processes occurring. With the aid of equation (25) we can often read out of spectra the energies of the stationary states of an atom, and thereby can predict the possible transfers of energy in collisions between atoms and electrons, or we can study these energy transfers in discharge tubes and can state with confidence that certain lines will occur in the spectrum of the material studied. But there is a limit to the information that can be gained in this way, and the directions in which progress can be made are best seen by writing down the questions which suggest themselves, relative to the choice of an atomic model:

1. What is to be our picture of the constituent parts of the atom?

2. What are the dynamical laws governing the motion of these parts?

3. What conditions are imposed to determine the stationary states of motion which actually exist?

4. What is our idea of the emission process, of the quantum of light emitted, of the interaction of matter with radiation, or of matter with matter, as in a collision of two atoms?

The fact is emphasized that a great variety of theories might be proposed to answer the above questions, all of which would yield the same relations between *observable quantities.* Clerk Maxwell pointed out long ago that an infinity of hidden mechanisms can be imagined, all of which will produce a given motion of the observable parts of a dynamical system. This is obvious from the equations of motion; suppose that some of the quantities occurring in them specify the position of a body while others determine certain forces acting on the body, since they describe the configuration of the bodies which exert these forces. The geometrical interpretation of the latter coordinates could be changed in any way, and still the former would vary in the same fashion, since the mathematical connections are unchanged. *There is probably no unique physical solution of the problem of atomic structure.* Indeed it is problematic whether we need to answer some of the above questions at all. It seems possible (Chap. XVII) to obtain equations which describe the connections between observable quantities without referring to any model, but it helps greatly if we have a model to think about. An excellent explanation of a vast body of experimental facts is obtained if we use the model proposed by Bohr. He assumed that electrons and nuclei inside the atom maintain their independent existence as point charges surrounded by inverse square fields of force and that Newton's laws of motion are obeyed. The accepted answer to question (3) can be understood better after we have given some illustrations.

7. THEORY OF THE HYDROGEN ATOM AND THE TWO-DIMENSIONAL OSCILLATOR

Anticipating a complete discussion in Chap. V, we give the simplest conceivable theory of the hydrogen atom and others of similar structure. Consider a single electron of mass m, revolving in a circle of radius a about a nucleus having the charge $+Ze$, so heavy by comparison that it may be assumed to be at rest. If $Z = 1$, we are dealing with the neutral hydrogen atom; if $Z = 2$ we have a singly ionized helium atom, and so on. Since the electrostatic attraction, directed toward the nucleus, is equal to the mass of the electron times its radial acceleration, we have

$$\frac{Ze^2}{a^2} = \frac{mv^2}{a}, \tag{26}$$

where v is the velocity of the electron. The kinetic energy is $mv^2/2$. The potential energy is $-Ze^2/a$ provided we arbitrarily make it equal to zero when the electron is at infinity, for we must do an amount of work Ze^2/a on the system in order to remove the electron, initially at rest in the orbit of radius a, to a position of rest at an infinite distance. Therefore, the total energy E is given by

$$E = \frac{1}{2}mv^2 - \frac{Ze^2}{a}. \tag{27}$$

Let p be the angular momentum of the electron about the nucleus, that is

$$p = mav. \tag{28}$$

By equations (26) and (28) we eliminate v and a from the equation for the energy and, thus,

$$E = -\frac{me^4Z^2}{2p^2}. \tag{29}$$

At this point we postulate that the "allowed orbits" which actually occur in nature are those for which

$$2\pi p = nh, \tag{30}$$

where n is an integer. This *quantum condition* is a pure assumption. It is introduced independently to supplement the postulate 1, above. It leads to the energy values,

$$E_n = -\frac{2\pi^2 me^4 Z^2}{n^2 h^2}, \; n = 1, 2, \; \cdots \tag{31}$$

In a transition from the orbit characterized by $n = n_2$ to that for which $n = n_1$, (where n_2 is greater than n_1), the frequency emitted can be calculated by the aid of postulate 2,

$$h\nu = E_{n_2} - E_{n_1} = \frac{2\pi^2 me^4 Z^2}{h^2}\left(\frac{1}{n_1{}^2} - \frac{1}{n_2{}^2}\right). \tag{32}$$

Now it is a fact (Chap. V) that the most conspicuous lines in the visible and near ultra-violet spectrum of hydrogen—the famous Balmer series—have the frequencies which are obtained from equation (32) by substituting the usual values of m, e, and h, and placing $Z = 1$, $n_1 = 2$, and $n_2 = 3, 4, 5, \cdots$.   In fact, all the lines of hydrogen, ionized helium etc., predicted by equation (32) which lie in regions accessible to observation have actually been found at the expected places.

From equations (26), (28), and (30) we obtain the radius of the orbit as a function of the quantum number n:

$$a = \frac{n^2h^2}{4\pi^2Ze^2m} = \frac{n^2a_1}{Z}, \tag{33}$$

where a_1 is the radius of the innermost orbit of the hydrogen atom, obtained by putting $n = 1$, $Z = 1$.   Equations (28), (30), and (33) together show that the velocity decreases as the radius increases, and the limiting case $n \to \infty$ corresponds to an atom with its electron *at rest* at an infinite distance from the nucleus.   The total energy is zero, since we so determined the constant in the potential energy that it approaches zero when a approaches ∞.

In addition to these quantized orbits, the electron can move on orbits (hyperbolas or parabolas) in which it can scarcely be said to belong to the nucleus, since it passes near it only once and moves away to an infinite distance.   Such orbits are usually called unquantized, because their shapes and dimensions may vary continuously and thus they have a continuous range of energies.   The quantum conditions are not applied to systems which are not periodic.   A simple calculation shows that for such orbits the total energy of the nucleus and the electron (we can scarcely refer to the combination as an atom) is always positive. From an unquantized orbit, the electron can pass into one of the quantized orbits with emission of radiation.   If the transition begins when the electron has velocity v and is at a distance r from the nucleus, the initial energy is $\frac{1}{2}mv^2 - Ze^2/r$ and the final energy is given by equation (31).   The frequency of the emitted radiation is the difference of these energies divided by h, for Bohr's second postulate applies to *all* emission and absorption processes, whether the orbits are quantized or not. In particular, if the electron falls into the lowest quantized orbit we have

$$h\nu = \frac{1}{2}mv^2 - \frac{Ze^2}{r} + \frac{2\pi^2me^4Z^2}{h^2}. \tag{34}$$

Equation (34) predicts a continuous spectrum because r and v can take all values.   The continuous spectrum lies at frequencies higher than any which can be emitted in a transition between quantized orbits.

The whole situation is summed up neatly by the use of an *energy diagram*, in which horizontal lines are plotted at ordinates proportional to the energies of the atom in its various quantized states.   The state of zero energy (ionized atom with the missing electron at rest at infinity) is placed near the top. Figure 2 is such a diagram for hydrogen. The energy equation (31) is more often written in the form,

$$E_n = -\frac{RhcZ^2}{n^2},\qquad(35)$$

where R is the *Rydberg constant,* $2\pi^2me^4/h^3c$. The energies are written on the left. It is customary, however, to use another quantity as a measure of the energy, namely, the wave number. If an electron falls from the infinite orbit to an orbit of energy E, the wave length emitted is given by $hc/\lambda = E$, or $1/\lambda = E/hc$; $1/\lambda$ is the number of waves per centimeter and is a quantity of convenient magnitude (20,000 cm.$^{-1}$ for green light of wave length 5,000Å). It is called the "wave-number" or "spectroscopic term" of the orbit, and is denoted by $\tilde{\nu}$ or T. Quite similarly, a light quantum is often described by giving its wave number, in which case only the symbol $\tilde{\nu}$ is used. In the energy diagram, a spectrum line is designated by drawing an arrow from the initial to the final level. In the diagram for hydrogen, beginning at the left, we have a series of arrows ending on the lowest level of the atom; the corresponding wave numbers are given by the formula,

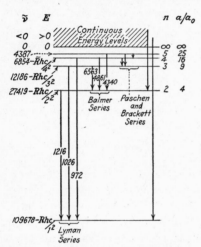

Fig. 2.—The energy diagram of the hydrogen atom.

$$\tilde{\nu} = R\left(\frac{1}{1^2} - \frac{1}{n^2}\right),\ n = 2, 3, 4 \cdots,$$

and the lines emitted in these transitions are collectively known as the Lyman series, after their discoverer. The wave lengths in this series converge to a limiting position as $n \to \infty$ and the wave number $R/1^2$ is called the limit of the series. Next, we come to the Balmer lines, the final orbit being the one for which $n = 2$. The formula giving their wave numbers is

$$\tilde{\nu} = R\left(\frac{1}{2^2} - \frac{1}{n^2}\right),\ n = 3, 4, 5, \cdots,$$

so that the limit is at $R/2^2$. A few other transitions are marked. On the extreme right, we have two arrows representing transitions from unquantized states (indicated by a shaded band) into the two most firmly bound orbits of the atom. Obviously, transitions of the kind shown by the longest arrow correspond to a continuous spectrum beginning at the limit of the Lyman series and extending toward higher frequencies. Similarly, the other arrow represents a typical emission process giving a continuous spectrum on the short-wave side of the Balmer series limit. Both of these continuous bands are actually observed.

We now take up a problem with two degrees of freedom—the two-dimensional analogue of the linear oscillator. Let a mass m be acted on by a force $-k_1x$ parallel to the x-axis, and a force $-k_2y$ parallel to the y-axis. Write $p_x = m\dot{x}$, $p_y = m\dot{y}$, so that the kinetic energy is

$$T = \frac{1}{2m}(p_x{}^2 + p_y{}^2). \tag{36}$$

The potential energy is

$$V = \tfrac{1}{2}(k_1x^2 + k_2y^2). \tag{37}$$

Since the x-component of force depends only on the x-coordinate, and the y-component only on the y-coordinate, the motion is a superposition of two simple harmonic vibrations performed at right angles,

$$x = A \cos (2\pi\nu_1 t + a), \tag{38}$$
$$y = B \cos (2\pi\nu_2 t + b),$$

where $\nu_1 = (k_1/m)^{\frac{1}{2}}/2\pi$, $\nu_2 = (k_2/m)^{\frac{1}{2}}/2\pi$.

In agreement with Planck's postulate about the possible energy levels of harmonic oscillators, we assume that the energy of the first is

$$E_1 = n_1 h\nu_1,$$

and that of the second is

$$E_2 = n_2 h\nu_2.$$

This illustrates a general feature of such problems. We need one extraneous equation, or quantum condition, for each degree of freedom, to determine the values of the constants of integration introduced in the solution of the equations of motion, so that the allowed energy values can be calculated.

Applying the frequency condition of Postulate 2 to this problem we see that the theory leads us to expect that light will be emitted and absorbed having the frequencies,

$$\nu = \frac{E' - E''}{h} = (n_1' - n_1'')\nu_1 + (n_2' - n_2'')\nu_2, \tag{39}$$

where n_1' and n_2' are the quantum numbers for the initial state and n_1'' and n_2'' those for the final state. Spectra of this kind are known in the infra-red; thus hydrogen chloride which has only one vibrational degree of freedom and therefore only one characteristic frequency of vibration, ν_1, has absorption bands at $\lambda\lambda 3.46\mu$ and 1.76μ, or wave numbers $\tilde{\nu} = 2,877$ and $5,657$, respectively, corresponding approximately to the prediction of equation (39), if $\nu_2 = 0, \nu_1 = 2,877c$ and $n_1' - n_1'' = 1$ and 2, respectively. Further examples of this type of spectrum will be given in Chap. XII.

8. THE QUANTUM CONDITIONS

The allowed energy levels of the hydrogen atom are picked out by assuming that its angular momentum is a multiple of $h/2\pi$, while the oscillator is quantized by setting its energy equal to a multiple of $h\nu$. The problem is, what is the general rule of which these assumptions are special cases? A set of rules which is found to yield a great variety of correct formulas was discovered independently and about simultaneously by W. Wilson,[1] Sommerfeld,[2] and Ishiwara.[3] They are usually referred to as the Sommerfeld quantum conditions. They apply to systems having periodic coordinates, like isolated atoms and molecules. Consider such a system, having n degrees of freedom.[4] *Suppose we can choose coordinates q such that each generalized momentum p_k is a function only of the corresponding q_k. Then the stationary states are those for which*

$$\oint p_k dq_k = n_k h, \tag{40}$$

where n_k is an integer and each integral is extended over a complete cycle of the variable q_k. The symbol $\oint$ is used to indicate that the integral extends over a cycle of q_k. In the case of a coordinate which does not pass through a cycle of values, like the azimuth φ of the electron in hydrogen, the integral is taken over a range which brings the system back to its original configuration. The important thing is the physical periodicity of the system, not the periodicity of its coordinates.

Let us apply these conditions to the examples just given. For the hydrogen atom with its electron on a circular orbit, the kinetic energy is

$$T = \tfrac{1}{2} m a^2 \dot{\varphi}^2, \tag{41}$$

where φ is the azimuth. We have,

$$p_\varphi = \frac{\partial T}{\partial \dot{\varphi}} = m a^2 \dot{\varphi}, \tag{42}$$

so that the momentum variable conjugate to φ is simply the angular momentum. There is only one quantum condition because the system has only one degree of freedom. It is

$$\int_0^{2\pi} p_\varphi d\varphi = nh. \tag{43}$$

Now p_φ is constant so

$$2\pi p_\varphi = nh, \tag{44}$$

which is exactly the condition used in our previous treatment.

In the case of the two-dimensional oscillator,

$$T = \tfrac{1}{2} m (\dot{x}^2 + \dot{y}^2),$$

[1] *Phil. Mag.*, **29**, 795 (1913).

[2] *Ann. Physik*, **51**, 1 (1916).

[3] *Tokyo Math. Phys. Proc.*, **8**, 106, (1915).

[4] If unfamiliar with generalized coordinates, the reader should refer to Chap. IV, Sec. **3**.

and

$$p_x = \frac{\partial T}{\partial \dot{x}} = m\dot{x}, \quad p_y = \frac{\partial T}{\partial \dot{y}} = m\dot{y}.$$

We must now express these quantities in terms of the coordinates, as given by equation (38). We have

$$m\dot{x} = -2\pi\nu_1 mA \sin (2\pi\nu_1 t + a) = -2\pi\nu_1 m(\pm \sqrt{A^2 - x^2}), \quad (45)$$

and a similar equation for $m\dot{y}$. Since p_x depends only on x, and p_y only on y, we see that x and y are coordinates suitable for use in applying the quantum conditions, in the form

$$\oint p_x dx = n_1 h, \qquad \oint p_y dy = n_2 h. \quad (46)$$

The range of integration for x is one complete oscillation, from 0 to $+A$, to $-A$, and back to 0 again. A similar statement holds for y. The question now arises, how can this integration yield a finite result, since the upper limit $x = 0$, is the same as the lower limit? The point is, p_x is a *double valued* function of x, as indicated by the $\pm$ sign in equation (45). At each abscissa, the momentum p_x can be either positive or negative, depending on whether the direction of travel is right or left. The situation is easily understood by plotting p_x as a function of x (Fig. 3). This must not be confounded with a diagram of the actual motion. Starting at $x = 0$, with p_x positive, we pass to $x = +A$, and the contribution to the integral is represented by the area Q in the first quadrant. At A the veloc-

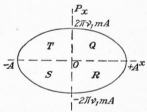

FIG. 3.—Phase diagram for the harmonic oscillator.

ity reverses, p_x becomes negative and the areas R and S in the diagram are traversed from right to left. At $-A$ the velocity reverses again and area T is added to the value of the integral as x passes from $-A$ to 0. Without carrying out the integration we can get the result from simple geometry, for the area of the ellipse is

$$\pi \cdot A \cdot 2\pi\nu_1 mA = 2\pi^2\nu_1 mA^2, \quad (47)$$

and this must be equal to $n_1 h$. Finally, the quantized values of the x- and y-amplitudes are given by

$$A^2 = \frac{n_1 h}{2\pi^2 \nu_1 m}, \quad B^2 = \frac{n_2 h}{2\pi^2 \nu_2 m}. \quad (48)$$

We can get the energy in a variety of ways. By use of equations (45), (47), and (48), the contribution to the energy due to the motion parallel to OX is found to be

$$E_x = \tfrac{1}{2}(m\dot{x}^2 + k_1 x^2) = \tfrac{1}{2}[m4\pi^2\nu_1^2(A^2 - x^2) + k_1 x^2],$$
$$= 2\pi^2\nu_1^2 mA^2 = n_1 h\nu_1.$$

Similarly, the contribution due to the y-oscillation is $n_2 h\nu_2$. These results agree with Planck's assumption mentioned at the end of Sec. **7**.

Summing up, the spectral evidence discussed here is overwhelmingly in favor of the fundamental assumptions and of the quantum conditions. We now discuss evidence of a quite different kind bearing on the Bohr postulates, but not on the quantum conditions.

9. THE RITZ COMBINATION PRINCIPLE AND THE CONSTANCY OF h

Long before Bohr gave his theory of the hydrogen atom, careful studies of spectra had revealed a regularity which was clearly formulated by Ritz. It bears his name and may be stated empirically as follows: If $\tilde{\nu}_a$ and $\tilde{\nu}_b$ are the wave numbers of two lines in the spectrum of a certain atom, it often happens that lines also occur at the wave numbers $\tilde{\nu}_a + \tilde{\nu}_b$ or $\tilde{\nu}_a - \tilde{\nu}_b$. This was a powerful tool in the analysis of spectra. It is explainable at once by means of the second Bohr postulate. If the energy levels involved in the emission of $\tilde{\nu}_a$ are E_1 and E_2, and those involved in the emission of $\tilde{\nu}_b$ are E_2 and E_3, where $E_1 < E_2 < E_3$, then

$$hc\tilde{\nu}_a = E_2 - E_1,$$
$$hc\tilde{\nu}_b = E_3 - E_2,$$

and
$$hc(\tilde{\nu}_a + \tilde{\nu}_b) = E_3 - E_1,$$

so that $\tilde{\nu}_a + \tilde{\nu}_b$ will be emitted in the jump from E_3 to E_1. Obviously, the emission of the difference frequency $\nu_a - \nu_b$ will not occur in this case. With the aid of an energy diagram like Fig. 2, the reader can easily see under what circumstances a difference frequency will be emitted. More often than not, lines which are predicted by naïve application of Ritz's principle do not occur. This failure to appear may usually be ascribed to the dynamical impossibility of a direct transition between the orbits in question.

The combination principle may be invoked to prove that in the equation $\epsilon = hc/\lambda$ the quantity hc is constant, within the accuracy of our spectroscopic measurements over the entire range from the infra-red to the shortest X-rays. This is reassuring, for quantum theory would have to be altered considerably if h were variable. Of course, the accuracy with which this is known to be true will vary in different parts of the range. What we know experimentally is that spectral lines a, b, c, are often found for which $\tilde{\nu}_a + \tilde{\nu}_b = \tilde{\nu}_c$. Starting with this, the proof that hc is not a function of wave length depends on our acceptance of an equation of the form $\epsilon = hc/\lambda$ for each spectral line, where ϵ simply means a definite number belonging to the initial state minus a definite number belonging to the final state.

The degree of reliance to be placed on the combination principle may be seen from an example of its application to the iron spectrum by Meggers.[1] Below, we compare the sum of the wave numbers of two

[1] *Astrophys. J.*, **60**, 60 (1924).

lines with that of two others which should yield the same value if the Ritz principle is correct.

$$\tilde{\nu}_{ab} = 18,184.979 \qquad \tilde{\nu}_{ad} = 19,404.864$$
$$\tilde{\nu}_{bc} = 19,169.445 \qquad \tilde{\nu}_{dc} = 17,949.554$$

$$37,354.424 \qquad\qquad 37,354.418$$

Today, the spectroscopist uses the Ritz principle as a sharp criterion, in deciding whether four lines arise from a group of four energy levels in the way described above.

10. CRITICAL POTENTIALS

When an atom or molecule is struck by a moving electron, the collision may or may not result in the transfer of energy between the electron and the internal mechanism of the atom. If the energy exchanged is entirely energy of translation of the collision-partners, the collision is termed "elastic," while, if the atom gains or loses internal energy, the collision is designated an "inelastic one." A similar nomenclature is applied to encounters between atoms and molecules. Inelastic collisions are further classified according to whether translational energy of the atoms or electrons is transferred to the internal mechanism of the atom, or the reverse. These two cases are termed "collisions of the first and second kinds," respectively.

The way in which these energy transfers occur has been studied principally by bombarding the atoms of a rarefied gas or vapor with rapidly moving electrons, though recently the interaction of excited atoms with unexcited ones has claimed much attention. This is partly due to the ease with which electrons can be obtained from a hot cathode, but principally to the fact that they are quite insensitive to elastic collisions, from the standpoint of energy loss, so that effects due to inelastic collisions can be clearly distinguished. A simple calculation based on the conservation of energy and of momentum gives us the loss of energy of an electron in an elastic collision with an atom of mass M originally at rest. Relative to stationary coordinates, on the average, the electron will lose a fraction of its energy equal to $2m/M$. Even for a gas of H atoms, this is only $1/922$, while for Hg atoms it is 200 times smaller. On the other hand, the fractional kinetic energy changes in a collision between two atoms are much larger.

Judging from our observations on macroscopic bodies, we should expect energy to be interchanged between electrons and the internal mechanism of atoms, regardless of their relative velocities. As mentioned in Chap. I, this is not true, a fact which furnishes one of the strongest supports of the theory of stationary states. The collisions of electrons of sufficiently low velocities with atoms or molecules are elastic. In describing what takes place at higher velocities it will be best to restrict ourselves here to the phenomena characteristic of atoms. As the energy of the electrons is increased a point is reached where the collisions are inelastic and energy is transferred to the atoms. This results in a quantum transition, in which the atom is carried to a stationary state of higher energy, and the potential at which this first occurs is called the "resonance potential." Often, though not always, the level reached by the atom is the one lying nearest to the normal energy level. At all potentials above the resonance potential, inelastic collisions occur which may have the same result as far as the atom is concerned, but the bombarding electron has kinetic energy left over after the collision. Increasing the potential further, we reach a value at which the energy of the electron is sufficient to raise the atom to another stationary state, and so on. Each potential at which a transition to a new energy level becomes possible is called a "resonance potential." The various resonance voltages are distinguished by calling them first, second, and so on, beginning with the lowest. All energy levels other than the one normally occupied are called "excited states" or "excited energy levels." When the atom has been brought into one of these states by direct electron impact, usually it can return to the normal level by emission of light. Sometimes, however, there are dynamical restrictions which prevent its return, in which case the atom is said to be in a "metastable" state. Eventually, a voltage is reached at which the bombarding electrons can completely separate an electron from the atom, leaving a positive ion which is eventually neutralized by picking up a stray electron. The minimum potential at which this occurs is called the "ionization potential," while critical potential is a more general term referring to both resonance and ionization. Obviously, an atom or molecule has many resonance potentials. Except in the case of hydrogen and helium, it also has a number of ionization potentials, since different electrons are bound to the atom with different amounts of energy.

In experiments on inelastic collisions, the energy of the electrons is imparted to them by allowing them to fall through known electric fields, so that the kinetic energy is given by the relation

$$V'e = \frac{mv^2}{2}, \tag{49}$$

where V' is the potential applied in electrostatic units. Now 300 volts correspond to one electrostatic unit of potential, so we have $V = 300\ V'$, if V is the value of V' expressed in volts, and the relation above becomes

$$\frac{Ve}{300} = \frac{mv^2}{2}. \tag{50}$$

An electron which has fallen through a potential difference of 5 volts is often called a 5-volt electron, and it is customary to refer to the critical energies required for inelastic collisions in terms of volts. Thus, we say "mercury has a resonance potential of 4.9 volts," or "the energy of the electrons was 60 volts." Of course, the volt is not a unit of energy, but convenience dictates this practice. There has been some talk of introducing an energy unit called the electron-volt, equal to the energy of an electron which has fallen through a potential difference of 1 volt. From equation (50), this unit is equal to $1.591 \cdot 10^{-12}$ ergs. It is used but little at present.

11. EXPERIMENTS ON CRITICAL POTENTIALS

Long before the advent of Bohr's theory, it was believed that a definite amount of energy is necessary to ionize an atom, and various experiments were devised to measure this quantity. An estimate which is correct as to order of magnitude can be obtained from studies of the discharge in an ordinary tube with two cold electrodes, combined with an approximate theory of the complicated phenomena of such a tube. Details of such studies are given by Townsend.[1]

Bergen Davis[2] approached the matter in a simpler way, by the use of the electrodeless ring discharge. If an alternating current of high frequency (perhaps several hundred kilocycles) is passed through a few turns of wire wound loosely around a bulb containing gas at a pressure of a few hundredths of a millimeter, a bright ring of luminosity is formed in the plane of the coil. Under suitable conditions this is due mainly to the electromotive force induced in the gas by the change of magnetic flux through the coil. The maximum potential gradient is easily calculated from the current in the coil and the constants of the circuit, so the energy acquired by an electron in traversing its mean free path can be found. If the pressure is gradually increased, the mean free path becomes smaller, until at last the great majority of the electrons have energies insufficient to ionize the atoms, and the discharge ceases to be luminous. The maximum potential gradient occurring during a cycle of the current multiplied by the kinetic theory value of the mean free path at this pressure of extinction may be taken as a measure of the voltage required for ionization.

The difficulty with all such methods is that the energies of the electrons are distributed over a broad range, and that it is difficult to ascertain the nature of the distribution. An arrangement in which the current and the potential can be varied independently is essential, and it is also very desirable that the velocity distribution of the electrons reaching a given point should be a narrow one. An apparatus satisfying these requirements was devised by Lenard,[3] the essentials of which are shown diagrammatically in Fig. 4. F is a hot-wire cathode, heated by a battery A. G is a metal gauze or grid. A voltage V_1, variable by means of a potentiometer arrangement B_1 is maintained between F and G, the

---

[1] "Electricity in Gases," Clarendon Press (1915).

[2] *Phys. Rev.*, **20**, 129 (1905).

[3] *Ann. Physik*, **8**, 149 (1902).

positive side being as shown, so that electrons are accelerated from
F to G. The gas pressure in the apparatus is so chosen that the mean
free path is comparable with the distance between electrodes. An
opposing field V_2, greater than V_1, is maintained between G and a metal
plate P. Electrons which pass through the grid are thrown back by
V_2, and do not reach P. If some of these electrons cause the atoms to
radiate, and if the wave lengths emitted are short enough, the light

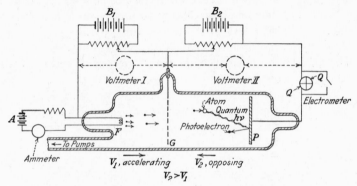

FIG. 4.—Lenard's critical potential apparatus.

ejects photoelectrons from P, charging the electrometer quadrants Q
positively. If some of the electrons ionize the atoms, the ions pass to P
and also charge the quadrants Q, positively. At certain values of V_1
the rate of charging shows fairly abrupt increases, which are interpreted
as due to the occurrence of inelastic collisions. Breaks due to resonance
and to ionization cannot be told apart by this method.

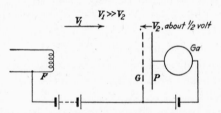

FIG. 5.—Franck and Hertz' critical potential apparatus.

The first work on critical potentials which yielded results of importance for quantum theory was done by Franck and Hertz.[1] Figure 5
shows the arrangement of their apparatus. It is similar to that of
Lenard, except that a galvanometer is used, and the retarding potential
V_2 is made small—about 0.5 volt, say. Further, the spacing of the
electrodes and the pressure of the gas in the apparatus are so adjusted

[1] FRANCK, J., and HERTZ, G. *Verh. d. Phys. Ges.* **16**, 10 (1914).

that the average electron makes many collisions in passing from F to G. V_1 is varied by small steps from zero up, and the galvanometer current is noted for each value of V_1.

As long as the collisions of electrons with gas molecules are elastic they lose little energy, and those which pass through openings in gauze G are able to move against the small opposing potential V_2, and will cause a current to flow through Ga. (The conventional direction of this current in the metallic parts of the circuit will be toward P.) But when the collisions become inelastic energy will be lost and many of the electrons will not have sufficient energy to reach P. Figure 6 shows a plot of galvanometer readings against V_1, in an experiment with Hg vapor. At first the current increases very much as the

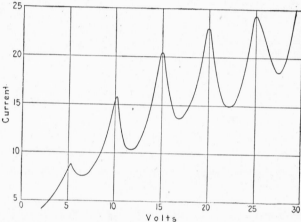

Fig. 6.—Inelastic collisions of electrons with Hg atoms.   (*After Mohler, unpublished figure.*)

current from a filament in a high vacuum does, approximately in accord with the $V^{3/2}$ law (see Chap. XIII, Sec. 1). At a point slightly above 5 volts the current starts to decrease quite suddenly, showing that inelastic collisions begin to occur at this point. It falls to a minimum and rises again. This means that many electrons having initial energies somewhat in excess of 5 volts do not lose all their energy in an inelastic collision. They retain enough to reach P against the voltage V_2. When the voltage V_1 becomes equal to twice the resonance potential, the electron loses its energy in two successive inelastic collisions and again cannot reach the plate P, causing the second drop in the curve. The third and higher maxima are explained in a similar way. The value of the first maximum on this curve cannot be taken as the critical potential since the electrons emitted by the filament have an initial energy distribution which is unknown. This is due not only to the normal Maxwellian velocity distribution of electrons obtained from a thermionic source, but also to the contact potentials between the electrodes. However, the difference between two successive maxima should give a correct value of the resonance potential. Franck and Hertz found it to be 4.9 ± 0.1 volts. Similarly, experiments on helium give a first resonance potential at 19.75 volts, and several others slightly higher. Helium has a higher first resonance potential than any other atom. The lowest value is that for cesium at 1.48 volts.

12. THE CONTROLLED EXCITATION OF SPECTRA

Consider the conditions when the bombarding electrons in a hot cathode tube have just enough energy to raise the atom from the normal level to the nearest excited state. For example, referring to the simplified energy diagram of sodium (Fig. 7), which is very similar to the diagrams of all other alkali metal atoms, the lowest level is called 1S by spectroscopists, and the nearest excited state is

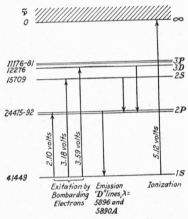

FIG. 7.—Simplified energy diagram of sodium.

called 2P for reasons discussed in Chap. VII. Experimentally, it is found that electrons which have fallen through a potential difference of 2.1 volts can raise sodium atoms from 1S to 2P. When this has been done, the atoms are in a position to return to 1S, and so they do, emitting the yellow D-lines, and these alone. This emission is referred to as a single-line spectrum. (Strictly, there are two D-lines forming a narrow doublet, because there are two levels at 2P, close together. See Chap. VII. For our present purpose we may treat these two levels as though there were but one.) The energy transformations are these. When a bombarding electron falls through a voltage V, it gains an amount of energy $Ve/300$. This is transformed into internal energy of the atom which is struck, except for a small fraction which increases its translational energy, and then this energy is given up as a quantum hc/λ. We have therefore,

$$\frac{Ve}{300} = \frac{hc}{\lambda}. \qquad (51)$$

Substituting $V = 2.1$ volts in this equation, we obtain $\lambda = 5.88 \cdot 10^{-5}$ cm. = 5,880 Ångström units (designated by Å), which agrees with the observed wave lengths 5,890 and 5,896Å., closer than could be expected considering the limits of error of the experiment. Similarly, if the atom is raised to a still higher level (e.g., 3D), it can return to the normal level in a series of transitions emitting spectral lines with the wave numbers $\bar{\nu}_1$, $\bar{\nu}_2$, etc. In this case, the equation replacing equation (51) is

$$\frac{Ve}{300} = \Sigma_i hc\bar{\nu}_i. \tag{52}$$

This is the fundamental equation in correlating critical potentials with spectral data.

The ideas presented here lead to the expectation that a spectrum can be excited step by step, one group of lines after another coming in as the voltage of the bombarding electrons is increased, and such is indeed the case. The first investigation in this field which yielded definite results was that of Franck and Hertz, already referred to. A good illustration of the important results which can be obtained is the work of Foote, Meggers, and Mohler[1] on the excitation of the magnesium spectrum, described in Chap. XIII, Sec. **3**.

13. UNIDIRECTIONAL QUANTA

In discussing the photoelectric effect we mentioned Einstein's suggestion that light of frequency ν consists of units called "photons," having the energy $h\nu$, each one traveling in a definite direction without dividing, as though it were effectively a particle. It is a theorem of electrodynamics that a unidirectional beam of light, carrying energy E, has momentum E/c associated with it, so each quantum should have the momentum $h\nu/c$. Special relativity leads us to associate the mass $h\nu/c^2$ with the energy $h\nu$. We shall see that there is much utility in treating light quanta as particles having these properties.

This theory had a vast handicap to overcome, for the electromagnetic theory of light was successful in explaining nearly all gross optical phenomena on the assumption that each emitting atom sends out a spherical wave. When it became evident that this picture could not account for the absorption of energy by distant atoms in quanta, or for the photoelectric effect, attempts were made to imagine emitting mechanisms which would produce directed quanta. These attempts to provide the atom with an ideal parabolic reflector have all been very unconvincing. Gradually, the opinion spread that neither wave theory nor photon theory could explain all the phenomena. It was often said that physics was confronted with an impassé; that the wave theory should be used in studying problems of diffraction or interference, while the hypothesis of light quanta should be used to describe the photoelectric effect and others of similar nature with which we shall soon become acquainted. We may say at once that the two theories may be reconciled by reinterpreting the electric and magnetic forces **E** and **H** which charac-

---

[1] *Phil. Mag.*, **42**, 1002 (1921); **43**, 639 (1922).

terize a radiation field. In classic electrodynamics, it is supposed that $E^2 + H^2$ is a measure of the energy density in the radiation field. *E and H serve as a "ghost field" which determines in a statistical way the paths which the quanta are to take.* On a screen which receives an interference pattern, the value of $E^2 + H^2$ at any point is proportional to the number of quanta which strike at that point.[1]

14. EXPERIMENTS WITH WEAK LIGHT

We now present experimental evidence bearing on these views. G. I. Taylor[2] performed the following experiment. The rays of a very weak light source (Fig. 8) passed through absorbing screens A and fell on a slit S. Behind this slit were two others at B, arranged as in Young's interference experiment. A photographic plate P was so placed that it would record the interference pattern. Knowing the constants of the absorbing screens, the incident intensity and the number of screens

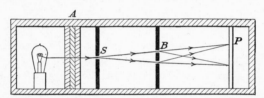

Fig. 8.—Taylor's arrangement for studying the interference of weak light.

were so chosen that only a few quanta per second would pass the first slit S. If each of these passes through only one of the slits B, it is difficult to see how interference can occur. As a matter of fact, the weak-light interference pattern was identical with that produced by strong light. This experiment allows us to conclude that *either* the spherical wave theory is correct *or* the original form of the light-dart theory needs to be supplemented by a statistical postulate prescribing the density of quanta along any path in space. According to this picture, the significant factor in the production of the interference pattern is the structure of the ghost electromagnetic field, determined by the slit arrangement and the behavior of the emitting atoms. Taylor's result is supported by the experiments of several other investigators. For example, Dempster and Batho[3] found that the diffraction pattern of an echelon grating showed no observable peculiarities when formed by very weak light.

[1] In the case of radio waves, this ghost field has a certain physical reality. It seems certain that E does represent an intensity of the electric field in the case of such long waves.

[2] *Proc. Camb. Phil. Soc.*, **15**, 114 (1909).

[3] *Phys. Rev.*, **30**, 644 (1927).

15. JOFFÉ'S EXPERIMENT ON THE UNIDIRECTIONALITY OF QUANTA; THE RAPID INTERRUPTION OF A LIGHT BEAM

It is customary to say that the light quantum does not spread sidewise as it passes through space—that it is rigorously unidirectional. If we could be sure that a light quantum strikes only a single atom when it ejects an electron from a metal surface, this would be satisfactory proof of its unidirectionality. We cannot be quite certain, however, that the energy is not collected by the whole metal surface and delivered to a single atom in some unexplained way. Joffé and Dobronravoff[1] performed an experiment to show that a quantum can be received by a very minute metal surface. A small X-ray tube was constructed, with a thin sheet of aluminium forming one of its walls. This was used as the anticathode, and also as the lower plate of a Millikan condenser. Conditions were so arranged that the tube emitted only about 10^3 quanta per second. A bismuth particle, positively charged, was caused to float in the Millikan condenser, close to the anticathode. Stray effects were satisfactorily eliminated and then it was found that about every 30 minutes the charge of the particle increased, due to the ejection of an electron by the X-rays. The particle was between $1 \cdot 10^{-5}$ and $5 \cdot 10^{-5}$ cm. in diameter, so the whole quantum was absorbed inside a circle of this diameter. At the source, such a circle subtended a solid angle smaller than 10^{-5}.

There is also good evidence that the quantum behaves as though it were very short in the direction of its propagation. Lawrence and Beams[2] constructed an electromagnetic shutter capable of interrupting a beam of light more than 10^9 times a second. The shutter consists of two crossed Nicol prisms with two Kerr cells placed between them at right angles to each other. The Kerr cell consists of two condenser plates with a suitable organic liquid, usually carbon bisulfide, chloroform, or nitrobenzene, placed between them. If an electric field is placed across these condenser plates, plane polarized light passing between them becomes elliptically polarized. The second Kerr cell perpendicular to the first and with the same field across its plates just compensates for this so that plane polarized light emerges from the second Kerr cell; this cannot pass through the second Nicol. As long as the fields across the two cells are equal, no light can pass the shutter, but if these fields differ the elliptical polarization introduced by the first cell is not exactly compensated by the second and thus the light emerging from the second cell has a component which can be transmitted by the second Nicol. A spark gap and the two Kerr cells are wired in parallel to each other across a transformer. At a certain potential the spark jumps

---

[1] *Z. Physik*, **34**, 889 (1925).

[2] See *Phys. Rev.*, **32**, 478 (1928) and *J. Franklin Inst.* **206**, 169 (1928), where the latest results are presented and references to earlier work are given.

which starts light quanta through the shutter, lowers the potential across the transformer, and starts a potential wave down the wires to the Kerr cells. No light can pass the shutter until this potential wave reaches the first cell; then light can pass the shutter until it reaches the second cell, after which no light passes the shutter again. Thus, the shutter is open only during the time that the potential wave takes to travel from the one cell to the other. By this arrangement, Lawrence and Beams found that quanta passed through the cells in less than 10^{-9} seconds, so that the quanta are not over a few centimeters in length. Similar experiments were performed by Breit,[1] using frequencies up to about 10^7 seconds^{-1}. Now if the quantum emitted by a single atom were longer than ct, where t is the time the shutter remains open, it seems reasonable to believe it would be cut when the shutter closes. A very naïve consideration suggests that the division of a quantum would give rise to two quanta of smaller energy and therefore of greater wave length. However, Breit, Ruark, and Brickwedde[2] showed that a correct application of Bohr's postulates leads to the same result as optical theory, which predicts a very slight frequency change due to the modulation. The experiments are in agreement with this view, and a treatment in terms of wave mechanics also supports it.

16. THE COMPTON EFFECT

The theory of unidirectional quanta has received extremely strong support from studies arising out of a fundamental discovery by A. H. Compton.[3] He found that if the monochromatic X-radiation of molybdenum of wave length 0.7 Å. is allowed to fall on light elements, the spectrum of the scattered X-rays contains not only the incident wave length, but also a greater wave length, very close to the original one, but generally separated from it. The apparatus is shown diagrammatically in Fig. 9. Light from the X-ray tube strikes a scatterer of carbon, let us say, which is made quite small to avoid multiple scattering within the block, and to fulfill the condition that the rays incident on the block must come from a definite direction. The radiation scattered at a given angle θ with the incident rays passes through a system of slits and is allowed to fall on the crystal of a Bragg spectrometer (see Chap. VIII for a description of the methods for studying X-ray spectra). Figure 10 illustrates Woo's[4] measurements on scattering from graphite at various angles. It shows the spectral distribution of the scattered light. In each diagram, the peak on the left occurs in the position of the

---

[1] Nature, 119, 280 (1927).

[2] Phil. Mag., 3, 1306 (1927).

[3] Bull. Nat. Research Council, 20, 10 (1922); Phys. Rev., 21, 483 (1923).

[4] Phys. Rev., 21, 715 and 22, 409 (1923); COMPTON "X-Rays and Electrons," p. 263, D. Van Nostrand Co., Inc., New York (1926).

original unscattered wave length coming from the X-ray tube, while that on the right is shifted in the direction of greater wave lengths by an amount which increases as the scattering angle becomes greater. At 90°, the difference in the wave lengths of the two peaks is 0.024 A.

Simultaneously, Compton published a theory of the effect, based on the unidirectional quantum. Debye[1] developed a similar theory independently. The simple classical theory of X-ray scattering is based on the conception that the bound electrons in the scatterer are set into forced oscillation by the electric force of the incident waves. They send out radiation having the same frequency as the incident waves in all directions. This picture contains no provision for a shift of wave length. On the other hand, if the scattering entities are free, they will be accelerated in the direction of the incident X-ray beam by radiation pressure. Their velocities will continually increase until reduced to zero by a collision. This forward component

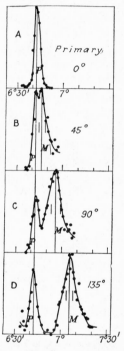

FIG. 10.—Compton effect. The MoKα line scattered by graphite at different angles.

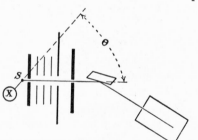

FIG. 9.—Experimental arrangement for studying the Compton effect.

of velocity gives rise to a Doppler shift in the scattered light. The frequency $\nu (\theta)$ scattered at an angle θ with the direction of the incident beam when the forward velocity is v, is obtained as follows, neglecting modifications due to relativity. If frequency ν_0 is incident on the electron, it oscillates perpendicular to the line of motion with the frequency,

$$\nu_e = \nu_0(1 - \beta), \beta = \frac{v}{c}.$$

Radiation scattered at the angle θ will have a frequency given by

$$\nu_e = \nu(\theta) \cdot (1 - \beta \cos \theta),$$

as seen by a resting observer, whence

$$\nu(\theta) \cdot (1 - \beta \cos \theta) = \nu_0(1 - \beta). \qquad (53)$$

[1] *Physik. Z.*, **24**, 161 (1923).

From this equation, radiation scattered parallel to the original beam suffers no change of wave length. As θ increases, $\nu(\theta)$ decreases to the value $\nu(1 - \beta)/(1 + \beta)$, for scattering at 180°. As we shall see, the Compton wave-length shift behaves in this fashion, and E. Bauer,[1] followed by others, attempted to interpret the shift as above. The difficulty is that the electrons should have a continuous range of velocities and at each value of θ a continuous band of frequencies should be observed, extending from the original spectrum line toward greater wave lengths. Such a band is not observed. The shifted line is definitely separated from the position of the incident wave length. Compton's treatment of the effect accounted for the experimental results so accurately that it was generally accepted until the advent of wave dynamics. It is as follows:

Let ν_0 be the frequency of the original X-ray quantum and ν be its frequency after a collision with an electron. Figure 11 shows the paths

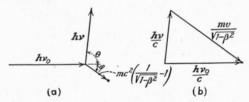

FIG. 11.—Collision between a light quantum and an electron. (a) Energy relations, (b) momentum diagram.

of the original quantum $h\nu_0$ and the electron e and quantum $h\nu$ after the collision. θ is the angle between the direction of the original quantum and the scattered quantum and φ is the angle between the direction of the original quantum and that of the electron struck. The directions of the quanta and the recoil electron must lie in a plane in order that momentum may be conserved. Conservation of energy and of the x- and y-components of momentum (as illustrated by the momentum triangle in Fig. 11b) yields the equations,

$$h\nu_0 = h\nu + mc^2\left(\frac{1}{(1 - \beta^2)^{1/2}} - 1\right), \tag{54}$$

$$\frac{h\nu_0}{c} = \frac{h\nu}{c}\cos\theta + \frac{mv}{(1 - \beta^2)^{1/2}}\cos\varphi, \tag{55}$$

$$0 = -\frac{h\nu}{c}\sin\theta + \frac{mv}{(1 - \beta^2)^{1/2}}\sin\varphi. \tag{56}$$

In equations (55) and (56) we transpose the terms in θ to the left, square, and add, to eliminate φ. Then, eliminating v between the result and equation (54), we find,

$$\nu = \frac{\nu_0}{1 + \alpha(1 - \cos\theta)} = \frac{\nu_0}{1 + 2\alpha\sin^2\theta/2}, \text{ where } \alpha = \frac{h\nu_0}{mc^2}. \tag{57}$$

[1] *Comptes rendus*, **177**, 1031, (1923).

The wave-length shift of a quantum scattered at angle θ is

$$\Delta\lambda = \frac{c}{\nu} - \frac{c}{\nu_0} = \frac{h}{mc}(1 - \cos\theta). \tag{58}$$

It is worth noting that this change in wave length is independent of the frequency of the light scattered. h/mc is the change in wave length of the light scattered at right angles to the original beam and has the numerical value $2.42 \cdot 10^{-10}$ cm. or 0.0242 Å. This is frequently called the "wave length of the Compton shift." It is the wave length which would be produced if the energy of an electron were transformed entirely into a light quantum. Using equations (55), (56), and (57), we find that

$$\tan\varphi = \frac{\cot(\theta/2)}{1 + \alpha}, \tag{59}$$

so that the recoil angle decreases from 90° to 0° as the scattering angle is altered from 0° to 180°. ($v = 0$, and φ is indeterminate, when $\theta = 0$.)

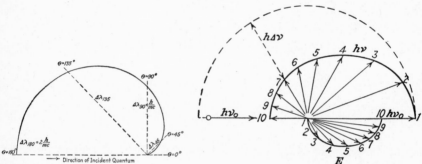

FIG. 12.—Polar graph of the Compton shift.   FIG. 13.—Debye diagram of the energies of recoil electrons.

Figure 12 is a polar graph in which $\Delta\lambda$ is plotted as a function of θ, while Fig. 13 is a diagram of Debye, showing the energy of the recoil electron and of the scattered quantum for ten different directions of scattering, the incident wave length being h/mc. Any radius vector of the upper solid curve, such as the one marked 3, is proportional to the energy of a quantum scattered through the angle which that radius makes with the direction of the incident beam. The energy of the corresponding recoil electron is shown by radius vector 3 of the lower curve, drawn at the appropriate recoil angle φ.

The agreement of equation (58) with the wave-length interval between the peaks in Fig. 10 is excellent. It is probable that the original wave length appears in the scattered light because some quanta are scattered by atoms as a whole. When this occurs, the mass of the electron must be replaced by the mass of the atom in the equation for $\Delta\lambda$, and the shift becomes negligible.

It remains to examine why the above theory based on the recoil of free electrons is satisfactory, for the electrons in the carbon atom are certainly not free. If the quantum must give up energy to eject the recoil electron from the atom, we should expect a greater shift than that given above. As a matter of fact, the shifted peak is usually broader than the unshifted one, so this factor must be taken into account. Its effect is relatively unimportant, however, when the ionization potential of the average electron in the atom is small compared with the energy of the incident quantum. Such is the case in the experiments quoted above, where the X-rays were of fairly short wave length and the scatterer was an element of low atomic number. See Chap. XI, Sec. 6.

17. THE CONSERVATION OF ENERGY AND MOMENTUM IN THE SCATTERING OF X-RAYS

If X-rays are scattered by the atoms of a gas or vapor, it should be possible to detect the recoil electrons by the Wilson cloud-track method (Chap. II). Independently, C. T. R. Wilson[1] and Bothe[2] showed that such electrons are present by photographing their tracks. Compton and Simon[3] made use of this fact to show that the direction of recoil and the direction in which the scattered quantum move are related in the way required by the light-quantum theory. A beam of X-rays was allowed to enter a Wilson cloud-track chamber, and photographs were taken in the usual way in order to detect any recoil electrons produced in the scattering process, and also any secondary electrons ejected by the scattered light quantum from the walls of the chamber. In order to make this latter process more probable, they suspended thin sheets of lead in the chamber. In most of the photographs only the path of a recoil electron was observed, but in a small fraction of them there appeared also the track of

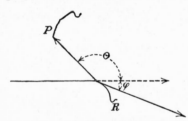

Fig. 14.—R is the recoil electron path and P the photoelectron path.

the photoelectron ejected by the scattered light quantum. The origin of the recoil electron path showed the point at which the scattering took place, and the initial direction of this path showed the direction in which the recoil electron was ejected by the light quantum. The direction of the scattered light quantum was secured by drawing a straight line from the point of scattering to the beginning of the photoelectron path. Since two photographs were taken at an angle to each other, the angles between the direction of the original beam and the directions of the scattered light quantum and of the recoil electron could be determined. The relations are shown diagrammatically in Fig. 14. In this way, it was possible to see whether the angles φ and θ were related to each other according to equation (59).

[1] Proc. Roy. Soc., **104**, 1 (1923).
[2] Z. Physik, **16**, 319 (1923).
[3] Phys. Rev., **26**, 289 (1925).

Within the limits of experimental error, which were necessarily quite large, the experiments agreed with the requirements of this equation and they show that energy and momentum are conserved when a light quantum is scattered by an electron. It should be noted that the experiment could not determine the energy of the recoil electron. The energy of the scattered quantum is known from the experiments on the Compton effect described in the preceding paragraph.

Bothe and Geiger[1] showed that the ejection of the recoil electron and the deflection of the quantum occur at the same time. Their apparatus consisted of two point counters one of which was open, while the other was closed with a thin platinum foil. These were mounted facing each other, with a narrow space between. A beam of X-rays passed between the counters. If a scattering process occurs in the neighborhood of the platinum foil, and the scattered quantum is absorbed in the foil, the electron which it ejects may enter the closed counter, while the recoil electron is recorded by the other counter. Therefore, a certain fraction of the events recorded by the two counters should be simultaneous. The fraction observed by Bothe and Geiger agrees well with what we might expect from the constants of the apparatus, and the assumption that each scattered quantum produces one recoil electron.

These experiments disproved the theory of Bohr, Kramers, and Slater,[2] who suggested that energy and momentum are not conserved in the interaction of a single light quantum with a single atom, but are only conserved statistically for large numbers of such processes.

18. THE STERN-GERLACH EXPERIMENT

The orbital motion of the electrons in an atom produces a magnetic field of such a kind that the atom may be considered as a permanent bar magnet when discussing its behavior in an external field constant in time and uniform in space. We consider first an atom with only one electron.[3] By Kepler's law of areas, the rate dA/dt at which the radius r drawn from the nucleus to the electron describes area is such that

$$\frac{2m\,dA}{dt} = mr^2\dot{\varphi} = p; \tag{60}$$

φ is the azimuthal angle and p the angular momentum. Integrating for one complete period T we get,

$$\text{Area of orbit} = A = \frac{Tp}{2m}. \tag{61}$$

---

[1] *Z. Physik*, **32**, 639 (1925).

[2] *Z. Physik*, **24**, 69 (1924).

[3] The theory developed in this section neglects the intrinsic magnetic moment of the electron (Sec. **19**) and must be corrected in the manner indicated in Chap. X, Sec. **8**.

As a consequence of the quantum conditions, the angular momentum of any atom is

$$\frac{jh}{2\pi},\tag{62}$$

where j is an integer or an integer plus $\frac{1}{2}$, and is called the inner quantum number, so equation (61) can be written

$$A = \frac{Tjh}{4\pi m}.$$

The electron passes a given point on its orbit $1/T$ times a second, and, therefore, is equivalent to a current $i = -e/T$. We shall express e and i in electromagnetic units. Now, if a current i flows in a closed circuit of area A, then at a great distance it produces a field practically identical with that of a magnet having a moment

$$\mu = iA.\tag{63}$$

Proof of Equation (63).—The pattern of force lines at a great distance does not depend appreciably on the shape of the circuit, so we shall suppose the current flows in a circle of wire, for simplicity, and shall compare its field at a point P on its axis OP

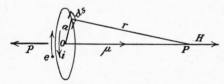

with that of a magnetic dipole having a moment μ directed along OP. By symmetry, the force at P is along OP (Fig. 15). The field at P, due to an element ds of the circular current, is ids/r^2, by Ampere's law, and the component of force along the axis is $aids/r^3$. The

FIG. 15.—The magnetic field of a rotating charge.

component along the axis due to the whole circle is $2\pi a^2 i/r^3$ and the sum of the components perpendicular to the axis is zero. But the field due to the dipole would be $2\mu/r^3$ and this will be the same as that due to the current if $\mu = i\pi a^2 = iA$.

From equation (63),

$$\mathbf{\mu} = -\frac{jhe}{4\pi mc} = -\frac{\mathbf{p} \cdot e}{2mc},\tag{64}$$

where e is now in electrostatic units.

This is easily generalized for an atom having several electrons by simply summing the contributions of all of them. If $jh/2\pi$ now denotes the resultant angular momentum of all the electrons and $\mathbf{\mu}$ the magnetic moment of the atom, we obtain an equation identical with equation (64). It is to be noted that this is a vectorial equation, and that $\mathbf{\mu}$ is opposed to $\mathbf{p}$ in direction because the charge of the electron is negative, as shown in Fig. 15. This simple theory requires therefore that the magnetic moments of atoms shall be multiples (or half-multiples, if j is an integer plus $\frac{1}{2}$) of an elementary unit called the "Bohr magneton," given by the equation,

$$M_B = \frac{eh}{4\pi mc} = 9.22 \cdot 10^{-21} \text{ gauss centimeter},\tag{65}$$

with e in e.s.u. Often, it is more convenient to deal with the magnetic moment associated with a gram-mole, without regard to the orientations of the separate atoms, that is, M_B times the Avogadro number N. This quantity is

$$\mu_B = 5{,}589 \text{ gauss centimeter per mole.} \tag{66}$$

However, magnetic moments are usually reported in the literature in terms of the Weiss magneton μ_W which is an empirical unit equal to 1,123.5 gauss centimeter per mole, so that it is almost exactly one-fifth of μ_B. This unit was introduced by Weiss as a result of careful measurements of the magnetic susceptibility of Te and Ni. It was believed that the magnetic moments of all molecules were multiples of μ_W/N. The fact is, they are not multiples of either μ_W/N or μ_B/N. The true state of affairs is more complicated due to the magnetic moment of the electron (Chap. X, Sec. 8).

Stern and Gerlach[1] proved by ingenious experiments that certain atoms have magnetic moments equal to the Bohr magneton. Their first experiments dealt with the magnetic moment of the silver atom in the vapor state. The work was later extended to many atoms and molecules. It is very interesting to know that the result was predicted before the experiments were carried out. In order to understand these remarkable experiments, it must be pointed out that

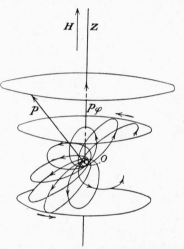

FIG. 16.—Orientation of the hydrogen atom in a magnetic field.

while, according to the classical theory, all orientations are possible for atoms in a uniform magnetic field, the quantum theory predicts *discrete orientations* such that *the component of the total angular momentum vector directed along the lines of force is a multiple or a half-multiple of $h/2\pi$.* The argument for discrete orientations can be easily seen by considering the hydrogen atom (again without the spinning electron, Sec. 19). In the presence of a magnetic field, the motion of the electron is changed in a very simple way. To a close approximation, the plane of its orbit rotates uniformly around an axis drawn through the nucleus parallel to the lines of force. A person rotating with the same angular speed around this axis would say the motion of the electron in its orbital plane was the same as it

[1] STERN, *Z. Physik*, **7**, 249 (1921); GERLACH and STERN, *ibid.*, **8**, 10 (1921); **9**, 349 and 353 (1922); STERN, *ibid.*, **39**, 751 (1926); KNAUER and STERN, *ibid.*, **39**, 764 (1926); LEU, *ibid.*, **41**, 551 (1927); STERN, *ibid.*, **41**, 563 (1927); WREDE, *ibid.*, **41**, 569 (1927); LEU, *ibid.*, **49**, 498 (1928); GERLACH, *Ann. Physik*, **76**, 163 (1925).

was in the stationary reference system before the field was applied. In Fig. 16, the normal to the plane of the orbit always makes the same angle with the direction of the field, and so the component of angular momentum parallel to the field is constant. Let us call this p_φ, φ being an angle measured around the axis OZ. Then, as we shall see in Chap. X, Sec. 8,

$$p_\varphi = \frac{mh}{2\pi},\tag{67}$$

where m is called the "magnetic quantum number" and takes the value 0, ± 1, $\cdots \pm j$. In the case of other atoms, silver being an example, m can take the values $\pm\frac{1}{2}$, $\pm\frac{3}{2}$, $\cdots \pm j$; for such atoms j is always an integer plus one-half. The angle between the field **H** and the vector

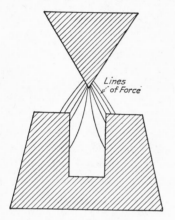

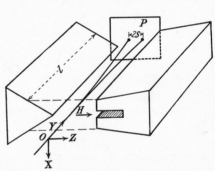

Fig. 17.—An inhomogeneous magnetic field.

Fig. 18.—The Stern-Gerlach experimental arrangement.

j is such that $\cos \alpha = m/j$ and the atom can take up only $2j + 1$ orientations in the field. This restriction was first pointed out by Sommerfeld[1] and Debye,[2] and the atoms are said to be space-quantized.

The experimental proof of space-quantization depends on the deflection of elementary magnets moving through an inhomogeneous magnetic field. There is no resultant force on a small magnet placed in a homogeneous magnetic field, for the force exerted on one pole will be exactly equal, but opposite in direction, to that exerted on the other. If the field is inhomogeneous, however, it will experience an acceleration. Consider an inhomogeneous field having force lines of the type shown in Fig. 17, where conditions do not vary perpendicular to the diagram. Such a field may be obtained with the aid of pole pieces having the cross-section shown in the figure. A unidirectional beam of atoms is produced in vacuo, by heating the metal to be studied in a furnace, and

[1] *Physik. Z.*, **17**, 491 (1916); *Ann. Physik*, **51**, 1 (1916).
[2] *Physik. Z.*, **17**, 507 (1916).

passing the vapor stream which comes from its mouth through minute apertures in accurate alignment. The beam passes close to the edge of the wedge-shaped pole piece (Fig. 18) and is received on a glass plate P. Along the path of the beam the lines of force are nearly parallel to OZ and the field strength changes rapidly in that direction. At any instant, an atom of moment μ will be deflected along OZ, by the force

$$\mu_x \frac{\partial H_z}{\partial x} + \mu_y \frac{\partial H_z}{\partial y} + \mu_z \frac{\partial H_z}{\partial z}, \tag{68}$$

where μ_x, μ_y, and μ_z are the components of μ along the axes.

Proof.—Let the atom be represented by a bar magnet with poles of strength m, with its south pole at the origin. The south pole is urged along OZ by a force mH_z (H_z being evaluated at the origin), while the north pole, at x, y, z, experiences a force along OZ equal to

$$m\left(H_z + \frac{\partial H_z}{\partial x}x + \frac{\partial H_z}{\partial y}y + \frac{\partial H_z}{\partial z}z + \cdots \right),$$

the derivatives being taken at the origin. The higher terms are neglected and the resultant force along OZ is

$$mx\frac{\partial H_z}{\partial x} + my\frac{\partial H_z}{\partial y} + mz\frac{\partial H_z}{\partial z}$$

which is equal to expression (68) because $mx = \mu_x$, etc., by definition.

As explained above, the atom will precess about the Z-axis, the value of μ_z remaining constant. Now $\partial H_z/\partial y$ is zero over practically the complete trajectory of the atom; $\partial H_z/\partial x$ is zero in the median plane of the magnet and is small for positions very close to this plane and $\partial H_z/\partial z$ is constant over small distances. But still better, the *mean* values of μ_x and μ_y are zero over a period of the precession, which is small compared with the time the atom is in the field, so the average force on the atom is very nearly

$$f = \mu_z \frac{\partial H_z}{\partial z} = \mu \frac{\partial H_z}{\partial z} \cos \theta, \tag{69}$$

θ being the constant angle between μ and the lines of force. Accordingly, each atom moves on a parabolic path, with the axis of the parabola parallel to OZ, and if we take its z-coordinate to be zero when it enters the field, after a time t it will be

$$z = \frac{ft^2}{2m}.$$

If the velocity is v, and the distance traveled through the field in reaching the plate is l, then the deflection at the plate is

$$s = \frac{f}{2m}\left(\frac{l}{v}\right)^2. \tag{70}$$

Since, in actuality, the atoms have a rather broad velocity distribution, the deflections at the plate cover a range of values. The z-coordinate of the centroid of the spot thus formed will be obtained by using in equation (70) the average value of $1/v^2$ for all the atoms in the beam, which is $m/4kT$ from kinetic theory.[1]

Substituting in equation (70),

$$s = \frac{1}{2} \mu \cos \theta \frac{\partial H_z}{\partial z} \frac{l^2}{4kT}. \tag{71}$$

In this equation, all quantities except $\mu \cos \theta$ can be measured, and so this combination can be evaluated. Figure 19a shows the pattern obtained in the case of silver, when no field is applied, and Fig. 19b shows the pattern obtained when the field is present. Twenty scale divisions correspond to 1 mm. The Z-axis runs horizontally through the center of the pattern and the drawn-out unsymmetrical portion on the right is

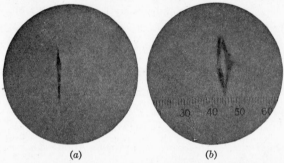

(a)   (b)

Fig. 19.—The deflection of silver atoms in the Stern-Gerlach experiment. (*After Stern and Gerlach.*)

due to the very large value of $\partial H_z/\partial z$ in the immediate neighborhood of the edge of the wedge-shaped pole piece. Above and below the Z-axis the value of $\partial H_z/\partial z$ rapidly decreases to zero with a corresponding diminution in the deviation of the beam. From spectroscopic evidence, there is every reason to believe that the silver atom in its normal state can take only two positions with respect to the field, namely, with its magnetic moment parallel or antiparallel to the force-lines, so $\cos \theta = \pm 1$. From measurements of $\partial H_z/\partial z$ in the plane of symmetry of the magnet, made by use of a thin bismuth wire mounted parallel to the edge of the wedge, the following values of s were computed, assuming that μ is one Bohr magneton. (See Chap. X, Sec. **8**.) These agree excellently with the observed values.

Deviation s

Observed Millimeters	Computed Millimeters
0.10	0.11
0.15	0.15

This experiment is excellent proof that the silver atom is space-quantized. If it were able to take up any orientation whatever in

[1] STERN, Z. *Physik*, **2**, 49, and **3**, 417 (1920).

the field, the two lines in Fig. 19 would be replaced by a continuous deposit filling the entire region which these lines enclose. Indeed, we should expect the densest part of the deposit to be in the center, for the number of atoms whose axis makes an angle between θ and $\theta + d\theta$ with the lines of force is nearly proportional to sin θ; thus a large fraction of the atoms are oriented nearly transverse to the field and will suffer very small deflections.

Similar experiments were performed by Phipps and Taylor[1] and by Wrede,[2] using a hydrogen discharge tube as a source of monatomic hydrogen and a plate coated with molybdenum oxide as a detecting screen. Two reduced areas of the molybdenum oxide show that the beam of hydrogen atoms is split by the field into two parts and the distance between the two reduced spots agrees very closely with that calculated on the assumption that the hydrogen atom has a magnetic moment of one Bohr magneton when in its state of lowest energy.

19. THE MAGNETIC MOMENT OF THE ELECTRON

While a model of the electron can be very useful in guiding our ideas of electrical phenomena, all attempts to endow it with an extended structure should be regarded as a conventional way of summing up its properties. When we say the electron has the properties of a point charge, we mean by *definition* that in its neighborhood nuclei and other electrons undergo accelerations toward or away from a very small region of space, and that the acceleration depends only on the distance from that region.   The great utility of attributing to the electron not only charge but also *magnetic moment*, not only mass and momentum but also *angular momentum*, has become apparent through the study of atomic spectra, so it is natural to think of the electron as an extended charged body in rapid rotation, which will possess these properties if the laws of gross mechanics and electrical theory can be applied to it.   The phenomena which led to the hypothesis of the spinning electron can not be fully explained until we reach Chap. X, but the main facts will be stated at once. Studies of the behavior of spectral lines when a magnetic field is applied to a luminous gas or vapor give us the ratio of the magnetic moment to the angular momentum of the atom. According to equation (64), this should be

$$\frac{\mu}{p} = -\frac{e}{2mc} \text{ (electrostatic units).} \tag{72}$$

Sometimes the spectral data also give this value, but in the majority of cases the result is

$$\frac{\mu}{p} = -g\frac{e}{2mc}, \tag{73}$$

[1] *Phys. Rev.*, **29**, 309 (1927).
[2] *Z. Physik.* **41**, 569 (1927).

where g is a ratio of two integers. The lowest value of g is 0, often it is in the neighborhood of 1, and values higher than 2 are rare. It is natural to explain this behavior as due to the presence in the atom of entities for which the ratio of magnetic moment and angular momentum is not given by equation (72). Independently, Uhlenbeck and Goudsmit[1] and Bichowsky and Urey[2] assumed that these entities were the electrons themselves. On this view, the contribution of an electron to the angular momentum of the atom consists of that due to the motion of its center of inertia around the nucleus and that due to its own internal motions around its own center of inertia, which may be called its "intrinsic" angular momentum.

Experiment has shown that *the intrinsic angular momentum of the electron is* $\dfrac{1}{2}\dfrac{h}{2\pi}$ *and its magnetic moment is one Bohr magneton,* $\dfrac{h}{2\pi}\dfrac{e}{2mc}$.

Thus the ratio μ/p is e/mc for the electron, twice as great as the value of equation (72) belonging to a point charge revolving around a fixed center of force. The value of g depends on the way in which the external and intrinsic angular momentum vectors of the several electrons in the atom combine to form its resultant angular momentum vector.

Evidence that positive nuclei have intrinsic angular momenta and magnetic moments has been obtained by Hund and others from band spectra, by Back and Goudsmit from the fine structure of spectral lines, and by Stern and Knauer from measurements of the magnetic moments of molecules. These moments are small compared with a Bohr magneton.

In conclusion, it is not surprising that the discovery of the electron spin was delayed until 1926. Most of the effects it produces are quite small, and some of the more prominent ones could be explained by other hypotheses.

References

1. *Black Body Radiation:*
    JEANS, J. H., "Report on Radiation and the Quantum Theory," 2nd ed., Fleetway Press, London (1924). Also "Kinetic Theory of Gases," 4th ed., Cambridge University Press. The Report gives an excellent but brief account; that in "Kinetic Theory" is more complete. The only detailed book on this subject is PLANCK's "Wärmestrahlung," 5th ed., Barth, Leipzig (1923). There is an English translation by M. P. Masius.
2. *Photoelectricity:*
    HUGHES, A. L., "Report on Photoelectricity," *Bull.* 10 of the National Research Council, Washington (1921).
    ALLEN, H. S., "Photoelectricity," 2nd ed., Longmans, Green and Co., New York.
    GUDDEN, B., "Lichtelektrische Erscheinungen," Springer, Berlin (1928).

[1] *Nature,* **117,** 264 (1926); *Physica* **5,** 266 (1925).

[2] *Proc. Nat. Acad. Sci.,* **12,** 80 (1926). Owing to an algebraic error, the ratio of angular momentum to magnetic moment given in this paper is incorrect by a factor of 4.

3. *Unidirectional Quanta; Compton Effect:*
  COMPTON, A. H., "X-rays and Electrons," D. Van Nostrand, Inc., New York (1926).
4. *Stern Gerlach Experiment:*
  STONER, E. C., "Magnetism and Atomic Structure," Dutton, New York (1926).

CHAPTER IV

REVIEW OF DYNAMICAL PRINCIPLES

Note to the Reader. Much of the material in this chapter is not essential to the understanding of the Bohr theory, although it is extensively used in Chap. VI and in the chapters on the new mechanics. Exceptions to this statement must be made in the case of generalized coordinates, Sec. **3**; the motion of a particle about a center of force, Sec. **5**; the inverse square law of force, Sec. **6**; and the Hamilton-Jacobi differential equation, Sec. **10**. The subject matter of these sections is constantly applied in the remainder of the book. If desired, the reader may pass at once to the study of the hydrogen atom, with the understanding that from time to time it will be necessary to refer to the results in the present chapter.

1. APPLICATION OF MECHANICS TO ATOMIC STRUCTURE

In so far as the atom can be treated by ordinary mechanics, the problems of its structure are very similar to those of astronomy. We deal with the orbits of bodies which are very small compared with the distances between them. In many cases these bodies may be treated with negligible error as mathematical points possessing mass. First, we study the *Lagrangian form* of the equations of motion and then the so-called "canonical equations of Hamilton." Both are formulations of the physical content of Newton's second law of motion, and can be applied in any system of coordinates. however complicated; both are well suited for the easy proof of general theorems. Next, we discuss *canonical transformations* of variables, which are the most general transformations leaving the form of the Hamilton equations unaltered. Then the concepts of *action* and of Hamilton's principal function are introduced, in preparation for a discussion of the *Hamilton-Jacobi differential equation*, which is especially suited for treating the problems of quantum theory.

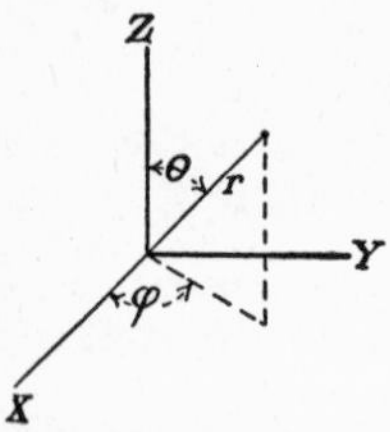

Fig. 1.—Coordinate systems used in this book.

2. CHOICE OF AXES

Throughout the book we use a *right-handed* system of Cartesian axes, and polar coordinates related to them in the fashion shown in Fig. 1. By right-handed, we mean that when we look along the positive Z-axis, a rotation of x toward y will cause a right-handed screw to advance along z.

3. GENERALIZED COORDINATES AND LAGRANGE'S EQUATIONS

Even for comparatively simple systems, it often happens that a great deal of geometrical reasoning and resolution of forces are necessary to

98

obtain the components of force acting on one of the particles of the system; often, when this has been accomplished, the expressions for these components are so complicated that they cannot be used for solution of the dynamical problem, and the labor must be repeated, using another type of coordinates. Much of this difficulty can be avoided, and the method of so doing is especially easy for conservative systems. In such systems, the equations of motion can be derived from a knowledge of the Lagrangian function L, which is equal to the kinetic energy T minus the potential energy V, both being expressed as functions of the velocities and coordinates. Essentially, the method is to express the equations of motion in a form which is valid in any system of coordinates. The configuration of a system of r particles having n degrees of freedom (where $n = 3r$) is completely determined when the values of n quantities, $q_1, q_2, \ldots q_n$, are specified. These n quantities are called the generalized coordinates of the system. They must be so chosen as to determine its configuration uniquely. In a Cartesian frame of reference, these are lengths; in polar coordinates, they are lengths or angles; and in other systems, they may have still other dimensions. The Cartesian coordinates of a particle of the system are functions of all or part of the q's and possibly of the time also, as in the case where we transform to a moving system of coordinates. In the study of the atom we shall often wish to transform to a rotating system, or to a system moving with the center of mass of the atom, so we consider the general case. Let any Cartesian coordinate x, y, or z of a particle of the system be represented by x_i and the component of force acting on it in the direction of that coordinate by X_i. Unless otherwise specified, all summations are to be extended from $i = 1$ to $i = n$, i.e., over all the x-, y-, and z-coordinates of all the r particles. We have then

$$x_i = x_i(q_1, \cdots q_n, t), \tag{1}$$
$$X_i = X_i(q_1, \cdots q_n, t).$$

First, we shall give some definitions and develop auxiliary equations, (5), (7), (8), and (9). The work which would be done on the system if the coordinates could be changed by the amounts $\delta x_1, \ldots, \delta x_n$ with t held constant is

$$\delta W = \Sigma X_i \delta x_i. \tag{2}$$

But

$$\delta x_i = \frac{\partial x_i}{\partial q_1} \delta q_1 + \cdots + \frac{\partial x_i}{\partial q_n} \delta q_n, \tag{3}$$

so that

$$\delta W = X_1\left(\frac{\partial x_1}{\partial q_1}\delta q_1 + \cdots \frac{\partial x_1}{\partial q_n}\delta q_n\right) + \cdots$$

$$+ X_n\left(\frac{\partial x_n}{\partial q_1}\delta q_1 + \cdots + \frac{\partial x_n}{\partial q_n}\delta q_n\right) \quad (4)$$

$$= \left(X_1\frac{\partial x_1}{\partial q_1} + X_2\frac{\partial x_2}{\partial q_1} + \cdots X_n\frac{\partial x_n}{\partial q_1}\right)\delta q_1 + \cdots$$

$$+ \left(X_1\frac{\partial x_1}{\partial q_n} + X_2\frac{\partial x_2}{\partial q_n} + \cdots X_n\frac{\partial x_n}{\partial q_n}\right)\delta q_n,$$

that is,

$$\delta W = \Sigma_k Q_k \delta q_k,$$

where

$$Q_k = X_1\frac{\partial x_1}{\partial q_k} + \cdots + X_n\frac{\partial x_n}{\partial q_k}, \quad (5)$$

and is called the "generalized force" corresponding to the coordinate q_k. Q_k has the dimensions of a force only when q_k has the dimensions of length; if q_k is an angle, Q_k has the dimensions of a moment of force. Its dimensions must always be such that the product of Q_k and q_k has the dimensions of work.

Example.—Consider a single particle referred to Cartesian and to polar coordinates. Let $x_1 = x$, $x_2 = y$, $x_3 = z$, $q_1 = r$, $q_2 = \theta$ and $q_3 = \varphi$; the quantities $X_1 = X$, $X_2 = Y$, and $X_3 = Z$ are the Cartesian components of force, and $Q_1 = R$, $Q_2 = \Theta$, $Q_3 = \Phi$ are the "generalized components of force." Then,

$$x_1 = x(r,\ \theta,\ \varphi) = r\sin\theta\cos\varphi,$$
$$x_2 = y(r,\ \theta,\ \varphi) = r\sin\theta\sin\varphi, \quad (1a)$$
$$x_3 = z(r,\ \theta,\ \varphi) = r\cos\theta.$$

We follow through the transformation just as above:

$$\delta W = X\delta x + Y\delta y + Z\delta z, \quad (2a)$$
$$\delta x = \sin\theta\cos\varphi\delta r + r\cos\theta\cos\varphi\delta\theta - r\sin\theta\sin\varphi\delta\varphi,$$
$$\delta y = \sin\theta\sin\varphi\delta r + r\cos\theta\sin\varphi\delta\theta + r\sin\theta\cos\varphi\delta\varphi, \quad (3a)$$
$$\delta z = \cos\theta\delta r - r\sin\theta\delta\theta.$$

Substituting in δW we get

$$\delta W = R\delta r + \Theta\delta\theta + \Phi\delta\varphi, \quad (4a)$$

where

$$R = X\sin\theta\cos\varphi + Y\sin\theta\sin\varphi + Z\cos\theta,$$
$$\Theta = r(X\cos\theta\cos\varphi + Y\cos\theta\sin\varphi - Z\sin\theta), \quad (5a)$$
$$\Phi = r(-X\sin\theta\sin\varphi + Y\sin\theta\cos\varphi).$$

In this simple case the values of the Q's could be obtained just as easily from geometrical reasoning, by observing that R is the component of the force in the direction of increasing r; that Φ is the moment of force about the Z-axis in the direction of increasing φ; while Θ is that component of the moment of force which causes an increase in θ, i.e., it is the moment of force about a line perpendicular to the Z-axis and the radius vector **r**. To specialize still further, X, Y, and Z may be the components of a force **F** directed toward the origin, so that

$$X = -F\sin\theta\cos\varphi,\ Y = -F\sin\theta\sin\varphi,\ Z = -F\cos\theta.$$

Substituting these values in (5a) we secure

$$R = -F, \ \Theta = 0, \ \Phi = 0.$$

The last two sets of equations show that in the case of central forces polar coordinates are generally much more convenient than Cartesian.

For convenience, let x_1, x_2, and x_3 represent the Cartesian coordinates of the first particle; x_4, x_5, and x_6, those of the second, and so on, while m_1, m_2, m_3 are all equal to the mass of the first particle, and so on. Then the kinetic energy of a system of $n/3$ particles is

$$T = \sum_{i=1}^{i=n} \frac{m_i \dot{x}_i^2}{2}. \tag{6}$$

Differentiating equation (1) with respect to t,

$$\dot{x}_i = \frac{\partial x_i}{\partial q_1} \dot{q}_1 + \cdots \frac{\partial x_i}{\partial q_n} \dot{q}_n + \frac{\partial x_i}{\partial t}. \tag{7}$$

Thus each $\dot{x}_i$ is a *linear* function of the $\dot{q}$'s, and also a function of the q's and of t, since the partial derivatives are functions of the q's and of t. Usually x_i does not depend on the time explicitly. When such is the case, we find from equations (6) and (7) that

$$T = \sum_i \frac{1}{2} m_i \left[\left(\frac{\partial x_i}{\partial q_1} \right)^2 \dot{q}_1{}^2 + \cdots + 2 \frac{\partial x_i}{\partial q_k} \frac{\partial x_i}{\partial q_l} \dot{q}_k \dot{q}_l + \cdots \right.$$

$$= \sum_i \sum_k \sum_l \frac{1}{2} m_i \frac{\partial x_i}{\partial q_k} \frac{\partial x_i}{\partial q_l} \dot{q}_k \dot{q}_l, \tag{6'}$$

so that T is a quadratic function of the $\dot{q}$'s; the coefficient of each product of the form $\dot{q}_k \dot{q}_l$ is a function of the q's.

The components of momentum when Cartesian coordinates are used are equal to the partial derivatives of $T(\dot{x}_i)$ with respect to the corresponding velocity component,

$$\frac{\partial T}{\partial \dot{x}_i} = m \dot{x}_i. \tag{8}$$

By analogy, we call the partial derivatives of the kinetic energy $T(q, \dot{q})$, with respect to the $\dot{q}$'s *generalized momenta*,

$$\frac{\partial T(q, \dot{q})}{\partial \dot{q}_k} = p_k(q, \dot{q}) = \sum_i \sum_l m_i \frac{\partial x_i}{\partial q_k} \frac{\partial x_i}{\partial q_l} \dot{q}_l. \tag{9}$$

(We use the notation $T(q, \dot{q})$ in place of $T(q_1, \ldots q_n, \dot{q}_1, \ldots \dot{q}_n)$ for brevity.) The p's are sometimes called "momentoids," for p_k has the dimensions of momentum only if q_k is a length. For example, in space polar coordinates p_θ and p_φ have the dimensions of angular momentum.

In forming the partial derivative of $\dot{x}_i$ with respect to one of the variables on which it depends, we shall adopt the *convention* that all other variables are treated as constants during the differentiation. For example, when writing out $\partial \dot{x}_i / \partial \dot{q}_k$, we hold

$q_1, \ldots, q_n, \dot{q}_1, \ldots \dot{q}_{k-1}, \dot{q}_{k+1}, \ldots \dot{q}_n$, and t all constant. The reader who is unfamiliar with such a convention will object that $\dot{x}_i$ will not change when the coordinates and the time are held constant. This is true; but we are not considering what happens in nature if the coordinates and the time are kept fixed. We are simply holding certain symbols constant in a mathematical expression. All partial derivatives occurring in the discussion of Lagrange's equation are to be understood in this sense. The point is that we can consider the relations of two similar systems of particles occupying the same positions but having different velocities or two systems having the same velocities but not located at the same positions. The kinetic energies of two systems having the same q's but slightly different velocities,—say $\dot{q}$ and $\dot{q} + \Delta\dot{q}$,—will differ by ΔT. By definition, $\partial T/\partial\dot{q}_k$ is the limit of $\Delta T/\Delta\dot{q}_k$ when $\Delta\dot{q}_k$ approaches zero.

From equation (7), by actual differentiation,

$$\frac{\partial \dot{x}_i}{\partial \dot{q}_k} = \frac{\partial x_i}{\partial q_k}. \tag{10}$$

Also,

$$\frac{\partial \dot{x}_i}{\partial q_k} = \frac{\partial}{\partial q_k}\left(\frac{\partial x_i}{\partial q_1}\dot{q}_1 + \cdots + \frac{\partial x_i}{\partial t}\right)$$

$$= \dot{q}_1\frac{\partial}{\partial q_1}\left(\frac{\partial x_i}{\partial q_k}\right) + \cdots + \dot{q}_n\frac{\partial}{\partial q_n}\left(\frac{\partial x_i}{\partial q_k}\right) + \frac{\partial}{\partial t}\left(\frac{\partial x_i}{\partial q_k}\right),$$

which tells us that

$$\frac{\partial \dot{x}_i}{\partial q_k} = \frac{d}{dt}\frac{\partial x_i}{\partial q_k}. \tag{11}$$

So much for auxiliary relations. Now we are in a position to prove that the equations of motion in the coordinates q are

$$\frac{d}{dt}\left(\frac{\partial T}{\partial \dot{q}_k}\right) - \frac{\partial T}{\partial q_k} = Q_k, \quad k = 1, \cdots n. \tag{12}$$

Here T must be expressed as a function of the q's, $\dot{q}$'s, and of t. If written in any other way, equation (12) is not valid. To do this we shall prove that the left side of equation (12) is identical with the right side of equation (5).

$$\frac{\partial T(q,\dot{q})}{\partial \dot{q}_k} = \sum_i \frac{\partial T(\dot{x})}{\partial \dot{x}_i}\frac{\partial \dot{x}_i}{\partial \dot{q}_k} = \sum_i m_i\dot{x}_i\frac{\partial \dot{x}_i}{\partial \dot{q}_k},$$

and, therefore,

$$\frac{d}{dt}\frac{\partial T}{\partial \dot{q}_k} - \frac{\partial T}{\partial q_k} = \sum_i \frac{d}{dt}(m_i\dot{x}_i)\cdot\frac{\partial \dot{x}_i}{\partial \dot{q}_k} + \sum_i m_i\dot{x}_i\frac{d}{dt}\left(\frac{\partial \dot{x}_i}{\partial \dot{q}_k}\right) - \frac{\partial T}{\partial q_k}. \tag{13}$$

By the ordinary equations of motion,

$$\frac{d(m_i\dot{x}_i)}{dt} = X_i.$$

This relation, together with equations (10) and (11), enables us to recast the right side of equation (13) in the form

$$\sum_i X_i\frac{\partial x_i}{\partial q_k} + \sum_i m_i\dot{x}_i\frac{\partial \dot{x}_i}{\partial q_k} - \frac{\partial T}{\partial q_k}.$$

The middle term here is $\dfrac{\partial}{\partial q_k}\sum_i \dfrac{1}{2}m_i \dot{x}_i^2$. Thus it is equal to the last term

and the right side of equation (13) is simply Q_k, as we see from the definition of this quantity, in equation (5). This completes the proof of Lagrange's equations (12).

The solution of equations (12) yields the same information as the solution of the Newtonian equations in Cartesian coordinates. They are n in number and of the second order. Their solution gives the values of the q's as functions of the time as soon as we specify the values of $2n$ constants of integration, which may be the values of the q's and $\dot{q}$'s at a given time. The values of the x's are then found from equation (1).

Example.—We continue the example used above, where the transformation of the forces from Cartesian to polar coordinates is carried out. To express T in polar coordinates, we abandon the procedure outlined above, and use the relation $T = (m/2)\,(ds/dt)^2$, where the square of the element of arc, ds^2, equals $dr^2 + r^2 d\theta^2 + r^2 \sin^2\theta\, d\varphi^2$. This yields,

$$T = (m/2)(\dot{r}^2 + r^2\dot{\theta}^2 + r^2\sin^2\theta\,\dot{\varphi}^2). \tag{6a}$$

This is a quadratic function of $\dot{r}$, $\dot{\theta}$, and $\dot{\varphi}$, and the coefficients are functions of the coordinates—in this case of only two of the coordinates, r and θ. No cross-product terms of the kind $\dot{r}\dot{\theta}$, $\dot{\theta}\dot{\varphi}$, etc., appear in the expression for the kinetic energy in polar coordinates. This is the case whenever the coordinate system is orthogonal, *i.e.*, when the coordinate lines are perpendicular to each other everywhere in space except possibly at a limited number of singular points, lines, or surfaces. In the present example, the origin is such a singular point and the Z-axis a singular line through which an infinite number of coordinate surfaces pass. The generalized momenta are

$$\frac{\partial T}{\partial \dot{r}} = m\dot{r} = p_r, \quad \frac{\partial T}{\partial \dot{\theta}} = mr^2\dot{\theta} = p_\theta, \quad \frac{\partial T}{\partial \dot{\varphi}} = mr^2\sin^2\theta\,\dot{\varphi} = p_\varphi.$$

In these coordinates Lagrange's equations are

$$\frac{d}{dt}\frac{\partial T}{\partial \dot{r}} - \frac{\partial T}{\partial r} = R,$$

$$\frac{d}{dt}\frac{\partial T}{\partial \dot{\theta}} - \frac{\partial T}{\partial \theta} = \Theta, \tag{12a}$$

$$\frac{d}{dt}\frac{\partial T}{\partial \dot{\varphi}} - \frac{\partial T}{\partial \varphi_{\,\lrcorner}} = \Phi.$$

To prove the right side of these equivalent to the expressions given in equation (5a) above, we could follow the method given above. Written out in full, equation (12a) becomes,

$$m(\ddot{r} - r\dot{\theta}^2 - r\sin^2\theta\,\dot{\varphi}^2) = R,$$

$$\frac{d}{dt}(mr^2\dot{\theta}) - mr^2\sin\theta\cos\theta\,\dot{\varphi}^2 = \Theta, \tag{12b}$$

$$\frac{d}{dt}(mr^2\sin^2\theta\,\dot{\varphi}) = \Phi.$$

Equations (12) are very general but they have some limitations. They must be replaced by others if parts of the system are obliged to remain on certain surfaces—like a ball rolling in a trough—or if there are other constraints which prevent the possible changes of the coordinates from being *independent and quite arbitrary*. These cases are seldom met in atomic problems.[1]

There is a special case of equations (12) which is worth mentioning. If we are dealing with a conservative system in which the Cartesian components of force are functions of the coordinates alone, then they are expressible in the form

$$X_i = -\frac{\partial V}{\partial x_i},$$

where V is the potential energy. Then equation (5) reduces to

$$Q_k = -\frac{\partial V}{\partial x_1}\frac{\partial x_1}{\partial q_k} - \cdots - \frac{\partial V}{\partial x_n}\frac{\partial x_n}{\partial q_k} = -\frac{\partial V}{\partial q_k}. \tag{5b}$$

Remembering that $\partial V/\partial \dot{q}_k = 0$, we can write equation (12) in the form,

$$\frac{d}{dt}\frac{\partial(T - V)}{\partial \dot{q}_k} - \frac{\partial(T - V)}{\partial q_k} = 0. \tag{14}$$

The function $T - V$ is called the Lagrangian function and is usually denoted by L. The Lagrangian equations become

$$\frac{d}{dt}\frac{\partial L}{\partial \dot{q}_k} - \frac{\partial L}{\partial q_k} = 0, k = 1, 2, \cdots \tag{15}$$

From equation (15) we can obtain the equation of energy. Multiply equation (15) by $\dot{q}_k$, obtaining

$$\dot{q}_k\frac{d}{dt}\frac{\partial L}{\partial \dot{q}_k} - \frac{\partial L}{\partial q_k}\dot{q}_k = 0.$$

Add the identity,

$$\frac{\partial L}{\partial \dot{q}_k}\ddot{q}_k - \frac{\partial L}{\partial \dot{q}_k}\ddot{q}_k = 0,$$

and sum the result over all values of k to obtain

$$\frac{d}{dt}\left(\Sigma \dot{q}_k \frac{\partial L}{\partial \dot{q}_k}\right) - \frac{dL}{dt} = 0.$$

$\partial L/\partial \dot{q}_k$ is the same as $\partial T/\partial \dot{q}_k$. T is a quadratic function of the velocities, so by Euler's theorem the summation in this equation is equal to $2T$. Integrating,
$$2T - L = T + V = E.$$

The constant of integration E is the total energy.

Equation (15) shows us that the whole motion of a conservative system can be derived from the single function L together with the initial conditions. Sometimes it may occur that equation (12) can be thrown into the form of equation (15) even when the forces depend on the

---

[1] See Chaps. II and VIII of Whittaker's "Analytical Dynamics."

velocities and on higher derivatives of the coordinates. Then, of course, these derivatives will appear in the function V. These cases are not unimportant, but have received very little attention.[1] A case in point is a charged particle moving in a magnetic field, so that the force acting on it depends on its velocity. The equations for this problem are given in Appendix VIII.

4. LAGRANGE'S EQUATIONS IN RELATIVITY MECHANICS

When the mass varies with the velocity the above proof must be modified. It might be thought that the relativity expression for the kinetic energy, namely, $mc^2\left(\dfrac{1}{(1 - \beta^2)^{1/2}} - 1\right)$, should be substituted for the Newtonian expression in writing Lagrange's equations for non-relativity mechanics; but this is not the case. One of the most valuable properties of the classical expression for the kinetic energy is that its derivative with respect to a generalized velocity is the expression for the corresponding generalized momentum; but this is not true of the relativity expression for the kinetic energy. Therefore, we define a new function which *does* have this property. For a system of particles it is

$$T^* = \sum_i m_i c^2 (1 - \sqrt{1 - \beta_i^2}),\, \beta_i = \frac{v_i}{c}, \tag{16}$$

where the summation is extended over all the particles of the system. The radical can be expanded for small values of β, and then T^* reduces to

$$T^* = \sum \frac{1}{2} m_i v_i^2 \left(1 + \frac{1}{4}\frac{v_i^2}{c^2} + \cdots\right).$$

For small values of v_i^2/c^2, this approaches $\Sigma \frac{1}{2} m_i v_i^2$. Now

$$\frac{\partial T^*}{\partial \dot{q}_k} = p_k. \tag{17}$$

In Cartesian coordinates, we have

$$\frac{\partial T^*}{\partial \dot{x}_i} = \frac{m_i \dot{x}_i}{(1 - \beta_i^2)^{1/2}} = p_{x_i}.$$

This expression is the actual mass multiplied by $\dot{x}$, which is *defined* to be the x-component of momentum. Using T^* instead of T, the equations (5), (7), (10), (11), and (13) are unaltered and we find that

$$\frac{d}{dt}\frac{\partial T^*}{\partial \dot{q}_k} - \frac{\partial T^*}{\partial q_k} = Q_k. \tag{18}$$

If we write

$$L = T^* - V,$$

Lagrange's equations for a conservative system take the form of equation (15), as before.

[1] See WHITTAKER, *loc. cit.*, pp. 45 and 266.

5. MOTION OF A PARTICLE ABOUT A CENTER OF FORCE

Suppose a particle P is acted on by a force directed toward or away from a fixed point O, the magnitude of the force F being some function of its distance r from the fixed point. At any moment the particle is moving in a plane determined by r and its velocity v, and it continues to move in this plane, for the total force acting upon it lies in the plane. We, therefore, use coordinates r, φ, in the plane of motion, the fixed

FIG. 2.—Particle moving in a central field.

point being taken as the origin. The velocity is resolved into components $\dot{r}$ and $r\dot{\varphi}$, as in Fig. 2. We have,

$$T = \tfrac{1}{2}m(\dot{r}^2 + r^2\dot{\varphi}^2), \tag{19}$$

while the potential energy is

$$V = \int_\infty^r -Fdr. \tag{20}$$

Lagrange's function is

$$L \equiv \tfrac{1}{2}m(\dot{r}^2 + r^2\dot{\varphi}^2) - V, \tag{21}$$

and the Lagrangian equations of motion are

$$\frac{d}{dt}\left(\frac{\partial L}{\partial \dot{\varphi}}\right) - \frac{\partial L}{\partial \varphi} = \frac{d}{dt}(mr^2\dot{\varphi}) = 0, \tag{22}$$

$$\frac{d}{dt}\left(\frac{\partial L}{\partial \dot{r}}\right) - \frac{\partial L}{\partial r} = \frac{d}{dt}(m\dot{r}) - mr\dot{\varphi}^2 + \frac{\partial V}{\partial r} = 0.$$

The integration of the first equation gives

$$mr^2\dot{\varphi} = p, \tag{23}$$

where the constant p is the total angular momentum of the system. The energy integral may be secured by multiplying equations (22) by $\dot{\varphi}dt = d\varphi$, and $\dot{r}dt = dr$; but this is unnecessary for we know the result will be $T + V = E$, that is,

$$\tfrac{1}{2}m(\dot{r}^2 + r^2\dot{\varphi}^2) + V = E. \tag{24}$$

Eliminating $\dot{\varphi}$ from equations (23) and (24),

$$\dot{r} = \left(\frac{2E}{m} - \frac{2V}{m} - \frac{p^2}{m^2r^2}\right)^{\frac{1}{2}}. \tag{25}$$

When the value of V is substituted in this equation it can be integrated, thus giving r as a function of the time. This value of r substituted in equation (23) gives a differential equation for φ as a function of the time. To secure the differential equation for the orbit we eliminate the time from equations (23) and (25).

$$\frac{dr}{dt} = \frac{dr}{d\varphi}\frac{d\varphi}{dt} = \frac{dr}{d\varphi}\frac{p}{mr^2} = \left(\frac{2E}{m} - \frac{2V}{m} - \frac{p^2}{m^2r^2}\right)^{\frac{1}{2}}. \tag{26}$$

The last equation can be integrated when V is known as a function of r, and gives the polar equation of the orbit.

6. INVERSE SQUARE LAW OF FORCE

The force acting between two electrically charged particles varies as the inverse square of the distance between them and is proportional to the product of their charges. The force is positive, *i.e.*, in the direction of increasing r, if the charges are of like sign and negative if of unlike sign. The electrostatic unit of charge is so chosen that the constant of proportionality is unity so that for two charges, e_1 and e_2,

$$F = \frac{e_1 e_2}{r^2}.$$

The potential energy is, therefore,

$$V = \int -Fdr = \int_{\infty}^{r} -\frac{e_1 e_2}{r^2}dr = \frac{e_1 e_2}{r}, \qquad (27)$$

the value of V being taken equal to zero for $r = \infty$.

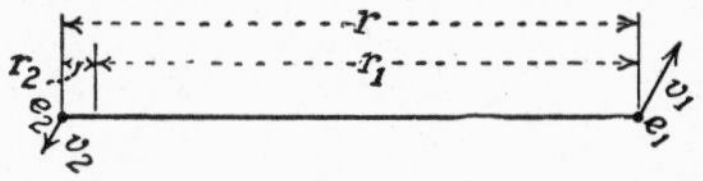

Let the masses of the two particles be m_1 and m_2 and their coordinates with respect to their center of gravity as origin be r_1, φ_1 and r_2, φ_2; and let $r = r_1 + r_2$ (Fig. 3). Then,

FIG. 3.

$$m_1 r_1 = m_2 r_2 \text{ and } \varphi_1 = \varphi_2 + \pi,$$

$$r_1 = r\frac{m_2}{m_1 + m_2}, \ r_2 = r\frac{m_1}{m_1 + m_2},$$

and

$$\dot{r}_1 = \dot{r}\frac{m_2}{m_1 + m_2}, \ \dot{r}_2 = \dot{r}\frac{m_1}{m_1 + m_2}, \ \dot{\varphi}_1 = \dot{\varphi}_2.$$

The kinetic energy is

$$\frac{m_1}{2}(\dot{r}_1{}^2 + r_1{}^2\dot{\varphi}_1{}^2) + \frac{m_2}{2}(\dot{r}_2{}^2 + r_2{}^2\dot{\varphi}_2{}^2).$$

On substituting the above values for r_1, r_2, φ_1 and φ_2,

$$T = \frac{\mu}{2}(\dot{r}^2 + r^2\dot{\varphi}^2), \qquad (28)$$

where $\dot{\varphi} = \dot{\varphi}_1 = \dot{\varphi}_2$, and $\mu = m_1 m_2/(m_1 + m_2)$; μ is called the reduced mass.

Equations (27) and (28) show that r varies just as though we were dealing with a particle of mass μ, moving about a fixed center under forces having the potential $V(r)$. Having solved this problem, the behavior of r_1 and r_2 is obtained from the relations preceding equation (28). The angular momentum of the system is $m_1 r_1{}^2\dot{\varphi}_1 + m_2 r_2{}^2\dot{\varphi}_2$ which is equal to $\mu r^2\dot{\varphi}$. It follows that the equations for the motion of a body about a fixed center of force will hold for the motion of one body about another if the reduced mass μ is substituted for m throughout. When the value of V is substituted in equation (26) and μ is used in place of m, we have on integrating,

$$\frac{\dfrac{p}{\mu r} + \dfrac{e_1 e_2}{p}}{\left(\dfrac{2E}{\mu} + \dfrac{e_1^2 e_2^2}{p^2}\right)^{1/2}} = \cos(\varphi + \varphi_0).$$

Rearranging, this gives

$$r = \frac{-p^2/\mu e_1 e_2}{1 - \epsilon \cos(\varphi + \varphi_0)}, \tag{29}$$

where we have written

$$\epsilon^2 = 1 + \frac{2Ep^2}{\mu e_1^2 e_2^2}.$$

Equation (29) is the equation of a conic section with parameter $-p^2/\mu e_1 e_2$ and eccentricity ϵ.   The semimajor axis a is such that

$$a(1 - \epsilon^2) = -\frac{p^2}{\mu e_1 e_2}.$$

In order that $\varphi = 0$ may coincide with the major axis of the conic, φ_0 must be equal to 0 or π.

The conic is an ellipse, parabola, or hyperbola when ϵ is less than, equal to, or greater than 1, respectively; that is, when E is negative, zero, or positive, respectively.

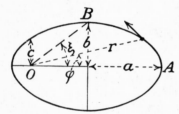

FIG. 4.—Kepler ellipse.

We shall consider the case in which the energy is negative and the path an ellipse. Figure 4 shows the orbit; a and b are the semimajor and semiminor axes, respectively, $\epsilon = \cos\xi$, and c is the parameter. The maximum value of r is OA and is secured by substituting $\varphi = 0$ in equation (29) when φ_0 is set equal to 0;

$$r_{\max} = -\frac{p^2}{\mu e_1 e_2 (1 - \epsilon)}.$$

The minimum value of r is

$$r_{\min} = -\frac{p^2}{\mu e_1 e_2 (1 + \epsilon)}.$$

Further,

$$2a \equiv r_{\max} + r_{\min} = -\frac{2p^2}{\mu e_1 e_2 (1 - \epsilon^2)},$$

whence, from the definition of ϵ, $a = e_1 e_2 / 2E$.   The distance OB is equal to a so that

$$b = \overline{OB} \sin\xi = a(1 - \epsilon^2)^{1/2}.$$

Substituting the values of a and ϵ, we have

$$b = \frac{p}{(-2E\mu)^{1/2}}.$$

Thus, the semimajor axis depends on the total energy but not on the angular momentum; the semiminor axis, on both the energy and the angular momentum; and the parameter on the angular momentum alone. All orbits having the same major axis have the same energy though the angular momentum may be different and all orbits having the same parameter have the same angular momentum though the energy may vary.

By substituting $V = e_1e_2/r$ in equation (25), and integrating between the limits r_{min} and r_{max}, we get the time required for a half revolution,

$$\int_{r_{min}}^{r_{max}} \frac{\mu r \, dr}{(2E\mu r^2 - 2\mu e_1 e_2 r - p^2)^{1/2}} = \frac{-e_1 e_2 \mu^{1/2} \pi}{(-2E)^{3/2}},$$

or

$$\tau = \frac{-2\pi e_1 e_2 \mu^{1/2}}{(-2E)^{3/2}}$$

where τ is the period. The frequency is

$$\omega = -\frac{(-2E)^{3/2}}{2\pi e_1 e_2 \mu^{1/2}}.$$

The frequency depends on the energy, but not on the angular momentum. If instead of the energy we substitute the semimajor axis a, the frequency is

$$\omega = \frac{|e_1^{1/2} e_2^{1/2}|}{2\pi a^{3/2} \mu^{1/2}}.$$

The three laws of Kepler for the motion of the planets about the sun apply to this motion: (1) the path of one body with respect to the other is an ellipse; (2) the area swept out per unit time by the line joining the bodies is a constant. This follows from equation (23), for $r\dot{\varphi}$ is the base of a triangle swept out per unit time and its altitude is r, so that the area is $\frac{1}{2}r^2\dot{\varphi}$. Since $\mu r^2\dot{\varphi}$ is a constant, and μ is a constant, this law is true; (3) the frequency of the rotation is inversely proportional to the $\frac{3}{2}$-power of the semimajor axis. All the results of this section are useful in the study of the hydrogen atom (Chap. V).

7. HAMILTON'S EQUATIONS

The Lagrangian equations are n in number, and are of the second order, so that $2n$ constants of integration are introduced in their solution. Often it is convenient to replace them by $2n$ equations of the first order, as follows: When the equations of motion are of the form of equation (15), p_k is defined to be $\partial L/\partial \dot{q}_k$, whether $\partial L/\partial \dot{q}_k = \partial T/\partial \dot{q}_k$ or not. This definition replaces equation (8).

$$p_k = \frac{\partial L}{\partial \dot{q}_k}, \tag{30}$$

so that Lagrange's equations are

$$\dot{p}_k = \frac{\partial L(q, \dot{q})}{\partial q_k}. \tag{31}$$

We introduce a new function

$$H = \Sigma p_k \dot{q}_k - L(q, \dot{q}).$$ (32)

At first sight this is formally a function of the p's, q's, and $\dot{q}$'s, but taking its total differential we have,

$$dH = \Sigma \dot{q}_k dp_k + \Sigma p_k d\dot{q}_k - \sum \frac{\partial L}{\partial \dot{q}_k} d\dot{q}_k - \sum \frac{\partial L}{\partial q_k} dq_k.$$

By equation (30), the second term cancels the third, and

$$dH = \Sigma \dot{q}_k dp_k - \sum \frac{\partial L}{\partial q_k} dq_k.$$

This shows that H depends only on the p's and q's.   But then

$$dH = \sum \frac{\partial H}{\partial p_k} dp_k + \sum \frac{\partial H}{\partial q_k} dq_k.$$

Each differential is quite arbitrary, so the corresponding coefficients in these equations must be equal.   Using equation (31),

$$\frac{dq_k}{dt} = \frac{\partial H(p, q)}{\partial p_k} ; \frac{dp_k}{dt} = -\frac{\partial H(p, q)}{\partial q_k}.$$ (33)

It is essential that H be a function of the p's and q's; otherwise, the equations are not valid.   These equations of first order are equivalent to the Lagrangian equations of second order and are called *the canonical form of the equations of motion*, or *Hamilton's equations*. $H(p, q)$ is called the Hamiltonian function and q_k and p_k are said to be *canonically conjugate variables*.   Taking the derivative of H with respect to the time and using equations (33),

$$\frac{dH}{dt} = \sum \left[\frac{\partial H}{\partial q_k} \dot{q}_k + \frac{\partial H}{\partial p_k} \dot{p}_k \right] = 0,$$

so that H is a constant.   The meaning of this constant is easily seen when T is a homogeneous quadratic function of the velocities, for then by Euler's theorem

$$\Sigma p_k \dot{q}_k = \sum \frac{\partial T}{\partial \dot{q}_k} \dot{q}_k = 2T,$$

and

$$H = 2T - L = T + V,$$

which is the total energy of the system.   We derived Lagrange's equations for the case of conservative forces.   As far as the above reasoning is concerned, then, Hamilton's equations have been proved only for conservative forces.   However, it is true that the equations of motion can often be thrown into this form even when the system is not conservative.   When such is the case, the relation $H = $ constant always furnishes an integral of the equations, whatever H may be.

8. HAMILTON'S PRINCIPLE

With a view to applications in this chapter and in Chap. XV *ff*, we now discuss Hamilton's principle, which is a statement of the laws of dynamics in integral form.   This principle has the advantage that it is the same in form for all systems of coordinates.   Let a dynamical system move from a fixed configuration A at time t_1 to a fixed configuration B at time t_2.   Hamilton's principle states that the path chosen in nature is such that

$$\int_{t_1}^{t_2} L\, dt$$

takes an extreme value as compared with all conceivable neighboring paths.   The condition for this is that

$$\delta \int_{t_1}^{t_2} L\, dt = 0, \tag{34}$$

where $\delta \int L\, dt$ means the variation which the integral undergoes if the system moves from A to B, on a path infinitesimally different from the natural one (Fig. 5).   Suppose the coordinates and velocities on the natural path are $q_1, q_2, \ldots, \dot{q}_1, \dot{q}_2$ $\ldots$ at time t.   At the same instant the coordinates and velocities on a neighboring path are $q_1 + \delta q_1, q_2 + \delta q_2, \ldots \dot{q}_1 + \delta \dot{q}_1, \dot{q}_2 + \delta \dot{q}_2, \ldots$ We wish to express $\delta \int L\, dt$ as a function of the q's and $\dot{q}$'s and their variations.   In varying the path the time is not changed, and so the order

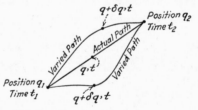

Fig. 5.—Actual and varied paths.

of the variation and integration can be interchanged.   That is,

$$\delta \int L\, dt = \int \delta L\, dt.$$

Now

$$\delta L = \sum \frac{\partial L}{\partial \dot{q}_k} \delta \dot{q}_k + \sum \frac{\partial L}{\partial q_k} \delta q_k$$

$$= \sum \frac{\partial L}{\partial \dot{q}_k} \frac{d\delta q_k}{dt} + \sum \frac{\partial L}{\partial q_k} \delta q_k$$

$$= \frac{d}{dt} \left[\sum \frac{\partial L}{\partial \dot{q}_k} \delta q_k \right] - \sum \left[\delta q_k \frac{d}{dt} \left(\frac{\partial L}{\partial \dot{q}_k} \right) \right] + \sum \frac{\partial L}{\partial q_k} \delta q_k.$$

On integrating, the first term yields

$$\left[\sum \frac{\partial L}{\partial \dot{q}_k} \delta q_k \right]_{t_1}^{t_2}$$

which is zero because the variations of all the coordinates are zero at t_1 and t_2, by hypothesis. Therefore,

$$\int \delta L dt = \int \sum \left[\frac{\partial L}{\partial q_k} - \frac{d}{dt}\left(\frac{\partial L}{\partial \dot{q}_k} \right) \right] \delta q_k dt$$

and this must be zero, regardless of our choice of the quantities δq_k, that is, for all varied paths. Choosing all the δq's except δq_1 equal to zero, we see that the coefficient of δq_1 must be zero; and similarly for the coefficients of all the other δq's. Therefore, the equations

$$\frac{d}{dt}\left(\frac{\partial L}{\partial \dot{q}_k} \right) - \frac{\partial L}{\partial q_k} = 0,$$

must hold true if Hamilton's requirement, equation (34), is to be satisfied, and these are simply the Lagrangian equations, from which we derived the canonical equations, above. By substituting $\Sigma p_k \dot{q}_k - H$ for L in equation (34), and finding the conditions which H must satisfy, we can derive the canonical equations (33) directly from equation (34).

9. CANONICAL TRANSFORMATIONS

It is often convenient to solve the equations of motion by introducing new variables P_k and Q_k, having the following properties: (1) The transformation equations are

$$p_k = p_k(Q_1, Q_2, \cdots P_1, P_2, \cdots , t),$$
$$q_k = q_k(Q_1, Q_2, \cdots P_1, P_2, \cdots , t). \tag{35}$$

This transformation is much more general than that of equation (1), where the new coordinates depend only on the old coordinates and perhaps on t. (2) In the new variables the equations of motion must be in the Hamiltonian form

$$\frac{dP_k}{dt} = -\frac{\partial H^*}{\partial Q_k}, \frac{dQ_k}{dt} = \frac{\partial H^*}{\partial P_k}, \tag{36}$$

where H^* is not necessarily the same as H, the Hamilton function in the original coordinates. When equations (36) are obeyed, the transformation is said to be *canonical*.

We now proceed to determine the relation between H^* and H, and the conditions which equation (35) must satisfy in order that the transformation may be canonical. Since the canonical equations can be derived from the variational principle that $\int L dt$ shall have an extreme value for the actual motion, regardless of the coordinates used, we have

$$\int_{t_1}^{t_2} L dt = \int_{t_1}^{t_2} [\Sigma p_k \dot{q}_k - H(q_1, p_1, \cdots t)] dt = \text{extreme},$$

and

$$\int_{t_1}^{t_2} [\Sigma P_k \dot{Q}_k - H^*(Q_1, P_1, \cdots t)] dt = \text{extreme}.$$

The integrals are taken between fixed values of t, and the final and initial configurations are fixed. The last equation will be true if the difference between the two integrands is the total derivative with respect to time of a function which depends on t and on any group of $2n$ variables chosen at will from both the old and new coordinates. Usually, this function is taken in one of the four forms,

$$F(q, P, t), F(q, Q, t), F(p, P, t), \text{ or } F(p, Q, t).$$

The first of these four forms is most often used and we shall illustrate this one only. If

$$\Sigma p_k \dot{q}_k - H(q_1, p_1 \cdots t) = \Sigma P_k \dot{Q}_k - H^*(Q_1, P_1, \cdots t) + \frac{d}{dt}(F - \Sigma P_k Q_k), \quad (37)$$

then multiplying by dt and integrating we have

$$\int_{t_1}^{t_2} \Big[\Sigma p_k \dot{q}_k - H(q_1, p_1 \cdots t) \Big] dt = \int_{t_1}^{t_2} \Big[\Sigma P_k \dot{Q}_k - H^*(Q_1, P_1, \cdots t) \Big] dt + (F - \Sigma P_k Q_k) \Big]_{t_1}^{t_2}$$

Therefore if the left hand side of the equation is a maximum or minimum, the right hand side enjoys the same property. The variation of the last term depends only on the variations of its independent variables at the times t_1 and t_2 but the variation of the integral depends on their variations at all times from t_1 to t_2. We may conclude that at all times, with the possible exception of t_1 and t_2 the equations of motion will be of the canonical form in the new coordinates. Rewriting,

$$\Sigma p_k \dot{q}_k - H(q_1, p_1, \cdots t) = -\Sigma Q_k \dot{P}_k - H^*(Q_1, P_1, \cdots t) + \sum \frac{\partial F}{\partial q_k} \dot{q}_k + \sum \frac{\partial F}{\partial P_k} \dot{P}_k + \frac{\partial F}{\partial t}. \quad (37')$$

This is true whatever be the values of the $\dot{q}_k$ and the $\dot{P}_k$. Therefore, the coefficients of these quantities on both sides must be equal and the terms free of them must also be equal, which yields the relations,

$$p_k = \frac{\partial F}{\partial q_k}, \ Q_k = \frac{\partial F}{\partial P_k}, \quad (38)$$

and

$$H = H^* - \frac{\partial F}{\partial t}. \quad (39)$$

The $2n$ equations (38) when solved for the p_k and q_k, yield the transformation relations of equation (35). All equations of transformation in the form of equation (38) preserve the canonical form of the Hamilton equations, as in equation (36), regardless of the nature of F. It must be remembered in applying equations (38) and (39) that F is a function of q, P, and t.

Illustration.—In transforming from plane polar to Cartesian coordinates, the appropriate function is

$$F = p_x\, r \cos \varphi + p_y\, r \sin \varphi,$$

whence

$$p_r = p_x \cos \varphi + p_y \sin \varphi,\ p_\varphi = r(-p_x \sin \varphi + p_y \cos \varphi),$$
$$x = r \cos \varphi,\ y = r \sin \varphi.$$

10. ACTION, HAMILTON'S PRINCIPAL FUNCTION, AND THE HAMILTON-JACOBI DIFFERENTIAL EQUATION

The *action function* S is defined by the equation

$$S = \int_{t_0}^{t} 2T dt, \tag{40}$$

where t_0 is an arbitrary initial value of the time-variable. A change of t_0 results in adding an unimportant constant to S. We shall set $t_0 = 0$ for simplicity. Now $2T = \Sigma p_k \dot{q}_k$, so that

$$S = \int \Sigma p_k dq_k \tag{41}$$

and, therefore,

$$p_k = \frac{\partial S}{\partial q_k}. \tag{42}$$

Thus, for a single particle moving with constant velocity,

$$S = \int_0^{t} m[\dot{x}^2 + \dot{y}^2 + \dot{z}^2]dt = \int p_x dx + p_y dy + p_z dz$$
$$= p_x x + p_y y + p_z z,$$

if we so choose the coordinates that $x = y = z = 0$ when $t = 0$. Obviously, equation (42) is verified in this case. For all dynamical systems, S is an increasing function of the time. The *Hamilton principal function* is closely related to S and is defined by

$$W = -Et + S, \tag{43}$$

so that

$$\frac{\partial W}{\partial q_k} = p_k,\ \frac{\partial W}{\partial t} = -E. \tag{44}$$

These functions owe much of their importance to their appearance in the *Hamilton-Jacobi differential equation*. Consider the relation

$$H(p, q) = E,$$

which is an integral of the Hamilton equations of motion for a conservative system. If we substitute the values of the p's from equation (42) in this relation, we have the *Hamilton-Jacobi equation* for the determination of S, as a function of the q's and of n constants of integration. It will often be referred to as the H. J. equation, and has the form

$$H\left(\frac{\partial S}{\partial q_k}, q_k\right) = E. \tag{45}$$

For a single particle, the equation $H(p, q) = E$ takes the form

$$\frac{1}{2m}(p_x{}^2 + p_y{}^2 + p_z{}^2) + V = E, \tag{46}$$

and the H. J. equation is

$$\frac{1}{2m}\left[\left(\frac{\partial S}{\partial x}\right)^2 + \left(\frac{\partial S}{\partial y}\right)^2 + \left(\frac{\partial S}{\partial z}\right)^2\right] + V = E, \tag{47}$$

where E is a constant of integration. To solve this, we must know the form of V.

Example 1. V = 0. Free Particle.—We solve equation (47) by the usual device of separation of variables. Multiplying by $2m$ we assume the solution is of the form,

$$S = S_x + S_y + S_z, \tag{48}$$

where S_x is a function of x alone; S_y, of y alone; and S_z, of z alone. Then $\partial S/\partial x = \partial S_x/\partial x$ and this is a function of x alone; similarly, $\partial S/\partial y = \partial S_y/\partial y$ and is a function of y, etc. Transposing all terms except $(\partial S/\partial x)^2$ to the right, we have on the left a function of x alone and on the right a function of y and z. But a function of x can be equal to a function of y and z only if both are constants. Calling the constant value of each side $2mE_x$ we have,

$$\left(\frac{\partial S_x}{\partial x}\right)^2 = 2mE_x. \tag{49}$$

Solving, and omitting an unessential additive constant of integration,

$$S_x = (2mE_x)^{\frac{1}{2}}x, \tag{50}$$

and likewise,

$$S_y = (2mE_y)^{\frac{1}{2}}y \text{ and } S_z = (2mE_z)^{\frac{1}{2}}z,$$

where

$$E_x + E_y + E_z = E.$$

From equation (49), $(2mE_x)^{\frac{1}{2}} = p_x = $ constant so S may be written

$$S = p_x x + p_y y + p_z z. \tag{51}$$

Here the constant p's play the rôle of integration constants, of which there must be three since the H. J. equation is of first order and has three variables.

Example 2. V = $-e^2/r$. Particle Attracted to Origin by the Inverse Square Law of Force; the Problem of the Hydrogen Atom.—Plane polar coordinates are especially suited to this problem. Equation (47) becomes

$$\left(\frac{\partial S}{\partial r}\right)^2 + \frac{1}{r^2}\left(\frac{\partial S}{\partial \varphi}\right)^2 = 2mE + \frac{2me^2}{r} \tag{47'}$$

We have,

$$\frac{\partial S}{\partial \varphi} = p_\varphi = \text{constant, say } \alpha_\varphi,$$

since the force is radial. This can be shown also by the method used in example 1. But

$$S = S_r + S_\varphi.$$

Then,

$$S_\varphi = \alpha_\varphi \varphi$$

and

$$\left(\frac{\partial S_r}{\partial r}\right)^2 = 2mE + \frac{2me^2}{r} - \frac{\alpha_\varphi{}^2}{r^2},$$

so that finally,

$$S = \alpha_\varphi \varphi + \int^r \left(2mE + \frac{2me^2}{r} - \frac{\alpha_\varphi{}^2}{r^2}\right)^{\frac{1}{2}} dr. \tag{52}$$

S is a function of φ, r, and two constants of integration, α_φ and E.

11. CYCLIC VARIABLES

The function S owes much of its importance to the fact that it is useful in reducing the Hamilton equations to an especially simple form. Suppose we try to find a transformation of the type given in equations (38) and (39), such that $\partial F/\partial t = 0$ and the function H^* depends only on the new momenta   Then

$$H = H^* = H^*(P_1, \cdots P_n).$$ (53)

Then the equations of motion (33) tell us that

$$\frac{dP_k}{dt} = -\frac{\partial H^*}{\partial Q_k} = 0,$$ (54)

so that *all the momentum variables are constants*, say $\alpha_1, \ldots \alpha_n$;

$$P_k = \alpha_k = \text{constant.}$$ (55)

Now

$$\frac{dQ_k}{dt} = \frac{\partial H^*}{\partial P_k},$$

and so dQ_k/dt is a function only of the P's. We call its constant value ω_k, and then

$$Q_k = \omega_k t + \delta_k.$$ (56)

The great advantage of using such coordinates is seen at once, for the equations (55) and (56) represent the complete solution of the problem. The apparent simplicity of equation (56) is misleading; often the coordinates Q_k have a very complicated meaning. Coordinates of this kind, which do not appear explicitly in the Lagrange equations (54), are called "cyclic variables." To find such variables we begin by requiring that

$$H^* = P_1$$ (53')

a special case of equation (53), so that the energy constant E is one of the new momenta. From equation (38), we have $p_k = \partial F/\partial q_k$. But the action S obeys the same relations, so that aside from a possible term containing the time, *the transformation function F is the action S.* The procedure for finding cyclic variables is therefore the following:

Solving the H. J. equation.

$$H\left(\frac{\partial S}{\partial q_k}, q_k\right) = E,$$

we obtain S as a function of the q's, of E, and of $n - 1$ other constants of integration, $\alpha_2, \ldots \alpha_n$, which we make our new momentum variables, $P_2 \ldots P_n$; so that

$$S = S(q_1 \cdots q_n, E, \alpha_2, \cdots \alpha_n).$$ (57)

Then, because of equation (53'), we have satisfied equation (53), and equations (54) to (56) follow. To get the formulas of transformation, we use the relations

$$p_k = \frac{\partial S}{\partial q_k}, \; Q_1 = \frac{\partial S}{\partial E}, \; Q_2 = \frac{\partial S}{\partial \alpha_2} = \frac{\partial S}{\partial P_2}, \text{ etc.}$$ (38')

The solution of the problem is then given by equations (55) and (56), where

$$\omega_1 = \frac{\partial H^*}{\partial P_1} = 1, \; \omega_2 = \cdots \omega_n = 0,$$

so that all the Q's are constant except Q_1, and $Q_1 = t + \delta_1$. The procedure has led to the discovery of $2n - 1$ functions of the original coordinates and momenta, $P_1, \ldots P_n, Q_2, \ldots Q_n$, which remain constant during the motion and another function Q_1 which increases uniformly.

Example.—In example 1 of the preceding section, the appropriate transformation which makes all coordinates constant except Q_1 is geometrically obvious. We need only pass to new Cartesian coordinates, X, Y, Z, with the axis of X parallel to the motion of the particle. The axes of Y and Z can occupy any positions in the plane at right angles to OX. As for the scale of the X-coordinate, we choose it so that the velocity $\omega_1 = dX/dt$ is unity, that is the unit of length is equal to $(p_x{}^2 + p_y{}^2 + p_z{}^2)^{\frac{1}{2}}/m$. To obtain this transformation by the analytic method outlined above would be quite tedious. In all such problems, it is well to remember that in the new frame of reference the path of the particle is a coordinate line.

Often it is convenient to replace the variables P by other variables P', each P' being a function only of the P's. Then new coordinates Q' conjugate to the P' can be found. It can be proved that each Q' is a linear function of the Q's, with coefficients depending on the old P's.[1] Thus each Q' is a cyclic variable and the Hamilton function is of the form $H'(P')$.

12. A GENERALIZATION OF THE HAMILTON-JACOBI EQUATION

The transformation theory of the preceding section refers to problems in which H does not contain t, so that it has the significance of the total energy. When H does contain t, another artifice is adopted. We seek to find a moving frame of reference in which all the new coordinates and momenta are constant, so the equations of transformation must involve t. (In the case of a freely moving particle, for instance, we choose any set of curvilinear coordinates which has a translational motion like that of the particle.) Now, when the coordinates and momenta are all constant, we see from the canonical equations in these coordinates that

$$\frac{\partial H^*}{\partial P_k} = 0, \; \frac{\partial H^*}{\partial Q_k} = 0.$$

Therefore, H^* does not depend on the Q's and P's, although it may be a function of t. We are free to choose $H^* = 0$, because any function of t which might be chosen can be incorporated in $\partial F/\partial t$ in equation (39). Adopting this assumption we have,

$$H(p,q,t) + \frac{\partial F}{\partial t} = 0. \tag{58}$$

[1] Born, "*Atommechanik*," p. 36.

Replacing p_k by $\partial F/\partial q_k$, we have a generalization of equation (45). If H does not contain t, we put

$$F = -Et + S(q, \alpha).$$ (59)

Substituting this in equation (58), we find that the equation to determine S is equation (45), so that S is the action; and since $\partial F/\partial t = -E$, we conclude that F is the Hamilton principal function W. When H contains t, the solution of equation (58) cannot generally be put in the form of equation (59), but it is still convenient to *define* the Hamilton principal function as the solution of

$$H\left(\frac{\partial W}{\partial q_k}, t\right) + \frac{\partial W}{\partial t} = 0.$$ (60)

13. ANGLE VARIABLES; CONDITIONALLY PERIODIC SYSTEMS[1]

A particular kind of cyclic variables called "angle variables" are very frequently used in the mechanics of the atom, which has borrowed them from astronomy. For simplicity, we shall suppose the system is conservative, and that its motion has n distinct fundamental frequencies, $\omega_1, \ldots \omega_n$. By *distinct*, we mean that there is no relation of the type

$$\tau_1\omega_1 + \cdots + \tau_n\omega_n = 0$$ (61)

where the τ's are integers. The concept of distinctness is a generalization of the idea of the incommensurability of two frequencies. When the frequencies are distinct, the system is said to be non-degenerate; otherwise it is degenerate. There are important differences in the methods of treating these two classes of systems. We call the angle variables $w_1 \ldots w_n$, and the corresponding momenta $J_1, \ldots J_n$, and require that they satisfy the following conditions, the first two of which apply to any set of cyclic variables as described above:

1. The time does not enter in the equations of transformation from the variables p, q to w, J, so that H^*, the new Hamilton function, is the energy E.

2. H^* is a function of the J's alone, so that

$$J_k = \text{constant} = \alpha_k, \ w_k = \omega_k t + \delta_k, \ \omega_k = \frac{\partial H^*}{\partial J_k}.$$ (62)

3. The system returns to its original configuration when any one of the w's, *varying separately*, increases by unity. This means that any one of the coordinates q_i can be expanded in a multiple Fourier series,

$$q_i = \Sigma A_{\tau_1} \cdots \tau_n \cos [2\pi(\tau_1 w_1 + \cdots + \tau_n w_n) + \epsilon_{\tau_1} \cdots \tau_n].$$ (63)

Here the quantities τ_1, τ_2, etc. are integers, and the summation is n-fold, with each of the τ's running from $-\infty$ to $+\infty$.

[1] An excellent treatment is given in VAN VLECK's "Quantum Principles and Line Spectra."

4. The action S can also be expanded in a Fourier series of this kind when expressed in terms of the w's and J's.

In these Fourier series the amplitudes and phase constants are functions only of the J's. A system whose coordinates are of the type of equation (63) is called *conditionally periodic*. It must be understood that in general such a system is really not periodic. The system never passes twice through the same configuration if it is non-degenerate, simply because the periods are distinct. However, it can be proved that it passes indefinitely close to any specified point. The term conditionally periodic is to be understood as meaning that if the frequencies were allowed to become commensurable the system would be truly periodic.

The reason for the name angle variables is that the w's actually are dimensionless. The J's have the dimensions of angular momentum, or action.

14. ANGLE VARIABLES FOR A SEPARABLE SYSTEM

Suppose that we can put S into the form

$$S_1(q_1; \alpha_1, \ldots \alpha_n) + S_2(q_2; \alpha_1, \cdots \alpha_n) + \cdots, \tag{64}$$

and that each q varies between a maximum and a minimum value, like the coordinate of a linear oscillator. Then, writing

$$\frac{\partial S}{\partial q_k} = F_k(q_k; \alpha_1, \cdots \alpha_n),$$

it is possible to define n phase integrals by the relations

$$J_k = \oint \left(\frac{\partial S}{\partial q_k} \right) dq_k = \oint F_k(q_k; \alpha_1, \cdots \alpha_n) dq_k. \tag{65}$$

The symbol $\oint$ indicates integration around a complete cycle of q_k, that is, from the minimum to the maximum value and back again. Each J_k is a function of the constants of integration, and the equations

$$J_k = J_k(\alpha_1, \alpha_2, \alpha_3, \cdots)$$

may be solved for the α's so that

$$\alpha_k = \alpha_k(J_1, J_2, J_3, \cdots).$$

Then these values may be substituted in S. Ordinarily, we obtain S from the functions F, so that

$$S = \sum_1^n \int^{q_k} F_k(q_k; J_1, \cdots J_n) dq_k. \tag{66}$$

The function S determines a canonical transformation of variables,

$$p_k = \frac{\partial S}{\partial q_k}, \ w_k = \frac{\partial S}{\partial J_k}, \tag{67}$$

such that

$$H = H(J_1, J_2, J_3, \cdots).$$

We must prove that the w's in equation (67) actually enjoy the property that the system repeats its configuration when any w is changed by unity, the others being held constant. Consider the change of one of the w's, say w_i, when any *one* of the old coordinates, say q_k, is carried through a cycle, the other q's being constant. It is

$$\Delta w_i = \oint \left(\frac{\partial w_i}{\partial q_k}\right) dq_k,$$

but by equations (67) and (64),

$$\frac{\partial w_i}{\partial q_k} = \frac{\partial^2 S}{\partial J_i \partial q_k} = \frac{\partial}{\partial J_i}\frac{\partial S_k}{\partial q_k},$$

so that

$$\Delta w_i = \frac{\partial}{\partial J_i} \oint \frac{\partial S_k}{\partial q_k} dq_k = \frac{\partial J_k}{\partial J_i};$$

and since the J's are independent variables, $\partial J_k/\partial J_i$ is unity when $k = i$, and zero otherwise. That is, when q_k passes through a cycle, $\Delta w_k = 1$, and the change of the other w's is zero. They may vary during the process, but at the end they have returned to their original values. This proves that the w's fulfill the third condition mentioned in Sec. 13.

15. THE ANGLE VARIABLES OF THE HARMONIC OSCILLATOR

As an illustration of the use of cyclic variables we shall consider the linear harmonic oscillator. If we draw a circle using the path of vibration as a diameter, the motion of the projection of a point rotating uniformly on this circle describes a simple harmonic motion. Then the variable which increases uniformly with the time is the angle between the radius vector to the moving point and the path of the particle. If we set this angle equal to $2\pi w$, w will increase by unity during one oscillation so that

$$w = \omega t + \delta,$$

where ω is the frequency of vibration and δ a phase constant. Thus w is the angle variable for the oscillator.

We now show this independently by the methods developed in the preceding paragraphs. Here $V = kx^2/2$, so that the H. J. equation (47) becomes

$$\frac{1}{2m}\left(\frac{\partial S}{\partial x}\right)^2 + \frac{kx^2}{2} = E,$$

and thus,

$$S = S_x = \int^x (2mE - mkx^2)^{1/2} dx = \frac{x}{2}(2mE - mkx^2)^{1/2} + E\left(\frac{m}{k}\right)^{1/2} \sin^{-1}\left(x\sqrt{\frac{k}{2E}}\right). \quad (68)$$

The oscillation takes place between two limits for which the momentum is zero and this occurs at the values of x for which $\partial S/\partial x = 0$. Therefore, x varies between the limits $\pm(2E/k)^{1/2}$. Now

$$J_x = \oint \left(\frac{\partial S}{\partial x}\right) dx = 2\int_{x_{min}}^{x_{max}} (2mE - mkx^2)^{1/2} dx = 2\pi E\left(\frac{m}{k}\right)^{1/2},$$

or

$$2mE = (mk)^{\frac{1}{2}}\frac{J_x}{\pi}.$$

Substituting this value of E in equation (68), we have

$$S = \int^x \left[(mk)^{\frac{1}{2}}\frac{J_x}{\pi} - mkx^2 \right]^{\frac{1}{2}} dx,$$

and

$$w = \frac{\partial S}{\partial J_x} = \frac{1}{2\pi} \int^x \left[\frac{J_x}{(mk)^{\frac{1}{2}}\pi} - x^2 \right]^{-\frac{1}{2}} dx = -\frac{1}{2\pi} \cos^{-1}\left(\frac{x}{a}\right),$$

or

$$\frac{x}{a} = \cos 2\pi w,$$

where

$$a = \left(\frac{J}{\pi(mk)^{\frac{1}{2}}} \right)^{\frac{1}{2}} = \left(\frac{2E}{k} \right)^{\frac{1}{2}},$$

and is the amplitude of the vibration. The value of w obtained in this way is the same as that derived above by direct consideration of the motion. This method, though more involved for this simple case, is a most powerful method when applied to more complicated mechanical systems.

References

Born, M., "Vorlesungen über Atommechanik," Springer, Berlin (1925). There is an English edition, entitled, "The Mechanics of the Atom," translated by J. W. Fisher and revised by D. R. Hartree, Bell, London (1927).

Van Vleck's "Bulletin," described at the end of Chap. I.

Webster, A. G., "Dynamics." Teubner, Leipzig.

Whittaker, E. T., "Analytical Dynamics." Cambridge University Press.

CHAPTER V

HYDROGENIC ATOMS AND THEIR SPECTRA

1. THE SPECTRA OF HYDROGEN AND IONIZED HELIUM

The first clew to our present knowledge of the quantized character of atomic systems and their radiations came from Balmer's discovery (1884) of simple numerical relations between the frequencies of hydrogen lines. The spectrum of a hydrogen vacuum tube is quite complex, but among all its lines there are four which catch the eye by their intensity. These lines are brightened relative to the others by increasing the current and can appear under conditions where the gas is largely dissociated, as in certain stars, so they are definitely assigned to the neutral hydrogen atom. Their names, wave lengths and wave numbers are tabulated below:

Hα.................	$\lambda = 6,562.79$ Å	$\bar{\nu} = 15,233.22$ cm.$^{-1}$
Hβ.................	4,861.33	20,564.79
Hγ.................	4,340.47	23,032.54
Hδ.................	4,101.74	24,373.07

The series can be followed with diminishing intensity to 35 lines in the solar chromosphere. In Fig. 1 is shown the series as absorption lines in the spectrum of a star. The lines become closer together in the

Fig. 1.—Spectrum of a star (α Lyrae) showing the Balmer lines of hydrogen in absorption. (*After Hulburt.*)

neighborhood of a limiting wave length, namely, 3645.98 Å. In certain stellar spectra a continuous absorption begins at this point and extends to shorter wave lengths, rising to a maximum of intensity and then fading away again.[1] Balmer was acquainted with six of these lines and found a formula for their wave lengths, which converted to wave numbers, is

$$\bar{\nu} = R_H\left(\frac{1}{2^2} - \frac{1}{m^2}\right), \quad m = 3, 4, 5, \cdots \quad (1)$$

R_H is an empirical constant called the "Rydberg constant for hydrogen," having the value[2]

$$R_H = 109,677.759 \pm 0.05 \text{ cm.}^{-1}.$$

[1] HARTMANN, *Physik. Z.*, **18**, 429, (1917).
[2] HOUSTON, *Phys. Rev.*, **30**, 608 (1927).

We place $m = 3$ to obtain the wave number of $H\alpha$, $m = 4$ for $H\beta$, and so on. Placing $m = \infty$ we get the wave number of the series limit, at 3645.98 Å.

Investigations in the ultra-violet and infra-red showed that similar series exist in these regions. Lyman[1] found a series which can be represented by the formula,

$$\bar{\nu} = R_H\left(\frac{1}{1^2} - \frac{1}{m^2}\right), \tag{2}$$

while Paschen[2] and Brackett discovered[3] series in which $\frac{1}{2}^2$ of the Balmer formula is replaced by $\frac{1}{3}^2$ and $\frac{1}{4}^2$, respectively. More recently Pfund[4] found the series having $\frac{1}{5}^2$ as the first term and Poettker[5] has extended the Paschen series to 8 members. All lines known to be due to the H atom are given by

$$\bar{\nu} = R_H\left(\frac{1}{n^2} - \frac{1}{m^2}\right), \ n < m, \tag{3}$$

where n and m are integers. Similarly, it is found that all observed lines of singly ionized helium are given by the formula,

$$\bar{\nu} = 4R_{He}\left(\frac{1}{n^2} - \frac{1}{m^2}\right), \ R_{He} = 109,722.403 \pm 0.05 \ \text{cm.}^{-1} \tag{4}$$

If $n = 4$, $m = 6$, 8, etc., equation (4) yields wave numbers which lie very close to those of the Balmer series of hydrogen; for this reason the whole series for which $n = 4$ was attributed to hydrogen when first discovered.[6] In the spectra of other elements a great many series have been found, which are in many cases rather similar to those of hydrogenic atoms.

When examined with spectroscopes of high dispersion, the first few members of the Balmer series can be resolved into very close doublets. The difference in the wave numbers of the two components is nearly constant for all these doublets. Ionized helium lines of the series with $n = 3$ and $n = 4$ have been studied by Paschen and by Leo, under high dispersion, and are found to consist of a number of components (Sec. **6**). Theory predicts that all the lines of a hydrogenic atom (that is, an atom with one electron) should be multiple, although experimental difficulties make it impossible to observe their structures except in a few instances.

2. BOHR'S THEORY OF HYDROGENIC ATOMS

In Chap. III we derived equation (3), by quantizing the motion of an electron on circular orbits around a nucleus. We now treat the

[1] See references at end of Chap. X.
[2] *Ann. Physik*, **27**, 537 (1908).
[3] *Astrophys. J.* **56**, 154 (1922).
[4] *J. O. S. A.* **9**, 193 (1924).
[5] *Phys. Rev.*, **30**, 418 (1927).
[6] A detailed account is given in Fowler's "Report on Series in Line Spectra."

problem in a more general way essentially as Bohr[1] did, to make clear the physical ideas which led him to propose his theory.   He supposed that the dimensions of the particles in the atom are so small in comparison with the distance between them that effects due to their finite size do not influence the problem.   (A little later this restriction will be removed and we shall study the modifications due to the spin of the electron.)   He assumed that they attract each other with a force varying as the inverse square of the distance between them.   Let the distances of the nucleus and electron from their center of mass be r_1 and r_2, respectively, and the distance between them be r.   The kinetic and potential energies are then

$$T = \frac{\mu}{2}(\dot{r}^2 + r^2\dot{\varphi}^2) \text{ and } V = -\frac{Ze^2}{r}, \tag{5}$$

where μ is the reduced mass $mM/(m + M)$, and the total energy is $E = T + V$.   This dynamical problem was solved in Chap. IV.   The nucleus and the electron move on *Kepler ellipses* just as the planets do. (Chap. IV, Fig. 4; and Fig. 6 of this chapter.)   The equation describing their relative motion is

$$\frac{p^2}{Ze^2\mu}\frac{1}{r} = 1 - \left(1 + \frac{2Ep^2}{Z^2e^4\mu}\right)^{1/2}\cos\varphi,$$

p being the total angular momentum of the sytem about its mass center. This can be put in the form,

$$r = \frac{a(1 - \epsilon^2)}{1 - \epsilon\cos\varphi}, \tag{6}$$

wnere the eccentricity is

$$\epsilon = \left(1 + \frac{2Ep^2}{Z^2e^4\mu}\right)^{1/2}, \tag{7}$$

and the semimajor axis is

$$a = -\frac{Ze^2}{2E}. \tag{7a}$$

The distances of the nucleus and electron from the center of gravity are

$$r_1 = \frac{m}{m + M}r \text{ and } r_2 = \frac{M}{m + M}r.$$

The frequency is

$$\omega = \frac{1}{2\pi}\left(\frac{-8E^3}{Z^2e^4\mu}\right)^{1/2}. \tag{8}$$

[1] *Phil. Mag.*, **26**, 1, 476, and 857 (1913).   In 1910, Arthur Haas had arrived at the formula for Rydberg's constant (*Sitz. Ber. der Wiener Akad., math. nat. Kl.*, IIa, p. 119) while Nicholson (Monthly Notices of the Royal Astronomical Society, 72, (1912)) had applied the quantum condition to the rotator; however, the mechanical frequency was set equal to the emission frequency in his theory.

If the electron radiated energy according to the Maxwell theory of light it would emit the frequencies ω, 2ω, etc., while the observed frequencies of the emitted light are given by equation (3). We have seen that classical electrodynamics agrees very well with experiment in the region of long wave lengths. Therefore, Bohr made the very probable assumption that the classical expression for the frequency should agree with the experimental values for the region of low frequencies. Equation (3) can be written

$$\nu = cRZ^2\left(\frac{1}{n^2} - \frac{1}{(n+\Delta n)^2}\right),$$

where $n + \Delta n$ has been substituted for m. This is equivalent to

$$\nu = cRZ^2\frac{(2n+\Delta n)\Delta n}{n^2(n+\Delta n)^2},$$

and for the region of low frequencies where Δn is small compared to n, we have approximately,

$$\nu = cRZ^2 \cdot \frac{2\Delta n}{n^3}.$$

Putting $\Delta n = 1$, the fundamental frequency is $2cRZ^2/n^3$. Combining with equation (8), we have

$$\omega = \frac{1}{2\pi}\left(\frac{-8E^3}{Z^2e^4\mu}\right)^{1/2} = \frac{2cRZ^2}{n^3}. \tag{9}$$

On the other hand, Bohr's second postulate and the Balmer formula give

$$\nu = \frac{E_{n+\Delta n} - E_n}{h} = -\frac{cRZ^2}{(n+\Delta n)^2} + \frac{cRZ^2}{n^2},$$

so that aside from an additive arbitrary constant which we take equal to zero, we must have

$$E_n = -\frac{RhcZ^2}{n^2}.$$

Substituting this value of E_n in equation (9) and solving for R, we have

$$R = \frac{2\pi^2\mu e^4}{h^3c}. \tag{10}$$

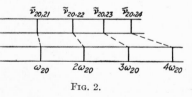

Fig. 2.

The substitution of the values of the universal constants determined by methods independent of spectroscopy, gives $R = 1.09 \cdot 10^5$ cm.$^{-1}$, a result in agreement with the spectroscopic value of R within the limits of experimental error. Figure 2 shows the asymptotic agreement between the actual frequencies and the multiples of ω. The upper spectrum is that calculated from equation (3) for $n = 20$, $m = 21, 22, \cdots$, and the lower spectrum is obtained by plotting

$$\omega_{20}\frac{\Delta n}{c} = \frac{2R\Delta n}{20^3}, \quad \Delta n = 1, 2, 3 \cdots$$

R varies with the mass of the nucleus since μ depends on M as well as m. Precise spectroscopic values of R for hydrogen and ionized helium are known. Thus,

$$\frac{R_{\mathrm{H}}}{R_{\mathrm{He}}} = \frac{M_{\mathrm{H}}}{m + M_{\mathrm{H}}} \cdot \frac{m + M_{\mathrm{He}}}{M_{\mathrm{He}}} = \frac{1 + \dfrac{m}{M_{\mathrm{He}}}}{1 + \dfrac{m}{M_{\mathrm{H}}}},$$

and using the known values of m, M_{H}, and M_{He} this ratio is 0.999596, while the value calculated from Houston's spectroscopic measurements is 0.999593. This accounts at least qualitatively for the difference in wave length of the Balmer lines and the ionized helium lines. Bohr[1] predicted in 1913 that this difference should exist. The subsequent experimental confirmation was one of the striking triumphs of the theory. If the mass of the nucleus is very large R approaches the value

$$R_{\infty} = \frac{2\pi^2 m e^4}{h^3 c}.$$

This can be calculated from the spectroscopic value of R_{H} using the relation $R_{\mathrm{H}} = R_{\infty} \dfrac{M_{\mathrm{H}}}{m + M_{\mathrm{H}}}$, or from the value of R_{He} in similar manner. The best value is

$$R_{\infty} = (109737.42 \pm 0.06)\mathrm{cm.}^{-1}.$$

The theory as developed by Bohr requires then, that only those orbits exist for which the total energy is given by the equation

$$E = -\frac{2\pi^2 Z^2 e^4 \mu}{n^2 h^2}, \; n = 1, 2, 3, \cdots \infty. \tag{11}$$

The relation of equation (7a) shows that the possible values of the semi-major axis of the elliptical orbits are

$$a = \frac{n^2 h^2}{4\pi^2 Z e^2 \mu}, \; n = 1, 2, 3 \cdots \tag{12}$$

In this computation the value of the angular momentum is *not* fixed and thus the semiminor axis and the eccentricity may vary continuously, so that associated with each energy level there should be an infinite number of possible elliptic orbits having the same semimajor axis. The energy levels required by the theory are shown in the energy diagram, Chap. III, Fig. 2. As mentioned in Chap. III, the quantity

$$T = -\frac{E_n}{hc}$$

is called the "spectroscopic" term, or "term-value," corresponding to the energy E_n. If the atom passes from higher levels to the lowest

[1] *Nature*, **92**, 231 (1913).

level, the Lyman series lines are emitted.   If from higher levels to the second level, the Balmer series lines are emitted and so on for the Paschen, Brackett, and Pfund series.   In the absorption of light the atom is raised to a higher energy level and the frequency of the light absorbed is the same as that of the light emitted when the reverse transition takes place.

3. THE PROOF OF BOHR'S THEORY BY THE METHOD OF ELECTRON COLLISIONS

The resonance potentials of the hydrogen atom can be calculated from its energy levels by Bohr's theory, or from the observed spectral

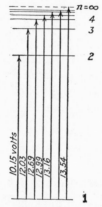

FIG. 3.—Transitions corresponding to the resonance potentials of hydrogen.

lines.   These potentials are the voltages required to raise the electron from the first orbit to the higher orbits.   They are indicated in Fig. 3 and are given by the equation

$$h c \tilde{\nu} = \frac{V e}{300} = R h c \left(\frac{1}{1^2} - \frac{1}{n^2} \right), n = 2, 3 \cdots \infty.$$

The constant $300 R h c / e = 13.54$ volts.[1]   The resonance potentials and corresponding wave numbers from this equation are given in Table 1.

TABLE 1

n	$\tilde{\nu}$	Volts (calculated)	Volts (observed)
2	82,258	10.154	10.15
3	97,491	12.034	12.05
4	102,823	12.692	12.70
5	105,291	12.997	13.00
6	106,631	13.162	13.17
7	107,440	13.262	13.27
. .	. . . .	. . . . .	. . . . .
∞	109,678	13.539	13.54

[1] Birge gives a slightly different value, 13.529₉ abs. volts.

The last column gives the critical potentials observed by Olmstead and Compton.[1] At the pressure and temperature used the hydrogen was 99 per cent dissociated. No critical potentials that could be assigned to molecular hydrogen were observed. The agreement between calculated and observed values is extremely satisfactory in view of the experimental difficulties.

4. QUANTUM CONDITIONS AND THE QUANTIZATION OF ELLIPTIC ORBITS

We have seen that Bohr's method of quantizing the hydrogen atom involves the following steps: (1) solving the two-body problem, we obtain the frequency of revolution of the electron in terms of the energy; (2) we equate the frequency of revolution to the frequency of the light emitted in the region of high quantum numbers and small quantum transitions, *i.e.*, the region of low frequencies. The possibility of using this method depends on our possession of an accurate empirical formula such as that of Balmer. In principle, similar methods could be applied to dynamical systems having several degrees of freedom, but usually we do not have a sufficiently precise empirical formula for the emission-frequencies. This prevents an application of the method to the fine structure of the lines of hydrogenic atoms. Instead, we utilize the Sommerfeld quantum conditions described in Chap. III. For convenience we repeat them here: If there are coordinates for a mechanical system such that each generalized momentum,

$$p_k = \frac{\partial L}{\partial q_k},$$

is a function of the corresponding q_k only, then the stationary states are those for which

$$\oint p_k dq_k = n_k h, \ n_k = 1, 2, 3 \cdots , \tag{13}$$

where each integral is to be extended over a complete cycle of the variable q_k. If one of the q's is the azimuthal angle φ of an electron, the integral is extended over the interval 2π. These equations, one for each degree of freedom, serve to determine a number of constants of integration equal to the number of degrees of freedom of the system. The reasons underlying the adoption of these equations are described in Chap. VI.

Let us quantize the elliptic orbits of the hydrogenic atom following Sommerfeld.[2] The energy equation is separable in polar coordinates r, φ (Chap. IV). The kinetic energy is

$$T = \frac{1}{2u}\left[p_r{}^2 + \frac{1}{r^2}p_\varphi{}^2\right], \tag{14}$$

[1] *Phys. Rev.*, **22**, 559 (1923).
[2] *Ann. Physik*, **51**, 1 (1916).

where $p_r = \mu\dot{r}$, $p_\varphi = \mu\dot{r}^2$ = angular momentum = constant. The quantum conditions are

$$\int_0^{2\pi} p_\varphi d\varphi = kh, \int p_r dr = n_r h. \tag{15}$$

Here k is called the "azimuthal quantum number" because it depends for its value on the variation of φ, while n_r is called the "radial quantum number." The second integral is extended from the minimum value of r to the maximum value and back again. When the electron is receding from the nucleus, both p_r and dr are $+$, while they are both $-$ when the electron approaches the nucleus. We have

$$p_\varphi = \frac{kh}{2\pi}. \tag{16}$$

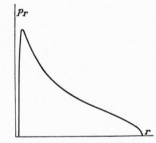

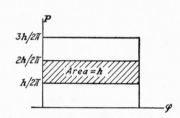

Fig. 4.—Radial momentum diagram for hydrogen.

Fig. 5.—Angular momentum diagram for hydrogen.

To obtain an expression for p_r we write the Hamilton equation,

$$H = \frac{1}{2\mu}\left[p_r^2 + \frac{1}{r^2}p_\varphi^2 \right] - \frac{Ze^2}{r} = E. \tag{17}$$

The radial quantum condition then can be written,

$$\oint p_r dr = 2\sqrt{-2\mu E} \int_{r_{\min}}^{r_{\max}} \left(-r^2 - \frac{Ze^2}{E}r + \frac{p_\varphi^2}{2\mu E} \right)^{\frac{1}{2}} \frac{dr}{r}, \tag{18}$$

where $r_{\min}$ and $r_{\max}$ are the values of r when $p_r = 0$; they are the roots of the equation $p_r = 0$, that is,

$$-r^2 - \frac{Ze^2}{E}r + \frac{p_\varphi^2}{2\mu E} = 0.$$

The integration can be carried out by ordinary methods. Perhaps the meaning of the phase integral is more clearly seen from Fig. 4 where p_r is plotted against r for the case of a hydrogen orbit with $k = 1$ and $n_r = 1$. The quantum condition requires that the energy and eccentricity of the orbit shall be such that twice the area enclosed within the curve shall be $n_r h$. Similarly, the phase integral for the coordinate φ requires that the area enclosed within the rectangle of Fig. 5 shall be equal to kh.

It is more convenient to evaluate the radial integral by expressing it in terms of φ as follows:

$$p_r dr = \mu \dot{r} dr = \mu \frac{dr \cdot}{d\varphi} \dot{\varphi} \frac{dr}{d\varphi} d\varphi,$$

and on substituting $\dot{\varphi}$ and $dr/d\varphi$ from $\mu r^2 \dot{\varphi} = p_\varphi$ and r from equation (6), we get

$$p_\varphi \int_0^{2\pi} \frac{\epsilon^2 \sin^2 \varphi d\varphi}{(1 - \epsilon \cos \varphi)^2} = n_r h. \tag{19}$$

After substituting $p_\varphi = kh/2\pi$, the integration of this equation gives

$$1 - \epsilon^2 = \frac{k^2}{(k + n_r)^2} = \frac{k^2}{n^2}, \tag{20}$$

where n has been substituted for $k + n_r$.

To prove this we observe that

$$\int_0^{2\pi} \frac{\epsilon^2 \sin^2 \varphi d\varphi}{(1 - \epsilon \cos \varphi)^2} = \frac{-\epsilon \sin \varphi}{1 - \epsilon \cos \varphi}\bigg]_0^{2\pi} + \epsilon \int_0^{2\pi} \frac{\cos \varphi d\varphi}{1 - \epsilon \cos \varphi}.$$

The integrated term is zero and the second may be written

$$\int_0^{2\pi} \left(\frac{1}{1 - \epsilon \cos \varphi} - 1 \right) d\varphi,$$

which is equal to

$$\frac{1}{(1 - \epsilon^2)^{1/2}} \tan^{-1} \frac{(1 - \epsilon^2)^{1/2} \sin \varphi}{-\epsilon + \cos \varphi}\bigg]_0^{2\pi} - 2\pi, \text{ or } \frac{2\pi}{(1 - \epsilon^2)^{1/2}} - 2\pi,$$

since the inverse tangent in this expression increases by 2π when its argument runs through its cycle of values from 0 to $+\infty$, to $-\infty$ and back to 0 again.

The energy is obtained from equation (20) by using the expression of equation (7) for ϵ in terms of the energy. Then,

$$1 - \left(1 + \frac{2E p_\varphi^2}{\mu Z^2 e^4} \right) = \frac{k^2}{(k + n_r)^2} = \frac{k^2}{n^2}.$$

Remembering that $p_\varphi = kh/2\pi$, this gives

$$E = -\frac{2\pi^2 \mu Z^2 e^4}{h^2 (k + n_r)^2} = -\frac{2\pi^2 \mu Z^2 e^4}{n^2 h^2}, \tag{21}$$

which is the result secured by the original method. Using the expressions for the semimajor axis a, the semiminor axis $b (= a\sqrt{1 - \epsilon^2})$, the parameter c and frequency ω, respectively, we have

$$a = \frac{n^2 h^2}{4\pi^2 Z e^2 \mu}; \ b = \frac{nk h^2}{4\pi^2 Z e^2 \mu}; \ \therefore \frac{b}{a} = \frac{k}{n}; \tag{22}$$

$$c = \frac{k^2 h^2}{4\pi^2 Z e^2 \mu}; \ \omega = \frac{4\pi^2 Z^2 e^4 \mu}{n^3 h^3}.$$

Next, we have the possibility $n = 1$, $k = 1$.   The 1_1 orbit is the normal state of the hydrogenic atom, and is of course a circle, since $\epsilon = 0$.   If $n = 2$, we have a circular 2_2 orbit and an elliptical 2_1 orbit. The following table gives the values of the energy, eccentricity, and semimajor and semiminor axes of several orbits of the H atom.   The radius a_1 of the 1_1 orbit is $0.528 \cdot 10^{-8}$ cm., a value consistent with kinetic theory estimates of the size of atoms.

E	n_k	n	k	n_r	ϵ^2	a/a_1	b/a_1
$-Rhc$	1_1	1	1	0	0	1	1
$-Rhc/4$	2_1	2	1	1	$(1 - \frac{1}{4})$	4	2
$-Rhc/4$	2_2	2	2	0	0	4	4
$-Rhc/9$	3_1	3	1	2	$(1 - \frac{1}{9})$	9	3
$-Rhc/9$	3_2	3	2	1	$(1 - \frac{4}{9})$	9	6
$-Rhc/9$	3_3	3	3	0	0	9	9

It is customary to refer to an orbit having principal quantum number n and azimuthal number k as an n_k orbit.   In conclusion, equations (20) and (16) determine both the major axis and the eccentricity of an n_k orbit.   Figure 6 illustrates a few of the possibilities.   If $k = 0$, $\epsilon = 1$, and the ellipse degenerates to a straight line so that the electron would hit the nucleus.   This state is customarily excluded as dynamically impossible, and, in fact, it is generally stated that orbits with $k = 0$ do not occur in any atom.   J. W. Nicholson[1] suggested that orbits passing through the nucleus are dynamically possible and gave a derivation of the energy of such orbits, arriving at equation (21).   His calculation is probably at fault, because in the quantum condition $\int m\dot{x}\,dx = nh$, he uses the rest mass of the electron instead of the actual mass. When the actual mass is used, difficulties are encountered because of the way in which $m\dot{x}$ approaches infinity in the neighborhood of the nucleus. R. B. Lindsay[2] showed that the law of force can be modified in such a way that these difficulties are avoided and yet the energy levels coincide with the Balmer terms except for quantities which cannot be detected experimentally.   There is no indication from either spectroscopic or X-ray data, however, that such energy levels exist.

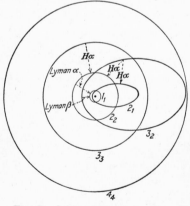

FIG. 6.—Orbits of the electron in hydrogen.

[1] *Phil. Mag.*, **45**, 801 (1923).
[2] *Proc. Nat. Acad. Sci.*, **13**, 413 (1927).

5. THE RELATIVITY CORRECTION

At first sight, the requirement that only definite values of the semi-minor axis can occur seems inaccessible to experimental verification, since the formula for the energy of an orbit is independent of its eccentricity. In fact, the energy in Keplerian motion depends only on the major axis of the orbit. In his earliest papers, Bohr suggested that the relativistic variation of mass of the electron should be taken into account in determining the energy levels, since its velocity on the innermost orbit of hydrogen is 0.007 of the velocity of light. In the paper in which Sommerfeld introduced the use of two quantum numbers to determine elliptic orbits, he also treated the problem from the standpoint of special relativity. With this improvement, it is found that the energy depends not only on n but also on k, so that ellipses of different eccentricity have different energies. This gives rise to slightly different frequencies when the electron passes between orbits of the same principal quantum numbers, depending on the azimuthal numbers of the orbits involved, so that every line in the spectrum of a hydrogenic atom should be complex. This prediction is verified by experiment.

The relativistic expression for the kinetic energy of an electron moving about the nucleus (assumed to be at rest) with velocity $v = c\beta$, is

$$T = m_0 c^2 \left(\frac{1}{(1 - \beta^2)^{\frac{1}{2}}} - 1 \right).$$

$$(23)$$

The potential energy is $-Ze^2/r$, as before, and the Lagrangian function (Chap. IV, Sec. 4) is

$$L = m_0 c^2 [1 - (1 - \beta^2)^{\frac{1}{2}}] + \frac{Ze^2}{r}.$$

Replacing β^2 by $(\dot{r}^2 + r^2\dot{\varphi}^2)/c^2$ and writing the Lagrangian equation of motion for φ, we have

$$\frac{d}{dt} \frac{m_0 r^2 \dot{\varphi}}{(1 - \beta^2)^{\frac{1}{2}}} = 0,$$

so that the angular momentum is a constant:

$$\frac{m_0 r^2 \dot{\varphi}}{(1 - \beta^2)^{\frac{1}{2}}} = m r^2 \dot{\varphi} = p.$$

The quantum condition for the φ coordinate is $2\pi p = kh$, as before. The radial momentum is

$$p_r = \frac{\partial L}{\partial \dot{r}} = \frac{m_0 \dot{r}}{\left[1 - \frac{1}{c^2}(\dot{r}^2 + r^2\dot{\varphi}^2) \right]^{\frac{1}{2}}}.$$

$$(24)$$

By direct calculation we find,

$$\frac{1}{c^2 m_0^2}\left(p_r^2 + \frac{p^2}{r^2}\right) = \frac{v^2/c^2}{1 - \frac{v^2}{c^2}}.$$

Solving this for v^2 and substituting in equation (23), we have

$$T = m_0 c^2 \left[\sqrt{1 + \frac{1}{m_0^2 c^2}\left(p_r^2 + \frac{p^2}{r^2}\right)} - 1\right].$$

The sum of the kinetic and potential energies is equal to the Hamiltonian function:

$$H = m_0 c^2 \left[\sqrt{1 + \frac{1}{m_0^2 c^2}\left(p_r^2 + \frac{p^2}{r^2}\right)} - 1\right] - \frac{Ze^2}{r} = E. \tag{25}$$

This equation, solved for p_r^2, gives

$$p_r^2 = Em_0\left(2 + \frac{E}{m_0 c^2}\right) + 2m_0 Ze^2\left(1 + \frac{E}{m_0 c^2}\right)\frac{1}{r} - p^2\left(1 - \frac{Z^2 e^4}{p^2 c^2}\right)\frac{1}{r^2}.$$

This is a function only of r and the fundamental constants, so we can apply the quantum condition of equation (13) directly, but we shall first secure the equation of the orbit. To simplify the computation we introduce the variable $u = 1/r$. Then

$$p_r = m\dot{r} = m\frac{dr}{d\varphi}\dot{\varphi} = -\frac{m}{u^2}\frac{du}{d\varphi}\dot{\varphi},$$

and substituting p for $m\dot{\varphi}/u^2$, we have $p_r = -p\,du/d\varphi$. Making these substitutions in the equation for p_r^2, it becomes

$$\left(\frac{du}{d\varphi}\right)^2 = -\left(1 - \frac{Z^2 e^4}{p^2 c^2}\right)u^2 + \frac{2m_0 Ze^2}{p^2}\left(1 + \frac{E}{m_0 c^2}\right)u + \frac{Em_0}{p^2}\left(2 + \frac{E}{m_0 c^2}\right).$$

Writing

$$1 - \frac{Z^2 e^4}{p^2 c^2} = \gamma^2, \tag{26}$$

$$\left(\frac{du}{d\varphi}\right)^2 = -\gamma^2 u^2 + 2\gamma^2 u \frac{Ze^2 m_0}{p^2 \gamma^2}\left(1 + \frac{E}{m_0 c^2}\right) + \frac{\gamma^2 Em_0}{p^2 \gamma^2}\left(2 + \frac{E}{m_0 c^2}\right).$$

Letting $\gamma\varphi = \psi$, we get

$$\left(\frac{du}{d\psi}\right)^2 + u^2 - 2u\frac{Ze^2 m_0}{\gamma^2 p^2}\left(1 + \frac{E}{m_0 c^2}\right) = \frac{Em_0}{\gamma^2 p^2}\left(2 + \frac{E}{m_0 c^2}\right).$$

To solve this equation, we add the square of the coefficient of $2u$ to both sides of the equation. It takes the form

$$\left(\frac{d(u - A)}{d\psi}\right)^2 + (u - A)^2 = B^2,$$

where

$$A = \frac{Ze^2 m_0}{\gamma^2 p^2}\left(1 + \frac{E}{m_0 c^2}\right), \tag{27}$$

$$B^2 = \frac{Em_0}{\gamma^2 p^2}\left(2 + \frac{E}{m_0 c^2}\right) + \frac{Z^2 e^4 m_0^2}{\gamma^4 p^4}\left(1 + \frac{E}{m_0 c^2}\right)^2.$$

If $x = (u - A)/B$, this becomes

$$\left(\frac{dx}{d\psi}\right)^2 + x^2 = 1,$$

which has the integral,

$$x = \frac{(u - A)}{B} = \sin \psi \text{ or } \cos \psi.$$

Returning to the coordinates r and φ, and measuring φ from a position where r is a minimum, we have the equation of the orbit,

$$u = \frac{1}{r} = \frac{1 + \epsilon \cos \gamma\varphi}{a(1 - \epsilon^2)}, \text{ or } r = \frac{a(1 - \epsilon^2)}{1 + \epsilon \cos \gamma\varphi}, \tag{28}$$

where the constants a and ϵ are such that

$$a(1 - \epsilon^2) = \frac{1}{A}, \quad \frac{a(1 - \epsilon^2)}{\epsilon} = \frac{1}{B}. \tag{29}$$

Now r does not return to a given value when φ increases by 2π, but only when it increases by $2\pi/\gamma$, which is greater than 2π since γ is less than one. The perihelion of the orbit precesses in the same direction as the rotation of the electron. It is incorrect, however, to describe the orbit as a *uniformly* rotating ellipse, so ϵ cannot be regarded as the eccentricity of an ellipse but only as a constant having a geometrical meaning somewhat similar to an eccentricity. The advance of perihelion per revolution is $2\pi(\gamma^{-1} - 1)$. Substituting $p = kh/2\pi$, in equation (26), and introducing the dimensionless *fine-structure constant*,

$$\alpha = \frac{2\pi e^2}{hc} = (7.284 \pm 0.006) \cdot 10^{-3},$$

we get

$$\gamma^2 = 1 - \frac{Z^2\alpha^2}{k^2} = 1 - \frac{Z^2}{k^2} \cdot 5.305 \cdot 10^{-5}. \tag{30}$$

When Z^2/k^2 is small, the advance of perihelion per revolution approximates to

$$\pi\left(\frac{Z^2}{k^2}\right) \cdot 5.305 \cdot 10^{-5} \text{ radians.} \tag{31}$$

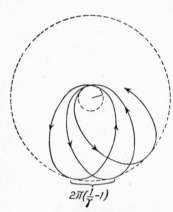

$2\pi(\frac{1}{\gamma}-1)$

FIG. 7.—Relativity precession of an orbit in the H atom.

Figure 7 shows the approximate character of the orbit. The radial quantum condition could have been applied by using p_r expressed in terms of r in equation (13), but can be calculated more easily by expressing p_r and dr in terms of φ. Then

$$\oint p_r dr = \int \frac{mr^2\dot{\varphi}}{r^2} \frac{dr}{d\varphi} dr = p\epsilon^2\gamma^2 \int_0^{2\pi/\gamma} \frac{\sin^2(\gamma\varphi)d\varphi}{(1 + \epsilon \cos \gamma\varphi)^2}.$$

The limits of integration are from 0 to $2\pi/\gamma$, since r passes from its minimum to its maximum value and back again when φ increases from 0 to $2\pi/\gamma$. This is equal to

$$p\gamma \int_0^{2\pi} \frac{\epsilon^2 \sin^2 \psi \, d\psi}{(1 + \epsilon \cos \psi)^2} = 2\pi p\gamma\left(\frac{1}{(1 - \epsilon^2)^{1/2}} - 1\right) = n_r h, \; n_r = 1, 2 \cdots, \quad (32)$$

and since $kh/2\pi = p$,

$$1 - \epsilon^2 = \frac{k^2\gamma^2}{(n_r + k\gamma)^2}.$$

6. THE RELATIVISTIC ENERGY LEVELS AND THE FINE STRUCTURE OF H AND He⁺ LINES

Using equations (27) and (29) to obtain E in terms of ϵ and p, we find

$$E = m_0 c^2 \left(\sqrt{\frac{p^2\gamma^2}{p^2 - \epsilon^2 \dfrac{Z^2 e^4}{c^2}}} - 1\right), \quad (33)$$

and substituting the value of ϵ we have

$$1 + \frac{E}{m_0 c^2} = \left(1 + \frac{\alpha^2 Z^2}{[n_r + (k^2 - \alpha^2 Z^2)^{1/2}]^2}\right)^{-1/2}. \quad (34)$$

An expression for E can now be obtained to any desired degree of accuracy by expanding the radicals of this equation in ascending powers of the small quantity $\alpha^2 Z^2$.[1] The term value, $-E/hc$, which results from this computation is

$$\begin{aligned}
T(n, k) = \; & \frac{RZ^2}{n^2} + \frac{RZ^4\alpha^2}{n^4}\left(\frac{n}{k} - \frac{3}{4}\right) \\
& + \frac{RZ^6\alpha^4}{n^6}\left[\frac{1}{4}\left(\frac{n}{k}\right)^3 + \frac{3}{4}\left(\frac{n}{k}\right)^2 - \frac{3}{2}\left(\frac{n}{k}\right) + \frac{5}{8}\right] \\
& + \frac{RZ^8\alpha^6}{n^8}\left[\frac{1}{8}\left(\frac{n}{k}\right)^5 + \frac{3}{8}\left(\frac{n}{k}\right)^4 + \frac{1}{8}\left(\frac{n}{k}\right)^3 - \frac{15}{8}\left(\frac{n}{k}\right)^2 + \frac{15}{8}\left(\frac{n}{k}\right) - \frac{35}{64}\right] \\
& + \cdots
\end{aligned} \quad (35)$$

The term in α^2 is the only one of importance in visible and ultra-violet spectra, but the higher terms are useful in discussing X-ray spectra, where large values of Z come into play. Dropping these higher terms for the present, the change of the n_k term of a hydrogenic atom due to the variation of electronic mass with velocity is given, in cm.⁻¹, by

$$\Delta T(n, k) = R\alpha^2\left(\frac{Z}{n}\right)^4\left(\frac{n}{k} - \frac{3}{4}\right) = 5.82\left(\frac{Z}{n}\right)^4\left(\frac{n}{k} - \frac{3}{4}\right). \quad (36)$$

This is always positive for k is always less than n. We shall calculate only the shifts of the hydrogen terms since the shifts for other atoms are

[1] The work is given in detail on p. 420 of Sommerfeld's "Atombau," 4th ed.

obtained by simply inserting the factor Z^4. Remembering that orbits with $k = 0$ are excluded, we have the following values of $\Delta T / R\alpha^2$:

n \ k	1		2		3		4	
1	$\dfrac{1}{4}$							
2	$\dfrac{1}{2^4}$	$\dfrac{5}{4}$	$\dfrac{1}{2^4}$	$\dfrac{1}{4}$				
3	$\dfrac{1}{3^4}$	$\dfrac{9}{4}$	$\dfrac{1}{3^4}$	$\dfrac{3}{4}$	$\dfrac{1}{3^4}$	$\dfrac{1}{4}$		
4	$\dfrac{1}{4^4}$	$\dfrac{13}{4}$	$\dfrac{1}{4^4}$	$\dfrac{5}{4}$	$\dfrac{1}{4^4}$	$\dfrac{7}{12}$	$\dfrac{1}{4^4}$	$\dfrac{1}{4}$

These results are illustrated by Fig. 8 in which horizontal distances from the left are proportional to ΔT. If the relativity correction were neg-

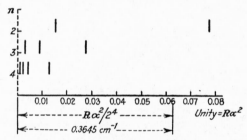

FIG. 8.—Shifts of hydrogen terms caused by relatively.

lected, all the levels in each
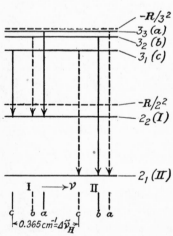

FIG. 9.—Fine structure of Hα according to the relativity theory.

diagram would coincide with the dotted line on the left, which represents the position of the Balmer term. Actually they are shifted to the positions indicated by the solid vertical lines. The shifts are given in terms of both $R\alpha^2$ and 1 cm.$^{-1}$ as units. We omit the figure for $n = 1$ to avoid an unfavorable scale for the more complicated patterns. Now we wish to obtain the positions of the lines emitted in transitions between these relativistic energy levels. We begin with the jump from orbits of total quantum number 3 to those with total number 2, which yield the fine structure of the line Hα. Figure 9 shows the energy levels for this emission, taken directly from Fig. 8. The arrows represent transitions, and would be thousands of times longer if drawn to scale. The light dotted lines represent the

Balmer levels, $-R/2^2$ and $-R/3^2$. Below the energy diagram is a horizontal scale of wave numbers on which the spectral lines are plotted in their true relation. Each arrow in the upper diagram is placed above the line arising in the corresponding transition. Because of the comparatively small separation of the 3-quantum levels, the lines fall into two groups of three. Proceeding similarly with other lines of the Balmer series, we should expect that Hβ would consist of two groups of four lines each (Fig. 10), each group being narrower than those in Hα because of the factor n^4 in the denominator of equation (36) and so on. As a matter of fact, these groups are so narrow that they have not been resolved even for Hα. All the Balmer lines appear as doublets when examined with spectroscopes of high resolving power. This is due mainly

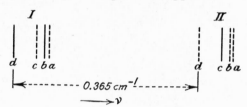

Fig. 10.—Fine structure of Hβ.

to the small mass of the H-atom, which endows it with high thermal velocity, so that its lines show a large Doppler effect. Further, the velocities acquired by light atoms in collisions with fast electrons cause a broadening which is large enough for detection with the best interference spectroscopes.

The interval of the hydrogen doublets is discussed in Sec. **19.** Here we consider the data on the lines of ionized helium, obtained in an investigation by Paschen[1] and in later work by Leo.[2] In helium, the pattern of a line arising in a certain transition is sixteen times as broad in the wave-number scale as that of the corresponding line in hydrogen, but it lies at a wave length four times smaller, so that the breadth is constant in the wave-length scale. Thus the pattern of the first Balmer line of helium, at 1,640 Å, will be of no more help to us than that of Hα. The lines which Paschen investigated belong to the Fowler series

$$\bar{\nu} = 4R\left(\frac{1}{3^2} - \frac{1}{n^2}\right); \lambda = 4{,}686, \ 3{,}203, \ 2{,}733, \ \text{etc.}; \ n = 4, \ 5, \ 6, \ \text{etc.},$$

and the Pickering series

$$\bar{\nu} = 4R\left(\frac{1}{4^2} - \frac{1}{n^2}\right); \lambda = 10{,}123, \ 6{,}560, \ 5{,}411, \ 4{,}859, \ \text{etc.}; n = 5, 6, 7, 8, \text{etc.}$$

We shall restrict our discussion to the line at 4,686, the first member of the three-quantum series. This line should have twelve components,

[1] *Ann. Physik*, **50**, 901 (1916).

[2] *Ann. Physik*, **81**, 757 (1926).

whose positions, obtained from equation (36), are shown in Fig. 11. Below these components we plot curves showing the intensity distribution in the lines which Paschen observed in a strong discharge (Funkenentladung), and still further below, the lines observed in a direct current discharge.[1] The agreement of calculated and observed line positions may be considered as very good. The trend of the intensities merits

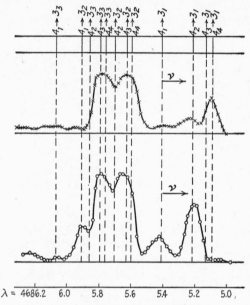

Fig. 11.—Structure of λ 4686 of helium.

careful notice, however. We observe that components arising from the transitions $4_4 \rightarrow 3_1$ and $4_3 \rightarrow 3_1$ are extremely weak in the direct-current discharge. It is probable these components would be entirely absent in a very weak discharge. This is due to the action of so-called selection principles, which will now be explained.

7. THE SELECTION PRINCIPLES FOR THE INNER AND AZIMUTHAL QUANTUM NUMBERS

The total angular momentum associated with the electrons of an atom may always be expressed as $jh/2\pi$, where j is either an integer or an integer plus one-half, and is referred to as the *inner quantum number*. Before the spinning electron was discovered, the inner quantum number of the hydrogen atom was thought to be identical with the azimuthal quantum number of its electron. Now, we know that it is the resultant of the "spin" angular momentum of the electron and that due to its revolution

[1] The curves are redrawn with ordinates somewhat reduced from photometer curves obtained by Paschen and reproduced in Sommerfeld's "Atombau," 4th ed., p. 439.

around the nucleus. It is found (Chaps. VII and X) that the spin vector must be either parallel or antiparallel to the vector $kh/2\pi$, in hydrogenic atoms. Here a peculiar circumstance shows itself. It is found that the inner quantum number takes the values $(k - 1) \pm \frac{1}{2}$ instead of $k \pm \frac{1}{2}$, as we should expect, and we shall have to postpone explanation to Chap. XVI, where the hydrogen atom is treated by the new mechanics. The important point for our present purpose is that *the inner quantum number of an atom can change by only* $+1$, -1, *or* 0 *when light is emitted or absorbed.*

$$\Delta j = \pm 1 \ or \ 0. \tag{37}$$

This is the *selection principle for j*, which applies to all atoms. Further, there is a selection principle for k, which is as follows for hydrogenic atoms and certain other simple atoms (see Chap. X, Sec. **3** for a generalization):

The azimuthal number of the electron of a hydrogenic atom can change only by ± 1 *when light is emitted or absorbed.*

$$\Delta k = \pm 1. \tag{38}$$

These two principles go a long way toward explaining the fact that in all spectra the majority of the lines predicted by naïve application of the Ritz combination principle fail to appear. In 1918, Rubinowicz[1] and Bohr[2] gave explanations of this behavior by two different methods. Bohr's procedure is based on his correspondence principle, and is explained in Chap. VI. It yields restrictions on the possible changes of both the azimuthal and the inner numbers during a quantum transition. The reasoning of Rubinowicz specifies only the possible changes of the inner quantum number. At the outset we call attention to the fact that both restrictions are altered in the presence of an external field, so that exceptions to the rules derived are frequently met with in practice, due to the use of high electric fields or to the disturbances caused by atoms and ions in the neighborhood of the emitting atom. Rubinowicz (and also Bohr, independently) applied the law of conservation of angular momentum to the system consisting of an atom and its field of radiation as specified by classical electrodynamics. The most important term in the force exerted upon a moving charge by its own radiation is

$$\mathbf{f}_r = \frac{2e^2\ddot{\mathbf{v}}}{3c^3(1 - \beta^2)}, \ \beta = \frac{v}{c}, \tag{39}$$

where $\mathbf{v}$ is the velocity. In general, this force has a component at right angles to $\mathbf{v}$ so that the angular momentum of the system is altered. The

[1] *Physik. Z.*, **19**, 441 and 465 (1918).

[2] "On the Quantum Theory of Line Spectra," Det Kgl. Danske Videnskab. Selskabs Skrifter, 8th series, vol. 4, No. 1. In English.

angular momentum lost must appear again as angular momentum of the field of radiation. Let us take our origin at the center of the emitting atom, and consider the angular momentum about the origin associated with an element of volume dV at a distance r. At this element there is a flow of radiant energy in a direction perpendicular to the electric and magnetic vectors $\mathbf{E}$ and $\mathbf{H}$. Since it can exert pressure in the direction of propagation, momentum is associated with it, and the momentum vector lies in the direction of flow. The momentum reckoned per unit volume, *i.e.*, the momentum density, is,

$$\mathbf{M} = \frac{[\mathbf{EH}]}{4\pi c},$$

where $[\mathbf{EH}]$ is a vector perpendicular to the plane of $\mathbf{E}$ and $\mathbf{H}$ having magnitude $EH \sin \theta$, and where θ is the angle between $\mathbf{E}$ and $\mathbf{H}$. This is called the vector product of $\mathbf{E}$ and $\mathbf{H}$. Associated with dV there is a momentum $\mathbf{M}dV$, and this will have a certain lever arm $r \sin \alpha$ about the origin. Its angular momentum is therefore $MdVr \sin \alpha$ in exact analogy to the expression $mr^2\dot\theta$ applying to a particle. By definition, the angular momentum vector is perpendicular to $\mathbf{M}dV$ and to $\mathbf{r}$, so it is the vector product of these two quantities, $[\mathbf{r}\mathbf{M}dV]$. The reader may find it difficult to see how the waves sent out by an atom can possess angular momentum about their origin, for at first sight it seems that $\mathbf{E}$ and $\mathbf{H}$ are always at right angles to the wave front, so that the vector $\mathbf{M}$ is directed straight away from the origin. Thus, the vector product of $\mathbf{M}$ and $\mathbf{r}$ becomes zero. Except in special cases, this view is wrong because of the incorrect supposition that $\mathbf{E}$ and $\mathbf{H}$ are perpendicular to $\mathbf{r}$. In the equatorial plane of the field due to a rotator, the vector $\mathbf{E}$ is tangent to a spiral of Archimedes, not to a circle concentric with the path of the rotator, and the prolongation of the vector $\mathbf{M}$ does not pass through the origin. In the field of a linear oscillator however, the total angular momentum is zero, as it must be since the oscillator has zero angular momentum at all stages of its motion.

We shall illustrate the physical ideas involved by considering the emission from an elliptic rotator with coordinates

$$x = a \cos 2\pi\nu t, \quad y = b \sin 2\pi\nu t. \tag{40}$$

Let ΔE be the loss of energy in a quantum transition and ΔP the loss of angular momentum. Then it can be proved, following Rubinowicz, that

$$\frac{\Delta P}{\Delta E} = \frac{2ab}{(a^2 + b^2)2\pi\nu}. \tag{41}$$

Putting $\Delta E = h\nu$,

$$\Delta P = \left(\frac{h}{2\pi}\right) \cdot \frac{2ab}{(a^2 + b^2)},$$

and since

$$2ab \leqq a^2 + b^2,$$

$$\Delta P \leqq \frac{h}{2\pi}. \qquad (42)$$

Considerations of symmetry show that the plane of the rotator is not changed during the emission so Δj is collinear with $\Delta \mathbf{P}$. Since the angular momentum of the rotator must be a multiple of $h/2\pi$, the only values Δj can take are ± 1 or 0, which is the selection rule. In Chap. VI, we show that the same rule is obtained by other methods in a more general case. Of course, it is somewhat illogical to apply a theory of this kind, based mainly on classical considerations, to a quantized atom. The above treatment is very useful, however, in trying to understand how the selection rule arises.

8. POLARIZATION RULES

From the selection principle we can obtain information as to the state of polarization of the emitted light. Suppose, first, that $\Delta j = \pm 1$. Then $\Delta P = h/2\pi$, and we must have $a = b$, so the electron moves in a circle, and the axis of the circularly polarized emission is normal to the plane of its orbit. Suppose now that $\Delta j = 0$. Then $\Delta P = 0$, and we see that either $a = 0$ or $b = 0$. The rotator becomes a linear oscillator, and emits a linearly polarized wave with axis parallel to the direction of motion. In the absence of an external field, the atoms are oriented at random, and these predictions cannot be tested. When a field is applied, a test becomes possible, for the atoms then take up definite orientations with respect to the lines of force, as we saw in the discussion of the Stern-Gerlach experiments (Chap. III, Sec. 18). Before passing to the study of the spinning electron, we take up the behavior of the hydrogenic atom as a spatial configuration, both in the absence and the presence of external fields.

9. SPACE QUANTIZATION

Consider a hydrogen atom subjected to a weak field which serves to indicate a fixed direction in space. In general, the motion of the electron will be three-dimensional and will contain three frequencies, so that three quantum conditions are necessary for fixing the energy states. One of these quantum conditions restricts the atom to a finite number of possible orientations in the external field. For uniform electric and magnetic fields, the component of the total angular momentum in the direction of the field is constant, though the plane containing the nucleus and the velocity vector of the electron continually changes its position. In these and similar cases it is customary to speak of an orientation of the atom. or to say that the atom is space quantized. Anticipating, we may say that when the field is very slowly reduced to zero the expression for the energy becomes identical with that obtained by quantizing the undisturbed atom and the atom is left with its angular momentum vector in one of a discrete set of possible positions with respect to the direction of the original field. The positions may not be the same for all types of force fields.

In Fig. 12a, let OZ be the direction of the lines of force. Let the angle γ determine the position of the electron in the plane of the orbit. φ and θ are the space polar coordinates of the electron with OZ as the pole. The kinetic energy in terms of r and γ is

$$T = \frac{(p_r \dot{r} + p_\gamma \dot{\gamma})}{2},$$

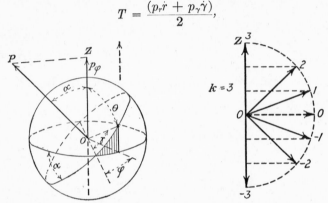

Fig. 12a and 12b.—Spatial quantization of hydrogen.

while in the space polar coordinates r, φ, and θ, it is

$$\frac{(p_r \dot{r} + p_\theta \dot{\theta} + p_\varphi \dot{\varphi})}{2},$$

so that

$$p_r \dot{r} + p_\gamma \dot{\gamma} = p_r r + p_\theta \theta + p_\varphi \dot{\varphi},$$

and, therefore,

$$p_\gamma d\gamma = p_\theta d\theta + p_\varphi d\varphi. \tag{43}$$

Then

$$\oint p_\gamma d\gamma = \oint p_\theta d\theta + \oint p_\varphi d\varphi. \tag{44}$$

The quantum conditions require that

$$\int_0^{2\pi} p_\gamma d\gamma = kh, \quad \int_0^{2\pi} p_\varphi d\varphi = k_1 h \text{ and } \oint p_\theta d\theta = k_2 h, \tag{45}$$

and therefore that $k = k_1 + k_2$. p_φ is the angular momentum about the line OZ and is constant as can be shown from the Lagrangian equation of motion; p_γ is the total angular momentum of the electron and is also constant; p_γ and p_φ are connected by the relations $p_\varphi = p_\gamma \cos \alpha$, where α is the angle between $p_\sim$ and the direction of the field before its removal. That is,

$$\cos \alpha = \frac{k_1}{k}, \quad k_1 = \pm(1, 2, 3 \cdots k), \quad k = 1, 2, 3 \cdots n. \tag{46}$$

Figure 12b shows the possible orientations of the angular momentum vector with respect to the (vanishing) external field for the value $k = 3$. The numbers placed at the end of each vector are the values of k_1. The expressions for the energy and the constants of the orbit are the same as before but in addition the orbits are oriented in such a way that the cosine of the angle between the angular momentum vector and the direction of the field can take only the values required by equation (46).

An experimental test of the existence of space quantization in the case of the hydrogen atom was carried through by Phipps and Taylor, and by Wrede (Chap. III, Sec. **18**), who performed the Stern-Gerlach experiment with a beam of atomic hydrogen produced by allowing the atoms to escape from a discharge tube, through a system of narrow slits.

10. CLASSICAL THEORY OF THE ZEEMAN EFFECT

We now proceed to study the behavior of the hydrogen atom in a magnetic field, and especially the effect of such a field on its spectrum. Zeeman discovered, in 1896, that if a light source is placed in an external magnetic field of a few thousand gauss, each line of its spectrum (with few exceptions) is split into a number of polarized components. In the case of hydrogenic atoms (and in the singlet series of other atoms), a so-called "normal triplet" is observed if the line of vision is perpendicular to the lines of force. As shown in Fig. 13, the electric vector of the outer components is perpendicular to the lines of force; that of the undisplaced, parallel. The letters s (senkrecht) and p (parallel) are used in referring to the components.

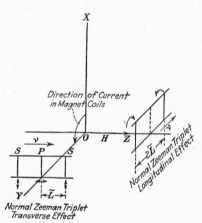

Fig. 13.—Normal Zeeman triplet.

Along the lines of force, the s-components are circularly polarized; the p-component is absent, as in Fig. 13.

The displacement of an s-component in the frequency scale is

$$\Delta\nu = \frac{e}{m}\frac{H}{4\pi c} = L,$$

where L is called the frequency of the Larmor precession, for reasons now to be explained, and in the wave-number scale,

$$\Delta\bar{\nu} = \frac{e}{m}\frac{H}{4\pi c^2} = 4.70 \cdot 10^{-5}\, H, \tag{47}$$

where e is the absolute value of the electronic charge in electrostatic units.

The classical interpretation of Lorentz is based on the motion of an oscillator carrying the charge e and having the fundamental frequency v. The component of its motion parallel to the field is unchanged in frequency. The radiation due to this component is a spherical wave, plane polarized parallel to **H**. An observer looking along **H** will receive no energy from this wave; seen perpendicular to the field, it yields the p-components in the Zeeman patterns of all lines emitted by the atom.

Now Larmor's theorem (Appendix VIII) tells us that when a uniform constant magnetic field is applied to a system of particles having identical e/m ratios, the resultant motion is the same as that which is performed in the absence of the field, except that a uniform precession of the whole system around the lines of force is superposed. This uniform rotation is called the Larmor precession. In the case of the harmonic oscillator, the fixed center of attraction is the center of rotation. Looking along the Z-axis, which is chosen as the direction of the field, consider the projection of the motion of the field free atom on the xy plane. If the coordinates of the electron are

$$x' = A \cos (2\pi vt - \alpha), \quad y' = B \cos (2\pi vt - \beta), \tag{48}$$

then, by Larmor's theorem, after the field is applied these are also the coordinates in axes which turn around the direction of H with frequency L, so that the coordinates in resting axes will be

$$x = x' \cos 2\pi Lt - y' \sin 2\pi Lt, \quad y = x' \sin 2\pi Lt + y' \cos 2\pi Lt. \tag{49}$$

Substituting equation (48) in (49), we have

$$x = C \cos [2\pi(v + L)t + \delta] + D \cos [2\pi(v - L)t + \epsilon], \tag{50}$$
$$y = C \sin [2\pi(v + L)t + \delta] - D \sin [2\pi(v - L)t + \epsilon],$$

where C, δ, D, and ϵ are found from the defining equations,

$$2Ce^{i\delta} = Ae^{-i\alpha} + Be^{i\left(\frac{\pi}{2}-\beta\right)}, \quad 2De^{-i\epsilon} = Ae^{i\alpha} + Be^{i\left(\frac{\pi}{2}+\beta\right)}.$$

Since the axes are right-handed, the vibration with frequency $\left\{ \begin{array}{c} v + L \\ v - L \end{array} \right\}$

represents a $\left\{ \begin{array}{c} \text{right-handed} \\ \text{left-handed} \end{array} \right\}$ circularly polarized wave when the observer looks along **H**. Seen from a position in their equatorial plane, these waves appear plane polarized and give rise to the s-components of the triplet.

In the absence of the field, the resultant amplitudes of each spectral line parallel to the x-, y-, and z-axes are equal. From this fact and the above equations we find that the Zeeman pattern as a whole should show no polarization. Experimentally, this is true in many cases although exceptions are known, and have been studied by Wiechert and his colleagues.[1]   The theory outlined here was considered a striking triumph since it yields a complete explanation of the normal triplet. Its defect is that it predicts normal triplets for every atom, since x, y, and z can be regarded as the coordinates of the electric "center of gravity" when there are several electrons, in complete disagreement with the existence of so-called "anomalous" Zeeman effects in which more complex patterns are observed (Chap. X, Sec. **8**).   This is a defect of the model used, and not of electrodynamic theory.   We can see this from the fact that Voigt arrived at an interpretation of the Zeeman pattern of the D-lines of sodium by the use of coupling forces depending on the velocities of the electrons.

11. QUANTUM THEORY OF THE ZEEMAN EFFECT OF HYDROGEN

In quantum theory, the splitting of a spectrum line into several components must be traced to changes in the allowed energy values of the emitter.   The energy levels of hydrogenic atoms in the presence of a magnetic field were obtained independently by Debye[2] and Sommerfeld.[3] In agreement with experiment, the result is the normal triplet.   This is a lucky coincidence, for the same result is obtained when the electron spin is taken into account.   Such is not the case in non-hydrogenic atoms, where the spin must be considered in order to get correct results. However, we shall give here a theory which applies to any atom, neglecting the electronic magnetic moment.   Let r, θ, φ, be the polar coordinates of an electron in a resting frame of reference and r, θ, χ, its coordinates in a frame which turns around the axis $\theta = 0$ (the direction of the field **H**) with angular velocity $2\pi L$.   When the field is zero, the kinetic energy of the system is given by

$$2T_0 = \Sigma m(\dot{r}^2 + r^2\dot{\theta}^2 + r^2 \sin^2\theta\ \dot{\varphi}^2), \tag{51}$$

where the summation extends over all the electrons.

If we replace $\dot{\varphi}$ by $\dot{\chi}$, this becomes the kinetic energy measured in the rotating system when the field is H.   The kinetic energy referred to the resting system T_H is still given by the function on the right side of equation (51), but the *value of $\dot{\varphi}$ is changed*.   In fact, $\dot{\varphi}_i = \dot{\chi}_i + 2\pi L$, and

$$2T_H = \Sigma m(\dot{r}^2 + r^2\dot{\theta}^2 + r^2 \sin^2\theta\ \dot{\chi}^2 + 2r^2 \sin^2\theta\ \dot{\chi} \cdot 2\pi L + \\ r^2 \sin^2\theta \cdot 4\pi^2 L^2). \tag{52}$$

Neglecting the term in L^2, this shows that

$$\Delta T_H = T_H - T_0 = 2\pi L p_\chi. \tag{53}$$

[1] See Summary in GRAETZ' "Handbuch d. Elek. und. Mag."
[2] *Physik. Z.*, **17**, 491 (1916)
[3] *Physik. Z.*, **17**, 507 (1916)

For an observer in the rotating system, the space quantization of Sec. **9** will be valid and if j denotes the inner quantum number,

$$p_x = \frac{mh}{2\pi}, \quad -j \leq m \leq j, \quad m = 0 \text{ excluded.} \tag{54}$$

The level $m = 0$ does not occur for dynamical reasons (Compare Sec. **13**). The potential energy depends only on the distances between the particles and is the same in both systems of coordinates, so that the change of the total energy is equal to ΔT_H;

$$\Delta E = mhL. \tag{55}$$

Consider two stationary states, with energies E_i and E_f in the absence of the field, which combine to give a spectral line

$$h\nu = E_i - E_f.$$

The frequencies emitted in the presence of the field will be

$$h(\nu + \Delta\nu) = E_i + \Delta E_i - E_f - \Delta E_f.$$

Therefore,

$$\Delta\nu = (m_i - m_f)L. \tag{56}$$

(Often the symbols $o/2\pi$ or $\Delta\nu_n$ are used in place of L; the subscript n indicates that $\Delta\nu_n$ is the value of $\Delta\nu$ appropriate for the normal triplet.) This equation predicts lines which lie symmetrically on either side of the original line, at intervals of the magnitude L. Thus, if the greatest values of $|m_i|$ and $|m_f|$ are j_i and j_f, we should expect lines at the positions,

$$0, \pm 1, \pm 2, \cdots \pm (j_i + j_f),$$

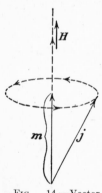

times L, with the origin at the position of the field-free line. In general, each line could arise from several transitions. As a matter of fact, only the normal triplet is observed.

Aside from very small oscillations in magnitude and direction occurring with the orbital frequency of the electron, the vector **j** precesses uniformly around **H** with frequency L; to the same approximation, its component along the field is constant, as shown in

FIG. 14.—Vector diagram for hydrogen atom in a uniform magnetic field.

Fig. 14. It must be noted that the quantum conditions of Sec. **4** are applied in the rotating coordinates. However, it is customary to refer to the angular momentum vector and its z-component in the resting coordinates as m and j, though they are neither quantized, constant, nor identical with the m and j used in the paragraphs on space quantization. This is justifiable to a high degree of approximation.

The fact that only the components 0, ± 1 exist is due to the action of a selection principle. Considerations of the angular momentum lost in the radiation process cannot be applied here, because conservation of angular momentum holds true only for the system composed of the atom and the apparatus producing the field. The correspondence principle yields a definite result. The reader may refer to Chap. VI, Sec. **6** for an exposition of the basis for the following remarks. To derive the selection principle for m, we note that the z-component of the electric moment contains only the original frequencies of the motion. The coefficient of $2\pi Lt$ in the Fourier series for the z-component is zero, so that the corresponding quantum number m must remain unaltered in any transitions giving light polarized with the electric vector parallel to H. But $2\pi Lt$ appears in the series for x and y with the coefficients $+1$ and -1, so m must change by ± 1 in transitions giving light with the electric vector perpendicular to H, that is,

$$\Delta m = 0 \text{ for p-components}, \pm 1 \text{ for s-components},$$

and we have the Lorentz triplet. The circular polarization of the waves giving the s-components is concluded from the amplitudes and phases of the corresponding terms in equation (50). In very strong fields, this selection principle is violated, and components appear at ± 2, and ± 3.[1] This was pointed out by Bohr, who detected the additional components in photographs published by Paschen and Back, and is explained as due to the increasing importance of terms in L^2, for L is proportional to H.

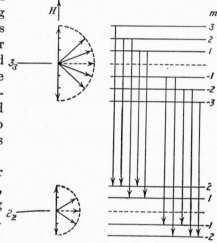

The physical significance of our results will be clear from Fig. 15, which shows the Zeeman splitting of the levels 3_3 and 2_2 of hydrogen. At the left are the field-free levels. The allowed orientations of j in the field are shown in the center and the corresponding energies on the right, as given by equation (55). The selection rule allows only the transitions $\Delta m = \pm 1$ or 0 as indicated by arrows.

Fig. 15.—Magnetic energy levels of hydrogen.

12. THE STARK EFFECT

It is rather surprising that the influence of an electric field on spectral lines was discovered many years after the Zeeman effect, for the shifts of wave length which can be produced with usual laboratory facilities are large compared with those due to the strongest magnetic fields.

[1] Paschen and Back, *Ann. Physik*, **39**, 897 (1912), and **40**, 960 (1913).

In 1913, Stark[1] demonstrated that in a field of the order of 100,000 volts per centimeter the hydrogen Balmer lines observed transverse to the field are split into a number of linearly polarized components. The difficulty which had thwarted previous attempts was twofold: First, the Stark effect is much smaller in non-hydrogenic atoms than for hydrogen; and second, it is difficult to increase the potential gradient in the ordinary discharge tube because any attempt to raise the applied potential simply increases the ionization and decreases the resistance of the tube. Stark overcame this trouble by placing an auxiliary electrode E close behind the cathode C, which is perforated, as shown in Fig. 16. Then, due to the fact that this electrode is inside the cathode dark space, no discharge takes place in EC. Positive ions are accelerated toward C and some will pick up electrons on the way, forming neutral H atoms. The fast atoms (and ions also) which pass through the perforations and emit light in EC are called "canal rays." Soon after Stark's dis-

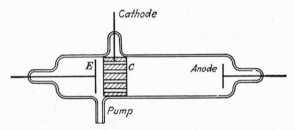

Fig. 16.—Tube for studying the Stark effect.

covery, Lo Surdo[2] found that the faint light emitted in the cathode dark space also shows the effects described above. For descriptions of experimental details and for an account of the Stark effect in non-hydrogenic atoms, we refer the reader to Chap. XI. Here we shall calculate the energy levels of the H atom in a uniform electric field and the orbits of its electron. The field is supposed so strong that the modifications due to relativity and electron spin may be neglected. (The energy levels in a weak field are discussed in Sec. 15.) The solution of this problem was obtained independently by Schwarzschild[3] and Epstein[4] in 1916 and was a real triumph for the quantum theory because classical theory was powerless to attack the problem. Suppose the field is directed along the positive Z-axis. Then, the potential energy of a positive charge ϵ may be taken as $-\epsilon Fz$, and that of an electron will be eFz. To solve the problem, we use the Hamilton-Jacobi equation. This is not separable in polar or Cartesian coordinates, but becomes

[1] *Berl. Sitzungsberichte* (1913), *Ann. Physik*, **43**, 965, 983 (1914).
[2] *Accad. dei Lincei*, **23** (1914).
[3] *Berl. Sitzungsberichte*, April (1916).
[4] *Ann. Physik*, **50**, 489 (1916).

so in parabolic coordinates, ξ, η, φ, which are defined by the relations

$$x = \xi\eta\cos\varphi, \, y = \xi\eta\sin\varphi, \, z = \frac{(\xi^2 - \eta^2)}{2}, \tag{57}$$

from which we see that φ is the polar angle in the xy plane.   If we write

$$\rho^2 = x^2 + y^2, \, r^2 = x^2 + y^2 + z^2,$$

we have

$$\rho^2 = \xi^2\eta^2, \, \xi^2 = r + z, \, \eta^2 = r - z, \, r = \frac{(\xi^2 + \eta^2)}{2}. \tag{58}$$

The coordinate surfaces ξ = constant and η = constant are paraboloids of revolution.   Figure 17 shows the parabolas in which they intersect the yz plane, having the equations

$$y^2 = -2\xi^2\left(z - \frac{\xi^2}{2}\right); \, y^2 = 2\eta^2\left(z + \frac{\eta^2}{2}\right). \tag{59}$$

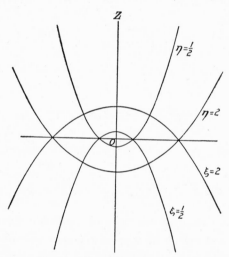

Fig. 17.—Parabolic coordinates.

The origin is the focus of all these curves; the segment of the y-axis intercepted between the two branches is the latus rectum; for the first family it is $2\xi^2$ and for the second $2\eta^2$.   This property helps us to visualize the positions of these curves.   The curve $\eta = 0$ is the positive z-axis (twice covered), while $\xi = 0$ is the negative z-axis.   As ξ and η increase, the parabolas become wider, with vertices farther from the origin.   To find the expression for the element of arc, it is convenient to consider its familiar value in cylindrical coordinates,

$$ds^2 = d\rho^2 + \rho^2 d\varphi^2 + dz^2,$$

whence, by equation (58),

$$ds^2 = (\xi^2 + \eta^2)(d\xi^2 + d\eta^2) + \xi^2\eta^2 d\varphi^2, \tag{60}$$

and the kinetic energy is

$$T = \left(\frac{m_0}{2}\right)[(\xi^2 + \eta^2)(\dot{\xi}^2 + \dot{\eta}^2) + \xi^2\eta^2\dot{\varphi}^2]. \tag{61}$$

From this we find the momenta,

$$p_\xi = m_0(\xi^2 + \eta^2)\dot{\xi}, \; p_\eta = m_0(\xi^2 + \eta^2)\dot{\eta}, \; p_\varphi = m_0\xi^2\eta^2\dot{\varphi}. \tag{62}$$

Thus, p_φ is the component of angular momentum around OZ. The significance of p_ξ, p_η is not simple; but they may be rewritten as

$$p_\xi = m_0(\dot{r} + \dot{z})\frac{r}{\xi}, \; p_\eta = m_0(\dot{r} - \dot{z})\frac{r}{\eta}.$$

When T is expressed in terms of the p's, we get for the energy function

$$\frac{1}{2m_0(\xi^2 + \eta^2)}\left[p_\xi{}^2 + p_\eta{}^2 + \left(\frac{1}{\xi^2} + \frac{1}{\eta^2}\right)p_\varphi{}^2\right] -$$
$$\frac{Ze^2}{\dfrac{(\xi^2 + \eta^2)}{2}} + eF\frac{(\xi^2 - \eta^2)}{2} = E. \tag{63}$$

Since φ does not appear in this, we see from the canonical equation, $dp_\varphi/dt = -\partial H/\partial\varphi$, that p_φ is constant. Multiplying equation (63) by $2m_0(\xi^2 + \eta^2)$, we get

$$p_\xi{}^2 + p_\eta{}^2 + (\xi^{-2} + \eta^{-2})p_\varphi{}^2 - 4m_0Ze^2 + m_0eF(\xi^4 - \eta^4) -$$
$$2m_0(\xi^2 + \eta^2)E = 0, \tag{63a}$$

which is separable. We can write

$$p_\xi{}^2 = 2m_0E\xi^2 + 2\alpha_1 - \frac{p_\varphi{}^2}{\xi^2} - m_0eF\xi^4, \tag{64a}$$

$$p_\eta{}^2 = 2m_0E\eta^2 + 2\alpha_2 - \frac{p_\varphi{}^2}{\eta^2} + m_0eF\eta^4, \tag{64b}$$

where

$$\alpha_1 + \alpha_2 = 2m_0Ze^2. \tag{65}$$

Then the quantized orbits are picked out by applying the conditions

$$\oint p_\xi d\xi = n_1 h, \; \oint p_\eta d\eta = n_2 h, \; \oint p_\varphi d\varphi = mh,$$

whence we have

$$p_\varphi = \frac{mh}{2\pi}.$$

To obtain the range of integration for the other two integrals we note that p_ξ(or p_η) is the square root of a rational function of ξ(or η). Since the p's must be real, the limits of variation of ξ and η will lie at the points where the values of $p_\xi{}^2$ and $p_\eta{}^2$ are changing from plus to minus, that is, at points where they are zero. When F is zero, the expression on the right of equation (64a) becomes quadratic after multiplication by ξ^2, and therefore gives us two limiting values of ξ^2. On taking the square root, we have 4 limiting values of ξ, but the negative ones have no physical meaning, so we restrict our attention to the positive roots. When F is not zero, there is a third root of the equation which is very large and which does not concern us when dealing with values of F obtainable in the laboratory. We are interested only in the two roots, ξ_{max} and ξ_{min}, which correspond to the pair existing when $F = 0$. These considerations show that the orbit is restricted to an annular space bounded by the surfaces $\xi = \xi_{min}$, $\xi = \xi_{max}$; $\eta = \eta_{min}$, $\eta = \eta_{max}$.

If we substitute $\xi^2 = x$ or $\eta^2 = x$ both integrals reduce to the form

$$nh = \frac{1}{2} \oint \left(A + \frac{2B}{x} + \frac{C}{x^2} + Dx \right)^{\frac{1}{2}} dx, \tag{66}$$

where in the integral for ξ,

$$A = 2m_0E, \; B = \alpha_1, \; C = -p_\varphi{}^2, \; D = -m_0eF, \tag{67}$$

and in the integral for η,

$$A = 2m_0E, \; B = \alpha_2, \; C = -p_\varphi{}^2, \; D = +m_0eF. \tag{67a}$$

Evaluating these integrals, we have two equations containing E, α_1, and α_2. Using equation (65), we eliminate the α's and obtain

$$E = -\frac{2\pi^2m_0e^4Z^2}{n^2h^2} - \frac{3h^2F}{8\pi^2m_0Ze}n(n_2 - n_1), \tag{68}$$

where the total quantum number n, is given by

$$n = n_1 + n_2 + m. \tag{69}$$

States for which m takes a specified value $-a$ have the same energy as those for which $m = +a$. Therefore, we restrict m to positive values in this formula.

A term in the energy proportional to F^2 has been computed by Epstein, and gives rise to effects which have been observed at very high fields by Takamine and Kokubu.

The details of obtaining equation (68) are as follows:
Integral 66 is evaluated in Appendix II by expanding the integrand in powers of the small quantity D. The result is

$$2nh = -2\pi i(C^{\frac{1}{2}} - BA^{-\frac{1}{2}}) + \left(\frac{\pi iD}{2A^{\frac{3}{2}}} \right)\left(\frac{3B^2}{A} - C \right). \tag{66b}$$

Since the term containing D gives the Stark effect it is small compared with the first two terms. Without appreciable error we may use an approximate value of B^2/A in this term. To get this we drop the terms in D and solve the resulting equation, obtaining

$$\frac{B^2}{A} = \left(C^{\frac{1}{2}} - \frac{nhi}{\pi} \right)^2,$$

and

$$\frac{3B^2}{A} - C = 2C - 6nhi\frac{C^{\frac{1}{2}}}{\pi} - 3\left(\frac{nh}{\pi} \right)^2.$$

Putting this in the last term of equation (66b), and solving for B, we have an equation giving B in terms of A, C, and D. It represents two equations, in which B and D take the values given in equations (67) and (67a), respectively, while n takes the values n_1 and n_2, respectively. Writing down these two equations and adding them we have

$$2m_0Ze^2 = A^{\frac{1}{2}}\left(2C^{\frac{1}{2}} - \frac{n_1 + n_2)hi}{\pi}\right) + \left(\frac{m_0eF}{2A}\right)\left(\frac{3}{2}\frac{(n_2{}^2 - n_1{}^2)h^2}{\pi^2} + \frac{3(n_2 - n_1)hiC^{\frac{1}{2}}}{\pi}\right)$$

Now, we put $C^{\frac{1}{2}} = -mhi/2\pi$, and calculate an approximate value of A, neglecting the terms in F:

$$A = -\frac{4\pi^2m_0{}^2Z^2e^4}{h^2(n_1 + n_2 + m)^2}$$

We use this value in the correction term in equation (66b). Writing $n_1 + n_2 + m = n$, we calculate a new value of A, and then, by equation (67), we arrive at the energy equation (68).

13. ENERGY LEVELS, SELECTION PRINCIPLES, AND POLARIZATION RULES IN THE STARK EFFECT

As mentioned before, Stark and Lo Surdo found that in the electric field each Balmer line is split into a number of components. When the line of vision is transverse to the field, all components are linearly polarized. For some components, the electric vector vibrates perpendicular to the field (s-components), and for others, parallel to it (p-components). Observing longitudinally, only the s-components appear, and these are unpolarized. These facts are fully explained by ideas similar to those in Secs. **7** and **8**. The application of the field does not alter the angular momentum component of the electron around the z-axis, p_φ, although the two components at right angles to it are continually changing, for the force on the electron is parallel to the z-axis. If we suppose the atom replaced by a harmonic oscillator radiating the actual emission frequency, having amplitudes a, b, and c parallel to the x-, y-, and z-axes then the z-component of the impulse moment of the radiated quantum will be

$$P_z = \left(\frac{h}{2\pi}\right)2ab\,\frac{\sin(\alpha - \beta)}{a^2 + b^2 + c^2}$$

α and β are the phases of the x- and y-components of the electric moment. This must be equal to the change of p_φ, namely $h\Delta m/2\pi$, and by reasoning like that leading to equation (42) we arrive at the following possible cases:

1. $\Delta m = +1$, $a = b$, $c = 0$, and $\sin(\alpha - \beta) = \pm 1$.

This corresponds to circularly polarized light with axis parallel to OZ. Observed at right angles to the lines of force, such waves appear linearly polarized with electric vector perpendicular to OZ, and give rise to the s-components. In the longitudinal Stark effect these components are unpolarized, for there is no preferred direction of rotation around the lines of force. For each atom yielding a certain frequency there will be another yielding the same frequency which is the mirror image of the first in a plane parallel to the force-lines.

2. $\Delta m = 0$; a or b or $\sin(\alpha - \beta)$ must be zero. There is no preferred direction in a plane perpendicular to the lines of force. Therefore, there is no reason why $\sin(\alpha - \beta)$ should be zero, and no reason why a should be zero while b is finite, or *vice versa*. The only way to avoid giving preference to some one direction is to make $a = b = 0$. Then we have only a linear oscillation parallel to OZ which gives rise to the p-components in the transverse Stark effect, and is not observed in the longitudinal effect. Summarizing, the selection principle for the equatorial number m states that $\Delta m = \pm 1$ *or* 0; *transitions in which* $\Delta m = \pm 1$ *yield s-components; those in which* $\Delta m = 0$ *yield p-components.*

By the energy equation (68), the Balmer energy level having a given total quantum number n is split by the field into a number of neighboring levels characterized by different values of n_1, n_2, and m. The wave-number interval between one of these levels and the Balmer level is

$$\Delta \bar{\nu} = \left(\frac{3hF}{8\pi^2 m_0 Zec} \right) n(n_2 - n_1). \tag{70}$$

If F is in volts/cm., this has the value

$$\Delta \bar{\nu} = 6.45 \cdot 10^{-5} \left(\frac{F}{Z} \right) n(n_2 - n_1). \tag{71}$$

Let us consider the possible values of n_1, n_2, and m for a given n. The value $m = 0$ is excluded. It corresponds to an orbit located entirely in a plane through the nucleus, parallel to the lines of force. The limits of its motion are determined by finding the roots of equations (64a) and (64b) after putting $p_\varphi = 0$. The minimum values of ξ and η are zero, and this means that the orbit will cross the negative and positive z-axes. The region swept over by the orbit is contained between two parabolas $\eta = \eta_{max}$ and $\xi = \xi_{max}$. It can be proved[1] that if the system is not degenerate, the electron will eventually pass indefinitely close to any point of this domain, and so it must approach arbitrarily close to the nucleus. For this reason, such orbits are considered impossible and are excluded from further consideration. It follows that n_1 and n_2 can take values from 0 to $n - m$ inclusive, subject to the condition $n_1 + n_2 + m = n$. For each positive value of $n_2 - n_1$ in equation (71), there is a negative value, equal in magnitude, which means that the displaced terms are disposed symmetrically about the original term, and thus the pattern of displaced lines is symmetrical about the original line. We illustrate this by listing the possible combinations of n_1, n_2, and m, together with the corresponding values of $n(n_2 - n_1)$ for the initial and final orbits of $H\alpha$.

[1] Born, "Atommechanik," p. 342.

	n_1	n_2	m	$n(n_2 - n_1)$
$n = 3$	2	0	1	−6
	1	1	1	0
	0	2	1	+6
	1	0	2	−3
	0	1	2	+3
	0	0	3	0
$n = 2$	1	0	1	−2
	0	1	1	+2
	0	0	2	0

Figure 18 illustrates the facts presented in the table. The displacements of the lines emitted from the field-free Balmer line are obtained from the formula,

$$\Delta \bar{\nu} = 6.45 \cdot 10^{-5} \left(\frac{F}{Z}\right)[n_f(n_{2f} - n_{1f}) - n_i(n_{2i} - n_{1i})], \qquad (72)$$

derived from equation (71). The subscripts i anf f refer to the initial and final quantum states. Figure 19 shows the parallel and perpendicular components of the first four lines in the Balmer series. Lines which were

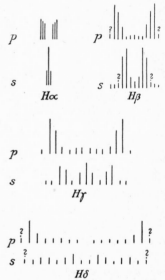

FIG. 19.—Components of $H\alpha$, $H\beta$ and $H\gamma$ in an electric field.

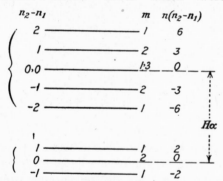

FIG. 18.—Energy diagram: Stark effect of $H\alpha$.

observed by Stark are drawn in full, while additional components predicted by the theory are shown by question marks. Intensities are indicated roughly by the heights of the lines. Photographs of the Stark effect of $H\gamma$, obtained with a Lo Surdo tube,[1] are presented in Fig. 20. These are reproduced from plates kindly placed at our disposal by Dr. J. S. Foster. The separation of the lines is due to the increase in field strength as the surface of the cathode is approached. To give

[1] *Phys. Rev.*, **23**, 667 (1924).

an idea of the scale of these patterns, it may be stated that the strong outer parallel components of $H\gamma$ are displaced by 0.23 Å and 0.19 Å, respectively, when the field strength is increased 1 kilovolt per centimeter. At 38 kilovolts per centimeter, the total spread of the parallel pattern in Fig. 20 is more than 17 Å. Foster found that the displacements are rigorously proportional to field strength up to this value, in agreement with theory.

The agreement between theory and experiment in the Stark effect of hydrogen may be described as practically perfect and has been one of the strongest supports of Bohr's postulates and the quantum conditions.

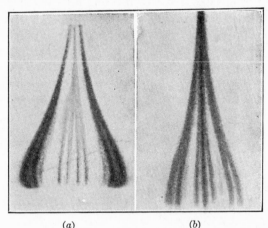

(a)   (b)

FIG. 20.—Stark effect of $H\gamma$; a, p-components; b, s-components.   (*After Foster.*)

14. THE MOTION OF THE ELECTRON IN THE STARK EFFECT

In certain cases, the motion of the hydrogen electron in a strong electric field is very simple. If $n_1 = n_2 = 0$, then $n = m$ and the orbit is a circle perpendicular to the field. It lies upfield from the nucleus, and both the radius and the energy are changed only by quantities of the second order. In other cases, the motion is more complex. As we have mentioned, the orbit eventually fills up the ring-like space between two paraboloids of the η-family and two of the ξ-family. In a single circuit around the nucleus the orbit varies but little from a Kepler ellipse, but in the course of time the eccentricity of the orbit and its inclination to the lines of force will vary, and the orbital plane precesses around the direction of the field. Methods of calculating the secular changes of the ellipse have been given by Bohr,[1] Lenz,[2] and Klein.[3]

[1] "Quantum Theory of Line Spectra," Kopenhagen Academy (1918).
[2] *Z. Physik*, **24**, 197 (1924).
[3] *Z. Physik*, **22**, 109 (1924). The papers of Lenz and Klein discuss the more general case in which both an electric and magnetic field are present.

Referring to Fig. 21, B is the *electrical center* of the orbit. If the electron were permanently located at B, its potential energy in the external field would be equal to the average potential energy, taken with respect to time over the unperturbed orbit. That is, if $\bar{z}$ is the z-coordinate of B, then

$$eF\bar{z} = \frac{1}{\tau}\int_0^\tau eFz\,dt. \tag{73}$$

τ is the period of the undisturbed motion. The result is that

$$\bar{z} = \frac{3\epsilon a \cos \alpha}{2}, \tag{74}$$

where ϵ is the eccentricity of the ellipse, and a its semimajor axis, while α is the angle between OZ and the major axis. Thus, for reasons of

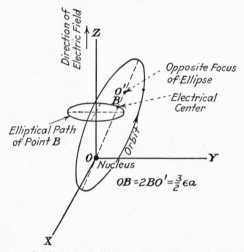

Fig. 21.—Orbit of the hydrogen electron in an electric field.

symmetry, B lies on the major axis at a distance $\frac{3}{2}\epsilon a$ from the nucleus. Since the average potential energy over a revolution of the electron is the same for all its revolutions, $\bar{z}$ is constant, and the electrical center moves in a plane perpendicular to Z. As a matter of fact, the path of the center is an ellipse, which it traverses with simple harmonic motion, having the frequency

$$\nu_F = \frac{3hF}{8\pi^2 mZe}n. \tag{75}$$

From this we can obtain the energy change caused by the field. The center of gravity of the charge moves like a Planck oscillator, and the energy due to this motion must be $\Delta E = n_F h\nu_F$, where n_F is a new quantum number. In fact ΔE is found to be identical with the value in equation (68), if we put

$$n_F = n_1 - n_2. \tag{76}$$

15. THE STARK EFFECT IN WEAK FIELDS

Up to this point, the precession frequency ν_F due to the electric field was supposed to be large in comparison with the frequency of the relativity precession. In the opposite case of a very weak field, Kramers[1] showed that the formula for the energy change is

$$\Delta E = -\frac{9}{4}\left(\frac{h}{2\pi}\right)^8 \frac{c^2 F^2}{Z^6 e^{10} m_0{}^3} n^5 k(n^2 - 2k^2 + m^2); \qquad (77)$$

n and k are the total and azimuthal numbers, while m is a quantum number measuring the component of angular momentum parallel to the field. At intermediate field strengths, the formula contains terms in both F and F^2. The reason for the absence of a term proportional to F in equation (77) is easily explained. When the field is strong, it suppresses the relativity precession, and the electrical center of gravity lies always on one side of the plane through the nucleus and perpendicular to the field (Fig. 21); but when the field is very weak, the relativity precession carries the electrical center first to one side of this plane and then to the other. The first-order term in the energy is first positive and then negative and its time average is zero, so that the quadratic term, equation (77), is the largest term in ΔE.

16. THE EFFECT OF ELECTRON SPIN

As stated in Chap. III, Sec. **19**, the electron behaves to a high degree of approximation as though it possessed an intrinsic angular momentum $h/4\pi$ and a magnetic moment of one Bohr magneton, $(h/2\pi)(e/2mc)$. Abraham[2] calculated the ratio of angular momentum and magnetic moment for a rigid spherical shell having a charge e uniformly distributed over its surface, obtaining the result e/mc, which agrees with the ratio of the quantities assigned above. Since the charge of the electron is $-e$, we have the vector equation

$$\mathbf{\mu} = -\left(\frac{e}{mc}\right)\mathbf{p_s}, \qquad (78)$$

expressing the fact that the spin vector $\mathbf{p_s}$ and the magnetic moment vector $\mathbf{\mu}$ are opposite in direction. Now the electron moves with velocity $\mathbf{v}$ through the electric field $\mathbf{E}$ of the nucleus. If it were uncharged, its velocity would not change in either amount or direction, and the electron-magnet $\mathbf{\mu}$ would behave as though it were subject to a magnetic field

$$\mathbf{H'} = -\frac{[\mathbf{vE}]}{c}, \qquad (79)$$

where $[\mathbf{vE}]$ means the vector product of $\mathbf{v}$ and $\mathbf{E}$. (See Appendix VIII; $\mathbf{H'}$ is analogous to the field $\mathbf{E'} = [\mathbf{vH}]/c$ which acts on a charge moving

---

[1] *Z. Physik*, **3**, 199 (1920). The results of this paper are discussed in VAN VLECK'S "Bulletin" and PAULI'S Handbuch article in considerable detail.

[2] *Ann. Physik*, **10**, 105 (1903).

with velocity **v** through a magnetic field **H**.) However, the motion of the electron is not uniform and so the energy change is not obtained from equation (79). At first, this fact was overlooked and the energy change caused by the existence of $\mathbf{\mu}$ was calculated as follows:

In the magnetic field $\mathbf{H}'$ the moment $\mathbf{\mu}$ will precess around the lines of force with angular velocity $\omega' = eH'/mc$ in accordance with an easily proved extension of Larmor's theorem (Appendix VIII). Just as we found the change of energy ΔT_H in equation (53), neglecting electron spin, so we prove that this precession gives rise to an instantaneous energy change

$$\Delta E' = (\mathbf{\omega'} \cdot \mathbf{p_s}) = -(\mathbf{\mu} \cdot \mathbf{H'}), \tag{80}$$

where $(\mathbf{\omega'} \cdot \mathbf{p_s})$ stands for the scalar product of $\mathbf{\omega'}$ and $\mathbf{p_s}$. The precession will not be uniform because $\mathbf{H'}$ varies as the electron traverses an elliptic orbit. We shall assume that it follows the change of $\mathbf{H'}$ without appreciable lag.

The procedure is nearly the same when the non-uniform motion of the electron is taken into account. We shall see in Sec. **18** that the velocity of precession of the spin vector, as seen by an observer at rest with respect to the nucleus, is

$$\omega = \frac{eH'}{2mc}, \tag{81}$$

which is just one-half the value used above, and so equation (80) is replaced by

$$\Delta E = (\mathbf{\omega} \cdot \mathbf{p_s}) = -\frac{(\mathbf{\mu} \cdot \mathbf{H'})}{2}. \tag{82}$$

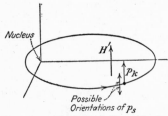

Fig. 22.—Motion of the spinning electron.

In Chap. VI, Sec. **10**, it is proved that the presence of a small perturbing term ΔE gives rise to a change $\overline{\Delta E}$ of the total energy, where $\overline{\Delta E}$ is the time average of ΔE, taken over the unperturbed orbit; so we proceed to calculate $\overline{\Delta E}$. Since the components of the electric vector are

$$E_x = -\frac{Zex}{r^3}, \; E_y = -\frac{Zey}{r^3}, \; E_z = -\frac{Zez}{r^3},$$

the vector itself may be written

$$\mathbf{E} = -\frac{Ze\mathbf{r}}{r^3}, \tag{83}$$

and

$$\mathbf{H'} = -\frac{[\mathbf{vE}]}{c} = \left(\frac{Ze}{r^3mc}\right)m[\mathbf{rv}]; \tag{84}$$

but $m[\mathbf{rv}]$ is the angular momentum vector $\mathbf{p_k}$ associated with the revolution of the electron around the nucleus, and is directed perpendicular to the plane of the orbit, as shown in Fig. 22, so

$$\mathbf{H'} = \left(\frac{Ze}{r^3mc}\right)\mathbf{p_k}. \tag{85}$$

Putting the values of equations (81) and (85) into equation (82), we have

$$\Delta E = \frac{Ze^2}{2 \cdot m^2c^2r^3}(\mathbf{p_s} \cdot \mathbf{p_k}). \tag{82a}$$

Now $p_s = sh/2\pi$, where $s = \pm\frac{1}{2}$; $p_k = kh/2\pi$; and so

$$(\mathbf{p_s} \cdot \mathbf{p_k}) = \frac{skh^2 \cos\theta}{4\pi^2} \tag{86}$$

where θ is the angle between $\mathbf{p_s}$ and $\mathbf{p_k}$. As a matter of fact, $\mathbf{p_s}$ is space quantized in the field $\mathbf{H'}$, and $\theta = 0^0$ or 180°, so that the total angular momentum of the atom is

$$\frac{jh}{2\pi} = \frac{(\mathbf{k} \pm \mathbf{s})h}{2\pi},$$

and

$$j = k \pm \frac{1}{2}. \tag{87}$$

Therefore, by equation (82a),

$$\overline{\Delta E} = \frac{Ze^2skh^2}{8\pi^2m^2c^2}\left(\overline{\frac{1}{r^3}}\right).$$

For a Keplerian ellipse of semiminor axis b,

$$\overline{\frac{1}{r^3}} = \frac{1}{b^3},$$

and by equation (22),

$$\frac{1}{b^3} = \left(\frac{4\pi^2Ze^2m}{nkh^2}\right)^3, \tag{88}$$

so finally,

$$\overline{\Delta E} = Rhc\alpha^2Z^4\frac{s}{n^3k^2}.$$

Adding this to the relativity correction of equation (36), the correction of the energy value due to both relativity and electron spin is found to be

$$\Delta E(n, k, s) = \frac{Rhc\alpha^2Z^4}{n^4}\left(\frac{3}{4} - \frac{n}{k} + \frac{sn}{k^2}\right). \tag{89}$$

It is understood that s is positive if p_s and p_k have the same direction. The alteration of the spectral term is

$$\Delta T(n, k, s) = \frac{R\alpha^2Z^4}{n^4}\left(\frac{n}{k} - \frac{3}{4} - \frac{sn}{k^2}\right). \tag{90}$$

As emphasized in the preceding sections and in the sections on X-ray spectra, the first two terms of equation (90) are in good agreement with experiment, so there does not appear to be room for the existence of the term sn/k^2, which splits each relativistic level into two levels, corresponding to the values $s = \pm\frac{1}{2}$.

17. MODIFICATIONS OF THE ENERGY FORMULA CAUSED BY THE NEW MECHANICS

Preparatory to the removal of this difficulty, it will be convenient to rewrite the last term of equation (90) in a more general form. Let us suppose for the instant that θ is not zero or π. Then in accord with principles established in Chap. X, Sec. **14**, the vectors $\mathbf{p}_k$ and $\mathbf{p}_s$ will precess around their resultant, which will have only certain quantized values. Calling the resultant $jh/2\pi$, we see that

$$j^2 = k^2 + s^2 + 2ks \cos \theta,$$

and

$$\cos \theta = \frac{j^2 - k^2 - s^2}{2ks}. \tag{91}$$

Using this value in equation (86), the result is that the last term of equation (90) is changed to

$$-\frac{R\alpha^2 Z^4(j^2 - k^2 - s^2)}{2n^3 k^3}. \tag{92}$$

Heisenberg and Jordan[1] and also Richter[2] showed by the new mechanics that equation (90) must be replaced by[3]

$$\Delta T = \frac{R\alpha^2 Z^4}{n^4}\left(-\frac{3}{4} + \frac{n}{l + \frac{1}{2}} - \frac{n[j(j+1) - l(l+1) - s(s+1)]}{2l(l + \frac{1}{2})(l+1)} \right). \tag{93}$$

The number n takes the same values as before, but $l = k - 1$, and takes values from 0 to $n - 1$ inclusive; the definition of j is now the vector sum of l and s, $\cdots$ that is, $j = l \pm \frac{1}{2}$. If $l = 0$, the third term in equation (93) is replaced by $-n/2(l + \frac{1}{2})$. The levels predicted by equation (93) are identical with those obtained from the relativity correction of Sommerfeld, so we can say that the spin correction in equation (93), superposed on a relativity correction term in which k is replaced by $k - \frac{1}{2}$, gives results in agreement with experiment, a fact which is essential for the interpretation of both X-ray and optical spectra. As an example, we may compute the displacements of the hydrogen energy levels when $n = 2$, expressing them as multiples of $R\alpha^2 Z^4/n^4$. The terms of Sommerfeld's theory are given by the values of $\frac{n}{k} - \frac{3}{4}$. Putting $k = 1$ and $k = 2$, these terms lie at the positions $\frac{5}{4}$ and $\frac{1}{4}$, measuring down from the position of the Balmer term in the energy diagram, Fig. 23. The following table shows how these

---

[1] *Z. Physik*, **37**, 263 (1926).

[2] *Phys. Rev.*, **28**, 849 (1926); *Proc. Nat. Acad. Sci.*, **13**, 476 (1927).

[3] Here s is always taken positive.

same terms arise from the combination of the relativity correction $\dfrac{n}{l+\frac{1}{2}} - \dfrac{3}{4}$ and the spin correction, while the second and third columns of Fig. 23 also show their origin:

l	$\dfrac{n}{l+\frac{1}{2}} - \dfrac{3}{4}$	s	j	Spin correction	Total correction
1	$\frac{7}{12}$	$\left\{\begin{array}{l} +\frac{1}{2} \\ -\frac{1}{2} \end{array}\right.$	$\begin{array}{c} \frac{3}{2} \\ \frac{1}{2} \end{array}$	$\begin{array}{c} -\frac{1}{3} \\ +\frac{5}{12} \end{array}$	$\begin{array}{c} \frac{1}{4} \\ \frac{5}{4} \end{array}$
0	$1\frac{3}{4}$	$\frac{1}{2}$	$\frac{1}{2}$	-2	$\frac{5}{4}$

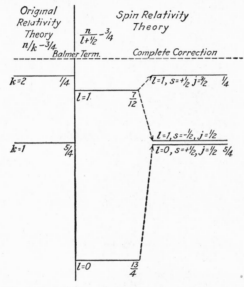

FIG. 23.—Effect of relativity and electron spin on the terms of hydrogen.

We see that the term $\frac{5}{4}$ arises from two combinations of quantum numbers. In the case of X-ray spectra, the effect of the other electrons in the atom is to separate these two coincident terms, because of the different shapes of the orbits involved, a matter which is discussed in detail in Chap. VIII.

For a considerable time the riddle which is solved in this section caused great confusion. One set of facts seemed to point conclusively to the relativistic origin of the hydrogen and helium fine structures and their analogues in the X-ray region. Evidence drawn from the spectra of non-hydrogenic atoms indicated just as strongly that these phenomena originated from the presence of a magnetic moment within the atom. The combination of the two explanations, using quantum numbers which apparently take half-integral values, seemed artificial until the new mechanics demonstrated the validity of the procedure.

18. THE PRECESSION OF THE SPINNING ELECTRON

In this section we prove that the angular velocity with which the spin vector precesses as seen by an observer at rest with respect to the nucleus is given by equation (81). This proof is not needed for the understanding of what follows, and it may be passed over if the reader desires. Frenkel[1] and Thomas[2] proved equation (81) independently. We shall give a treatment like that of Thomas, but much simplified. Let x, y, z, t be coordinates and time in a frame of reference R in which the nucleus is at rest, and in which the electron is momentarily at the origin, while x_0, y_0, z_0, and t_0 are measured in a frame O which moves with the instantaneous velocity of the electron at zero time, measured in R. For simplicity, we take z perpendicular to the orbital plane, and both x and x_0 parallel to the velocity vector $\mathbf{v}_0$ (Fig. 24). We pass from R to O by a Lorentz transformation,

$$x_0 = k_0(x - v_0 t),\ y_0 = y,\ z_0 = z,\ t_0 = k_0\left(t - \frac{xv_0}{c^2}\right),\qquad (94)$$

where

$$k_0 = \left(1 - \frac{v_0^2}{c^2}\right)^{-\frac{1}{2}}\qquad (95)$$

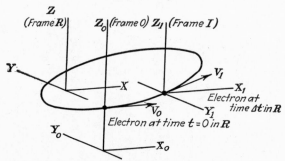

FIG. 24.—Coordinate systems for study of electron spin.

Similarly, let x_1, y_1, z_1, t_1 be measured in a system I in which the electron is instantaneously at rest at the origin at time Δt measured in R. As before, the axis x_1 is parallel to x. The relative velocity of the two systems is given by

$$\mathbf{v}_1 = \mathbf{v}_0 + \mathbf{f}\Delta t\qquad (96)$$

where $\mathbf{f}$ is the acceleration of the electron, and since $\mathbf{v}_1$ is not parallel to the x- and x_1-axes, the formulas for Lorentz transformation from R to I are more complicated. In R let the coordinates of the electron be a_x, a_y, a_z, and let $\mathbf{r}$ and $\mathbf{r}_1$ be vectors with the components x, y, z and x_1, y_1, z_1, respectively. Then the transformation[3] is

$$\mathbf{r}_1 = \mathbf{r} - \mathbf{a} + (k_1 - 1)\frac{(\{\mathbf{r} - \mathbf{a}\}\cdot\mathbf{v}_1)}{v_1^2}\mathbf{v}_1 - k_1\mathbf{v}_1(t - \Delta t)$$

$$t_1 = k_1\left\{t - \Delta t - \frac{(\{\mathbf{r} - \mathbf{a}\}\cdot\mathbf{v}_1)}{c^2}\right\}.\qquad (97)$$

By eliminating x, y, z, t, between equations (94) and (97) we obtain the formulas of transformation from O to I. The result is this: I can be obtained from O by applying two transformations in succession: first, a rotation around the z-axis through an angle

$$\frac{(k_0 - 1)[\mathbf{v}_0 d\mathbf{v}_0]}{v_0^2},\qquad (98)$$

[1] Z. Physik, 37, 243 (1926).
[2] Phil. Mag., 3, 1 (1926).
[3] MADELUNG, Math. Hilfsmittel des Physikers, 1st ed., p. 209.

where $d\mathbf{v}_0 = \mathbf{f}_0 dt_0$, and second, a Lorentz transformation characterized by the vector velocity

$$k_0 \, d\mathbf{v}_0 + k_0(k_0 - 1) \frac{(\mathbf{v}_0 \cdot d\mathbf{v}_0)\mathbf{v}_0}{v_0^2}. \tag{99}$$

The second does not concern us. In the first, the vector product of $\mathbf{v}_0$ and $d\mathbf{v}_0$ has the value $[\mathbf{v}_0\mathbf{f}_0]dt$ and $k_0 - 1 \cong v_0^2/2c^2$, so equation (98) takes the form $[\mathbf{v}_0\,\mathbf{f}_0]dt/2c^2$. Therefore, an observer in R believes that the axes of O and I are parallel to his own, but an observer in O is equally sure that the x-axis of I makes an angle with his own x-axis. This result of relativity kinematics cannot be understood in terms of our usual ideas of space and time except with the aid of specially constructed hypotheses like the Fitzgerald contraction.

Suppose for the sake of generality that the atom is exposed to an external magnetic field $\mathbf{H}$ parallel to the z-axis, and let $\mathbf{E}_0$ and $\mathbf{H}_0$ be the electric and magnetic field strengths as measured in the system O. To a first approximation,

$$m\mathbf{f}_0 = -e\mathbf{E}_0 \tag{100}$$

and the rate of precession of the spin vector s is

$$\omega_0 = \frac{eH_0}{mc} \tag{101}$$

when measured in O. Suppose that the projection of $\mathbf{s}$ on the $x_0 y_0$ plane is directed along x_0. For the "resting" observer it will be along x. After time dt, an observer in I will find by equations (101) and (98), that the projection of $\mathbf{s}$ has rotated through an angle

$$d\mathbf{A} = \boldsymbol{\omega}_0 dt - \frac{[\mathbf{v}_0\,\mathbf{f}_0]dt}{2c^2}, \tag{102}$$

(aside from negligible quantities introduced by the Lorentz transformation of the time). The resting observer will conclude, applying the transformation (97) in the reverse direction, that $\mathbf{s}$ has rotated an amount $d\mathbf{A}$ with respect to R. Now $d\mathbf{A}$ is expressed in terms of the field strengths $\mathbf{E}_0$ and $\mathbf{H}_0$. We proceed to express it in terms of $\mathbf{E}$ and $\mathbf{H}$, as measured in R. To a sufficient approximation, the transformation equations are

$$\mathbf{E}_0 = k_0 \left(\mathbf{E} + \frac{[\mathbf{vH}]}{c} \right), \mathbf{H}_0 = k_0 \left(\mathbf{H} - \frac{[\mathbf{vE}]}{c} \right), \tag{103}$$

in accord with the explanation given in Appendix VIII. Using equations (100), (101), and (103), we obtain

$$\frac{d\mathbf{A}}{dt} = \frac{e}{mc} \left\{ \mathbf{H} - \frac{k_0}{1 + k_0} \frac{[\mathbf{vE}]}{c} \right\} \cong \frac{e}{mc} \left\{ \mathbf{H} - \frac{[\mathbf{vE}]}{2c} \right\}. \tag{104}$$

The first term gives the Larmor precession of the electron in an external field $\mathbf{H}$. If $\mathbf{H} = 0$, $|d\mathbf{A}/dt|$ reduces to the value ω of equation (81).

In conclusion, we must point out that Dirac[1] has developed a more general theory of the electron. According to his conceptions it behaves like a spinning body only under certain simple circumstances. However, this does not affect any of the applications we shall make.

19. REVISED SELECTION PRINCIPLES FOR HYDROGEN

In Sec. 7, we stated that the selection principles for a hydrogenic atom are $\Delta j = \pm 1$ or 0; $\Delta k = \pm 1$. The introduction of the spinning electron makes it necessary to distinguish between k and j, and therefore new components are predicted in the fine structure of hydrogen and

[1] *Proc. Roy. Soc.*, **117**, 610 and **118**, 351 (1928).

ionized helium lines. Even before the advent of the spinning electron this revision was suggested by Slater[1] and by Sommerfeld and Unsöld,[2] independently.

As an illustration, we shall consider the fine structures predicted for $H\alpha$ by the two theories. Let us compare Fig. 9 with a similar energy diagram constructed in the same way as Fig. 23 with the aid of both relativity and spin corrections. This diagram is shown in Fig. 25. Levels which correspond to two configurations of the atom are shown slightly separated for the sake of ease in listing the various possible transitions, although they are actually coincident. Three quantum numbers n, l, and j (or s) are now required to determine a quantum state, and the values of these numbers are shown on the right of each level. In discussing X-ray levels it is convenient to use the symbol n_{k_1,k_2} where k_1 is identical with the azimuthal number k. These symbols are

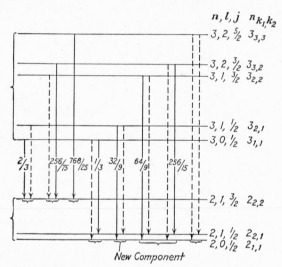

Fig. 25.—Fine structure of $H\alpha$ on the spinning electron theory.

also shown in the diagram. The transitions allowed by both selection principles are shown by full lines while those which are forbidden by one or both of the principles are indicated by dotted lines. Whereas the lowest initial level was formerly assigned the azimuthal number $k = 1$, it now consists of two coincident levels for which $k = 2$ or 1. The transition from 3, 1, ½ to 2, 0, ½ is allowed, and furnishes a new component. Similarly, a jump from 3, 2, ¾ to 2, 1, ¾ yields a new line. The relative intensities of the permitted transitions as predicted by wave mechanics are given by the numbers placed on the arrows. We are now in a position to compare these predictions with experiment.

[1] *Proc. Nat. Acad. Sci.*, **11**, 732 (1925).

[2] *Z. Physik*, **36**, 259 and **38**, 237 (1926).

Only one of the new components, namely, 3, 1, $\frac{1}{2}$ → 2, 0, $\frac{1}{2}$, is far enough from its nearest neighbor to give us hope of detecting it. As a matter of fact, experiments which are not inconsistent with the existence of this component have been made by Hansen,[1] Kent, Taylor and Pearson,[2] and W. V. Houston.[3] The results of Kent and his colleagues will be discussed here. Density measurements of plates showing the Hα doublet were made with the aid of a microphotometer. One of the curves showing density as a function of wave length is reproduced in Fig. 26, with wave lengths increasing toward the right. The amplitude of the original microphotometer curve for the peak of shorter wave length was about 15 cm. The asymmetry of the shorter component is attributed to the existence of the faint line at c', predicted by the spinning electron theory. Houston's curves are similar.

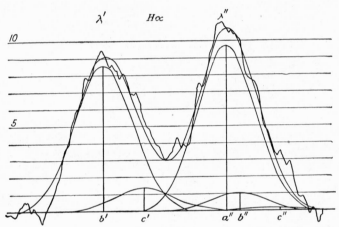

Fig. 26.—Microphotometer curves showing structure of Hα.   (*After Kent.*)

The new theory predicts additional components of other Balmer lines. On the basis of the older selection principle we should expect each Balmer line to consist of three components, corresponding to the changes 3 → 2, 1 → 2, and 2 → 1 of the azimuthal number k. The separation between the first two components should be very small compared with their distance from the third, and should approach zero as we pass to higher series members, because the spread of the n-quantum terms decreases as n grows larger. All the lines should appear as doublets with separations which approach 0.365 cm.$^{-1}$ for the higher series members. The changes predicted by the new theory are not so prominent as in the case of Hα. Kent, Taylor, and Pearson have obtained density curves for Hβ and Hγ. In the case of Hβ, these favor the new theory

[1] *Ann. Physik*, **78**, 558 (1925).

[2] *Phys. Rev.*, **30**, 266 (1927).

[3] *Astrophys. J.* **64**, 81 (1926); *Phys. Rev.*, **30**, 608 (1927).

but the data for Hγ do not permit any definite conclusions. The slight increase in width on the wave number scale as we pass to higher series members is borne out by the data.

The measurement of these small doublet differences is beset with many sources of error which have been successively discovered and eliminated by a number of careful investigators. Kent and his colleagues give references to the older literature. To show the status of the subject, we list the results of five recent investigations, giving the separations in milli-Angstroms. Below, the mean values of the separations are compared with those obtained with the aid of theoretical intensity computations.

Observers	Hα	Hβ	Hγ
SHRUM and JANICKI, *Ann. Physik*, **76**, 561 (1925)...	130	76	60
HANSEN (*loc. cit.*)............................	135–8	75	62
JANICKI and LAU, *Z. Physik*, **35**, 1 (1925).........	132	72	59
HOUSTON (*loc. cit.*)............................	135.8	78.2	66.5
KENT, TAYLOR, and PEARSON (*loc. cit.*)...........	137.0	79.1	66.6
Means..	134.5	76.1	62.8
Observed means in cm.$^{-1}$......................	0.313	0.322	0.334
Predicted means:			
Old theory....................................	0.328	0.350	0.357
Spinning electron theory.......................	0.320	0.345	0.354

More definite evidence in favor of the new selection principles can be obtained from the lines of ionized helium, as Slater pointed out (*loc. cit.*). Referring to Fig. 11, we may note the following alterations: On the new theory, Ib, IIc and IIId are allowed, though previously forbidden. In fact IIc and IIId can each arise in two ways. IIb, IId, and IIIc each have two possibilities of realization as against one before. Most of these changes are not amenable to test by the aid of Fig. 11, but the presence of IIId in considerable strength is favorable to the new selection principles. Previously, its presence was explained by assuming an external electric field.

20. SUGGESTED CORRECTIONS OF THE HYDROGEN ENERGY LEVELS

The evidence in favor of equation (36) obtained from the H and He$^+$-spectra, interpreted with the aid of the correct selection principles, may be considered fairly conclusive. Various refinements and modifications of equation (36) have been proposed. The alteration of E due to possible asphericity of the nucleus was thoroughly discussed by Silberstein[1] who obtained a result applicable to any rigid axially symmetrical nucleus. To explain the fine structures of the Balmer lines and the lines of He on such a basis it is necessary to assume a nucleus whose dimensions are of the order of $2 \cdot 10^{-11}$ cm. Even then it is difficult to force the data into the frame provided by the theory. H. A. Wilson[2]

[1] *Phil. Mag.*, **39**, 46 (1919); *Proc. Roy. Soc.*, A, **98**, 1 (1920).

[2] *Astrophys. J.*, **56**, 34 (1922).

suggested that the potential energy of the atom should be regarded as distributed through the space surrounding it, so that this energy (endowed with mass in the sense of the theory of relativity) will partake of the motion of the electron. This theory predicts shifts of the spectrum lines which are too large to escape detection, but which have not been observed. H. S. Allen[1] calculated the correction due to a nuclear magnetic moment for the case of circular orbits. His results were extended to elliptical orbits by Ruark.[2] The calculation unfortunately is in error, but a reconsideration of the question shows that the final result is of the correct order of magnitude. The conclusion drawn was that experiment decides against the existence of a nuclear moment as large as one Bohr magneton. This is in agreement with our present belief that the moment of the nucleus is $\sim m/M_H$ Bohr magnetons. In the same paper, effects due to a possible asphericity of the electron are discussed, and all the above corrections are shown to be in disagreement with experiment.

There is a slight error in the relativistic quantization presented in Sec. 5. The motion of the nucleus is neglected, and cannot be taken into account by modifications similar to those used in the classical calculations, because in special relativity the theorems concerning the motion of the center of mass break down, and are replaced by equations which are so complicated as to be useless. Then too, retarded potentials and magnetic forces due to the translational motion of electron and nucleus have not been used in our derivations. All these defects were remedied by Darwin.[3] Schwarzschild[4] showed that the equations of motion of a charged particle in an electromagnetic field can be put in the Lagrangian form if we use for L an expression given in Appendix VIII. Darwin generalized this result for any number of particles, obtaining a Lagrangian function which is symmetrical in the coordinates and angles characteristic of each particle. He then applied this Lagrangian to the case of two bodies, and found that the term in parentheses in equation (36) should be modified to read

$$\frac{n}{k} - \frac{3}{4} + \frac{1}{4}\frac{Mm}{(M+m)^2}.$$

The last term is too small to detect in visible spectra, and in X-ray spectra other terms arise which mask its effect.

References

Extensive references on hydrogenic spectra are given in van Vleck's " Bulletin, " p. 67.

[1] *Phil. Mag.*, **29**, 40 and 714 (1915).
[2] *Astrophys. J.*, **58**, 46 (1923).
[3] *Phil. Mag.*, **39**, 537 (1920).
[4] *Göttinger Nachrichten* (1903).

CHAPTER VI

GENERAL THEOREMS OF THE OLDER QUANTUM THEORY

Most of the general theorems of the older quantum theory must be modified in the light of the new quantum mechanics, and it might seem that they are now of little value. However, they are often very useful in giving hints as to the solution of problems in the new mechanics, for Bohr's theory is a first approximation to wave dynamics, and they form a necessary background for reading papers which appeared prior to 1925. Orbital models, both atomic and molecular, as treated by ordinary dynamics, give concrete mental pictures which are very valuable in thinking about atomic systems, though exact relations must be secured from mathematical formulas of quite another kind. A number of theorems based on the Bohr theory will be presented in this chapter.

1. CLASSICAL THEORY OF LIGHT EMISSION

We begin with a study of the light emitted by a conditionally periodic system (Chap. IV, Sec. **13**) on the classical theory. As stated in Chap. I, Sec. **4**, it is assumed that the emission frequencies are identical with those occurring in the various terms of the Fourier series representing the coordinates of the charged particles in the atom.

As shown in Appendix VIII, electromagnetic theory requires that the instantaneous rate at which an accelerated charge radiates energy shall be

$$\frac{-dE}{dt} = \frac{2e^2 \dot{\mathbf{v}}^2}{3c^3}, \tag{1}$$

where $\dot{\mathbf{v}}$ is the vector acceleration and c the velocity of light. For a harmonic oscillator, $x = A_x \cos (2\pi\omega t + \delta_x)$, ω being the frequency, and

$$\ddot{x} = -A_x (2\pi\omega)^2 \cos (2\pi\omega t + \delta_x). \tag{2}$$

There are similar expressions for the y- and z-components of acceleration and

$$\dot{v}^2 = \ddot{x}^2 + \ddot{y}^2 + \ddot{z}^2,$$

so that equation (1) becomes

$$\frac{-dE}{dt} = \left(\frac{2e^2}{3c^3}\right)(2\pi\omega)^4[A_x{}^2 \cos^2 (2\pi\omega t + \delta_x)$$
$$+ A_y{}^2 \cos^2 (2\pi\omega t + \delta_y) + A_z{}^2 \cos^2 (2\pi\omega t + \delta_z)]. \tag{3}$$

The average rate of emission by the oscillator is

$$\frac{-\overline{dE}}{dt} = \left(\frac{e^2}{3c^3}\right)(2\pi\omega)^4(A_x{}^2 + A_y{}^2 + A_z{}^2), \tag{4}$$

for the time average of the cosine squared is $\frac{1}{2}$.

A similar result is obtained for a conditionally periodic system having the fundamental frequencies $\omega_1, \ldots \omega_n$. By the methods of Chap. IV it is possible to express the coordinates of a particle in such a system as functions of the canonical variables, the J's and w's; the former are constants and the latter linear functions of the time of the form,

$$w_k = \omega_k t + \frac{\delta_k}{2\pi} \tag{5}$$

where ω_k is the frequency of oscillation of the kth coordinate and δ_k is a phase quantity. In general, a coordinate will be represented by a multiple Fourier series containing the w's only as arguments of the sine and cosine terms and having coefficients which are functions of the J's; thus

$$q_k = \Sigma A_{\tau_1}, \cdots \tau_s, k \cos 2\pi[(\tau_1\omega_1 + \cdots \tau_s\omega_s)t + (\delta_1 + \cdots \delta_s)_k], \tag{6}$$

where each τ ranges over all integer values from $-\infty$ to $+\infty$, *subject to the restriction that* $\tau_1\omega_1 +$ *etc. must be positive.* We shall usually employ the following abbreviations:

$$A_{\tau_1} \cdots \tau_s, k = A_{\tau,k}; \; (\delta_1 + \cdots \delta_s)_k = \Sigma\delta_k; \; \tau_1\omega_1 + \cdots$$
$$+ \tau_s\omega_s = \Sigma\tau\omega, \tag{7}$$

so that

$$q_k = \Sigma A_{\tau,k} \cos (2\pi\Sigma\tau\omega t + \Sigma\delta_k). \tag{8}$$

Then,

$$x = \Sigma A_{\tau,x} \cos (2\pi\Sigma\tau\omega t + \Sigma\delta_x), \tag{9}$$

and

$$\ddot{x} = -\Sigma A_{\tau,x}(2\pi\Sigma\tau\omega)^2 \cos (2\pi\Sigma\tau\omega t + \Sigma\delta_x) \tag{10}$$

and there are similar expressions for the y- and z-components. Inspection of equation (10) shows that $\ddot{x}^2$ contains squared terms of the form

$$A_{\tau,x}^2(2\pi\Sigma\tau\omega)^4 \cos^2 (2\pi\Sigma\tau\omega t + \Sigma\delta_x)$$

and cross-product terms of the form.

$$A_{\tau',x}A_{\tau',x}(2\pi\Sigma\tau\omega)^2(2\pi\Sigma\tau'\omega)^2 \cos (2\pi\Sigma\tau\omega t + \Sigma\delta_x) \cos (2\pi\Sigma\tau'\omega t + \Sigma\delta'_x),$$

which give rise to rapid fluctuations of the rate of radiation. Similar terms will occur in $\ddot{y}^2$ and $\ddot{z}^2$. The mean value of each squared term in equation (10) is equal to one-half its coefficient, while that of each cross-product term is zero. Therefore, the mean rate of radiation by an accelerated charged particle is

$$\frac{-\overline{dE}}{dt} = \left(\frac{2e^2}{3c^3}\right)\sum_\tau \frac{1}{2}(A_{\tau,x}^2 + A_{\tau,y}^2 + A_{\tau,z}^2)(2\pi\Sigma\tau\omega)^4. \tag{11}$$

This represents the simultaneous radiation of a number of frequencies of the form $\tau_1\omega_1 + \cdots + \tau_s\omega_s$. The rate at which energy is carried away by one of these is given by the corresponding term in the summation of equation (11).

If the system contains several charged particles, equation (1) is replaced by

$$-\frac{dE}{dt} = \frac{2\ddot{P}^2}{3c^3},$$ (12)

where $\mathbf{P}$ is the electric moment vector of the atom, whose components are

$$P_x = \sum_{i=1}^{i=n} e_i x_i, \; P_y = \sum_{i=1}^{i=n} e_i y_i, \; P_z = \sum_{i=1}^{i=n} e_i z_i.$$ (13)

The summations extend over all the particles of the system with due regard to the signs of the charges $e_1, \ldots e_n$. Just as before, we express the function $\mathbf{P}^2$ as a multiple Fourier series in order to obtain the rate of emission of light of a given frequency, obtaining

$$-\frac{\overline{dE}}{dt} = \left(\frac{1}{3c^3}\right)\sum_{\tau}(P_{\tau,x}^2 + P_{\tau,y}^2 + P_{\tau,z}^2)(2\pi\Sigma\tau\omega)^4.$$ (14)

Usually, it is convenient to use exponential notation in dealing with multiple Fourier series. In place of equation (8), we write

$$q_k = \Sigma C_{\tau,k} \exp 2\pi i \Sigma\tau\omega t,$$ (8a)

where *the τ's now take all integral values both positive and negative.* The two terms,

$$C_{\tau,k} \exp 2\pi i \Sigma\tau\omega t + C_{-\tau,k} \exp 2\pi i \Sigma(-\tau\omega)t,$$

must be identical with

$$A_{\tau,k} \cos (2\pi\Sigma\tau\omega t + \Sigma\delta_k)$$

which is a real quantity. This will be the case if

$$2C_{\tau,k} = A_{\tau,k} \exp i\Sigma\delta_k, \; 2C_{-\tau,k} = A_{\tau,k} \exp - i\Sigma\delta_k.$$ (15)

In place of equation (9), we write

$$x = \Sigma C_{\tau,x} \exp 2\pi i \Sigma\tau\omega t.$$ (9a)

Then

$$\ddot{x} = - \Sigma C_{\tau,x}(2\pi\Sigma\tau\omega)^2 \exp 2\pi i \Sigma\tau\omega t,$$ (16)

and

$$\ddot{x}^2 = \sum_{\tau}\sum_{\tau'}C_{\tau,x}C_{\tau',x}(2\pi\Sigma\tau\omega)^2(2\pi\Sigma\tau'\omega)^2 \exp 2\pi i \Sigma(\tau + \tau')\omega t.$$

The average of each exponential term is zero unless $\tau = -\tau'$, which means $\tau_1 = -\tau_1', \cdots, \tau_s = -\tau_s'$. Thus, the double summation reduces to a single summation, and, since there are two terms with frequency $\Sigma\tau\omega$ in equation (8a), we finally get,

$$-\frac{\overline{dE}}{dt} = \frac{2e^2}{3c^3}\sum_{\tau}2(C_{\tau,x}C_{-\tau,x} + C_{\tau,y}C_{-\tau,y} + C_{\tau,z}C_{-\tau,z})(2\pi\Sigma\tau\omega)^4,$$ (17)

which, by using the relations in equation (15), is found to be identical with equation (11). In equation (17), τ runs only from $+1$ to $+\infty$.

2. THE CORRESPONDENCE THEOREM AND THE CORRESPONDENCE PRINCIPLES

We have seen that on the classical theory each atom simultaneously emits all its spectral lines. In the absence of definite quantum conditions the amplitude of a given harmonic in the motion might vary from atom to atom. If a light source were actually made up of a vast number of atoms radiating in this fashion, the intensity of a spectral line of frequency ω would be proportional to

$$\frac{(2\pi\omega)^4 e^2 \Sigma A^2}{3c^3},\tag{18}$$

where A is the amplitude of the corresponding harmonic in the motion of a typical atom, and the summation sign now indicates addition of the contributions of all atoms. (We add *intensities* because the atoms radiate with random phases.) Therefore,

$$i = \frac{(2\pi\omega)^4 e^2 \overline{A^2}}{3c^3},\tag{19}$$

where i is the intensity per atom and $\overline{A^2}$ is the average squared amplitude of the harmonic of frequency ω.

On the Bohr theory the picture is quite different. The emission frequencies are not usually identical with those assumed to be present in the motion of the charged particles. Further, the intensity is calculated on the basis of a radically different mechanism. An atomic system remains in a steady state without radiating energy for some finite length of time and then radiates one quantum, presumably in a very short time, after which it remains in the state of lower energy for a finite time without radiating or absorbing additional energy. The time an atom remains in an excited state is, in the absence of a radiation field, governed by a probability which depends only on the internal structure of the atom in the two steady states. Einstein represents this probability by A_{12} and thus the rate of emission of light per atom by a gas containing N_1 atoms in the higher state will be

$$-\frac{h\nu}{N_1}\frac{dN_1}{dt} = -\frac{dE}{dt} = h\nu A_{12}.\tag{20}$$

In spite of these differences, it is possible and extremely useful to trace a correspondence between the frequencies and amplitudes of orbital models and those of the light they emit. This is especially true in the region of large quantum numbers and small changes of the quantum numbers—which usually means that we are dealing with large wave lengths—for in this region both the exact wave mechanics and the Bohr theory yield frequencies which approach those of classical theory. Bohr's derivation of the Balmer formula (Chap. V, Sec. 2) is an excellent illustration. As regards intensities, the *statistical formulas* of Bohr theory approach those of classical theory in this region. For example, the

Rayleigh-Jeans formula for the distribution of intensity in the spectrum of a black body agrees with Planck's formula in the region of great wave lengths, and the values of equations (19) and (20) approach equality. There is no implication that the mechanism of emission from an individual atom merges into that of classical theory.

While it is customary to speak of the complex of facts associated with this asymptotic agreement as the Bohr correspondence principle, it is important to state accurately the various hypotheses and theorems which are involved, as van Vleck has done in "Quantum Principles and Line Spectra." We shall discuss this subject under three headings—the correspondence theorem for frequencies, the correspondence hypothesis for intensities, and the correspondence hypothesis for polarization.

3. THE CORRESPONDENCE THEOREM FOR FREQUENCIES

Consider an atomic system which passes from a state characterized by the quantum integrals,

$$J_1' = n_1'h, \quad \cdots \quad J_s' = n_s'h, \tag{21}$$

to a state for which these integrals take the values,

$$J_1'' = n_1''h, \quad \cdots \quad J_s'' = n_s''h. \tag{22}$$

The frequency emitted in the transition is given by the frequency condition,

$$h\nu(n', n'') = E(J_1', \cdots J_n') - E(J_1'' \cdots J_n'') = \Delta E \tag{23}$$

while by Sec. 1 and Chap. IV, Sec. 13, the classical frequencies appearing in the Fourier expansion of the motion of the charged particles and emitted according to electromagnetic theory are

$$\omega_\tau = \Sigma\tau\omega = \tau_1\frac{\partial E}{\partial J_1} + \tau_2\frac{\partial E}{\partial J_2} + \cdots + \tau_s\frac{\partial E}{\partial J_s}. \tag{24}$$

If the quantum numbers involved are large and the changes of the quantum numbers are small, we have

$$h\nu(n', n'') = \Delta E \cong \frac{\partial E}{\partial J_1}\Delta J_1 + \frac{\partial E}{\partial J_2}\Delta J_2 + \cdots \frac{\partial E}{\partial J_s}\Delta J_s. \tag{25}$$

Setting

$$\Delta J_1 = (n_1' - n_1'')h, \Delta J_2 = (n_2' - n_2'')h, \cdots \Delta J_s = (n_s' - n_s'')h,$$

gives

$$\nu(n', n'') \cong \omega_1(n_1' - n_1'') + \omega_2(n_2' - n_2'') + \cdots \omega_s(n_s' - n_s''), \tag{26}$$

and this is equal to $\Sigma\tau\omega$ of equation (24), if

$$\tau_1 = n_1' - n_1'', \tau_2 = n_2' - n_2'', \cdots \tau_s = n_s' - n_s''. \tag{27}$$

The quantum frequency, determined by equation (26), approaches asymptotically to the classical frequency, $\Sigma\tau\omega$, for which the τ's are given by equation (27). The frequencies $\nu(n', n'')$ and $\Sigma\tau\omega$ related in this way are said to be *corresponding frequencies*.

Regardless of the magnitude of the quantum numbers and their changes, the quantum frequency is a mean value of the frequency in equation (24) averaged over all intermediate orbits in such a way that the J's vary linearly from the one state to the other. To prove this let

$$J_k = n_k''h + \lambda(n_k' - n_k'')h, \quad dJ_k = h(n_k' - n_k'')d\lambda, \tag{28}$$

where λ is a quantity which increases from 0 to 1. Then the mean value sought for is $\displaystyle\int_{\lambda=0}^{\lambda=1} \Sigma\omega\tau d\lambda$, but using equations (24) and (27) this takes the form,

$$\int_{\lambda=0}^{\lambda=1} \left(\frac{\partial E}{\partial J_1}(n_1' - n_1'') + \cdots \frac{\partial E}{\partial J_s}(n_s' - n_s'') \right)d\lambda.$$

Substituting from equation (28) this becomes

$$\frac{1}{h}\int_{\lambda=0}^{\lambda=1} \left(\frac{\partial E}{\partial J_1}dJ_1 + \cdots \frac{\partial E}{\partial J_s}dJ_s \right) = \frac{E' - E''}{h} = \nu(n',n''), \tag{29}$$

which is the correspondence theorem for frequencies.

4. THE CORRESPONDENCE PRINCIPLE FOR INTENSITIES

The correspondence principle for intensities is not a theorem, but a postulate, which may be stated as follows:

In the region of high quantum numbers and small changes of the quantum numbers, the rate of emission per atom approaches the value given by the classical formulas. That is, if we compute the frequencies and amplitudes of the various harmonics in the motion of the atom in either the initial or the final state, and substitute them in equations (11) or (13), a correct result is obtained. The frequencies and amplitudes in both states are nearly equal because of the restriction to high quantum numbers and small quantum number changes. Therefore, equating the right member of equation (20) to the corresponding term in the right member of equation (14) and substituting for $\Sigma\tau\omega$ its approximate value ν we have

$$h\nu A_{12} \cong \frac{(2\pi\nu)^4}{3c^3}(P_{\tau,x}{}^2 + P_{\tau,y}{}^2 + P_{\tau,z}{}^2) \tag{30}$$

for the relation between the probability constant A_{12} and the Fourier coefficients $P_{\tau,x}$, $P_{\tau,y}$, $P_{\tau,z}$ belonging to the terms of corresponding frequency in the components of the electric moment P. Knowing A_{12}, it is possible to calculate the coefficients of induced emission and absorption by the relations $A_{12}/B_{12} = 8\pi h\nu^3/c^3$ and $p_1B_{12} = p_2B_{21}$, derived in Chap. III, Sec. **4.** When the attempt is made to extend the relation in equation (30) to the region of small quantum numbers, it is necessary to use some means of averaging the amplitudes of the corresponding harmonics. Almost without exception, the various suggestions made prior to 1926 as to the proper type of average failed to yield results in agreement with experiment, so we shall not discuss them here in extenso.

However, there is a very important special case in which exact results are obtained. If the classical Fourier coefficient of a certain harmonic is zero, both for the initial and final states, then we may expect that the probability of spontaneous transition between these two states will also be zero and light of the corresponding frequency will be neither emitted nor absorbed. This gives a method of deriving the selection rules for spectral lines, which are only special cases of the more general problem of relative intensities.

5. THE CORRESPONDENCE PRINCIPLE FOR POLARIZATION

This principle is a postulate, due to Bohr, which states that for high quantum numbers and small changes of the numbers, light of a given frequency ν has the polarization predicted by classical theory for the corresponding frequency $\Sigma\tau\omega$. For example, consider the emission of a group of atoms all of which are similarly oriented, as in the Zeeman effect. The amplitudes of the electric vector parallel to the x-, y-, and z-axes for a certain spectral line are proportional to $P_{\tau,x}$, $P_{\tau,y}$ and $P_{\tau,z}$. Further, the phases of the x- and y-components are such that we observe circular polarization in the longitudinal Zeeman pattern.

6. THE SELECTION PRINCIPLES FOR k AND j

Let r and φ be the coordinates of an electron moving in a central field of force. Because the force field is symmetrical about a center, each loop of the orbit will be similar to every other loop (Fig. 7, Chap. V). The motion may therefore be described as a periodic motion in a closed orbit with frequency ω_r, upon which a uniform rotation is superposed, such that in the time of one complete oscillation from maximum r to minimum r and back again, the orbit is carried forward by an amount equal to the actual advance of its aphelion point per revolution. Let the angular velocity of this rotation be $2\pi\omega_\varphi$. Then, in a system of coordinates x', y', rotating with this angular velocity, any coordinate is expressible as a Fourier series of the type $\Sigma A_\tau \cos (2\pi\tau\omega_r t + \delta_\tau)$. Now if $\alpha = 2\pi\omega_\varphi t$, then

$$x = x' \cos \alpha - y' \sin \alpha,$$
$$y = x' \sin \alpha + y' \cos \alpha.$$

which may be written for purposes of easy computation in the form

$$x + iy = (x' + iy') \exp (2\pi i\omega_\varphi t).$$

But

$$x' + iy' = \Sigma D_\tau \exp (2\pi i\tau\omega_r t),$$

and so,

$$x + iy = \Sigma D_\tau \exp [2\pi i(\tau\omega_r + \omega_\varphi)t]. \tag{31}$$

Similarly,

$$x - iy = \Sigma E_\tau \exp [2\pi i(\tau\omega_r - \omega_\varphi)t]. \tag{32}$$

We may add these equations to get x, and subtract the second from the first to get y. When this is done, we see that both x and y contain terms with the frequencies $\tau\omega_r \pm \omega_\varphi$.[1] Since ω_φ appears only with the coefficients ± 1, we conclude in accordance with the assumption of Sec. 4 that the azimuthal number changes only by ± 1. On the other hand, τ can take any value whatsoever and therefore the changes of the radial quantum number are unrestricted. The above argument is valid only when the electron moves on a plane orbit. If its interaction with the remainder of the atom causes the motion to be of a more complex kind, we expect a breakdown of the selection principle.

The selection principle for the inner quantum number is derivable in much the same fashion for an atom with one valence electron. The resultant angular momentum vector $jh/2\pi$ is composed of the contributions $kh/2\pi$ arising from the orbital motion and $sh/2\pi$ due to electron spin. These two vectors must precess around their resultant, which is fixed in magnitude and direction, and it can be shown (Chap. X, Sec. 14) that this precession is uniform, that is, the orbital plane precesses around the direction of j. Just as before, we obtain the Fourier expansions of the electronic coordinates, and find that the precessional frequency ω appears with the coefficients ± 1 or 0, and these alone. The conclusion is that Δj can be ± 1 or 0, for it can be shown that the quantum integral jh is the momentum variable conjugate to $2\pi\omega$. However, a more general proof requiring no detailed knowledge of the atomic motions is the following:

To describe the position of the pth electron let us use cylindrical coordinates r_p, z_p, φ_p, where z_p is the distance of the electron from the invariable plane perpendicular to the vector j, and φ_p is its azimuth in that plane. Then we can arrange that one of the φ's (say φ_1) shall not appear in the expression for the energy; for the φ's do not occur in the kinetic energy and the potential energy depends only on the *relative* azimuths $\Phi_2 = \varphi_2 - \varphi_1$, $\Phi_3 = \varphi_3 - \varphi_1$, etc. We take φ and these relative azimuths as new coordinates. The kinetic energy is

$$T = \tfrac{1}{2}[m_1 r_1{}^2 \dot{\varphi}_1{}^2 + \cdots] \tag{33}$$
$$= \tfrac{1}{2}[m_1 r_1{}^2 \dot{\varphi}_1{}^2 + m_2 r_2{}^2(\dot{\Phi}_2 + \dot{\varphi}_1)^2 + \cdots]$$

and

$$\frac{\partial T}{\partial \dot{\varphi}_1} = m_1 r_1{}^2 \dot{\varphi}_1 + m_2 r_2{}^2(\dot{\Phi}_2 + \dot{\varphi}_1) + \cdots$$
$$= m_1 r_1{}^2 \dot{\varphi}_1 + m_2 r_2{}^2 \dot{\varphi}_2 + \cdots ,$$

for the partial differentiation is carried out holding the Φ's constant. We see now that $\partial T/\partial \dot{\varphi}_1$, the momentum conjugate to φ_1, is the total angular momentum, which takes the quantized value $jh/2\pi$. Now,

$$x_p + iy_p = r_p \exp i\varphi_p = r_p \exp i\varphi_1 \exp i\Phi_p \tag{34}$$

---

[1] Alternatively we could prove this without the use of imaginaries by using the relation $2 \cos a \cos b = \cos (a + b) + \cos (a - b)$, and similar trigonometric formulas. An excellent alternative discussion is given in VAN VLECK's "Bulletin," p. 294.

where x and y are coordinates taken in the invariable plane. If P_x and P_y are components of the electric moment, we have

$$P_x + iP_y = \exp i\varphi_1 \cdot F(\Phi, r) \tag{35}$$
$$P_z = G(\Phi, r).$$

The functions F and G can be expressed as Fourier series which do not contain φ_1. Thus, P_x and P_y contain sine and cosine terms with arguments of the type

$$2\pi(\Sigma\tau\omega t \pm \varphi_1),$$

in which φ_1 has the coefficient $+1$ or -1. On the other hand, φ_1 does not occur in P_z. We conclude that Δj may take the values ± 1 or 0, and these only. As to polarization, the terms of a given frequency in P_x and P_y have phases and amplitudes such that they represent a circular motion in the xy plane, while each term in P_z represents a vibration parallel to the z-axis. By the correspondence principle for polarization, we conclude that *quantum transitions in which $\Delta j = \pm 1$ give rise to circularly polarized light with its oscillation plane parallel to the invariable plane, while those in which $\Delta j = 0$ give rise to light linearly polarized perpendicular to that plane.*

Enough has been said to illustrate the spirit of the correspondence principle in its application to the derivation of selection rules. Other examples will be given throughout the text, as the necessity arises.

7. THE ADIABATIC PRINCIPLE

We have emphasized the fact that after a transient disturbance has passed over an atomic system it will be found in a quantized state, in contradiction with classical mechanics. Similarly, if an external field of force is established and is then maintained at a steady value, the atom is still in an allowed state. This fact imposes certain restrictions on the quantum conditions. The energy of an atom depends on the charges and masses of its constituent particles, and on the strength of any external fields of force which may be present. Any quantity of this kind which is treated as a constant in solving the equations of motion will be called a "parameter." The parameters c_1, c_2, . . . will appear in the quantum conditions, which will therefore be of the form

$$F_1(c_1, c_2, \cdots) = n_1 h,$$
$$F_2(c_1, c_2, \cdots) = n_2 h, \tag{36}$$

and so on. If the parameters are very slowly changed, the left members of these equations retain their values because the system is in a state characterized by the same quantum numbers. Since this is true for any alterations of the c's, we must have

$$\frac{\partial F_1}{\partial c_i} = 0, \quad \frac{\partial F_2}{\partial c_i} = 0, \text{ etc.,} \tag{37}$$

where c_i is any one of the c's.   In other words, the functions F which appear in the quantum conditions must be invariant during changes of the kind described.

In general, as we said above, classical mechanics does not predict that the atom will be in a quantized state after a disturbance, but under special circumstances now to be explained the changes in its motion can be calculated with the aid of the usual equations.   Consider a quantized atom which is *not degenerate*, that is, the fundamental frequencies in its motion are all distinct, and are equal in number to the number of degrees of freedom.   We change its condition *infinitely slowly* and in a way not systematically correlated with the motion of the system, either by altering the strength of an external field of force, or by changing the internal constitution of the system, at least in imagination if not in actuality.   For example, we may suppose the charge on the nucleus of the H atom is increased to $+2e$, or we may alter the distance between nuclei in a diatomic molecule.

It can be proved that *the new state of the system is the quantized state appropriate to the new values of the parameters, such as the external field, and the quantum numbers are the same as those of the original system.*

This is the principle of slow mechanical transformability introduced by Ehrenfest[1] and called by him the adiabatic hypothesis because of thermodynamic applications which he made.   It is not an hypothesis however, but a definite theorem.

Proof.—The following demonstration is essentially due to Burgers.[2]   It employs straightforward methods to find an expression for the change of each quantum integral J when the atom is disturbed, and to show that this change is zero.   Let the Hamiltonian function of the system be $H(q, p, c)$ where c is a parameter which we intend to vary.   Holding c constant, we transform to the angle variables w and the associated momentum variables J.   Instead of making the transformation function W a function of the q's and J's, as we did in Chap. IV, Sec. **9**, we give it the form $W(q, w, t)$.   Then, an argument exactly like that in Chap. IV gives us the relations between the old and new variables and the form of the new Hamiltonian function, $\overline{H}$.   They are,

$$p_k = \frac{\partial W}{\partial q_k}, \quad J_k = -\frac{\partial W}{\partial w_k}, \quad \overline{H} = H + \frac{\partial W}{\partial t}. \tag{38}$$

The new equations of motion tell us that

$$\frac{dJ_k}{dt} = -\frac{\partial \overline{H}}{\partial w_k} = -\frac{\partial H}{\partial w_k} - \frac{\partial}{\partial w_k}\left(\frac{\partial W}{\partial t}\right). \tag{39}$$

When forming $\partial W/\partial t$ in equations (38) and (39), W must be written as a function of q, w, and t; but we must then transform $\partial W/\partial t$ into a function of w, J, and t, before carrying out the differentiation with respect to w_k; for in the new Hamilton equations, $\overline{H}$ must be written in terms of w and J.   As long as c is constant $dJ_k/dt = 0$, because W is so chosen that the J's will be constant, and the quantum conditions state that $J_k = n_k h$.   But when c is allowed to vary, the system is no longer conservative and the

[1] *Ann. Physik*, **36**, 91 (1911).

[2] Dissertation, Leiden, 1919.

situation is changed.   To compute the change in one of the J's, we note that H, the energy, is independent of the w's, and so

$$J_k = -\frac{\partial}{\partial w_k}\left(\frac{\partial W}{\partial c}\frac{dc}{dt}\right). \tag{40}$$

The change in J_k in a specified time interval, very long compared with any period of the system, will be

$$\Delta J_k = -\int \frac{\partial}{\partial w_k}\left(\frac{\partial W}{\partial c}\frac{dc}{dt}\right)dt. \tag{41}$$

It was stated above that the change in c must be quite unsystematic.   That is, we must not apply the increments in any definite relation to the phases of the atomic motion, as we would in starting a swing by appropriate pushes at the moments when it comes to rest.   This condition will be satisfied, for example, if we give dc/dt a constant value.   With this understanding, ΔJ_k will be of the same order of magnitude as the quantity

$$\frac{\overline{dc}}{dt}\int \frac{\partial}{\partial w_k}\left(\frac{\partial W}{\partial c}\right)dt, \tag{41a}$$

where $\overline{dc/dt}$ is an average value of dc/dt.   Now $\partial W/\partial c$ can be represented by a multiple Fourier series containing the w's, and so the integrand in equation $(41a)$ is a similar series without a constant term.   This is the essential point in the proof, for it means that the integral always remains below a certain finite value.   Thus it is possible to make ΔJ_k as small as we please by decreasing the rate of variation of c.   Special attention must be paid to the restriction that the system must not become degenerate.   If it were to happen at some stage of the process, that the frequencies obeyed a relation of the type,

$$\tau_1\omega_1 + \cdots + \tau_n\omega_n = 0,$$

the τ's being integers, then a term in the Fourier series for $\partial^2 W/\partial c\partial w_k$, containing this combination of frequencies, would reduce to a constant.   The value of the integral would then increase without limit, and we could not make ΔJ_k as small as we please.

The result of this section may be expressed by stating that the quantum integrals of a non-degenerate system are *adiabatic invariants*. This is a theorem of great power which enables us to avoid lengthy calculations in many problems.   For example, if an atom is subjected to a weak magnetic or electric field, the component of angular momentum parallel to the field is equal to a quantum integral divided by 2π.   We can conclude at once that the same will be true in a very strong field.

8. THE ADIABATIC INVARIANT $2\overline{T}/\omega$

The following theorem of Ehrenfest is often very useful.   Let $\overline{T}$ be the average kinetic energy of a *singly periodic* system, and ω the common frequency of all the coordinates.   If the system is altered adiabatically by changing parameters c_i which occur only in the potential energy function, $2\overline{T}/\omega$ is unaltered.

The proof is very simple.   Each coordinate q may be expressed as a Fourier series containing terms of the type $\cos (2\pi\tau w + \delta_\tau)$, where $w = \omega t$.   In equation (39), $\partial W/\partial t$ will be a Fourier series similar to those for the coordinates q. $\partial^2 W/\partial t\partial w$ will be a Fourier series without a constant term.   Further—and this is the crucial point— none of the terms $\cos (2\pi\tau\omega t + \delta_\tau)$ can reduce to a constant unless ω itself vanishes.

If that were to occur there would be no motion. Leaving this trivial case aside, we can prove as before that the momentum variable conjugate to w is invariant. This variable, J, can be found from the definition-equation

$$J = \frac{\partial S}{\partial w},$$

S being the action (see Chap. IV, Sec. **13**). Now

$$\int_0^{1/\omega} 2T dt = \oint \frac{\partial S}{\partial w} dw = J \int_0^1 dw = J; \tag{42}$$

but

$$2\overline{T} = \frac{\int_0^{1/\omega} 2T dt}{1/\omega} \tag{43}$$

and so $2\overline{T}/\omega$ is adiabatically invariant, being equal to J.

9. JUSTIFICATION OF THE QUANTUM CONDITIONS

If we assume the quantum condition $J = nh$ for the Planck oscillator, it is possible to justify the conditions

$$J_i = n_i h, \ i = 1, 2, \cdots \tag{44}$$

which are applied to conditionally periodic non-degenerate systems with any number of degrees of freedom. Let such a system be altered adiabatically, by changing the forces acting on its particles, or in other ways, until the motion of each particle is a superposition of three simple harmonic vibrations, mutually at right angles. The physical significance of the J's will alter until they become identical with the momentum components of the particles along the axes of their vibration. This follows from the way in which the J's and w's are found. The transformation equations connecting the sets of variables p, q and J, w are determined by solving the Hamilton-Jacobi differential equation. As the potential energy is adiabatically altered, the value of the transformation function S (or W) of Chap. IV, Sec. **10** is also changed, eventually becoming identical with the action function for an assemblage of oscillators. Since the J's and w's are completely determined by S, they must merge into the values appropriate to the oscillators. Further, the J's are unaltered in value if the change is made in such a way that the system never becomes degenerate. But each component oscillation is independent of the others, and is quantized by applying the condition $J = nh$, which justifies the equations (44).

10. A THEOREM FOR CALCULATING ENERGY PERTURBATIONS

Consider a non-degenerate atom described by variables w, J, the energy function being $H_0(J)$. Let it be disturbed by conservative forces which contribute a term $\lambda H_1(J, w)$ to the energy, so that it takes the form

$$H = H_0 + \lambda H_1, \tag{45}$$

λ being a small quantity which measures the strength of the force field. Then, *the additional quantized energy in the presence of the field is equal* to the average value of λH_1, taken over the unperturbed motion, except for negligible terms containing λ^2 and higher powers of λ.   This theorem enables us to obtain the energy without any knowledge of the changes in the motion.

The following derivation is nearly the same as one given by van Vleck.[1]   Although it is stated for a single particle the extension to other systems is easy.   Let the total energy be

$$E = \tfrac{1}{2}m(\dot{x}^2 + \dot{y}^2 + \dot{z}^2) + V + \lambda H_1, \tag{46}$$

where V is the unperturbed potential energy, and suppose for the purposes of this proof that λ increases slowly and uniformly from zero to its final value.   The rate of change of the energy is

$$\frac{dE}{dt} = \left(m\dot{x}\ddot{x} + \frac{\partial V}{\partial x}\dot{x} + \lambda\frac{\partial H_1}{\partial x}\dot{x} \right) + \text{etc.} + \frac{d\lambda}{dt}H_1, \tag{47}$$

but the equations of motion tell us that $m\ddot{x} + \dfrac{\partial V}{\partial x} + \dfrac{\lambda\partial H_1}{\partial x} = 0$, etc.   Therefore

$$dE = H_1 d\lambda. \tag{48}$$

Let $\overline{H}_1$ be the time average of H_1 over an interval which comprises many periods of the undisturbed motion, but which is small compared with the interval in which λ attains its final value. H_1 is expressible as a Fourier series, with periods equal to those of the atomic motion corresponding to the instantaneous value of λ. $\overline{H}_1$ is equal to the constant term of this series, and so $H_1 - \overline{H}_1$ is a Fourier series without a constant term. Therefore,

$$\int (H_1 - \overline{H}_1)\frac{d\lambda}{dt}dt \cong \frac{d\lambda}{dt}\int (H_1 - \overline{H}_1)dt.$$

The last integral remains finite because the integrand is alternately positive and negative, and $d\lambda/dt$ can be chosen as small as we like.   Therefore, in obtaining the change of E we may replace $\int H_1 d\lambda$ by $\int \overline{H}_1 d\lambda$, and

$$E - E_0 = \int_0^\lambda \overline{H}_1 d\lambda. \tag{49}$$

$\overline{H}_1$ will change as λ increases, and we may write it in the form

$$\overline{H}_1 = (\overline{H}_1)_{\lambda = 0} + \lambda\left(\frac{\partial \overline{H}_1}{\partial \lambda}\right)_{\lambda = 0} + \cdots \tag{50}$$

The second term and all higher ones contain λ^2 and higher powers of λ, and may be neglected for our present purpose, so

$$E - E_0 = \lambda\overline{H}_{10}. \tag{51}$$

(The subscript zero indicates that $\overline{H}_1$ is taken over the unperturbed motion.)   This proves our theorem.   If we desire closer approximations, we use additional terms in the expansion in equation (50), obtaining

$$E - E_0 = \lambda\overline{H}_{10} + \frac{1}{2}\lambda^2\left(\frac{\partial \overline{H}_1}{\partial \lambda}\right)_0 + \cdots \tag{52}$$

References

(See end of Chap. IV.)

"Quantum Principles and Line Spectra," p. 205.

CHAPTER VII

INTRODUCTION TO OPTICAL SPECTRA

1. THE TYPES OF SPECTRA EMITTED BY ATOMS

The line spectra emitted by atoms or atomic ions when they pass from an excited stationary state to another of lower energy are very different from the spectra of molecules; the latter consist of regular series of lines, usually quite closely spaced, which have the appearance of continuous bands under low dispersion and therefore are called "band spectra." (See Chap. XII and especially Fig. 1.) The line spectra of the neutral atoms in the first and second columns and the second subgroup of the third column of the periodic table, are especially simple, being characterized by series of lines not unlike those of hydrogen. The wave numbers of the lines in a series can usually be calculated with fair accuracy from the so-called "Rydberg formula,"

$$\tilde{\nu} = \tilde{\nu}_\infty - \frac{RZ^2}{(m + \varphi)^2}. \tag{1}$$

In this formula, R is a constant nearly equal to the Rydberg constant for infinite mass; $Z = 1$ for neutral atoms, 2 for singly charged ions, etc.; m is an integer, and φ is a common fraction which is reasonably constant for all lines of the series, while $\tilde{\nu}_\infty$ is the wave number of the series limit, obtained by placing $m = \infty$. The obvious interpretation of equation (1) is that the atom has a sequence of levels with the energies

$$E_m = -\frac{Z^2 Rhc}{(m + \varphi)^2}, \tag{2}$$

and that it can pass from any of these to a level with the energy $-\tilde{\nu}_\infty hc$.

While well-defined series are to be expected in all atomic spectra, they are usually short and difficult to trace for elements in the center and on the right of the periodic table. The characteristic feature of these spectra is their richness in lines, brought about by the existence of many energy levels, which, in turn, is due to the manifold possibilities of internal arrangement arising when the atom possesses several loosely bound "valence" electrons. Such spectra contain groups of lines called "multiplets," which arise from transitions between groups of physically related energy levels, referred to as multiple or polyfold levels.

The discovery and interpretation of spectral regularities is a science in itself. Given a table of the spectral lines characteristic of a substance, the modern spectroscopist wishes to gain all the information he can about

181

the entities which emit that spectrum.   We shall outline the procedure
he follows, and shall then describe the structure of some simple spectra,
the modes for exciting and studying them, and their interpretation:

1. The wave-length table will contain lines due to impurities.   These
must be eliminated by careful experiments, and by comparison with
published spectral tables.

2. The revised table will contain lines due not only to the neutral
atom but also to the singly charged ion, and quite frequently, lines
belonging to the atom in still higher stages of ionization.   The relative
intensities of lines, due to different emitters, are changed by almost any
alteration in the physical conditions, such as variations of the voltage
or current when the spectra are excited electrically; or changes of temperature in the case of flame spectra or furnace spectra; or the addition
of varying amounts of a foreign gas or vapor.   There are many ways of
separating the lines into classes each of which is due to only one type
of emitter.   Among the more powerful and trustworthy methods we
may mention the study of the influence of a magnetic field on the lines
(Zeeman effect), and the determination of the energy which an electron
must possess in order to excite a given group of lines (Chaps. III and
XIII).   In the case of furnace spectra, the study of the growth of
intensity with increase of temperature is particularly valuable for
elements of rather high, but not too high, boiling point.

3. The separation accomplished, let us fix our attention on the
lines due to a given emitter, the neutral atom for example.   It is necessary
to ascertain whether the wave lengths are expressed in Rowland's scale,
or in International Ångströms (I.Å.)   The latter have superseded the
former.   Descriptions of both scales are given in Fowler's "Report
on Series in Line Spectra," described in Chap. X, Sec. 1.   Assuming
that the wave lengths are in International Ångstroms, they have been
measured with respect to those of a standard element such as cadmium,
and the latter are determined in dry air at 15°C. and 760 mm.; so we
must reduce the tabulated values to the values which would be obtained
if our experiments were carried on *in vacuo;* reciprocals are then taken
to obtain the wave numbers of the lines.   Now the real task begins—to
discover from these wave numbers the arrangement of energy levels
which can give rise to the lines in accordance with the relation, $\Delta E = h\nu$.
This is an empirical process.   In the case of the more complicated spectra,
it consists mainly of searching for constant *differences* between pairs
of wave numbers in the table, although Zeeman-effect data, physical
characteristics of the lines, critical potential data and indications of a
theoretical character are almost indispensable aids.   At some stage
in the investigation it may appear probable that certain energy levels
are so distributed as to form a sequence of levels, with energies given
by equation (2).   After the identification of series of lines arising in

transitions from such a sequence of levels to other lower lying levels, the problem is one of interpretation.   In general, it will be found that many of the mathematically possible transitions between energy levels do not actually give rise to spectral lines.   It is important to explain such absent lines, by showing that if they appeared some dynamical principle would be violated.   Theories must be constructed to predict the existence as well as the energy values of the observed stationary states, and to explain the absence of missing lines.

2. METHODS FOR PRODUCING LINE EMISSION SPECTRA; SPECTRAL CHARACTERISTICS OF VARIOUS SOURCES

The reader should understand clearly that by the spectrum of a neutral atom we mean the spectrum emitted due to the return of an electron after the atom has been singly ionized; or, the spectrum emitted when the atom has been raised to a high energy level and performs transitions to lower energy levels.   Similarly, the spectrum of a singly charged ion is the aggregate of lines emitted by atoms which have been doubly ionized and to which an electron is returning; and so on.   It must be observed that two electrons of a neutral atom can be raised to higher orbits simultaneously; the lines emitted when one or both return are a part of the spectrum of the neutral atom.

In general, it may be said that when atoms are excited by subjecting them to the action of high temperatures or to bombardment by electrons, any increase in the strength of excitation is accompanied by greater complexity of the spectrum and by a shift of the center of intensity toward the shorter wave lengths.   To take the simplest possible case, the introduction of a tiny bit of NaCl into the Bunsen flame causes the abundant emission of the familiar yellow D-lines ($\lambda = 5.890$-6 Å) while other lines are so faint that they are completely lost in the weak background of continuous radiation.   In the spectrum of sodium, obtained by heating the metal in a carbon tube furnace *in vacuo*,[1] these are the first lines to appear.   On raising the temperature other lines due to the neutral atom are observed.

If we study the spectrum of an arc between carbon poles which are bored lengthwise and packed with a mixture of carbon dust and some sodium salt, we obtain practically all the lines which have been definitely identified as due to the neutral Na atom; since this is approximately true for many elements, the spectrum of a neutral atom is often called the "arc spectrum," regardless of the means by which it is produced. If an element is caused to emit light by passing a high tension discharge between poles of the material, the spectrum contains, in addition, the lines of the singly charged ion, and very frequently the lines due to atoms in still higher stages of ionization.   The spectrum of the singly charged

[1] KING, A. S., *Astrophys. J.*, **27**, 353 (1908); and numerous later papers.

ion is often called the "spark spectrum," and that due to the doubly charged ion the "double-spark spectrum." It is desirable to abandon these ambiguous terms and to designate the spectrum of neutral Hg, for example, as Hg I; that of once ionized Hg, as Hg II, etc.

3. THE SPECTRUM OF A NEUTRAL ALKALI ATOM

In the spectrum of a neutral alkali atom, such as cesium (Fig. 1),[1] one readily picks out three main sequences of lines, known as the "principal," "sharp," and "diffuse" series. This designation arises from the fact that the principal series is especially strong in the alkalies, while sharp series lines are really quite narrow, and diffuse series lines quite broad. There is also a "Bergmann" series, or "fundamental" series, lying entirely in the infrared except in the case of cesium. The term "fundamental" is a misnomer, arising from the mistaken idea that the frequencies of the lines in this series represent the lowest frequencies associated with the motions in the atom. This terminology is extended to series arising from the same types of electron transitions in other atoms, even though the physical characteristics of the lines may be radically different from the simple state of affairs described above. The next point to be noticed is that each member of the principal, the sharp, and the diffuse series is double. The early members, at least, of the diffuse series may be described as doublets in which the component of longer wave length is accompanied by a faint companion, or satellite. (The term satellite is used also in another sense, see Chap. XI, Sec. **3**.) In the higher members the satellite fuses together with the main line. Further information is easily acquired from Table 1. The first column contains the wave lengths of the more prominent lines due to the neutral cesium atom. In succeeding columns the wave numbers of the lines are listed under the names of the series to which they belong, and doublet differences are given. The wave lengths of series limits are placed in parentheses. These limits cannot be directly observed, except in the principal series, the limit of which can be clearly seen in the absorption

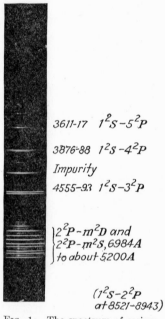

$3611\text{-}17 \quad 1^2S-5^2P$

$3876\text{-}88 \quad 1^2S-4^2P$

Impurity

$4555\text{-}93 \quad 1^2S-3^2P$

$\left.\begin{array}{l}2^2P-m^2D \text{ and} \\ 2^2P-m^2S, 6984A \\ \text{to about } 5200A\end{array}\right\}$

$(1^2S-2^2P$
$at\, 8521\text{-}8943)$

Fig. 1.—The spectrum of cesium.

---

[1] This spectrum was kindly prepared for us by Dr. F. L. Mohler.

TABLE 1.—SERIES IN THE SPECTRUM OF NEUTRAL CESIUM

Wave lengths, International Ångströms	Principal series		Sharp series		Diffuse series		Bergmann series	
	$\bar{\nu}$	$\Delta\bar{\nu}$	$\bar{\nu}$	$\Delta\bar{\nu}$	$\bar{\nu}$	$\Delta\bar{\nu}$	$\bar{\nu}$	$\Delta\bar{\nu}$
36,127.0	....	.....	....	.....	2,767.3	97.9		
34,892.0	....	.....	....	.....	2,865.2	554.1		
30,100.0	....	.....	....	.....	3,321.4			
14,694.8	....	.....	6,803.3	554.1				
13,588.1	....	.....	7,357.4					
10,124.1	....	.....	....	.....	....	.....	9,874.8	97.2
10,025.4	....	.....	....	.....	....	.....	9,972.0	
9,208.40	....	.....	....	.....	10,856.7	42.8		
9,172.23	....	.....	....	.....	10,899.5	554.0		
8,761.35	....	.....	....	.....	11,410.7			
8,943.46R	11,178.3	554.0						
8,521.12R	11,732.3							
8,079.24	....	.....	....	.....	....	.....	12,374.0	97.8
8,015.90	....	.....	....	.....	....	.....	12,471.8	
7,944.11	....	.....	12,584.5	554.0				
7,609.13	....	.....	13,138.5					
6,983.37	....	.....	....	.....	14,315.8	20.9		
6,973.17	....	.....	....	.....	14,336.7	554.0		
6,723.18	....	.....	....	.....	14,869.8			
6,586.94	....	.....	15,177.4	554.0				
6,354.98	....	.....	15,731.4					
(5,948.23)	....	.....	....	.....	....	.....	$3^2D_{5/2}$	97.9
(5,913.77)	....	.....	....	.....	....	.....	$3^2D_{3/2}$	
(5,081.88)	....	.....	$2^2P_{3/2}$	554.0	$2^2P_{3/2}$	554.0		
(4,942.67)	....	.....	$2^2P_{1/2}$	.....	$2P_{1/2}$			
4,593.16	21,765.4	181.4						
4,555.26	21,946.5							
3,888.65	25,709.3	80.6						
3,876.39	25,789.9							
3,617.41	27,636.2	45.1						
3,611.52	27,681.3							
(3,183.33)	$1^2S_{1/2}$, limit.							

spectrum of cesium vapor. This spectrum contains only the principal series lines. Bevan [1] was able to obtain 31 members of the principal series of cesium, while Wood[2] photographed 57 members in sodium.

[1] *Proc. Roy. Soc.*, **83**, 421; **85**, 54; and **86**, 320 (1910 to 1912).
[2] *Astrophys. J.*, **43**, 73 (1916).

The cesium sharp series has been photographed to 7 members; the diffuse to 10; and the fundamental to 9.

There are several important facts in regard to the doublet separations in alkali spectra:

1. In the principal series, the difference of the wave numbers of the components of a doublet decreases rapidly as we pass toward the ultra-violet.

2. The wave number differences $\Delta \bar{\nu}_s$ of sharp series doublets remain constant as far as the series can be followed, and in the diffuse series the same is true of the difference $\Delta \bar{\nu}_d$ between the shorter component of the doublet, and the satellite.

3. $\Delta \bar{\nu}_s = \Delta \bar{\nu}_d$.

4. The wave-number difference of the first doublet in the principal series is equal to $\Delta \bar{\nu}_s$.

Let us now consider the interpretation of these regularities. Many facts in regard to the arc spectra of alkali atoms can be explained by assuming that each stationary state corresponds to a different orbit of a single loosely bound valence electron. In a transition giving rise to an arc line only the quantum numbers of the valence electron are changed.[1]

The arc spectrum of cesium, or of any alkali, arises in transitions between stationary states occurring generally in close pairs, as shown in the *energy diagram* (Fig. 2). In this diagram, horizontal lines are drawn at ordinates proportional to the energies of the atom in its various stationary states. We start with zero energy at the top, which corresponds to complete removal of one electron. At the left is a scale from which we can read off the wave number T of the quantum which would be emitted if the valence electron fell from a position at rest at infinity into any given orbit. If E is the energy of the atom when the valence electron is on that orbit, then $T = -E/hc$. T is called the "term" or the "term value" belonging to that state.

This gives us a schematic method of indicating transitions between states by drawing an arrow to connect their representative lines. Downward arrows correspond to emission; upward, to absorption. To aid

---

[1] For many purposes, the details of the motion of the other electrons may be neglected, and the atom may be treated as though it consisted of a single electron moving in a central field of force. For this reason it became customary during the early development of the subject to think of optical energy levels in general as determined by the nature of the orbit of a single electron called the "light electron," and to speak of an energy level as an orbit. Thus, we may say, "the atom is on the 2P orbit." These practices present no difficulties in dealing with the arc spectra of the alkalies and some portions of the spectra of the alkaline earths, but in other cases, they lead to confusion because, in general, several electrons play an active part in determining the energy levels. In our study of alkali spectra, then, we shall speak freely of the orbits of the valence electron.

the eye in picking out the levels which belong to a physically related sequence of states, such as the initial levels for the emission of a series, the horizontal lines are separated into several groups. The lowest stationary state of an alkali atom is single, and is designated as $1^2S_{1/2}$ for reasons partly historical and partly logical. This symbol is read "one doublet S sub one-half" or "one doublet S one-half." It is the first or lowest state of a set designated as the S sequence. The letter S shows that this sequence of levels consists of the initial states for the emission of the *sharp* series. The superscript "2" shows that the state belongs to a sequence of levels denoted by $m^2S_{1/2}$ and giving rise to a doublet spectrum. The particular state under discussion happens to be unaccompanied

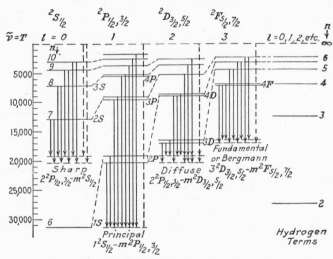

FIG. 2.—Energy diagram of cesium.

by another state of closely neighboring energy. The reason why the S states are not double will soon be given. In these states the atom possesses a total angular momentum $\dfrac{1}{2}\dfrac{h}{2\pi}$ so that $j = \dfrac{1}{2}$. The subscript indicates the inner quantum number. (Many authors use $j + \frac{1}{2}$ instead, when j is half-integral, in order to avoid the use of fractional subscripts.)

We come now to the closely neighboring sequences designated as $m^2P_{1/2}$ and $m^2P_{3/2}$, where m is an integer. The lowest pair of states belonging to these sequences is called $2^2P_{1/2}$ and $2^2P_{3/2}$. The number j varies as we pass from level to level within the limits of a given multiplet level. The reader will see that the ^2P states are the initial levels for the emission of the principal series, whence the letter P, and will recognize sequences labeled $m^2D_{3/2}$ and $m^2D_{1/2}$, with $m = 3, 4, \cdots$, which are initial orbits for the diffuse series. Other sequences are also present, such as mF, mG, mH, . . . , with m starting at the values 4, 5, 6, . . . , respectively. All the terms of the sequences G, H, etc., lie extremely close to the F-terms and cannot well be indicated in the figure.

Symbols such as $2^2P_{1/2}$ are customarily used, not only to designate a spectral term, but also to mean the actual numerical value of the spectral term, T. Thus the term values for the states $1^2S_{1/2}$ and $2^2P_{1/2}$ of sodium are 41,449 and 24,493. The wave number of the line emitted in a fall from $2^2P_{1/2}$ to $1^2S_{1/2}$ is

$$\bar{\nu} = 41,449 - 24,493 = 16,956, \quad (\lambda = 5,896\,\text{Å})$$

which is expressed by

$$\bar{\nu} = 1^2S_{1/2} - 2^2P_{1/2}.$$

Therefore the line itself is referred to as $1^2S_{1/2} - 2^2P_{1/2}$.

Where no confusion can arise, we shall omit the superscript which shows the degree of multiplicity of the spectrum (doublets, triplets, etc.) and also the subscript indicating the angular momentum of the atom. To summarize, an alkali spectrum contains the following main series:

Series		Satellite	Component of greater wave length	Component of smaller wave length
Principal..............	$m \geqq 2$	....	$1S_{1/2} - mP_{1/2}$	$1S_{1/2} - mP_{3/2}$
Sharp................	$m \geqq 2$	....	$2P_{3/2} - mS_{1/2}$	$2P_{1/2} - mS_{1/2}$
Diffuse..............	$m \geqq 3$	$2P_{3/2} - mD_{3/2}$	$2P_{3/2} - mD_{5/2}$	$2P_{1/2} - mD_{3/2}$
Fundamental........	$m \geqq 4$	$3D_{5/2} - mF_{5/2}$	$3D_{5/2} - mF_{7/2}$	$3D_{3/2} - mF_{5/2}$

The number m runs parallel to the total quantum number of the valence electron, but often is not equal to it. The connection between m and the total number is discussed in Chap. X, Sec. 1. The energy diagram shows clearly why only the principal series lines appear in the absorption spectrum. In the absorption of light the atom is raised from a level of lower energy to one of higher energy and since at low temperatures all but a negligible fraction of the atoms must be in the lowest energy state these lines must arise in transitions from this lowest level to higher ones. We see also, from Fig. 2, that the variation of the doublet difference in the principal series, and its constancy in the sharp and diffuse series, is at once explained. The $\bar{\nu}$-difference of the lines $1S - mP_{1/2}$ and $1S - mP_{3/2}$ is simply $mP_{1/2} - mP_{3/2}$, which decreases as m increases. On the other hand, the frequency difference of the members of the sharp or diffuse doublet arises from the fact that the two lines have different final orbits, $2P_{1/2}$ or $2P_{3/2}$, the same for all members of the series,

4. SELECTION PRINCIPLES

The question now arises, why do many lines which seem to be possible from consideration of the energy diagram fail to occur?   Prior to the introduction of the spinning electron, it was supposed that the electron of an atom in an S-level has the azimuthal quantum number $k = 1$; while the P, D, F, etc. orbits were assigned the azimuthal numbers, $2, 3, 4, \ldots$, respectively.   Some authors preferred to assume azimuthal numbers $\frac{1}{2}$, $\frac{3}{2}$, $\ldots$ for the S, P, $\ldots$ levels, for reasons connected with the energy of the various states.   As a purely empirical rule to be justified later, we may say:

Only those transitions ordinarily occur for which the change in k is ± 1.
Thus we have the combinations $S - P$, $P - S$, $P - D$, but such series as $1S - mS$, or $2P - mF$ are either entirely lacking or very faint.   It remains to mention a rule governing the non-appearance of the lines $2^2P_{\frac{1}{2}} - m^2D_{\frac{3}{2}}$, which would be satellites of the shorter main components in the diffuse series:

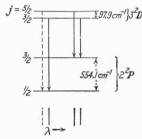

Only those transitions ordinarily occur for which the change in the inner quantum number j is ± 1 or 0.

FIG. 3.—The $2^2P_{\frac{1}{2}}$, $\frac{3}{2}$–$3^2D_{\frac{3}{2}}$, $\frac{5}{2}$ cesium multiplet.

Thus, we have in Fig. 3 the following transitions of j:

$\frac{3}{2} \rightarrow \frac{3}{2}$, satellite;

$\frac{5}{2} \rightarrow \frac{3}{2}$, longer main component;

$\frac{3}{2} \rightarrow \frac{1}{2}$, shorter main component;

but the line for which j changes from $\frac{5}{2}$ to $\frac{1}{2}$ fails to appear.   A diagram of the spectral lines produced in these transitions is given at the bottom of the figure.

5. THE QUANTUM STATES OF A ONE-ELECTRON SYSTEM

In Chap. X, we shall describe a scheme which enables us to predict with almost complete success the existence of every term in the X-ray and optical spectra of the atoms.   Here we describe its application to atoms with only one valence electron.   Many features of a doublet spectrum can be interpreted by considering the orbits of a single electron moving about a kernel which has an electron configuration like that of a rare gas atom.   It is an empirical fact that the electrons of the kernel have zero resultant angular momentum.   The existence of the terms in the energy diagram can be deduced almost without reference to the structure of the kernel, and many of their properties can be expressed entirely by means of the quantum numbers of the valence electron.   As mentioned in the case of the hydrogen atom, four quantum numbers must be assigned to this electron.   They are as follows:

1. n, the total quantum number of the electron orbit, which takes integral values and does not measure a vector magnitude.

2. $l = k - 1$, which takes the values 0, 1, 2 for S, P, D, etc. terms, respectively. The number l is found to behave exactly as we should expect k to behave if the old quantum mechanics were valid. The reason for this cannot be understood in terms of the model we are using, but is easily understandable when using the model suggested by wave mechanics (Chap. XVI).

3. s, a vector having the magnitude $\frac{1}{2}$. The theory can be applied independent of any assumption about the physical nature of s, and the method was freely used to predict spectral terms before any hypothesis was made to explain this quantum number. However, $sh/2\pi$ is the angular momentum of the electron spinning about its own axis.

4. j, defined as the vector sum of l and s. We now inquire for the possible values of j. Both l and s have fixed values, and their vectorial sum j must be constant in the absence of an external field since it represents the total angular momentum of the atom. This means that both the normal to the orbital plane and the spin axis of the electron must precess about the vector j. The strict application of Sommerfeld's quantum conditions to this motion requires that j should be an integer. The new mechanics leads to the result that j can take the values

$$l + s, l + s - 1, \cdots |l - s|. \tag{3}$$

That is, for a one-electron system,

$$j = l \pm \tfrac{1}{2}. \tag{4}$$

These quantum numbers apply to hydrogen as well as to the alkalies.

The enumeration of the possible spectral terms is now only a question of listing all the possible values of the quantum numbers n, l, and j, for s is always $\frac{1}{2}$. When l and s are given, the corresponding j values are found by using equation (4). In the case of atoms with more than 1 valence electron, this procedure usually results in the prediction of some terms which do not exist. To exclude these terms, we must apply the so-called Pauli exclusion principle to the energy levels in a magnetic or electric field, introduced to make the system non-degenerate, as described in Chap. X, Sec. **10.** This difficulty is not encountered in our discussion of alkali atoms in the absence of a field. Table 2 illustrates some of the possibilities for those low-lying terms of cesium in which the total quantum number is 6 or 7, as well as a few others.

The reader will observe how naturally the singleness of the S terms fits into the scheme. When $l = 0$ there is only one possible value for j, that is, the value of s itself. The S term is single in all other spectra for a similar reason. The numeration of the terms in column six of the table is purely conventional and is explained in Chap. X, Sec **1.**

TABLE 2.—QUANTUM NUMBERS FOR THE TERMS OF Cs

n k l	s	$l + s = j$	Term	Angular momentum diagram
6 1 0	½	½	$1^2S_{\frac{1}{2}}$	
7 1 0	½	½	$2^2S_{\frac{1}{2}}$	
6 2 1	½	½	$2^2P_{\frac{1}{2}}$	
6 2 1	½	³⁄₂	$2^2P_{\frac{3}{2}}$	
5 3 2	½	³⁄₂	$3^2D_{\frac{3}{2}}$	
		⁵⁄₂	$3^2D_{\frac{5}{2}}$	
4 4 3	½	⁵⁄₂	$4^2F_{\frac{5}{2}}$	
		⁷⁄₂	$4^2F_{\frac{7}{2}}$	

6. ZEEMAN PATTERNS OF ALKALI ATOMS

We now describe the Zeeman patterns of the principal and sharp series in alkali spectra. Only the patterns observed perpendicular to the field will be discussed since the longitudinal patterns do not show components polarized parallel to the field. If the frequency changes due to the field are large (or small) compared to the doublet interval we say that the field is strong (or weak). Obviously, no hard and fast distinction is intended. As we increase the field, the patterns undergo a change known as the "Paschen-Back effect." Hence, we must describe the weak- and strong-field patterns separately. In weak fields, the line of greater wave length in a principal series doublet yields four components as shown at the bottom of Fig. 4. Expressed in terms of the wave number L corresponding to the Larmor precession (Chap.

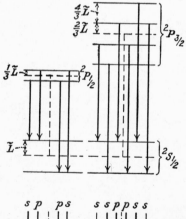

FIG. 4.—The Zeeman patterns of a principal series doublet in a weak field.

V, Sec. **11**) as a unit, their wave number displacements from the postion of the field-free line are $\pm \frac{2}{3}$, $\pm \frac{4}{3}$, respectively. Similarly, the shorter member has components at $\pm \frac{1}{3}$, $\pm \frac{3}{3}$, $\pm \frac{5}{3}$, respectively. The energy levels from which the components arise are shown above by full lines, while the energy levels in the absence of the field are represented by dotted lines. The letters s (senkrecht) or p (parallel) indicate the components polarized perpendicular and parallel to the field respectively. The atoms are space-quantized in the field, in accordance with Chap. V, Sec. **9,** and each energy level in the figure corresponds to a definite orientation of the vector j with respect to the lines of force. The component of j parallel to the field is m, which is called the magnetic quantum number. The

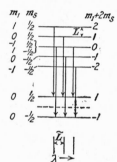

facts in regard to these patterns may be summed up by saying that the displacements of the energy levels are given by the formula

$$\Delta \tilde{\nu} = mg\tilde{L}, \qquad (5)$$

where m takes half-integer values from $-j$ to $+j$ and $g = \frac{2}{3}$ for $^2P_{1/2}$, $\frac{4}{3}$ for $^2P_{3/2}$, 2 for $^2S_{1/2}$. This formula differs from that for the normal Zeeman effect only through the factor g (Chap. X, Sec. **8**).

Fig. 5.—The Zeeman pattern of a principal series doublet line in a strong field.

Equation (5) is valid when the forces due to the magnetic field do not appreciably affect the coupling between l and s, which causes them to form a quantized resultant j. This condition is not met if a strong magnetic field is applied to the atom for then the electron will orient itself with its axis of rotation parallel to the field so that the projection of its angular momentum vector along the field is identical in value with the vector itself, being either $\frac{1}{2}\frac{h}{2\pi}$ or $-\frac{1}{2}\frac{h}{2\pi}$. We call this projection $m_s h/2\pi$, so that the magnetic quantum number of the electron in such a field is m_s. Further, in a strong magnetic field the orbit of the valence electron is independently space-quantized, so that the component of l along the field is m_l. Hence the restriction $-l \leqq m_l \leqq l$. If $l = 0$, we may suppose the orientation is indeterminate. The energy levels in a strong field are obtained exactly as in the treatment of the Zeeman effect of hydrogen (Chap. V, Sec. **11**) and are given by the formula

$$\Delta \tilde{\nu} = (m_l + 2m_s)\tilde{L}. \qquad (6)$$

The factor 2 appears here because the electron has a magnetic moment of one Bohr magneton though its s is $\frac{1}{2}$, so that it precesses with twice the frequency of the Larmor precession. As an illustration, we show in Fig. 5 the strong-field patterns of principal and sharp series lines, as given by equation (6). The values of m_l, m_s, and $m_l + 2m_s$ are indicated at the sides of the figure.

7. SERIES FORMULAS FOR ALKALI ATOMS

As we said at the beginning of this chapter, Rydberg[1] showed in 1889 that the terms of the series spectra known at that time and belonging to the elements of the first few columns in the periodic table follow a formula

$$T = \frac{RZ^2}{(m + \varphi)^2}. \tag{7}$$

Here we shall follow the numeration of Paschen, in which the terms of the various sequences are numbered as follows:

$$mS: \quad m = 1, 2, \cdots$$
$$mP: \quad m = 2, 3, \cdots$$
$$mD: \quad m = 3, 4, \cdots$$
$$mF: \quad m = 4, 5, \cdots$$

A résumé of the various systems of numeration is given in Chap. X, Sec. **1**. Only the combination $m + \varphi$ is determined by the magnitude of the term, so that the value of m is quite immaterial. This number serves only for the convenient identification of the terms in a sequence. φ is very nearly constant for all the terms of a given sequence such as the $^2S_{\frac{1}{2}}$, $^2P_{\frac{1}{2}}$, or $^2P_{\frac{3}{2}}$ terms of the alkali metals, but changes when we pass to another sequence. Since these are associated with different values of l, this means that φ is a function of l and also of s. Ritz[2] modified the formula (7) to give definite expression to the variation of φ with the running number m, and showed that it was capable of representing many series terms with high accuracy. His formula is

$$T = \frac{RZ^2}{(m + a + bT)^2}. \tag{8}$$

where a and b are constants. Usually it is quite satisfactory to use the alternative formulas

$$T = \frac{RZ^2}{\left(m + a + \dfrac{b'}{(m + a)^2}\right)^2} \text{ or } \frac{RZ^2}{\left(m + a + \dfrac{b''}{m^2}\right)^2} \tag{8a}$$

In fact we may regard $a + bT$ in equation (8) as the first two terms of a series in ascending powers of T, which reduces to its first term a as m approaches infinity. Both a and b are functions of both l and s, and approach zero as l increases. The same remarks apply to the formula of Hicks,

$$T = \frac{RZ^2}{\left(m + a + \dfrac{\alpha}{m}\right)^2} \tag{8b}$$

---

[1] *K. Swenska Akad. Handl.*, Vol. **23**.

[2] *Ann. Physik*, **12**, 264 (1903); *Physik. Z.*, **9**, 521 (1908).

Ordinarily we shall use the Ritz formula. The Rydberg and Ritz terms are customarily indicated by the symbols (m, φ) and (m, a, b), respectively. It is often convenient to write $m + a + bT$ in the form

$$n + A + BT, \tag{10}$$

where n is the total quantum number of the valence electron. The quantity in equation (10) is sometimes called the "Rydberg" or "Ritz denominator," although it is actually the square root of the denominator of equation (8), but more often we speak of it as the effective quantum number, n^*. Further, the so-called "quantum defect" is

$$Q = n - n^* = -A - BT. \tag{12}$$

Rewriting equation (8) in the form

$$T = \frac{RZ^2}{n^{*2}},$$

we see that the quantum defect is a measure of the departure of the spectral term from the hydrogenic term having the same total quantum number. Without exception, the terms of neutral alkali atoms are greater than the corresponding hydrogenic terms, so $n - n^*$ is positive for these atoms. Table 3 gives effective quantum numbers for certain terms of alkali atoms. The value of n for each doublet level can easily be found with the aid of this table, and of approximate atomic models now to be explained.

8. APPROXIMATE MECHANICAL MODELS

Many ingenious attempts have been made to calculate the energy levels of the simpler non-hydrogenic atoms with the aid of classical mechanics and the quantum conditions. Of course the mathematical difficulties are great. Even the three-body problem can be solved only by successive approximations and then only for certain special configurations, such as that in which both electrons move on identical orbits or one moves on a much larger orbit than the other. The problem of the lithium atom is still more difficult and no attempts worthy of serious consideration have been made to obtain the term values of atoms having three or more electrons. Calculations for the helium atom, assuming that the two electrons move on identical orbits, have been made by Bohr,[1] Van Vleck[2] and Kramers.[3] It is found that none of the models studied give the observed value of the ionizing potential and moreover the models are dynamically unstable; i.e., the electrons will not continue to move on orbits which are even approximately identical if their motion is slightly disturbed. Born and Heisenberg[4] have calculated the excited terms of helium and find that these also do not agree with the observed values.

[1] Phil. Mag., **26**, 476 (1913).
[2] Phys. Rev., **21**, 372 (1923).
[3] Z. Physik, **13**, 312 (1923).
[4] Z. Physik, **16**, 229 (1923).

If the laws of mechanics held, atoms having many electrons would exhibit similar instability. Thus the energy of one electron in such an atom might increase, while the others lost energy until it was spontaneously ejected from the atom, in evident contradiction with fact. Or, one electron might move so close to the nucleus that it would collide with it. The experimental behavior of atoms is characterized by a regularity and relative simplicity which cannot be explained on the basis of ordinary mechanics. These facts alone point out the necessity of the new systems of dynamics.

In order to secure approximate models of the alkali metal atoms and thus a partial explanation of the energy levels, we can make non-mechanical assumptions which simplify the problem. An alkali atom can readily lose its valence electron to form a singly charged positive ion, a fact which led us to conclude that this electron alone is responsible for the doublet spectrum of the neutral atom. Similarly, the divalent elements of the second column of the periodic table and the trivalent elements of the third column readily lose two or three electrons, forming doubly and triply charged ions, respectively.

The singly charged ion of a second group metal or the doubly charged ion of a third group metal has a single valence electron moving about a very stable electron group. Thus, the ions Mg^{++} and Al^{+++} have the same electron configuration as the very inert gas neon, while Hg^{++} and Tl^{+++} must be similar to platinum, which is also very inert chemically. Mg^+, Hg^+, Al^{++}, and Tl^{++} are called "alkali-like" because they possess a single valence electron. The stable electron group obtained when this electron is removed is called the "kernel" or the "core."[1]

The model of atoms (or ions) with one valence electron, used first by Sommerfeld,[2] rests on the assumption that the force field of the kernel is central in character so that the electron moves in an orbit similar to a precessing ellipse; whatever the law of central force between the kernel and the electron may be, the successive loops of the orbit have the same shape (Fig. 6). Therefore, the same energy and angular momentum are to be associated with the electron at corresponding points of these loops. Thus, the difficulties of spontaneous ionization or of collision with the nucleus do not arise with this model. At large distances from the kernel, its force field should approximate to the inverse square law. The kernel is not to be considered as a uniformly charged spherical surface of definite radius. The electrons within the kernel are rather to be regarded as moving (approximately) on elliptical or circular orbits

---

[1] We shall use the term "kernel" as the equivalent of the German *atomrest* or *rumpf*. It was first used by Lewis (*J. Am. Chem. Soc.*, **10**, 1121 (1916)), and we believe that it is a better English equivalent than other terms suggested since that time.

[2] *Ann. Physik*, **51**, 15 (1916).

of differing semimajor axes and eccentricities, giving rise to an average field not unlike that of a spherical volume charge with density which varies in a radial direction. The electron will induce a polarization of the kernel so that the field at points outside will be somewhat greater than the inverse square. At internal points, some of the electrons of the kernel will not "screen" the nucleus and therefore the force exerted on the valence electron will be much greater than the force outside. Within the innermost shell of electrons the nucleus is not screened by any of the electrons of the kernel and therefore the force will be

$$F = -\frac{Ze^2}{r^2},$$

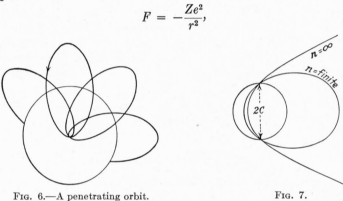

Fig. 6.—A penetrating orbit.	Fig. 7.

where Z is the atomic number. It is convenient to represent the force at any distance from the nucleus as

$$F = -\frac{Z(r)e^2}{r^2}, \tag{13}$$

where $Z(r)$ is a function of r, which decreases from the value of the atomic number at $r = 0$ to a value of 1, 2, 3 $\cdots$ at $r = \infty$ for neutral, singly or doubly charged atoms, respectively. However, in order to show qualitatively the various types of orbits of an electron moving in the field of an atomic kernel, we can use a simpler model for the kernel, namely, a positive nucleus surrounded by a uniformly charged spherical surface, so that the net attracting charge is $Z'e$ outside of the spherical surface and Ze inside this surface. To determine the possible types of orbit, consider the situation when the path of the valence electron lies entirely outside the kernel. Its minimum distance of approach is

$$r_{\min} = a(1 - \epsilon) = \frac{n^2 a_1}{Z'}\left[1 - \left(1 - \frac{k^2}{n^2}\right)^{\frac{1}{2}}\right] \tag{14}$$

for an elliptical orbit of semimajor axis a, where the energy is negative and n is finite. a_1 is the radius of the first orbit of hydrogen. For the parabolic orbit, where the energy is zero and n is infinite, this becomes

$$\frac{k^2 a_1}{2Z'}.$$

All orbits having the same value of k have the same parameter,

$$c = \frac{k^2 a_1}{Z'}.$$

An orbit having n finite and the orbit with n infinite are shown in Fig. 7. If for some particular value of k, the radius of the spherical shell ρ is less than $k^2 a_1 / 2Z'$, all the orbits of a sequence having the azimuthal quantum number k will lie outside the shell and will be elliptical orbits just as in the case of the inverse square field of force of a bare nucleus. If ρ is greater than c, all orbits with azimuthal number k will penetrate the shell, and the circular orbit for which $n = k$ will lie completely inside. Finally, if ρ lies between c and $c/2$, the orbits of low total quantum number will not penetrate the shell but those of higher total quantum number will do so. Examples of all three of these types are known, although the types are not as sharply defined as this simple model would predict, since the kernel may have several shells of electrons and the valence electron may penetrate more than one of these shells. We now consider these three cases in turn.

9. NON-PENETRATING ORBITS

These will have energy values lying very near those of the hydrogenic atom having an atomic number equal to the number of charges on the kernel. For such orbits the effective quantum number must lie very close to integral values and it is possible to pick them out in most cases from tables similar to Table 3. Thus the ^2P, ^2D, and ^2F levels of the single electron spectra of Li I and the other elements in the first horizontal line of the periodic table have effective quantum numbers lying very close to the hydrogenic values. The ^2D terms of Na I, K I, Mg II, Al III, and Si IV and the $^2F_{5/2,7/2}$ terms of these spectra as well as Rb I, Cs I, Ca II, Sr II, Ba II, Zn II and Cd II have effective quantum numbers which are nearly integral, and, therefore, belong to non-penetrating orbits. These terms follow the Ritz formula fairly well, although there are some minor deviations. This behavior is predicted by simple theory.

The field of force outside the kernel may be represented by a series in descending powers of r,

$$F = -\frac{Ze^2}{r^2}\left(1 + C_1\frac{2}{r} + C_2\frac{3}{r^2} + C_3\frac{4}{r^3} + \cdots\right) \tag{15}$$

It may be, of course, that certain terms in this series are much more important than others. Born and Heisenberg[1] came to the conclusion

---

[1] *Z. Physik*, **23**, 388 (1924); Born, "Vorlesungen über Atommechanik," p. 189. Springer (1925).

that the term containing r^{-5} is probably more important then any of the others except the inverse square term. The inverse fifth power term appears because the kernel is polarized by the field of the valence electron.

Table 3.—Effective Quantum Numbers for Neutral Alkalies and Ionized Alkaline Earths

	Li	Na	K	Rb	Cs
$1S_{1/2}$	1.588	1.626	1.771	1.805	1.869
$2S_{1/2}$	2.596	2.643	2.802	2.846	2.920
$3S_{1/2}$	3.598	3.647	3.800	3.856	3.934
Q	0.40	1.35	2.18	3.14	4.06
$2P_{1/2}$	1.966	2.116	2.232	2.280	2.392
$3P_{1/2}$	2.956	3.133	3.263	3.317	3.374
$4P_{1/2}$	3.954	4.138	4.272	4.329	4.390
Q	0.05	0.86	1.72	2.66	3.60
$3D_{3/2}$	2.999	2.990	2.854	2.767	2.548
$4D_{3/2}$	3.998	3.988	3.797	3.706	3.528
$5D_{3/2}$	5.000	4.987	4.770	4.684	4.526
Q	0.001	0.02	0.25	1.33(?)	2.47(?)
$4F_{5/2}$	4.000	3.999	3.994	3.989	3.977
$5F_{5/2}$	5.005	5.000	4.991	4.984	4.975
Q	0.001(?)	−0.00	0.01	0.01	0.03

	Mg^+	Cd^+	Sr^+	Ba^+
$1S_{1/2}$	1.903	1.791	2.222	2.333
$2S_{1/2}$	2.920	2.868	3.267	3.403
$3S_{1/2}$	3.925	.....	4.286	4.404
Q	1.07	3.10	2.70	3.60
$2P_{1/2}$	2.265	2.181	2.595	2.696
$3P_{1/2}$	3.286	3.245		
$4P_{1/2}$	4.293	4.276		
Q	0.70	2.71	2.4	3.3
$3D_{3/2}$[1]	2.970[1]	3.066	2.431	2.407
$4D_{3/2}$[1]	3.962[1]	4.093	3.513	3.557
$5D_{3/2}$[1]	4.960[1]	5.104	4.536	4.588
$6D_{3/2}$[1]	5.957[1]	6.108	5.552	5.603
Q	0.04	1.89	1.45	2.40
$4F_{5/2}$	4.00	3.962	3.962	3.681
$5F_{5/2}$	5.00	.....	4.966	4.495
$6F_{5/2}$	6.00	5.953	5.970	5.209
Q	0.00	0.05	0.03	0.79

[1] These refer to the $^2D_{5/2}$ levels.

To a first approximation the electric moment p of the induced dipole is proportional to the intensity of this field at a distance r from the center of the kernel so that

$$p = \frac{\alpha e}{r^2}, \qquad (16)$$

where α is a constant called the "polarizability." The dipole can be regarded as two equal charges of unlike sign and magnitude p/l at a small distance l from each other. The axis of the dipole always points toward the electron (Fig. 8) and the force tending to increase the distance between them is

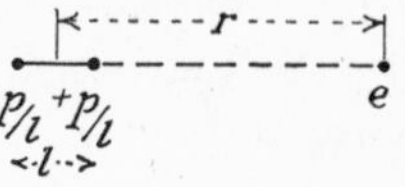

FIG. 8.

$$ep\left[\frac{1}{(r + \frac{1}{2}l)^2} - \frac{1}{(r - \frac{1}{2}l)^2}\right] \cong -\frac{2pe}{r^3} = -\frac{2\alpha e^2}{r^5}. \qquad (17)$$

The expression for the total force between the kernel and electron is therefore

$$F = -\frac{Ze^2}{r^2} - \frac{2\alpha e^2}{r^5} \qquad (18)$$

The potential energy is

$$V = -\int_\infty^r F dr = -\frac{Ze^2}{r} - \frac{\alpha e^2}{2r^4}, \qquad (19)$$

and the kinetic energy is $m(\dot{r}^2 + r^2\dot{\varphi}^2)/2$. The radial and azimuthal quantum conditions are thus

$$\oint p_r dr = \oint \left[2mE + \frac{2mZe^2}{r} - \frac{p_\varphi^2}{r^2} + \frac{\alpha me^2}{r^4}\right]^{\frac{1}{2}} dr = n_r h \qquad (20)$$

and

$$\int_0^{2\pi} p_\varphi d\varphi = 2\pi p_\varphi = kh. \qquad (21)$$

The integral in equation (20) is evaluated in Appendix II and leads to the energy value,

$$E = -\frac{RhcZ^2}{\left(n + \delta_1 + \frac{\delta_2}{n^2}\right)^2}, \quad \delta_1 = -\frac{3Z^2\alpha}{4k^5 a_1^3}, \quad \delta_2 = \frac{Z^2\alpha}{4k^3 a_1^3}, \qquad (22)$$

where a_1 is the radius of the first Bohr orbit of hydrogen. The constant can be calculated from the experimental values of δ_1 and δ_2 independently and may then be compared with a value found in the following way.

The kernel of each of the alkali metal atoms has the same number of electrons as one of the inert gases and undoubtedly has the same electron configuration. The electrons of the inert gases are bound less firmly however than those of the kernels of the alkali metals immediately following them in the periodic table, because of the smaller charges on their nuclei. Therefore, the polarizabilities of these atoms should be greater than those of the alkali metal kernels, though we can expect that the constants will be of the same order of magnitude. The value of the constant α for a rare gas can be calculated from its dielectric constant ϵ or from its refractive index n for infinitely long wave lengths by the Lorentz-Lorenz formula,

$$\alpha = \frac{3}{4\pi N} \frac{\epsilon - 1}{\epsilon + 2} = \frac{3}{4\pi N} \frac{n^2 - 1}{n^2 + 2},$$

where N is the number of atoms per unit volume; n is obtained by extrapolating the refractive index curve to very large wave lengths. In the following, Table 4, the first row contains values of α calculated from refractive indices. The second shows values obtained from spectroscopic data, assuming that $k = 1, 2, 3, \cdots$ for the $S, P, D, \cdots$ sequences, respectively. The third row is obtained in the same manner as the second row except that k is taken equal to $\frac{1}{2}, \frac{3}{2}, \frac{5}{2}$ etc. Rubidium is not included because of the irregular character of its terms.

TABLE 4.—POLARIZABILITY CONSTANTS

Inert gases.....................	He	Ne	A	Kr	X
$10^{24}\alpha$..........................	0.20	0.39	1.63	2.46	4.00
Alkali metal ions.................	Li$^+$	Na$^+$	K$^+$	Rb$^+$	Cs$^+$
With k integral, $10^{24}\alpha$.............	0.314	0.405	0.68	....	6.48
or, with k half-integral, $10^{24}\alpha$.......	0.075	0.21	0.87	....	3.36

It will be noted that the half quantum numbers for k give values of α lower than those of the corresponding inert gases, as they should be, while whole quantum numbers do not. This appears to be an argument for the half quantum numbers but it cannot be taken as conclusive. Hartree[1] and Schrödinger[2] pointed out that different values of α can be secured by using different sequences of terms. The calculations show that the order of magnitude of α calculated with either set of values of k is that to be expected from the refractive indices of the rare gases.

10. PENETRATING ORBITS

Schrödinger[3] first showed that the ^2S orbits of the alkali valence electron must penetrate the kernel. In order to understand the difference between the energy values of penetrating and non-penetrating orbits, we may assume that the kernel consists of a nucleus surrounded by a spherical shell, with the charge of q electrons uniformly distributed over its surface. Schrödinger considered the more general case of several shells with different radii, but the essential points can be understood by considering a simple model for the sodium-like atoms and then extending the results to atoms of higher atomic number. Let us suppose that a sodium-like atom consists of a nucleus of charge Ze ($Z = 11, 12,$

[1] *Proc. Camb. Phil. Soc.*, **21**, 625 (1923); **22**, 409 and 464 (1924); *Proc. Roy. Soc.*, **106**, 552 (1924).

[2] *Ann. Physik.*, **77**, 43 (1925).

[3] *Z. Physik.*, **4**, 347 (1921).

13, . . . for Na I, Mg II, Si III, . . . , respectively) surrounded by a
very small sphere carrying a charge $-2e$ and a larger shell of charge
$-8e$, and radius ρ. This distribution is based on the facts in regard
to X-ray spectra presented in Chap. VIII. The two electrons of the
inner shell may be considered as coincident with the nucleus for our
purpose. *Outside* the kernel the effective charge attracting the valence
electron is Z_o, where

$$Z_o = Z - 10, \tag{23}$$

while *inside* the kernel it is

$$Z_i = Z - 2. \tag{24}$$

Neglecting the effect of polarization, the potential energy of the system
when the valence electron is outside the shell is

$$V = \frac{-Z_o e^2}{r}, r > \rho, \tag{25}$$

while inside the shell it is

$$V = \int_\infty^\rho \frac{Z_o e^2}{r^2} dr + \int_\rho^r \frac{Z_i e^2}{r^2} dr = -\frac{Z_o e^2}{\rho} - \frac{Z_i e^2}{r} + \frac{Z_i e^2}{\rho}, r < \rho. \tag{26}$$

The total energy and angular momentum of the electron are the same
both inside and outside, and its path consists of sections of ellipses
(Fig. 6). The equations of the outside and inside orbits and their
semimajor axes are, respectively,

$$\frac{p^2}{m Z_o e^2} \frac{1}{r} = 1 - \left[1 + \frac{2E p^2}{m Z_o{}^2 e^4}\right]^{\frac{1}{2}} \cos\theta, a_o = \frac{-Z_o e^2}{2E}, \tag{27}$$

and

$$\frac{p^2}{m Z_i e^2} \frac{1}{r} = 1 - \left[1 + \frac{2E_i p^2}{m Z_i{}^2 e^4}\right]^{\frac{1}{2}} \cos\theta, a_i = -\frac{Z_i e^2}{2E_i},$$

where

$$E_i = E - \frac{(Z_i - Z_o)e^2}{\rho}.$$

In applying the azimuthal quantum condition to this orbit the range
of integration is 2π, and so

$$p = \frac{kh}{2\pi}, \tag{28}$$

but the range of integration for the radial quantum condition is made up
of an outer loop and an inner loop, for after traversing this path the
electron repeats its motion. The radial integral is

$$2\int_{r_{min}}^\rho \left[2mE_i + \frac{2m Z_i e^2}{r} - \frac{p^2}{r^2}\right]^{\frac{1}{2}} dr$$
$$+ 2\int_\rho^{r_{max}} \left[2mE + \frac{2m Z_o e^2}{r} - \frac{p^2}{r^2}\right]^{\frac{1}{2}} dr = n_r h. \tag{29}$$

The integration can easily be carried out, but the graphical method used by Wentzel,[1] Sommerfeld,[2] and others shows more clearly the meaning of this integral. In Fig. 9, which is a modification of one given by Sommerfeld, p_r is plotted against r so that the area under the curve $ABCD$ is the radial integral and according to the quantum conditions must be equal to $n_r h$. The radial integral of another orbit is outlined by the curve $A'B'C'D'$, and that of an orbit which just falls within the kernel by the curve $A''C''D''$.

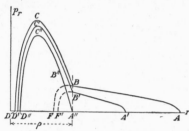

FIG. 9.—Radial phase integrals of penetrating orbits.

The energy E of the quantized orbit must be such that the azimuthal and radial quantum conditions are fulfilled. The area under the curve ABF is the radial integral of an orbit having the same energy and angular momentum as the actual one but which lies entirely in the inverse square field of force of a positive charge $Z_o e$.

The area under this curve is not a multiple of Planck's constant. We set

$$\oint \left[2mE + \frac{2mZe^2}{r} - \frac{p^2}{r^2} \right]^{\frac{1}{2}} dr = n_r {}^* h \tag{30}$$

and then

$$E = -\frac{Rhc}{(n_r{}^* + k)^2} = -\frac{Rhc}{n^{*2}}, \tag{31}$$

where $n_r{}^*$ and n^* are not whole numbers and n^* is obviously the effective quantum number defined in Sec. 7. Further,

$$nh = n^* h + Qh, \tag{32}$$

where Q is the quantum defect defined in equation (12), and so

$$n_r h = n_r{}^* h + Qh. \tag{33}$$

The geometric meaning of Qh is now clear. It is the area $FBCDF$. The figure shows that this area is nearly independent of the total quantum number; that is, Q is nearly constant for all lines of a given spectral series.

When the approximate distribution of the inner electrons is known, the radius ρ of the electron shell can be specified roughly; curves like those of Fig. 9 can be constructed and the value of Q can be determined for each orbit. Approximate considerations of this kind were extensively used by Bohr in determining the total quantum numbers of the alkali valence electrons in their normal ^2S orbits. Anticipating, these numbers are 2, 3, 4, 5, and 6 for Li, Na, K, Rb, and Cs, respectively. Cu, Ag, and

[1] Z. Physik, **19**, 53 (1923).
[2] "Atombau," 4th ed., p. 537.

Au have the valence electron in the $^2S_{1/2}$ states in 4, 5 and 6 quantum orbits, respectively. The values of Q assigned to the energy states of the doublet spectra considered here are given in Table 3 and the values of the total quantum numbers of the orbits are obtained by adding Q to the effective quantum number and taking the nearest whole number.

11. PARTIALLY PENETRATING ORBITS

As stated above, it may happen that the orbits of higher total quantum number in a sequence may penetrate the kernel while those of lower quantum number do not. This occurs, if the radius of the kernel lies between k^2a_1 and $k^2a_1/2$, as shown in Fig. 7. An example of this was found by Wentzel (*loc. cit.*) in the ^1P sequence of terms of the mercury arc spectrum. The higher members of this sequence have large quantum defects while the lower terms have small quantum defects. This sequence belongs to an atom with two valence electrons, however, and, therefore, the irregularity of the effective quantum number may be partly due to causes other than the one considered here.

12. MODELS OF MORE COMPLICATED ATOMS, AND THE RITZ FORMULA

The results obtained from our penetrating-orbit model of the sodium-like atom, such as the derivation of the Rydberg formula, are surprising in view of its simplicity. Of course many modifications suggest themselves. The force field outside the kernel is not exactly an inverse square field as assumed, partly because of polarization forces and partly because the electrons of the kernel cannot be replaced by a uniformly charged spherical surface. Moreover, in dealing with more complicated atoms, the effect of the electrons should be approximated by several shells of charge. The orbit of a valence electron would then consist of parts of several ellipses with different major and minor axes. It can be shown by methods like those of Sec. 9 that the spectral terms of such a model are given by the Ritz formula (8). According to the theory the constant a should be negative, and b positive. Ordinarily this is found to be the case.

Much attention has been devoted to the computation of spectral terms on the basis of the shell model, and in simple cases fair agreement with the spectra has been attained. Appropriate distributions of the inner electrons must be determined with the aid of information gained from X-ray spectra.

13. THE ORIGIN OF THE ALKALI DOUBLETS

We have seen that the difference between the orbits $m^2P_{3/2}$ and and $m^2P_{1/2}$ of the valence electron of an alkali lies in the orientation of the electron-spin vector with respect to its angular momentum. The quantum numbers n, l, and s are the same for both orbits, but s and l are parallel and antiparallel for these two states, respectively. Therefore, we should be able to calculate the wave-number difference of these terms by a method like that used in Chap. V, Secs. **16** to **19,** to obtain the difference of the terms 2, 1, $\frac{3}{2}$ and 2, 1, $\frac{1}{2}$ of hydrogen. The parallelism of the two cases is most easily seen by considering the element lithium, whose P orbits do not penetrate the kernel, the term values being very close to those of hydrogen. At the left of Fig. 10 the positions of the two-quantum states of hydrogen are indicated on a much exaggerated scale. The 2, 1, $\frac{1}{2}$, and 2, 0, $\frac{1}{2}$ terms are shown separately though they are actually coincident. The slight displacements of these terms from the positions predicted by the simple Balmer formula are due to the combined effects of relativity and electron spin, as summed up in equation (93), Chap. V. The corresponding terms of lithium are shown on the

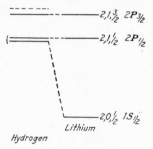

Hydrogen

FIG. 10.—The correlation of hydrogen and lithuim terms.

right, also on a distorted scale. The $1^2S_{\frac{1}{2}}$ orbit penetrates the kernel, as we recognize immediately from Table 3. Its quantum numbers are $n = 2$, $l = 0$, $j = \frac{1}{2}$, so that it corresponds to the 2, 0, $\frac{1}{2}$ orbit of hydrogen and is denoted by the same symbol. Similarly, the $2^2P_{\frac{1}{2}}$ and $2^2P_{\frac{3}{2}}$ orbits correspond to 2, 1, $\frac{1}{2}$ and 2, 1, $\frac{3}{2}$ of hydrogen. The interval between these two states is small, for the orbits have the same total and azimuthal numbers, and are practically coincident. In fact, the interval is due to the electron spin. The energy of the penetrating 2, 0, $\frac{1}{2}$ orbit is also affected by the electron spin and the relativity change of mass, though these are small compared to the increase of the term due to penetration. The interval between $1S$ and $2P$ is usually called a "screening doublet," for the difference of their energies is due to the fact that on the average an electron on a $1S$ orbit is not screened from the powerful attraction of the nucleus to the extent it would be in traversing a $2P$ orbit. Likewise, the interval between the $2^2P_{\frac{1}{2}}$ and $2^2P_{\frac{3}{2}}$ orbits is called a "spin doublet." A better name would be "spin-relativity doublet."

A quantitative test of the adequacy of this explanation is easily made. From equation (93) of Chap. V, the interval between two levels with quantum numbers n, l, $l + \frac{1}{2}$ and n, l, $l - \frac{1}{2}$ is

$$\Delta \bar{\nu} = \frac{R\alpha^2 Z^4}{n^3 l(l+1)}. \tag{33}$$

Now, in dealing with lithium, instead of employing an effective quantum number, we may think of the non-penetrating $2P$ orbits as hydrogenic orbits moving in the field of a nucleus with an effective charge Z_{eff}, so that the spectral term is

$$T = \frac{R Z_{\text{eff}}^2}{2^2}. \tag{34}$$

Using the known value of T, namely 28,582.5, we find that $Z_{eff} = 1.021$. This value is used in equation (33) to calculate the relativity and spin corrections of the two orbits in question. The result is

$$\Delta\bar{\nu}_{Li} = \frac{Z^4_{eff}}{1^4}\Delta\bar{\nu}_H, \tag{35}$$

where $\Delta\bar{\nu}_H$ is the separation of the two quantum orbits of hydrogen, 0.365 cm.$^{-1}$. Therefore,

$$\Delta\bar{\nu}_{Li} = 0.386 \text{ cm.}^{-1}.$$

Kent[1] has found the separation of the $2P$ orbits to be 0.34 cm.$^{-1}$, which is a satisfactory agreement in view of the approximate nature of our model.

In order to apply these ideas to the penetrating orbits of the other alkalies, it is necessary to consider the contributions of the inner and outer parts of the orbits. On the outer part of its orbit, the electron moves in a field corresponding to an effective atomic number Z_o and in an orbit whose dimensions are determined by the quantum numbers n^* and l. For an electron moving in a complete orbit of the same shape as this outer loop, the difference in wave number for the two possible orientations of the electron spin relative to the orbital angular momentum will be

$$\Delta\bar{\nu}_o = \frac{R\alpha^2 Z_o^4}{n^{*3}l(l+1)}. \tag{36}$$

Similarly, the wave number separation for the two orientations for an electron moving in a complete ellipse having the same constants as the inner loop will be

$$\Delta\bar{\nu}_i = \frac{R\alpha^2 Z_i^4}{n_i^3 l(l+1)}. \tag{37}$$

To get the value of $\Delta\bar{\nu}$ for the actual orbit consisting of an outer and inner loop (Fig. 6), we weight these two values in proportion to the relative times spent by the electron in the two parts of the orbit. This procedure is partially justified by the theorem of Chap. VI, Sec. **10**.

The time τ required for the electron to move from the position of maximum distance from the nucleus to the minimum distance and back again in the actual orbit is nearly equal to the time τ_o required for it to traverse the whole outer ellipse, a result easily verified by the study of a few examples. Therefore,

$$\tau \cong \tau_o = \frac{n^{*3}h^3}{4\pi^2 m e^4 Z_o^2}. \tag{38}$$

Similarly, the time spent in the inner loop of the orbit is very nearly equal to the time of revolution in a completed internal orbit, so that

$$\tau_i \cong \frac{n_i^3 h^3}{4\pi^2 m e^4 Z_i^2}. \tag{39}$$

[1] *Astrophys. J.*, **46**, 343 (1914).

and

$$\Delta \bar{\nu} = \Delta \bar{\nu}_o \frac{\tau_o}{\tau} + \Delta \bar{\nu}_i \frac{\tau_i}{\tau} \cong \Delta \bar{\nu}_o + \Delta \nu_i \frac{\tau_i}{\tau_o}$$

$$\cong \frac{R\alpha^2 Z_o^2}{n^{*3} l(l+1)} (Z_o^2 + Z_i^2). \tag{40}$$

14. THE CALCULATION OF ORBITAL PROPERTIES FROM DOUBLET SEPARATIONS

If Z_o is small compared to Z_i, the first term in the parenthesis can be neglected. In this form Landé[1] used equation (40) to calculate values of Z_i for the penetrating P levels of a large number of atoms and found that Z_i differed from the atomic number by only a few units in all cases. This was interpreted as showing that the electron penetrates close to the nucleus in all these orbits.

For the doublet separations of ionized atoms of low atomic number it is not justifiable to neglect Z_o^2 in the equation above. The Z_i values for the doublet spectrum of Na and for ions which have the same number of electrons as Na (namely, 11), are given in Table 5.

TABLE 5

	Z_o	$2^2P_{1/2} - 2^2P_{3/2}$	n^*	Z_i	$3^2P_{1/2} - 3^2P_{3/2}$	n^*	Z_i
Na I.	1	17.18	2.117	7.58	5.49	3.134	7.55
Mg II.	2	91.55	2.265	9.34	30.05	3.287	9.36
Al III.	3	238	2.370	10.58	80.13	3.392	10.50
Si IV.	4	460	2.450	11.37	162.06	3.471	11.38
P V.	5	795	2.509	12.14			
S VI.	6	1279	2.556	12.85			

	$4^2P_{1/2} - 4^2P_{3/2}$	n^*	Z_i	Average Z_i	$Z - Z_i$
Na I.	2.49	4.139	7.72	7.62	3.38
Mg II.	14.07	4.294	9.57	9.42	2.58
Al III.	39.15	4.399	10.85	10.62	2.36
Si IV.	75	4.478	11.34	11.36	2.64
P V.	.....	.....	.....	12.14	2.86
S VI.	.....	.....	.....	12.95	3.05

The last column of the table gives the value of the so-called screening constant for the inner part of the orbit. It is the difference between the atomic number and the calculated value of Z_i for the ^2P orbits of these atoms. The data indicate that the P orbits of these atoms plunge inside a shell of about 7 electrons and remain outside the region occupied

[1] Z. Physik., **25**, 46 (1924). See also MILLIKAN and BOWEN, Phys. Rev., **24**, 209 (1924).

by about 3 electrons. This agrees fairly well with the arrangement
of electrons discussed in Chap. IX, according to which there is an inner
shell of 2, and a second shell of 8. Since the quantum defect Q is greater
for the ^2S levels it seems very probable that the electron in these steady
states penetrates the inner shell.

Such calculations make possible the extrapolation from the known
doublet separations of atoms to unknown separations of other atoms.
Bowen and Millikan[1] used this method to aid in identifying the series
lines of P V and S VI, used in making the calculations of Table 5, and the
method has been particularly useful in studying the doublets of stripped
atoms of the long periods.[2] The cause of the separations of systems of
higher multiplicity (triplets, quartets, etc.) to be taken up immediately
is similar, and similar methods can be used for extrapolating from known
to unknown multiplet separations.

15. BOHR-GROTRIAN DIAGRAMS

In studying approximate orbits, it is very convenient to use energy
diagrams like those in Fig. 11. The energy increases toward the right

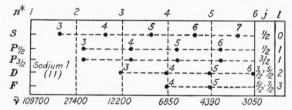

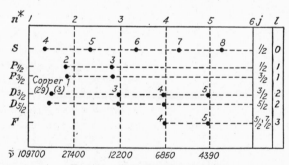

FIG. 11.—Bohr-Grotrian diagrams.

and the point of zero energy is represented by the line at the extreme
right of the diagram. The energy values of the terms S, P, D, etc.,
as given at the left, or of the l values 0, 1, 2, etc., as given at the right,
are indicated by dots. The vertical lines represent the energy levels

[1] *Phys. Rev.*, **25**, 295 (1925).

[2] GIBBS and WHITE, *Proc. Nat. Acad. Sci.*, **12**, 675 (1926).

of hydrogenic atoms. The total quantum numbers n are written beside the terms. If an energy level falls close to the corresponding hydrogenic level, the orbit is ordinarily assumed to be non-penetrating and is given the same quantum numbers as the corresponding hydrogenic level; the doublet separation must also be small in order that this may be justifiable. Thus in Cu I, the ^2P levels fall near the two-quantum level of hydrogen so that they might be assigned the numbers $n, l = 2, 1$. The doublet separation is large, however, and it is probable that this is a penetrating orbit with the quantum numbers $n, l = 4, 1$. The assignment of total quantum numbers is largely determined from such general studies of the building up of the entire periodic system of the elements, which will be taken up in Chap. IX after X-ray spectra have been discussed.

16. THE SCHEME OF QUANTUM NUMBERS FOR AN ATOM HAVING ANY NUMBER OF VALENCE ELECTRONS[1]

We are now in a position to discuss the spectra of atoms having several valence electrons. New phenomena will be encountered because the properties of the atom, *e.g.*, its energy, and its behavior when external fields are applied, will depend on the quantum numbers of all the electrons in the uncompleted outside group. In the presence of a uniform external force field, which we assume to be magnetic for simplicity, each electron in the outer group may be characterized by five quantum numbers. We denote the quantum numbers of the pth electron by

$$n_p, \ l_p, \ m_{lp}, \ s_p, \ m_{sp}. \tag{41}$$

Here n_p is the total number, l_p the reduced azimuthal number, and m_{lp} the component of l_p along the lines of force; s_p is the spin quantum number while m_{sp} is the component of s_p along the lines of force.[2] When there is no external field, the system is degenerate and the situation is simplified. Let us suppose that the values of n_p and l_p for each electron

---

[1] The quantum numbers l, s, and j are vectors and should be indicated in bold-face type; but, since this is not customary, they have been indicated in this way only when it was especially necessary to emphasize their vector character.

[2] These five quantum numbers do not constitute a unique choice, and we shall sometimes use other systems, *e.g.*, we shall replace s_p by j_p, where j_p is the resultant of s_p and l_p. The reader may wonder why the spinning electron is assigned only five quantum numbers. The fact is, there should be six quantum numbers if we think of the electron as a rigid body spinning on an axis. To specify the position of such a body, we may give the coordinates of a point on the axis, and three other coordinates which specify the motion of the electron about its center of gravity. The quantum numbers for the motion of a symmetric rigid body in the absence of a field of force are discussed in Chap. XII, Sec. **24.** A third quantum number specifying the orientation of the angular momentum vector is necessary when a field of force is applied. This corresponds to m_{sp}. In the case of the spinning electron, it appears probable that the other two have the same physical significance, so that apparently we deal with only one of them.

are specified. The value of s_p is always $\frac{1}{2}$. This will not make the energy of the atom determinate, for the l and s vectors of the various electrons may assume various orientations with respect to each other, each one corresponding to a different energy level. In practice, many of these possibilities are not realized at all; or, if they are, they give rise to very weak spectral lines. We have seen that in the case of the alkali metals, the l_p and s_p vectors of the valence electron combine to form a quantized resultant j_p, but in an atom with several valence electrons it is not generally true that the l_p and s_p vectors of each electron combine to form a quantized resultant, because of the influence of the other electrons. Two limiting cases are to be distinguished: (1) that in which the vectors s_p are closely coupled, and the vectors l_p are also closely coupled, with little interaction between the s_p and l_p of each electron; (2) that in which the s_p and l_p vectors are closely coupled while there is little interaction between the individual electrons. Between these extremes, all possible intermediate strengths of coupling are supposed to exist. The exact nature of the coupling is immaterial in enumerating the spectral terms, because either case (1) or (2) leads us to predict the existence of the same number of terms. The relative positions of the terms in these two cases, however, will be quite different. Case (1) corresponds to the term arrangements found in the spectra of elements in the first three columns of the periodic table and in many multiplet spectra, while case (2) is well illustrated by neon and other rare gases. All the spectra considered in the remainder of this chapter can be explained on the basis of case (1). Therefore, we assume, as an *approximation*, that when no external field is present,

(1) The spin vectors s_p will form a quantized resultant

$$s = \Sigma s_p, \tag{42}$$

and each s_p will precess about this resultant.

(2) The reduced azimuthal quantum number l_p likewise form a quantized resultant

$$l = \Sigma l_p, \tag{43}$$

and each l_p precesses about the resultant l.

(3) The vectors l and s form a resultant j around which they precess,

$$\mathbf{j} = \mathbf{l} + \mathbf{s}. \tag{44}$$

The behavior of these vectors in the presence of an external field will be discussed in Chap. X, Sec. **8**.

We must now explain the part played by the numbers l, s, and j in the analysis of spectra, anticipating the descriptions to be given in the next few sections. Before the discovery of the spin of the electron, the study of spectra emitted by atoms with several valence electrons had led to the introduction of an azimuthal number k and an inner number for each spectral term, just as in the case of alkali metal spectra. The term sequences were given the names, S, P, D, etc., and the values $k = 1, 2$, and 3, etc. were assigned to these sequences, exactly as described in Sec. **3**. Naturally, it was believed that the azimuthal number of a spectral term was actually the azimuthal number of a single electron, called the "leuchtelektron" or "emitting electron." Today, we know that $k - 1$ is identical with l, the resultant of the l_p, so that $l = 0, 1, 2, \cdots$ etc. for the S, P, D, etc. terms, respectively. When $s = 0, \frac{1}{2}, 1$, etc. we are dealing with singlets, doublets, triplets, etc. The multiplicity of the system of terms is indicated by a superscript in front of the symbol S, P, etc. Thus a triplet term for which $l = 1$ and $j = 2$ is written $^3P_2$.

17. DESCRIPTION OF SECOND-GROUP SPECTRA

The spectra of the neutral atoms of second group elements are more complicated than those of the alkalies because there are two sets of energy levels, a singlet system and a triplet system. We have spectral lines due to the combination of single levels, and groups of spectrum lines, three or six in number, due to the combination of triplet levels with other triplet levels. In addition, there are lines caused by the change from a triplet level to a single level, and *vice versa*, which are called "intercombination lines." In these spectra, the terms and their combinations may be described by means of numbers l, j, and s, just as in the case of the alkali atoms. These numbers are characteristic of the term and *not* of any single electron. It is found empirically that when they are assigned to the terms in the way indicated in the energy diagram (Fig. 12), the selection rules as given above for doublet spectra hold true, *i.e.*, l changes by ± 1, except in the case of combinations with the so-called primed terms, which will be discussed presently; and j changes by ± 1 or 0, with the additional restriction that the change $0 \to 0$ is forbidden.

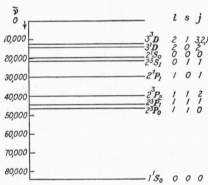

Fig. 12.—The energy diagram of mercury.

We use the Hg spectrum (Fig. 13) as the first example because of its importance in experimental work. The physical properties of Hg are such that it is widely used in testing spectroscopic theories as well as in photochemistry and biological work, and the reader cannot be too familiar with its spectrum. Anticipating, we may say that all the terms which we shall define in discussing this element correspond to configurations in which one of the two valence electrons is on an excited orbit, while the other is on an unexcited orbit. The frequency differences between the components of the more important triplet levels of Hg are very large; *e.g.*, $2^3P_1 - 2^3P_2 = 4,631$ cm.$^{-1}$. Quite generally, the separations of the components of multiple terms increase as we pass from low to high atomic numbers in a given group of the periodic table. The large $\bar{\nu}$ difference of the 2^3P terms of Hg causes successive groups in the sharp and diffuse triplet series to overlap, so that it is difficult to detect series in this element by eye. The lowest term of the spectrum is the singlet term 1^1S_0 which lies at 84,178 cm.$^{-1}$. There is no triplet S state having a term value comparable with 1^1S_0. 2^1S_0 is found at 20,353 cm.$^{-1}$ and an S level of the triplet system lies nearby at 21,831 cm.$^{-1}$. Because of the close agreement in energy value with the 2^1S_0 orbit, this state is also given the number 2 and is called 2^3S_1. The first lines of the singlet and intercombination principal series, $1^1S_0 - 2^1P_1$ at 1,849 Å, and $1^1S_0 - 2^3P_1$ at 2,536.7 Å, are the important *resonance lines*. They are the only lines in the absorption spectrum which lie in accessible regions. Often conditions are such that $\lambda 1,849$ is the strongest line of the

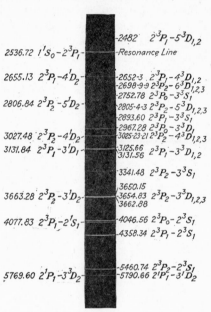

Fig. 13.—The mercury spectrum.

emission spectrum. The most important series of Hg are as follows: (In reading across a horizontal line the wave length decreases.)

Singlet System:

Principal..............	$m \geqq 2$	$1^1S_0 - m^1P_1$; $m \geqq 3$, $2^1S_0 - m^1P_1$.
Sharp.................	$m \geqq 2$	$2^1P_1 - m^1S_0$.
Diffuse...............	$m \geqq 3$	$2^1P_1 - m^1D_2$.

Triplet System:

Principal..............	......	..........; $m \geqq 3$, $2^3S_1 - m^3P_{0,1,2}$.
Sharp.................	$m \geqq 2$	$2^3P_2 - m^3S_1$; $2^3P_1 - m^3S_1$; $2^3P_0 - m^3S_1$.
Diffuse...............	$m \geqq 3$	$2^3P_2 - m^3D_{1,2,3}$; $2^3P_1 - m^3D_{1,2}$; $2^3P_0 - m^3D_1$.

Intercombination:

Principal..............	$m \geqq 2$	$1^1S_0 - m^3P_1$.

It is unnecessary to illustrate the nature of the singlet series, so we begin with the first triplet of the sharp series. The wave lengths, wave numbers, and wave-number differences of its three lines are as follows:

Classification	λ	$\tilde{\nu}$	$\Delta\tilde{\nu}$
$2^3P_2 - 2^3S_1$	5,460.74	18,307.5	4,630.6
$2^3P_1 - 2^3S_1$	4,358.34	22,938.1	1,767.3
$2^3P_0 - 2^3S_1$	4,046.56	24,705.4	

Higher members of the series are similar and, obviously, have the wave number differences listed for the first triplet. A diffuse triplet is more complicated, since it is obtained by the combination of two triplet levels. Thus it would be expected to contain nine lines, but three of these are

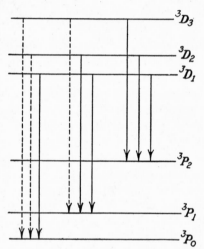

Fig. 14.—Transitions of a $^3P - {}^3D$ multiplet.

eliminated by the operation of the selection principle for j. In Fig. 14 we see how this occurs. Numerical data for the diffuse triplet $2^3P - 3^3D$ of the related element cadmium are given below:

Classification	λ	$\tilde{\nu}$	$\Delta\tilde{\nu}_{3D}$	$\Delta\tilde{\nu}_{2P}$
$2^3P_2 - 3^3D_1$	3,614.43	27,659.0	11.8	
$\quad - 3^3D_2$	3,612.89	27,670.8	18.2	1,171.1
$\quad - 3^3D_3$	3,610.51	27,689.0		
$2^3P_1 - 3^3D_1$	3,467.61	28,830.1	18.9	
$\quad - 3^3D_2$	3,466.18	28,842.0		542.2
$2^3P_0 - 3^3D_1$	3,403.60	29,372.3		

As for the intercombination principal series, the lines $1^1S_0 - m^3P_2$ are ruled out by the j selection principle, while $1^1S_0 - m^3P_0$ is absent because of the additional restriction that transitions do not occur between states for both of which $j = 0$.

In addition to the series systems mentioned in the above tabulation, any second-group metal has sequences of so-called "primed terms," corresponding to configurations in which both valence electrons are on excited orbits. Mercury does not furnish a good illustration of these terms so we shall study them in magnesium instead. Before discussing the primed terms, however, it will be best to study the combinations of quantum numbers giving rise to the terms already described.

18. ORDINARY SERIES OF A TWO-ELECTRON SYSTEM, ILLUSTRATED BY MAGNESIUM

We deal first with terms of magnesium in which 1 electron remains on an s orbit, starting with the lowest term. The quantum numbers of this electron are indicated by the subscript 1, those of the "excited" electron by the subscript 2. Referring to Table 6, consider the assignment of quantum numbers written in the first line. The resultant of l_1 and l_2 is zero, while that of s_1 and s_2 may have the values zero or one, according as the spin vectors of the 2 electrons are opposed or parallel. In the first case, the vectorial sum of l and s is zero, and this is the value of j. In the second case, this sum is one. The level arising from the first arrangement is a singlet term. It is an S term, for l is zero, and its subscript gives the value of the inner quantum number. The second is called a triplet term for reasons similar to those given in Sec. **3** where the S levels of an alkali were called doublet S terms, even though they are single. The formation of the remainder of the table will be obvious. It should be noted that the triplet terms owe their threefold

TABLE 6.—QUANTUM NUMBERS FOR ORDINARY SERIES TERMS OF MG

n_1 s_1 l_1	n_2 s_2 l_2	s	l	j	Term
3 ½ 0	3 ½ 0	0	0	0	1^1S_0
		1	0	1	1^3S_1 (absent; explained in Sec. **19**)
3 ½ 0	3 ½ 1	0	1	1	2^1P_1
				0	2^3P_0
		1	1	1	2^3P_1
				2	2^3P_2
3 ½ 0	3 ½ 2	0	2	2	3^1D_2
				1	3^3D^1
		1	2	2	3^3D_2
				3	3^3D_3
3 ½ 0	4 ½ 0	0	0	0	2^1S_0
		1	0	1	2^3S_1
	etc.	etc.			etc.

character to the three possible quantized orientations of the s vector with respect to the l vector. In general, the number of levels corresponding to a given l and s is $2s + 1$.

The part of the table above the solid dividing line exhausts the possibilities of obtaining terms from a 3, 0 electron and a second three-quantum electron; the highest value of l which can arise from such an arrangement is 2 since $l_p < n_p$. To obtain F terms, we must place the second electron on a four-quantum orbit. Then, $l = l_2 = 0, 1, 2,$ or 3, and we obtain the second members of the S, P, and D sequences as well as the first member of the F sequence. In all the terms in this table, $l_2 = l$, so that l_2 determines the azimuthal character of the terms. In any atom containing only one valence electron with an l value different from zero, that electron may be considered as the "leuchtelektron," and all the others may reasonably be referred to the kernel; but, on the whole, such a distinction is of little benefit.

19. PAULI'S EQUIVALENCE PRINCIPLE

In the energy diagram of Hg and in Table 6, we note that the triplet system has no deep-lying level which might be called 1^3S_1 in analogy to the lowest level of the atom, 1^1S_0. This is due to the operation of Pauli's[1] equivalence principle, a far-reaching hypothesis now to be explained. In order to understand this principle we must become acquainted with the behavior of an atom in a magnetic field, discussed in Chap. X, Secs. **8** and **9**. In the presence of a weak field the vector j precesses about the direction of the lines of force. Just as in the cases of hydrogen and of the alkali metals, the atom is space-quantized in the field and the component of j in the direction of the field is called the magnetic quantum number m. On the other hand, in the presence of a very strong field the coupling of the various l_p and s_p vectors is broken down, and each of these vectors is independently space-quantized in the field. Their orientations follow the usual quantum rules, so that m_{l_p} takes integral values obeying the conditions,

$$-l_p \leqq m_{l_p} \leqq l_p, \tag{45}$$

while m_{s_p} has the values,

$$s_p \leqq m_{s_p} \leqq s_p, \text{ or } m_{s_p} = \pm \frac{1}{2}. \tag{46}$$

It is often more convenient to consider the case of a strong field because each electron is then definitely characterized by the five quantum numbers n_p, l_p, s_p, m_{s_p}, and m_{l_p}. The assignment of numbers for an intermediate field is not so simple as in either a weak or a strong field.

Pauli's principle is as follows:

There are never two or more equivalent electrons in the atom, such that the values of all five of their quantum numbers will be identical when a strong magnetic field is applied.

[1] *Z. Physik,* **31,** 765 (1925).

This assumption limits the number of ways in which the electrons in a field-free atom may be coupled, and also explains the structure of the periodic table of the elements (Chap. IX). We may use it at once to explain the absence of the 1^3S_1 term in Table 6. For this state, the total quantum numbers of both valence electrons are equal. Their l vectors are each equal to zero, and their s vectors are parallel. The orbits of these electrons are therefore completely equivalent, and if a strong field is applied parallel to the common direction of the s vectors, both electrons would be characterized by the magnetic quantum numbers $m_l = 0$, $m_s = +\frac{1}{2}$, or $m_l = 0$, $m_s = -\frac{1}{2}$, for both of them must behave similarly. This configuration would not be in agreement with Pauli's principle and, therefore, the level 1^3S_1 does not occur in the absence of a field. Other illustrations will be encountered continually.

20. QUANTUM NUMBERS FOR THE HIGHER SERIES SYSTEMS OF SECOND-GROUP ELEMENTS

Let us now return to the study of the Mg spectrum. If we place the first electron on a 4, 0 orbit and the second on a 3, 0 orbit, we obtain the terms 2^1S_0 and 2^3S_1, as before; but the configuration of a 4, 0 orbit together with any possible orbit other than 3, 0 yields a series system similar to that in Table 6. Of course, all the terms lie at much higher levels on the energy diagram than their analogues in Table 6, and the series converges to a different limit. The triplet S term corresponding to the arrangement 4, 0; 4, 0 is missing, by Pauli's rule. Similar systems are obtained if the first electron is on the 5, 0 orbit, and so on. Even the 4, 0 system must be expected to be extremely weak, and in Mg no such terms are known. They might be discovered by using a high-current arc. Series of this type are well known, however, in the spectra of other elements.

When the first electron is on a 3, 1 orbit instead of its normal position 3, 0, we encounter new relationships. Corresponding to given values of the l_p's, we can have *different* values for the resultant l; that is, *spectral terms having various l values are found to correspond to one and the same set of l_p values, the difference between them arising from the various possible orientations of the vectors l_p.* The way in which such terms arise is shown in Table 7. In this table some of the term symbols are provided with primes. The meaning of this notation is given in Sec. **21**.

It is not convenient at this stage to explain in detail the exclusions mentioned in the column of remarks for such explanation involves a knowledge of the strong field Zeeman effect of these terms, but we may describe the way in which these terms could arise, neglecting the fact that some of the possibilities listed are excluded. The resultant, s, of s_1 and s_2, may take the values $\frac{1}{2} - \frac{1}{2}$ or $\frac{1}{2} + \frac{1}{2}$. The first value yields *singlet* terms; for when $s = 0$, the resultant, j, of l and s is l itself;

TABLE 7.—SPECTRAL TERMS OF MG WITH 1 ELECTRON ON A 3, 1 ORBIT

n_2	l_2	s	l	j	Term	$\bar{\nu}$	Remarks
3	1	0	0	0	$^1S_0$	. . . .	Undiscovered in Mg.
			1	1	$^1P_1'$	. . . .	Excluded by Pauli's principle.
			2	2	$^1D_2$	3,649	Identical in position with 6^1D_2 in the ordinary ^1D series.
3	1	1	0	1	$^3S_1$	. . . .	Excluded by Pauli's principle.
			1	0, 1, 2	$^3P_0'$, $^3P_1'$, $^3P_2'$	3,798–3,860	$^3P_2'$, $_{1, 0}$ in Paschen notation.
			2	1, 2, 3	$^3D_1$, $^3D_2$, $^3D_3$	. . . .	Excluded by Pauli's principle.

that is, only *one* j-value arises from this set of values of l and s. But the value $s = 1$ gives rise to triplet terms. Whatever l may be, the addition of the vector $s = 1$ to the vector l gives *three* quantized resultants, $l + 1$, l, and $l - 1$; except that when $l = 0$, we have only one quantized resultant and $j = s$. This gives an isolated S term, $^3S_1$, called a triplet S term because it has the same s value as all the actual triplet terms. Now in the table the possible resultants of the vectors $l_1 = 1$ and $l_2 = 1$ are $l = 2$, 1, or 0. Taking each of these l values with each of the possible s values, we get the 6 multiple terms of Table 7. For experimental information on these terms the reader may consult a paper by Green and Petersen,[1] and another by Ruark,[2] dealing with the excitation potentials of lines involving some of these levels. We do not list terms in which the first electron is in a state of higher excitation, such as the 3, 2 orbit, for such terms are not known in the Mg spectrum. Terms due to a configuration consisting of one n, 2 and one n, 1 electron are strongly developed in Ca, Sr, and Ba.

21. PRIMED TERMS AND DISPLACED SEQUENCES

In the spectral tables for second-group elements there are many illustrations of terms which arise from electron configurations of the kind described in the last section. As an illustration we shall consider groups of lines in second-group spectra which may be interpreted as combinations of two triplet P terms. An excellent illustration is the strong multiplet near 4,300 Å in the Ca spectrum, which has the structure shown in Fig. 15. The lower level involved in the emission of this group is a ^3P level, which belongs to a sequence corresponding to that described in Table 6. When the atom is in one of these states, one valence electron is on a 4, 0 orbit and the second has the quantum numbers n, 1, where n is equal to or greater than 4. If we put $n = \infty$, the second electron is removed, and the ion which remains is similar to an alkali atom in its normal state. If we assign the wave number zero to this

[1] *Astrophys. J.*, **60**, 301, (1924).
[2] *J. O. S. A.*, **11**, 199 (1925).

state in the customary fashion, the ^3P levels of calcium are found to have wave numbers which obey a Ritz formula. However, this is not true of the upper levels for the emission of the multiplet at 4,300 Å, which are designated by m^3P', with m equal to 2, 3, etc. It was formerly customary to refer to such levels as primed levels, or primed terms, but the meaning of the term has been altered in recent years. Its present-day significance is described in Chap. X, Sec. 3.

Let us now examine the origin of the P' levels of calcium. When the atom is in a P' state the valence electrons are on 4, 2 and n, 1 orbits, respectively, with the understanding that n is greater than or equal to 4. When n becomes infinite, the atom is ionized; as before, the ion is similar to the atom of potassium, but it is not in the normal state, for the valence electron is on a ^2D orbit. The energy of this state is positive and its wave number is negative, if the normal state of the ion is taken as the origin and therefore the wave numbers of the mP' levels converge to a negative value and cannot be expected to follow a Ritz formula.

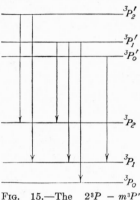

FIG. 15.—The $2^3P - m^3P'$ multiplet of calcium.

For example, the terms of the m^3P' sequence of Ca have been assigned the following wave numbers by Russell and Saunders:[1]

$2^3P'$	10,753,	10,840,	10,887
$3^3P'$	741,	767,	781
$4^3P'$	$-5,000,$	$-4,984,$	$-4,978$
$5^3P'$	$-8,334,$	$-8,313,$	$-8,306$
$6^3P'$	$-10,086,$	$-10,063,$	....

The fact that these terms extend into the region of negative wave numbers is worthy of notice. When the term is negative, the atom possesses more energy than would be required to eject a single valence electron from the unexcited atom.

All sequences which converge, as this one does, at an excited state of the ion, may be called "displaced;" they are neither anomalous nor infrequent, and it often happens that their wave numbers will obey a Ritz formula if the origin is shifted to the limit of the sequence. Thus, in the case of calcium, Russell and Saunders showed that the lines $2^3P_2 - m^3P_2'$ are well represented by the formula

$$\bar{\nu} = 47,950 - \frac{R}{[m - 0.8202 + 3.75 \cdot 10^{-5}(47,950 - \bar{\nu})]^2}, \ m \geq 2. \quad (47)$$

Since the final orbit involved in the emission of these lines is 2^3P_2, having the wave number 33,989 cm.$^{-1}$, the series limit lies at $2^3P_2 -$

[1] *Astrophys. J.*, **61**, 38 (1925).

$\infty \, ^3P_2' = 33,989 - 47,950 = -13,961$ cm.$^{-1}$. Let us now examine the evidence in favor of the statement made above, that the $\infty P'$ state is the ^2D state of the ion. We see that the ion will emit a quantum $\tilde{\nu} = 13,961$ in falling to its normal state which has wave number zero in our present scheme of reckoning. The lowest terms of Ca$^+$ (with zero at the principal series limit, corresponding to removal of the valence electron) are as follows: 1^2S at 95,740, 3^2D at $82,028 - 82,089$, and 2^2P at $70,325 - 70,548$ cm.$^{-1}$. Now $1^2S_{1/2} - 3^2D_{5/2} = 13,711$, and this agrees with 13,961 within the error involved in determining the limit for the mP' sequence, which is somewhat irregular.

This alone would not be sufficient proof of the assignment of quantum numbers cited above, but similar relationships are found in strontium and barium, and the question may be regarded as settled. In the elements Be and Mg, on the other hand, the situation is different, and a controversy arose before the matter was completely understood. Some authors claimed that the P' terms of all second-group elements arise from the configuration $l_1 = 2$, $l_2 = 1$, while others believed that the l values of both electrons are equal to one. Theoretically, there should be term systems corresponding to both configurations, and the question involved is really that of their relative prominence. For example, there should be Mg terms arising from the electron grouping 3, 1; 3, 2, but lines involving them should be very faint for these terms lie much higher on the energy diagram than those corresponding to 3, 1; 3, 1. This is due to the fact that the 2^2P level of Mg$^+$ is lower than 3^2D. On the other hand, in the spectra of Ca, Sr, and Ba, 3^3D is very close to 2^3P, and in Ba, 3^3D is actually lower than 2^3P. Further in the spectra Ca II, Sr II, and Ba II, 3^2D is greater than 2^2P. Therefore, in these three ions this term lies closer to the normal level, 1^2S, than any other level, and is metastable because of the operation of the azimuthal selection principle. It is well adapted to give rise to prominent terms when an electron is picked up by the ion to form a neutral atom.

22. SELECTION PRINCIPLES

Anticipating the explanations given in Chap. X, Sec. **3**, we may state the following selection principles for second-group spectra, which are a generalization of the ones used up to this point. The selection rule for j is $\Delta j = \pm 1$ or 0; that for l may be expressed by saying that only those transitions occur in which the l_p of one electron changes by ± 1, and that of a second by 0 or ± 2. If the l value of only one electron is altered, then it changes by ± 1. This rule is obeyed with only a few exceptions in all spectra.

CHAPTER VIII

X-RAYS AND X-RAY SPECTRA

1. THE DISCOVERY AND PRODUCTION OF X-RAYS

While experimenting with a cathode ray tube, Röntgen[1] discovered that rays capable of passing through opaque objects originate wherever the cathode particles fall on the glass walls of the tube. These rays cause the air through which they pass to become ionized and thus conductive, affect a photographic plate, and cause many substances to fluoresce. They spread from the point of origin in all directions in straight lines and are not deflected by electric and magnetic fields. Because of these properties, Röntgen gave the correct explanation that they are electromagnetic waves, similar to ordinary light but of much shorter wave length. However, experimental difficulties prevented him from demonstrating any interference phenomena such as are known for light. He observed that the ability of the rays to pass through thin layers of any substance varies greatly when the pressure of the residual gas in the tube is changed. Low pressure is favorable to the production of more penetrating or "harder" radiations, which have the shorter wave lengths. The

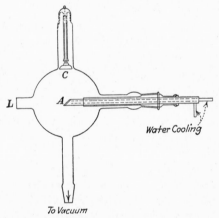

Fig. 1.—An ion X-ray tube. (*After Siegbahn.*)

stopping power of different elements for rays of the same hardness increases rapidly with the atomic number.

X-rays are emitted by any substance upon which high velocity electrons fall, the kinetic energy of translation of the electrons being converted into the energy of the X-rays. In present practice, the electrons are caused to impinge on a metal disk, the *anticathode*, instead of on the walls of the tube. The many types of tubes designed for the study of the rays themselves, of crystal structure, or of medical problems, vary in the means used for producing the free electrons and in the

[1] *Sitz.-Ber. phys.-med. Ges.*, Würzburgh, 1895. English translation in *The Electrician*, Jan. 24, 1896, and Apr. 24, 1897.

arrangement of the electrodes. We shall distinguish two main types, differing in the manner of producing the electron current. In *ion tubes*, the electrons are liberated when ions bombard the cathode. Such a tube is illustrated in Fig. 1 and consists of a disk-shaped cathode C, and anticathode A sealed in a glass bulb containing hydrogen at low pressures. A high potential (10 to 300 kilovolts), supplied by a transformer and rectifier or by a battery of cells, is placed between C and A. The residual positive ions present in the gas are accelerated toward the cathode and cause the emission of electrons from the cold metal when they impinge on it with high velocities. The free electrons produced in this way fall on the anticathode causing the emission of X-rays. By colliding with the H_2 molecules they maintain an abundant supply of ions which in turn maintain the electron supply. The electrons leave the cathode along lines perpendicular to its surface since nearly the entire potential drop from the cathode to the anode is very near the cathode and the electric force is nearly perpendicular to its surface. By making the cathode concave, the electrons can be focused on a small area of the anticathode. X-rays emitted at A can pass out through the glass walls or through a window of thin metal foil (usually aluminium) at L. The anticathode is often water-cooled as in the figure and can be removed from the tube so that different substances can be placed upon it. The kinetic energy of the electrons hitting the anticathode depends on the applied potential, and on the energy loss to molecules of the gas, that is, on the pressure. When the voltage across the tube, which determines the hardness of the radiation, is varied, the current is changed. The impossibility of varying these two factors independently is a marked disadvantage.

Highly evacuated X-ray tubes differ from the ion tubes in that few gaseous ions are produced. Practically no electrons are liberated from the cathode by ionic bombardment. Other means are used to secure free electrons from the cathode such as thermal or photoelectric emission. The most common method is to use a hot filament, usually tungsten, as the cathode. The advantage of this type of tube over the ion tube is that both the potential drop and electron current and thus the hardness and intensity of the X-rays can be easily and exactly controlled.

2. THE NATURE OF X-RAYS

When a beam of X-rays falls on matter a portion of its energy is dissipated in a variety of ways. This energy is usually said to disappear by a process of absorption or by one of scattering. In absorption processes the energy is taken up by the atoms, raising them to higher quantized states or ionizing them. In the return to the normal condition these atoms can emit radiations which are definitely characteristic of the type of atom involved and are commonly called the "fluorescent" or "characteristic radiations." In scattering processes the atoms and electrons of the scattering material serve merely to deflect the X-ray quanta and in some cases to change their energy slightly, as explained in our discussion of the Compton effect in Chap. IV. Aside from this minor alteration of wave length, the properties of the secondary X-rays are determined by the character of the primary beam.

We now discuss the experimental proofs that X-rays possess all the essential properties of ordinary light; in fact, many of their properties can be successfully predicted over a wide range of wave lengths by the electromagnetic theory of light. The existence of polarized X-rays was first demonstrated by studying the properties of scattered rays. In a beam of unpolarized X-rays, the electric vector shows no preference, on the average, for any direction perpendicular to the beam. It may be resolved into two components aa and bb perpendicular to each other. In Fig. 2, OA represents the direction of the beam. At A is placed a body which partially scatters this primary beam. According to electrodynamic laws, electrons in A vibrate with the frequency of the light beam and send out secondary wavelets in all directions which have the intensity and polarization required for the light emitted by an oscillating doublet (Appendix

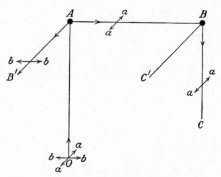

Fig. 2.—The polarization of X-rays by scattering.

VIII). The component of motion of an electron which is due to the aa component of the electric vector produces light with electric vector in the direction of the meridians of a sphere, having its poles in the direction aa, as shown in Fig. 2, Chap. I. At a distance r from the scatterer in a direction making an angle θ with aa, the intensity of this light should be proportional to

$$\frac{e^2\dot{\mathbf{v}}^2 \sin^2 \theta}{4\pi c^3 r^2},\tag{1}$$

where $\dot{\mathbf{v}}$ is the acceleration produced by the electric field of the primary beam. From this formula the intensity of the light excited by aa is zero in the direction AB' and a maximum along AB. Similarly, the bb component of the primary beam will give rise to scattered light with its electric vector in the direction of the meridians of a sphere having its poles in the direction of bb. The intensity of this light is zero in the direction AB, and a maximum in the direction AB' perpendicular to this. Thus the beam scattered along AB, perpendicular to the primary beam should be completely polarized with its electric vector parallel to aa, while that in the direction AB' should be completely polarized along bb. The light scattered along the primary beam and that scattered backwards should be unpolarized, and in intermediate directions partial polarization should occur. The polarization of the scattered rays can be detected by allowing them to fall on a second scatterer, either at B or B'. Reasoning similar to that above shows that the light scattered at B should have its electric vector along the meridians of a sphere with poles in the direction aa and this should have zero intensity along BC' and maximum intensity along BC. Similar relations hold for the beam scattered at B'. Barkla[1] detected a difference in intensity for

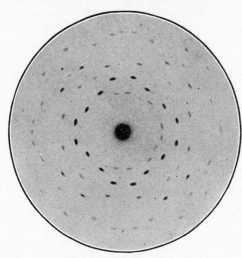

Fig. 3.—The Laue pattern of ZnS. (*After Laue, Friedrich, and Knipping.*)

the beams BC and BC' which indicated that the beam AB was 70 per cent polarized. A. H. Compton and Hagenow,[2] repeating this work, took precautions to avoid multiple scattering at A and B. They found polarization which was complete, within an experimental error of 1 or 2 per cent, showing that in this respect X-rays obey electromagnetic theory.

Additional evidence can be obtained from interference phenomena. Röntgen attempted to observe X-ray diffraction but was unsuccessful.

Haga and Wind[3] and Walter and Pohl[4] detected a slight broadening of a beam of rays which had passed through a wedge-shaped slit having a width of about 0.001 mm. at the broad end. Sommerfeld calculated the wave length of the X-rays used by these investigators as $1.3 \cdot 10^{-8}$ and $0.4 \cdot 10^{-8}$ cm., respectively. The experiments showed that the harder X-rays had the shorter wave lengths. Walter[5] and Rabinov[6] have made further studies of this subject.

Definite evidence of another kind was provided by Laue's discovery (1912) that X-rays can be diffracted by crystals. It occurred to him that regularly spaced layers of atoms separated by distances of the same order

[1] *Proc. Roy. Soc.*, **77**, 247 (1906).

[2] *J. O. S. A.* and *R. S. I.*, **8**, 487 (1924).

[3] *Ann. Physik*, **68**, 884 (1899).

[4] *Ann. Physik*, **29**, 331 (1909). See also Sommerfeld, *Physik. Z.*, **2**, 59 (1900); Sommerfeld and Koch, *Ann. Physik*, **38**, 507 (1912).

[5] *Ann. Physik*, **74**, 661 (1924); **75**, 189 (1924).

[6] *Proc. Nat. Acad. Sci.*, **11**, 222 (1925).

of magnitude as the wave length of the X-rays should act as a diffraction grating. At Laue's suggestion, Friedrich and Knipping performed an experiment to test the idea which was immediately successful.[1] A beam of X-rays, selected by narrow slits, fell on a crystal of ZnS about 0.5 mm. thick and struck a photographic plate mounted perpendicular to the beam. Most of the radiation passed the crystal without deflection, and a part was scattered in all directions, but beams of high intensity were scattered in certain definite directions so that a "point diagram" appeared on the plate as shown in Fig. 3. The theory of this pattern was developed by Laue, assuming that the atoms of the crystal were arranged regularly in space and that they acted as point charges in scattering the rays. Such patterns are valuable in the study of crystal structure but are not adapted to precise measurement of X-ray wave lengths. Arrangements for this purpose are discussed farther on.

3. REFLECTION AND REFRACTION IN THE X-RAY REGION

Recently, the wave lengths of X-rays have been measured without the use of crystals, the results agreeing with crystal determinations. The two methods used are refraction in prisms which may be either crystalline or amorphous, and diffraction at the surface of a ruled grating.

In considering the results of both types of experiment, we must remember that the refractive indices of solid substances (and presumably also of substances in other states) for X-rays are in general very slightly less than unity, for the same reason that we encounter refractive indices less than unity in the case of ordinary light—namely, we are dealing with a region lying at smaller wave lengths than a strong absorption band, a region of so-called "anomalous dispersion," though it is not in any way anomalous. As we can see from Chap. VII, Sec. **9**, the refractive index n of an amorphous substance is given by the equation

$$n^2 = \frac{1 + \left(\dfrac{8\pi}{3}\right)N\alpha}{1 - \left(\dfrac{4\pi}{3}\right)N\alpha}, \tag{2}$$

where N is the number of molecules per unit volume, and α the electric moment induced in a single molecule by unit electric field. If the medium contains harmonically bound electrons,

$$\alpha = \sum_i \frac{e^2}{4\pi^2 m} \frac{F_i}{\nu_i{}^2 - \nu^2}, \tag{3}$$

in a region of slight absorption, ν_i being a typical resonant frequency of the electrons. The constant F_i corresponding to each frequency ν_i is the number of electrons in each molecule having that frequency.

[1] *Sitzungsber. Bayer. Akad. Wiss. (Math.- Phys. Klasse)*, p. 303 (1912); *Ann. Physik*, **41**, 971 (1913).

n will be greater or less than unity depending on whether α is positive or negative and this depends on the relative magnitudes of ν_i and ν. If ν is less than all ν_i, n is greater than unity, but if ν is greater than all or a part of the resonant frequencies, n may be less than unity. In most of the refractive index experiments discussed here the wave lengths used are shorter than the resonance wave lengths of all the electrons in the atom; α is small and negative and, therefore,

$$n \cong 1 - N \sum_i \frac{F_i e^2}{2\pi m \nu^2}.$$

In deriving this equation, ν_i^2 is neglected in comparison with ν^2. The last term in this equation is of the order 5×10^{-6} for the refraction of the wave length 1.3 Å. in a glass prism of density 2.5. This formula is well confirmed by the measurements of Davis, Siegbahn, Compton, and their colleagues. This extension of the dispersion formula to the X-ray region could not have been expected confidently, since the assumptions for its derivation are so simple that we might well feel inclined to distrust an extrapolation of such great range.

The refraction of X-rays by solids has been used by Larson, Siegbahn and Waller[1] and by Davis and Slack[2] to secure prism spectrograms of K-series X-rays. The refracted beam is bent toward the apex of the wedge, because n is less than one. This method confirms the results of the more precise crystal grating methods of Sec. **7**.

Laby, Shearer, and Bingham[3] have recently made the discovery that X-rays having a wave length of about 50 Å. are reflected regularly from glass and quartz up to glancing angles of 45 degrees. (The *glancing angle* is the complement of the angle of incidence.) They state that the angle of incidence is accurately equal to the angle of reflection. The reflection coefficient is about 50 per cent for glancing angles up to 35 degrees. Check experiments were made to show that the radiation dealt with does not consist of electrons, or of light of longer wave length. These observations are especially interesting because they open the possibility that X-rays can be reflected from spherical surfaces and brought to a focus. If this is correct, it makes possible new methods for the study of long X-rays. For shorter X-rays, such reflection has not been observed, but since $n - 1$ is small and negative, it is possible to secure total reflection, if the glancing angle is sufficiently small— of the order of 30'. At any interface, total reflection occurs on the side of higher refractive index, which is the air side in the case of X-rays. Working within this small angle where total reflection occurs, Compton and

[1] *Phys. Rev.*, **25**, 235 (1925); *Naturwissenschaften*, **52**, 1212 (1924).

[2] *Phys. Rev.*, **25**, 881 (1925); *Ibid.*, **27**, 37 (1926); also SLACK, *ibid.*, **27**, 691 (1926).

[3] *Nature* **122**, 96 (1928). See also HENDERSON and LAIRD, *Proc. Nat. Acad. Sci.*, **14**, 773 (1928).

Doan[1] succeeded in securing an X-ray spectrum from a ruled speculum grating. Their photographs show an unreflected beam and diffracted beams of several orders at the positions predicted by the simple theory of the diffraction grating. The wave length of the $K\alpha_1$ line of molybdenum was found to be 0.707 Å. Within the error of experiment, this agrees with the value 0.70759 Å., obtained with crystal gratings. Similar spectra have been obtained by Thibaud,[2] Hunt,[3] and Weatherby,[4] who photographed lines with wave lengths between 6 and 46 Å. Figure 4 is a spectrogram, the original of which shows three orders of the carbon line known as $K\alpha$, at 44.6 Å. The direct beam (D) and a reflected beam (R) are also shown.

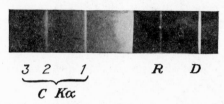

Fig. 4.—X-ray spectrogram of the carbon $K\ \alpha$ line. (*After Weatherby.*) D is the direct beam, R the reflected beam, and 1, 2, and 3 are the first, second, and third order spectra.

By a clever use of the phenomenon of total reflection, Prins[5] has brought forward evidence of anomalous dispersion in the X-ray region. His method consists in the determination of the limiting angle of total reflection of the X-rays at the surface of a mirror, with X-rays of various wave lengths. If the refractive index of the mirror is $1 - \delta$, then the limiting angle is approximately $\sqrt{2\delta}$. Prins was able to show that this angle varies considerably when the wave length passes through certain critical regions.

4. DIFFRACTION OF X-RAYS BY CRYSTALS

There are many useful arrangements of apparatus for studying the diffraction of X-rays by crystals. Some are especially adapted for the determination of crystal structures, the wave lengths utilized being known from the results of previous work, while others are especially suited to the independent determination of wave lengths. The methods introduced by W. H. and W. L. Bragg with their many modifications are equally useful in both these fields and depend on the use of a well-formed perfect crystal placed in definite orientations with respect to the incident X-ray beam. The method associated with the names of Debye and

[1] *Proc. Nat. Acad. Sci.*, **11**, 598 (1925).

[2] *C. R.*, **182**, 1141 (1926); *Revue d'optique*, **5**, 97 (1926).

[3] *Phys. Rev.*, **30**, 227 (1927).

[4] *Phys. Rev.*, **32**, 707 (1928).

[5] See *Naturwis.*, **16**, 555 (1928) for bibliography and for a summary of the results obtained; also *Z. Physik*, **47**, 479 (1928).

Scherrer and of Hull and frequently called the "powder method" has its main applications in the field of crystal structure and has the advantage that it depends on the use of a diffracting sample having numerous small crystals arranged at random, *e.g.*, a powder or a piece of steel. Before describing these methods, we shall first recall some of the leading facts of crystallography.

5. THE NATURE OF CRYSTAL LATTICES

The natural regularity of external form and the homogeneous character of crystals led Haüy (1784) to suggest the modern theory of their structure in a primitive form; namely, that they are built up by the repetition of unit cells having the same size and orientation throughout the crystal. The *unit cell* may be taken as the smallest group of atoms such that the entire crystal can be built up by repeating it in a definite way throughout the crystal. Isotopic atoms are regarded as equivalent in

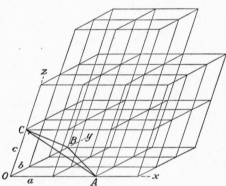

forming a cell. Such a group can be chosen in many ways, but in practice this leads to no confusion. Let us fix our attention on some arbitrary point within a cell, such as the nucleus of a certain atom. The assemblage of similar points in all the cells of an ideal infinite crystal forms a regular array which is called a "spacelattice." Whatever point in the unit cell we take to start with, the resulting space lattices are identical except for a transla-

FIG. 5.—A space lattice and a typical plane.

tional shift. In Fig. 5, we show a possible space lattice. Its points may be connected in a variety of ways by three sets of parallel lines, so that every point lies at the intersection of three lines, one from each set. This is simply to aid the eye in following the symmetry of crystals possessing such a space lattice. The lines themselves have no physical significance, and in general will be drawn in a simple way, so that the resulting parallelopipeds have edges of the same order of magnitude. For example, in a crystal with cubic symmetry the lines may be drawn at right angles. Having chosen a particular method of drawing the lines, we choose a lattice point as origin and take the lines passing through it as coordinate axes (Fig. 5) which will be called the axes of the crystal. We now introduce a method of naming the different planes of atoms in the crystal. Let ABC be a typical plane on which a set of points lie, including the points at A, B, and C

themselves. OA, OB, and OC are then multiples of the smallest distances a, b, c, between lattice points in the directions Ox, Oy, Oz, respectively. (We say the distance between lattice points, not the distance between particles. The distinction is apparent at once from Fig. 16, which shows the unit cell of NaCl, containing two species of atoms.) Then the ratios OA/a, OB/b, OC/c are the integers, i_1, i_2, i_3 and

$$\frac{a}{OA} : \frac{b}{OB} : \frac{c}{OC} = i_2 i_3 : i_3 i_1 : i_1 i_2. \tag{5}$$

Dividing the integers $i_2 i_3$, $i_3 i_1$, $i_1 i_2$ by their largest common factor we arrive at a triplet of integers h, k, l called the "Miller indices," used to designate the plane ABC and all similar planes of lattice points parallel to it. For a cubic crystal where $a = b = c$, these indices have a simple physical meaning. Taking the axes OA, OB, OC at right angles to each other the equation of plane ABC is

$$lx + my + nz = P \tag{6}$$

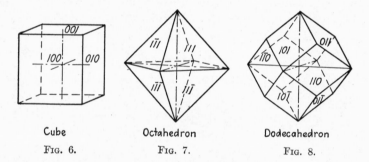

Cube
FIG. 6.

Octahedron
FIG. 7.

Dodecahedron
FIG. 8.

where l, m, n are the direction cosines of its normal and P its perpendicular distance from O. The intercept equation is

$$\frac{x}{OA} + \frac{y}{OB} + \frac{z}{OC} = 1; \text{ or, } \frac{i_2 i_3}{a}x + \frac{i_3 i_1}{b}y + \frac{i_1 i_2}{c}z = i_1 i_2 i_3. \tag{7}$$

So if $a = b = c$, then $l : m : n = i_2 i_3 : i_3 i_1 : i_1 i_2$, which is the ratio of the indices. Even for crystals whose axes are not at right angles, and for which a, b, c are not equal, this relation will serve as a *rough* means of visualizing the positions of the planes, although the above derivation does not hold for such crystals. In Figs. 6, 7, and 8, we show three common forms in which cubic crystals occur in nature. The symbol $11\bar{1}$ indicates the plane with indices 1, 1, -1; the minus sign is customarily written above to save space.

Study of the *external* symmetry of crystals has shown that it is possible to classify all known crystals into six systems distinguished by the relative lengths of a, b, c and by the angles α, β, γ, which the axes make with each other, as follows:

I. Cubic............... $a = b = c,\ \alpha = \beta = \gamma = 90°$

II. Tetragonal........... $a = b \neq c,\ \alpha = \beta = \gamma = 90°$

III. Rhombic............. $a \neq b \neq c,\ \alpha = \beta = \gamma = 90°$

IV. Monoclinic........... $a \neq b \neq c,\ \alpha = \beta = 90°,\ \gamma \neq 90°$

V. Triclinic............. $a \neq b \neq c,\ \alpha \neq \beta \neq \gamma \neq 90°$

VI. Hexagonal........... $a = b \neq c,\ \alpha = \beta = 90°,\ \gamma = 120°.$

Rhombohedral. The axes may be chosen as for the hexagonal, or

$$a = b = c,\ \alpha = \beta = \gamma \neq 90°.$$

These six systems of symmetry can be further subdivided into thirty-two classes on the basis of partial suppression of the maximum symmetry which the system can possibly possess. Both the system and class can be determined from the macroscopic crystalline form, but little can be said about the arrangement of the atoms within the unit cell without the aid of X-rays.

6. THE REFLECTION OF X-RAYS FROM CRYSTALS

It must be understood that the word reflection is not used here in the same sense as in optics. If a parallel beam of X-rays of a given

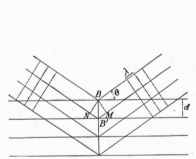

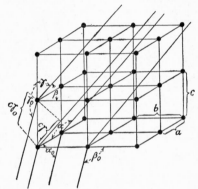

Fig. 9a.—The reflection of X-rays from lattice planes.

Fig. 9b.—The diffraction of X-rays by a simple cubic lattice.

wave length impinges on a crystal, there is an angle of incidence $\pi/2 - \theta$, (or better, several such angles), upon any set of crystal planes we may care to consider, such that a strong diffracted beam is sent off making an angle of $\pi/2 - \theta$ with the normal to these planes, just as in the optical case (Fig. 9a). The angle θ is called the glancing angle. The X-rays penetrate deep within the crystal, and the diffracted beam is formed by the interference of elementary beams scattered from all planes of the set under consideration. In position it obeys the ordinary law of reflection, but the mechanism of its production is not the same as that of a reflected beam of light. In some respects the action is like that of a diffraction grating with its spacings perpendicular to the surface of the crystal.

For simplicity, in giving the explanation of these facts, we begin with the case of a crystal having axes at right angles, the scattering centers being concentrated at the lattice points. Let a parallel beam of monochromatic X-rays be incident on the crystal. How can we choose its direction so that the secondary waves from all the atoms will reinforce to form diffracted beams of high intensity in definite directions? The answer is easily found if we assume that each lattice plane reflects in accordance with geometric optics. For, in Fig. 9a, "reflected" rays from the individual layers will interfere unless the paths of the beams diffracted by the successive layers differ by a whole number of wave lengths of the incident radiation, *i.e.*,

$$NB' + B'M = 2d \sin \theta = n\lambda, \tag{8}$$

which is known as "Bragg's law." The integer n must be less than $2d/\lambda$ because $\sin \theta$ is less than 1; n is called the order of the spectrum. This derivation has the disadvantage that one cannot be sure that it gives all the possible diffracted beams. Thus we might expect each layer of atoms to act as a two-dimensional grating, so that there would be additional diffracted beams. One might expect that such higher order beams from successive layers of atoms would reinforce in certain directions. However, a rigorous treatment (given below) shows that all of these higher order beams are destroyed by interference and that Bragg's formula gives all the possible reflections from the crystal.

Alternative Derivation of Bragg's Law.—In Fig. 9b, let α_0, β_0, γ_0, be the direction cosines of the incident beam and α, β, γ those of the reflected beam. Consider wave fronts of this beam which are separated by the distance λ. We draw the intersections of these wave fronts with the YZ plane at any instant and find the condition that a pair of adjacent scattering centers on the Z-axis should be excited in the same phase by these wave fronts. It is

$$(\gamma - \gamma_0)c = L\lambda,$$

where L is a positive integer or zero, for as we see from the figure, the difference in path of the beams which strike adjacent atoms is $c\gamma - c\gamma_0$. Similar conditions are obtained for reinforcement along the X- and Y-axes, so that

$$(\alpha - \alpha_0)a = H\lambda, \ (\beta - \beta_0)b = K\lambda, \ (\gamma - \gamma_0)c = L\lambda. \tag{9}$$

But if these conditions are satisfied, then the waves from all pairs of atoms reinforce, because for any such pair the path difference is a sum of multiples of the three elementary path differences written on the left side of equation (9). We have,

$$\alpha = \alpha_0 + \frac{H\lambda}{a}, \ \beta = \beta_0 + \frac{K\lambda}{b}, \ \gamma = \gamma_0 + \frac{L\lambda}{c}. \tag{10}$$

Squaring, adding, and utilizing the relations, $\alpha^2 + \beta^2 + \gamma^2 = 1$, $\alpha_0^2 + \beta_0^2 + \gamma_0^2 = 1$, we get,

$$\lambda = - \frac{2\left(\dfrac{H\alpha_0}{a} + \dfrac{K\beta_0}{b} + \dfrac{L\gamma_0}{c}\right)}{\left(\dfrac{H^2}{a^2} + \dfrac{K^2}{b^2} + \dfrac{L^2}{c^2}\right)}. \tag{11}$$

Here we exclude the simple case $H = K = L = 0$, giving the undeflected beam for which $\alpha = \alpha_0$, $\beta = \beta_0$, $\gamma = \gamma_0$. This beam is present regardless of the wave length used, but in all other cases, if α_0, β_0, γ_0, are given, by orienting the crystal in a particular way with respect to the incident beam, a diffracted beam can arise only if λ has one of the values obtained by substituting a possible set of values of H, K, and L into this equation. At first sight it appears that H, K, and L could always be chosen to satisfy this condition, since after all the light used is not strictly monochromatic. However, if very high values are chosen for any or all of H, K, and L, the diffracted beam is found by experiment to be very weak, a result quite analogous to the faintness of higher orders of diffraction grating spectra, which is easily explained by optical considerations.

For given values of H, K, and L, the angle 2θ between incident and reflected beams is given by

$$2 \sin \theta = \lambda \left(\frac{H^2}{a^2} + \frac{K^2}{b^2} + \frac{L^2}{c^2}\right)^{\frac{1}{2}}; \tag{12}$$

for squaring the relations in equation (10) and adding we have

$$2 - 2(\alpha\alpha_0 + \beta\beta_0 + \gamma\gamma_0) = \lambda^2\left(\frac{H^2}{a^2} + \frac{K^2}{b^2} + \frac{L^2}{c^2}\right)$$

or, since

$$\alpha\alpha_0 + \beta\beta_0 + \gamma\gamma_0 = \cos 2\theta,$$

$$4 \sin^2 \theta = \lambda^2\left(\frac{H^2}{a^2} + \frac{K^2}{b^2} + \frac{L^2}{c^2}\right);$$

and equation (12) follows. These relations are valid only for crystals having their axes mutually perpendicular.[1]

We can now prove that the diffracted beam behaves as though reflected from a set of atomic planes within the crystal. To do this, we write a condition which must be satisfied by the coordinates x, y, z of a point P in a plane which bisects the angle between the incident and diffracted beams and is perpendicular to the plane in which they lie. The line OP makes equal angles with these two beams. The equality of the cosines of these angles is expressed by

$$\alpha x + \beta y + \gamma z = \alpha_0 x + \beta_0 y + \gamma_0 z. \tag{13}$$

Combining with equation (9),

$$\frac{H}{a}x + \frac{K}{b}y + \frac{L}{c}z = 0, \tag{14}$$

which must be the equation of the reflecting plane.

H/a, K/b, and L/c are proportional to the direction cosines of its normal. Referring to equations (6) and (7), we see that this plane is parallel to the lattice planes having Miller indices proportional to H, K, and L. Thus if n is the greatest common factor of H, K, and L we put

$$H = nh, K = nk, L = nl, \tag{15}$$

and h, k, and l are the Miller indices of the plane. The X-rays are diffracted as though they were reflected from a lattice plane of Miller indices h, k, and l; thus equation (12) takes the form of Bragg's equation (8), if we put

$$d = \left(\frac{h^2}{a^2} + \frac{k^2}{b^2} + \frac{l^2}{c^2}\right)^{-\frac{1}{2}} \tag{16}$$

for this expression is the distance between two successive lattice planes of indices h, k, and l.

7. METHODS AND APPARATUS FOR X-RAY SPECTROSCOPY

The X-ray spectrometer used by the Braggs consists essentially of a system of slits which selects a narrow beam of rays from the radiation

---

[1] The general formulas holding for any crystal will be found on p. 99 of WYCKOFF, "The Structure of Crystals," Chemical Catalogue Co., 1924.

of the X-ray tube, a crystal mounted on a revolving table carrying a vernier and a graduated circle so that its position can be accurately determined, and a device for detecting the beam reflected from the crystal, also mounted so that it revolves about the same vertical axis as the table and carrying a vernier to determine its angular position (Fig. 10).

The Braggs used an ionization chamber as a detecting device. This is a metal chamber containing a vapor which absorbs the rays readily. Methyl bromide and SO_2 are often used. An electrode is mounted in the chamber just out of the way of the entering beam. The chamber is insulated and raised to a high potential and the electrode connected to a

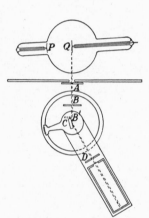

Fig. 10.—The Bragg spectrometer.

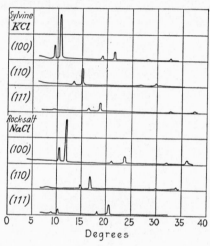

Fig. 11.—The intensity of reflection of the Pd $K\alpha_1$, and $K\alpha_2$ lines as a function of the angle, θ. (*After Bragg.*)

sensitive electrometer. When X-rays enter, ions are produced, and the electrometer is discharged. In operation the crystal is set at an angle with the direction of the primary beam and the detecting device at twice this angle, since the reflection angle must be equal to that of incidence; the crystal is rotated through successive small angles, the detecting device being rotated always through twice the change of the crystal angle. The ionization current is determined at each position and is then plotted as in the spectra of Fig. 11, which show the intensity of reflection of the K radiation of palladium from three natural faces of KCl and NaCl crystals. It is to be noted that all the peaks on the curves occur in pairs. This as well as other evidence shows that the K radiation consists of two wave lengths lying very close together and that these pairs of peaks are due to these two wave lengths. Figure 11 also shows the relative intensities for different spectral orders for the more intense wave length. W. H. and W. L. Bragg estimate that the intensities of the first five orders are approximately in the ratio $100:20:7:3:1$.

A photographic plate may be used to detect the reflected beam. An arrangement suited to this means of detection and known as the rotating crystal apparatus of de Broglie is shown in Fig. 12. X-rays enter at C and fall on crystal D which is continuously and slowly rotated about axis O by clock work. At some position 1 making angle θ_1 with the original beam, a spectrum line is obtained due to X-rays of wave length $\lambda_1 = 2d \sin \theta_1/n$. The rays, deviated through an angle $2\theta_1$ arrive at position I on the photographic plate AA'. As the crystal is turned to another position 2 at an angle θ_2 from the direction of the original beam, another wave length $\lambda_2 = 2d \sin \theta_2/n$ will be reflected through an angle $2\theta_2$ to another position II, and so on. The photographic plate is mounted on an arm so that its position can be determined relative to the direction of the original beam. Since each wave length is diffracted to a different position a spectrum similar to the usual optical spectrum appears on the photographic plate and the wave length can be determined very accurately from the position of the line on the plate. This method has the advantage that it is largely automatic in operation and requires little attention, but it is not so sensitive as the ionization chamber method.

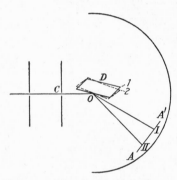

Fig. 12.—The de Broglie rotating crystal arrangement.

In order to avoid the necessity of rocking the crystal, M. de Broglie[1] has used a curved sheet of mica, and Trillat[2] made use of a similar device in studying the orientation of the molecules in a thin film of fatty acid on the surface of a liquid. The film is allowed to spread over the curved surface of a small drop of the liquid (mercury, for example), and the drop is placed in the beam of X-rays in the position ordinarily occupied by the crystal.

8. THE DETERMINATION OF CRYSTAL STRUCTURE BY THE USE OF X-RAYS

We must content ourselves with a few brief examples of the use of X-rays in studying the structure of crystals. References to many excellent treatises are given at the end of the chapter. Potassium chloride and sodium chloride have very simple space lattices, but they illustrate practically all the essential features involved in determining a structure. They may crystallize in cubes and on the basis of this crystalline form they must be assigned to the cubic system. The

[1] *C. R.*, **157**, 924 (1913). *Verhandl. d. D. Phys. Ges.*, **15**, 348 (1913).
[2] *C. R.*, **187**, 168 (1928).

elements of symmetry of these crystals as determined from a study of all the forms in which they occur, are shown in Fig. 13.[1] The planes drawn in the figure are so-called "reflection planes" dividing the crystal into two halves which are mirror images of each other. The lines con-

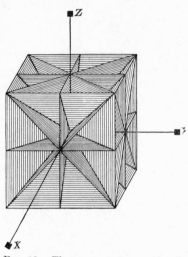

necting the face centers are fourfold axes of symmetry, since rotation about these axes through one-fourth of a revolution brings the crystal to a position indistinguishable from its first position. Similarly, lines connecting the opposite corners of the cube are threefold axes of symmetry and lines connecting the middle points of opposite edges are twofold axes. The center of a cube is a center of symmetry since a line drawn from it to any point in the crystal, when extended in the opposite direction an equal distance, will locate a point with properties similar to those of the first point. The possession of these elements of symmetry places a

FIG. 13.—The symmetry properties of rock salt crystal. (*After Wyckoff.*)

crystal in the holohedric class of the cubic system, by definition. We attribute to the unit cells of NaCl and KCl all of the symmetry properties of a cube. There are three possible space lattices having the type of symmetry exhibited by the holohedric class of the cubic system. These are the simple cubic, face-centered cubic, and body-centered cubic

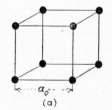

(a)

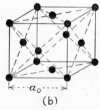

(b)

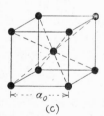

(c)

FIG. 14.—Simple, face-centered, and body-centered cubic lattices.

lattices shown in Fig. 14. The problem is to decide which of these is actually present in KCl or NaCl.

A possible procedure is to mount the crystal in a Bragg spectrometer, illuminate it with monochromatic X-rays (a reasonable amount of continuous background is not objectionable), and measure the glancing angle for reflection from various sets of atomic planes. The ratios

[1] Wyckoff, "The Structure of Crystals," Chemical Catalogue Co., New York. (1924).

of the interplanar distances for two sets of reflecting planes can be determined without a knowledge of the wave length used. For the two peaks to be considered we have θ-values given by

$$2d_1 \sin \theta_1 = n_1\lambda, \quad 2d_2 \sin \theta_2 = n_2\lambda, \qquad (17)$$

so that

$$\frac{d_1}{d_2} = \frac{n_1 \sin \theta_2}{n_2 \sin \theta_1}. \qquad (18)$$

Care must be taken in assigning the values of n for the different peaks. By inspecting the diagrams of the three possible lattices, or from the relation

$$d_{hkl} = \frac{a}{\sqrt{h^2 + k^2 + l^2}}$$

(obtained from equation (16) by putting $a = b = c$), we find that for each lattice

$$d_{100}:d_{110}:d_{111} = 1:\frac{1}{\sqrt{2}}:\frac{1}{\sqrt{3}}.$$

At first sight, then, we should predict identical Bragg diffraction patterns from all three lattices, as in Fig. 15a where the abscissa is proportional to

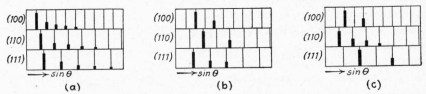

(a)   (b)   (c)

FIG. 15.—Reflection patterns from simple, face-centered and body-centered cubic lattices.

sin θ and the diffraction peaks of various orders from the three sets of planes considered are drawn in separate rows. The spaces between orders for the three types of planes are in the ratios $1:\sqrt{2}:\sqrt{3}$. The heights of the heavy lines indicate roughly the decreasing intensity. The simple cubic lattice actually gives a pattern of this kind, but with the face-centered lattice some of the peaks due to 100 and 110 planes are destroyed by interference, caused by atomic planes lying midway between those predicted by the formula and having the same number and arrangement of atoms as the latter planes. (This does not contradict the formula, for it was derived by considering an imaginary lattice, formed by taking one point in each unit cell, while the intermediate planes of which we speak are due to structures within the cell.) For all diffractions of odd order the length of path of the light diffracted by these intermediate planes will differ by one-half wave length from that of the light diffracted by the planes considered in deriving the formula. The light from these two sets of planes interferes and thus the diffraction beams of odd order are completely extinguished. The result is the same as would be secured by reducing the interplanar distances in a simple cubic crystal to one-half their value. The diffraction patterns for the 100, 110, and 111 planes of the face-centered lattices are shown in Fig. 15b. The 111 pattern is unaltered. Similarly, the body-centered lattice gives the patterns of Fig. 15c with odd orders missing from the 100 and 111 reflections. The diffraction patterns of the 100, 110, and 111 faces of NaCl are similar to those for the face-centered cubic lattice except that the odd-order diffractions from the 111 planes are relatively weaker than those predicted for this lattice. This pattern can be explained by the lattice of Fig. 16 where black dots represent positive metal ions and circles negative chlorine ions. The positive and negative ions are each placed on face-centered lattices which are displaced relative to each other by one-half their body diagonal. The diffractions by the 100 and 110 planes are the same as would be obtained if ions of either sign were present alone; for

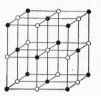

the addition of the negative-ion lattice to the positive-ion lattice produces no new 100 or 110 planes; but it *does* introduce new 111 planes, of negative ions only, midway between 111 planes of positive ions. The presence of these intermediate planes will reinforce the even-order diffractions and will cause only *partial* interference of odd orders, because the electron density near planes of positive charge is smaller than that near negative planes in the ratio 10:18. Thus, the weakening of odd 111 orders is explained.

Fig. 16.—The NaCl lattice.

With this definite information as to the arrangement of the atoms, we can compute the distance between 100 planes, which is called the "grating constant." Inspection of Fig. 16 shows that 4 molecules of NaCl are to be considered as belonging to each unit cell, and knowing the number of molecules in 1 cc. of rock salt from its density, molecular weight, and the Avogadro number, we find the number of unit cells in 1 cc., and, therefore, the side of each cell. Proceeding in this way we obtain the value 5.628 Å. Since relative measurements of X-ray wave lengths can be made to six significant figures, the grating constant is taken as 5.62800 Å. with the understanding that the last two digits have no physical significance.

Let us now consider KCl. Evidently, if the electron densities in planes containing only positive and negative charges are identical, the odd 111 orders disappear completely and the pattern becomes the same as that of a simple cubic lattice having the lattice constant $d_{100}/2$. KCl presents a case of this kind, for K^+ and Cl^- ions contain the same number of electrons and therefore should have nearly equal scattering powers. A glance at Fig. 15 shows that the diffraction pattern is that of a simple cubic lattice. The grating space as obtained from this pattern appears to be 3.138 Å. If KCl really has a face-centered lattice, its constant is twice this value, 6.276 Å, and $d(KCl)/d(NaCl) = 1.115$. This is much more reasonable than the ratio obtained by using 3.138 Å, for the K-ion should have a larger volume than the Na-ion.

By equation (8) we can now calculate the wave lengths of the X-rays, using the observed values of θ. Thus, for the second order,

$$\lambda = \frac{2d \sin \theta}{n} = \frac{2 \times 5.62800}{2} \times 0.0938,$$

$$\lambda = 0.576 \cdot 10^{-8} cm. = 0.576 \text{ Å}.$$

The theoretical maximum wave length which can be measured by using a given set of crystal planes is equal to $2d$ divided by the lowest value of n. This corresponds to $\sin \theta = 1$ or $\theta = 90°$. For intensity reasons 60° is about the working maximum so that the longest wave length which can be measured is considerably less than the theoretical limit. To avoid the excessive use of decimals it is customary to record X-ray wave lengths in terms of the X unit (abbreviated to X.U.) which is 10^{-3} Ångström units or 10^{-11} cm. Thus, the strong palladium line called $K\alpha$ has the wave length 0.576×10^{-8} cm. $= 0.576$ Å $= 576$ X.U.

Before leaving this subject, attention should be directed to X-ray diffraction patterns of liquids. While many investigations of these patterns have been made, the subject has developed rapidly only in recent years. We owe to G. W. Stewart and his colleagues, Morrow and Skinner,[1] the first extensive and systematic studies of X-ray diffraction in organic liquids, with spectrographs of adequate resolving power. The results give interesting information on the size and arrangement of molecules in the liquid state.

9. DISCOVERY OF THE K AND L RADIATIONS BY ABSORPTION MEASUREMENTS

Before Laue's fundamental discovery, some information about the wave lengths of X-rays was obtained by Barkla through study of their absorption. Just as the intensity of a monochromatic beam of light falls off exponentially as it penetrates an absorbing medium so X-rays follow the law

$$I = I_0 e^{-\mu d}, \tag{19}$$

where I is the intensity at depth d, I_0 the intensity at depth $d = 0$, and μ the absorption coefficient which depends on the absorbing material and the wave length. The values of μ for different substances are not directly comparable, for densities vary widely and in an irregular manner as we pass through the periodic system. It is convenient to substitute m/ρ for d where m is the mass contained in a column of length d, 1 cm.^{2} in cross-section, and ρ is the density. Then

$$I = I_0 e^{-\frac{\mu m}{\rho}}. \tag{20}$$

[1] Series of articles in *Phys. Rev.* (1927) and (1928). See especially **30**, 558 (1928) for a summary of theories concerning liquid diffraction patterns.

The μ/ρ value for any monochromatic constituent of a heterogeneous beam is called the "mass absorption coefficient for that wave length." It is a measure of the absorption in a beam of 1 sq. cm. cross-section in passing through unit mass, while μ measures the absorption of such a beam in unit volume. When many wave lengths are present, equation (20) is replaced by

$$I = I_0'e^{-\frac{\mu'}{\rho}m} + I_0''e^{-\frac{\mu''}{\rho}m} + \cdots, \tag{21}$$

and for continuous radiation the sum becomes an integral.

The primary rays produced in the anticathode cause a substance absorbing them to emit both electrons and secondary X-rays. The latter consists of two parts of different origin; the scattered radiation, which has an intensity distribution with respect to wave length determined primarily by the source of the primary rays, and the characteristic radiation, which varies with the material of the absorber.

Barkla showed that the absorption of secondary X-rays follows the law in equation (21) and that the characteristic radiation consists mainly of two types of rays which differ greatly in hardness. The harder constituents are called the K radiation and the softer the L radiation. Table 1 gives the values of the mass absorption coefficients in aluminium for the K and L radiations of a few elements.

TABLE 1.—COEFFICIENTS OF MASS ABSORPTION IN ALUMINIUM (After Barkla)

Atomic number	K-radiation	L-radiation
20	435	.....
24	136	.....
28	59.1	.....
33	22.5	.....
37	10.9	.....
42	4.8	.....
47	2.5	700
51	1.21	435
56	0.8	224
74	......	30.0
78	......	22.2
82	......	17.4
90	......	8.0
92	......	7.5

For example, silver produces a characteristic X radiation whose absorption by aluminium is given by equation (21) using $\mu'/\rho = 2.5$ and $\mu''/\rho = 700$. These two coefficients are characteristic of the K and L radiations, respectively. The corresponding thicknesses of aluminium which would reduce the K and L radiations separately to half their initial intensities are 0.103 and 3.7×10^{-4} cm. After the rays pass through a small thickness of aluminium foil, say 0.037 cm., the intensity of the L radiation will be reduced to a fraction of a per cent of its original value. That of the K radiation is practically unchanged. After this the K radiation, if monochromatic, should obey equation (20), and is found to do so.

The mass absorption coefficients in aluminium for the characteristic secondary radiation decrease continuously as the atomic number of the emitting element increases and show no periodic variations corresponding to the periodic variation in chemical properties. Facts of this kind led quite early to the speculation that X-rays arise from the inner portions of the atom, where the influence of the nucleus preponderates over those due to the electrons in the outer shells. However, this simple dependence of μ upon atomic number is not encountered in general. It occurs only when the atomic number of the absorber is *less* than those of the emitters under consideration, which is true for the combinations listed in Table 1. We shall return to this subject in Sec. **12.**

10. GENERAL SURVEY OF X-RAY EMISSION SPECTRA

The study of characteristic radiations received a great impetus when Moseley,[1] using de Broglie's method, first photographed the K spectra

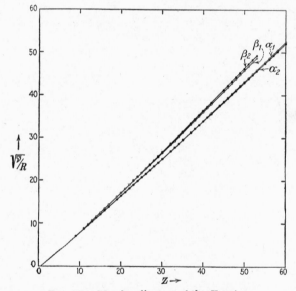

Fig. 17.—Moseley diagram of the K-series.

of a number of elements between Ca and Zn (Fig. 1, Chap. I). He used the second and third reflections from a crystal of potassium ferrocyanide. In agreement with Bragg's ionization measurements, the K radiation was found to consist of two distinct wave lengths for each element. The work of later investigators with higher dispersion shows that the typical K spectrum contains four strong lines known as $K\alpha_1$, $K\alpha_2$, $K\beta_1$, and $K\beta_2$. For atoms of atomic numbers less than 16 (sulfur) the $K\alpha_1$

[1] *Phil. Mag.*, **26**, 1024 (1913); **27**, 703 (1914).

and $K\alpha_2$ lines lie so close together that they have not been separated by X-ray methods. $K\beta_2$ has not been observed in atoms of atomic number lower than 22(Ti). In addition to these strong lines, a number of very much weaker ones have been observed, due, it is believed, to doubly ionized atoms and, therefore, having analogy to the spark lines of optical spectra. The order of decreasing intensity of the four strong lines is, α_1, α_2, β_1, β_2. Moseley's work showed that the K-lines shift toward shorter wave lengths in a regular way with increasing atomic number. The law connecting wave length and atomic number is most easily seen by plotting $\sqrt{\bar{\nu}/R}$ against the atomic number, where R is the Rydberg constant, inserted for reasons soon to be explained. Such a graph is called a "Moseley diagram." Figure 17 shows Moseley diagrams for the K-series lines, with circles indicating the experimental values. (They can be extrapolated to atoms of lower atomic number, but this is not done here since the structure of the spectra becomes more complex in this region, as described in Chap. X.) The curves of this diagram are very nearly straight lines, so that for each line we have

$$\sqrt{\frac{\bar{\nu}}{R}} = A(Z - s), \qquad (22)$$

where A and s are constant. Therefore,

$$\bar{\nu} = (Z - s)^2 R A^2. \qquad (23)$$

For the K lines, s is approximately one, A^2 is about equal to $\frac{1}{1^2} - \frac{1}{2^2}$ for the $K\alpha$ lines and is roughly equal to $\frac{1}{1^2} - \frac{1}{3^2}$ for $K\beta_1$. In other words, *the lines obey Bohr's formula for the lines of hydrogenic atoms, a result of profound importance.*

The general structure of the L-series, which consists of many more wave lengths than the K-series, is illustrated by the diagrammatic spectra in Fig. 18 together with two commonly used systems of designating the lines—neither system has any theoretical basis. The brackets indicate line groups which

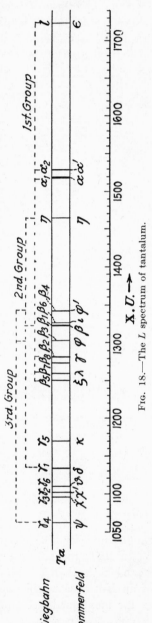

Fig. 18.—The L spectrum of tantalum.

appear successively as the tube voltage increases. The lines of group 1 in the case of tungsten are excited by potentials higher than 10.16 kilovolts, and those of group 2 come out above 11.6 kilovolts, while group 3 lines appear only at potentials higher than 12.0 kilovolts.[1] The relative intensities are indicated roughly by the weights of the lines. The regular shift in position of the L-series lines is shown by the Moseley diagram of

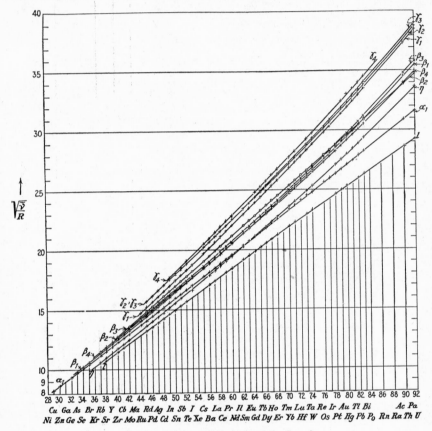

FIG. 19.—Moseley diagram of the L-series.

Fig. 19. The number of lines decreases below about $Z = 50$, due to the smaller number of electron shells in the atom.

In 1916, Siegbahn[2] discovered the M-series, lying at much greater wave lengths than the L-lines, while Dolejsek[3] demonstrated the existence of an N-series at still greater wave lengths. In no case do the series so far mentioned overlap. The existence of O- and P-series lying in

[1] WEBSTER, D. L., and H. CLARK, Phys. Rev., 9, 571 (1917). HOYT, Proc. Nat. Acad. Sci., 6, 639 (1920).

[2] Ver. d. Deutsch. Phys. Ges., 18, 278 (1916).

[3] Z. Physik, 10, 129 (1922).

experimentally difficult regions is made certain by a study of the energy levels which give rise to the above mentioned series and by critical potential measurements and other special methods. The observed M-series spectra consist of many lines which are usually designated by the symbols of the two energy levels involved, since they were first discovered after the energy levels were fairly well known. N-series spectra have been measured only for a few heavy elements.[1]

Just as the K-series lines obey approximately a formula like that of the Lyman series of hydrogen, so the stronger lines of the L, M, and N spectra are represented in a rough way by formulas of the type

$$\bar{\nu} = (Z - s)^2 R\left(\frac{1}{n_1^2} - \frac{1}{n_2^2}\right);$$ (24)

$n_1 = 2, 3, 4$ for the L-, M-, and N-series, respectively, n_2 is an integer greater than n_1; and for each series, s is a constant.

11. ABSORPTION SPECTRA

The intensity of the darkening of a photographic plate due to the action of light will depend among other things on two factors, the intensity of the light and the coefficient of absorption of the silver bromide

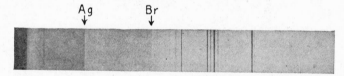

Fig. 20.—The K- and L-absorption limits of Ag and Br.   (*After de Broglie.*)

for that light.   De Broglie[2] noted on his first photographs of X-ray spectra a very sharp change in the darkening of the plate caused by the continuous spectrum, at two distinct wave lengths as shown in Fig. 20. These are the so-called "absorption limits" of Ag and Br. Large absorption means intense darkening, so we see that rays of shorter wave length than these limits are absorbed strongly by the Ag or Br, respectively, while those of longer wave lengths are absorbed only slightly. It is certain that these limits are associated with silver bromide, for their positions are independent of the anticathode material.

Similar abrupt changes in absorption coefficients can be detected by studying the absorption spectrum of the element in question.   To do this, a thin layer of the element (or of a compound containing the element) is placed between a source of continuous X radiation (*e.g.*, a tungsten target) and the slits of an X-ray spectrograph.   Absorption of certain wave-length regions by the layer is indicated, of course, by absence of darkening in certain parts of the spectrum plate.

[1] Hjalmar, *Z. Physik*, **15**, 55 (1923).
[2] *Jour. de Physique*, **6**, 161 (1916).

Figure 21 shows photographs of the K-absorption spectra of several elements. The edge marked "Ag" is due to silver in the plate, *i.e.*, wave lengths shorter than this are strongly absorbed by the silver (plate darkened) while longer wave lengths are absorbed only slightly. This limit is present in all the photographs. In addition, there is a limit due to the absorbing element. Its frequency is denoted by ν_K, its wave length by λ_K, and it is called the "K-absorption limit." Frequencies greater than ν_K are strongly absorbed; smaller frequencies are only slightly absorbed. The simple interpretation is that quanta

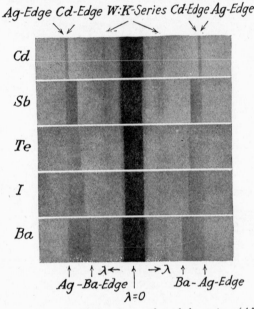

Fig. 21.—The K-absorption limits of a number of elements. (*After de Broglie.*)[1]

greater than $h\nu_K$ can eject tightly bound electrons, which cannot be removed by smaller quanta, from the atoms of the absorber. The darkening of the plate falls off rapidly with increasing ν in spite of the increased number of electrons which can be removed. This shows that as long as the number of electrons which can be ejected from each atom remains constant, the absorption coefficient decreases continuously with wave length. In fact, the absorption coefficient per atom is given approximately by the empirical formula,

$$kZ^4\lambda^3 + 0.8Z\sigma_0,$$

for wave lengths between 0.1 and 1.4 Å, for all elements having atomic number greater than 5. Z is the atomic number, and k and σ_0 are con-

---

[1] Fig. 21 is taken from Siegbahn, "Spektroskopie der Röngenstrahlen," p. 130, Springer Berlin, (1924).

stants.   The first term arises from the ejection of photoelectrons and
the second from scattering.

Similar relations are found in absorption spectra covering the range
of the L-series lines, but, here, three distinct limits are observed.   The
M-absorption spectra of a few heavy elements have been studied and
five absorption limits have been observed.   The general nature of the
absorption by a given element as a function of wave length and the
relative positions of the absorption limits and the emission lines are
illustrated in Figs. 22a and 22b for the K- and L-series, respectively.

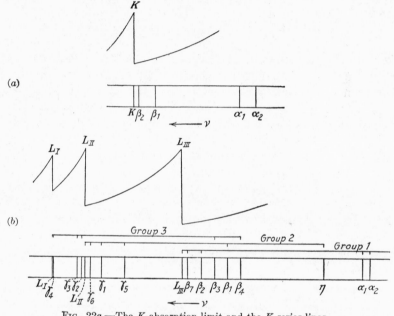

Fig. 22a.—The K-absorption limit and the K-series lines.
Fig. 22b.—The L-absorption limits and the L-series lines.

The K-absorption limit lies very slightly to the short wave-length side
of the shortest emitted wave length, $K\beta_2$.   The three L limits are often
designated L_I, L_{II}, and L_{III} in the order of increasing λ.   The L_I limit
has a wave length slightly shorter than the shortest L-emission line,
but the L_{II} and L_{III} limits fall among the L-emission lines.   Closer
examination shows that in Hoyt's classification of the lines according
to their excitation voltages (Sec. 10) L_{II} lies on the high frequency
side of groups 1 and 2, and L_{III} on the high frequency side of group 1
only.   Similarly, designating the M limits as M_I to M_V in the order of
increasing wave length, the M_I limit lies slightly to the short wave length
side of the shortest M emission line, the others falling among the emission
lines.

12. KOSSEL'S EXPLANATION OF X-RAY SPECTRA

The experimentally ascertained regularities just described can be explained by a very simple theory, the foundations of which were laid by Kossel.[1] He thought of the atom as built up of successive aggregates of electrons, often loosely referred to as shells. All the electrons in a given aggregate are supposed to have the same ionization potential. We may think of these aggregates as containing the maximum number of electrons which they can possess without dynamical catastrophe, except that the outer shells, having very small ionization potentials from the standpoint of X-rays, may be incomplete. Because of this situation, it will generally be impossible to move an electron from a tightly bound to a more loosely bound shell, either by electron impact, or by the absorption of X-rays. Any excitation of a deep lying shell of the atom must consist in the removal of one of its electrons to the exterior of the atom. If this is done by radiation, the energy of the quantum must be equal to or greater than the ionization potential of the shell in question, which yields an immediate explanation of the absorption bands just described. The sharp discontinuity in absorption at the long wave-length limit ν_0 of such an absorption band gives a direct measure of the ionization potential V of a shell through the equation $Ve = h\nu_0$. A quantum having the frequency ν_0 will eject an electron and leave it at rest outside the atom; a higher frequency ν will eject an electron and give it kinetic energy $h(\nu - \nu_0)$.

Similarly, a bombarding electron must fall through a potential at least as large as $h\nu_0/e$ in order to ionize the shell in question. This explains Webster and Clark's observation of well-defined excitation potentials for the L-lines of tungsten.[2] When a certain shell of the atom has been ionized, an electron may fall from an outer shell into the vacant place, causing the emission of light. It is important to remember that the X-ray spectrum originates in an ionized atom.

Evidence for this relation between the absorption and the emission spectra is found also in the variation of the absorption coefficients of an element for the characteristic X-rays of other elements immediately preceding and following it in the periodic system. Table 2 gives Barkla's[3] determinations of the absorption coefficients for characteristic X-rays of elements from Cr to Se using Fe and Ni as the absorbers.

A sharp increase in the coefficient of absorption for the characteristic X-rays occurs at the element having atomic number just two units higher than the absorber. Coincident with this increase in absorption there is a marked increase in the number of photoelectrons emitted and the characteristic K radiation of the absorber is first excited.

[1] Z. Physik, 1, 124 (1920).
[2] Loc. cit. Sec. 10.
[3] Phil. Mag., 17, 749 (1909).

Table 2

Emitter	Absorber	
	Fe	Ni
Cr............	103.8	129
Fe............	66.1	83.8
Co...........	67.2	67.2
Ni............	314	56.3
Cu...........	268	62.7
Zn............	221	265
As............	134	166
Se............	116.3	141.3

The reason for this is evident from Kossel's theory of the absorption limit and its relation to the emission lines. The K-absorption limit of Fe is at 1,737.7 X. U. and the K-emission lines of Fe, Co, and Ni are as follows:

	α_2	α_1	β_1	β_2
Fe......................	1,936.51	1,932.30	1,752.72	1,740.60
Co......................	1,789.56	1,785.28	1,617.13	1,605.4
Ni......................	1,658.54	1,654.61	1,497.03	1,485.4

The Ni radiation, having wave lengths shorter than the Fe absorption limit will be absorbed by Fe with the removal of one of its K electrons and the entire K spectrum of Fe will be excited. The Fe radiation and the strong α_1 and α_2 lines of Co will not be absorbed. Thus Barkla's experiments are in accord with the predictions of the theory.

13. THE GENERAL FEATURES OF X-RAY ENERGY LEVELS

In discussing X-ray energy levels, it is customary to assign zero energy to the normal state of the atom, in contradiction to the conventions used for optical energy diagrams. Approximate formulas for the wave numbers of K-, L-, and M-series lines were given in equation (24). The similarity of these formulas to those used in describing the spectrum of hydrogen leads at once to an arrangement of the X-ray energy levels, shown in Fig. 23, not unlike that for hydrogen. It must be understood at once that this figure is a diagram of *ionizing energies*, the different levels representing the energies required to remove electrons from the different electron groups. Alternatively, the levels represent the energies of the atom ionized in various ways referred to the normal atom as an origin. Let us suppose the neutral atom is ionized by removing one of its most firmly bound electrons belonging to the so-called "K shell." It will then be in the energy level marked K in Fig. 23 which we shall call the "K state." An electron in any of the looser-bound shells, which are called the L, M, etc. shells in order of decreasing ionization potential, could then fall into the K shell with emission of a K-series line. If this electron comes from the L shell, the line emitted has the wave number $RZ'^2\left(\dfrac{1}{1^2} - \dfrac{1}{2^2}\right)$ and is called $K\alpha$; if from the M shell,

it has the wave number $RZ''^2\left(\dfrac{1}{1^2} - \dfrac{1}{3^2}\right)$ and is called $K\beta$; and so on.

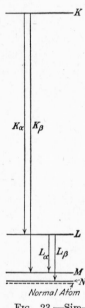

FIG. 23.—Simplified X-ray energy diagram.

(As we shall see farther on Z' and Z'' may be considered to be effective nuclear charges.) When any one of these events has occurred, the shell from which the electron fell is incomplete and may be filled by the transition of an electron from any shell of smaller ionization potential. Such jumps continue in cascade fashion until the outermost shell has lost an electron and is replenished by picking up a stray electron from regions outside the atom.

From the diagram, we can read off many combination relations at once. For example, the frequency of the $K\beta$ line is the sum of the frequencies of the $K\alpha$ and the $L\alpha$ lines. It is customary to use the names of the lines and the levels to denote their frequencies, or better, the corresponding values of $\bar{\nu}/R$, which are of convenient magnitude. Thus, the K level of uranium has a $\bar{\nu}/R$ value of 8,477, corresponding to a wave length of 0.1075 Å; this is the highest value encountered. Using this notation, we have relations of the type

$$K\alpha = K - L, \quad K\beta = K - M, \quad L\alpha = L - M, \quad K\beta = K\alpha + L\alpha.$$

Let us now consider X-ray transitions in more detail. If we ionize the atom from the L shell to begin with, leaving a full complement of electrons in all others, transitions from M to L, N to L, etc., will occur, giving rise to the emission of L-series lines. The principle is now obvious, and we may determine the energies of the various states in Fig. 23 referred to the normal atom as an origin. They are given approximately by the values $R(Z - s)^2/n^2$ where s is in the neighborhood of unity for the K state and assumes larger values for the other states. Each of these values is identical with the amount of energy required to remove an electron from an orbit of a hydrogenic atom having the nuclear charge $Z - s$. The explanation of this approximate regularity is very simple. The motion of an electron in the innermost shell of an atom of reasonably high atomic number is governed almost entirely by the overpowering attraction of the nucleus. The inner shell has 2 electrons as we shall see in Chap. IX, and the effect of each electron on the other is practically equivalent to a reduction of the nuclear charge by one unit. That is, the repulsive force which one electron exerts may be considered to screen off one unit of nuclear charge. This is the meaning of the value one assumed by the constant s for the K state. As for the other electrons in the atom, we shall see that their penetrating orbits (Chap. VII, Sec. **10**) may pass very close to the electrons of the K shell; but in these portions of the orbits their velocities are very high and they remain between the K electrons and the nucleus only a very small fraction of the time. The result is that the kinetic energy of a K electron plus its potential energy with respect to the nucleus and the other K electron is practically that of an electron in a hydrogenic atom of nuclear charge $Z - 1$. This energy is approximately the amount required to bring the neutral atom to the K state. Similar statements may be made in regard to the ionization of any other shell.

14. THE COMPLETE SCHEME OF X-RAY ENERGY LEVELS

The preceding description is only a rough approximation to the facts. The interaction of the electrons in the atom is very complicated, and we have not discussed modifications due to relativity and to electron spin, which may be quite large because of the high velocities of the electrons in the interior of the atom. These influences give rise to the existence of several classes of electrons in each shell except the K shell, each class having its own ionization potential. We said above that there are three L-absorption limits in the region covered by the L-series emission lines, five absorption limits corresponding to the ejection of M electrons from the atom by light, and so on. This complexity of the energy levels brings about a considerable increase in the complexity of the emission spectra. For example, there are two $K\alpha$ lines close together produced in transitions from the K state to two of the three L states.

An illustration will make these facts more concrete. We may determine the L levels of tungsten from its absorption spectrum; on numbering them L_{I}, L_{II}, L_{III} in descending order on the energy diagram, we find the $\bar{\nu}/R$ values shown in the tabulation below. In this tabulation we also list the $\bar{\nu}/R$ values for the individual lines of the L-series, divided into groups in accordance with the work of Webster and Clark and of Hoyt described in Sec. **10**. All the lines in group 1 arise in transitions to the L_{III} shell and are excited at 10.16 kilovolts, which is not far above the theoretical ionization potential of this shell, 9.7 kilovolts. The discrepancy is due to the fact that the probability of excitation is low when the energy of the bombarding electrons is very close to the value required for ionization. Similarly, the other two groups arise in transitions to the L_{II} and L_I shells and appear only when these levels are ionized.

TABLE 3.—$\bar{\nu}/R$ VALUES OF THE L LIMITS AND L LINES OF TUNGSTEN

	L_I	γ_4	β_3	β_4			
Group 3	889.9	887.77	723.23	701.66			
	L_{II}	γ_1	β_1	η			
Group 2	849.59	831.81	712.39	642.78			
	L_{III}	β_5	β_7	β_2	α_1	α_2	ι
Group 1	750.88	751.56	746.45	733.76	618.46	613.85	544.03

Table 4 gives the X-ray levels of uranium, thorium, and tungsten, obtainable by removing a single electron from the atom. The $\bar{\nu}/R$

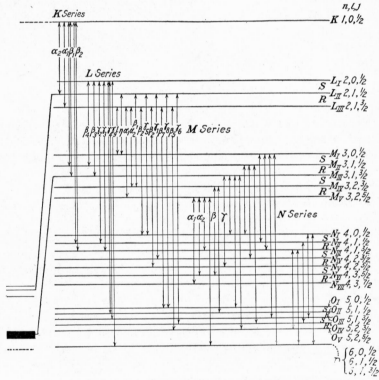

FIG. 24.—X-ray energy diagram of radon.

values for all observed emission lines are expressible as differences between these numbers, except for certain lines which have their origin in the doubly ionized atom. However, not all the differences give rise to emission lines because of selection rules similar to those found in optical spectra.

Table 4.—$\bar{\nu}/R$ Values of Uranium, Thorium, and Tungsten

Level	U	Th	W
K	8,477.0	8,073.5	5,113.8
L_I	1,603.5	1,509.7	893.0
L_{II}	1,543.1	1,451.5	850.6
L_{III}	1,264.3	1,200.6	752.1
M_I	408.9	381.6	208.1
M_{II}	382.1	354.4	191.3
M_{III}	317.2	298.0	169.8
M_{IV}	274.0	256.6	138.3
M_V	216.0	244.9	133.7
N_I	106.6	97.8	44.1
N_{II}	95.7	....	38.0
N_{III}	77.1	....	33.0
N_{IV}	56.3	51.2	18.8
N_V	53.6	47.8	18.4
N_{VI}	28.4	24.8	2.9
N_{VII}	27.6	24.1	2.8
O_I	26.2	....	5.7
$O_{II,III}$	15.4	....	5.2
$O_{IV,V}$	5.8	5.7	

The combinations which occur can be seen in Fig. 24 which shows the levels of the rare gas radon on an exaggerated scale. (The correct scale has been used in the small diagrams at the left.) For example, the diagram indicates that only two of the three possible transitions between the L levels and the K level occur with emission of radiation, so that there are two $K\alpha$ lines and not three. On the right are the symbols and quantum numbers for the levels. n and l are the total and reduced azimuthal numbers, respectively. j is not a quantum number of the removed electron but is the inner number of the ionized shell, and therefore of the whole atom, as we shall see in detail in Sec. **20.** Further, l is the vectorial sum of the angular momenta of the electrons in the ionized atom, due to their revolution around the nucleus. This is numerically identical with the l value of the missing electron. In the earlier attempts at an interpretation of X-ray terms, the numbers l and j were often thought of as belonging to the missing electron.[1]

As an empirical fact, the following selection principles are obeyed with extreme fidelity in X-ray emission spectra:

$$\Delta l = \pm 1, \ \Delta j = \pm 1 \text{ or } 0, \tag{25}$$

[1] Several different sets of quantum numbers have been used in place of the l and j used here. Before the complete scheme of quantum numbers now used to describe multiplet spectra was evolved, the quantum numbers k and j were used, and these are found in most treatises on X-ray spectra; k is equal to $l + 1$ and was assumed to take the values 1, 2, ... n; j as commonly used is equal to our j plus $\frac{1}{2}$.

or in the older notation of Sommerfeld,

$$\Delta k_1 = \pm 1, \ \Delta k_2 = \pm 1 \text{ or } 0.$$

These rules appear to be identical with the selection principles for the azimuthal and inner quantum numbers in optical spectra, and l and j are often called by these names in spite of our more detailed and exact knowledge of their significance. Few exceptions to these rules are known. A weak tungsten line, $K\alpha_3$, has been observed at the position expected for the $K - L_I$ transition. The quantum number l does not change in this transition and therefore this is a violation of the first selection rule.

Using the transitions indicated in the diagram, which obey the selection rules, very good agreement is obtained between the $\bar{\nu}/R$ values of the emission lines and those calculated from the experimentally determined absorption limits. When we have established the origin of a set of emission lines by comparison with the experimental absorption limits, using elements in which both are easily studied, the regularity of the Moseley diagrams enables us to classify the corresponding lines of other elements with confidence even though some of the absorption limits are inaccessible. Then, from the known absorption limits and the $\bar{\nu}/R$ values for the emission lines, we can find the unobserved limits. For example, we can secure the M levels of W and other elements whose M-absorption limits have not been measured. It is known (using Siegbahn's notation) that

$$L_I - L\beta_4 = M_{II}, \ L_I - L\beta_3 = M_{III}.$$

Substituting the numerical values from the tables of Siegbahn or Lindh,[1] we have

$$893.0 - 701.7 = M_{II} = 191.3,$$
$$893.0 - 723.2 = M_{III} = 169.8.$$

Using these values it is possible to show that the $K\beta_1$ line represents the combination of the M_{III} levels with the K level. Thus,

$$K - M_{III} = 5{,}113.8 - 169.8 = 4{,}944.0$$

while the measured value of $K\beta_1$ is 4,942.9.

Thus, the building up of the complete X-ray energy diagram requires the use of the usual spectroscopic methods of searching for combination relations, and needs no further illustration.

The values given in the case of these three elements refer to the atoms in chemical combination, for the spectra are obtained from their compounds. Experimentally this makes little or no difference, for the energy of interaction of an inner incomplete shell and an outer incomplete shell is of the same order of magnitude as the doublet or triplet differences occurring in optical spectra. From a theoretical standpoint, however,

---

[1] For reference, see end of chapter.

the number and arrangement of levels in Fig. 24 would be considerably altered if outer electrons were present. As it stands it applies only to an atom or ion having complete subshells, that is, having the electronic configuration of radon. Fine structures of the X-ray lines due to the existence of incomplete shells are well known in a number of cases, as we shall see in Sec. **22.** It will be understood that lighter atoms do not possess all the ionization potentials implied by the levels in Fig. 24 because they do not have as many electron shells. The X-ray spectra of the lightest atoms are very simple, and there is a steady increase in complexity as the atomic number increases. This will be discussed in the following chapter, since the exact number of levels cannot be deduced entirely from X-ray data but requires the use of facts and theories derived from the study of optical spectra and the periodic table.

For detailed tables of wave length and of $\bar{\nu}/R$ and $(\bar{\nu}/R)^{1/2}$ values, the reader should consult the references at the end of the chapter.

15. THE EMPIRICAL LAWS OF X-RAY DOUBLETS

Some of the most useful advances in our knowledge of atomic structure have come from the critical study of Moseley diagrams[1] showing the dependence of the $(\bar{\nu}/R)^{1/2}$ values of the X-ray levels on the atomic number. Figure 25 is such a diagram showing data for the K, L, and M levels, and Fig. 26, a similar diagram showing the M, N, and O levels on a larger scale. For the present, we may confine our attention to those portions of the curves which are quite uniform. It will be seen that the lines for the levels L_{II} and L_{III} diverge, but that the lines L_I and L_{II} are parallel. We shall refer to the frequency difference between two neighboring levels as a doublet. Intervals which behave like that between L_{II} and L_{III} are called "relativity doublets" or "relativity-spin doublets" and were first discovered by Sommerfeld, while those which resemble the interval between L_I and L_{II} are screening doublets, and were discovered by Hertz. At the right of Fig. 24 we indicate the character of the various doublets. It will be noted that spin (R) and screening (S) doublets alternate in passing down the energy diagram, a fact which is helpful in memorizing these regularities. It is apparent that the two levels belonging to a spin doublet have identical azimuthal numbers, but different inner numbers. On the other hand, the levels of a screening doublet have different azimuthal number, but the same inner number. These relations are recapitulated in Table 5.

The frequency difference $\Delta\bar{\nu}$ of a spin doublet increases as the fourth power of the atomic number diminished by a certain screening constant d. In fact, the data are well satisfied by an empirical formula of the type

$$\frac{\Delta\bar{\nu}}{R} = C(Z - d)^4[1 + a(Z - d)^2 + b(Z - d)^4]. \tag{26}$$

[1] See Bohr and Coster, *Z. Physik*, **12**, 342 (1923).

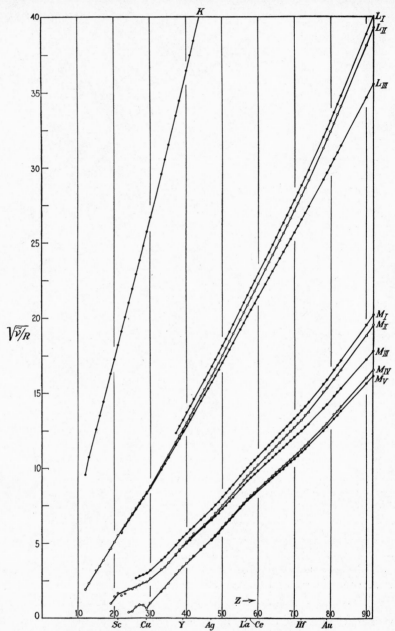

Fig. 25.—The Bohr-Coster diagrams for the K, L, and M levels. (*Revised.*)

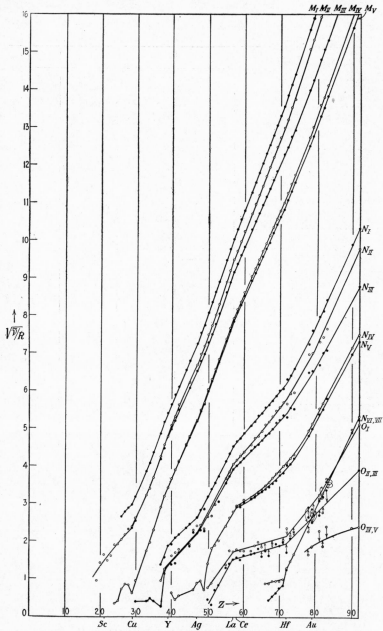

Fig. 26.—The Bohr-Coster diagrams for the L, M, N, and O levels.   (Revised.)

Table 5.—Quantum Numbers of X-ray Levels[1]

Level	Type of doublet	n	$k \equiv k_1$	$l \equiv k - 1$	$j \equiv k_2 - \tfrac{1}{2}$
K.................		1	1	0	$\tfrac{1}{2}$
L_{I}................		2	1	0	$\tfrac{1}{2}$
	S				
L_{II}................		2	2	1	$\tfrac{1}{2}$
	R				
L_{III}...............		2	2	1	$\tfrac{3}{2}$
M_{I}................		3	1	0	$\tfrac{1}{2}$
	S				
M_{II}...............		3	2	1	$\tfrac{1}{2}$
	R				
M_{III}..............		3	2	1	$\tfrac{3}{2}$
	S				
M_{IV}..............		3	3	2	$\tfrac{3}{2}$
	R				
M_{V}...............		3	3	2	$\tfrac{5}{2}$
N_{I}.................		4	1	0	$\tfrac{1}{2}$
	S				
N_{II}...............		4	2	1	$\tfrac{1}{2}$
	R				
N_{III}..............		4	2	1	$\tfrac{3}{2}$
	S				
N_{IV}..............		4	3	2	$\tfrac{3}{2}$
	R				
N_{V}...............		4	3	2	$\tfrac{5}{2}$
	S				
N_{VI}..............		4	4	3	$\tfrac{5}{2}$
	R				
N_{VII}.............		4	4	3	$\tfrac{7}{2}$
O_{I}................		5	1	0	$\tfrac{1}{2}$
	S				

[1] R = relativity-spin doublet; S = screening doublet. k_1 is the older azimuthal number assigned by Sommerfeld to these levels; l is the true azimuthal number.

Retaining only the first term in this formula, it is equivalent to the statement that $\Delta\lambda$ is constant for the spin doublets as we pass from element to element. We see this at once from the relation $\Delta\lambda = -\Delta\bar{\nu}/\bar{\nu}^2$, together with equation (24). As an experimental fact, easily interpreted by the theory we are about to outline, this law also holds approximately for the emission doublets. For example, in passing from uranium to silver the wave lengths of the L_{II} and L_{III} limits change by a factor of 6, but the wave length difference of L-series emission doublets which involve these limits changes by only 40 per cent. The law followed by the screening doublets is explained at once by the

Moseley term values, equation (24).   If we have two levels for which
the empirical screening constants are s_1 and s_2, we may write

$$\left(\frac{\bar{\nu}_1}{R}\right)^{\frac{1}{2}} = a(Z - s_1) \text{ and } \left(\frac{\bar{\nu}_2}{R}\right)^{\frac{1}{2}} = a(Z - s_2) \tag{27}$$

and, therefore,

$$\left(\frac{\bar{\nu}_1}{R}\right)^{\frac{1}{2}} - \left(\frac{\bar{\nu}_2}{R}\right)^{\frac{1}{2}} = a(s_1 - s_2); \tag{28}$$

that is, the difference of their $(\bar{\nu}/R)^{\frac{1}{2}}$ values should be a constant,
and their representative lines on the Moseley diagrams should be parallel.
That this is approximately but not exactly true is evident from Figs.
25 and 26.   A more exact theory of these doublets will be given in Sec. **18**.

16. SOMMERFELD'S FORMULA FOR THE SPIN-RELATIVITY DOUBLETS

We pointed out in Sec. **13** that the magnitudes of the X-ray energy
levels are equal to the ionization potentials of electrons in the inner
shells of the atom.   The approximately hydrogenic character of these
spectral terms is explained by the controlling influence of the nucleus;
the effect of the other electrons on the one which is to be removed to
give rise to an X-ray energy level is practically equivalent to a simple
reduction of the nuclear charge.   When an electron moves on an orbit
of low total quantum number in the field of a nucleus of high atomic
number its velocity may not be neglected in comparison with the velocity
of light, and it is essential to use a formula for its energy, which takes
account of the variation of mass with velocity.

Sommerfeld[1] showed that it is possible to obtain excellent agreement
with the observed X-ray energy levels by using a modification of the
relativistic formula for the energy of the hydrogenic atom.   This
modification consists in replacing Z by $Z - s$ in equation (35), Chap. V,
so that s represents the screening of the nucleus by other electrons.
Wentzel[2] further modified this by replacing Z by $Z - s$ in the first term
of equation (35), Chap. V, and by $Z - d$ in the other terms, so that the
formula becomes

$$
\begin{aligned}
\bar{\nu} = {}& \frac{R(Z - s)^2}{n^2} + \frac{R(Z - d)^4\alpha^2}{n^4}\left(\frac{n}{k} - \frac{3}{4}\right) \\
& + \frac{R(Z - d)^6\alpha^4}{n^6}\left[\frac{1}{4}\left(\frac{n}{k}\right)^3 + \frac{3}{4}\left(\frac{n}{k}\right)^2 - \frac{3}{2}\left(\frac{n}{k}\right) + \frac{5}{8}\right] \\
& + \frac{R(Z - d)^8\alpha^6}{n^8}\left[\frac{1}{8}\left(\frac{n}{k}\right)^5 + \frac{3}{8}\left(\frac{n}{k}\right)^4 + \frac{1}{8}\left(\frac{n}{k}\right)^3 - \frac{15}{8}\left(\frac{n}{k}\right)^2 + \frac{15}{8}\left(\frac{n}{k}\right) - \frac{35}{64}\right]
\end{aligned}
\tag{29}
$$

$$+ \cdots$$

[1] An excellent resumé is given in the chapters on X-rays in "Atombau," 4th ed.
[2] *Z. Physik*, **16**, 51 (1922).

The reason for the introduction of the two screening constants s and d can be seen from a consideration of the origin of the terms in this formula, using the simple shell model of Chap. VII, Sec. **10**. We can see that the screening constant s in the first term depends on the distribution of electrons in shells both inside and outside the one containing the electron in question. All other terms in equation (29) arise from the variation of mass with velocity and from electron spin. In accord with Chap. V, Sec. **16**, the values of these terms depend essentially on the velocity of the electron and this is determined by the field in which it moves, that is, on the screening due to the inner shells, regardless of the distribution of the outside shells. We may call s and d the total and partial screening constants, respectively.

17. DATA CONCERNING THE L AND M DOUBLETS

To obtain the formula for the separation of the L doublet, we write down the term values for L_{II} and L_{III}, as obtained from equation (29) by substituting the values of k and n given for these levels in Table 5. Assuming that s is the same for both these levels, the term containing $(Z - s)$ drops out in the difference and we obtain

$$\frac{\Delta\bar{\nu}}{R} = \frac{L_{II} - L_{III}}{R} = \frac{\alpha^2}{2^4}(Z - d)^4 \left[1 + \frac{5}{2}\frac{\alpha^2}{2^2}(Z - d)^2 \right.$$
$$\left. + \frac{53}{8}\frac{\alpha^4}{2^4}(Z - d)^4 + \cdots \right]. \tag{30}$$

The equations for the M doublets are

$$\frac{\Delta\bar{\nu}}{R} = \frac{M_{II} - M_{III}}{R} = \frac{\alpha^2}{3^4}(Z - d)^4 \left[\frac{3}{2} + \frac{279}{32}\frac{\alpha^2}{3^2}(Z - d)^2 + \cdots \right],$$
$$\frac{\Delta\bar{\nu}}{R} = \frac{M_{IV} - M_{V}}{R} = \frac{\alpha^2}{3^4}(Z - d)^4 \left[\frac{1}{2} + \frac{25}{32}\frac{\alpha^2}{3^2}(Z - d)^2 + \cdots \right], \tag{31}$$

and other doublet formulas are obtained similarly.

The precision with which the theory accounts for the spin doublets can best be seen by substituting the experimental values for the spin-doublet separations on the left-hand side of equations (30) and (31), and solving for the values of d. The degree of constancy of d for a given doublet, as the atomic number changes, is a measure of the applicability of equation (29). The constancy of the screening number for the L-doublet is shown by Table 6 which is an extract from a more extensive table compiled by Sommerfeld.[1]

Similar calculations for the M and N doublets give values which are nearly as constant as those for the L doublet. It is natural that the departure from the Sommerfeld formula should become greater for the outer shells where the physical conditions necessary for its validity

[1] "Atombau," 4th ed., p. 447.

TABLE 6

Z	Element	$\Delta\tilde{\nu}/R$	d
41	Nb	6.89	3.50
45	Rh	10.48	3.47
50	Sn	16.73	3.50
56	Ba	27.70	3.54
60	Nd	37.86	3.51
67	Ho	62.46	3.50
74	W	98.54	3.51
82	Pb	160.02	3.44
92	U	278.71	3.49

are not so well fulfilled. The screening constants for the L, M, and N doublets are assembled in Table 7.

TABLE 7

Level	d
L_{II}, L_{III}	3.50
M_{II}, M_{III}	8.5
M_{IV}, M_{V}	13.0
N_{II}, N_{III}	17.0
N_{IV}, N_{V}	24.4
N_{VI}, N_{VII}	34

18. SCREENING DOUBLETS

The values of the constant d can be secured by the method given in the preceding section, for all X-ray levels except K, L_I, M_I, N_I, O_I, etc. In these cases there is no relativity doublet and, therefore, the constant s cannot be eliminated as for the other levels. The values of s for the doublet levels can be calculated by substituting the values of d (Table 7) in equation (29) and solving for the term $\dfrac{R(Z-s)^2}{n^2}$. This is known as the "reduced term" and is represented by $\tilde{\nu}'$; it is the same for both levels of a relativity doublet. Following the reasoning used in deriving equation (28), but using the *reduced terms* instead of the actual terms, we secure the equation

$$\left(\frac{\tilde{\nu}_1'}{R}\right)^{\frac{1}{2}} - \left(\frac{\tilde{\nu}_2'}{R}\right)^{\frac{1}{2}} = \frac{\Delta s}{n}. \qquad (32)$$

When the reduced terms for the $M_{II,III}$ and the $M_{IV,V}$ levels are substituted in this formula it is found that $\Delta s/n$ is constant, with no indication of a trend such as we found in Sec. **15**. The same is true for the $N_{II,III}$ and $N_{IV,V}$ screening doublets, though the erratic variations of $\Delta s/n$ are greater.

To secure the reduced terms for the L_I, M_I, N_I, etc., levels further assumptions are necessary. It seems most natural to assume that $\Delta s/n$ should be constant, with increasing atomic number, for the screening doublets $L_I - L_{II,III}$, $M_I - M_{II,III}$, $N_I - N_{II,III}$, $O_I - O_{II,III}$, as well as for the screening doublets $M_{II,III} - M_{IV,V}$ and $N_{II,III} - N_{IV,V}$. Wentzel chose a value for d for the L_I level in such a way as to satisfy this assumption. That is, we calculate the reduced L_I term, by substituting Wentzel's d in equation (29), and call it $\bar{\nu}_1$; we also calculate the reduced term $\bar{\nu}_2$ corresponding to the L_{II} and L_{III} terms. Then, using equation (32) we obtain a value of $\Delta s/n$ which is practically independent of the atomic number. The same method was applied by Wentzel to the other single levels. The values of d thus secured are as follows:

	L_I	M_I	N_I
d	2.0	6.8	14

By comparison with Table 7, it will be seen that these values fit in with the trend of those for the other levels. The values of $\Delta s/n$ calculated from equation (32) for a number of elements are listed in Table 8, which

TABLE 8.—DIFFERENCES OF THE SQUARE ROOTS OF REDUCED TERMS FOR SCREENING DOUBLETS

Z	(L_I, $L_{II,III}$)	(M_I, $M_{II,III}$)	($M_{II,III}$, $M_{IV,V}$)	(N_I, $N_{II,III}$)	($N_{II,III}$, $N_{IV,V}$)	($N_{IV,V}$ $N_{VI,VII}$)	(O_I, $O_{II,III}$)	($O_{II,III}$, $O_{IV,V}$)
74	0.54	0.60	1.12	0.56	1.15	2.57	0.58	1.70
78	0.55	0.63	1.11	0.45	1.17	2.47	0.53	1.51
79	0.57	0.61	1.12	0.53	1.27	2.40	0.09	1.81
81	0.57	0.57	1.16	0.63	1.09	2.21	0.54	1.42
83	0.54	0.63	1.08	0.63	1.05	2.11	....	1.97
90	0.60	0.61	1.12	....	....	1.95	....	....
92	0.60	0.62	1.13	0.56	1.14	1.94	1.20	1.51

is similar to, but briefer than a table given by Wentzel. The constancy of these differences with respect to atomic number is very satisfactory; it is also evident that they are approximately multiples of 0.58 so that the reduced terms are given by the equation,

$$\frac{\bar{\nu}'}{R} = \left[\frac{Z - s_n}{n} - 0.58\varphi(l) \right]^2.$$

In this formula s_n is that value of s which will give the reduced term, $\frac{\bar{\nu}'}{R}$, for the L_1, M_1, N_1, O_1 . . . levels when n equals 2, 3, 4, 5, . . . , respectively; for these terms $\varphi(l)$ is zero. We cannot expect s_n to be independent of atomic number, since it depends on the number and distribution of electrons both nearer and farther from the nucleus than

the region occupied by the electrons under consideration.   The addition
of electrons to the outer part of the atom must change the value of s_n.
Since d depends only on the inner electron configurations, it should be

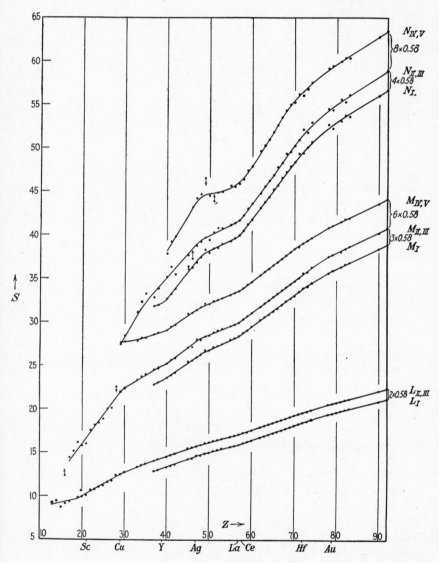

Fig. 27.—The screening constant s.

(and is) constant, so long as the electron shells lying nearer to the
nucleus than its own are complete.   The values of s_n do not follow any
simple law; Fig. 27 shows its trend as a function of the atomic number.

The empirical relations developed here for the dependence of the X-ray levels on the atomic number and the quantum numbers can be summarized in one formula due to Wentzel, partly theoretical and partly empirical, which gives an excellent representation of the experimental X-ray energy levels. This formula is,

$$\frac{\tilde{\nu}}{R} = \left[\frac{Z - s(Z,n)}{n} - 0.58\varphi(l)\right]^2 + \alpha^2\left(\frac{Z - d(n,l)}{n}\right)^4\left(\frac{n}{k} - \frac{3}{4}\right)$$
$$+ \alpha^4\left(\frac{Z - d(n,l)}{n}\right)^6\left[\frac{1}{4}\left(\frac{n}{k}\right)^3 + \frac{3}{4}\left(\frac{n}{k}\right)^2 - \frac{3}{2}\left(\frac{n}{k}\right) + \frac{5}{8}\right]$$
$$+ \alpha^6\left(\frac{Z - d(n,l)}{n}\right)^8\left[\frac{1}{8}\left(\frac{n}{k}\right)^5 + \frac{3}{8}\left(\frac{n}{k}\right)^4 + \frac{1}{8}\left(\frac{n}{k}\right)^3 - \frac{15}{8}\left(\frac{n}{k}\right)^2 + \frac{15}{8}\left(\frac{n}{k}\right) - \frac{35}{64}\right] + \cdots \quad (33)$$

$\varphi(l)$ and $d(n,l)$ take the values

$$\varphi(0) = 0, \ \varphi(1) = 1, \ \varphi(2) = 3, \ \cdots,$$
$$d(2,0) = 2.0, \ d(2,1) = 3.5,$$
$$d(3,0) = 6.8, \ d(3,1) = 8.5, \ d(3,2) = 13.0,$$
$$d(4,0) = 14.0, \ d(4,1) = 17.0, \ d(4,2) = 24.4, \ d(4,3) = 34. \quad (34)$$

The values of $s(Z,n)$ are those given in Fig. 27.

As yet there is no complete theoretical explanation of these very striking empirical relations. Fues[1] and Hartree[2] have shown that it is possible to account for the X-ray levels approximately by assuming stationary electron orbits in a central field and especially Fues has shown that it is not possible for electrons to be bound in orbits having the quantum numbers $n = 4$, $k = 4$, in the cesium atom, but that it is possible for such electrons to be present in atoms having atomic numbers only slightly higher than that of cesium. An investigation by Sugiura and Urey[3] shows that this is also true if k is assigned half-integral values and that the values of the inner screening constant, d, calculated on this basis agree fairly closely with the experimental values. The calculated and observed constants for cesium are

	$L_{II,III}$	$M_{II,III}$	$M_{IV,V}$
d: calculated....................	2.8	9.2	12.4
d: observed....................	3.5	8.4	13.0

Using similar assumptions, Pauling[4] secured values which agree about as well with the observed values as those given above.

[1] *Z. Physik*, **11**, 364 (1922); **12**, 1 (1923); **13**, 211 (1923); **21**, 265 (1924).

[2] *Proc. Camb. Phil. Soc.*, **21**, 625 (1925).

[3] *Kgl. Dan. Vidsk. Selskab. Math.-fys. Medd.*, **VII**, 13 (1926).

[4] *Z. Physik*, **40**, 344 (1927). Pauling has also applied the new mechanics to this problem. See *J. A. C. S.*, **50**, 1036 (1928) and *Proc. Roy. Soc.*, **114**, 181 (1927).

19. COMPARISON OF THE RELATIVITY AND THE SPIN-RELATIVITY THEORIES OF X-RAY DOUBLETS

We are now in a position to understand how and why Sommerfeld's original interpretation was replaced by another which takes the spin of the electron into account. We have seen that in Sommerfeld's theory it was necessary to assign the azimuthal number 1 to the L_I and L_{II} orbits, and the number 2 to L_{III}, and that similar assignments, conflicting with the spin theory, must be made for other levels. This leads to difficulties. The two levels associated with a relativity doublet have the same total screening constant, as we assumed when equations (30) and (31) were obtained by subtracting two equations of the form of equation (29), having the same value of s. It is difficult to see how this can be the case except in the case of a hydrogenic atom, for electrons having the same total but different azimuthal numbers will move on orbits of different shape. Even if this difficulty were overcome, there is another which may be illustrated by referring to the L levels. L_I and L_{II} form a screening doublet which obeys Hertz' law. If the total screening constants are different for these two levels, it seems reasonable to suppose that the relativity corrections should be different for them. As a matter of fact, the data would not permit this, as we see by considering the parallelism of the L_I and L_{II} curves on the Moseley diagram. Even in the region of high atomic numbers where the relativity doublet separation becomes large compared with the screening doublet there is no indication of such an effect.

It is possible to overcome the first difficulty by a different interpretation. We may suppose that the interval between L_I and L_{III} is a combined relativity and screening doublet, in which the difference of the screening constants is directly traceable to the difference in the azimuthal numbers. The difficulty is that we then are still confronted by the same trouble as before in attempting to explain the interval between L_I and L_{II}. Similar remarks may be made in regard to doublets of other series.

Further difficulties arise when an attempt is made to correlate the energies of the X-ray electrons with those of the valence electron of an alkali metal. The correlation is based on the similarity of the X-ray diagram and the energy diagram of a typical alkali atom. In Chap. VII, Sec. 13, we discuss the empirical laws describing the separations of the doublet levels in alkali atoms, and in ions having the same number of electrons as the neutral alkalies. The outstanding fact is that these doublets obey approximately the same law as the X-ray spin doublets, especially when we are dealing with highly charged ions. Because of the inhomogeneity of the field through which the electron moves in the case of the optical spectra it is necessary to introduce screening constants for both the inner and outer parts of the orbit, as we showed in equation (40), Chap. VII.

Even before the discovery of the spinning electron it was practically certain from evidence based on the Zeeman effect that the alkali doublets were principally due to differences in the orientation of two or more portions of the atom with respect to each other, and that the forces which held these parts in their quantized orientations were magnetic in origin. Because of the definite connection between magnetic moment and angular momentum, it appeared necessary to say that the levels forming an optical doublet have identical azimuthal numbers but different inner numbers. The selection principles for these numbers are identical in form with those for the X-ray quantum numbers by l and j in equation (25). Therefore, it appeared reasonable to call these numbers by the same names as the analogous numbers in optical spectra, and this is in complete disagreement with the assignment of quantum numbers based on the relativity theory.

For a time this difficulty remained unsolved. It appeared that the magnetic explanation, using the two possible orientations of a magnetic spinning electron relative to the magnetic moment of the orbital motion of the electron, left no room for the relativity correction, and *vice versa*, for either alone was able to yield a quantitative interpretation of the levels. As stated before, the true explanation lay in the fact that the combination of relativity and magnetic corrections, as calculated by the new mechanics, gives the original relativistic energy levels of Sommerfeld. The validity of the first-order term of Sommerfeld's formula was established by Heisenberg and Jordan[1] and by Richter.[2] Darwin[3] has proved that the wave-mechanical theory of the electron introduced by Dirac yields precisely the expression given by Sommerfeld. His formula is derived in such a way that the spin quantum number of the electron does not explicitly appear, but the selection principles appear in their usual form.

20. THE QUANTUM NUMBERS OF THE X-RAY LEVELS

Although the preceding discussion was based on a study of the energy of a single electron in the field of a partially screened nucleus, we must remember that this procedure yields only approximate results; for the negative energy of such an electron on its normal orbit, as determined by Sommerfeld's formula and measured from the state in which it is removed to infinity, is only approximately the same as the energy of the atom on the corresponding X-ray level, measured from the unexcited state as an origin. In Sec. **14** we stated the selection

---

[1] *Z. Physik*, **37**, 263 (1926).

[2] *Phys. Rev.*, **28**, 849 (1926) and *Proc. Nat. Acad. Sci.*, **13**, 476 (1927).

[3] *Proc. Roy. Soc.*, **118**, 654 (1928). Also GORDON, *Z. Physik*, **48**, 11 (1926).

principles for X-ray spectra and compared them with the strikingly similar rules for an alkali atom. Further, we have pointed out the similarity of the alkali metal and X-ray energy diagrams. The reason for this similarity was first clearly stated by Pauli.[1] When a single electron is removed from an atom, the number of X-ray levels which may result is equal to the number of essentially distinct ways in which the remaining electrons may be coupled to yield quantized states. Let us suppose that we are dealing with an atom in which the l vectors (Chap. VII, Sec. 5) of the individual electrons are coupled so as to form a quantized resultant $\bar{l}$, and that similarly the s vectors form a quantized resultant $\bar{s}$. Further, we suppose that the vectors $\bar{l}$ and $\bar{s}$ are so oriented with respect to each other that their resultant $\bar{j}$ is quantized. If the atom is built up of successive electron shells each of which has no resultant angular momentum or magnetic moment, *i.e.*, with the l and s vectors adding up to $\bar{l} = 0$ and $s = 0$, then the removal of one electron whose quantum numbers are l' and s' will leave an incomplete electron shell with its $\bar{l}$ and $\bar{s}$ values equal to l' and s', so coupled as to give a certain quantized resultant j'. Thus, the shell from which one electron is missing must have the same number of possible combinations of the l and s vectors of its electrons as the single electron removed from the shell and for this reason the X-ray levels are doublet levels just as in the case of the optical spectrum of an alkali.

The exact optical analogues of the X-ray energy values are the energies required to ionize atoms having completed subshells of electrons, such as the alkaline earths and inert gases. We may take neon and magnesium as the simplest examples. In Chap. IX, we shall see that the numbers of electrons in the two- and three-quantum shells of these elements are the following:

Element	Subshell		
	2, 0	2, 1	3, 0
Ne....................	2	6	0
Mg....................	2	6	2

The energy required to remove one of the 3, 0 valency electrons of Mg is the energy of the M_I X-ray level of magnesium. The 3, 0 subshell of Mg has $\bar{l} = 0$, $\bar{s} = 0$ and $\bar{j} = 0$. Each of the electrons of this subshell has the quantum numbers $l = 0$, $s = \frac{1}{2}$ and $j = \frac{1}{2}$. If one electron is

[1] *Z. Physik*, **31**, 765 (1925).

removed, we obtain the quantum numbers of the incomplete subshell left behind by subtraction, as follows:

$$\begin{array}{ccc}
\bar{l} = 0 & \bar{s} = 0 & \bar{j} = 0 \\
l = 0 & s = \frac{1}{2} & j = \frac{1}{2} \\
\hline
\bar{l} - l = 0 & \bar{s} - s = -\frac{1}{2} & \bar{j} - j = -\frac{1}{2}
\end{array}$$

The values in the last line are in fact the quantum numbers of the remaining electron of this subshell. The level is, therefore, a $^2S_{\frac{1}{2}}$ level from the standpoint of optical spectra, so that our assignment of quantum numbers for the M_I level in Sec. **15** is verified. The removal of one of the 2, 0 electrons of neon gives an exactly similar optical level except that the total quantum number of the remaining electron is 2 instead of 3, and the ionization energy of this subshell is the energy of the L_I level of neon.

The removal of one of the six 2, 1 electrons from either of these elements may leave the incomplete subshell with an angular momentum of $\frac{1}{2}$ or $\frac{3}{2}$, in terms of $h/2\pi$ as a unit. That is, the electron removed may carry with it an angular momentum corresponding either to $j = \frac{1}{2}$ or $j = \frac{3}{2}$; so that the quantum numbers of the ionized atom are formed as follows:

$$\begin{array}{ccc}
\bar{l} = 0 & \bar{s} = 0 & \bar{j} = 0 \\
l = 1 & s = \frac{1}{2} & j = \frac{1}{2} \text{ or } j = \frac{3}{2} \\
\hline
\bar{l} - l = -1 & \bar{s} - s = -\frac{1}{2} & \bar{j} - j = -\frac{1}{2} \text{ or } \bar{j} - j = -\frac{3}{2}
\end{array}$$

We conclude that two different ionizing potentials will be observed depending on whether the incomplete shell is left with j equal to $\frac{1}{2}$ or to $\frac{3}{2}$. As we shall see in Chap. X, Sec. **10**, these two levels of the ion are $^2P_{\frac{1}{2}}$ and $^2P_{\frac{3}{2}}$ levels. They are the L_{II} and L_{III} levels of neon, respectively. The L_{II} and L_{III} ionization potentials correspond to the two limits for the optical series spectra described in Chap. IX, Sec. **5**. L_{II} with $j = \frac{1}{2}$ is higher than L_{III} on the optical energy diagram so that these levels are an inverted ^2P level of Ne^+. The same is true of the low-lying ^2P levels of the halogens. This is not true of the alkali metals in their ^2P states, for here the level with $j = \frac{3}{2}$ has the greater energy. Quite generally, the low-lying states of atoms with incomplete subshells are similar to the X-ray energy states in their multiplicity, and just as in this simple example the levels correspond to inverted doublets of optical spectra. Table 9 gives the number of electrons in each of the subshells of the argon atom in its normal state and each of its X-ray states. That the assignment of electrons to the subshells of the normal atom is correct will be proved in Chap. IX. In the last two columns of the table we give the optical symbol for the level and the atom whose normal or low-lying state is similar to the X-ray level. The addition of completed subshells to the outside of the atom does not change the multiplet character of the level.

TABLE 9

X-ray level \ n, l	1, 0	2, 0	2, 1	3, 0	3, 1	Optical symbol	Analogous atom
Normal state..............	2	2	6	2	6	$^1S_0$	A
K...................	1	2	6	2	6	$^2S_{\frac{1}{2}}$	H
L_{I}...................	2	1	6	2	6	$^2S_{\frac{1}{2}}$	Li
L_{II}, L_{III}.................	2	2	5	2	6	$^2P_{\frac{1}{2},\frac{3}{2}}$	F
M_{I}.................	2	2	6	1	6	$^2S_{\frac{1}{2}}$	Na
M_{II}, M_{III}................	2	2	6	2	5	$^2P_{\frac{1}{2},\frac{3}{2}}$	Cl

21. X-RAY SPECTRA OF HIGHER ORDER

In addition to the lines of the K- and L-series which agree so well
with the energy level scheme developed in the preceding paragraphs,
a considerable number of weak lines have been observed, which cannot be
fitted into this scheme without seriously altering it. In general, they
lie on the short wave-length side of the stronger lines of the K- and
L-series. In the K-series these weak lines are resolved for elements of
atomic numbers 12 to 29 and in the L-series for elements of atomic numbers
lower than 51. Such additional lines were first discovered by Siegbahn
and Stenström and were greatly extended in number and in precision
of measurement by Dolejsek, Hjalmar, and Coster,[1] while Foote and
Mohler[2] have recorded critical potentials in the soft X-ray region which
may be related to some of these lines.

The $K\alpha$ group of lines consists of three doublets $\alpha_2\alpha_1$, $\alpha_3\alpha_4$, and $\alpha_5\alpha_6$,
in the order of decreasing wave lengths, and a line α_1' lying between the
$\alpha_1\alpha_2$ and $\alpha_3\alpha_4$ doublets. This complete group is observed only in the
elements Na, Mg, Al, and Si. The resolution of the $\alpha_3\alpha_4$ and $\alpha_5\alpha_6$
doublets becomes more difficult with increasing atomic number, and, in
this respect, they differ from the $\alpha_1\alpha_2$ doublet. The latter is due to
combinations between the K and the L_{II} and L_{III} levels. The five lines
α_1, α_3, α_4, α_5, and α_6 may be arranged in three pairs such that the frequency differences of the pairs is approximately constant;

$$\alpha_3 - \alpha_1 \cong \alpha_5 - \alpha_3 \cong \alpha_6 - \alpha_4. \tag{35}$$

Furthermore, the last of these differences for any one element is very
closely the same as the first of these differences for the element immediately following in the periodic system;

$$(\alpha_6 - \alpha_4)_Z = (\alpha_3 - \alpha_1)_{Z+1}. \tag{36}$$

These relationships expressed by equations (35) and (36) are illustrated
in Table 10.

---

[1] See SIEGBAHN, "Röntgenstrahlen," Springer, pp. 98, 108, 180–185, for a review
of the experimental data up to 1924, and LINDH, *Physik. Z.*, 28, 93 (1927) for more
recent work.

[2] "Origin of Spectra," p. 200*ff*.

Table 10[1]

	Na	Mg	Al	Si
$\alpha_3 - \alpha_1$	0.52	0.64	0.71	0.83
$\alpha_5 - \alpha_3$	0.57	0.67	0.76	0.91
$\alpha_6 - \alpha_4$	0.65	0.76	0.83	0.94

[1] Wetterblad, Z. Physik, **42**, 611 (1927).

Similar regularities are found in the L-series satellites though they are not so clear as the K-series relations, probably because of the more complicated structure of the L and M shells.

Wentzel[1] proposed that these faint lines represent the spark X-ray spectra emitted by atoms which have more than one electron removed. The X-ray spectra emitted by singly, doubly, and trebly ionized atoms may be referred to as the first, second, and third spectra, respectively. Two electrons may be removed from the same or different shells of the atom and the spectrum emitted by such multiply ionized atoms when electrons of outer shells fall to the inner shells will be of different character from that emitted by the singly ionized atom. A doubly ionized atom will have an energy diagram of the singlet and triplet type, and the trebly ionized atom or ion will have doublet and quartet multiplicities. These conclusions follow from the study of multiplicities of optical spectra to be described in Chap. X.

A word of explanation is necessary, however, in this connection. Many of the X-ray spectra ascribed to atoms are really characteristic of ions having closed subshells of electrons, or compounds with closed subshells, in the sense that the incomplete valence shell of one atom couples with those of other atoms in such a way that there is no resultant angular momentum or magnetic moment. For such ions and compounds the system of levels must be of the doublet type. But in many elements of transition groups, as for example the rare earths, the subshells are not all closed even for stable ions, as indicated by measurements of magnetic susceptibility. The X-ray levels of such an ion cannot be a doublet system; there must be closely spaced groups of levels in the neighborhood of each of the doublet levels.

Aside from these facts on which there is general agreement, the subject of X-ray spark spectra is rather involved and controversial. A description of the various theories proposed in regard to the transitions which give rise to the $K\alpha$ group would be quite lengthy, and we shall content ourselves with giving references to the more recent papers on the subject.[2]

[1] Ann. Physik, **66**, 487 (1921); ibid., **73**, 647 (1924); Z. Physik, **31**, 445 (1924).

[2] Bäcklin, Z. Physik, **27**, 30 (1924); Druyvesteyn, ibid., **43**, 707 (1927); Turner, Phys. Rev., **26**, 143 (1925); Richtmyer, Phil. Mag., **6**, 64 (1928).

22. THE EFFECTS OF CHEMICAL COMBINATION ON X-RAY SPECTRA[1]

Thus far, we have not considered changes in the spectra due to the state of chemical combination; they have been assumed to be characteristic of the individual atom and independent of its chemical combination with other atoms. This is found to be far from true when the fine structures of the absorption limits and lines and their exact wave lengths are determined. Though these effects have not been extensively investigated, it may be said that the absorption limits and emission lines of an element are different in position in nearly all of its chemical compounds and often there are differences in structure as well. The causes of these

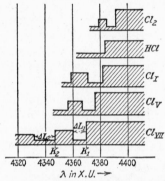

Fig. 28.—K-absorption limits of chlorine of different valences. (*After Lindh.*)

changes are imperfectly understood and the experimental data are as yet too meager for systematic classification.

Figure 28 gives the structure of the K-absorption limits of chlorine in its different valencies, according to Lindh, and illustrates two general features: the absorption limit is shifted toward higher frequency as the valence increases, and a distinct fine structure appears, the nature of which depends on the valence. In some cases, the fine structure consists of fairly sharp absorption lines. There are two distinct absorption limits for each valence, except in the case of HCl, though these two limits are not observed for all compounds having a particular type of valency. The average wave lengths of these limits, K_1 and K_2, observed in many compounds, and their variation with valence, are given in Table 11, together with the energy differences of these limits for free chlorine and for the element in combination. The change in wave length between the longest and shortest wave lengths is about 0.5 per cent, which is far from insignificant, though it corresponds only to an energy change of the

[1] For complete summaries, see the following papers and references there given: Lindh, *Physik. Z.*, **28**, 98 and 111 (1927); Stelling, *Z. f. anorg. Chem.*, **131**, 48 (1923); *Z. f. Phys. Chem.*, **117**, 161, 175, 194 (1925); *Chem. Ber.*, **60**, 650 (1927); "Über den Zusammenhang zwischen chemischer Konstitution und K-Röntgen Absorptionsspektren," Lund, May (1927); *Z. Physik*, **50**, 506 (1928).

TABLE 11

	Wave length		ΔV (volts) relative to Cl_2		$K_2 - K_1$ (volts)
	K_1	K_2	K_1	K_2	
Cl_2..................	4,393.8	4,381.6	0	0	7.8
HCl..................	4,385.3	....	5.4	....	....
Cl^-..................	4,382.9	4,360.0	7.0	13.8	14.6
Cl^{5+}..................	4,376.9	4,357.4	10.8	15.5	12.5
Cl^{7+}..................	4,369.8	4,347.8	15.3	21.6	14.1

order of magnitude of the binding energies of the compounds. There is some variation among the individual compounds containing the chlorine in any one valence type, though they group themselves rather closely about the values given in the table.

A study of the K limits of chlorine and sulfur compounds, as well as others, shows that there must be specific effects of the metal ions with regard to both the wave lengths of the limits and their fine structures. Stelling[1] pointed out that the variation in the wave length of the limit depends on the crystal structure, the interionic distances, and the electron configuration of the metal ion, and Fajans[2] has found that the experimental results agree fairly well with the assumption that the wave-length difference between the absorption limit of the free ion and of the ion in the crystal is proportional to the inverse fourth power of the interionic distance r if the metal ions have similar outside electron shells and the crystals have the same lattice; that is,

$$\lambda_\infty - \lambda = \frac{k}{r^4},$$

where λ_∞ is the wave length for the free ion and λ that for the ion bound in a lattice, and k is a constant. The following table shows how well this formula agrees with the experimental data on three sulfides, if $\lambda_\infty(S^{--})$ is taken as 5,009.3 X. U.

TABLE 12

Compound	λ	r	r^4	$\lambda_\infty - \lambda$	$(\lambda_\infty - \lambda)r^4 = k$
MgS	5,005.3	2.594	45.3	4.0	180
CaS	5,006.6	2.843	65.3	2.7	176
BaS	5,007.5	3.184	103.0	1.8	185

[1] Loc. cit.
[2] Z. Physik, **50**, 531 (1928).

The change of refractive index of the ions due to binding in a crystal follows a similar law[1] and this indicates that the variations due to the metal ions depend on the deformation of the outside electron shells of the negative ions. The complete explanation of these phenomena has not been given. It will probably be necessary to consider, in addition, the lattice energy with normal ions, with ions having a K electron missing, and with free electrons in the lattice, as has been done by Aoyama, Kimura, and Nishina,[2] and also to consider the deformation of the ion by the neighboring atoms or ions.

The dependence of emission spectra on the compound containing the element is even more prominent than that of the absorption edges, for here there appears to be a dependence on the metal of the target supporting the compound as well. Lines which appear when a compound is supported on a target of one metal will be absent, if the same compound is supported on another target, and the relative intensities of the lines may be changed. These spectra require much more research before any satisfactory classification and interpretation of the results can be made.

References

WYCKOFF, R. W. G., "The Structure of Crystals," Chemical Catalogue Co., New York (1924).

BRAGG, W. H. and W. L., "X-Rays and Crystal Structure," Bell, London (1924).

COMPTON, A. H., "X-Rays and Electrons," D. Van Nostrand Company, Inc., New York (1926).

SIEGBAHN, M., "Spektroskopie der Röntgenstrahlen," Springer, Berlin (1924).

CLARK, G. L., "Applied X-Rays," McGraw-Hill Book Company, Inc., New York (1927).

EWALD, P. P., "Kristalle und Röntgenstrahlen," Springer, Berlin (1924).

KAYE, G. W. C., "X-Rays," Longmans, Green and Co., London (1923).

LINDH, A. E., *Physik. Z.*, **28**, 24 and 93 (1927).

SOMMERFELD, "Atombau."

[1] FAJANS, *Z. f. Phys. Chem.*, **130**, 724 (1927).

[2] *Z. Physik*, **44**, 810 (1927).

CHAPTER IX

THE PERIODIC SYSTEM OF THE ELEMENTS

1. THE ARRANGEMENT OF ELECTRONS IN ATOMS

The periodic system of the elements consists of six completed periods and one incomplete period containing 2, 8, 8, 18, 18, 32, and 6 elements, respectively. Each increase in the length of period brings with it a number of elements with properties different from those of the preceding periods. The types of elements which first appear in the periods of 18 are known as the transition elements, and the period of 32 also contains the fourteen rare earths.

Figure 1 is the periodic table of Julius Thomsen[1] which agrees well with the structure of the electron configurations deduced by Bohr, which we shall now describe. In this table the rare gases, which were postulated by Thomsen before their discovery, the transition groups, and the rare earths have logical positions. Thomsen pointed out that the numbers of elements in the periods of the table, omitting the inert gases, are given by the expression

$$1 + 2 \times 3 + 2 \times 5 + \cdots,$$

which can be modified on including the inert gases to read

$$2 \times 1 + 2 \times 3 + 2 \times 5 + 2 \times 7 + \cdots; \tag{1}$$

by breaking this series at different points, the numbers 2, 8, 18, 32, etc., mentioned above are secured.

The approximate but unmistakable repetition of chemical and physical properties with these periods and the increasing length of the periods has been believed to be due to a regular building up of successive electron shells with increasing numbers of electrons since the original proposals of Sir J. J. Thomson to account for them in this way. We are confronted with several questions: (1) How many electrons are there in each shell or subshell? (2) What limits the number of electrons in a given shell? (3) How are the periodic properties of the elements related to the exterior electron configurations? These questions can now be answered in a broad way, as a result of our knowledge of the optical and X-ray spectra of the elements.

Bohr[2] first proposed a distribution of electrons into different shells and subshells which was based on an attempt to correlate spectral data

---

[1] *Z. anorg. Chem.*, **9**, 190 and 283 (1895).
[2] *Ann. Physik*, **71**, 228 (1923); *Z. Physik*, **9**, 1 (1922).

with the periodic system; this explained a wide range of phenomena. Bohr's assignment of the numbers of electrons in the shells defined by the total quantum number, n, for the atoms of the different periods has not been modified, but his assignment of the numbers in the subshells defined by the azimuthal number, l, has been modified by Stoner[1] and

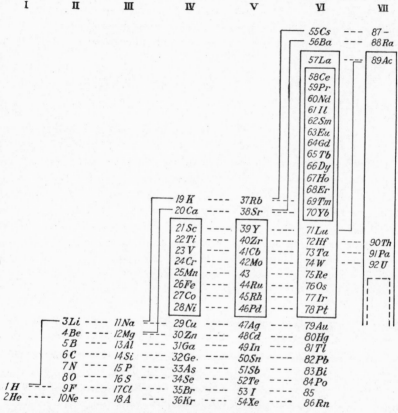

I	II	III	IV	V	VI	VII
					55Cs	87 –
					56Ba	88Ra
					57La	89Ac
					58Ce	
					59Pr	
					60Nd	
					61 Il	
					62Sm	
					63Eu	
					64Gd	
					65Tb	
					66Dy	
					67Ho	
					68Er	
			19K	37Rb	69Tm	
			20Ca	38Sr	70Yb	
			21Sc	39Y	71Lu	
			22Ti	40Zr	72Hf	90Th
			23V	41Cb	73Ta	91Pa
			24Cr	42Mo	74W	92U
			25Mn	43	75Re	
			26Fe	44Ru	76Os	
			27Co	45Rh	77Ir	
			28Ni	46Pd	78Pt	
		3Li	11Na	29Cu	47Ag	79Au
		4Be	12Mg	30Zn	48Cd	80Hg
		5B	13Al	31Ga	49In	81Tl
		6C	14Si	32Ge.	50Sn	82Pb
		7N	15P	33As	51Sb	83Bi
		8O	16S	34Se	52Te	84Po
1H		9F	17Cl	35Br	53 I	85
2He		10Ne	18A	36Kr	54Xe	86Rn

Fig. 1.—The Thomsen-Bohr periodic table (*modified*).

Main-Smith.[2] Following this work Pauli proposed his equivalence principle, which limits the possible numbers of electrons in each shell or subshell. There are two factors which are effective in determining the electron configuration of the normal state of an atom; first, the electron configuration must be one permitted by the Pauli equivalence principle, and second, it must be that which makes the energy of the atom a minimum. These two factors will now be taken up in order.

[1] *Phil. Mag.*, **48**, 719 (1924).
[2] *J. Chem. Ind.*, **43**, 323 (1924); "Chemistry and Atomic Structure," London (1924); *Phil. Mag.*, **50**, 878 (1925).

2. THE PAULI EQUIVALENCE PRINCIPLE AND THE ELECTRON SHELLS

Pauli's principle requires that no two electrons of an atom shall have all of their five quantum numbers identical (Chap. VII, Sec. **19**). These five quantum numbers may be taken as those required to fix the steady states of an atom in a strong magnetic field, since there is a one-to-one correspondence between these and the quantum numbers required to fix the steady states of the atom under any other conditions where the atomic system is not degenerate. These five quantum numbers and their possible values have been defined and illustrated in Chap. VII, but will be briefly reviewed here. They are,

$$n = 1, 2, 3, \cdots \infty,$$
$$l = 0, 1, \cdots n - 1, \text{ a vector,}$$
$$s = \tfrac{1}{2}, \text{ a vector,}$$
$$m_l = -l, -l + 1, \cdots, 0, \cdots l - 1, l,$$
$$m_s = \pm \tfrac{1}{2}.$$

Such a set of quantum numbers is required for each electron of an atom to fix the steady states in a strong magnetic field. In a weak magnetic field another set of quantum numbers must be used but there will still be $5Z$ such numbers. One of these will be the resultant angular momentum of all the electrons of the atom, in quantum units, and another the projection of this in the direction of the field. These two numbers are j and m, respectively. When the field vanishes, m loses its meaning, since the orientation in space becomes indeterminate. In the absence of the field many of the quantum numbers are no longer characteristic of the individual electrons, but of a group of electrons. However, the n, l, and s quantum numbers can still be assigned to individual electrons, and, therefore, the shells and subshells can be designated in terms of these numbers. Since s is always $\tfrac{1}{2}$ it is unnecessary to use it in designating the shells. We now wish to find the maximum numbers of electrons having given values of n and l, which an atom can possess without violating the Pauli principle.

We consider first the smallest values of n and l and proceed to the larger values, considering, at present, only the numbers of electrons which may enter any shell and not the question of whether these numbers are actually present in the case of any given atom. Taking $n = 1$, l can take only the value 0, and, therefore, m_l only the value 0, while m_s may take two values, $\pm \tfrac{1}{2}$; therefore there may be two electrons in an atom with n, $l = 1$, 0, one for each of the two possible values of m_s. These two electrons complete the first shell. If n equals 2, l may be either 0, or 1; with l equal to 0, m_l must be 0 and m_s may be $\pm \tfrac{1}{2}$, and thus two electrons may occupy the 2, 0 subshell; with l equal to 1, m_l may be -1, 0, 1; and, as before, m_s may be $\pm \tfrac{1}{2}$ for each of these three values of m_l, so that six electrons may occupy the 2, 1 subshell. The eight electrons of the second completed shell have the quantum numbers given in Table 1, if it is placed in a very strong magnetic field, and, as this field is allowed to vanish, they arrange themselves in two closed subshells of two and six electrons each.

TABLE 1

n	l	m_l	m_s
2	0	0	$-\frac{1}{2}$
2	0	0	$+\frac{1}{2}$
2	1	-1	$-\frac{1}{2}$
2	1	-1	$+\frac{1}{2}$
2	1	0	$-\frac{1}{2}$
2	1	0	$+\frac{1}{2}$
2	1	1	$-\frac{1}{2}$
2	1	1	$+\frac{1}{2}$

Similar reasoning can be applied to the other electron shells. It is immediately evident that m_l takes $2l + 1$ values and that m_s always has $2s + 1$ $(=2)$ values, so that there will be $2(2l + 1)$ electrons in any subshell. Summing over the possible values of l, the number of electrons in the nth shell is

$$\sum_{l=0}^{l=n-1} 2(2l + 1) = 2n^2. \tag{2}$$

TABLE 2

X-ray symbol	n, l	$2(2l + 1)$	$2n^2$
K...............	1, 0	2	2
L_I...............	2, 0	2	
$L_\text{II,III}$............	2, 1	6	8
M_I...............	3, 0	2	
$M_\text{II,III}$............	3, 1	6	
$M_\text{IV,V}$............	3, 2	10	18
N_I...............	4, 0	2	
$N_\text{II,III}$	4, 1	6	
$N_\text{IV,V}$	4, 2	10	
$N_\text{VI,VII}$	4, 3	14	32
O_I...............	5, 0	2	
$O_\text{II,III}$	5, 1	6	
$O_\text{IV,V}$	5, 2	10	
$O_\text{VI,VII}$	5, 3	14	
$O_\text{VIII,IX}$	5, 4	18	50
P_I...............	6, 0	2	
.			
.			
.			
$P_\text{X,XI}$............	6, 5	22	72

This equation is equivalent to Thomsen's rule given by the expression (1). It is interesting that the correct formula for the numbers of electrons in subshells was secured so many years before its theoretical interpretation. Table 2 gives the numbers of electrons in the completed shells and sub-shells to the sixth shell. The electron groups are not filled in the order in which they occur in this table.

The P and O levels having high l values are hypothetical, as we shall soon see. The numbers 2, 8, 18, and 32 appear here as the maximum numbers of electrons in the shells, but the repetition of the 8 and 18 periods found in the periodic system does not follow from the equivalence principle alone.

It is convenient to introduce a symbol to represent the numbers of electrons in each shell and subshell of the atom. This can be done by using a whole number to represent n and the letters s, p, d, etc. to indicate values of l equal to 0, 1, 2, etc., respectively. Superscripts on these letters indicate the numbers of electrons of each kind in the atom. The symbol will be clear from the following example: An atom having the following configuration;

n, l	1, 0	2, 0	2, 1	3, 0	3, 1	3, 2
Number of electrons	2	2	6	2	6	4

would be represented by the symbol,

$$1s^2 2s^2 2p^6 3s^2 3p^6 3d^4.$$

3. BOHR'S THEORY OF THE PERIODIC SYSTEM[1]

Bohr attacked the problem of assigning quantum numbers to the individual electrons of the atom by considering the building up of the

---

[1] The principal arguments of this section are due to Bohr, but the assignment of electrons to the subshells was given essentially by Stoner and Main-Smith (loc. cit.). Bohr divided the electrons in each completed shell equally among the subshells so that the assignment was the following:

n, l	1, 0	2, 0	2, 1	3, 0	3, 1	3, 2	· · ·
Number of electrons	2	4	4	6	6	6	· · ·

At the time there appeared to be no way of deciding whether this was correct or not. Stoner and Main-Smith assigned them as follows:

n, l, j	1, 0, ½	2, 0, ½	2, 1, ½	2, 1, 3⁄2	3, 0, ½	3, 1, ½	3, 1, 3⁄2
Number of electrons	2	2	2	4	2	2	4

3, 2, 3⁄2	3, 2, 5⁄2	· · ·
4	6	

The division of the subshells for $l > 0$ into two parts is not justified for the relativity doublet levels $L_{II,III}$, $M_{II,III}$, $M_{IV,V}$, etc. are due to two possible ways of orienting the vectors of the incomplete shell relative to each other. The quantum number j is not characteristic of the individual electron removed from these shells, but is a vector sum of the l and s vectors of all the remaining electrons and takes two possible values for a shell with one electron removed, if $l > 0$. See Chap VIII, Sec. **20**, and STONER, Proc. of Leeds Phil. Soc., **1**, 226 (1928), particularly p. 229.

electron shells starting with a bare nucleus of charge $+Ze$ and adding electrons successively to this nucleus.   He postulated that each successive electron could be added in such a way that the n and l quantum numbers of the previously bound electrons would not be changed.   This is called the "construction principle" (Aufbauprinzip).   Further, the normal state of the atom has that electron configuration which gives the atom as a whole the least possible internal energy of all possible configurations. It will not be true always that ions and atoms having the same total number of electrons, whatever their nuclear charges may be, will have the same number of electrons in each of the shells and subshells, and cases in which they do not are especially instructive; but in many cases,

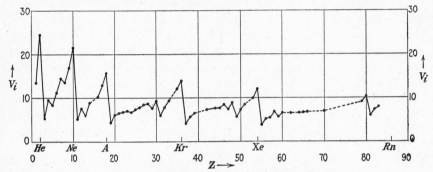

FIG. 2.—Ionizing potentials of the elements.

the $Z - 1$ electrons of the singly charged ion of an element are bound in the same way as the electrons of the neutral atom immediately preceding it in the periodic system.   For this reason, and in order to proceed from simpler to more complex atoms, it is well to begin the discussion of the building process with hydrogen.

In discussing the building up of the electron shells of elements with low atomic numbers, it is convenient to refer to the energy required to remove the most loosely bound electron.   Unfortunately, this energy is unknown for many elements, but Fig. 2 is a plot of the known values against the atomic number for the elements of the periodic table. The most striking features of this curve are the very sharp decreases between each inert gas and the following alkali metal.   The features of this curve will now be correlated with the electron configurations of the atoms.

The electron of the hydrogen atom and of the singly ionized helium atom, in their normal states, is known from their spectra to have the quantum numbers $n = 1$ and $l = 0$.   The binding energies are equal in wave numbers to R_H and $4R_{He}$, respectively.   Though the spectra of only these two hydrogenic atoms have been observed, one electron bound to a bare nucleus of any atomic number would enter the 1, 0 steady state, for this state has less energy than any other with higher quantum numbers. The second electron of helium is also bound in a 1, 0 orbit, as we can see from the following evidence.

An electron brought to the helium ion is attracted by the field of one unit of positive charge at large distances, and by a field of two positive units as a maximum at small distances. Therefore the energy liberated in binding the second electron in the 1, 0 shell should lie somewhere between R and $4R$, while the energy of binding in a state with $n = 2$ would be of the order of magnitude of $R/4$. The actual energy of binding calculated from the ionizing potential of 24.5 volts is $1.81R$, which shows that both electrons have the quantum numbers $n, l = 1, 0$. The configuration of the atom is represented therefore by the symbol $1s^2$. This is a possible configuration according to the preceding section and Table 2. Only the higher terms of the LiII spectrum are known, and these are similar to the higher terms of the HeI spectrum.

The third element lithium has an ionizing potential of 5.37 volts, so that the third electron is bound with an energy of $0.40\ R$. If the third electron entered the 1, 0 shell, its binding energy should be greater than R and probably larger than the energy of binding of the second electron of helium; if bound in a state with $n = 2$, its energy should be approximately that of the hydrogen atom in its orbits with $n = 2$, or about $\frac{1}{4}R$. The energies of the $2^2P_{\frac{1}{2},\frac{3}{2}}$ states of lithium are very nearly equal to this (Chap. VII, Table 3). The larger energy of binding of the normal state, $1^2S_{\frac{1}{2}}$, is in agreement with its assignment to a 2, 0 orbit, for due to its ellipticity such an orbit will pass very close to the 2 inner electrons or perhaps within the region of their orbits and, thus, be in the field of three positive charges for a part of the time, i.e., the orbit is a penetrating orbit (Chap. VII, Secs. 10 and 11). The lithium atom, therefore, has the configuration $1s^22s$. The normal states of Be^+, B^{2+}, and C^{3+} are known and these as well as the excited states show that the third electron is bound in the 2, 0 shell. The 1, 0 shell is evidently completed at helium and is filled with two electrons in all other atoms.

The fourth electron of beryllium, boron, or carbon is also bound in the 2, 0 shell. The normal states of these 4 electron atoms are $^1S_0$ states as they should be according to the theory of multiplets given in Chap. X. The energy of binding of this last electron increases above that of the lithium electron, for reasons similar to those which explain the increased binding energy of the second helium electron as compared with that of hydrogen. The normal beryllium atom and B^+ and C^{++} as well have the configuration $1s^22s^2$. The most loosely bound electron of boron requires considerably less energy for its removal than that of beryllium (Fig. 2). This indicates that it is bound in another type of orbit. The normal state of boron is a ^2P level showing that the last

electron is bound on a 2, 1 orbit.   Thus, the 2, 0 subshell is completed
with 2 electrons and the next one enters the 2, 1 subshell.

The assignment of quantum numbers to the electrons of the remaining
elements in the second period can be made from the study of their optical
spectra.   These spectra are of the more complex type considered in
Chap. X and, therefore, we shall not discuss these assignments here.
The following configurations are in accord with the known spectroscopic
data: C, $1s^2 2s^2 2p^2$; N, $1s^2 2s^2 2p^3$; O, $1s^2 2s^2 2p^4$; F, $1s^2 2s^2 2p^5$; and

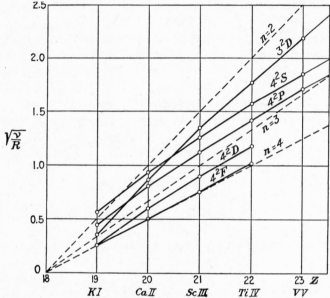

FIG. 3.—Optical Moseley diagram of the energy levels of the nineteenth electron.   (*After
Grotrian.*   See reference at the end of Chap. X.)
The numbers preceding the symbols ^2S, ^2P, etc. are the total quantum numbers.   Thus,
the 4^2S state of this figure is the 1^2S state in our nomenclature.

Ne, $1s^2 2s^2 2p^6$.   The binding energy of the last electron increases from
boron to neon except for a slight decrease at oxygen.

The ionizing potential of neon is 21.47 volts and that of sodium
only 5.13 volts.   This large change in the energy of binding indicates
that the last electron of sodium does not enter the 2, 1 subshell and therefore it has a total quantum number, $n = 3$.   The binding energy of this
electron is considerably greater than that of an electron of the same total
quantum number in hydrogen, indicating that its orbit penetrates
the completed shells.   The normal level is a $^2S_{1/2}$ state and so the eleventh
electron must enter a 3, 0 orbit.   The electron configurations of the
remaining elements of this period are similar to those of the preceding
period.   Argon has the configuration $3s^2 3p^6$.

Figure 3 illustrates certain regularities of optical spectra, which have
been partly discussed in Chap. VII, Secs. **13** and **14.**   The doublet separa-

tions (not shown in the figure) follow the law for the relativity-spin doublets of X-ray spectra. In addition, the screening-doublet law of X-ray spectra holds very well for these optical levels of stripped atoms. Thus the curves for ^2S, ^2P, and ^2D states with total quantum number 4 are very nearly parallel to each other, showing that the screening constants for these levels differ by a constant amount. Such regularities have been used to extrapolate from the known levels of certain atoms to unknown ones of others.[1]

4. THE LONG PERIODS

The first 18 electrons are bound in the order of increasing n and l and the subshells have the numbers of electrons required by the theory of Sec. 2. The curve of ionizing potentials (Fig. 2) shows that there is a very marked decrease in binding energy with increasing n, as in the case of He and Li or Ne and Na. There is a smaller decrease with increasing l, as we see by comparing Be and B, and Mg and Al. In fact, it is quite generally true that an increase in n produces a greater decrease in the binding energy than an increase of l. At potassium we meet the first irregularity in this respect. The quantum theory permits 10 electrons to occupy the 3, 2 subshell, but it is not filled in argon or potassium and from the spectrum of potassium we know that its last electron enters the 4, 0 subshell. The normal level is $^2S_{1/2}$ with the configuration $3s^2 3p^6 4s$, while the levels $^2D_{3/2, 5/2}$ with the configuration $3s^2 3p^6 3d$ have a higher energy. This is also true in ionized calcium and the second valence electron of calcium as well is in the 4, 0 subshell. But in doubly ionized scandium, the normal level is a $^2D_{3/2, 5/2}$ level, showing that the nineteenth electron in scandium enters the 3, 2 subshell. The change of the configuration $3s^2 3p^6 3d$ from an excited level of K and Ca$^+$ to the normal level of Sc^{2+} and other ions following it can be clearly seen from the Moseley diagram of Fig. 3. The normal states of the elements from Sc21 to Ni28, inclusive, have electrons in both the 3, 2 and 4, 0 subgroups and the variable valence and magnetic properties of these elements are due to these partially completed shells. Copper is the first element having enough electrons to fill completely the 3, 2 subshell, and 1 valence electron in addition. Its normal state is a $^2S_{1/2}$ state and its electron configuration is $3s^2 3p^6 3d^{10} 4s$. The building up of the 4, 0 and 4, 1 subshells from Cu29 to Kr36 is similar to that of the second and third periods. Krypton has the configuration $4s^2 4p^6$.

The electron configuration of copper differs from that of potassium only in having the third shell completed by the addition of 10 electrons to the 3, 2 subshell, and the different chemical properties of the two elements must be due to the different underlying shells. Since copper

[1] See, for example, MILLIKAN and BOWEN, Proc. Nat. Acad. Sci., 13, 531 (1927) and references given there, and GIBBS and WHITE, Phys. Rev., 31, 309 (1928) and references given there; Proc. Nat. Acad. Sci., 12, 598 (1926).

may be divalent, 1 electron of the 3, 2 subshell can be removed fairly easily, while in potassium, the electrons of the 3, 1 subshell are not thus easily removed. Moreover, the kernel of copper is undoubtedly much smaller than that of potassium. This can be seen to be in accord with theoretical expectations. The screening constants for the M_I, $M_{II,III}$, and $M_{IV,V}$, that is, the 3, 0, 3, 1, and 3, 2 subshells, are 6.8, 8.5, and 13.0, respectively (Chap. VIII, Secs. **16** to **19**), so that the effective nuclear charges for the 3, 0 and 3, 1 subshells of potassium are 12.2 and 10.5 while those for the 3, 0, 3, 1, and 3, 2 subshells of copper are 22.2, 20.5, and 16.0, respectively. Under these higher fields, the third-shell electrons will lie closer to the nucleus in the case of copper. At least part of the difference in chemical properties of potassium and copper and also of calcium and zinc and other similarly related elements of the long periods is due to this difference in size of the respective kernels (Sec. 7).

The fifth period is built up in the same way as the fourth period. The 4, 2 and 4, 3 subshells are both unfilled in Kr36, and in the second transition group of elements the 4, 2 subshell is completed with 10 electrons at Ag47; the 4, 3 subshell is still unfilled. Rb37 has the configuration $4s^2 4p^6 5s$ and its normal state is a ^2S state; but Y^{2+} has the configuration $4s^2 4p^6 4d$ and the normal state is the $^2D_{3/2,5/2}$ state. Ag47 has the configuration, $4s^2 4p^6 4d^{10} 5s$, and Xe54 the configuration, $4s^2-4p^6 4d^{10} 5s^2 5p^6$.

In the sixth period, Cs55 and Ba56 are similar to K and Ca, and Rb and Sr in the structure of their valence shells. With La57 one valence electron enters the 5, 2 subshell and the other two the 6, 0 subshell and throughout the rare earths the numbers of electrons in these two subshells remain the same. Beginning with Ce58 the additional electrons enter the 4, 3 subshell until La71 is reached, when this subshell has its complete quota of 14 electrons. Hf72 has the configuration,

$$4s^2 4p^6 4d^{10} 4f^{14} 5s^2 5p^6 5d^2 6s^2;$$

this is similar to that of Zr, namely,

$$4s^2 4p^6 4d^2 5s^2.$$

The marked similarity of these elements is undoubtedly due to this circumstance and the additional fact that the atomic volumes are very nearly the same. The effect of the additional charge of the Hf nucleus on the size of the kernel has just been compensated by the additional electron shells of higher total quantum number. From Hf72 to Au79 the 5, 2 subshell is filled to 10 electrons, so that this group of elements is similar again in chemical properties to the first and second transition groups. From Au79 to Rn86 the process of building the 6, 0 and 6, 1 shells to two and six electrons, respectively, is completed. Rn has the configuration,

$$5s^2 5p^6 5d^{10} 6s^2 6p^6.$$

The seventh group consists of the missing alkali metal 87, Ra88, Ac89, Th90, UX91, and U92. The properties of radium are similar to those of Ba and it undoubtedly has the Rn86 configuration with two additional valence electrons in the 7, 0 subshell. Thorium and uranium are similar to Hf and W in properties indicating that the additional valence electrons enter the 6, 2 subshell. They certainly are not similar

TABLE 3

Element	K 1,0 1s	L 2,0 2s	L 2,1 2p	M 3,0 3s	M 3,1 3p	M 3,2 3d	N 4,0 4s	N 4,1 4p	Normal term (theoretical)	V_i[1]
H 1	1	..	..	..	..	..	..	..	$^2S_{1/2}$	13.54
He 2	2	..	..	..	..	..	..	..	$^1S_0$	24.48
Li 3	2	1	..	..	..	..	..	..	$^2S_{1/2}$	5.37
Be 4	2	2	..	..	..	..	..	..	$^1S_0$	9.48
B 5	2	2	1	..	..	..	..	..	$^2P_{1/2}$	8.4
C 6	2	2	2	..	..	..	..	..	$^3P_0$	11.24
N 7	2	2	3	..	..	..	..	..	$^4S_{3/2}$	14.48
O 8	2	2	4	..	..	..	..	..	$^3P_2$	13.56
F 9	2	2	5	..	..	..	..	..	$^2P_{3/2}$	16.9
Ne 10	2	2	6	..	..	..	..	..	$^1S_0$	21.5
Na 11				1	..	..	..	..	$^2S_{1/2}$	5.12
Mg 12				2	..	..	..	..	$^1S_0$	7.61
Al 13				2	1	..	..	..	$^2P_{1/2}$	5.96
Si 14		Neon		2	2	..	..	..	$^3P_0$	8.19[2]
P 15		configuration		2	3	..	..	..	$^4S_{3/2}$	
S 16				2	4	..	..	..	$^3P_2$	10.31
Cl 17				2	5	..	..	..	$^2P_{3/2}$	12.96
A 18				2	6	..	..	..	$^1S_0$	15.69
K 19				..	1	..	$^2S_{1/2}$	4.32
Ca 20				..	2	..	$^1S_0$	6.09
Sc 21				1	2	..	$^2D_{3/2}$	6.57
Ti 22				2	2	..	$^3F_2$	6.80
V 23		Argon		3	2	..	$^4F_{3/2}$	6.76, 7.04[3]
Cr 24		configuration		5	1	..	$^7S_3$	6.74
Mn 25				5	2	..	$^6S_{5/2}$	7.40
Fe 26				6	2	..	$^5D_4$	7.83
Co 27				7	2	..	$^4F_{9/2}$	7.81, 8.25[3]
Ni 28				8	2	..	$^3F_4$	7.64, 8.65[3]
Cu 29				10	1	..	$^2S_{1/2}$	7.69
Zn 30				10	2	..	$^1S_0$	9.35
Ga 31				10	2	1	$^2P_{1/2}$	5.97
Ge 32		Argon		10	2	2	$^3P_0$	7.85
As 33		configuration		10	2	3	$^4S_{3/2}$	9.4
Se 34				10	2	4	$^3P_2$	
Br 35				10	2	5	$^2P_{3/2}$	12.2
Kr 36				10	2	6	$^1S_0$	13.940

TABLE 3.—(Continued)

Element	Configuration of inner shells	N 4,2 4d	N 4,3 4f	O 5,0 5s	O 5,1 5p	O 5,2 5d	P 6,0 6s	Normal term (theoretical)	V_i
Rb 37		..	..	1	..	..	..	$^2S_{1/2}$	4.16
Sr 38		..	..	2	..	..	..	$^1S_0$	5.67
Y 39		1	..	2	..	..	..	$^2D_{3/2}$	6.5
Zr 40		2	..	2	..	..	..	$^3F_2$	
Cb 41	Krypton con-	4	..	1	..	..	..	$^6D_{1/2}$	
Mo 42	figuration	5	..	1	..	..	..	$^7S_3$	7.35
43		(6)	..	(1)	..	..	..	$(^6D_{9/2})$	
Ru 44		7	..	1	..	..	..	$^5F_5$	7.7
Rh 45		8	..	1	..	..	..	$^4F_{9/2}$	7.7
Pd 46		10	..	..	..	..	..	$^1S_0$	8.5
Ag 47			..	1	..	..	..	$^2S_{1/2}$	7.54
Cd 48			..	2	..	..	..	$^1S_0$	8.95
In 49			..	2	1	..	..	$^2P_{1/2}$	5.76
Sn 50	Palladium configu-		..	2	2	..	..	$^3P_0$	7.37
Sb 51	ration		..	2	3	..	..	$^4S_{3/2}$	8.5
Te 52			..	2	4	..	..	$^3P_2$	
I 53			..	2	5	..	..	$^2P_{3/2}$	10
Xe 54			..	2	6	..	..	$^1S_0$	12.078
Cs 55			..			..	1	$^2S_{1/2}$	3.88
Ba 56			..			..	2	$^1S_0$	5.19
La 57			..			1	2	$^2D_{3/2}$	4
Ce 58			1	The shells 5s		1	2	$^3H_4$	4
Pr 59			2	to 5p con-		1	2	$^4K_{11/2}$	4
Nd 60			3	tain 8 elec-		1	2	$^5L_6$	4
Il 61	Xenon configura-		4	trons		1	2	$^5L_{9/2}$	
Sa 62	tion. The shells		5			1	2	$^7K_4$	4
Eu 63	1s to 4d contain		6			1	2	$^8H_{3/2}$	
Gd 64	46 electrons.		7			1	2	$^9D_2$	4
Tb 65			8			1	2	$^8H_{17/2}$	4
Dy 66			9			1	2	$^7K_{10}$	4
Ho 67			10			1	2	$^6L_{19/2}$	
Er 68			11			1	2	$^5L_{10}$	
Tu 69			12			1	2	$^4K_{17/2}$	
Yb 70			13			1	2	$^3H_6$	4
Lu 71			14			1	2	$^2D_{3/2}$	

Table 3.—(*Continued*)

Element	Configuration of inner shells	O		P		Q		Normal term (theoretical)	V_i
		5, 2 5d	5, 3 5f	6, 0 6s	6, 1 6p	6, 2 6d	7, 0 7s		
Hf 72		2	..	2	..	..	..	$^3F_2$	
Ta 73		3	..	2	..	..	..	$^4F_{3/2}$	
W 74		4	..	2	..	..	..	$^5D_0$	
Re 75		5	..	2	..	..	..	$^6S_{5/2}$	
	Shells 1s to 5p con-tain 68 electrons	6	..	1	..	..	..	$^6D_{9/2}$	
Os 76		6	..	2	..	..	..	$^5D_4$	
		7	..	1	..	..	..	$^5F_5$	
Ir 77		7	..	2	..	..	..	$^4F_{9/2}$	
		8	..	1	..	..	..	$^4F_{9/2}$	
Pt 78		9	..	1	..	..	..	$^3D_3$	
Au 79			..	1	..	..	..	$^2S_{1/2}$	9.20
Hg 80			..	2	..	..	..	$^1S_0$	10.39
Tl 81			..	2	1	..	..	$^2P_{1/2}$	6.08
Pb 82	Shells 1s to 5d contain 78 electrons		..	2	2	..	..	$^3P_0$	7.39
Bi 83			..	2	3	..	..	$^4S_{3/2}$	8.0
Po 84			..	2	4	..	..	$^3P_2$	
85			..	2	5	..	..	$^2P_{3/2}$	
Rn 86			..	2	6	..	..	$^1S_0$	
87			..				1	$^2S_{1/2}$	
Ra 88			..				2	$^1S_0$	
Ac 89			..			1	2	$^2D_{3/2}$	
Th 90	Radon configuration. The shells 1s to 5d contain 78 electrons		1	The shells 6s to 6p contain 8 electrons		1	2	$^3H_4$	
			..			2	2	$^3F_2$	
UX 91			2			1	2	$^4K_{11/2}$	
			..			3	2	$^4F_{3/2}$	
Ur 92			3			1	2	$^5L_6$	
			..			4	2	$^5D_0$	

[1] V_i is the energy in volts required to remove one electron and leave the ion in its lowest energy state except in the cases noted.

[2] McLennan and Shaver give 7.94 for the ionization potential of silicon.

[3] In the case of vanadium, cobalt, and nickel, values are given for ionization by two different routes; $d^{n-2}s^2 \to d^{n-1}$ and $d^{n-2}s^2 \to d^{n-2}s^1$. These two values are given in this order in the table.

[4] Estimates of the ionization potentials of a number of rare earths were made by Rolla and Piccardi (*Phil. Mag.*, **7**, 296 (1929)) using a method depending on the relative degrees of ionization produced in flames of equal temperature when known amounts of salts of these elements were vaporized. Their results are as follows: La, 5.49 volts; Ce, 6.91; Pr, 5.76; Nd, 6.31; Sa, 6.55; Gd, 6.65; Tb, 6.74; Dy, 6.82; Yb, 7.06.

to the rare earths, thus indicating that they do not enter the 5, 3 subshell. At Ce58 the configuration $4f5s^25p^65d6s^2$ is more stable than the configuration $5s^25p^65d^26s^2$, but even at U92 the configuration with the valence electrons in the 6, 2 and 7, 0 subshells is more stable than that with one or more electrons in the 5, 3 subshell. Calculations made by Sugiura and Urey[1] indicate that electrons should first enter the 5, 3

[1] *Kgl. Danske Videnskab. Selskab, Math.-fys. Medd.*, **7**, No. 13, 3 (1926) in English.

subshell at the element 94.   None of these arguments are conclusive, however; the configuration can be fixed only by more spectroscopic evidence.

Table 3 gives the electron configurations of all the elements so far as they are known at the present time.   The detailed assignments of the electrons of the transition elements to the electron shells can be made only from their spectral terms, which are of the complex multiplet type described in Chap. X.   In Chap. X, Sec. 4 the assignment is carried through for the chromium atom.   It is there proved that chromium has the configuration $3s^2 3d^5$, as given in the table.   The configurations of other atoms have been determined in a similar way (see Chap. X, Sec. 17).

5. X-RAY EVIDENCE FOR THE ASSIGNMENT OF ELECTRON CONFIGURATIONS[1]

The order in which the electrons enter the shells and subshells of atoms as the atomic number increases will affect the X-ray energy levels in two ways: (1) an X-ray energy level cannot appear until there is at least one electron in the subshell corresponding to that level, and this level cannot be of the regular doublet type until the subshell is completely filled, though the higher multiplicity may not be detectable experimentally; (2) the change in numerical values of the X-ray energy levels of completed subshells with atomic number shows irregularities at the elements where the electrons begin to enter a given subshell and where that subshell is completed.

In Table 4 are listed the elements where an electron first enters each subshell and where that subshell is first complete.   If, after the subshell is completed, it becomes incomplete again in some element of higher atomic number, the element where it is finally completed is also listed. The last row of the table gives the element of lowest atomic number for which the level has been observed by the methods of crystal spectroscopy.   The X-ray term is first observed for atoms of higher atomic number than that at which the shell is first occupied.   We cannot expect the second and fourth lines to agree, for the electron configurations of Table 3 apply to gaseous atoms, while the X-ray terms are usually observed for the elements in chemical combination and in the solid state.   In the case of metals, we do not know how many and which electrons are free, so that we do not know whether we are dealing with an atom or ion. In the case of salts, there is the question of lattice energy of the normal ion, the ion with an inner electron removed, and of the electron in the crystal, all of which must be considered.   Deviations from the regular doublet type also produce complications, especially for soft energy levels

[1] BOHR and COSTER, *Z. Physik*, **12**, 350 (1923).

TABLE 4[1]

Level	K	L_I	$L_{II,III}$	M_I	$M_{II,III}$	$M_{IV,V}$	N_I	$N_{II,III}$	$N_{IV,V}$	$N_{VI,VII}$
n, l..........	1, 0	2, 0	2, 1	3, 0	3, 1	3, 2	4, 0	4, 1	4, 2	4, 3
Subshell entered at.....	H1	Li3	B5	Na11	Al13	Sc21	K19	Ga31	Y39	Ce58
Subshell completed at....	He2	Be4	Ne10	Mg12	A18	Cu29	{Ca20 Zn30}	Kr36	Pd46	Lu71
First observed at.........	Na11	Cr24	Mg12	Fe26	P15	Cr24	Rb37	Cu29(?)	Zr40	Dy66

Level	O_I	$O_{II,III}$	$O_{IV,V}$	P_I	$P_{II,III}$	$P_{IV,V}$	Q_I	$Q_{II,III}$
n, l....................	5, 0	5, 1	5, 2	6, 0	6, 1	6, 2	7, 0	7, 1
Subshell entered at......	Rb37	In49	La57	Cs55	Tl81	Ac89(?)	87	Ac89(?)
Subshell completed at...	{Sr38 Cd48}	Xe54	Au79	{Ba56 Hg80}	Rn86	....	Ra88	
First observed at........	Sn50	Sn50	Pt78	Th90	Bi84			

[1] See THORAEUS, *Phil. Mag.*, **2**, 1007 (1926) and references at the end of Chap. VIII.

like those of the incomplete subshells. Only approximate values can be secured for these soft levels by the usual X-ray methods. Thus, the interpolation of levels between those determined by X-ray spectroscopy methods and those determined optically or by critical potential methods is not justified. Moreover, there are many experimental difficulties which sometimes prevent the observation of absorption limits or of the emission lines necessary to calculate all the terms. In general, however, there is a marked parallelism between the appearance of an electron shell and the observed X-ray term.

The K energy levels have been determined by the usual methods of X-ray spectroscopy only for Na 11 and elements of higher atomic number. The Moseley diagram of Chap. VIII, Fig. 25 rises uniformly with no evidence of sudden changes in slope and bends toward the $(\bar{\nu}/R)^{1/2}$ axis due to the change of mass with velocity and the spin of the electron.

The ionizing potentials of neutral lithium and beryllium are the L_I levels of these atoms, though the ions in the solid salts, theoretically, should not have such levels. From boron to neon the $L_{II,III}$ shell is built in and the true X-ray $L_{II,III}$ levels begin with neon. The observed ionizing potential of neon is 21.5 volts; but there are two sets of levels which approach different limits for large values of the quantum numbers. These two limits are separated by 782 cm.$^{-1}$ and therefore the atom really has two ionization potentials separated by this amount. Grotrian[1]

[1] *Z. Physik*, **8**, 116 (1921).

suggested that these two limits are due to two steady states in which the neon ion is left by the removal of the electron, namely the L_{II} and L_{III} states. Granting this hypothesis, the doublet separation should be given by equation (30) Chap. VIII, and therefore,

$$\frac{782}{R} = \frac{\alpha^2}{2^4}(Z - d)^4.$$

Solving this for the screening constant d, we secure $d = 3.2$, which is in fairly good agreement with the value 3.5 secured from the L_{II}, L_{III} doublets of elements of higher atomic number (Chap. VIII, Sec. **17**).

The $L_{II,III}$ curves (not separated at first in Chap. VIII, Fig. 25) rise rapidly from neon. There is a decided decrease in slope beginning with Sc21 and an increase in slope beginning with Cu29, as can most easily be seen by applying a straight edge to the curve. Other such changes in slope occur, but they are not so sharp as these two. Up to Sc21 electrons enter outside shells of the atom, but at this element, they begin to enter the underlying 3, 2 shell and this process continues up to Cu29, after which they again enter the outside shells.

To see, qualitatively, why the slope decreases, we must remember that the total screening constant s depends on the distribution of electrons outside the region of the orbit, as well as within this region, and, therefore, changes in the distribution of outside charge influence the energy. Consider the simple model of an atom with a number of electrons in an L shell surrounded by a spherical surface, having one unit of negative charge, to represent an electron in a higher shell. If an electron is taken from the L shell, it must be removed against the attractive force of a positive charge $Z_{eff}e$ until the charged sphere is passed, after which it must be removed against a field of $(Z_{eff} - 1)$ positive charges. The work of removal will therefore be greater, the larger the radius of the negatively charged sphere. Thus, if the twenty-first electron of scandium entered an outside 4, 1 orbit instead of an inner 3, 2 orbit more energy would be required to remove an L electron. The electron actually enters a 3, 2 orbit and the energy of the $L_{II,III}$ level should be lower than the value secured by extrapolating the $L_{II,III}$ curve from lower elements to scandium. This effect actually appears first at Ti or V probably because the X-ray levels have been determined for the ionized elements in the solid state and not for the gaseous atoms. The actual atom is not so simple as this model but the qualitative predictions of the model are followed. Also we can expect that the slope of the curve will increase when electrons begin again to enter outer shells. This happens at copper just as it should.

The M_I and the $M_{II,III}$ shells are built up from Na11 to A18. The curves show a very marked break at Cu29, where the slope increases. The $M_{IV,V}$ shell is filled in from Sc21 to Cu29. The M curves show well defined breaks at Y39 and Ag47, due to the building in of the 4, 2 sub-shell, and at La57 and Ce58 due to the beginning of the 5, 2 and 4, 3 subshells. The break at Au79 is not so pronounced because the completion of the 4, 3 subshell at Lu71 and of the 5, 2 subshell at Au79 are so close together that the net effect is a gradual change in slope in this region.

The N_I and $N_{II,III}$ subshells, which are built up from K19 to Kr36, show very sharp breaks in their Moseley curves at Y39, Ag47, and La57 and Ce58 and a pronounced break at Lu71 or Hf72 and a less definite one at Au79. Sharp breaks occur in the $N_{IV,V}$ curves at La57 and pronounced but gradual changes in slope between Lu71 and Au79. The $N_{VI,VII}$ shell is filled in at the rare earths. Its curve cuts the O_I and $O_{II,III}$ curves because these levels appear first at lower atomic numbers than the $N_{VI,VII}$ levels, but the energy of binding of the $N_{VI,VII}$ electrons increases more rapidly with increasing atomic number.

Summarizing these facts, we see that the X-ray energy levels do have periodic variations. New levels appear at different points in the periodic system and the points at which this occurs are related to the periodic properties of the elements; the square roots of the terms do not increase uniformly with increasing atomic number, but show decided breaks which are also related to the periods of the system.

6. VALENCE AND THE PERIODIC SYSTEM

The subject of the valence of the elements is very involved and has been the subject of innumerable researches. At the outset it is well to classify as clearly as possible the various types of valence. There are certain terms applied to the types of binding between the atomic constituents of a compound, which must be carefully defined. The binding between the atoms of a compound is said to be an "atomic binding," if the adiabatic separation of the atomic nuclei to large distances gives uncharged atoms as the final products; the binding is said to be "ionic," if the end products of this separation are positively and negatively charged ions. As an example of the first type we may take H_2. As the distance between the nuclei increases, the molecule separates into two neutral atoms. This can be deduced from the vibration states of the molecule as deduced from its band spectrum (Chap. XII, Sec. 10). As an example of an ionic type of binding, we may take NaCl, which in the gaseous state probably separates into two ions as the vibrational energy increases. Examples in the solid state are diamond and copper (atomic binding) and NaCl (ionic binding). The crystal structures of diamond and copper show that the atoms are equivalent and symmetrically arranged relative to each other and on evaporation they probably give a vapor of single atoms. The crystal structure of NaCl (Chap. VIII, Sec. 5) shows that the sodium and chlorine ions are arranged in a lattice, where the sodium ion is placed symmetrically relative to the chlorine ions with no evidence of any pairing of sodium and chlorine ions. On evaporation, this type of crystal gives molecules such as NaCl.

TABLE 5

1	1	Na	Na							
2	2	Mg	Cu₂Mg	Mg						
3	3	Al	Ag₃Al	......	Al					
4	4	Si	Na₄Sn	Mg₂Si	Al₄C₃	Si				
3	5	P	Na₃P	Mg₃P₂	AlN	Si₃N₄	P			
2	6	S	Na₂S	MgS	Al₂S₃	SiS₂	P₂S₃	S		
1	7	Cl	NaCl	MgCl₂	AlCl₃	SiCl₄	PCl₃	...	Cl₂	
0	8	Ne	Na	Mg	Al	Si	P	S	Cl	A

Valence toward hydrogen	Mendeléeff group										
		0	1	2	3	4	5	6	7	8	Mendeléeff group
		0	1	2	3	4	3	2	1	0	Valence toward hydrogen

The atomic valence types in the solid state may be further differentiated as (1) metallic, (2) diamond type, (3) non-metallic, and (4) inert gas type. Copper is an example of (1). This type is found in the elements at the top of Thomsen's table and also in compounds between these elements. Diamond, carborundum (SiC), aluminium nitride (AlN), and other compounds of two elements near the carbon group, such that the sum of the valence electrons is 8, are examples of atomic binding of the diamond type. They crystallize in the cubic system; the hardest known substances and those which are least volatile occur in this group.[1] The non-metallic valence type occurs in H_2, Cl_2, and other compounds of elements toward the bottom of Thomsen's table. These solids contain the molecule as a unit in the crystal lattice and evaporate in the form of molecules. They are in general low boiling and soft compounds. Finally, the inert gases in the solid state have atomic lattices. The salts with their ionic type of binding are formed by one element from the top and one from the bottom of the table. They conduct the electric current in both the fused and solid states by the transfer of ions. These characteristic binding types for substances in the solid state are very well summarized and illustrated by Table 5 due to Grimm.[2] This gives the valences toward hydrogen of the elements of the third period. The maximum valences toward hydrogen and oxygen as we pass from element to element through the short periods are illustrated by the following tabulation, where the elements in question

[1] See GRIMM and SOMMERFELD, Z. Physik, **36**, 49 (1926); HUGGINS, Phys. Rev., **27**, 286 (1926).

[2] "Handbuch d. Physik," **24**, 489.

are in combination with hydrogen and oxygen and not with more electro-positive and electronegative elements as in Table 5.

Hydrogen valence.......	1	2	3	4	3	2	1
	LiH Na$_2$O	BeH$_2$ MgO	BH$_3$ Al$_2$O$_3$	CH$_4$ SiO$_2$	NH$_3$ P$_2$O$_5$	OH$_2$ SO$_3$	FH Cl$_2$O$_7$
Oxygen valence.........	1	2	3	4	5	6	7

These valences are mostly of the atomic type. The increasing valency toward oxygen also occurs in the b subgroups of the Mendeléeff table (Chap. I, Sec. 2), that is, in the half periods beginning with Cu, Ag, and Au.

So far we have discussed only binary compounds, but obviously the same definitions will apply to those which contain more than two elements. In such compounds it may be possible to have both ionic and atomic bindings. Thus the solid salt ammonium sulfate undoubtedly consists of positive ammonium ions and negative sulfate ions, while the bindings between the nitrogen and hydrogen atoms and between the sulfur and oxygen atoms are probably of the atomic type.

The terms, "polar and non-polar valences," have also been used with the meaning that we have given to ionic and atomic bindings. We reserve the terms polar and non-polar to indicate whether the molecule has an electric moment or not. Thus in the absence of water, the HCl molecule is polar in the sense that it has a permanent electric moment, but the binding between the hydrogen and chlorine atoms is probably atomic so that the separation of the two nuclei would result in a hydrogen atom and a chlorine atom, and not in hydrogen and chlorine ions as has often been assumed. The hydrogen molecule is non-polar and has an atomic binding, while NaCl in the gaseous state is polar and has an ionic binding. It could hardly happen however, that a non-polar molecule should have an ionic binding.[1]

We are now in a position to discuss the relation of valence to the periodic table. Figure 4 gives a diagram of the kind first introduced by Kossel[2] and by Langmuir[3] showing the possible valences of the known elements. The valences toward hydrogen are shown as negative and those toward oxygen as positive. This arrangement is really quite arbitrary for the hydrogen valences are probably all atomic and therefore not due to a transfer of an electron from hydrogen to the element;

[1] See Chap. XII, Sec. 11 and the references there given on HCl, NaCl, and similar molecules.

[2] *Ann. Physik*, **49**, 229 (1916).

[3] *J. A. C. S.*, **41**, 868 (1919).

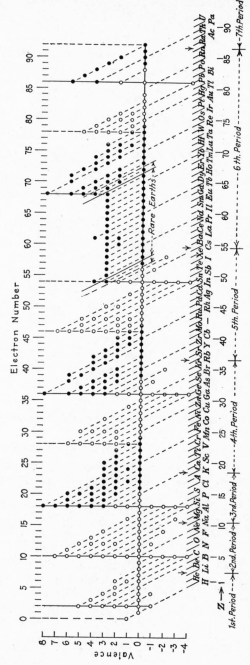

FIG. 4.—Atomic valences. Dots (•) indicate valences of the transition elements and circles (o) those of the non-transition elements. Elements which may be placed in either of the classifications are indicated by the symbol ◑. (We are indebted to F. T. Martin for help in preparing this figure.)

also many of the valences toward oxygen are certainly of the atomic type and not of the ionic type. Often it is impossible to be certain whether a binding is atomic or ionic. The positive and negative valences in the figure may therefore be regarded simply as valences toward more electropositive elements or more electronegative elements, whether they are ionic or atomic.

Lewis[1] and Langmuir[2] have emphasized the great tendency of elements from the extreme top and bottom of the Thomsen table to form ions having complete shells of eight outer electrons, and thus having the inert gas electron configurations. This is easily the most prominent feature of Fig. 4. Almost equally prominent is the tendency to form ions with completed shells of 18 electrons. There is also a tendency on the part of elements not belonging to the transition groups to have valences toward oxygen which differ by two units. However, this tendency is far less prominent than those mentioned above. Lewis pointed out the extreme rarity of molecules with odd numbers of electrons, the so called "odd molecules." This means that the number of electrons entering into the chemical bonds will be even and those electrons of each atom not so directly concerned with the bond must also be even in number. In general, atoms of odd atomic number have odd stable valences and those of even atomic number even valences. Still less prominent is the regularity that atoms having four valence electrons not entering into chemical combination are less common than those having two such valence electrons; thus, sulfur does not form compounds in which it is divalent nor phosphorus those in which it is monovalent.

These even numbers are due to the fact that the ultimate electron shell consists of two electrons with all quantum numbers identical except that the electron spins are reversed in direction.[3] The electron pair proposed by Lewis as a model for the chemical bond is probably such a pair of electrons.

In the transition groups indicated by solid circles we find the cases of multiple valence. In general, these valences fill triangular areas in Fig. 4 and suggest the possibility that the triangles may be filled in solid in the future. Some of these valences are more stable than others, at least in the sense that in the presence of oxidizing and reducing agents, the "unstable" ions readily change to others with other valences. (In practice, chemists mean by a "stable" compound one that is not readily decomposed by water, oxidized by oxygen, or reduced by common reducing agents, *i.e.*, that the compound is easily isolated.) Within

---

[1] *J. A. C. S.*, **38**, 762 (1916). Also, "Valence and the Structure of Atoms and Molecules." Chemical Catalogue Co., New York (1923).

[2] *loc. cit.*

[3] London, *Z. Physik*, **46**, 455 (1927) and Pauling, *Proc. Nat. Acad. Sci.*, **14**, 359 (1928).

limits, the filling in of these triangles appears to be mostly a matter of skill in isolating the compounds.

7. THE EFFECT OF SIZE AND CHARGE OF THE KERNEL ON CHEMICAL PROPERTIES

A great many chemical properties are characteristic of ions and not of neutral atoms and therefore in considering the relation of chemical properties to the periodic system, we should construct a periodic table in which all known ions have a place.   Figure 4 is in reality such a table and the addition of the strictly atomic valences as positive and negative ones can be justified because the properties of compounds in which they occur can be related to the size and charge of the kernel, and to the configurations of their electron shells.

On the basis of the electronic structure of the kernel, ions may be classified in the following groups:

1. The kernel has a rare gas configuration. This group may be further subdivided into ions with the closed shell of two electrons, *i.e.*, ions of the elements in the first period of eight, and those with the closed shell of eight electrons.

2. The kernel has a closed shell of 18 electrons immediately beneath the valence shell.

3. The kernel has incomplete shells and subshells.

The hydrogen ion H^+ is unique in having no electrons in its kernel and its many remarkable properties can undoubtedly be explained as due to this structure, as, for example, its high catalytic activity.[1] The marked differences between second period elements and similar ones in higher periods are to be ascribed partly to the fact that the outer electron shell of the kernel has two electrons, though perhaps more directly to the small radius of the kernel.   The evident differences of elements in the *a* and *b* subgroups of the Mendeléeff table are at least partly due to the electronic structures of the shells immediately beneath the valence shells.

The dependence of chemical properties on the ionic radius has been emphasized by Grimm,[2] v. Hevesy,[3] and Pauling,[4] among others.   Evidently the relative sizes and charges of ions are the predominating factors in determining the crystal structures of salts.   The removal of electrons from even a very electropositive element requires a large expenditure of energy, which must be partly compensated by the energy liberated in the formation of the negative ion and partly by the crystal lattice energy of the solid.   The lattice energy of an ionic solid is greater,

---

[1] See for example, BRÖNSTED, *Chem. Reviews*, **5**, 231 (1928).

[2] "Handbuch d. Physik" (see end of the chapter).

[3] *Z. anorg. allgem. Chem.*, **147**, 217 (1925).

[4] *J. A. C. S.*, **50**, 1036 (1928); *Proc. Roy. Soc.*, **114**, 181 (1927).

the more closely the ions approach each other. Also, the properties of ions in water solution are largely determined by charge and radius. The energy of hydration increases with decreasing radius and increasing charge of the ion and this energy partly compensates for the large energy of ionization in the case of aqueous solutions of salts.

Cartledge[1] has observed that the physical properties of ions in the solid state and in solution can be correlated very well with the ratio of charge to radius, which he calls the "ionic potential." In fact, many properties of both ionic and atomic compounds can be correlated with

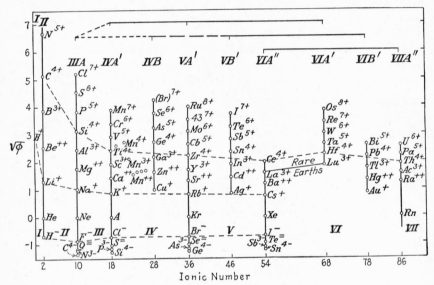

FIG. 5.—The ionic potentials. (*After Cartledge.*)

the ionic potential of the kernel obtained by removing all the valence electrons. Thus, the ionic potentials of P^{5+} and Cl^-, and of Cl^{7+} and O^{2-} may be calculated by using the radii of these ions as obtained theoretically by Pauling,[2] or as determined from the distances of nearest approach in crystals; from these ionic potentials certain properties of PCl_5 and Cl_2O_7 can be correctly predicted.

In order to work with numbers of convenient size, the ionic potential Φ may be expressed as the ratio of the number of elementary units of charge on the kernel divided by its radius in Ångström units; further, the square root of this quantity is more convenient for plotting against the number of electrons in the ion. This plot is given in Fig. 5 for ions whose radii have been estimated by the above methods. All those cations having $\Phi^{1/2} < 2.2$ are basic in water solutions, those having

[1] *J. A. C. S.*, **50**, 2855 and 2863 (1928).

[2] *Loc. cit.*

$\Phi^{1/2} > 3.2$ are acidic and those whose $\Phi^{1/2}$ values lie between 2.2 and 3.2 are amphoteric. The fused chlorides of those elements for which $\Phi^{1/2} < 2.2$ conduct the electric current, while those for which $\Phi^{1/2} > 2.2$ do not, and it will be noted that this limit is exactly the same as that for the change from acidic to amphoteric properties of the positive elements. Probably both these breaks in properties are due to a change from the ionic to the atomic type of binding. Cartledge has been able to show that, in general, other properties such as heat of hydration, discharge potential in the fused state, and hardness, vary continuously with the ionic potential, even though the ions differ in kernel structure and in valence. The $\Phi^{1/2}$ values of Zr^{4+} and Hf^{4+} are 2.24 and 2.25 and those of Cb^{5+} and Ta^{5+} are 2.66 and 2.65, respectively. These facts, together with the similarities of the underlying kernels (complete shells of 18 electrons), undoubtedly account for the marked similarity in chemical properties.

The justification for classifying the oxygen valences in Fig. 3 as positive is now evident. If a Cl^{7+} ion is introduced into water, its ionic potential is so large that it can remove O^{2-} from water leaving H^+ ions in solution and therefore it forms a negative ClO_4^- ion with atomic bindings between the Cl and O atoms, and is acidic. On the other hand, Al^{3+} can only remove O^{2-} from water if a base is present to remove the H^+ ions formed, and it is therefore amphoteric. Finally Na^+ has a low ionic potential and even in the presence of strong bases does not remove the O^{2-} from water.

8. THE NUMBER OF THE CHEMICAL ELEMENTS

It has often been suggested that elements with higher atomic numbers than 92 are so unstable that they did not long survive the genesis of the earth, but this is simply a speculation, and there is no adequate reason for believing uranium to be the heaviest element. However, there is fairly good evidence for a definite upper limit to the periodic system.

There are several ways in which it is possible to obtain an approximate upper limit to the atomic number. One of these, discussed by Bohr, depends on a peculiarity of the relativistic energy levels of the hydrogen atom. The inner electrons of a heavy atom are supposed to be on orbits which are approximately hydrogenic, so that equation (34) of Chap. V holds true for them. If the atomic number becomes so large that the square root in the denominator of this formula becomes imaginary, the orbit will no longer be stable. When $n = 1$ the value of Z for which this occurs is 137.

It is probably incorrect to treat the problem in this fashion. Modifications of the law of force should be taken into account at such small distances. Kossel[1] has made an attempt to take this into account in an approximate way. He assumes that the magnetic attraction of two electrons is proportional to r^{-4}, while the electrostatic repulsion is proportional to r^{-2}. Thus, if the diameter of a K orbit becomes too small, an electron on such an orbit might fall into the nucleus, reducing the nuclear charge.

[1] *Naturwis.*, **16**, 298 (1928).

Flint and Richardson[1] have approached the question from another standpoint. Certain considerations based on relativistic mechanics indicate that there is a minimum possible radius for a circular electron orbit. The limit obtained by their theory is $Z = 98$.

References

BOHR, "The Theory of Spectra and Atomic Constitution," Cambridge University Press (1922).

KRAMERS and HOLST, "The Atom and the Bohr Theory of its Structure," translated from the Danish by R. B. LINDSAY and RACHEL T. LINDSAY, Alfred A. Knopf, Inc., New York (1924).

GRIMM, "Handbuch d. Physik," Vol. **24**, Chap. 6, Springer, Berlin (1927).

DUSHMAN, *Chemical Reviews*, **5**, 109 (1928).

VON HEVESY, G., "Die seltenen Erden," Springer, Berlin (1927).

LEWIS, G. N. "Valence and the Structure of Atoms and Molecules," Chem. Cat. Co., New York (1923).

[1] *Proc. Roy. Soc.*, **117**, 637 (1928).

CHAPTER X

GENERAL THEORY OF ATOMIC SPECTRA

1. HISTORICAL INTRODUCTION

Before we proceed to a systematic study of the laws of spectra, the reader must be acquainted with some of the puzzling marches and countermarches which have brought us to our present position of mastery in this subject. In particular, he must understand the changes in term notation which have clouded the subject in recent years before he can read and understand the great majority of papers on spectra.

At the risk of some repetition we shall now review the salient points in the history of this subject in a connected manner. The analysis of the more complicated spectra began to make active progress in 1922, with the publication of Catalan's paper on the manganese spectrum[1] and that of Miss Gieseler[2] on chromium. Up to that time, only singlet, doublet, and triplet spectra had been studied systematically, and terms of higher multiplicity could not be satisfactorily described by the simple notation in use. Two books on series spectra appeared, in 1922, by Fowler,[3] and by Paschen and Götze,[4] and even now both of them are essential to a thorough knowledge of the subject. They contain discussions of the laws of spectral series, as well as a table, due to Rydberg, which is very useful in the discovery of series. However, the main part of each book consists of tables of all lines which had been classified in series up to 1922, arranged according to elements. The so-called revised Paschen notation has been used in the past much more widely than that of Fowler, and indeed it is occasionally used today, although it is now practically superseded by the notation adopted in this book. These notations are as follows:

	Singlets			Doublets					Triplets		
Fowler	S	P	D	σ	π_2	π_1	δ'	δ	s	$p_{3,2,1}$	$d_{3,2,1}$
Paschen	S	P	D	s	p_2	p_1	d_2	d_1	s	$p_{3,2,1}$	$d_{3,2,1}$
Modern	$^1S_0$	$^1P_1$	$^1D_2$	$^2S_{1/2}$	$^2P_{1/2}$	$^2P_{3/2}$	$^2D_{3/2}$	$^2D_{5/2}$	$^3S_1$	$^3P_{0,1,2}$	$^3D_{1,2,3}$

In the modern notation, we use the actual value of j as a subscript but it must be remembered that many authors use $j + \frac{1}{2}$ in the systems of

[1] *Phil. Trans.* A, **223**, 127 (1922).

[2] *Ann. Physik*, **69**, 147 (1922).

[3] FOWLER, A., "Report on Series in Line Spectra," London.

[4] "Seriengesetze der Linienspektren," Berlin.

even multiplicity to avoid fractional subscripts. The correlation between the Fowler and Paschen‧ notations, on the one hand, and the modern notation, on the other, must be altered when we meet with *inverted multiple terms*. The inner quantum numbers of the levels belonging to an inverted multiple term increase as we pass *down* the energy diagram; those of a normal term decrease. However, the subscripts of the Fowler and Paschen notations always increase as we pass down the energy diagram.

As a result of studies of simple ring models, the belief arose that the $S, P, D, \ldots$ states correspond to azimuthal numbers $1, 2, 3, \ldots$ of a single valence electron, so that the minimum total quantum number in a sequence should be equal to the azimuthal number for that sequence. Thus, in the Rydberg term $R/(m + \varphi)^2$, it seemed reasonable to write $m = 1, 2, \cdots$ in the S sequence, $m = 2, 3 \cdots$ for the P terms, etc. Paschen adopted this plan, throwing all the burden of accounting for the deviation from the Balmer formula on the quantity φ. This was correct for many D and F sequences and it led to reasonably small φ values in a large number of P and S sequences, so that the actual values of the total quantum numbers remained long undiscovered. Fowler thought it best to choose the m values in such a way as to make the value of φ fairly small. Thus, in his *Report* we encounter such terms as $1D$ and $3F$. The trouble is that this principle is not followed with complete consistency throughout the *Report*.[1]

Beginning in 1922, Bohr showed that the total quantum number of the valence electron in the S or P levels of an alkali atom is not closely related to the value of m which makes φ as small as possible, but varies from atom to atom (Chap. IX). After this discovery many authors used the actual quantum number of the valence electron for the value of m, in discussing one-electron spectra and those parts of the spectra of second-group elements which arise when one electron is unexcited. The trouble was that attempts were made to do the same for terms in which two or more electrons are excited. Then came Landé's discovery that many characteristics of multiplet spectra can be derived from a model consisting of a "leuchtelektron" with azimuthal number k and total number n, and kernel (atomrumpf) with impulse moment $rh/2\pi$. The term symbol n^r_{kj} was introduced, but difficulties of printing made it appear preferable to use $n^r S_j$, $n^r P_j$, etc. (When it is impossible to specify the quantum numbers of terms discovered empirically, it is quite usual to assign them arbitrary symbols pending a correct classification.)

The Landé model was inadequate in many respects and was soon superseded. The first step in this direction came from Russell and

---

[1] FOOTE and MOHLER give a clear treatment of this subject in "Origin of Spectra," p. 43.

TABLE 1.—COMPARISON OF QUANTUM NUMBER SYSTEMS[3]

	Name of quantum number	Notation of this book	Sommerfeld[1]	Landé	X-ray
Single electron. Doublet spectrum	Azimuthal.........	$k = 1, 2 \cdots$ for $S, P \cdots$	k	$K = k - \frac{1}{2}$	k_1 or k
	Reduced azimuthal......	$l \equiv k - 1$	$j_a = k - 1$	K is used instead of l	$l = k_1 - 1$
	Magnetic azimuthal......	$-l \leqq m_l \leqq l$	....	$-(K - \frac{1}{2}) \leqq m_K \leqq K - \frac{1}{2}$	
	Spin.........	$s = \frac{1}{2}$	$j_s = \frac{1}{2}$	$R = s + \frac{1}{2} = 1$	
	Magnetic spin.........	$m_s = \pm \frac{1}{2}$	....	$m_R = m_s$	
	Inner.........	$j = l + s$ (V)[2]	$j = j_s + j_a$ (V)	$I = j + \frac{1}{2}$	$k_2 = j = k_1$ or $k_1 - 1$
	Magnetic.........	$m_1 = m_s + m_l$ $-j \leqq m_1 \leqq j$ $m_2 = 2m_s + m_l$	$-j \leqq m \leqq j$	$-(I - \frac{1}{2}) \leqq m \leqq (I - \frac{1}{2})$	(Same as for atom with N valence electrons)
Resultant for several electrons, appropriate for normal multiplet spectra	Azimuthal.........	$l = \Sigma l_p$ (V)	$j_a = l$	$L = l + \frac{1}{2}$	
	Magnetic azimuthal......	$m_l = \Sigma m_{lp}$ (V) $-l \leqq m_l \leqq l$	....	$m_L = m_l$ $-(L - \frac{1}{2}) \leqq m_L \leqq (L - \frac{1}{2})$	
	Spin.........	$s = \Sigma s_p$ (V) $-s \leqq m_s \leqq s$	$j_s = s$		
	Magnetic spin.........	$m_s = \Sigma m_{sp}$ (V) $-s \leqq m_s \leqq s$	....	$m_R = m_s$ $-(R - \frac{1}{2}) \leqq m_R \leqq R - \frac{1}{2}$	
	Inner.........	$j = l + s$ (V)	j	$I = j + \frac{1}{2}$ $|R - L| + \frac{1}{2} \leqq I \leqq R + L - \frac{1}{2}$	
	Magnetic.........	$m_1 = m_s + m_l$ (V) $-j \leqq m_1 \leqq j$ $m_2 = 2m_s + m_l$	$m = m_l$	$m = m_1$ $-(I - \frac{1}{2}) \leqq m \leqq (I - \frac{1}{2})$	
	Multiplicity.........	$r = 2s + 1$	$r = 2j_s + 1$	$R = s + \frac{1}{2}; r = 2R$	

X-ray column groupings: *Singly ionized shell; analogous to doublet spectrum* — *N-fold ionized shell; analogous to spectrum due to N valence electrons*

[1] This notation is no longer used by Sommerfeld, but is included here because it has been extensively employed.

[2] (V) means that a sum is to be taken as a vectorial sum.

[3] The recommendations of a group of spectroscopists have recently been presented by Russell, Shenstone, and Turner. (Phys. Rev., **33**, 900 (1929)). The term notation is the one we have used except that half-integral quantum numbers are written in the form 1½, 2½, 3½, ... Also they recommend the use of L, S, and J for the resultant quantum numbers (our l, s, and j) and of l, s, and j for the quantum numbers of individual electrons (our l_p, s_p, and j_p). The reader should refer to this report for more complicated notations showing the electron configurations from which the term arises.

Saunders'[1] study of the primed terms of the alkaline earths. Their paper introduced the idea that the characteristics of the spectroscopic term are determined by the resultant quantum numbers of the atom as a whole, and not by the numbers of some privileged electron. This was followed by Pauli's[2] assignment of four quantum numbers to each electron, and by the introduction of the spinning electron, as described in Chap. VII, Sec. 16. These ideas were immediately applied to complicated spectra. In the hands of Goudsmit,[3] Heisenberg,[4] and especially of Hund[5] they showed their capacity to predict the existence of spectral terms with almost complete success.

The most recent treatise on spectral regularities is that of Hund.[6] It is devoted mainly to the study of the laws of spectra, and gives only as much information on individual spectra as is necessary to the proper illustration of the laws. A summary of various systems of quantum numbers is presented in Table 1.

2. MULTIPLET STRUCTURE

In Chap. VII, Sec. 16, we have described the quantum numbers belonging to each electron in the atom and have mentioned the most important ways in which the angular momentum vectors of the individual electrons may be coupled. In the early part of this chapter we shall deal almost exclusively with the so-called normal multiplets, which may be described on the assumptions that the l_p are strongly coupled to form a quantized l, that the s_p are likewise coupled so as to form a quantized s, and that the inner quantum number is the resultant of l and s. When cases of this kind have been studied there is little difficulty in tracing the corresponding relations for the other extreme type of coupling in which the l_p and s_p of each electron form a quantized resultant, let us say j_p for the pth electron, and j is the vectorial sum of the j_p.

For the present, we shall pay no attention to Pauli's principle, contenting ourselves with a simple enumeration of all the possibilities, regardless of whether they are allowed or not. In this connection, diagrams of the kind shown in Fig. 1 may be used to give us an idea of the arrangements of vectors which give rise to the various values of j when l and s are specified. We draw an arrow having a length proportional to l, and place at its tip another arrow representing s on the same scale. The maximum value of j, namely, $l + s$, occurs when these arrows are parallel. In Fig. 1a, this value is 5, in Fig. 1b, it is $\frac{7}{2}$. The arrangement

[1] *Astrophys. J.*, **61**, 38 (1925).

[2] *Z. Physik*, **31**, 765 (1925).

[3] *Z. Physik*, **32**, 794 (1925).

[4] *Z. Physik*, **32**, 841 (1925).

[5] *Z. Physik*, **33**, 345 and 855; **34**, 296 (1925).

[6] "Linienspektren und periodisches System der Elemente," Berlin (1927).

of l and s giving rise to the next smaller j value (4 or $\frac{5}{2}$ in the two cases, respectively) is obtained by laying off a circle with radius $s + l - 1$ around the point A as center. The intersection of this circle with one having radius s and center B is the end of the j vector of magnitude $s + l - 1$. Continuing the process, we obtain all possible configurations

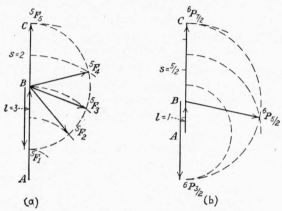

Fig. 1.—Quantized arrangements of l and s vectors.

of l and s. By constructing a few diagrams of this kind, or by simply counting up the possibilities, the reader will easily verify the list of j values corresponding to each pair of values of l and s presented in Table 2. The maximum multiplicity in an odd system of spectral terms is first encountered when we meet the value $j = 0$, and is equal to $2s + 1$.

TABLE 2.—j VALUES FOR NORMAL MULTIPLETS

l	j							j						
0	0					Singlets	$\frac{1}{2}$					Doublets		S
1		1				$s = 0$	$\frac{1}{2}$	$\frac{3}{2}$				$s = \frac{1}{2}$		P
2			2					$\frac{3}{2}$	$\frac{5}{2}$					D
3				3					$\frac{5}{2}$	$\frac{7}{2}$				F
0		1	2			Triplets		$\frac{3}{2}$				Quartets		S
1	0	1	2			$s = 1$	$\frac{1}{2}$	$\frac{3}{2}$	$\frac{5}{2}$			$s = \frac{3}{2}$		P
2		1	2	3			$\frac{1}{2}$	$\frac{3}{2}$	$\frac{5}{2}$	$\frac{7}{2}$				D
3			2	3	4			$\frac{3}{2}$	$\frac{5}{2}$	$\frac{7}{2}$	$\frac{9}{2}$			F
0			2			Quintets		$\frac{5}{2}$				Sextets		S
1		1	2	3		$s = 2$		$\frac{3}{2}$	$\frac{5}{2}$	$\frac{7}{2}$		$s = \frac{5}{2}$		P
2	0	1	2	3	4		$\frac{1}{2}$	$\frac{3}{2}$	$\frac{5}{2}$	$\frac{7}{2}$	$\frac{9}{2}$			D
3		1	2	3	4	5	$\frac{1}{2}$	$\frac{3}{2}$	$\frac{5}{2}$	$\frac{7}{2}$	$\frac{9}{2}$	$11\frac{1}{2}$		F
0			3			Septets		$\frac{7}{2}$				Octets		S
1		2	3	4	5	$s = 3$		$\frac{5}{2}$	$\frac{7}{2}$	$\frac{9}{2}$	$s = \frac{7}{2}$			P
2		1	2	3	4	5		$\frac{3}{2}$	$\frac{5}{2}$	$\frac{7}{2}$	$\frac{9}{2}$	$11\frac{1}{2}$		D
3	0	1	2	3	4	5	6	$\frac{1}{2}$	$\frac{3}{2}$	$\frac{5}{2}$	$\frac{7}{2}$	$\frac{9}{2}$	$11\frac{1}{2}$ $13\frac{1}{2}$	F
$\Delta \nu =$	1	2	3	4	5	6		$\frac{3}{2}$	$\frac{5}{2}$	$\frac{7}{2}$	$\frac{9}{2}$	$11\frac{1}{2}$	$13\frac{1}{2}$	

For example, a quintet S term has only one level, the P term, three, and the D term,[1] five. Similarly, we reach the maximum multiplicity in an even term system when the azimuthal number has grown sufficiently large to give us a term with $j = \frac{1}{2}$, for example, ^4P, ^6D, etc.

To summarize, when the number of electrons outside of closed shells is even, the values of s are integers, and we have odd spectral systems, but when they are odd in number, the values of s are half integral that is, integers plus $\frac{1}{2}$, and we have even spectral systems (Sec. 6).

A complete picture of an atomic configuration requires a statement of the value of n and l, as well as a description cf the orientations of the l and s vectors, for each electron. Thus, we give n, l, m_l, and m_s for each electron in the presence of a magnetic field. But frequently the value of n is immaterial. When so, we use a notation, due to H. N. Russell, writing the *small letters* s, p, . . . to indicate electrons for which $l = 0, 1, \cdots$, and indicating the number of each kind by a superscript; e.g., we write d^2s to describe a system of three electrons of the types n_1, 2, n_2, 2; and n_3, 0, respectively. If necessary, this notation may be modified to include the total quantum numbers; thus, $3d^25s$.

Now, we must determine the various l's and s's which can arise from a given number of electrons. If there are n electrons, the highest possible value for s is $n/2$, neglecting Pauli's principle. We might expect to have also the values $\frac{1}{2}(n - 1)$, $\frac{1}{2}(n - 2)$, etc. The highest multiplicity to be expected would be $n + 1$. In practice, Pauli's principle prevents the occurrence of such prodigious values of the multiplicity (93 in the case of uranium!). The existence of terms of such high multiplicity would require the s vectors of many electrons to coincide in direction. To avoid violations of the equivalence principle we should soon be obliged to utilize a great variety of values for m_l. But since m_l is always less than l, this involves high l_p values for the various electrons. Finally, n_p is greater than l_p, so extremely high stages of excitation characterized by large quantum numbers would be involved. In actuality, as the nuclear charge increases and more electrons are added, a given electron becomes more and more firmly bound. There is less possibility that the means of excitation at our disposal will change its state. Closed groups are formed, such as the rare gas shells, due to the equivalence principle, and the system of multiplicities starts over again.

3. THE AZIMUTHAL SELECTION PRINCIPLE AND THE DISTINCTION BETWEEN PRIMED AND UNPRIMED TERMS

It is found that the selection rule for j in multiplets involving primed or unprimed terms is $\Delta j = \pm 1$ or 0. A rule governing the changes of

---

[1] Strictly, we should call this a multiple term or set of terms. However, it has become customary to call such a set of levels a term, as though it were a single level. In practice, this causes no difficulty.

l was proposed independently by Laporte[1] and Russell[2] on the basis of experimental regularities. They observed that the terms of any atom may be divided into two great classes which they called primed and unprimed, such that the following rules hold true with relatively few exceptions: Primed terms combine with unprimed terms in such a way that $\Delta l = 0$ or ± 2, and with other primed terms according to the restriction $\Delta l = \pm 1$ (or sometimes ± 3). The latter rule is the same as the selection principle for combinations between unprimed terms.

These rules are not quite correct and may be replaced by others derived by Heisenberg[3] on the basis of the correspondence principle. We have seen (Chap. VI, Sec. **6**) that the motion of each electron in an atom contains the frequency ν_1 with which the perihelion of its orbit precesses. Heisenberg showed that the frequencies $\nu_1 \pm 2\nu_2$ also occur prominently, ν_2 being the corresponding precession frequency of a second electron. By the correspondence principle, we may expect that transitions will occur in which the l_p of one electron changes by ± 1, while that of a second changes by 0 or ± 2. This rule is obeyed with few exceptions in all spectra, and makes no mention of primed or unprimed terms, so that the separation of the terms into these two divisions appears superfluous. However, this is not the case from a practical standpoint. Heisenberg's rule operates in such a way that when a spectrum is being analyzed, it is very convenient to divide the terms into the two great classes, mentioned in the rule of Russell and Laporte, in the absence of information about the l_p values which characterize a given state. The rule itself furnishes no criterion for deciding which half of the term system is to be called primed. After the work is done, it is usually possible to state definitely the quantum numbers belonging to each term, and then we can determine which group is to be called "primed" by applying a convention adopted by Russell, and very generally by others. This convention is based on a definite physical distinction and is as follows:

Terms for which the sum of the absolute values of the l_p is even, belong to the category,

$$S \quad P' \quad D \quad F' \quad G \ldots ,$$

while those for which the sum of the absolute values of the l_p is odd, belong to the category,

$$S' \quad P \quad D' \quad F \quad G' \ldots$$

The reader may verify the fact that the primed terms of the alkaline earths are in agreement with this convention.

More recently, a committee of American spectroscopists[4] has proposed the replacement of this notation by another in which all terms with even l_p sums are left unprimed while those with odd l_p sums are provided

---

[1] *Z. Physik*, **23**, 135 (1924).
[2] *Science*, **51**, 512 (1924).
[3] *Z. Physik*, **32**, 841 (1925).
[4] *Phys. Rev.*, **33**, 900 (1929).

with a superscript°, as $^3P°$. The selection rules, where this nomenclature is used, are:

Odd → odd, and even → even: $\Delta l = 0, \pm 2$.
Odd → even, and even → odd: $\Delta l = \pm 1$ (or ± 3).

To be consistent, the P, F, etc. terms of the alkalies and the unprimed terms of the *alkaline earths* should be written S, $P°$, D, $F°$, etc. This is not done in these simple cases unless it is necessary to distinguish the two kinds of terms.

4. A TYPICAL MULTIPLET SPECTRUM—NEUTRAL CHROMIUM

We shall now illustrate these abstract considerations by applying them to the spectrum of chromium which displays most of the interesting features of multiplet spectra.

Chromium stands in the sixth place after argon in the periodic table and has atomic number 24. At this stage in the development of the periodic system, the 3, 0 and 3, 1 shells are complete. In potassium ($Z = 19$) and calcium ($Z = 20$) two 4, 0 electrons are added to the atom, for they are more firmly bound in these orbits than they would be in 3, 2 orbits. However, when the nuclear charge is increased sufficiently, the 3, 2 orbits become more strongly bound than the 4, 0 orbits. Thus, the most stable state of once ionized Cr has five valence electrons on 3, 2 orbits and none at all on 4, 0 orbits.

Most of the important terms of the CrII spectrum, giving rise to strong lines, arise from the above electron configuration, and from two others, obtained from it by raising one and two electrons, respectively, to 4, 0 orbits. These three configurations are referred to as d^5, d^4s^1, and d^3s^2.

The spectrum arising from the excitation of one or more of the five valence electrons contains quadruple and sextuple terms. Table 3 shows the terms to be expected in this spectrum on the basis of Hund's theory, soon to be explained, and their observed positions. One of the terms on the energy diagram is given the arbitrary value 90,000.00 cm.$^{-1}$,

TABLE 3

Electron configuration	Terms of CrII	Observed terms
d^5................	^6S	102,498.31
	^4G	81,900
	^6D	90,000.00–90,534.78
d^4s^1..............	^4D	82,472.76–82,968.43
	$^4H'$	72,104.87–72,338.75
	$^4F'$	71,277.20–71,413.74
d^3s^2..............	^4P	71,632.23–72,544.53

on the basis of an expert guess as to its probable value. It is recorded here to 7 significant figures because the wave numbers of the lines are measured with great accuracy, and only their differences are involved in the analysis of the spectrum.

The second column is derived by considering all the possible l and s values which can be obtained by vectorial additions of the l_p and s_p of the individual electrons, and excluding those which violate Pauli's principle. The third shows the highest and lowest levels of the multiple terms which result.

Practically all the prominent terms of CrI are obtained by adding an electron in an s orbit ($l = 0$) to the d^5 and d^4s^1 configurations of Cr$^+$, a surprising state of affairs when we consider the complexity of the spectrum. Partial classifications of the CrI spectrum have been published by Catalan,[1] Kiess and Kiess[2] and Gieseler.[3]

New measurements and extensive studies of the spectrum have been made by Dr. C. C. Kiess, to whose kindness we owe the opportunity to use much of the data as well as the illustrations in this section. Further, the absorption spectrum of chromium vapor has been obtained by Gieseler and Grotrian.[4]

Between 26,232 Å. and 1,994 Å., about 1,950 chromium lines are listed in Vol. 7 of Kayser's "Handbook." This list is by no means complete, for many faint and doubtful lines were omitted. On the whole, the arc spectrum and the spark spectrum are quite similar, both as to the general distribution of the lines which occur and the intensities of those lines. It is safe to say that little progress could be made in separating the spectra CrI and CrII on the basis of the listed intensities, but much information can be obtained from two papers by King[5] on the vacuum furnace spectrum of Cr. King measured the intensities of the stronger lines at temperatures of about 2000, 2300, and 2600°C. From 7,000 to 2,800 Å. the lines were observed in emission, while the region from 2,780 to 2,360 Å. was obtained in absorption. A supplementary list contains lines which appear in a prolonged exposure at 1730°C., the lowest temperature at which photographs could conveniently be obtained. All the lines on the supplementary list (except possibly 5,022.04 Å.) involve the three lowest multiple levels of the atom. Practically all the lines of the larger list have proved to be due to the neutral atom. The division of these lines into temperature classes has been of great value in classifying the

[1] *Phil. Trans. A*, **223**, 127 (1922) *Anales de la Soc. Española de fis. y. chim.*, **21**, 84 (1923).

[2] *Science*, **56**, 666 (1922).

[3] *Z. Physik*, **22**, 228 (1924).

[4] *Z. Physik*, **22**, 245 (1922).

[5] *Astrophys. J.*, **41**, 86 (1915), and **60**, 282 (1924); or, *Mt. Wilson Contributions*, 94, (1915) and 282 (1925).

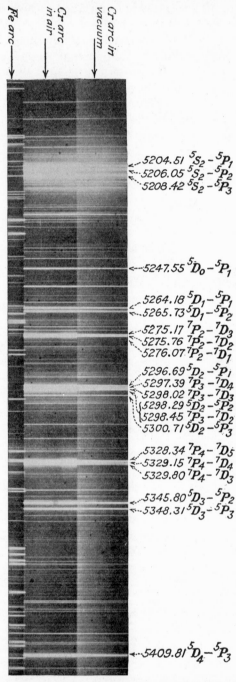

Fig. 2.—The chromium spectrum between 5,200 and 5,400 Å.

spectrum. Thus, all lines classified by Catalan which involve the three lowest terms belong in temperature classes I or II.

With the aid of these physical characteristics of the lines, the spectrum has been analyzed into triplets, quintets, and septets, of which the two latter systems are by far the most prominent. When a set of levels belonging to a multiple term combines with another such set of levels, the closely related lines which result are called a "multiplet." Much of the complex appearance of such a spectrum is due to the overlapping of the multiplets which compose it. In Fig. 2, we show the region between 5,400 and 5,200 Å. The lines of three important multiplets are marked in the figure, their wave lengths, wave numbers, intensities, and designations being as follows:

λ	$\tilde{\nu}$	Intensity	Classification
5,204.51	19,208.8	9R	$^5S_2-^5P_1$
06.05	203.1	9R	$^5S_2-^5P_2$
08.42	194.3	10R	$^5S_2-^5P_3$
5,247.55	051.2	40	$^5D_0-^5P_1$
64.18	18,991.0	50	$^5D_1-^5P_1$
65.73	985.5	25	$^5D_1-^5P_2$
75.17	951.5	20n	$^7P_2-^7D_3$
75.76	949.4	15n	$^7P_2-^7D_2$
76.07	948.3	20n	$^7P_2-^7D_1$
96.69	874.4	50	$^5D_2-^5P_1$
97.39	872.0	20n	$^7P_3-^7D_4$
98.02	869.7	15n	$^7P_3-^7D_3$
98.29	868.7	60	$^5D_2-^5P_2$
98.45	868.2	Calculated	$^7P_3-^7D_2$
5,300.71	860.2	25	$^5D_2-^5P_3$
28.34	762.4	50n	$^7P_4-^7D_5$
29.15	759.5	20n	$^7P_4-^7D_4$
29.80	757.2	5n	$^7P_4-^7D_3$
45.80	701.1	70	$^5D_3-^5P_2$
48.31	692.3	50	$^5D_3-^5P_3$
5,409.81	479.8	100	$^5D_4-^5P_3$

In the remaining tables and diagrams of this section, the wave numbers of the terms *increase* as we pass to higher energy, beginning at zero for the normal state of the atom. In spite of precedent, it is very convenient to proceed in this way when analyzing multiplet spectra. It is usually very easy to discover the *relative* position of the terms giving rise to strong combinations, but the difficulty of establishing series relationships prevents a determination of the distance of these terms from the normal energy state of the singly charged ion. (This remark does not apply to our example, chromium, for series have been established in its spectrum.)   Further, in atoms with several valence electrons there are several ionization potentials and there is little point in locating the zero of energy at a state of the ion which is obtained by removing any particular electron.

With wave numbers increasing upward, the levels involved in the production of the above multiplets are as follows:

$^7D_5$	42,261.3 cm.$^{-1}$
$^7D_4$	42,258.4
$^7D_3$	42,256.2
$^7D_2$	42,254.5
$^7D_1$	42,253.3
$^5P_1$	26,801.8
$^5P_2$	26,796.1
$^5P_3$	26,787.3
$^7P_4$	23,498.9
$^7P_3$	23,386.4
$^7P_2$	23,305.0
$^5D_4$	8,307.5
$^5D_3$	8,095.2
$^5D_2$	7,927.4
$^5D_1$	7,810.7
$^5D_0$	7,750.7
$^5S_2$	7,593.1

The quintet P levels are the initial levels for the emission of 5,204–06–08, while $^5S_2$ is the final level.   The remaining lines arise in transitions

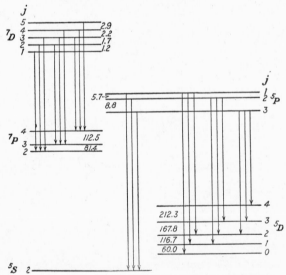

Fig. 3.—Energy diagram for three chromium multiplets.

from the same ^5P level to the ^5D levels, and from an initial ^7D level to a final ^7P level.   The combinations occurring are shown in Fig. 3.

The wave-number separations of the levels are indicated by their values, and the inner quantum numbers are seen at either side. The selection rule $\Delta j = \pm 1$ or 0 is obeyed; all missing combinations would violate this rule. To avoid the use of lists and the trouble of making energy diagrams, it is customary to illustrate a multiplet by a rectangular array like that in Table 4. At the left are written the names of the initial levels; at the top, those of the final levels. For each combination, λ, $\bar{\nu}$, and the intensity, in brackets, are written in the body of the table, below

TABLE 4.—A $^5P^5D$ MULTIPLET OF NEUTRAL Cr

	$^5D_4$	$^5D_3$	$^5D_2$	$^5D_1$	$^5D_0$
$^5P_1$			5,296.69 [50] 18,874.4 (116.6) (5.7)	5,264.18 [50] 18,991.0 (60.2) (5.5)	5,247.55 [40] 19,051.2
$^5P_2$		5,345.80 [70] 18,701.1 (167.6) (8.8)	5,298.29 [60] 18,868.7 (116.8) (8.5)	5,265.73 [25] 18,985.3	
$^5P_3$	5,409.81 [100] 18,479.8 (212.5)	5,348.31 [50] 18,692.3 (167.9)	5,300.71 [25] 18,860.2		

TABLE 5.—RELATION OF PROMINENT Cr AND Cr$^+$ TERMS

Cr$^+$			Cr		
l_p	Term	Empirical term value	l_p	Term	Empirical term value
d^5.............	^6S	0	d^5s............	^7S ^5S	0 7,593
			d^5p............	$^7P°$ $^5P°$	23,305–23,499 26,802–26,787
sd^4............	^6D	11,964–12,498	sd^4s............ sd^4d	^5D ^5G	7,750– 8,307 20,517–20,519
				^5F ^5D ^5P	not found 24,277–24,282 21,841–21,857
			sd^4p..........	$^7P°$ $^7D°$ $^7F°$	27,729–27,935 27,825–27,300 24,971–25,771
				$^5P°$ $^5D°$ $^5F°$	29,421–29,825 33,338–33,816 30,787–31,280

the final term and to the right of the initial term. The intervening numbers in parentheses are empirical values of $\Delta\bar{\nu}$ for the various pairs of levels.

In a case like this it is important to consider the various l values which arise by combining the l_p of the valence electrons. Table 5 shows how low lying terms of neutral chromium arise by adding a 4, 0 electron to the d^5 configuration of Cr^+, or by adding a 4, 0 or 3, 2 electron to the d^4s configuration. The terms listed are those which survive when Pauli's rule has been applied. Higher lying terms are gotten if the sixth electron is on an orbit 4, 1. Still higher stages of excitation are possible, giving rise to weaker lines.

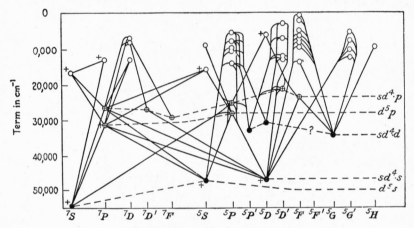

Fig. 4.—Complete energy diagram of neutral chromium.

In so far as it has been analyzed, the spectrum corresponds in every detail with the theory developed in this chapter. The empirical energy diagram is given in Fig. 4. To avoid detail, each multiple term is represented in the diagram by a circle drawn at the position of its center of gravity. For the lower levels, the character of the terms is known, and even and odd terms are distinguished by black circles and hollow circles with crosses, respectively. The combinations which occur are indicated by drawing solid lines between the circles representing the terms, and the electron configurations from which the terms arise are shown by the dotted lines, which run to the appropriate designations at the right of the diagram. At the bottom, the azimuthal character of each term is shown, and the division into primed and unprimed terms is indicated.

It will be observed that, in a general way, the terms fall into three groups, which are often called "low," "middle," and "high," respectively, though no sharp distinction is intended. The addition of an s electron to the configurations d^5 or sd^4 of the ion results in terms having even l_p-sums; for the l value of each s or d electron is itself even. Further, the addition of a d electron to sd^4 gives "even" terms. These three configurations are responsible for the prominent low-lying terms. In accordance with Sec. **3**, they are of the types S, P, D, F, etc.

The middle group is composed of "odd" terms of the types $S°$, $P°$, $D°$, $F°$, etc., which have their origin in the configurations d^5p and sd^4p. Their position is accounted for by the fact that the binding energy of a 4, 1 electron is considerably smaller than that of a 4, 0 or 3, 2 electron. Finally, the highest terms are obtained when one of the electrons is raised to an orbit of type 5, 0, or 4, 2.

In general, the low terms do not combine among themselves, but combine freely with the middle group of terms. The reason is easily seen, when we remember that the low terms belong to the types S, P, D, etc. The selection principle forbids combinations of S with P, P with D, S with $D°$, etc.; but low S terms may combine with $P°$ terms, which occur in the middle group; low P terms may combine with middle $S°$ and $D°$ terms; and so on. For similar reasons, the middle terms do not usually form combinations among themselves, but are free to serve as the final states for transitions from the high levels. Further, the high terms do not combine with the low terms. Exceptions to all these rules are encountered but the preceding statement gives a good idea of the general trend of affairs.

5. SERIES IN THE CHROMIUM I SPECTRUM

It is usually difficult to trace long series in the spectrum of an atom with several valence electrons, and this circumstance prevents us from calculating accurate term values for such atoms. However, Russell[1] made estimates for all elements in the first long period, based on a few related terms in each spectrum.

Just as in the case of the alkaline earths, it is possible in these atoms to have series which converge to different limits. Suppose we assign the wave number zero to a state in which a given electron—call it A—has been removed, all other electrons remaining on their normal orbits. The removal of another electron B, not having the same ionization potential, while A remains in its normal orbit, will leave the atom in a state whose term value is not zero. That is, the term sequences in which electron B is on large orbits do not converge to zero, as a limit. Again, it may occur that electron B remains on an excited orbit while A occupies one of a sequence of large orbits, or is removed. The term values for such a sequence of states will converge to an excited state of the ion. More complicated situations can easily be imagined. In the case of most of the atoms of the iron group there are many metastable states. The number of ionization potentials is also large, each one

[1] *Astrophys. J.*, **66**, 283 (1927).

corresponding to a different state of the ionized atom which can be reached by removing one electron. It is sufficient, however, to consider only those routes of ionization which involve the normal and the lowest metastable states of the atom or ion. The following summary of the more important methods of ionization is modeled on a discussion by Russell (*loc. cit.*) If an atom with n electrons outside the argon shell is doubly ionized, we have an ion with the electron configuration d^{n-2}. Let us consider only the lowest multiple term arising from this configuration. By adding a $4s$ electron we obtain a singly ionized atom in the configuration $d^{n-2}s$. The lowest multiple terms coming from this arrangement are of the same name as the parent terms, but of multiplicities 1 unit greater and less, due to the fact that the incoming s electron does not change the resultant l value of the atom but increases or decreases s by $\frac{1}{2}$ unit. These terms are denoted by (a) and (b) in the second line of the following diagram:

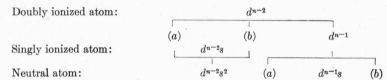

The addition of a second s electron gives rise to a single low multiple term, due to the configuration $d^{n-2}s^2$ of the neutral atom, for others are excluded by Pauli's principle. (Of course, other terms may be obtained by adding the second s electron to the atom while it is in one of the higher multiple terms of the arrangement $d^{n-2}s$, but such cases need not be considered for our present purpose.) Similarly, the addition of a d electron to the doubly ionized atom gives the configuration d^{n-1}, for which the lowest term is usually of a different name, and is of multiplicity higher by 1 unit, unless n exceeds 6, in which case it is lower by 1 unit. Adding one $4s$ electron gives two terms of the same name as the lowest term of the d^{n-1} arrangement. These are marked (a) and (b) in the third lines of the diagram. This shows that there are four principal routes of single ionization in these atoms. Four of these have been traced in the case of chromium.

We are indebted to Dr. Kiess for the following account of these series: The four sets of terms which form these series are marked in Fig. 4 by a small $+$ sign placed to the left of the dot representing the term. It is seen that in each set only two terms have been definitely recognized as being in sequence; therefore, we cannot hope to calculate the series limits with the same precision as is done in the case of the alkalies or the alkaline earths.

The relative separations of these terms are obtained from the measured wave lengths of lines resulting from the combination of these series-forming terms with other terms. For example, the two ^7S terms combine with a common term $^7P_3$ to give the lines at wave lengths 4274.80 Å. and 7400.27 Å., respectively. The vacuum wave numbers of these lines are 23,386.4 and 13,509.3 and their sum 36,895.7 gives the separation of the two ^7S terms. In like manner, we find from the combinations of the two series-forming ^5S terms with the same $^7P_3$ term that they are separated by 30,290.1 wave number units, and that the lower of the two lies 7,593 units above the low ^7S. For the two $^5D_4$ terms, we find a separation of 40,517.0 units and a distance of 8,307 units between the lower $^5D_4$ term and the base term ^7S.

The series of ^7S, ^5S and ^7P terms converge to the limit ^6S of the Cr ion, as is indicated in Table 5. The ^5D terms, however, converge to ^6D of the ion, the component $^5D_4$ in particular, having as its limit $^6D_{9/2}$, and this lies 12,498 wave-number units above ^6S, as we find from an analysis of CrII. Our problem is, therefore, one of finding the distances separating each series term from the appropriate limit. And this is easily accomplished by solving for each series a pair of simultaneous equations obtained by substitution of the known data in Rydberg's formula, as illustrated in Chap. IV and Appendix I of Fowler's Report, or in our Chap. VII, Sec. 7. Since the values of the series terms have been calculated and tabulated for all possible pairs of values of the parameters of the equation, we most readily effect our solution by simple interpolation from such a table (Table III of Fowler's Report).

With the value 36,896, the separation of the two ^7S terms, we interpolate from the table the values 55,933 and 19,037 for the terms and a value 0.4003 for the constant φ, to be used in Rydberg's formula for the calculation of the higher members of the ^7S series (Chap. VII, Sec. 7). We thus conclude that the basic term ^7S of neutral Cr lies 55,933 units below the basic term ^6S of the ion. With the separation 30,290 of the ^5S terms we again find from the table that they lie 47,586 and 17,296 units, respectively, below ^6S, and that for the ^5S series $\varphi = 0.5182$. However, we have seen that the low ^5S and ^7S terms are separated by 7,593 units. The sum of this and 47,586 gives 55,179 as an alternative value for the distance between ^7S and ^6S. A third series converging to ^6S consists of two ^7P terms. From the separation, 18,778 of the two $^7P_4$ terms, we find, from the table, 32,369 and 13,591, respectively, for their distances below ^6S, and a value 0.8408 for φ. Since the lower $^7P_4$ lies 23,499 units above ^7S, we get from this series a value of 55,867 for ^7S.

We again enter the table with the value 40,517 for the two $^5D_4$ terms and find that they lie 60,423 and 19,906 units, respectively, from their limit, $^6D_{9/2}$ of the ion, and that for the ^5D series, $\varphi = 0.3473$. To find their distances from the term ^6S we decrease these numbers by 12,498, giving 47,925 and 7,408. But we have seen that the term $^5D_4$ lies 8,307 units above ^7S. We thus find 56,232 as a fourth value for ^7S. The disagreement between the four values is not large considering that only two members are available in each series and we therefore adopt as the most probable value of ^7S the mean of the four, 55,803. In case more than two members of a series are known, a more rigorous solution is obtained by solving three simultaneous equations and using a formula, such as that of Ritz, which employs an additional parameter. In such a solution, it would then be desirable to use for the Rydberg number the value for the element in question and not that of hydrogen, although the error introduced by using the hydrogen value is not great.

6. ALTERNATION LAW, DISPLACEMENT LAW, AND BRANCHING RULE

Rydberg conjectured long ago that the spectra of neutral atoms alternate between doublet and triplet structure as the atomic number increases. This statement received many modifications, as the subject developed, which culminated in the generalization that even and odd multiplicities are found alternately as we pass through the periodic table, a regularity referred to as the "alternation law."

Further, Kossel and Sommerfeld[1] promulgated the displacement law, namely—*the spectrum of a singly charged ion resembles that of the neutral atom of the preceding element; the spectrum of a doubly charged ion resembles that of the element two places lower in the scale of atomic numbers, etc.* In general, the spectra of systems having the same number of electrons but different nuclear charges are similar. By "similar," we mean that, in general, they have the same multiplicities, and that the order and relative spacings of the terms are somewhat alike, but no hard and fast rule can be laid down; there are many exceptions to the statement about order and spacings. Much can be said as to the spectrum of a neutral atom from a knowledge of the spectrum of its singly charged ion, or of the preceding neutral atom. A knowledge of the ionic spectrum usually gives us a more reliable idea of the energy values of the neutral atom than a knowledge of that of the preceding neutral atom.

A correct statement of both the alternation and the displacement laws, applying for any element in any stage of ionization, is,

Even (odd) spectral multiplicities occur when the number of electrons is odd (even).

In practice, we need only count the number of electrons outside completed rare gas shells, for the total number of electrons will be odd or even according as the number of electrons in uncompleted shells is odd or even. Starting with an alkali, each l value of its valence electron has associated with it two j values, because the s vector $\frac{1}{2}$ has two possible orientations with respect to l. Now raise the nuclear

[1] *Verh. d. Phys. Ges.*, **21**, 240 (1919).

charge by 1, and add one more electron. The possible values of s are 0 and 1, and we obtain singlet and triplet terms.

Consider an atom in a singlet state ($s = 0$) and add one more electron, the arrangement of the two others remaining the same. The resultant s value is $\frac{1}{2}$, and we obtain doublet terms again. Also, consider a triplet term of the two-electron system ($s = 1$). Add one electron, again keeping the quantum numbers of the first two invariable. The s vector of the new electron can be oriented parallel or opposed to the vector $s_1 + s_2$. The resultant s values are $\frac{1}{2}$ and $\frac{3}{2}$, giving doublets and quartets, respectively. The question arises whether these doublet terms will be identical with those mentioned before. In general, they will not, for although the s vector is composed of contributions which we may write $+\frac{1}{2}$, $+\frac{1}{2}$, and $-\frac{1}{2}$ in both cases, the accompanying values of the other quantum numbers are not the same for both arrangements. For example, the third-group metal thallium has prominent doublet terms arising from the following quantum numbers of the three valence electrons,

$$
\begin{array}{cccc}
n_p & l_p & m_{lp} & m_{sp} \\
6 & 0 & 0 & +\frac{1}{2} \\
6 & 0 & 0 & -\frac{1}{2} \\
n_3 & l_3 & m_{l3} & +\frac{1}{2}.
\end{array}
$$

Other doublet terms could arise from the arrangement,

$$
\begin{array}{cccc}
n_p & l_p & m_{lp} & m_{sp} \\
6 & 0 & 0 & +\frac{1}{2} \\
6 & 1 & \pm 1 \text{ or } 0 & +\frac{1}{2} \\
n_3 & l_3 & m_{l3} & -\frac{1}{2}.
\end{array}
$$

The general principle is clear. Adding one electron with azimuthal number l_e to an atom with quantum numbers l_r, s_r, and j_r we have the following l values:

$$ l_r + l_e, \ l_r + l_e - 1, \ \cdots \ |l_r - l_e|. $$

Each of these l values may be combined with the resultant s values, namely, $s_r \pm \frac{1}{2}$, to form all possible j vectors. For example, the reader will easily find that the addition of an electron for which $l = 1$ to the $^2P_{3/2}$ term of an ion similar to an alkali atom gives rise to S, P, and D terms of both singlet and triplet systems.

Similarly, each term of a singly charged ion gives rise (at least theoretically) to two groups of terms of neighboring multiplicity in the spectrum of the neutral atom. This is the so-called "branching rule" (German, Verzweigungsprinzip), first proposed by Landé and Heisenberg.[1] An exception occurs for singlet terms, which give rise only to doublets. This process will certainly show us all the terms which can arise, but it will often occur that some of these are excluded by Pauli's

---

[1] *Z. Physik*, **25**, 279 (1924).

principle.   More satisfactory methods of predicting terms are discussed in Sec. 10.

7. THE INTERVAL RULE

It was early noted that the separations of the levels making up a triplet P term are approximately in the ratios $2:1$. Writing $\Delta P_{21} = m^3P_1 - m^3P_2$ and $\Delta P_{10} = m^3P_0 - m^3P_1$, we have, $\Delta P_{21}:\Delta P_{10} = 2:1$. For example, the separations of the 2^3P terms of cadmium are 1,171.1 and 541.9, which are in the ratio $2.16:1$. Heisenberg generalized this regularity, pointing out that to a rough approximation we often have

$$\Delta D_{32}:\Delta D_{21} = 3:2,$$
$$\Delta F_{43}:\Delta F_{32} = 4:3, \text{ etc.}$$

With the discovery of multiplet spectra, similar relations were quickly found by many workers, and Landé[1] proposed a more general interval rule, which bears his name and may be stated as follows:

The wave-number difference between two terms belonging to the same multiple term and having inner numbers j and $j - 1$ is proportional to j. This leads to the ratios of term intervals written in the bottom lines of Table 2. By way of illustration, the levels of a ^5D term have inner numbers from 4 to 0, inclusive. Beginning with the pair having inner numbers 4 and 3, we should have wave-number intervals in the ratios $4:3:2:1$. As a matter of fact, the quintet D term of chromium listed in Sec. 4 shows the separations,

$$212.3:167.8:116.7:60.0 = 4:3.16:2.20:1.13.$$

This illustration is neither very bad nor very good. Sometimes a set of terms will obey the rule within 1 or 2 per cent; again, we meet with terms in which the individual levels are not in the order to be expected from their inner numbers. The theory underlying this rule is postponed to Sec. 13, and will include the explanation of the so-called "inverted terms." In elements which lie near the end of a period, such as the iron group or the halogens, the normal situation is that the j values of a multiplet increase as we pass down the energy diagram. Thus, the lowest multiple level of neutral iron is a ^5D level with the following structure:

j	Term
0	59,022
1	59,112
2	59,296
3	59,584
4	60,000 (assumed).

Multiplets in which the j values decrease as we pass down the diagram are called "regular" to distinguish them from the inverted type. We also encounter multiplets in which the j values first increase and then decrease, or *vice versa*.

[1] *Z. Physik*, **15**, 189 (1923).

8. ZEEMAN PATTERNS IN WEAK FIELDS AND LANDÉ'S g FORMULA

In Chap. VII, Sec. 6, we described the Zeeman effect of the principal and sharp series of doublet lines, and the energy levels which give rise to the patterns obtained in the presence of a field. The behavior of lines of a normal multiplet spectrum in the presence of the field is qualitatively

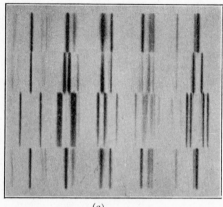

(a)

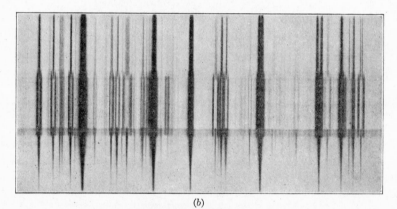

(b)

Fig. 5.—Typical Zeeman patterns.

similar to that of doublet lines. Each energy level of the atom splits into several components, which we shall call magnetic levels, equally spaced and symmetrically disposed with respect to the position of the field-free level. The combinations of these levels, suitably controlled by a selection principle and a polarization rule, give rise to a line pattern which is symmetrical with respect to the position of the parent line.

In Fig. 5,[1] we have illustrations of the Zeeman effect in chromium (Fig. 5a) at a field of about 32,000 gauss and in vanadium (Fig. 5b)

[1] This figure was kindly placed at our disposal by Dr. H. D. Babcock of the Mt Wilson Observatory.

at about 29,000 gauss. In Fig. 5a, the first and fourth strips show the chromium spectrum in the absence of a field. The third strip was taken through a polarizing prism so oriented that only light polarized with electric vector perpendicular to the field was transmitted. Therefore, this spectrum shows only the s-components of the Zeeman patterns. Similarly, the second strip shows only the p-components. In Fig. 5b, the upper strip shows the p-components; the center, the s-components, and the comparison spectrum is below.

Such patterns are most easily explained by discussing the energy levels which give rise to them. What we shall say about these levels applies only to the case of an ideal multiplet spectrum. In practice, many exceptions are encountered because the conditions for the validity of our theory are not fulfilled, but on the whole it works surprisingly well. Most of the exceptions occur in elements of high atomic number. For hydrogenic atoms and for lines belonging to singlet systems of other atoms, the weak-field Zeeman pattern is a normal triplet, arising from energy levels whose positions relative to the original level are given by the formula,

$$\Delta E = mLh. \tag{1}$$

L is the frequency of the Larmor precession (Appendix VIII) and is given by the formula

$$L = \frac{eH}{4\pi mc}, \tag{2}$$

where e is measured in electrostatic units. Energy levels of other multiplicities in normal multiplet spectra give rise to magnetic levels expressed by the formula

$$\Delta E = mgLh, \tag{3}$$

so that the term shift is

$$\Delta T = -mg\widetilde{L}. \tag{4}$$

As before, m is the magnetic quantum number, defined as the component of j along the field when seen from the rotating coordinate system described in connection with Larmor's theorem; g is known as Landé's splitting factor, and depends only on l, s, and j for the spectral term under consideration. Landé[1] discovered the correct formula for g empirically and gave a classical calculation which led to a similar formula. We know today that the new mechanics is required to derive the g-formula correctly, but it is of great interest to go as far as we can with the old mechanics. Consider an atom as represented by the aggregate of the vectors l_p, s_p, j_p belonging to its electrons, and let the coupling be that characteristic of a normal multiplet spectrum. Suppose that the coupling of the l and s vectors is so strong that it is not appre-

---

[1] *Z. Physik*, **15**, 189 (1923). See also E. Back, and A. Landé, "Zeemaneffekt und Multiplettstruktur der Spektrallinien," Springer, Berlin (1925).

ciably disturbed by the magnetic field. Then the vectors l and s precess about their resultant j (Sec. **14**), and j precesses about the direction of H. To obtain the energy of this configuration, we recollect that the potential energy of a magnetic doublet having the moment μ in a field **H** is $-\mu H$ cos (μ, H), or $-\mu_H H$, where μ_H is the component of μ in the direction of the field. The change in energy of a perturbed system is equal to the perturbing potential averaged over a cycle of the unperturbed motion (Chap. VI, Sec. 10) so that

$$\Delta E = -H\mu_H,$$

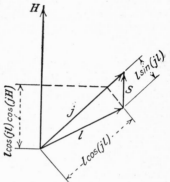

FIG. 6.—Angular momentum vectors of an atom in a weak field.

where the bar denotes a time average. To obtain the value of μ_H, we consider Fig. 6. The magnetic moment due to the spinning electron with its angular momentum $\frac{h}{4\pi}$ is $2\left(\frac{h}{4\pi}\right)\left(\frac{e}{2mc}\right)$. Therefore, the magnetic moment associated with the vector **s** is

$$-2s\left(\frac{h}{2\pi}\right)\left(\frac{e}{2mc}\right). \tag{5}$$

The minus sign is introduced because the magnetic moment vector due to the rotation of a negative charge is antiparallel to the angular momentum vector for that rotation. Further, the moment associated with l is

$$-1\left(\frac{h}{2\pi}\right)\left(\frac{e}{2mc}\right), \tag{6}$$

so that

$$-\mu_H = \left(\frac{eh}{4\pi mc}\right)[l \cos (lH) + 2s \cos (sH)] \tag{7}$$

while

$$\Delta E = Lh\overline{[l \cos (lH) + 2s \cos (sH)]} \tag{8}$$

by equations (2) and (3). To calculate $\overline{l \cos (lH)}$ we split l into components parallel and perpendicular to j, having magnitudes $l \cos (jl)$ and $l \sin (jl)$, and project these components on the direction of **H**. Since l precesses uniformly around **j**, the average value of the projection of l sin (jl) is zero (aside from terms proportional to H, which are negligible), but the projection of $l \cos (jl)$ on **H** is constant. Finally,

$$\overline{l \cos (lH)} = l \cos (jl) \cos (jH). \tag{9}$$

Similarly,

$$\overline{s \cos (sH)} = s \cos (js) \cos (jH). \tag{10}$$

From the geometry of the triangle formed by **j**, **l**, and **s**,

$$\cos (jl) = \frac{j^2 + l^2 - s^2}{2jl}, \cos (js) = \frac{j^2 + s^2 - l^2}{2js}, \cos (jH) = \frac{m}{j}. \tag{11}$$

Using equations (9), (10), and (11) in equation (8), we obtain

$$\Delta E = mLh\left(1 + \frac{j^2 + s^2 - l^2}{2j^2}\right). \tag{12}$$

Comparison with equation (4) shows that

$$g = 1 + \frac{j^2 + s^2 - l^2}{2j^2}.$$

As a matter of experimental fact this formula yields correct results only in the region of large quantum numbers, a situation which we might expect from the correspondence principle. The formula found empirically and by wave mechanics is very similar, however. It is

$$\begin{aligned} g &= 1 + \frac{j(j+1) + s(s+1) - l(l+1)}{2j(j+1)} \\ &= \frac{3}{2} + \frac{s(s+1) - l(l+1)}{2j(j+1)} \\ &= \frac{3}{2} + \frac{(s-l)(s+l+1)}{2j(j+1)}. \end{aligned} \tag{13}$$

In Table 6, the g values for the Zeeman effects of normal multiple levels are collected. (As a matter of fact, some of the most important earmarks of normality are obedience to the g formula and to the interval rule.) The value of g becomes indeterminate when the second fraction in equation (13) does so; that is, when $s = l$ and $j = 0$. In this case the energy levels should not be changed by the field, for $m = 0$ when $j = 0$. This conclusion is confirmed by experiment. By way of illustration, we may derive the g factor for the S terms of alkali spectra. For these terms $l = 0$, $s = \frac{1}{2}$, $j = \frac{1}{2}$, and substituting in equation (13) we have $g = 2$. Therefore, the magnetic levels arising from a ^2S term will lie at the positions

$$\Delta T = -2m\widetilde{L}.$$

Since m is the component of j along the field it can assume only two values, namely, $\pm\frac{1}{2}$, so that $\Delta T = \pm\widetilde{L}$, in agreement with Chap. VII, Sec. **6**. This arrangement is identical with that to be expected in the absence of electron spin, as we see from the treatment of the Larmor precession in Appendix VIII, Sec. **3**, but has its origin in a very different mechanism. The Zeeman pattern for any term may now be predicted, if we pay due attention to the selection principle for the magnetic quantum number. Empirically, and also as a result of the new mechanics, *the magnetic quantum number can change by only ± 1 or 0. When it changes by one unit, we have s-components in the transverse Zeeman pattern, and when it retains its value, we have p-components. A further restriction is that when j remains unchanged, the levels for which $m = 0$ cannot combine.*

Table 6.—The Splitting Factor g

l \ j	0	1	2	3	4	5	6	7	$\frac12$	$\frac32$	$\frac52$	$\frac72$	$\frac92$	$\frac{11}{2}$	$\frac{13}{2}$	$\frac{15}{2}$	
			Singlets $s=0$									Doublets $s=\frac12$					
0	$\frac{0}{0}$								2								S
1		1							$\frac{2}{3}$	$\frac{4}{3}$							P
2			1							$\frac{4}{5}$	$\frac{6}{5}$						D
3				1							$\frac{6}{7}$	$\frac{8}{7}$					F
4					1							$\frac{8}{9}$	$\frac{10}{9}$				G
			Triplets $s=1$									Quartets $s=\frac32$					
0		2								2							S
1	$\frac{0}{0}$	$\frac{3}{2}$	$\frac{3}{2}$						$\frac{8}{3}$	$\frac{26}{15}$	$\frac{8}{5}$						P
2		$\frac{1}{2}$	$\frac{7}{6}$	$\frac{4}{3}$					0	$\frac{6}{5}$	$\frac{48}{35}$	$\frac{10}{7}$					D
3			$\frac{2}{3}$	$\frac{13}{12}$	$\frac{5}{4}$					$\frac{2}{5}$	$\frac{36}{35}$	$\frac{78}{63}$	$\frac{4}{3}$				F
4				$\frac{3}{4}$	$\frac{21}{20}$	$\frac{6}{5}$					$\frac{4}{7}$	$\frac{62}{63}$	$\frac{116}{99}$	$\frac{14}{11}$			G
			Quintets $s=2$									Sextets $s=\frac52$					
0			2								2						S
1		$\frac{5}{2}$	$\frac{11}{6}$	$\frac{5}{3}$						$\frac{12}{5}$	$\frac{66}{35}$	$\frac{12}{7}$					P
2	$\frac{0}{0}$	$\frac{3}{2}$	$\frac{3}{2}$	$\frac{3}{2}$	$\frac{3}{2}$				$\frac{10}{3}$	$\frac{28}{15}$	$\frac{58}{35}$	$\frac{100}{63}$	$\frac{14}{9}$				D
3		0	1	$\frac{5}{4}$	$\frac{27}{20}$	$\frac{7}{5}$			$-\frac{2}{3}$	$\frac{16}{15}$	$\frac{46}{35}$	$\frac{88}{63}$	$\frac{142}{99}$	$\frac{16}{11}$			F
4			$\frac{1}{3}$	$\frac{11}{12}$	$\frac{23}{20}$	$\frac{19}{15}$	$\frac{4}{3}$			0	$\frac{6}{7}$	$\frac{8}{7}$	$\frac{14}{11}$	$\frac{192}{143}$	$\frac{18}{13}$		G
			Septets $s=3$									Octets $s=\frac72$					
0				2								2					S
1			$\frac{7}{3}$	$\frac{23}{12}$	$\frac{7}{4}$						$\frac{16}{7}$	$\frac{122}{63}$	$\frac{16}{9}$				P
2		3	2	$\frac{7}{4}$	$\frac{33}{20}$	$\frac{8}{5}$				$\frac{14}{5}$	$\frac{72}{35}$	$\frac{38}{21}$	$\frac{56}{33}$	$\frac{18}{11}$			D
3	$\frac{0}{0}$	$\frac{3}{2}$	$\frac{3}{2}$	$\frac{3}{2}$	$\frac{3}{2}$	$\frac{3}{2}$	$\frac{3}{2}$		4	2	$\frac{12}{7}$	$\frac{34}{21}$	$\frac{52}{33}$	$\frac{222}{143}$	$\frac{20}{13}$		F
4		$-\frac{1}{2}$	$\frac{5}{6}$	$\frac{7}{6}$	$\frac{13}{10}$	$\frac{41}{30}$	$\frac{59}{42}$	$\frac{10}{7}$	$-\frac{4}{3}$	$\frac{14}{15}$	$\frac{44}{35}$	$\frac{86}{63}$	$\frac{140}{99}$	$\frac{206}{143}$	$\frac{284}{195}$	$\frac{22}{15}$	G

In using the g formula and the selection principle to predict a Zeeman pattern, the following arrangement of the work is advantageous. Write in a row all the values of m which will be used, as in Table 7.

Table 7.—Calculation of Zeeman Pattern for $^2P_{3/2} - {}^2D_{5/2}$

$m =$	$-\frac52$	$-\frac32$	$-\frac12$	$+\frac12$	$+\frac32$	$+\frac52$
$^2D_{5/2}:\ g=\frac65$	$-\frac{15}{5}$	$-\frac{9}{5}$	$-\frac{3}{5}$	$\frac{3}{5}$	$\frac{9}{5}$	$\frac{15}{5}$
$^2P_{3/2}:\ g=\frac43$		$-\frac{6}{3}$	$-\frac{2}{3}$	$\frac{2}{3}$	$\frac{6}{3}$	
$m-1\to m;\ s$		$-\frac{15}{15}$	$-\frac{17}{15}$	$-\frac{19}{15}$	$-\frac{21}{15}$	
$m\to m;\ p$		$\frac{3}{15}$	$\frac{1}{15}$	$-\frac{1}{15}$	$-\frac{3}{15}$	
$m+1\to m;\ s$		$\frac{21}{15}$	$\frac{19}{15}$	$\frac{17}{15}$	$\frac{15}{15}$	

Below each value of m put the displacement mg of the magnetic level of the *initial* spectral term which has that m value. (It is customary to express the displacements of the levels in terms of the separation between the s- and p-components of the normal triplet as a unit. Note that this unit is not fixed, but is proportional to H.) Write similarly the displacements of the levels belonging to the final term, in the next line. The cross-lines indicate the combinations which obey the selection rules. Subtraction of any displacement in the lower line from a displacement in the upper line yields a component in the Zeeman pattern.

Below each m value we can write (in separate rows) the positions of the lines corresponding to the transitions $m - 1 \to m$, $m \to m$, and $m + 1 \to m$. The line positions may be expressed as multiples of $1/r$, where r is called the Runge denominator and is the least common multiple of the denominators in the values of mg. Thus, in Table 7, all mg values for the initial level are multiples of $\frac{1}{5}$ while those for the final levels are multiples of $\frac{1}{3}$. The Runge denominator is $3 \times 5 = 15$. The usual

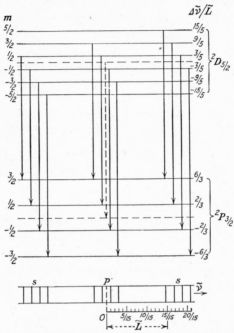

Fig. 7.—Zeeman pattern for $^2P_2 - {}^2D_3$.

notation for a Zeeman pattern consists of a long line with the Runge denominator beneath it and with integers above to show at what multiples of $1/r$ the components lie. Parallel components are enclosed in paren-theses. For example, the symbol for the pattern obtained in Table 7 is

$$\pm \frac{(1)\ (3)\ 15\ 17\ 19\ 21}{15}$$

or, in decimals, $\pm (0.07, 0.20), 1.00, 1.13, 1.27, 1.40$. The energy diagram (Fig. 7) shows all details of the way in which this pattern is produced.

Back and Landé give a table which shows the g values as decimal fractions, and tabulate a great many Zeeman patterns for lines of multi-plicities from 2 to 7, inclusive. Kiess and Meggers[1] have published very extensive tables of theoretical g values and Zeeman patterns. These are believed to be extensive enough to cover all possible term com-

[1] Bur. Standards *J. Research*, **1**, 641 (1928).

binations which are likely to occur in the spectra of elements other than the rare earths. By considerations based on the correspondence principle, Landé showed that the most intense parallel components should arise from configurations in which the angle between the vector j and the direction of the field is a maximum, while it should be a minimum for the most intense perpendicular components. Of course, there is some ambiguity in applying a rule like this in the region of small quantum numbers, for two atomic configurations are involved. Kiess and Meggers formulate the following approximate rule for determining the strongest components:

In case the j's of the combining terms are not equal, the vertical differences in the middle of the scheme and the diagonal differences at the ends give, respectively, the strongest p and s components. In case the j's are equal, the vertical differences at the end of the scheme and the diagonal differences at the center give, respectively, the strongest p and s components, with the added requirement that for terms of odd multiplicity the p-components corresponding to the transition $m = 0$ to $m = 0$ are forbidden; that is, their intensity is zero.

9. ZEEMAN PATTERNS IN STRONG FIELDS

In Chap. VII, Sec. 6, we saw that a strong magnetic field breaks down the coupling between the l and s vectors of the single valence electron in an alkali atom, with the result that the Zeeman patterns of its lines are completely altered. A similar phenomenon occurs in the case of atoms with several valence electrons, and is known as the "Paschen-Back effect." The original observations of Paschen and Back[1] were made on a number of rather narrow doublets and triplets. In a general way it is true that changes of Zeeman patterns with the field strength are most prominent in the case of narrow mutliplets. In this connection it is important to state just what we mean by the terms strong and weak. If we consider a line which is produced in a transition between two multiple levels with separations of the same order of magnitude, then we shall say the field is strong (weak) if the frequency changes produced by the field are large (small) compared with the multiplet separations. The Paschen-Back effect is encountered when the field strength is in the transition region. Consider also a line produced in a transition between a narrow multiple level and one which is broad. If the magnetic field is so chosen that the magnetic shifts are intermediate between the intervals characteristic of these levels, then the field may be considered strong with respect to one set of levels and weak with respect to the other. We shall not concern ourselves here with the complicated phenomena of the transition region between weak and strong fields, but shall examine the arrangement of the angular momentum vectors in the presence of a strong field. The coupling between the electrons is broken down, and

[1] *Ann. Physik*, **39**, 897 (1912), and **40**, 960 (1913).

the l_p and s_p vectors of each one take up quantized orientations with respect to the lines of force. This means that the s_p vector of each electron is oriented either parallel or antiparallel to the field. It follows as in Sec. 8 that the change of energy in the presence of the field is

$$\Delta E = -\mu_H H = (m_l + 2m_s) \frac{ehH}{4\pi mc}, \qquad (14)$$

where m_l is the sum of the magnetic quantum numbers m_{lp} corresponding to the orbital motions of the individual electrons, and m_s is the sum of the numbers m_{sp} corresponding to their spins. We may refer to $m_l + 2m_s$ as the strong-field magnetic quantum number. In a transition it usually changes only by ± 1 or 0, though exceptions have been noted. These changes correspond to the emission of perpendicular and of parallel components, respectively. This selection rule has the consequence that the strong-field pattern of all types of levels is a normal Zeeman triplet. The location of this triplet with respect to the original multiplet is described in Sec. 12.

10. THE ENUMERATION OF NORMAL MULTIPLET TERMS

We are now prepared for the problem of finding the terms which arise from a given configuration of electrons. This problem is attacked with the aid of Pauli's principle (Chap. VII, Sec. 19), namely, *there are never two or more equivalent electrons in the atom, such that the values of all five of their quantum numbers coincide when a strong magnetic field is applied, and cases which can be derived from one another by interchanging the quantum numbers of two electrons give only a single term.*

Equivalent electrons are those which have the same total and azimuthal numbers. We begin by considering the case of two such electrons, and shall place them first on s orbits. For each one $m_l = 0$, and therefore the resultant m_l is zero. In order to avoid having all five quantum numbers of both electrons the same, we must assume that $m_{s1} = +\frac{1}{2}$, $m_{s2} = -\frac{1}{2}$, and so the resultant $m_s = 0$. The array of possible pairs of m_l amd m_s values reduces to only one pair, namely 0, 0, which yields a single undisplaced level, representing the Zeeman pattern of a $^1S_0$ term. On removing the field, the single magnetic energy level passes adiabatically into a field-free $^1S_0$ term. This furnishes a complete explanation of the fact that the lowest singlet S term of an alkaline earth atom is not accompanied by a triplet S term. There cannot be more than two equivalent s electrons, for the m_s values of at least two of them would have to coincide.

The method of enumerating possible terms is quite similar in other cases. For example, Table 8 gives all the possible values of m_l and m_s which can arise from two p electrons having the same total quantum number.

Table 8.—Quantum Numbers for Two Equivalent p Electrons

m_{l1}	m_{l2}	m_{s1}	m_{s2}	m_l	m_s	Possible values of $m_l + 2m_s$
1	1	$\frac{1}{2}$	$-\frac{1}{2}$	2	0	2
1	0	$\pm\frac{1}{2}$	$\pm\frac{1}{2}$	1	1, 0, 0, −1	3, 1, 1, −1
1	−1	$\pm\frac{1}{2}$	$\pm\frac{1}{2}$	0	1, 0, 0, −1	2, 0, 0, −2
0	0	$\frac{1}{2}$	$-\frac{1}{2}$	0	0	0
0	−1	$\pm\frac{1}{2}$	$\pm\frac{1}{2}$	−1	1, 0, 0, −1	1, −1, −1, −3
−1	−1	$\frac{1}{2}$	$-\frac{1}{2}$	−2	0	−2

The quantum numbers of the two electrons are distinguished by the subscripts 1 and 2. We have,

$$l_1 = l_2 = 1.$$

If

$$m_{l1} = m_{l2} = 1,$$

then m_{s1} and m_{s2} must have opposite signs, and therefore,

$$m_l = 2, m_s = 0.$$

But if,

$$m_{l1} = 1 \text{ and } m_{l2} = 0,$$

then m_{s1} and m_{s2} can be either plus or minus, independently, so that there are four possible ways in which the resultant m_s can be formed, giving the values $1, 0, 0, -1$, in the second row of the m_s column. We do not obtain any new terms by considering the case $m_{l1} = 0$, $m_{l2} = 1$, for this is obtained from the previous one by simply interchanging the two electrons. Similar statements may be made for the combinations of m_{lp} values occurring in the third and fifth lines of the table. We must now consider the magnetic terms arising from these two p electrons. Each m_l value may occur with any of the m_s values which appear *in the same line* of the table; every such combination of m_l and m_s values gives rise to a physically distinct atomic configuration which must be counted as a separate term even though its energy may coincide with that of several other terms. The positions of the terms are given by the expression $(m_l + 2m_s)\tilde{L}$, the values of $m_l + 2m_s$ being listed in the last column of the table.

To find the field-free terms, we must determine what l and s values would give us the array of m_l and m_s values shown in the table. In the first place, the terms will all be even, since $\Sigma l_p = 2$. While there is a perfectly definite procedure for solving such problems, based on the dynamics of an atom with several magnetic parts, it is possible to answer the question also by the following method. The highest value of s must be the same as the highest value of m_s. In the case under discussion this is 1; now the magnetic levels for which $m_s = 1$ or -1 arise from field-free levels for which $s = 1$, since there is no tendency for the individual s vectors of the electrons to change their orientation if they are all either parallel or antiparallel to the lines of force at the beginning. We now look for the highest m_l value which goes with an m_s value of unity; this is also 1, and this must be the value of l for at least one term characterized by $s = 1$; so we see that some of the magnetic levels arise from a triplet P term ($l = 1$, $s = 1$). But we can write down at once all the combinations of m_l and m_s values which arise from a ^3P term, and can strike them out of the table. This eliminates nine integers from the m_s column in Table 8, for m_l and m_s can take on the values ± 1 or 0 independently.[1] The remaining $m_l m_s$ combinations are 2, 0; 1, 0; 0, 0; 0, 0; -1, 0; -2, 0; and we treat them by the same process. All the magnetic levels belonging to these combinations of integers have $m_s = 0$, and so we must have $s = 0$ for all the corresponding field-free terms, which are therefore singlets. The highest m_l value in the list is 2, and this must coincide with the value of l for one of the field-free terms, namely a singlet D term. As before, we construct the array of $m_l m_s$ combinations of a ^1D term, namely, 2, 0; 1, 0; 0,0; -1, 0; -2,0. Striking these out of the above list, we are left with 0, 0, which must belong to a ^1S term. Summarizing, the field-free terms arising from two equivalent p electrons are ^3P, ^1D, and ^1S.

The principle is now obvious. Table 9 analyzes the combinations of m_l and m_s which arise from three equivalent p electrons. The terms in this case are odd, since $\Sigma l_p = 3$.

TABLE 9.—QUANTUM NUMBERS FOR THREE EQUIVALENT p ELECTRONS

m_{l1}	m_{l2}	m_{l3}	m_{s1}	m_{s2}	m_{s3}	m_l	m_s
1	1	0	$+\frac{1}{2}$	$-\frac{1}{2}$	$\pm\frac{1}{2}$	2	$\pm\frac{1}{2}$
1	1	-1	$+\frac{1}{2}$	$-\frac{1}{2}$	$\pm\frac{1}{2}$	1	$\pm\frac{1}{2}$
1	0	0	$\pm\frac{1}{2}$	$\pm\frac{1}{2}$	$-\frac{1}{2}$	1	$\pm\frac{1}{2}$
1	0	-1	$\pm\frac{1}{2}$	$+\frac{1}{2}$	$\pm\frac{1}{2}$	0	$\pm\frac{1}{2}$, $\pm\frac{1}{2}$, $\pm\frac{1}{2}$, $\pm\frac{3}{2}$
1	-1	-1	$\pm\frac{1}{2}$	$+\frac{1}{2}$	$-\frac{1}{2}$	-1	$\pm\frac{1}{2}$
0	0	-1	$+\frac{1}{2}$	$-\frac{1}{2}$	$\pm\frac{1}{2}$	-1	$\pm\frac{1}{2}$
0	-1	-1	$\pm\frac{1}{2}$	$+\frac{1}{2}$	$-\frac{1}{2}$	-2	$\pm\frac{1}{2}$

Considerable thought is essential to the understanding of this table. For example, we may ask why the combination $m_{l1} = m_{l2} = m_{l3} = 1$ is absent. Let us consider what the m_s values must be if all the m_l values are equal to 1. In order that the first and second electrons may not violate Pauli's rule, we must have $m_{s1} = +\frac{1}{2}$, $m_{s2} = -\frac{1}{2}$, or $m_{s1} = -\frac{1}{2}$, $m_{s2} = +\frac{1}{2}$. Whichever possibility we choose, the third electron

[1] The reader will note that we can strike out the combination $m_l = 1$, $m_s = 0$ from the second line of the table in two independent ways, and the same situation occurs for the combinations 0, 0 and -1, 0. In each case only one of the two ways is correct, but for our present purpose it does not matter which one is chosen.

will then have all its quantum numbers the same as those of the first or the second, and so we cannot avoid breaking the rule. The conclusion is that the above combination of m values does not occur.

The configuration of three p electrons gives the terms $^2D^\circ$, $^2P^\circ$, $^4S^\circ$. The same process can be carried through for four, five, and six p electrons. These configurations have the same terms as those with two, one, and zero p electrons, respectively, which is a special case of a reciprocity theorem stated in Sec. 16.

Nothing new in principle is introduced when we consider several equivalent d or f electrons. The tabulations are more complicated and more field-free terms are obtained. Table 10 summarizes the terms which arise from any number of equivalent p electrons; Table 11 does the same for d electrons. The case of one s and any number of equivalent d electrons, which is quite important, is obtained from Table 11 on replacing each term by two terms of the same azimuthal number, but of multiplicities greater and less by one, respectively. For example, ^2D is replaced by ^3D and ^1D.

TABLE 10

Number of p electrons	Terms
1	$^2P^\circ$
2	$^3P\,^1D\,^1S$
3	$^4S^\circ\,^2D^\circ\,^2P^\circ$
4	$^3P\,^1D\,^1S$
5	$^2P^\circ$
6	^1S

TABLE 11

Number of d electrons	Terms		
1			^2D
2		$^3F^3P^1G^1D$	^1S
3		$^4F^4P^2H^2G^2F^2D^2P$	^2D
4	$^5D^3H^3G^3F^3D^3P^1J^1G^1F^1D^1S$	$^3F^3P^1G^1D$	^1S
5	$^6S^4G^4D^2J^2G^2F^2D^2S$	$^4F^4P^2H^2G^2F^2D^2P$	^2D
6	$^5D^3H^3G^3F^3D^3P^1J^1G^1F^1D^1S$	$^3F^3P^1G^1D$	^1S
7		$^4F^4P^2H^2G^2F^2D^2P$	^2D
8		$^3F^3P^1G^1D$	^1S
9		^2D	
10			^1S

11. CORRELATION OF MAGNETIC AND FIELD-FREE ENERGY LEVELS

In the case of two equivalent p electrons we showed how one can determine the aggregate of field-free terms from a knowledge of the strong-field magnetic levels. However, our discussion did not always give us the correlation between the field-free levels and those observed in a strong field. Now, we already possess complete knowledge of the connection between the field-free and the weak-field terms, so our problem reduces to finding the correlation between the terms in weak and strong fields. Pauli[1] solved it by studying the motions of a simple atom model containing two magnetic parts, which he called the electron and the core. The principal results of his theory are valid in a sufficient number of cases to make them very valuable, and we shall state them here without proof and without qualifications. If we specify a certain weak-field level by giving the values of l, s, j, and m, the m_l and m_s values of the corresponding level in a strong field are as follows:

For Regular Multiplets:

$$\text{If } m \geqq s - l, \text{ then } m_s = j - l, \ m_l = m - (j - l).$$
$$\text{If } m \leqq s - l, \text{ then } m_s = m - (s - j), \ m_l = s - j. \tag{15}$$

For Inverted Multiplets:

$$\text{If } m \leqq l - s, \text{ then } m_s = l - j, \ m_l = (j - l) + m.$$
$$\text{If } m \geqq l - s, \text{ then } m_s = (s - j) + m, \ m_l = j - s. \tag{15a}$$

For partially inverted multiplets, where the values of j first increase, and then decrease, no general rule can be given, although any definite numerical case could be treated by a direct study of the vector-precessions in Pauli's model.

As an example we take $^2P_{3/2}$ and $^2P_{1/2}$, for which $s = \frac{1}{2}$ and $l = 1$. The m_s and m_l values belonging to each weak-field level are tabulated below, together with $2m_s + m_l$, which determines the energy. Figure 8a shows the correlation diagrammatically.

Term	m	m_s	m_l	$2m_s + m_l$
$^2P_{3/2}$....................	$\frac{3}{2}$	$\frac{1}{2}$	1	2
	$\frac{1}{2}$	$\frac{1}{2}$	0	1
	$-\frac{1}{2}$	$\frac{1}{2}$	-1	0
	$-\frac{3}{2}$	$-\frac{1}{2}$	-1	-2
$^2P_{1/2}$....................	$\frac{1}{2}$	$-\frac{1}{2}$	1	0
	$-\frac{1}{2}$	$-\frac{1}{2}$	0	-1

The strong-field levels are measured from the center of gravity of the multiplet. The dotted connecting lines serve to show the correlation and do not indicate the rather complicated course taken by the energy levels as the field changes.

Breit[2] has given a speedy and easy method for carrying out such correlations. Suppose we specify the multiplet to be studied, giving its l and s values. We then draw up an array, having $2s + 1$ rows and $2l + 1$ columns. In the spaces of this array we write all the possible m values of the multiplet, arranged in a way which will be obvious on inspecting the following example:

[1] Z. Physik, **20**, 371 (1924).
[2] Phys. Rev., **28**, 334 (1926).

Each m value is written in the form $m_s + m_l$. It will be understood that the entries $s + (l - 2)$ and $(s - 2) + l$ symbolize different atomic configurations. The former means that $m_s = s$, $m_l = l - 2$; the latter, that $m_s = s - 2$, $m_l = l$. We now assert that *beginning at the upper right, the m values blocked off by the division lines belong in succession to the various terms of the multiplet, beginning with the term of highest j, provided that the multiplet is regular; but, if it is inverted, the division lines must be drawn in the shape of the capital latter L.* Then the left side and bottom edge of the array belong to the lowest term, which has the highest j, and so on. From these schemes we can read off at once the m_s and m_l values arising from a given term, and can find the positions of the strong-field levels with ease. For a normal ^2P "multiplet" the m array appears as follows:

$$\frac{\frac{1}{2} + 1 \qquad \frac{1}{2} \qquad \frac{1}{2} - 1}{-\frac{1}{2} + 1 \quad -\frac{1}{2} \;\rceil\; -\frac{1}{2} - 1}$$

From this we construct an array showing the corresponding values of $2m_s + m_l$, thus:

$$\frac{2 \qquad 1 \qquad 0}{0 \qquad -1 \;\rceil\; -2.}$$

On comparison with the tabulation following the equations (15), we see that this gives the correct result. For an inverted ^2P multiplet (like that of helium), the numbers in the m array and the energy array are the same as before, but the correlation is as follows:

Values of m: $\dfrac{1}{2} + 1 \; \Big\lfloor \; \dfrac{1}{2} \qquad \dfrac{1}{2} - 1$
$\qquad\qquad -\dfrac{1}{2} + 1 \qquad -\dfrac{1}{2} \qquad -\dfrac{1}{2} - 1$.

Values of $2m_s + m_l$: $2 \; \Big\lfloor \; 1 \qquad 0$
$\qquad\qquad\qquad 0 \qquad -1 \qquad -2$.

This case is further illustrated by Fig. 8*b*.

There is another interesting way of carrying out these correlations, depending on the hypothesis that levels which have the same m do not cross when the field strength is increased. Shenstone[1] has recently shown that certain incorrect predictions of the series limits approached by an atom, when one electron is removed, can be traced back to the

[1] *Nature*, **122**, 727 (1928).

inadequacy of this hypothesis. His paper should be consulted for a statement of the cases in which it is known to be correct. To illustrate the use of this hypothesis, we may consider all levels arising from a given regular multiplet, which have a certain value of m_l. These levels will have different m_s values. The highest m_s yields the highest energy in this selected group of magnetic levels, and must be correlated with the highest level of the field-free multiplet—that for which $j = j_{max}$. The next lower m_s value is correlated with the level for which $j = j_{max} -$

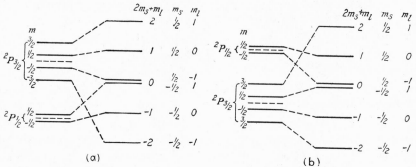

(a)

(b)

FIG. 8a.—Correlation of strong- and weak-field levels for regular ^2P terms.   FIG. 8b.—Correlation of strong- and weak-field levels for inverted ^2P terms.

1, and so on. These facts are most easily dealt with by drawing up a table similar to Table 12, which refers to doublet levels.

TABLE 12.—CORRELATION OF STRONG-FIELD AND FIELD-FREE LEVELS FOR DOUBLETS

| m_l.. | -3 | | -2 | | -1 | | 0 | | 1 | | 2 | | 3 | |
m_s..	$-\frac{1}{2}$	$\frac{1}{2}$	$-\frac{1}{2}$	$\frac{1}{2}$	$-\frac{1}{2}$	$\frac{1}{2}$	$-\frac{1}{2}$	$\frac{1}{2}$	$-\frac{1}{2}$	$\frac{1}{2}$	$-\frac{1}{2}$	$\frac{1}{2}$	$-\frac{1}{2}$	$\frac{1}{2}$
S...							$\frac{1}{2}$	$\frac{1}{2}$						
P...					$\frac{3}{2}$	$\frac{3}{2}$	$\frac{1}{2}$	$\frac{3}{2}$	$\frac{1}{2}$	$\frac{3}{2}$				
D...			$\frac{5}{2}$	$\frac{5}{2}$	$\frac{3}{2}$	$\frac{5}{2}$	$\frac{3}{2}$	$\frac{5}{2}$	$\frac{3}{2}$	$\frac{5}{2}$	$\frac{3}{2}$	$\frac{5}{2}$		

To illustrate the construction of this table, let us take the second row, referring to the P levels, $^2P_{3/2}$ and $^2P_{1/2}$. Consider the magnetic levels for which $m_l = 1$, arising from both these terms. For one of these magnetic levels m_s will be $+\frac{1}{2}$, and for the other it will be $-\frac{1}{2}$. The first is higher on the energy diagram and is therefore assigned to $^2P_{3/2}$; the second, to $^2P_{1/2}$. To indicate this, the inner number $\frac{3}{2}$ is written in the body of the table under $m_l = 1$, $m_s = \frac{1}{2}$, while the inner number $\frac{1}{2}$ is written under $m_l = 1$, $m_s = -\frac{1}{2}$. We follow through the same reasoning with the two magnetic levels for which $m = 0$, but when we come to the pair of levels for which $m_l = -1$, the procedure must be changed. As before, we assign the higher level $m_l = -1$, $m_s = \frac{1}{2}$, to the term of *higher* energy, $^2P_{3/2}$, but the other level, $m_l = -1$, $m_s = -\frac{1}{2}$, cannot now be assigned to $^2P_{1/2}$, for if the field is decreased it passes into a weak-field level with $m = -\frac{3}{2}$. This must be assigned to $^2P_{3/2}$ since a level with $m = -\frac{3}{2}$ cannot arise from a term for which $j = \frac{1}{2}$.

Hund[1] has given correlation tables similar to our Table 12, for terms of all multiplicities up to 8. The modifications to be introduced in the case of inverted multiplets are simple; the magnetic levels of *lowest* m_s belong to the highest j values, and so on.[2]

12. THE ZEEMAN EFFECT IN INTERMEDIATE FIELDS AND THE PERMANENCE RULES FOR g SUMS AND γ SUMS

We now consider the changes which take place in the Zeeman patterns of normal multiplet lines when the field becomes so large that the Zeeman separations are of the same order of magnitude as the separations in the field-free multiplet. The wave number of a given magnetic level may always be written in the form

$$\tilde{\nu} = \tilde{\nu}_c + \gamma\tilde{\omega} + mg\tilde{L} \tag{17}$$

where $m = m_l + m_s$, and g is a generalization of the Landé splitting factor. In this expression the first term in equation (17) is the wave number of the optical center of gravity of the multiple term and is an average of the wave numbers of the individual levels. In taking this average, each level is assigned the weight $2j + 1$. $\tilde{\omega}$ is the wave number corresponding to the frequency of precession of l and s about j, and γ is a quantity introduced by Landé and called by him the interval factor; e.g., for an alkali P doublet the level $j = \frac{3}{2}$ has the weight 4, while the level $j = \frac{1}{2}$ has the weight 2, and so the center of gravity lies at a distance $\tilde{\omega}/3$ from the former line, $\tilde{\omega}$ being the doublet difference. Hence the interval factor is $\frac{1}{3}$ for $^2P_{3/2}$ and $-\frac{2}{3}$ for $^2P_{1/2}$. Table 13 gives the values of the interval factor *in weak fields* for all multiplicities up to 8. This table is taken from Back and Landé's[3] book on the Zeeman effect, and is computed from the formula

$$\gamma_{\text{weak}} = \frac{(j + \frac{1}{2})^2 - (s + \frac{1}{2})^2 - (l + \frac{1}{2})^2 + \frac{1}{4}}{2(s + \frac{1}{2})(l + \frac{1}{2})} = \frac{j(j + 1) - s(s + 1) - l(l + 1)}{2(s + \frac{1}{2})(l + \frac{1}{2})} \tag{18}$$

which may be derived in much the same fashion as the g formula.

The effect of increasing the field until the Paschen-Back effect sets in is to change both g and γ. For doublets, a classical theory governing this change was long ago worked out by Voigt.[4] It is very remarkable

[1] Table 36, at the end of his book "Linienspektren."

[2] See, however, a paper which discusses the matter more thoroughly: HUND, Z. *Physik*, **52**, 601 (1928).

[3] "Zeemaneffekt und Multiplettstruktur der Spektrallinien," p. 73, Springer, Berlin (1925). See also LANDÉ, Z. *Physik*, **19**, 112 (1923).

[4] *Ann. Physik*, **41**, 403 and **42**, 210 (1913).

TABLE 13.—LANDÉ'S INTERVAL FACTORS IN WEAK FIELDS

Integer j (Singlets, Triplets, Quintets, Septets)

l	0	1	2	3	4	5	6	7
Singlets: $s = 0$								
0	0							
1		0						
2			0					
3				0				
4					0			
Triplets: $s = 1$								
0		0						
1	−8/9	−4/9	4/9					
2		−12/15	−4/15	8/15				
3			−16/21	−4/21	12/21			
4				−20/27	−4/27	16/27		
Quintets: $s = 2$								
0			0					
1		−12/15	−4/15	8/15				
2	−24/25	−20/25	−12/25	0	16/25			
3		−32/35	−24/35	−12/35	4/35	24/35		
4			−40/45	−28/45	−12/45	8/45	32/45	
Septets: $s = 3$								
0				0				
1			−16/21	−4/21	12/21			
2		−32/35	−24/35	−12/35	4/35	24/35		
3	−48/49	−44/49	−36/49	−24/49	−8/49	12/49	36/49	
4		−60/63	−52/63	−40/63	−24/63	−4/63	20/63	48/63

Half-integer j (Doublets, Quartets, Sextets, Octets)

l	½	3/2	5/2	7/2	9/2	11/2	13/2	15/2
Doublets: $s = \tfrac{1}{2}$								
0	0							
1	−2/3	1/3						
2		−3/5	2/5					
3			−4/7	3/7				
4				−5/9	4/9			
Quartets: $s = \tfrac{3}{2}$								
0		0						
1	−5/6	−2/6	3/6					
2	−9/10	−6/10	−1/10	6/10				
3		−12/14	−7/14	0	9/14			
4			−15/18	−8/18	1/18	12/18		
Sextets: $s = \tfrac{5}{2}$								
0			0					
1		−7/9	−2/9	5/9				
2	−14/15	−11/15	−6/15	1/15	10/15			
3	−20/21	−17/21	−12/21	−5/21	4/21	15/21		
4		−25/27	−20/27	−13/27	−4/27	7/27	20/27	
Octets: $s = \tfrac{7}{2}$								
0				0				
1			−9/12	−2/12	7/12			
2		−18/20	−13/20	−6/20	3/20	14/20		
3	−27/28	−24/28	−19/28	−12/28	−3/28	8/28	21/28	
4	−35/36	−32/36	−27/36	−20/36	−11/36	0	13/36	28/36

that he was led to a formula which can also be derived on the basis of the older quantum theory as Sommerfeld[1] has shown. The formula for the position of a level, referred to the doublet center of gravity is

$$\frac{\Delta \tilde{\nu}}{L} = m - \frac{v}{4(l + \frac{1}{2})} \pm \frac{1}{2}\left(1 + \frac{2mv}{l + \frac{1}{2}} + v^2\right)^{\frac{1}{2}}, \; v = \frac{\tilde{\omega}}{L}, \quad (19)$$

where the plus (minus) sign refers to the higher (lower) level. This formula is well established by experiment. Much remains to be done in generalizing it to other multiplicities and in testing such generalizations.

The g's and γ's obey two interesting laws known as the permanence rules for g and γ sums, and associated with the names of Heisenberg, Pauli, and Landé. The g-sum rule may be expressed as follows: Having chosen a multiplet, we fix our attention on all magnetic levels with the same magnetic quantum number. For each of these components, there will be a different g, depending on the value of j for the corresponding field-free level. Summing these g values over all j's, the value is found to be independent of the field strength. This may be otherwise expressed by stating that *the sum of the energy values which belong to definite values of l, s, and m is a linear function of the field strength.* The permanence of g sums is a phenomenon extremely well verified by experiment. Its validity extends beyond the case of normal multiplet spectra, and it is interesting from another standpoint, for it gives an alternative means of calculating the g's in weak fields from those in strong fields, or *vice versa*. For this application it is more convenient to write the principle in the form

$$\sum_j mg = \text{constant, with } m, l, \text{ and } s \text{ fixed.} \quad (20)$$

For example, we may consider the triplet P terms. The strong-field values of Σmg may be obtained by methods given in Sec. **11,** which do not involve a knowledge of the weak-field g's. The values found for $m = 2, 1$, and 0 are 3, 3, and 0, respectively. Applying equation (20) to each of these cases, and letting g_2, g_1, and g_0 be the g's for the $^3P_2$, $^3P_1$, and $^3P_0$ states, respectively, in a weak field, we have,

$$2g_2 = 3, \; g_2 + g_1 = 3, \; 0(g_2 + g_1 + g_0) = 0.$$

We must remember that only $^3P_2$ can give a term with $m = 2$, that both $^3P_2$ and $^3P_1$ can give terms with $m = 1$ and that all three of the ^3P levels can give terms with $m = 0$. These equations lead to the values $g_2 = \frac{3}{2}$, $g_1 = \frac{3}{2}$, g_0 indeterminate, in agreement with Landé's table.

Similarly, the sum of the γ values for levels having fixed l, s, and m, but variable j, is independent of the field strength:

$$\sum_j \gamma = \text{constant, with } m, l, \text{ and } s \text{ fixed.} \quad (21)$$

[1] *Z. Physik*, **8**, 257 (1922).

The value of γ in a strong field is found to be

$$\gamma = \frac{m_s m_l}{(s + \frac{1}{2})(l + \frac{1}{2})}. \tag{22}$$

Other interesting regularities are these:

$$\sum_m \sum_j \gamma = 0, \tag{23}$$

$$\sum_m \sum_j mg = 0. \tag{24}$$

As mentioned by Back and Landé,[1] these relations lead to the following conclusion: If we attribute the weight one to every magnetic level, then the position of the center of gravity of all magnetic levels arising from a multiplet is independent of the field.

13. EXPLANATION OF THE INTERVAL RULE AND OF INVERTED TERMS

The interval rule of Landé may be explained by ideas very similar to those used in deriving the g formula. Let us represent the atom by an aggregate of angular momentum vectors, l_i and s_i. Each electron, say the pth, will be considered as a magnet of moment $s_i he/4\pi mc$. We suppose that the average field acting on this magnet to orient it is composed of two parts. First, there is a torque due to all the other s_i vectors, which causes the s_i vectors to form a quantized resultant s. Second, there is a torque on s_i due to the revolution of the *same* electron on its orbit with quantum number l_i. It is supposed to be insensitive to the fields produced by the revolution of other electrons, for reasons not fully understood. Under these circumstances, the potential energy of interaction of l_i and s_i is equal to (Chap. V, Secs. **16** and **17**)

$$E_i = hRc\alpha^2 l_i s_i \overline{\cos (l_i s_i) \frac{Z_i a^3}{r^3}}. \tag{25}$$

Z_i is the effective nuclear charge to which the electron is exposed when at a distance r from the nucleus and a is the radius of the first hydrogen orbit. To a first approximation, the vectors l_i have a precessional motion around their resultant l, the nature of which is explained in more detail in Sec. **14,** and the vectors s_i precess around s; while l and s turn much more slowly around the resultant j. In general, the frequencies of these precessions will all be different and will be of an order of magnitude quite distinct from that of the orbital frequency. If we write each term under the bar in equation (25) as a Fourier series, then on multiplying these series and averaging, all the terms will vanish, except the first one, which does not contain the time. This term is the product of the constant terms in these series, that is, the product of the average values of the individual series. This proves that the average in equation

[1] "Zeemaneffekt," p. 74.

(25) is equal to the products of the averages of each of its factors. We write $2C_i$ for the average of $Z_i a^3/r^3$. Further,

$$l_i s_i \cos (l_i s_i) = l_i \cos (l_i l) s_i \cos (s_i s) \cos (ls). \tag{26}$$

Proof.—$l_i s_i \cos (l_i s_i)$ is the scalar product $(\mathbf{l}_i \cdot \mathbf{s}_i)$. Since the precession of l and s around j is supposed to be slow compared with the precessions of the l_i and s_i vectors, we may obtain a first approximation to this scalar product by calculating just as though l and s were fixed in space. Figure 9 illustrates the case of two electrons. We resolve l_i int a component $l_i \cos (l_i l)$ parallel to l, and a component $l_i \sin (l_i l)$ perpendicular thereto: s_i is resolved similarly. In the scalar product $(\mathbf{l}_i \cdot \mathbf{s}_i)$, we write each vector as the sum of its two components. Multiplying out, we have the sum of four scalar products. Now, in taking the time average only the product $(l_i \cos (l_i l) \cdot s_i \cos (s_i s))$ yields a finite contribution to the result, namely, the expression on the right of equation (26). This is true because the frequencies of the l_i and s_i are supposed incommensurable. The cosine of the angle between the vectors $l_i \sin (l_i l)$ and $s_i \cos (s_i s)$ is as often positive as it is negative; and similar statements may be made concerning the products $(l_i \cos (l_i l) \cdot s_i \sin (s_i s))$ and $(l_i \sin (l_i l) \cdot s_i \sin (s_i s))$, so that their time averages are zero.

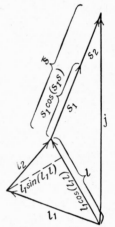

Fig. 9.—Quantized arrangements of l_i and s_i vectors.

Summing over all the electrons, and remembering that s_i is always $\frac{1}{2}$, we have the total magnetic energy of the atom:

$$E = hRc\alpha^2 \cos (ls) \sum_p C_i l_i \cos (l_i l) \cos (s_i s). \tag{27}$$

When the sum in this equation does not depend materially on the relative orientations of l and s, we may replace it by its approximately constant value, C. Then, replacing $\cos (ls)$ by its value in terms of the sides of the triangle j, l, s, we have,

$$E = hRc\alpha^2 C \frac{j^2 - l^2 - s^2}{2ls}. \tag{28}$$

The new mechanics requires us to replace this formula by

$$E = hRc\alpha^2 C \frac{(j + \tfrac{1}{2})^2 - (l + \tfrac{1}{2})^2 - (s + \tfrac{1}{2})^2 + \tfrac{1}{4}}{2(s + \tfrac{1}{2})(l + \tfrac{1}{2})}$$

$$= hRc\alpha^2 C \frac{j(j + 1) - s(s + 1) - l(l + 1)}{2(s + \tfrac{1}{2})(l + \tfrac{1}{2})}. \tag{29}$$

The difference of energy of two terms having the same l and s, but j's which differ by unity, is,

$$E_j - E_{j-1} = hRc\alpha^2 C \frac{j}{(l + \tfrac{1}{2})(s + \tfrac{1}{2})}. \tag{30}$$

The linear dependence of this energy difference on j gives us the interval rule (Sec. **7**), and consideration of the assumptions on which equation (30) is derived gives us insight into the physical conditions which exist when this rule is approximately fulfilled. Many interesting conclusions may be drawn from equation (27), such as the following:

If we have two outer electrons, one of which is on an s orbit, the sum in equation (27) reduces to a single term, let us say $c_2 l_2 \cos (s_2 s)$, and

$$E = hRc\alpha^2 \cos (ls) C_2 l_2 \cos (s_2 s).$$

For a triplet, $\cos (s_2 s)$ takes the value $+1$, and therefore the interval between the outside levels of the triplet is $2hRc\alpha^2 C_2 l_2$, which is to say, the total spread of the triplet is the same as that of a doublet term of the same l, and having the same effective total quantum number. This is often found to be the case. Other regularities which are predicted by equation (27) have been studied by Bechert and Catalan.[1]

We come now to the explanation of inverted terms. A multiplet will be regular or inverted, according as the summation in equation (27) is positive or negative. Now for excited states in which the constants C_i may be quite different for the various outer electrons, the possibilities are numerous and complicated. Let us limit our attention, therefore, to the case of equivalent electrons, for which $l_i = \lambda$ and all the C_i's are equal to a constant k, let us say. If all the s_i vectors are parallel, $\cos (s_i s)$ is positive in every term of the summation of equation (27), and it reduces to $k\lambda\Sigma \cos (l_i l)$. But this sum must be positive, for there are more electrons with l_i in the direction of l than in the opposite direction. This means that *there cannot be inverted terms having the highest possible value of s*, that is, having a multiplicity greater by one than the number of equivalent electrons involved. Therefore, we must consider terms of lower multiplicity. Perhaps the simplest illustration is that of the lowest terms ^3P of the sixth group elements, O, Se, and Te. We need only consider the four p electrons of the outer shell. In discussing these terms, Slater assumed (Sec. **14**) that the s_i vectors are all either parallel or antiparallel to their resultant, no reason being given save that this supposition leads to correct results. Since we are dealing with triplet terms, three of the s_i vectors must be parallel to s, the fourth being antiparallel. Thus for three of the terms in the summation of equation (27), $\cos (s_i s)$ is positive, and for the fourth it is negative. Slater was able to show that for a simple vector model of this kind the resultant l' of the l_i vectors which have their s_i vectors parallel to s, is conjugate to an angle variable, and must be a multiple of $h/2\pi$; and the same is true of l'', the resultant of the l_i vectors which have their s_i vectors antiparallel to s. For the ^3P term under consideration, $l'' = 1$, since there is only one electron for which s_i is antiparallel to s, but l' may be

[1] Z. Physik, **37**, 658 (1926).

2, 1, or 0, and the whole problem is to find which of these possibilities actually occurs. Slater answered this question by making a new assumption—that Pauli's exclusion principle applies separately to l' and l'', so that no state is allowed which would become a forbidden state by simply removing electrons from the atom. On this basis, the three electrons giving rise to l' must form an allowed configuration for which $s = \frac{3}{2}$. Looking at Table 10, we see that the only term of this kind is ^4S, so that $l' = 0$. Thus, the sum in equation (27) reduces to a single term, $-C_4 l_4 \cos (l_4 l)$, and $\cos (l_4 l)$ is unity because $l_4 = l$. Therefore, we have an inverted term.

By applying the same method we can determine the nature of the lowest term in every case. So long as we are dealing with normal multiplet spectra, the result is as follows: Consider, first, an atom with an outer shell composed entirely of p electrons. If there are less than three of them, it is possible to have terms for which the multiplicity is one greater than the number of electrons without violating Pauli's principle (see Table 10). Since the energy of interaction of the s_i vectors is ordinarily greater than that of the l_i vectors, these terms of highest multiplicity must be the lowest terms. As stated above, a term of the highest multiplicity must be regular. Now, if there are exactly three p electrons, we have a ^4S term, and if there are more p electrons we have $l' = 0$.[1] From this it follows that all surviving terms of the summation of equation (27) are negative and we have inverted terms. Similar relations are encountered in the case of atoms which have only equivalent d electrons or equivalent f electrons. The general statement is this:

In building an outer subshell of equivalent electrons we have regular terms in the first half of the subperiod, an S term at the middle, and inverted terms in the second half.

To make this more concrete, we may say that regular terms are obtained from less than three p, five d, or seven f electrons, and so on.

14. A DYNAMICAL MODEL FOR A COMPLEX ATOM

In preceding sections we have made free use of a model in which the atom is replaced by a set of angular momentum vectors. Slater[2] has made a thorough investigation of the motions in such a model on the basis of certain simplifying assumptions. Any one of the vectors is supposed to act on another with a torque which is proportional to the sine of the angle between them. To show that this assumption is a natural one, we may recall that under these circumstances the potential

---

[1] This follows because in the lowest term s must have as large a value as possible consistent with Pauli's principle. The largest value of s is obtained when as many s_i vectors as possible are in the direction of s; but when this is the case, on taking away the electrons with s_i vectors antiparallel to s, we are left with a configuration giving rise to a term with $l' = 0$, just as in the illustration dealing with sixth-group elements.

[2] *Phys. Rev.*, **28**, 291 (1926).

energy of any pair of vectors will be proportional to the cosine of the angle between them, just as in the case of two magnets. It may be well at this point to consider the *sign* of the energy of such a pair of vectors. The fact that the alkali doublets are regular shows that the state of higher energy corresponds to the case in which l and s are parallel. Now, before the advent of the spinning electron, it was difficult to understand this as Breit[1] first clearly pointed out. His argument is as follows:

The vector s is supposed to represent the angular momentum of the kernel and is, therefore, localized, at least approximately, at the center of the atom. At the center there is a magnetic field **H**, due to the orbital revolution of the valence electron. If the magnetic moment of the kernel is **μ**, and if **μ** makes an angle θ with the direction of **H**, the magnetic energy is $-\mu H \cos \theta$. But when l and s are parallel, **H** and **μ** are parallel, so that the state of higher j should have the lower energy. This difficulty was abolished when it was found that s is located on the electron itself, as we may see by considering the calculations in Secs. **16** and **17** of Chap. V.

The practical consequence for our discussion of Slater's work is that we must choose the proper signs for the torques between the vectors in his rather abstract model, guided by our knowledge that the alkali doublets are regular, and by other pertinent facts. In order to restrict the discussion to normal multiplet spectra, Slater begins by assuming that the coupling of the l vectors among themselves, or of the s vectors among themselves, is strong compared to that between the l's and s's. In other words, the separation between multiplets is to be large compared with that between adjacent levels of a multiplet. It is assumed that the s vectors are all either parallel or antiparallel to their resultant. Further, the problem is simplified by the assumption that there is no torque between the l of one electron and the s of another. With these restrictions, Slater obtains the motions of the vectors for a shell of equivalent electrons and for such a shell in combination with another non-equivalent electron. His method of attack is as follows:

Suppose that $\mathbf{p}_i$ is one vector and $\mathbf{p}_j$ another. The torque exerted on $\mathbf{p}_i$ by $\mathbf{p}_j$ is proportional to the sine of the angle between, if the energy is proportional to the cosine. It is a vector, at right angles to $\mathbf{p}_i$ and $\mathbf{p}_j$. That is, it can be written as a constant times the vector product: $A_{ij}[\mathbf{p}_i\mathbf{p}_j]$. Taking the torque as the vector product of the force and the lever arm, it is readily verified that a positive A_{ij} means that $\mathbf{p}_i$ is being pulled toward $\mathbf{p}_j$. The total torque on $\mathbf{p}_i$ is then the sum of the torques from all other angular momentum vectors:

$$\Sigma(j)A_{ij}[\mathbf{p}_i\mathbf{p}_j].$$

The equation of motion for $\mathbf{p}_i$ now is simply that the time rate of change of the angular momentum equals the torque acting:

$$\frac{d\mathbf{p}_i}{dt} = \sum_j A_{ij}[\mathbf{p}_i\mathbf{p}_j] = \left[\mathbf{p}_i \sum_j A_{ij}\mathbf{p}_j\right].$$

[1] *Nature*, Sept. 15, 1923.

The law of action and reaction states that the reaction of $\mathbf{p}_j$ on $\mathbf{p}_i$, $A_{ji}[\mathbf{p}_i\mathbf{p}_i]$, is equal and opposite to the action of $\mathbf{p}_i$ on $\mathbf{p}_j$, so that $A_{ij} = A_{ji}$.

The device used in solving the equations of motion of this type is very simple in principle. First, we neglect the interaction of the l's and s's and consider the system of l vectors independently. As stated several times before, the motion of the l's consists in a uniform rigid rotation around their resultant. The proof is very simple for the case of a shell of equivalent electrons: The constant A_{ij} will be the same for each pair of electrons and may be written as A. Then the equation for l_i is,

$$\frac{dl_i}{dt} = [l_i A \, \Sigma l_j],$$

where the summation sign indicates a vectorial sum which extends over all the electrons except the ith. Now the vector product, $A[l_il_i]$, is zero, and so it may be added to the right side of this equation, which becomes

$$\frac{dl_i}{dt} = [l_i A l], \tag{31}$$

since $\Sigma l_j = 1$. It is well known[1] that when a vector is subject to a law of this kind, its motion is simply a uniform precession around the vector Al with angular velocity Al, which we shall call ω_l. Similarly, in the case of the s vectors, the whole system rotates around s with angular velocity $Bs = \omega_s$. Now we introduce a small coupling torque of the form $\mu[l_is_i]$ in the equation for l_i, and a similar term in the equation for s_i. This causes a slow precession of both l and s around j. The detailed solution shows that small periodic terms of higher frequencies are also present in the motion; but still more important, it turns out that new quantities suitable for use as quantum integrals make their appearance. They are, l', the vector sum of those l_i's which have s_i's parallel to s, and l'', the vector sum of those l_i's which have s_i's antiparallel to s, so that $l = l' + l''$. To show that these vectors are suitable for quantization, we only need to prove that they are constant (except for quantities of the order of μ^2), and this is easily carried through. The motion of the l_i may be described as follows: Each l_i precesses with angular velocity ω_l' about l', or ω_l'' about l'', as the case may be; further l' and l'' precess about $\bar{l}$ with velocity ω_l, where $\bar{l}$ is a vector differing from l only by a quantity containing the first power of μ; $\bar{l}$ has the interesting property of precessing uniformly around j, although l does not. The energy of the atom is finally shown to be

$$E = \frac{A\bar{l}^2}{2} + \frac{Bs^2}{2} + \mu s\bar{l}\left(\frac{l'^2 - l''^2}{\bar{l}^2}\right)\frac{j^2 - s^2 - \bar{l}^2}{2s\bar{l}}. \tag{32}$$

[1] For example, see Page, "Introduction to Theoretical Physics," D. Van Nostrand Company, New York (1928).

By taking the derivative of E with respect to j we obtain the angular velocity of the precession around j, and ω_l, ω_l', etc., can be obtained similarly (Chap. IV, Sec. **13**).

The results are more complicated when one non-equivalent electron is added to the atom, and they will not be quoted here. Further study of Slater's paper is recommended to anyone who wishes to appreciate the great value of the vector model in giving qualitative explanations of spectral phenomena.

15. DETERMINATION OF THE SERIES LIMIT APPROACHED BY A MULTIPLET TERM

Let us suppose that the total quantum number of one electron in an atom is adiabatically increased until it is very large. The state of the atom approaches that of a singly charged ion. In general, this ion will have a number of low-lying states, and we desire to know which one of these will be attained when the electron in question is completely removed. The answer depends on the nature of the multiplet level in which the atom was found when the process began. In some cases it is possible to examine this question experimentally by observing the behavior of individual terms of successive multiplets in a series. The simplest case would be that of the sharp or the diffuse series of an alkaline earth where the sequences head for the same wave number and the atom approaches the same ionic state regardless of the j values of the terms through which it passes. The question involved here may be formulated as follows:

Considering the case of two electrons solely to simplify the notation (a quite unimportant restriction), what is the correlation of the terms described by the quantum numbers

$$l_1, \ l_2, \ s_1, \ s_2, \ s, \ l, \ \text{and } j \tag{33}$$

with the terms of the ion, described by the numbers

$$l_1, \ s_1, \ j_1.$$

This question can be answered by the following artifice, introduced for the sole purpose of allowing us to use the results of Sec. **12** and others like them. If we expose the neutral atom to a strong magnetic field, we can follow in detail the way in which each term described by the quantum numbers of expression (33) gives rise to magnetic levels characterized by certain sets of values of

$$l_1, \ s_1, \ m_{l1}, \ m_{s1}, \ l_2, \ s_2, \ m_{l2}, \ m_{s2}.$$

The atom will now occupy a state specified by a definite set of these quantum numbers; which one it occupies is of no significance. Now, with the field still applied, we take away the second electron, leaving an ion with the same values of l_1, s_1, m_{l1}, and m_{s1}. Finally, the field is removed, and we have the ion in the state $l_1 s_1 j_1$ which is approached by the atom as a series limit when n_2 is gradually increased. The physical principle involved here is very simple, but in practice the details of the correlation are complicated and we shall illustrate it by the simplest possible case, that of an atom with two electrons on p orbits. The problem is attacked in reverse order. First we consult a table, showing the correlation of pairs of values of l_1, j_1 with pairs of values of m_{l1}, m_{s1}. (Table 12 is an example.) We then begin the construction of the scheme shown in Table 14, writing down the chosen l values, and the possible m_{l1} and m_{s1} values. Now with each m_{l1}, we can have $m_{l2} = +1$, 0, or -1, and for each of these possibilities there are two possible values

TABLE 14.—SERIES LIMITS FOR TERMS ARISING FROM 2 p-ELECTRONS

l_1 l_2	j_1	m_{l1} m_{l2}	m_{s1} m_{s2}	m_l	m_s	Terms
1　1	$\frac{1}{2}$	1　　1	$-\frac{1}{2}$　$\frac{1}{2}$	2	0	
			$-\frac{1}{2}$		-1	
		0	$\frac{1}{2}$	1	0	
			$-\frac{1}{2}$		-1	
		-1	$\frac{1}{2}$	0	0	
			$-\frac{1}{2}$		-1	$^3D_2$ $^3D_1$
		0　　1	$-\frac{1}{2}$　$\frac{1}{2}$	1	0	$^3P_1$ $^3P_0$
			$-\frac{1}{2}$		-1	
		0	$\frac{1}{2}$	0	0	
			$-\frac{1}{2}$		-1	
		-1	$\frac{1}{2}$	-1	0	
			$-\frac{1}{2}$		-1	
	$\frac{3}{2}$	1　　1	$\frac{1}{2}$　$\frac{1}{2}$	2	1	
			$-\frac{1}{2}$		0	
		0	$\frac{1}{2}$	1	1	
			$-\frac{1}{2}$		0	
		-1	$\frac{1}{2}$	0	1	
			$-\frac{1}{2}$		0	
		0　　1	$\frac{1}{2}$　$\frac{1}{2}$	1	1	
			$-\frac{1}{2}$		0	
		0	$\frac{1}{2}$	0	1	
			$-\frac{1}{2}$		0	
		-1	$\frac{1}{2}$	-1	1	$^3D_3$ $^3P_2$ $^3S_1$
			$-\frac{1}{2}$		0	$^1D_2$ $^1P_1$ $^1S_0$
		-1　1	$\frac{1}{2}$　$\frac{1}{2}$	0	1	
			$-\frac{1}{2}$		0	
		0	$\frac{1}{2}$	-1	1	
			$-\frac{1}{2}$		0	
		-1	$\frac{1}{2}$	-2	1	
			$-\frac{1}{2}$		0	
		-1　1	$-\frac{1}{2}$　$\frac{1}{2}$	0	0	
			$-\frac{1}{2}$		-1	
		0	$\frac{1}{2}$	-1	0	
			$-\frac{1}{2}$		-1	
		-1	$\frac{1}{2}$	-2	0	
			$-\frac{1}{2}$		-1	

of m_{s2}, namely $+\frac{1}{2}$ and $-\frac{1}{2}$. (It must be remembered that we are dealing with a case in which the electrons are not equivalent, and that Pauli's rule does not apply.) We list all these cases, and form the resultants, m_l and m_s. These are the strong-field values of m_l and m_s for the terms of the neutral atom arising from the ionic configuration l_1, j_1.

The first twelve lines of Table 14 give the m_l and m_s values belonging to the magnetic levels of the neutral atom which arise from the ionic configuration $l_1 = 1$, $j_1 = \frac{1}{2}$; and the remainder of the table contains those coming from the ionic term $l_1 = 1$, $j_1 = \frac{3}{2}$. The next problem is to pick out the field-free terms to which these magnetic levels belong. This is done in the following way:

We know that the terms coming from two p electrons must be triplet and singlet S, P, and D. We construct Table 15 in precisely the same way in which Table 12 was obtained, to show the correlation of m_l, m_s pairs with the field-free terms of the neutral atom.

TABLE 15.—CORRELATION OF FIELD-FREE TRIPLET TERMS WITH STRONG-FIELD LEVELS

m_l	-2			-1			0			1			2		
m_s	-1	0	1	-1	0	1	-1	0	1	-1	0	1	-1	0	1
S							1	1	1						
P				2	2	2	1	1	2	0	1	2			
D	3	3	3	2	2	3	1	2	3	1	2	3	1	2	3

We see that the combination $m_l = 2$, $m_s = 1$, belongs only to the $^3D_3$ term. In Table 14 this combination stands only in the group of magnetic terms arising from the spark term $j_1 = \frac{3}{2}$. From inspection of Table 15 we find that $^3D_3$ also gives rise to the combinations 1, 1; 0, 1; -1, 1; -2, 1; -2, 0; and $-2,-1$. We strike all of these out of the table and turn our attention to $^3D_2$. Here we find that the highest magnetic level belonging to this term, namely that represented by the combination 2, 0, is in the part of Table 14 belonging to the spark term $j_1 = \frac{1}{2}$. Again we strike out all magnetic levels of $^3D_2$, and continue the process, first for the triplet and then for the singlet terms. At the end we see that four of the terms go to the limit $^2P_{\frac{1}{2}}$, namely $^3D_2$, $^3D_1$, $^3P_1$, and $^3P_0$; the others approach the limit $^2P_{\frac{3}{2}}$.

The principle by which such questions are attacked is now clear. It will be seen that the limits approached by inverted terms arising from two p electrons are different from those approached by regular terms of the same name. For a discussion of some of the difficulties which arise, in the case where the series electron is a p or d electron, we may refer to papers by Shenstone[1] and Hund.[2]

[1] *Nature*, **121**, 619, and **122**, 727 (1928).

[2] *Z. Physik*, **52**, 601 (1928).

16. RECIPROCITY THEOREMS

Consider the energy levels of an atom in which one electron has been removed from a completed group, and (for simplicity) all other groups are closed. We have already considered such levels in our study of X-ray terms and it is our present purpose to generalize the remarks made in that section.

For a closed group, $\Sigma m_{sp} = 0$ and $\Sigma m_{lp} = 0$. If we remove an electron characterized by the numbers l_1, m_{s1}, m_{l1} while the remaining electrons retain their numbers, the resultant m_s and m_l of the ionized group will be $-m_{s1}$ and $-m_{l1}$. To every set of quantum numbers n_1, l_1, m_{s1}, m_{l1} of an atom with only one electron in the n-quantum group, there corresponds uniquely a set of numbers n_1, l_1, $-m_{s1}$, $-m_{l1}$ characterizing an energy state of an atom in which that group lacks only the electron with numbers n_1, l_1, m_{s1}, m_{l1}. The generalization to the case where the group has lost r electrons is obvious and constitutes Pauli's reciprocity theorem. In the absence of a strong external field a somewhat similar statement may be made, as we see from the fact that when the field is removed adiabatically the statistical weights of the various states are unaltered. However, the situation can be better appreciated from the following statement: For a closed group $\Sigma l = \Sigma s = \Sigma j = 0$. If an electron having numbers n_1, l_1, s_1, j_1 is removed the remainder is characterized by the numbers n_1, $-l_1$, $-s_1$, $-j_1$. Similarly, to every configuration of r electrons of total quantum number n, characterized by the resultant numbers l, s, and j, there corresponds a configuration of $2n^2 - r$ electrons occupying all the places left vacant by the r electrons and having the quantum numbers $-l$, $-s$, and $-j$.

17. THE NORMAL STATES OF THE TRANSITION ELEMENTS

The spectral characteristics of the lowest lying terms of the elements of the first and second transition groups are known from studies of the type described in the preceding sections and from these the number of electrons in each subshell can be determined. Figure 10a taken from Gibbs and White[1] is a plot of lower lying terms corresponding to the different numbers of electrons in the 4, 1 and 3, 2 types of orbits in the elements from K to Cu, inclusive. The terms as given are referred to the term with one s electron and $n - 1$ d electrons as zero, since the ionizing energies of these atoms are not known accurately, and therefore the more usual method of referring to the ion and electron as having zero energy cannot be used. The curves are designated by the number of d, s, and p electrons which combine to give the terms. There are usually many terms for each of these configurations; the plot shows the lowest term of each configuration.

[1] *Proc. Nat. Acad. Sci.*, **14**, 559 (1928).

The assignment of electrons to the subshells for the normal states is now evident. Ca, Sc, Ti, V, Mn, Fe, and Co have two valence electrons in the 4, 0 orbits and the remainder in 3, 2 orbits. Cr has one 4, 0 electron and five 3, 2 electrons. The assignment in nickel is two 4, 0 and eight 3, 2 electrons, though the energy levels of this configuration and those of the configuration consisting of one 4, 0 electron and nine 3, 2 electrons lie very close together. Figure 10b is a similar diagram for the second transition group and the electron configurations as given in Table 3, Chap. IX follow from these curves. It is interesting to note the

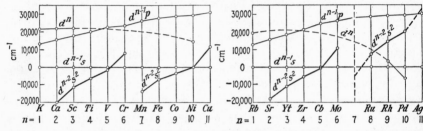

FIG. 10a.—Plot of low terms of K to Cu, inclusive. (*After Gibbs and White.*)   FIG. 10b.—Plot of low terms of Rb to Ag, inclusive. (*After Gibbs and White.*)

similarity of these two sets of curves though they show that the normal states of the Fe, Co, Ni and Ru, Rh, Pd triads have quite different electron configurations.

References

KAYSER, H., and KONEN, H., "Handbuch der Spektroscopie," 1–4 (1907); 5 (1910); 6 (1912); 7 (1924), Hirzel, Leipzig.

KAYSER, H., "Tabelle der Hauptlinien der Linienspektren aller Elements," Springer, Berlin (1926).

KAYSER, H., "Tabelle der Schwingungszahlen," Hirzel, Leipzig (1925).

BALY, E. C. C., "Spectroscopy," 4 vols., Longmans, Green and Co., London (1927).

FOWLER, A., "Report on Series in Line Spectra," Fleetway Press, London (1922).

PASCHEN and GÖTZE, "Seriengesetze der Linienspektren," Springer, Berlin (1922).

HICKS, W. M., "The Analysis of Spectra," Cambridge University Press (1922).

UHLER, H. S., and R. W. WOOD, "Atlas of Absorption Spectra," *Pub.* 71, Carnegie Institution of Washington (1907).

MEES, C. E. K., "An Atlas of Absorption Spectra," Longmans, Green and Co., London (1909).

HAGENBACH and KONEN, "Atlas of Emission Spectra of Most of the Elements," translated by A. S. King, W. Wesley and Son, London (1905).

JONES and UHLER, "Hydrates in Aqueous Solution," *Pub.* 60; JONES and ANDERSON, "Spectra of Solutions," *Pub.* 110; JONES and STRONG, "Spectra of Solutions," *Pub.* 130 and 160; Carnegie Institution of Washington.

LYMAN, "The Spectroscopy of the Extreme Ultra-violet," 2nd ed., Longmans, Green and Co., New York (1928).

LE COMTE, "Le Spectre Infra-rouge," Les Presses Universitaires de France, Paris (1928).

GROTRIAN, W., "Graphische Darstellung der Spektren von Atomen und Ionen mit ein, zwei und drei Valenzelektronen," Vols. I and II, Springer, Berlin (1928).

EDER and VALENTA, "Atlas Typischer Spektren," Hölder, Wien (1911).

JOOS, G., see reference at end of Chap. XI.

CHAPTER XI

SPECIAL TOPICS IN SPECTROSCOPY

1. THE STARK EFFECT OF NON-HYDROGENIC ATOMS

The Stark effect of non-hydrogenic atoms is qualitatively similar to that of hydrogenic atoms presented in Chap. V, Secs. **12** to **15**. In weak electric fields the energy change of the atom is proportional to the square of the field strength, but in sufficiently high fields it becomes proportional to the first power of the field. This gradual transition from the second-order to the first-order effect occurs, in general, at much higher electric fields in the case of non-hydrogenic atoms than in the case of hydrogenic atoms. Further, it occurs at greater fields in the case of energy levels which differ by large amounts from the corresponding hydrogenic levels. In Chap. V, Sec. **14**, we showed that the additional energy due to the external field is equal to the mean value of the perturbation term in the potential energy taken over the unperturbed orbit. This term is eFz, where z is the displacement of the electron from the nucleus in the direction of the field. The orbit of an electron moving in a central field of force, which deviates from the inverse square law, is not closed, but precesses in a plane. (In the hydrogenic atom, the precession is caused by the change of mass with velocity.) In the case of a precessing orbit, z is as often positive as negative and the mean value of eFz is zero. Therefore, an energy term proportional to F is absent. The largest energy term must be secured by taking account of the small changes in the orbit and is proportional to F^2. If the field is sufficiently large, it will displace the electron relative to the nucleus by an appreciable distance. If it is strong enough to suppress the precession, the energy term proportional to F becomes important and, in fact, much larger than that proportional to F^2. The smaller the quantum defect is, the less is the deviation from the inverse square field and the more easily is the electron displaced in the direction of the field; therefore, only those levels having small quantum defects will be expected to have large first-order Stark effects in electric fields which can be produced by present experimental methods.

The effect of an electric field on the spectra of non-hydrogenic atoms has been investigated by Stark[1] and his pupils,[2] by Nyquist,[3] Takamine

---

[1] *Ann. Physik*, **43**, 965 (1914); **56**, 577 (1918).
[2] LEIBERT, *Ann. Physik*, **56**, 589 (1918).
[3] *Phys. Rev.*, **10**, 226 (1917).

and Kokubu,[1] Ishida,[2] and a number of other physicists. The most complete investigations of this kind are those of J. S. Foster[3] on the He I

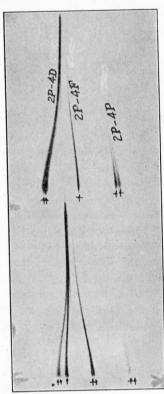

FIG. 1.—Stark effect of helium lines.
(*After J. S. Foster.*)

spectrum, and of Foster and his colleagues on neon and the secondary spectrum of hydrogen. The work on helium is of special interest because Foster has also given the theoretical explanation using matrix mechanics. Figure 1 is a reproduction of one of Foster's photographs showing the Stark effect components of the $2^1P - 4^1P$, $2^1P - 4^1D$, and $2^1P - 4^1F$ lines, for which he used a modified Lo Surdo[4] tube as a source. The polarizations are marked at the side of the two figures. In the case of a maximum field of 44.5 kilovolts per centimeter the corresponding maximum displacements of the $2^1P - 4^1D$ parallel components are 15.5 and 16.8 cm.$^{-1}$, respectively, which gives the order of magnitude of the displacements secured.

Table 1 classifies the various combinations of field-free terms on the basis of the number of parallel (p) and perpendicular (s) components observed in the field. It is always possible that the maximum number of components has not been observed, for their separations may be too small to be resolved.

The $^1P - {}^1F$ transition has only one parallel and two perpendicular components according to Foster's experiments (Fig. 1), and therefore

TABLE 1

p/s	$\frac{1}{0}$	$\frac{1}{1}$	$\frac{2}{2}$	$\frac{2}{3}$
Term combinations........	$^1S - {}^1S$ $^3S - {}^3S$	$^1S - {}^1P$ $^1P - {}^1S$	$^1P - {}^1P$ $^3P - {}^3P$ $^3P - {}^3D(?)$	$^1P - {}^1D$ $^3P - {}^3D(?)$ $^1P - {}^1F(?)$ $^3P - {}^3F$

---

[1] TAKAMINE, *Astrophys. J.*, **50**, 23 (1919); TAKAMINE and KOKUBU, *Mem. Coll. Sci.*, Kyoto, **3**, 275 (1919).

[2] *Nature*, **122**, 277 (1928).

[3] *Proc. Roy. Soc.* **114**, 47 (1927); **117**, 137 (1927); See also FUJIOKA, Inst. of Phys. and Chem. Res., 181, Tokio, (1929).

[4] See Foster's original article for the experimental details, and Chap. V Fig. 16.

does not belong in any column of Table 1. Theoretically, it belongs in the $\frac{2}{3}$ column and it is placed there for that reason. Similarly, the $^3P - {}^3D$ lines have two parallel and two perpendicular observed components though theoretically they belong to the $\frac{2}{3}$ column. They have been placed in both columns and the uncertainty has been indicated by question marks.

Figure 2 is the theoretical energy-level diagram calculated by Foster for the transitions from the levels of total quantum number 4 to those of total quantum number 2. The arrows indicate the permitted trans-

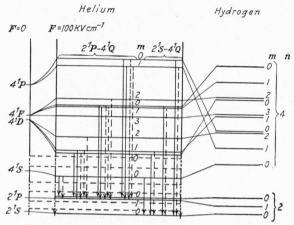

Fig. 2.—Energy diagram for Stark effect of helium.

itions; the perpendicular components $\Delta m = \pm 1$ are indicated by broken lines and parallel components, $\Delta m = 0$, by solid lines. At the right we show the energy diagram of the corresponding levels of hydrogen calculated from equation (70) of Chap. V; the broken connecting lines show the correlations between the levels of the two atoms.[1] The formulas for the energy levels of helium are not simple and the calculation can be made only by the perturbation methods of quantum mechanics. The diagram shows the number of parallel and perpendicular components to be expected and the agreement with the experimental data of Table 1 is complete except for the $^3P - {}^3D$ and $^1P - {}^1F$ combinations as already mentioned. Moreover, the theoretical values agree quantitatively with the observed displacements.

Similar patterns are to be expected in the case of atoms of higher atomic number. It is to be noted, however, that large effects are secured only when the orbits do not penetrate the kernel. In lines belonging to a diffuse series, it often happens that almost the entire displacement of a Stark effect component is due to the D term. Conversely, in a

[1] See Kramers, *Z. Physik*, **3**, 199 (1920).

sharp series, for which the initial states correspond to penetrating S orbits, the final P term may contribute most of the displacement. This is well illustrated by the work of Foster and Rowles[1] on neon. As for non-penetrating orbits, they find that the displacements D of the diffuse terms of neon in theoretically low fields are well represented by $D = a - bx$, where a and b are constants and x is the wave-number difference between the field-free term and the corresponding hydrogen term.

In this element most of the patterns of the sharp, diffuse, and combination lines are identical with those observed by Foster in parhelium. Foster and Rowles observed a phenomenon like the Paschen-Back effect for a number of neon lines. At sufficiently high fields the various levels of a multiple term fuse together, yielding an unsymmetrical Stark effect. Now, the electric field brings out new lines corresponding to violations of the azimuthal selection rule (Sec. 2) and the group of Stark patterns, belonging to a group of such lines, shows a symmetry like that encountered in the Paschen-Back effect.

The quadratic Stark effect of the sodium D lines was studied in absorption by Ladenburg.[2] At a field strength of 160,000 volts per centimeter, the p-components for the two lines were displaced to the red about 0.025 Å. The s-component of $1^2S_{\frac{1}{2}} - 2^2P_{\frac{1}{2}}$ is shifted a similar amount, but that of $1^2S_{\frac{1}{2}} - 2^2P_{\frac{3}{2}}$ is displaced by a smaller amount. Grotrian[3] has found that the second and third members of the sodium principal series are displaced to the violet. Grotrian and Ramsauer[4] studied the principal series of potassium, and found that their results agree well with a theory of Becker[5] as extended by Thomas.[6]

Ions, which are present under the more common experimental conditions used for exciting atoms, may cause a Stark effect of the lines emitted by atoms in their neighborhood. The ionic fields, in which the atom finds itself, are not homogeneous and vary with time. The net effect is to broaden the line emitted by the many atoms in different fields. This is certainly one cause for the diffuse character of certain lines. The sharp series lines, so called because of their narrowness, are emitted by transitions between two penetrating orbits, which are very slightly affected by electric fields; the diffuse series line, on the other hand, are broad because the initial non-penetrating D orbits are strongly affected by electric fields of neighboring ions. Holtzmark[7] has used such

[1] Proc. Roy. Soc., **123**, 80 (1929). The Stark effect in neon was studied also by NYQUIST, Phys. Rev., **10**, 226 (1917).

[2] Physik, Z., **22**, 549 (1921); Z. Physik, **28**, 51 (1924).

[3] Z. Physik, **49**, 541 (1928).

[4] Physik Z., **28**, 846 (1927).

[5] Z. Physik, **9**, 332 (1922).

[6] Z. Physik, **34**, 586 (1925).

[7] Ann. Physik, **58**, 577 (1919); Physik. Z., **25**, 73 (1924).

considerations in calculating the observed widths of spectral lines and obtained good agreement with experimental values, while Hulburt[1] has discussed the broadening of the Balmer lines from a similar point of view.

In the derivation of the formula for the first-order Stark effect of hydrogenic atoms in Chap. V, Sec. **12,** we found that the dynamical problem is separable in parabolic coordinates ξ, η, and that the limits of libration are secured by setting cubic expressions in ξ^2 and η^2 equal to zero, and solving these equations. Only two roots were considered, namely, those of importance when the field intensity F is small. The third root leads to significant solutions, when F is large, as in the cases considered in this section, and when the electron is on an orbit of high total quantum number. Robertson and Dewey[2] have considered the limitations of the derivation more closely and find that non-periodic orbits with negative energy can exist. Thus, no quantizable orbits exist whose energy is greater than $-\dfrac{3}{2}\left(\dfrac{eFp_\varphi}{m^{1/2}}\right)^{2/3}$ and then only, if $|p_\varphi| <$ $\dfrac{8}{9}\left(\dfrac{me^3}{(3eF)^{1/2}}\right)^{1/2}$. This means that with sufficiently large fields and angular momenta, continuous energy states with negative energy are possible. The same conclusions can be drawn in the case of non-hydrogenic atoms.

It is well known that the continuous spectra usually found on the shorter wave-length side of the series limits extend in many cases well to the long wave-length side of these limits. This continuous spectrum is due to the recombination of electrons and ions. The minimum energy available for emission is the energy of recombination of an electron and ion at rest relative to each other to form an atom in a quantized state; this energy is that of the series limit. Oldenberg[3] suggested that this extension of the continuous spectrum into the longer wave lengths might be due to a Stark effect displacement of the series limits. Robertson and Dewey show that the existence of continuous energy states with energy less than zero as required by their theory accounts for the overlapping of the continuous and discrete spectra, assuming that the Stark effect is due to neighboring ions present under the conditions of excitation. Mohler's recombination spectra, described in Chap. XIII, Sec. **6,** and illustrated by Fig. 14*B*, Chap. XIII, were taken under just such conditions and illustrate the effect very well. Sharp lines also appear along with the continuous spectrum, probably because many atoms radiate at considerable distances from ions and thus have sharply quantized energy states.

[1] *Astrophys. J.,* **55,** 399 (1922); and **59,** 177 (1924); *Phys. Rev.,* **22,** 24 (1923).

[2] *Phys. Rev.,* **31,** 973 (1928).

[3] *Z. Physik,* **41,** 1 (1927).

2. EXCEPTIONS TO SELECTION PRINCIPLES

In our study of the Stark effect (Sec. 1) we saw that the selection rule for the azimuthal number breaks down if a strong electric field is present. As pointed out above, atoms may be subjected to electric fields of other atoms or ions under the usual conditions of excitation, and therefore derivations of selection rules for isolated atoms based on the correspondence principle, which are qualitative at best, or by means of the new mechanics, may not be applicable.

As a general rule, violations of the azimuthal selection principle alone are quite frequent. Cases where Δl and Δj both take anomalous values are less often encountered but are still numerous, but violations of the rule for Δj alone are very rare and it is especially hard to produce lines for which j is zero in both the initial and final orbits.

Leaving the effect of *external* magnetic and electric fields out of account, let us discuss the exceptions which occur in ordinary spectroscopic practice. The production of forbidden lines is usually more difficult, the greater the amount by which Δl or Δj deviates from the prescribed values. In the tables there are many instances of series such as $P - P$, $S - D$, and $P - F$. There are only a few instances, however, in which it was definitely proved that the applied potential, or the fields of ions and electrons in the discharge are not responsible for or at any rate connected with the production of the lines. Foote, Meggers, and Mohler[1] observed the potassium lines $1^2S_{1/2} - 3^2D_{3/2,5/2}$ in the low voltage arc, in a space which was shielded from the applied potential of 7 volts. This observation was made at rather high currents, but the line was also found by Mohler[1] with a current density of the order of 10^{-4} amperes per cm.[2] Datta[3] obtained the first two members of this series in absorption at a vapor pressure of $2\frac{1}{2}$ mm. At this pressure, lines due to the potassium atom were very sharp, but this does not indicate that breakdown of the selection rule is not due to the fields of neighboring atoms. It is in accord with our knowledge of the effect of weak fields on atoms to assume that even in this case intermolecular fields are responsible.

In many cases, violations of the selection rule for l are necessarily accompanied by failure of the rule for j. Hansen, Takamine, and Werner[4] obtained mercury lines for which $\Delta l = 8$ in the condensed discharge. For metals of Group 2, all lines ending on P orbits for which $\Delta l \geq 4$ involve a violation of the rule for j. Fukuda, Kuyama, and Uchida[5] excited Zn and Cd lines which violate both rules by the use of heavy currents in the vacuum arc at only 30 volts.

[1] *Astrophys. J.*, **55**, 145 (1922); *Phil. Mag.*, **43**, 659 (1922).

[2] *Sci. Papers*, Bureau of Standards, **20**, 167 (1925).

[3] *Proc. Roy. Soc.*, **101**, 539 (1922).

[4] *Det Kgl. Danske Videnskabernes Selskab. Math.-fys. Meddelelser*, **5**, 3 (1923).

[5] *Sci. Papers*, Inst. Phys. Chem. Research, Tokyo, **4**, 177 (1926).

Hansen, Takamine, and Werner obtained $1^1S_0 - 2^3P_2$ of Hg in a condensed discharge, but concluded that it cannot be produced by either a homogeneous electric or magnetic field alone. This line was obtained in Zn, Cd, and Hg by Foote, Takamine, and Chenault[1] using a hot cathode arc having a low voltage gradient. Only in the case of Cd was it possible to excite $1^1S_0 - 2^3P_0$ by this method. Finally, Fukuda[2] obtained this line in both Cd and Hg by the use of a heavy condensed discharge in a Geissler tube with a narrow capillary, but was unable to excite the line in Zn except by using a high-current vacuum arc.

Wood and Gaviola[3] have shown that this line of mercury is especially intense relative to lines which are not forbidden when Hg vapor is excited with its 2,536.7 Å. line in the presence of nitrogen or water vapor. Collisions of the second kind (Chap. XIV) between nitrogen or water molecules and mercury atoms in the 2^3P_1 state are very effective in throwing the mercury atoms into the 2^3P_0 state, so that a high concentration of such atoms is secured. In this case no ions or electrons are present and the electric fields must be due to neutral atoms. It may be that transitions to the normal state occur only during collisions with other atoms. The line observed is sharp, however, so that, if such is the case, none of the energy of excitation appears as translational energy of the atoms; the Stark effect of the energy states involved would be small, because the electrons are moving in penetrating orbits.

These violations of the selection rules are only apparent violations, if the radiating atoms are in high electric fields. In such fields the azimuthal number l is no longer a quantum number, for the quantum numbers of the field-free atom must be replaced by m, n_1, and n_2 of Chap. V, Sec. **12**, and analogous numbers in the case of atoms with more than one valence electron. The selection rule is now $\Delta m = \pm 1$, or 0. The j of the field-free atom must also be replaced by a number equal to the vector sum of m and s, and it is this number which must change by ± 1 or 0, instead of j. While for convenience we have spoken as though the selection rules for l and j break down in strong fields, this is not an accurate statement of the situation. The quantum numbers of the atom have changed and the selection rules apply to the new numbers. The question is then whether or not the new rules are obeyed. In some of the experiments referred to above, high fields are present, and in these cases the violations of the rules are probably not real; but, in others, it would seem that the electric fields must be quite small and thus that true failures of the rules occur.

[1] *Phys. Rev.*, **26**, 165 (1925); see also TAKAMINE and FUKUDA, *Phys. Rev.*, **25**, 23 (1925).

[2] *Sci. Papers*, Inst. Phys. Chem. Research, Tokyo, **4**, 171 (1926).

[3] WOOD, *Phil. Mag.*, **4**, 466 (1927); WOOD and GAVIOLA, *ibid.*, **6**, 271 (1928).

Forbidden lines appear strongly in the spectra of certain nebulas, a discovery we owe to Bowen[1] and Fowler.[2] Prior to their work, many lines in nebular spectra were of unknown origin and were often ascribed to elements unknown on earth. It is certain that only light elements occur in an extremely tenuous galactic nebula. The Balmer series of hydrogen and the spectrum of helium are prominent features of many nebular spectra and lines belonging to the spark spectra of carbon, oxygen, and nitrogen are also frequently found. Bowen has found that many of these unknown lines arise from transitions between metastable states of ionized oxygen and nitrogen and their lower lying energy levels. Two strong nebular lines have the wave lengths 4,363.21 and 7,325 Å.; while the calculated wave lengths for the transitions $^1D_2 - {}^1S_0$ of O^{2+} and $^2D° - {}^2P°$ of O^{2+} are 4,362.54 and 7,326.2, respectively; the agreement is within the limits of error of the calculated values. The strong nebular lines at 5,006.84 and 4,958.91, known respectively as the N_1 and N_2 lines, have a wave number separation of 193 cm.$^{-1}$, which agrees with the separation of $^3P_1 - {}^3P_2$ of O^{2+}, namely, 192 cm.$^{-1}$. This quite certainly identifies these lines as due to the $^3P_2 - {}^1D_2$ and $^3P_1 - {}^1D_2$ transitions of this ion. Similarly, the 6,583.6 and 6,548.1 Å. nebular lines are emitted in the analogous transitions of N^+. In all these transitions the l's of the individual electrons remain unchanged, in violation of the selection principle stated in Chap. X, Sec. **3**. The $^1D_2 - {}^1S_0$ transition of O^{2+} is also a violation of the selection principle for j. On the other hand, the line due to the transition $^3P_0 - {}^1D_2$ of O^{2+} is not observed. Intercombination lines of this type are comparatively rare and weak[3] in the case of these light elements.

These lines appear in nebulas having a density of about 10^{-17} or 10^{-18} grams per cm.^{3} For an atom of oxygen or nitrogen in a gas of this density and at the probable temperatures of nebulas (10^5 to 10^6 degrees) the mean free path will be of the order of 10^3 kilometers and the mean free time 10^3 or more seconds. A metastable atom may radiate spontaneously in these long times and this accounts for the appearance of forbidden lines in nebulas. The presence of lines of unknown origin in the solar corona led to the assumption of a new element, coronium. This too will probably find its explanation in forbidden transitions of elements present in the corona.

3. FINE STRUCTURES OF SPECTRAL LINES

Shortly after Michelson constructed his interferometer, he discovered by its aid that some spectral lines have a complex structure. Since that

[1] *Nature*, **120**, 473 (1927); *Astrophys. J.*, **67**, 1 (1928).

[2] *Nature*, **120**, 617 (1927).

[3] Croze and Mihul, *Comptes Rendus*, **185**, 702 (1927); Fowler, *Nature*, **120**, 617 (1927).

time the structure of many lines has been investigated with spectroscopes of high resolving power, such as the Lummer-Gehrcke plate and the Fabry-Perot etalon. In some cases, the lines of a multiplet lie so close together that they are referred to as a single complex line. Such is the case with the line 5,876 Å. of helium, for example. However, we are concerned here with the structure of individual lines of a multiplet, which is not predicted by the theories of Chap. X, and which is often referred to as hyper-fine structure to distinguish it from multiplet structure. To illustrate the type of results which are obtained, let us consider the fine structure of the 2,537 Hg line as measured by Wood[1] and later by Macnair.[2] Earlier investigators had reported a structure which differs considerably from that recorded here, due to self-reversal of the components and false lines produced by the spectroscopes employed. It is now certain that the line consists of five components, as follows:

$$-25.6, \ -10.3, \ 0.0, \ +11.6, \text{ and } +22.1 \text{ milli-Ångströms.}$$

It is customary to use the milli-Ångström and one-thousandth of the reciprocal centimeter in dealing with fine structures.

Much of the earlier data on fine structures is untrustworthy for experimental reasons. They have been studied by Joos[3] and by Ruark and Chenault,[4] who showed that fine structures of the spectral terms are responsible for the fine structures of the lines. A *fine quantum number*, f, was introduced to distinguish the various levels of a complex spectral term, and showed that in some cases this quantum number obeys the selection rule $\Delta f = \pm 1$ or 0. Kimura[5] has analyzed a number of terms of thallium, using the data of Back[6] and of Mohammad and Mathur.[7] He was able to explain the observed pattern on the basis of the above rule, together with the restriction that transitions between levels for which $f = 0$ are forbidden. A fine-structure energy diagram for the three cadmium lines at 5,085, 4,799, and 4,678 Å. is shown in Fig. 3, taken from a paper by Macnair.[8] The phenomena of fine structures are extremely varied, and it is perhaps impossible to explain all of them

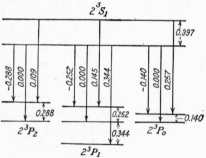

Fig. 3.—Energy diagram for fine structures of three cadmium lines.

[1] *Phil. Mag.*, **50**, 761 (1925).

[2] *Proc. Nat. Acad. Sci.*, **13**, 430 (1927).

[3] *Physik. Z.*, **26**, 380 (1925).

[4] *Phil. Mag.*, **50**, 937 (1925).

[5] *Sci. Papers*, Inst. Phys. and Chem. Research, Tokyo, **9**, 51 (1928).

[6] *Ann. Physik*, **70**, 333 (1923).

[7] *Phil. Mag.*, **5**, 1111 (1928).

[8] *Phil. Mag.*, **2**, 613 (1926).

by the use of a single principle. Nagaoka, Sugiura, and Mishima[1] suggested that the various components of a spectral line are emitted by different isotopes. It seems, however, that this is generally not the case. Fine structures are found both in elements which consist of a mixture of isotopes and those which do not. To be sure, there are changes in atomic spectra due to variations in the mass of the nucleus. Aronberg[2] showed that the wave lengths of 4,058 Å. obtained from ordinary lead and from radio lead are different by 0.0044 Å., and Merton[3] measured shifts of the same order of magnitude for 4,058 Å. and other lead lines.

Pauli[4] suggested that the origin of the fine structures may be explained by assuming that the nucleus possesses angular momentum and magnetic moment. It may be well to point out that if the angular momentum is of the order of $h/2\pi$, the magnetic moment is much smaller than one Bohr magneton. The ratio of magnetic moment to angular momentum contains the mass in the denominator and, therefore, the magnetic moment of a nucleus of mass M will be of the order of m/M Bohr magnetons, m being the mass of the electron. This assumption leads to frequency differences of the proper order of magnitude. If it is further assumed that the relative motion of the electronic and nuclear structures is a uniform precession around the vector representing the total impulse moment of the atom, a simple theory of the possible quantized states leads us to expect that complex levels will resemble tiny multiplet levels, which is sometimes true, but not always. Pauli states that these assumptions as to the origin of satellites require that in an external magnetic field they should undergo a transformation. In weak fields they should have a new and perhaps complicated Zeeman pattern, which should change, in stronger fields, into the anomalous Zeeman pattern appropriate to the spectral line in question. There are data which are in good qualitative agreement with these predictions. In particular, the Zeeman patterns of certain complex mercury lines show a behavior like that predicted above.[5] Further evidence in favor of Pauli's hypothesis has been obtained by Goudsmit and Back[6] in a study of the fine structures of bismuth lines. They conclude that the fine quantum number is to be interpreted as the resultant impulse moment of both the nucleus and the electron shells, and find the value $\dfrac{9}{2}\dfrac{h}{2\pi}$ for the moment of the bismuth nucleus. There is nothing impossible about this value, considering the high atomic number of bismuth. While Pauli's hypothesis seems

[1] *Japanese J. Phys.*, **2**, Nos. 6–10 (1923).

[2] *Astrophys. J.*, **47**, 96 (1918).

[3] *Proc. Roy. Soc.*, **96**, 388 (1920).

[4] *Naturwis.*, **12**, 741 (1927).

[5] Data of NAGAOKA and TAKAMINE, *Phil. Mag.*, **27**, 333 (1914) and **29**, 241 (1915); analyzed by RUARK, *Phil. Mag.*, **51**, 977 (1925).

[6] *Z. Physik*, **43**, 321 (1927).

likely to be of very general application, it may not be amiss to point out some of the difficulties which confront it. Fine structures are quite capricious in their occurrence, and analogous elements do not have similar fine structures. Copper and silver, cadmium and mercury offer good illustrations. Further, we should anticipate that different isotopes of an element would have different nuclear moments, and therefore would have different fine structures. Data which bear on this point are few in number. Jenkins[1] compared the spectra of ordinary Hg and Cl with those of samples in which certain isotopes were enriched. In the case of mercury, the proportions of isotopes 198 and 204 in these samples differed by about 20 and 27 per cent from their normal values, respectively. No wave-length shifts greater than $3 \cdot 10^{-4}$ A. were observed in the lines 5,461, 4,358, 4,078 and 4,047 Å.; and the relative intensities of the satellites were visually identical. In the case of chlorine the two specimens differed by 0.097 atomic-weight units, and distinct evidence of wave-length shifts was obtained. The chlorine lines examined probably have no satellites.

With few exceptions, elements which have abundant fine structures lie in those parts of the periodic table in which either the valence shell or the next underlying shell is well on its way to completion. It is worthy of note that nearly one-fifth of the lines of lanthanum have fine structures, which have been studied by Meggers and Burns.[2]

4. THE POLARIZATION OF RESONANCE RADIATION

Wood and Ellett[3] observed that the resonance radiation of mercury and sodium is polarized, and that this polarization is related to the plane of polarization of the exciting light and is changed by a magnetic field. Figures 4 and 5 show the experimental results of Wood and Ellett,[4] except that the angle of 54° for zero polarization in Fig. 5 is that obtained by Hanle[5] and by Ellett in his later work, instead of 45° originally reported by the former authors. The incident light comes from the left in the direction of the X-axis; its electric vector is shown by arrows. The direction of the magnetic field H is indicated by an arrow and the polarization of the light observed along the axes is shown by crossed double-headed arrows which are not drawn to scale, and by the percentage of polarization. This is defined as

$$P = 100\frac{I_p - I_s}{I_p + I_s},$$ (1)

[1] *Nature*, **117**, 893 (1926); *Phys. Rev.*, **29**, 50 (1927).
[2] *J. O. S. A.*, **14**, 449 (1927).
[3] *Phys. Rev.*, **24**, 243 (1924).
[4] WOOD and ELLETT, *loc. cit.*; ELLETT, *J. O. S. A.*, **10**, 427 (1925).
[5] *Z. Physik*, **30**, 93 (1924).

where I_p and I_s are the intensities of the components parallel and perpendicular to the magnetic field respectively, or, in the absence of the field, of the two components referred to the axes as shown.   This polarization changes in most cases with the field intensity and the recorded values are the maximum polarizations observed.   In the case of the mercury 2,536.7 Å. line the maximum is reached at a few gauss, and

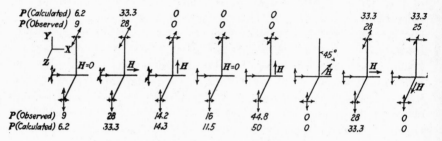

FIG. 4.—Polarization of Resonance Radiation of Sodium.

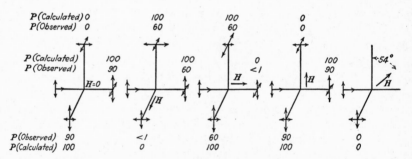

FIG. 5.—Polarization of Resonance Radiation of Mercury.

in the case of the sodium D lines at 60 gauss; higher fields do not change the polarization.   The experimental errors are fairly large and within the limits of these errors the results of Wood and Ellett are in substantial agreement with other work by Hanle and by Gaviola and Pringsheim.[1]

The theory of this effect was developed by Breit,[2] Pringsheim,[3] Joos,[4] Gaviola and Pringsheim (*loc. cit.*) and Van Vleck,[5] following

[1] *Z. Physik*, **24**, 24 (1924).

[2] *Phil. Mag.*, **47**, 832 (1924).

[3] *Naturwis.*, **12**, 247 (1924); *Z. Physik*, **23**, 324 (1924).

[4] *Physik. Z.*, **2ℂ**, 130, 298, 400 (1924).

[5] *Proc. Nat. Acad. Sci.*, **11**, 612 (1925).   Van Vleck has applied more recent intensity rules for the Zeeman components of the two D-lines to the previous calculations and it is largely his numerical results that are quoted here.

somewhat the suggestions of Foote, Ruark, and Mohler[1] and Hanle.[2] Since most of the observations have been made for the cases in which the magnetic field is zero or lies in the plane defined by the electric vector and the direction of the incident light, *i.e.*, the XY plane (Fig. 4), we shall develop the theory for this case only. The other cases are handled quite simply by similar methods.

Let the angle between the direction of the electric vector and that of the magnetic field be θ. The magnetic field is assumed to be sufficiently intense to orient the atoms and to split the lines into parallel and perpendicular Zeeman components, but it must not be sufficiently intense to change the energy levels to such an extent that the outside Zeeman components fail to fall within the band of frequencies covered by the exciting line. The probability of absorption of linearly polarized light by a parallel Zeeman component is proportional to the square of the electric vector component parallel to the direction of the magnetic field, that is $E^2 \cos^2 \theta$, where E is the electric intensity of the light. The "corresponding" circular oscillator which absorbs a perpendicular component can be resolved into two linear oscillators at right angles to each other as shown in Fig. 6. The one oscillator is perpendicular to E and, therefore, the prob-

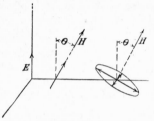

Fig. 6.

ability for the absorption of the linear light by this component is zero; the probability of absorption by the other is proportional to $E^2 \sin^2 \theta$.

It is necessary to consider the relative probability of absorption by the corresponding linear and circular oscillators. The so-called principle of spectroscopic stability is a statement of the experimental fact that the percentage of polarization and the total intensity of the light emitted by a gas *excited isotropically* or absorbed by a gas do not change when a magnetic field is applied. With isotropic excitation the sums of the intensities of the parallel components and of the circular components viewed perpendicular to the field must be equal and the sum of the intensities of all components when viewed perpendicular to the field must be equal to the sum of the intensities of the circular components viewed parallel to the field. This requires that the intensity of the circular components viewed parallel to the field must be twice that of the same components viewed perpendicular to the field. Integration of the intensities over all directions in space shows that the total energy emitted by the circular components in all directions is twice the energy emitted by the parallel components in all directions so that the sum of all the probabilities of spontaneous transition for the circular

[1] *J. O. S. A.*, **7**, 415 (1923).

[2] *Naturwis.*, **11**, 690 (1923).

components must be twice the same sum for the parallel components. Obviously, the same relations must hold for the probabilities of absorption of unpolarized light.[1]

Let A_i and a_i be the probabilities of spontaneous emission in all directions in transitions from the ith excited Zeeman level for the perpendicular and parallel components, respectively. There is at most only one such perpendicular component and one such parallel component in the cases we are considering. Then, because of the requirements of spectroscopic stability just considered, the probabilities of absorption of unpolarized light from a direction perpendicular to the field, by the ith parallel and perpendicular components are a_i and $\frac{1}{2}A_i$, respectively, and taking account of the factors $\cos^2 \theta$ and $\sin^2 \theta$ arising from the use of plane polarized light with angle θ between the electric vector and the magnetic field, the probability of exciting the ith level is proportional to

$$E^2 a_i \cos^2 \theta + \frac{1}{2}E^2 A_i \sin^2 \theta. \tag{2}$$

To see how the polarization of the emitted light may be obtained, we shall consider a representative case. The magnetic energy levels of the $1^2S_{\frac{1}{2}} - 2^2P_{\frac{1}{2},\frac{3}{2}}$ transitions of sodium are as given in Fig. 7. The relative probabilities of emission A or a, and the relative intensities I of the various Zeeman lines when viewed in a direction perpendicular to the magnetic field are indicated beneath the diagrams (Chap. XX). Substituting the values of A_i and a_i in expression (2), we get the probability of exciting an atom to the ith state. If the $^2P_{\frac{3}{2}}$ states with $m = \pm\frac{3}{2}$ are excited, the atom can return to a lower level by one transition only, but in the case of all other excited levels there are two such transitions. To secure the resultant probability of the return to a lower level by one route, we divide the emission probability (either A_i or a_i) by $A_i + a_i$, and multiply by the probability of excitation of the higher level. In the case of perpendicular components we must multiply by $\frac{1}{2}$ to get the intensity as compared to the parallel components, for the reasons

---

[1] The requirements of the principle of spectroscopic stability are readily derived for the case of classical linear oscillators. Three linear oscillators of unit amplitude oriented parallel to the X-, Y-, and Z-axes, respectively will emit unpolarized light with equal intensity in all directions. In the presence of a magnetic field parallel to the Z-axis, the motion of the three oscillators will be changed as follows: (1) the linear oscillator parallel to the field will be unchanged; (2) each of the other two oscillators will be split into right and left circularly polarized components of amplitude $\frac{1}{2}$. The total emission of the linear component is proportional to 1^2 and the intensity of light emitted by this component perpendicular to the Z direction is also proportional to 1^2. Each circular oscillator may be resolved into two linear oscillators with amplitude $\frac{1}{2}$, and the emission of each of these is proportional to $(\frac{1}{2})^2$, making the total intensity due to all circular components proportional to 2. Similarly, the intensity of each circular component viewed perpendicular to the field is proportional to $\frac{1}{2}$, and the intensity of each circular component viewed parallel to the field is proportional to 1. Thus the requirements of spectroscopic stability are met.

given in the preceding paragraph.   The intensities of the light due to all transitions polarized parallel and perpendicular to the field are, therefore,

$$I_p \propto \frac{a_i}{A_i + a_i}(a_i \cos^2 \theta + \frac{1}{2}A_i \sin^2 \theta)E^2,$$

$$I_s \propto \frac{1}{2}\frac{A_i}{A_i + a_i}(a_i \cos^2 \theta + \frac{1}{2}A_i \sin^2 \theta)E^2. \tag{3}$$

The percentage of polarization secured by substituting the numerical values of the A_i's and a_i's and simplifying is

$$P = 100\frac{I_p - I_s}{I_p + I_s} = \frac{3\cos^2\theta - 1}{3 + \cos^2\theta}. \tag{4}$$

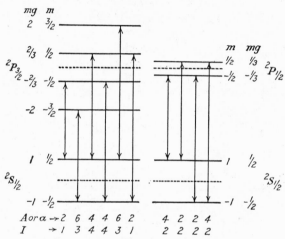

FIG. 7.—Magnetic energy levels of sodium.

This is the polarization at all azimuths in the plane perpendicular to the direction of H.   The angle for zero polarization is secured by setting this expression equal to zero.   This gives

$$\cos^2 \theta = \tfrac{1}{3}, \ \theta = 54.7°.$$

The polarizations calculated from this formula for the cases for which it applies are given in Fig. 4.   The calculation for the case when H is perpendicular to E and to the direction of illumination is made by exactly similar methods, with the results given in the figure.   In this case the parallel components are not absorbed.   The calculation for the case of zero field has been made by using an assumption due to Breit, namely, by calculating the average effect of magnetic fields oriented at random. The value for the case of unpolarized light is obtained by combining the results for two beams linearly polarized at right angles to each other.

The agreement between calculated and observed values is quite close, but not exact, and seems to be outside the experimental limits of error.   All known sources of error cause depolarization.   Such is the effect, for example, of foreign gas, and of divergence of the exciting and the excited beams. In fact, the observed values are all too small, except that determined in zero magnetic field.

The 2,536.7 Å. resonance radiation of mercury is almost completely polarized in the absence of a magnetic field and it may safely be assumed that the deviation from complete polarization is due to unavoidable experimental difficulties. The polarization does not change when a field is applied parallel to the electric vector of the exciting light; this is in marked contrast to the behavior of sodium. This line is split by a magnetic field into two perpendicular components and one parallel component. The levels are given in Fig. 8. If the field is in the direction of the electric vector only the parallel component is excited, the atoms are raised only to the upper magnetic level $m = 0$, and only the parallel

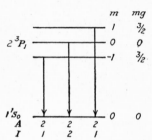

FIG. 8.—Magnetic levels for λ2537 of Mercury.

component should be emitted; that is, the light emitted should be completely polarized parallel to the field, in good agreement with the observed value of 90 per cent. If the field is parallel to the direction of the exciting beam, or perpendicular to both this direction and the electric vector, only the perpendicular components should be excited and emitted and the light should be unpolarized when viewed along the field. This is in agreement with experiment. Further it should be completely polarized perpendicular to the field when viewed perpendicular to the field, but the observed percentage of polarization is only 60 per cent. The semi-classical method of calculating the polarization in the absence of the field used in the case of sodium resonance does not agree with the observed value of 90 per cent. Heisenberg[1] suggested that the polarization should not change when a magnetic field is applied parallel to the electric vector of the exciting light. This appears to be correct in the case of the mercury 2,536.7 Å. line, but not for the D-lines of sodium. The depolarization angle for mercury should be 54.7°, as in the case of the sodium D-lines, while Hanle obtained 54°.

A weak magnetic field perpendicular to the electric vector and the direction of the illuminating beam might be expected at first sight to destroy the polarization of the (unresolved) light observed along the field, for with this arrangement we are dealing with the longitudinal Zeeman effect. However, this is not the case. The polarization measured relative to two axes parallel to the electric vector and the direction of the incident beam, respectively, decreases with increasing field. The explanation is as follows. The number of atoms of mercury in the 2^3P_1 state which radiate during the time t to $t + dt$ after excitation is

$$dN = -AN dt = -AN_0 e^{-At} dt,$$

[1] Z. Physik, **31**, 617 (1925).

and during the time t a linear oscillator attached to such an atom will be rotated by the field through an angle

$$\varphi = 2\pi gLt,$$

where g is Landé's splitting factor and L the frequency of the Larmor precession.

The intensities of the components along the two axes parallel and perpendicular to the electric vector of the incident light contributed by atoms radiating in the time dt are,

$$dI_y = h\nu AN_0 e^{-At} \cos^2 (2\pi gLt)dt, \; dI_x = h\nu AN_0 e^{-At} \sin^2 (2\pi gLt)dt.$$

The percentage of polarization is

$$P = \frac{\displaystyle\int_{t=0}^{\infty} dI_y - \int_{t=0}^{\infty} dI_x}{\displaystyle\int_{t=0}^{\infty} dI_y + \int_{=0}^{\infty} dI_x} 100 = \frac{100}{1 + \left(\dfrac{4\pi gL}{A}\right)^2}. \tag{5}$$

The integrals are extended from $t = 0$ to $t = \infty$ since at any instant we are observing the effect of all atoms previously excited. However, the plane of maximum polarization is displaced about the axis of the magnetic field in the direction of the Larmor precession. The angle Φ between the plane of maximum polarization in the presence of the field and that in its absence varies with the field according to the equation

$$\tan 2\Phi = \frac{4\pi gL}{A} \tag{6a}$$

and the percentage of polarization measured relative to axes parallel and perpendicular to the direction of maximum polarization is,

$$P^2 = \frac{P_0^2}{1 + \left(\dfrac{4\pi gL}{A}\right)^2}, \tag{6b}$$

where P_0 is the per cent polarization with zero field.[1] These formulas show that $\Phi = 45°$ and $P = 0$ at $H = \infty$.

Equations (6a) and (6b) can be derived in the following way. Let the angle $\varphi(= 2\pi gLt)$ be the angle between the direction of polarization in the absence of the field and the direction of polarization of the light emitted by atoms emitting in the time t to $t + dt$ and let Φ be the angle defining the direction of maximum polarization (as yet unknown). Then the components parallel and perpendicular to the direction of Φ are,

$$I_\parallel = \int_{t=0}^{\infty} h\nu AN_0 e^{-At} \cos^2 (\Phi - \varphi)dt, \; I_\perp = \int_{t=0}^{\infty} h\nu AN_0 e^{-At} \sin^2 (\Phi - \varphi)dt.$$

Then,

$$P = \frac{(I_\parallel - I_\perp)100}{I_\parallel + I_\perp} = \frac{a}{a^2 + 4} (a \cos 2\Phi + 2 \sin 2\Phi)100 \tag{6b'}$$

[1] For the relations given here see Eldridge, *Phys. Rev.*, **24**, 234 (1924); Breit, *J. O. S. A.*, **10**, 439 and **11**, 465 (1925); and v. Keussler, *Phys. Zeit.*, **27**, 313 (1926).

where $a = A/2\pi gL$. By taking $\partial P/\partial \Phi$ and setting this equal to zero, we secure a value for Φ which makes P a maximum and this gives $(6a)$. Substitution of $(6a)$ into $(6b')$ gives $(6b)$ with the factor $P_0 = 100$. In order to secure $(6b)$ for any value of P_0 it is necessary to consider the contribution to $I_\parallel$ and $I_\perp$ by other oscillators at right angles to the one considered, which must be present if P_0 is not 100.

5. THE RAMAN EFFECT

It has been known for many years that light is scattered without change of wave length by small particles suspended in a gas or liquid; this phenomenon is the so-called "Tyndall effect." The fraction of the incident light which is scattered decreases rapidly with decreasing radius of the particle; the fraction is small in the case of molecules, but is still observable and constitutes a "molecular" Tyndall effect. The scattered light is highly polarized perpendicular to the direction of the primary beam and is coherent. Its intensity varies as the inverse fourth power of the wave length, so that shorter wave lengths are scattered with much greater intensity than long wave lengths. Rayleigh first recognized that molecular scattering is the cause of diffuse daylight and that the greater scattering in the shorter wave lengths causes the blue color of the sky. Kramers,[1] in connection with his quantum theory of dispersion, predicted that the displaced frequencies, $\nu_0 \pm \nu_i$, should appear in the scattered light in addition to the incident frequency, ν_0; here ν_i represents one of the characteristic frequencies absorbed or emitted by the molecule. Smekal[2] extended the argument of Compton and Epstein (Chap. III, Sec. **16**) in regard to collisions between atoms or molecules and light quanta to include possible changes in the internal quantized energy. He suggested that the incident quantum might give up part of its energy to increase the internal energy, the remainder being scattered as a quantum of lower energy and therefore of lower frequency, or that energy might be added to the incident quantum and the scattered quantum might have a correspondingly greater energy and higher frequency.

Raman[3] observed that such displaced frequencies do appear in scattered light. He found that this effect is shown by many liquids, by the gases CO_2 and N_2O under high pressure, and by transparent solids. The effect in the case of solids was discovered independently by Landsberg and Mandelstamm.[4] This displaced radiation resembles the undisplaced radiation in several important respects. Its intensity follows the intensity of the undisplaced radiation rather closely in its

[1] *Nature*, **113**, 673 (1924); also KRAMERS and HEISENBERG, *Nature*, **114**, 310 (1924).

[2] *Naturwis.*, **11**, 873 (1923).

[3] *Indian Journal of Physics*, **2**, 1 (1928). Discovered Feb. 28, 1928.

[4] *Naturwis.*, **28**, 557 (1928).

dependence on the wave length of the incident light. Some of the displaced lines are more highly polarized than the Tyndall scattering, but others are only slightly polarized.

Raman and Krishnan[1] and other investigators have studied the spectrum of the scattered light. The principal experimental difficulties are due to the very low intensity of the displaced light. The spectra contain the undisplaced lines of the incident light, new lines displaced mostly to the long wave-length side and also weaker lines displaced to shorter wave lengths. These lines are often referred to as the "Stokes and anti-Stokes lines," in analogy to similar lines in fluorescent spectra. Figure 9 is a reproduction of a photograph by Raman showing the spectrum of the light of the mercury arc scattered by carbon tetrachloride. The pattern is particularly clear in the neighborhood of the 4,358 Å. line.

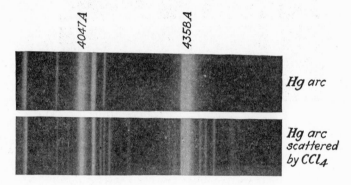

FIG. 9.—Raman spectrum of CCl₄.   (*After Raman.*)

(There is a weaker line of the mercury arc at 4,347 Å. whose Raman lines are so much fainter than those due to the 4,358 Å. line that they are not observed.) There are four lines on either side of this line, those on the long wave-length side being decidedly more intense than those on the short wave-length side. The latter decrease in intensity as we go farther from the 4,358 Å. line and in fact the fourth line is barely visible on the original. The displaced lines are usually quite sharp. Wood[2] has found that some of the displaced lines of benzene are only twice as broad as the exciting line. In other cases, the displaced lines are very broad. Figure 10 (also after Raman) shows such an effect in the case of water.

Each line of the exciting spectrum is accompanied in the scattered spectrum by its own group of Raman lines and if the exciting spectrum contains many lines, the scattered spectrum is so complex that it is difficult to correlate the Raman lines with the correct exciting line.

[1] *Indian Journal of Physics,* **2,** 399 (1928).

[2] Private communication.

Wood[1] has devised a method of excitation in which only the 3,888 Å. line of helium is effective. A tube containing the scattering liquid is surrounded by a tube of nickel-oxide glass and then by a coiled helium discharge tube. The glass transmits only the 3,888 Å. line and a few very weak lines in its neighborhood and the Raman lines observed are due to 3,888 alone. Figure 11 is a reproduction of the spectrum of

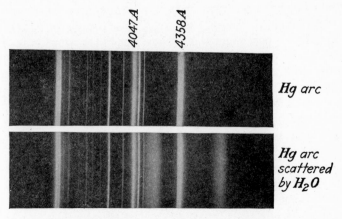

FIG. 10.—Raman spectrum of water. (*After Raman.*)

benzene secured in this way, using a high dispersion spectrograph and quite narrow slits. It will be noted that the spectrum is very simple and that the fainter displaced lines are very narrow.

The phenomenological explanation of the Raman effect is that given by Smekal. The lines displaced toward longer wave lengths are due to quanta which have made inelastic collisions of the first kind with the molecules, while those displaced to the shorter wave lengths have

FIG. 11.—Raman spectrum of benzene excited by He 3888. (*After Wood.*)

made collisions of the second kind with excited molecules, so that their energy has been added to that of the incident quantum; and, finally, the undisplaced line is due to quanta which have made elastic collisions. The Raman effect presents another good example of similarity between the behavior of light quanta and electrons (Chap. XXI). At ordinary temperatures only a small fraction of the molecules will possess energy associated with any degree of freedom for which the energy steps are

[1] Private communication.

more than a few times the mean thermal energy; thus, the anti-Stokes lines are less intense than the corresponding Stokes lines. For Stokes lines of about the same intensity, the intensity of the corresponding anti-Stokes lines decreases as the frequency difference between these lines and the exciting line increases. This is in agreement with observation, as shown by Fig. 9.[1]

A comparison of the wave lengths of infra-red bands, calculated from the Raman displacements and observed in the infra-red, brings out some very striking facts. With few exceptions, the displaced Raman lines correspond to observed infra-red bands, but there seems to be little or no correlation between the. relative intensities of the displaced lines and the intensities of the corresponding infra-red absorption bands. Thus benzene has a very strong absorption band at 9.75μ, toluene one at 6.86μ, and chlorbenzene at 6.77μ, while Pringsheim finds no evidence for any scattered lines displaced by the corresponding frequencies. Moreover, the most intense Raman lines of these substances are displaced by frequencies corresponding to the 10.3, 10.2, and 10.0μ infra-red bands, respectively, and these are not the strongest infra-red bands of these substances. Pringsheim has further observed that cases in which the vibrational energy changes by $2\nu_i, 3\nu_i, \ldots$, are very rare.

Langer[2] and Rasetti[3] have given the following explanation of such peculiarities. Let ν be the frequency of the incident light, and let ν_{kl} be the frequency corresponding to a transition of the scattering molecule from state k to state l. Further, let A_{kn} and A_{ln} be the amplitudes corresponding to the intensities of the lines emitted in jumps from k to n, and from l to n, respectively. Then it is a consequence of wave mechanics that the intensity of the Raman lines $\nu \pm \nu_{kl}$ is proportional to a sum of terms of the type

$$A_{kn}A_{ln}\left[\frac{1}{\nu_{kn} \pm \nu} + \frac{1}{\nu_{ln} \mp \nu}\right](\nu_{kl} \pm \nu)^2.$$

Thus, the Raman lines $\nu \pm \nu_{kl}$ will appear only when we can find at least one level n such that both A_{kn} and A_{ln} are different from zero; that is, when there is at least one level with which both k and l can combine.

These considerations show that we may have a Raman shift corresponding to an infra-red transition forbidden by the selection rules, so that we have the possibility of getting energy levels of molecules which cannot be detected in other ways. Langer has analyzed his data on the Raman effect in CCl_4 from this point of view and finds excellent agreement.

---

[1] See also PRINGSHEIM, *Z. Physik*, **50,** 741 (1928).

[2] *Nature*, **123,** 345 (1929).

[3] *Proc. Nat. Acad. Sci.* **15,** 234 (1929).

Rasetti[1] has secured the displaced mercury lines scattered by CO and CO_2 at atmospheric pressure. CO gives a line displaced by the frequency of its infra-red band, while CO_2 does not. Instead, the observed Raman line of CO_2 is displaced by the difference in frequency of two infra-red bands. McLennan and McLeod have secured Raman lines from liquid oxygen, nitrogen, and hydrogen. The observed changes in frequency correspond to changes in the vibration quantum number from 0 to 1 and from 0 to 2 in the case of oxygen and nitrogen, and from 0 to 1 in the case of hydrogen. In addition, changes in frequency corresponding to changes in the rotational quantum number from 0 to 2 and 1 to 3 are observed in the case of hydrogen. None of the corresponding infra-red bands have been observed and in fact these transitions are violations of the selection rules for band spectra.

Ramdas[2] has found that the Raman effect is less intense in gaseous CO_2 than in liquid CO_2 at the same density, that is, near the critical temperature, and he succeeded in getting the effect in ether vapor. Wood[3] has observed a displaced line corresponding to the 3.46 μ band of HCl, by illuminating this gas at one atmosphere pressure by an intense mercury arc. The Raman line is very sharp, and is displaced slightly less toward the red from the exciting line than would be expected for a line at the middle of this band. It appears that the Q branch of this band is excited; this is the group of lines for which the vibrational quantum number changes from 0 to 1 and the rotational quantum number does not change. Using formulas which will be developed in Chap. XII, the frequencies of these lines can be calculated; the line corresponding to a transition from the rotational state present in largest numbers at ordinary temperatures should have a wave number about 3.5 cm.$^{-1}$ less than that of the middle of the band, which agrees with Wood's observation. As we shall see in Chap. XII, this Q branch is not observed in the infra-red.

It is important to consider whether the displaced radiation is coherent or incoherent. Brickwedde and Peters[4] have shown that it is incoherent in the case of scattering from quartz by studying the variation of intensity of the displaced lines as a function of the temperature. Undisplaced radiation scattered by crystals at low temperatures is very weak, because it is destroyed (except in the direction of the original beam) by interference between wave trains from the regularly arranged atoms of the crystal; its intensity increases with the absolute temperature because of the increased irregularity in the crystal.

[1] Nature, **123**, 205 (1928).

[2] Indian Journal of Physics, **3**, 131 (1928).

[3] Private communication.

[4] Private communication of work done in the cryogenic laboratory of the Bureau of Standards.

For an incoherent scattering, in which there is no phase relationship between the light scattered by different particles, local variations in density of the crystal would have no effect upon the intensity of the scattered light. Thus we have an experimental test for determining whether the modified scattering is coherent or incoherent. Figure 12 is a spectrogram obtained by Brickwedde and Peters, showing Raman lines of quartz excited by 2,537 of mercury, which is greatly overexposed. These lines, marked $S21\mu$ and $A21\mu$, are shifted by a frequency corresponding to an absorption band at 21.5μ. The figure shows the large increase in the intensity of the anti-Stokes line in going from 55 to 525°C. The Stokes line, however, decreases slightly in intensity with rising

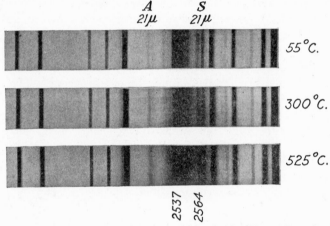

FIG. 12.—Raman spectra of quartz. (*After Brickwedde and Peters.*)

temperatures. The intensities of the mercury lines increase with rising temperatures because they come from the Tyndall scattering. Comparing the intensities of the Stokes line $S21$ and the mercury line 2,564, it will be seen that at 55°C, $S21$ is more intense than the mercury line 2,564; at 300°C. they are of about equal intensity, and at 525°C., the mercury line 2,564 is more intense than $S21$. The temperature variation of the Raman scattering in crystalline media is, therefore, different from that of the Tyndall scattering which increases as the absolute temperature. The results obtained are in qualitative agreement with the explanation that the intensities of these Raman lines vary as the density of population of the initial states which give rise to them, the density of population varying with temperature in accordance with the Boltzmann distribution law. If the Raman scattering were coherent, the intensity of the Stokes line $S21$ should increase with temperature and it should be more intense than 2,564 at 525°C.

There is the further question of a possible time lag in the scattering process, though it seems doubtful if there is any lag of the order of that observed in fluorescence ($10^{-8} - 10^{-9}$ seconds).[1] It seems more likely that the cause of the incoherence lies in the random phases of the scattering molecules,[2] *i.e.*, at the same time that the energy changes there is a random change of phase.

6. DISPLACED X RADIATION

Davis and Mitchell[3] discovered that scattered X radiation may be displaced toward longer wave lengths in a way similar to the Raman effect for ordinary light; this was made independently of Raman's discovery and almost simultaneously with it. They studied the Mo $K\alpha_1$, α_2 radiation, scattered from metallic beryllium and aluminium, and from graphite, with the double X-ray spectrometer developed by Davis and Purks.[4] In addition to the undisplaced $K\alpha_1$ and $K\alpha_2$ lines, the latter being very weak, they found lines which were displaced toward longer wave lengths by amounts to be expected, if part of the energy of the incident quantum of $K\alpha_1$ was used to ionize the K shell of the atom and the remainder scattered as a quantum of less energy.   The displaced lines are very narrow so that the electron removed from the atom must receive only a small kinetic energy, or always the same kinetic energy. The agreement between the values for K-energy levels secured from the change in frequency of the scattered light and from other measurements is especially good.

If no kinetic energy is given to the electron, the shift in wave length will be

$$\Delta\lambda = \frac{\lambda^2}{(\lambda_K - \lambda)},\tag{7}$$

where λ is the wave length of Mo $K\alpha_1$ and λ_K is the wave length of the K-absorption limit of the scattering element.   In the case of carbon and aluminium the observed displacements in wave length and those calculated from equation (7) are:

	C	Al
$\Delta\lambda$(calculated)	0.0117 A.	0.069 Å.
$\Delta\lambda$(observed)	0.0113 $\pm$ 0.00015 Å.	0.069 $\pm$ 0.002 Å.

The agreement is so good that there can be little doubt that the interpretation is correct.   They have also observed lines displaced by smaller distances and the energy lost by the quantum is of the order of magnitude of the L-absorption limits of these atoms, though we cannot make an

---

[1] RUARK, *Nature*, **122**, 312 (1928); GAVIOLA, *Z. Physik*, **42**, 862 (1927).

[2] PRINGSHEIM, *Naturwis.*, **16**, 44 (1928).

[3] *Phys. Rev.* **31**, 119 (1928); **32**, 331 (1928).   The discovery was made on Mar. 9, 1928.   The authors are indebted to Mr. Mitchell for the privilege of seeing another manuscript before going to press.

[4] *Proc. Nat. Acad. Sci.*, **13**, 419 (1927); **14**, 172 (1928).

exact comparison because the *L*-absorption limits for the solids under consideration are not known with sufficient precision.

In the case of beryllium, a line is observed displaced toward shorter wave lengths by an amount to be expected if the energy of the quantum is increased by 16 volts. The ionizing potential of gaseous beryllium is about 8 volts. Considering our uncertain knowledge of the binding of outer electrons in metallic beryllium, it may be that the 16 volts is the energy liberated when an electron falls into the outer shell of beryllium. This would be the X-ray effect analogous to the anti-Stokes Raman effect. Due to the small number of ionized atoms which should be present, this explanation cannot be accepted with confidence.

REFERENCES

Joos, G., "Ergebnisse und Anwendungen der Spektroskopie," and "Ramaneffekt," Wien-Harms Handbuch der Physik, Vol. 22, Akademische Verlagsgesellschaft, Leipzig (1926).

CHAPTER XII

MOLECULAR SPECTRA

Molecular spectra are rivaled in complexity and number of lines only by the most complex atomic spectra. Under low dispersion they appear as continuous bands, and for this reason they are often called "band spectra." Usually a band has a sharp intense edge or head on one side, and gradually decreases in intensity toward the other side. Under higher dispersion a band can usually be resolved into groups of monochromatic lines, well ordered according to fairly simple laws. Near the intense head of the band these lines are close together and in some instances, they overlap completely, forming a continuum. As they recede from the band head, the lines become more widely separated and also weaker. The names, band and line spectra used to distinguish molecular and atomic spectra are therefore not distinctive, since both types are in reality composed of monochromatic lines having approximately the same width. Figure 1a and 1b show the emission bands of the NO and CN molecules under low and high dispersion, which may be compared with the atomic spectra of Figs. 1 and 13, Chap. VII.

In point of experimental methods and theoretical significance, molecular spectra fall into three groups according as they lie in the far infra-red $(20 - 150\mu$, let us say), in the near infra-red, or in the visible or ultra-violet regions. The first two groups are simple in structure and theory, and their study leads naturally to an understanding of the more complex and extensive visible spectra. Therefore, we take them up in the order in which they are named. Anticipating the experimental evidence, these three types of bands are correlated respectively with (1) changes in the rotational energy; (2) simultaneous changes of the rotational and vibrational energy; and (3) simultaneous changes in the rotational, vibrational, and electronic energy of the molecule. Most of the data and theoretical considerations available at present deal with diatomic molecules, which therefore take up the major part of the discussion in this chapter.

Under heading A, dealing with infra-red rotation and rotation-vibration spectra, all the molecules discussed are of the HCl type, and have closed electron shells like those of the inert gases. The simple theories developed for them must be modified when we consider molecules whose electron shells have a resultant electronic angular momentum, under heading B. Further modifications in the theory of rotational

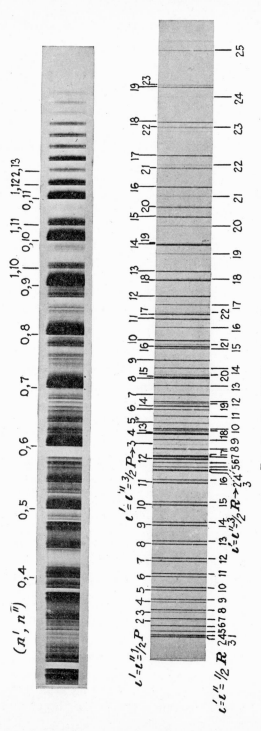

Fig. 1a.—The β NO bands. (*After Jenkins.*)

The upper figure shows the band system under low dispersion. The (0, 7) band is shown below in the second order of a 21-foot grating. The numbers given are equal to j″ +½. Short Q branches are present but are too weak to show in the reproduction.

bands are necessary in the case of polyatomic molecules, discussed under heading *C*.

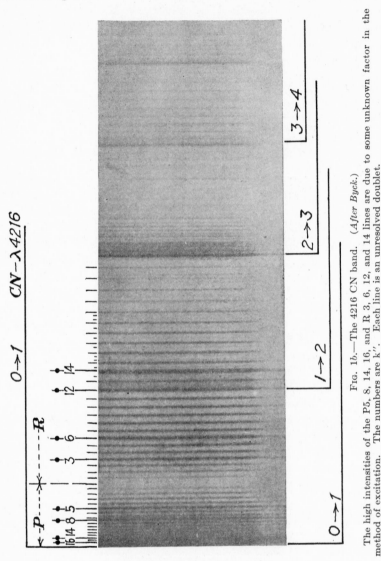

Fig. 1b.—The 4216 CN band. (*After Byck.*)

The high intensities of the P5, 8, 14, 16, and R 3, 6, 12, and 14 lines are due to some unknown factor in the method of excitation. The numbers are k″. Each line is an unresolved doublet.

A. Infra-red Spectra

1. ROTATION SPECTRA

The far infra-red spectra are known only in absorption, and only for the molecules HCl, HBr, HI, HF, H_2O, and NH_3 have they been studied in any detail. The H_2O lines have been only imperfectly resolved and the classification is uncertain.[1] Recently, Badger[2] has observed six absorption lines of NH_3 which follow a simple formula. We cannot obtain much information about the structure of such a complex molecule from this spectrum because it must be incomplete (Sec. **24**). The absorption spectra of the hydrogen halides have been investigated by Czerny[3] who finds a number of lines in the region from 40 to 130μ. For each molecule these lines are nearly equally spaced in the frequency scale and can be represented by the formulas

HF; $\bar{\nu} = 41.086M - 0.011879M^3$, $M = 2, 4, 5$,
HCl; $\bar{\nu} = 20.8411M - 0.001814M^3$, $M = 4, 6, 7, 8, 9, 10, 11$,
HBr; $\bar{\nu} = 16.7092M - 0.001457M^3$, $M = 5, 6, 7, 10, 11, 12, 13, 14$,
HI; $\bar{\nu} = 12.840M - 0.000820M^3$, $M = 6, 7, 8, 9$.   (1)

Lines of greater wave length are to be expected with wave numbers given by substituting M values beginning with 1 in these formulas, but the region in which they would lie has not been investigated by spectroscopic methods. The wave number for $M = 1$ for HCl would be 20.84 and the corresponding wave length would be 480μ or about 0.5 mm. Radiations having approximately this wave length have been produced electrically by Nichols and Tear,[4] who analyzed them with an inteferometer arrangement, but such methods have not yet been applied to the study of absorption spectra. A plot of wave numbers observed by Czerny for HCl is shown in Fig. 4.

Long before this work was done, much evidence had accumulated indicating that there should be infra-red spectra due entirely to changes in the rotational energy of molecules. The most conclusive evidence that Czerny's bands arise in this way comes from the detailed study of the near infra-red bands, to be described in Sec. **3**. The quantum theory of the rotating molecule, which will now be given, together with the Bohr frequency condition, gives an exact explanation of the structure of the far infra-red spectra.

2. THE THEORY OF THE ROTATING DIATOMIC MOLECULE

The energy of a rotating rigid diatomic molecule may be considered entirely kinetic as a first approximation. Using plane polar coordinates, the energy is

$$E = T = \frac{1}{2}\mu r^2 \dot{\varphi}^2 = \frac{p_\varphi^2}{2\mu r^2},\qquad(2)$$

[1] SLEATOR and PHELPS, *Astrophys. J.*, **62**, 28 (1925).
[2] *Nature*, **121**, 942 (1928).
[3] *Z. Physik*, **34**, 227 (1925); **44**, 235 (1927); **45**, 476 (1927).
[4] *Phys. Rev.*, **21**, 587 (1923).

where r is the distance between the nuclei and μ the reduced mass. Applying the quantum condition

$$\int^{2\pi} p_\varphi d\varphi = 2\pi p_\varphi = jh, \, j = 0, 1, \, \cdots \tag{3}$$

we have, if I is the moment of inertia,

$$E_j = \frac{j^2 h^2}{8\pi^2 \mu r^2} = \frac{j^2 h^2}{8\pi^2 I}. \tag{4}$$

This formula is modified by quantum mechanics (Chap. XV, Sec. **9**) to the form

$$E_j = \frac{j(j+1)h^2}{8\pi^2 I} + \text{a constant independent of } j, \tag{5}$$

$$j = 0, 1, \, \cdots \, .$$

If we use the so-called "half-integral" values $j = \frac{1}{2}, \frac{3}{2}, \cdots$ in equation (4) instead of $j = 0, 1, \cdots$, we obtain a sequence of energy levels identical with those obtained from $j(j+1)h^2/8\pi^2 I$, except for a constant term $\dfrac{1}{4} \dfrac{h^2}{8\pi^2 I}$. This follows from the fact that $(a + \frac{1}{2})^2 = a(a + 1) + \frac{1}{4}$. Since the differences of the energy levels determine the spectral frequencies, both formulas give identical spectra. As a matter of fact, we must use equation (4) with half quantum numbers or equation (5) with whole quantum numbers to explain formula (1), for either supposition tells us that the wave number emitted in the transition from $j + 1$ to j is

$$\tilde{\nu} = \frac{E_{j+1} - E_j}{hc} = \frac{(j+1)h}{4\pi^2 I c}.$$

The use of equation (4) with j equal to an integer would give $j + \frac{1}{2}$ in place of $j + 1$ in this formula, which would then disagree with the fact that the empirical ordinal number M is an integer. We shall adopt the formula (5) in all that follows.

The model assumed above is inadequate, for the molecule cannot be truly rigid and the centrifugal force due to rotation changes the distance between the nuclei slightly. To take this into account, we write the energy in the form

$$E = \frac{p_\varphi^2}{2\mu r^2} + V. \tag{6}$$

As a first approximation we assume that

$$V = \frac{k(r - r_0)^2}{2}, \tag{7}$$

where r_0 is the equilibrium distance between the nuclei when the molecule is not rotating and k is a constant, so that the law of force is harmonic. The centrifugal and centripetal forces must be equal when the new equilibrium is attained and so,

$$\mu r \dot{\varphi}^2 = k(r - r_0).$$

The angular momentum will again be constant, and, therefore,

$$p_\varphi{}^2 = \mu k r^3 (r - r_0).$$ (8)

Let $r - r_0 = \Delta$. An approximate value of Δ/r_0 may be obtained from equation (8) on replacing r^3 by $r_0{}^3$. It is,

$$\frac{\Delta}{r_0} = \frac{p_\varphi{}^2}{\mu k r_0{}^4}.$$ (9)

The energy is approximately

$$E = \frac{p_\varphi{}^2}{2\mu r^2} + V = \frac{p_\varphi{}^2}{2\mu r_0{}^2}\left(1 - \frac{2\Delta}{r_0}\right) + \frac{1}{2}k r_0{}^2\left(\frac{\Delta}{r_0}\right)^2$$

and to a sufficient approximation for our purpose we may substitute the above value of Δ/r_0, obtaining

$$E = \frac{p_\varphi{}^2}{2\mu r_0{}^2}\left(1 - \frac{p_\varphi{}^2}{\mu k r_0{}^4}\right).$$

Using the quantum condition equation (3)

$$E = B_0 h c j^2 (1 - u^2 j^2),$$ (10)

where

$$u^2 = \frac{\mu h^2}{4\pi^2 I_0{}^2 k}, \text{ and } B_0 = \frac{h}{8\pi^2 I_0 c}.$$ (11)

The new mechanics modifies this formula to

$$E = B_0 h c [j(j + 1) - u^2 j^2 (j + 1)^2], j = 0, 1, \cdots,$$ (12)

and this is the expression we shall use. This procedure is nearly equivalent to the use of half-integral j's in equation (10).

The selection rule for j may be derived by the correspondence principle. The molecule rotates with uniform angular velocity in a plane which may be taken as the xy plane. If it has an electric moment P in the direction of the line of nuclei, the x- and y-components will be

$$P_x = P \cos 2\pi\omega t, P_y = P \sin 2\pi\omega t,$$ (13)

where ω is the frequency of revolution and is equal to $\partial E/\partial jh$ and $2\pi\omega t$ is the angle between the x-axis and the line of nuclei. Since only the fundamental frequency occurs in these expansions, the quantum number will decrease by 1 in emission and increase by 1 in absorption. This is the selection rule for rotation bands. Molecules which do not have a permanent electric moment such as O_2, N_2, H_2, etc. will not absorb in the infra-red, for in this case, $P = 0$ and the rate of emission is zero. (Chap. VI, Sec. **4**).

Using the Bohr frequency condition, equation (12), and the above selection rule, the wave numbers which will be absorbed by a rotating hydrogen halide molecule are,

$$\tilde{\nu} = \frac{E(j + 1) - E(j)}{hc} = \frac{h}{4\pi^2 c I_0}[(j + 1) - 2u^2(j + 1)^3],$$

$$j = 0, 1, \cdots,$$ (14)

This is of the same form as equation (1), if $M = j + 1$. Equating the constants of this equation to those of equation (1) it is possible to secure values for the constants I_0 and u, and thus the distance between the nuclei. The results of such calculations are given in Table 1. In particular, from equations (9) and (11)

$$\frac{\Delta}{r_0} = j^2 u^2, \tag{15}$$

and from the values of u given in the table it is evident that the assumption that Δ/r_0 is small in equation (9) is justified.

The transitions involved in the absorption of these far infra-red lines are shown by the arrows at the left in Fig. 5. The permitted transitions are $0 \rightarrow 1$, $1 \rightarrow 2$, $2 \rightarrow 3$, etc., and neglecting the effect of the small term in the energy proportional to $j^2(j + 1)^2$, the wave numbers of the light absorbed are $2B_0$, $4B_0$, $6B_0$, etc., respectively. These are plotted in Fig. 4 for the case of HCl, taking into account the cubic term of equation (1) or equation (14); the lines plotted in this way become closer together as we go to higher frequencies.

3. NEAR INFRA-RED ROTATION-VIBRATION SPECTRA

Lord Rayleigh[1] showed that a rotating vibrating diatomic molecule having an electric moment should emit and absorb light of frequencies $\omega_v \pm \omega_r$ with approximately equal intensities; ω_v and ω_r are the frequencies of vibration and rotation, respectively. Bjerrum[2] pointed out that as a result of the Maxwell-Boltzmann distribution law there should be a most probable value for $\omega_v + \omega_r$ and for $\omega_v - \omega_r$. Thus the number of molecules dN having frequencies of rotation between ω_r and $\omega_r + d\omega_r$ is

$$dN = N \exp\left(\frac{-2\pi^2 I \omega_r^2}{kT}\right) \cdot \frac{4\pi^2 I}{kT} \omega_r d\omega_r.$$

The intensity of absorption for $\omega_v + \omega_r$ or $\omega_v - \omega_r$ should be proportional to $dN/d\omega_r$ and this will be zero for $\omega_r = 0$ and $\omega_r = \infty$, and a maximum for $\omega_r = \frac{1}{2\pi}\left(\frac{kT}{I}\right)^{\frac{1}{2}}$. The absorption band will have a minimum intensity at ω_v and two maxima on either side at a distance $\frac{1}{2\pi}\left(\frac{kT}{I}\right)^{\frac{1}{2}}$ in the frequency scale.[3] Figure 2 shows a band at 4.7μ discovered by Miss von Bahr,[4] who found that the separation of the two maxima increases approx-

---

[1] *Phil. Mag.*, (5) **34**, 410 (1892).

[2] "Nernst Festschrift," Halle (1912).

[3] KEMBLE, in the *Bull.* of the National Research Council entitled "Molecular Spectra in Gases"; see references, end of chapter. Henceforth this publication will be referred to as "Molecular Spectra."

[4] *Verh. deut. Physik. Ges.*, **15**, 710, 731 (1913). See also SPENCE and HALLEY. *J. O. S. A.* and *R. S. I.*, **7**, 169 (1923).

imately as the square root of the absolute temperature. This doublet
character has now been established for many of the near infra-red bands.

Under higher dispersion, the rotation vibration bands of a number
of molecules have been resolved into fairly narrow lines; of these the
hydrogen halide bands have been most carefully studied, and will be
considered in detail, since they illustrate very well the general structure

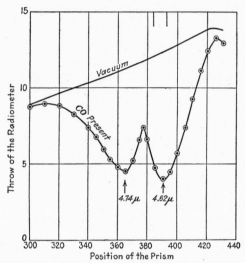

FIG. 2.—The vibration-rotation band of CO.   (*After von Bahr.*)

of the bands of diatomic molecules in the infra-red, as well as in the
visible and ultra-violet.   Imes[1] has studied the fundamental bands of
HF, HCl, and HBr and the first harmonic of HCl.   Colby, Meyer, and
Bronk[2] have extended the HCl fundamental band at 3.4μ to twenty
lines on either side of the mid-point of the band.   In Fig. 3, we reproduce
their absorption curve for this band and, in Fig. 4, we show a plot of the

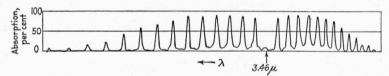

FIG. 3.—The 3.4 μ absorption band of HCl.   (*After Colby, Meyer, and Bronk, Reprinted
by permission of the University of Chicago Press.*)

frequencies of the lines together with a plot of Czerny's rotation spectrum
placed so that the zero frequency coincides with the "missing line"
of the 3.4μ band (shown broken in this figure and indicated by the weak
absorption at the mid-point in Fig. 3).   The band consists of approximately equally spaced lines which become closer together toward the

[1] *Astrophys. J.*, **50**, 251 (1919).

[2] *Astrophys. J.*, **57**, 7 (1923).   See also CZERNY, *Z. Physik*, **45**, 476 (1927).

high frequency side; at the mid-point the intensity is very low (probably zero) and the intensity increases to a maximum on either side and then decreases slowly to zero. These two branches, as they are called, are of nearly equal intensity, the low frequency branch being slightly weaker than the other. The high frequency branch is known as the "R branch," and the low frequency branch as the "P branch." The wave numbers of these two branches can be represented by the formula,

$$\bar{\nu} = 2,886.20 + 20.5379M - 0.30318M^2 - 0.001814M^3, \quad (16)$$

where $M = 1, 2, 3, \cdots$ for the R branch and $-1, -2, -3, \cdots$ for the P branch. This formula contains the first, second, and third powers of the ordinal number M and, in order to account for its structure, it is necessary to consider the model of the diatomic molecule in greater detail.

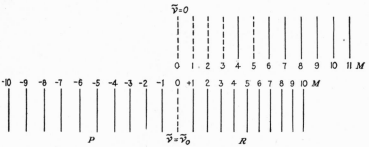

FIG. 4.—Diagram of the rotation and vibration-rotation bands of HCl.

4. KRATZER'S THEORY OF THE VIBRATING ROTATING DIATOMIC MOLECULE

Kratzer[1] has calculated the energy states for a diatomic molecule taking account of both the rotation and the vibration of the nuclei, assuming that the molecule is not rigid, and that the force acting between the nuclei is harmonic to a first approximation. Using plane polar coordinates, the energy of a diatomic molecule is

$$E = \tfrac{1}{2}\mu\dot{r}^2 + \tfrac{1}{2}\mu r^2\dot{\varphi}^2 + V, \quad (17)$$

where r is the internuclear distance, φ the angular coordinate, and μ the reduced mass. Our first concern is to determine a suitable form for V. Kratzer assumed that the hydrogen halides have an ionic binding, i.e., the molecule passes to two ions when the distance between the two nuclei becomes large, and he therefore assumed that the force between the two nuclei consists of an attractive force proportional to $1/r^2$, a repulsive force proportional to $1/r^3$, and of smaller terms proportional to higher negative powers of r. All investigators who have recently studied the question of whether the binding of these molecules is atomic or ionic have concluded that it is atomic, and that the expansion of the

[1] Z. Physik, **3**, 289 (1920).

force as an inverse power series should begin with higher negative powers of r than $1/r^2$. Kemble[1] used an expansion in powers of the displacement of the nuclei from the equilibrium position. The two potential energy curves are identical over the range used by Kratzer.[2] It is convenient to use Kratzer's expression for the potential energy which will hold true for small oscillations regardless of whether the binding is atomic or ionic in character.

His potential energy function may be written,

$$V = C - k\left(\frac{r_0}{r} - \frac{r_0^2}{2r^2} + c_3\left(\frac{r - r_0}{r_0}\right)^3 + c_4\left(\frac{r - r_0}{r_0}\right)^4 + \cdots\right) \quad (18)$$

where C, k, c_3, and c_4 are constants and r_0 is the equilibrium distance between the nuclei. Setting $r = r_0$, we have

$$V_0 = C - \frac{k}{2}, \quad (19)$$

which is the energy of dissociation if we take V equal to zero for $r = \infty$. If the distance $r = r_0$ is to be an equilibrium position, $(dV/dr)_{r=r_0}$ must equal zero and this is easily found to be true. The frequency of vibration for an infinitesimal amplitude ω_0 is given by

$$(2\pi\omega_0)^2 = \frac{1}{\mu}\left(\frac{d^2V}{dr^2}\right)_{r=r_0} = \frac{k}{\mu r_0^2} = \frac{k}{I_0}, \quad (20)$$

and, thus, $k = (2\pi\omega_0)^2 I_0$. The kinetic energy is

$$T = \tfrac{1}{2}\mu(\dot{r}^2 + r^2\dot{\varphi}^2); \quad (21)$$

and substituting $\partial T/\partial \dot{r} = p_r$ and $\partial T/\partial \dot{\varphi} = p$, the Hamiltonian function becomes

$$H = \frac{p_r^2}{2\mu} + \frac{p^2}{2\mu r^2} + V = E. \quad (22)$$

The quantum conditions are

$$\int_0^{2\pi} pd\varphi = 2\pi p = jh, \quad (23)$$

and

$$\oint p_r dr = \oint \left[2\mu(E - C) + 2\mu(2\pi\omega_0)^2 I_0\left\{\frac{r_0}{r} - \left(r_0^2 + \frac{p^2}{(2\pi\omega_0)^2 I_0}\right)\frac{1}{2r^2}\right.\right.$$
$$\left.\left. + c_3\left(\frac{r - r_0}{r_0}\right)^3 + c_4\left(\frac{r - r_0}{r_0}\right)^4 + \cdots\right\}\right]^{\frac{1}{2}}dr. \quad (24)$$

The terms in $\left(\dfrac{r - r_0}{r_0}\right)^3$ and $\left(\dfrac{r - r_0}{r_0}\right)^4$ are small compared to the remainder of the bracket; therefore, the integrand may be expanded in terms of these small quantities and the integration carried out term by term.

---

[1] J. O. S. A., **12**, 1 (1926).

[2] Kemble did not compare his potential energy curve with that of Kratzer but Prof. R. T. Birge has informed us that he has done so, with the above result.

(See Appendix II for an illustration of this procedure.) Finally, solving for E, and neglecting an additive constant, we have

$$E = nh\omega_0(1 - xn) + j^2\left(\frac{h^2}{8\pi^2 I_0}\right)(1 - u^2j^2) - j^2n\alpha h, \qquad (25)$$

where

$$x = u(\tfrac{3}{2} + 1\tfrac{5}{2}c_3 + \tfrac{3}{2}c_4 + 1\tfrac{5}{4}c_3{}^2),$$

$$\alpha = \frac{3\omega_0 u^2}{2}(1 + 2c_3 + \cdots), \qquad (26)$$

and

$$u = \frac{h}{4\pi^2 I_0 \omega_0}.$$

The energy of the diatomic molecule has been calculated by Fues, using wave mechanics and employing the potential energy given in equation (18) (Chap. XIX, Sec. 4). The formula obtained is identical with Kratzer's except that half integral quantum numbers must be used throughout. However, if we wish to use integral quantum numbers, Fues' formula can be secured by replacing n and j of equation (25) by $n + \frac{1}{2}$ and $j + \frac{1}{2}$, respectively. The equation for the energy then becomes

$$E = \left(n + \frac{1}{2}\right)\left(h\omega_0 - \frac{\alpha h}{4}\right) - xh\omega_0\left(n + \frac{1}{2}\right)^2$$
$$+ \left(\frac{h^2}{8\pi^2 I_0} - \frac{u^2 h^2}{16\pi^2 I_0} - \frac{\alpha h}{2}\right)j(j + 1) - \frac{h^2}{8\pi^2 I_0}u^2 j^2(j + 1)^2$$
$$- \alpha hnj(j + 1) + \frac{h^2}{32\pi^2 I_0}\left(1 - \frac{u^2}{4}\right), \quad (27)$$

where $n = 0, 1, 2, \cdots$ and $j = 0, 1, 2, \cdots$. This equation can be further simplified by writing

$$h\omega_0 - \frac{\alpha h}{4} = h\omega, \text{ and } \frac{h^2}{8\pi^2 I_0} - \frac{u^2 h^2}{16\pi^2 I_0} - \frac{\alpha h}{2} = \frac{h^2}{8\pi^2 I}, \qquad (28)$$

so that ω is an "effective" frequency of vibration for zero amplitude ($n = 0$), and I is an "effective" moment of inertia for zero rotation ($j = 0$); finally, the constant term of equation (27) may be neglected for most purposes since it drops out in taking the difference of two energies, which determines the frequency of the radiation. Then since α and u are small, equation (27) becomes

$$E = \left(n + \frac{1}{2}\right)h\omega - xh\omega\left(n + \frac{1}{2}\right)^2 + \frac{h^2}{8\pi^2 I}j(j + 1)$$
$$- u^2\frac{h^2}{8\pi^2 I}j^2(j + 1)^2 - \alpha hnj(j + 1). \quad (29)$$

It is convenient to substitute the simpler symbol B for $h/8\pi^2 I c$. Then equation (29) becomes

$$E = (n + \tfrac{1}{2})h\omega - xh\omega(n + \tfrac{1}{2})^2 + hcBj(j + 1) - u^2 hcBj^2(j + 1)^2$$
$$- \alpha hnj(j + 1). \quad (30)$$

We see from equation (26) and the definition of B that

$$u = \frac{2Bc}{\omega} = \frac{2B}{\bar{\omega}}.$$

For most purposes equations (29) and (30) will be satisfactory, though there may be occasions when it will be necessary to use equation (27) or even more complicated formulas containing higher powers of $(n + \frac{1}{2})$ and $j(j + 1)$. The change from equation (27) to equation (29) means a change in the electronic energy by the amount of the last constant term of equation (27).

The total energy E_t is

$$E_t = E_e + E,$$

where E_e is the energy of the electronic motions and E is given by equation (27). We see that the energy for $n = 0$ and $j = 0$ is

$$E_t(n = 0, j = 0) = E_e + \frac{1}{2}\left(h\omega_0 - \frac{\alpha h}{4}\right) + \frac{h^2}{32\pi^2 I_0}\left(1 - \frac{u^2}{4}\right).$$

From the study of electronic bands (i.e., bands the emission of which is accompanied by a change in the electronic configuration of the molecule), it is possible to secure the difference between $E_t(n = 0, j = 0)$ for two electronic states of the molecule. It is,

$$E_t'(n = 0, j = 0) - E_t''(n = 0, j = 0) = E_e' - E_e'' + \frac{1}{2}\left(h(\omega_0' - \omega_0'')\right)$$

$$- \frac{(\alpha' - \alpha'')h}{4}\right) + \frac{h^2}{32\pi^2}\left(\frac{1}{I_0'} - \frac{1}{I_0''}\right) - \frac{h^2}{128\pi^2}\left(\frac{u'^2}{I_0'} - \frac{u''^2}{I_0''}\right).$$

Primed quantities refer to the higher electronic level and are in general different from the corresponding double-primed quantities, which refer to the lower electronic level. If the molecule is composed of atoms having isotopes, the values of E_e' and E_e'' for the isotopic molecules formed from them will differ only by very small amounts of the order expected for the isotope effect in atomic spectra (Sec. 7). The constants ω_0', ω_0'', α', α'', etc. depend on the masses of the nuclei, equation (28), and differ appreciably for different isotopic molecules, so that it is possible to decide whether the constant terms of equation (27) are present or not. Mulliken showed in this way that the term $h\omega_0/2$ must be present and it is included in equation (29) for this reason. The presence of the other constant terms has not been proved experimentally, probably because the constants themselves are small, so that the alterations of frequency resulting from their differences cannot be detected. For the sake of brevity these unproved terms have been omitted from equation (29).

5. SELECTION PRINCIPLES FOR ROTATION-VIBRATION BANDS

The selection rules may be derived by extending the reasoning of Sec. 2. The electric moment increases and decreases as the nuclei vibrate. The Fourier expansion for the vibrational motion of the nuclei, when the force holding them to their position of equilibrium is nearly harmonic will be assumed to be of the form

$$r = r_0 + r_1 \cos 2\pi\omega_v t + r_2 \cos 2\pi 2\omega_v t + \cdots,$$

where ω_v is equal to $\partial E/\partial nh$. Though the electric moment of the molecule may not be exactly proportional to this displacement, we may assume that the same frequencies will appear in the Fourier expansion of this moment and, therefore, we write

$$P = P_0 + P_1 \cos 2\pi\omega_v t + P_2 \cos 2\pi 2\omega_v t + \cdots \qquad (31)$$

The substitution of this expression for P in equation (13) gives equations for the x- and y-components of P as functions of the time and of ω_v and ω_r. The result is,

$$P_x = P_0 \cos 2\pi\omega_r t + \frac{P_1}{2}[\cos 2\pi(\omega_v + \omega_r)t + \cos 2\pi(\omega_v - \omega_r)t]$$

$$+ \frac{P_2}{2}[\cos 2\pi(2\omega_v + \omega_r)t + \cos 2\pi(2\omega_v - \omega_r)t] + \cdots \; ;$$

$$P_y = P_0 \sin 2\pi\omega_r t + \frac{P_1}{2}[\sin 2\pi(\omega_v + \omega_r)t - \sin 2\pi(\omega_v - \omega_r)t]$$

$$+ \frac{P_2}{2}[\sin 2\pi(2\omega_v + \omega_r)t - \sin 2\pi(2\omega_v - \omega_r)t] + \cdots \qquad (32)$$

The frequencies appearing in these expressions are ω_r, $\omega_v \pm \omega_r$, $2\omega_v \pm \omega_r$, etc., and according to classical theory these frequencies will occur in the light emitted. By the correspondence principle, the following changes in the quantum numbers will occur with the emission of light;

$$\Delta n = 0, \Delta j = 1,$$
$$\Delta n = 1, \Delta j = \pm 1,$$
$$\Delta n = 2, \Delta j = \pm 1,$$
$$\cdots\cdots\cdots\cdots\cdots \qquad (33)$$

and the same changes with opposite signs will occur in the absorption process.

6. APPLICATION OF KRATZER'S THEORY TO THE HYDROGEN HALIDES

If we calculate the frequencies emitted, using equation (30), and the first selection rule of equation (33), we secure equation (14) previously derived for the rotation bands. From the other selection rules of equation (33) we secure the wave numbers of the rotation-vibration bands;

$$\bar{\nu}(n', n''; j+1, j) = (n' - n'')\bar{\omega} - x\bar{\omega}[(n' + \tfrac{1}{2})^2 - (n'' + \tfrac{1}{2})^2]$$

$$+ \left(2B - \frac{\alpha}{c}(n' + n'')\right)(j + 1) - \frac{\alpha}{c}(n' - n'')(j+1)^2 - 4u^2 B(j+1)^3,$$

$$j = 0, 1, 2, \cdots, \text{ for } \Delta j = +1, \qquad (34a)$$

and

$$\bar{\nu}(n', n''; j-1, j) = (n' - n'')\bar{\omega} - x\bar{\omega}[(n' + \tfrac{1}{2})^2 - (n'' + \tfrac{1}{2})^2]$$

$$- \left(2B - \frac{\alpha}{c}(n' + n'')\right)j - \frac{\alpha}{c}(n' - n'')j^2 + 4u^2 B j^3,$$

$$j = 1, 2, \cdots, \text{ for } \Delta j = -1. \qquad (34b)$$

In these formulas j is the quantum number of the lower energy state. These relations are of the same form as the empirical equation (16) for the 3.46μ HCl band, if we use the equation (34a) with $M = j + 1$ for the R branch, and the equation (34b) with $M = -j$ for the P branch. The R branch consists of lines emitted when j decreases by unity, and the P branch of lines for which j increases by unity; therefore, the R branch extends toward higher frequencies. The values of n' and n'' for the absorption bands of HCl can be determined as follows: The application of the Maxwell-Boltzmann distribution law shows that all but a small fraction of the molecules will be in the zero vibrational level at ordinary temperatures; thus the fraction of the molecules in the second vibrational state will be

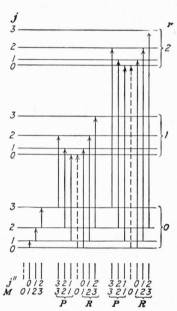

$$\frac{N_1}{N_0} = \exp\left(\frac{-\Delta E}{kT}\right)$$

where ΔE is the difference in energy between the levels with vibrational quantum number 1 and 0. The frequency of the missing line of the 3.46μ band is about $2,886c$, so that for a temperature of $300° K, \Delta E/kT \cong 14$ and thus $\exp(-\Delta E/kT)$ is a small quantity of the order of 10^{-6}. Transitions in which the wave lengths 3.46μ and 1.76μ are absorbed must originate from the lowest level and terminate on the first and second vibration levels as shown in the diagram, Fig. 5. This assignment is made because there is no band between the one at 3.46μ and the rotation bands.

FIG. 5.—The vibrational and rotational energy levels of HCl. The rotational levels are plotted on ten times the scale of the vibrational levels.

The numerical values of the constants of equation (34) are obtained by comparison with equation (16a)·

$$(n' - n'')\bar{\omega} - x\bar{\omega}[(n' + \tfrac{1}{2})^2 - (n'' + \tfrac{1}{2})^2] = 2{,}886.20$$

$$2B - \frac{\alpha}{c}(n' + n'') = 20.5379$$

$$\frac{\alpha}{c}(n' - n'') = 0.30318$$

$$4u^2B = 0.001814. \qquad (35)$$

The equations can be solved for the values of B, α, and u^2 as soon as the values of n' and n'' have been decided upon, but $\bar{\omega}$ and $x\bar{\omega}$ cannot be calculated from one band. Using $n' = 1$, $n'' = 0$, we find the values,

$$2B = 20.8411, \quad \frac{\alpha}{c} = 0.30318, \quad u = 6.592 \cdot 10^{-3}. \qquad (36)$$

The value of B calculated here and that found from the rotation bands equation (14) are identical, but this is because the empirical equations (1) and (16a) were calculated by Czerny so as to make them agree. There is some slight systematic error in the experimental data of either the rotation band or the rotation-vibration band. Because of the experimental difficulties such an error is easily possible.

The wave number of the missing line of the band is secured by setting $(j + 1)$ in equation (34a) or j in equation (34b) equal to zero. This gives

$$\bar{\nu}(n', n'') = (n' - n'')\bar{\omega} - x\bar{\omega}[(n' + \tfrac{1}{2})^2 - (n'' + \tfrac{1}{2})^2] \qquad (37)$$

and, for the case of the absorption bands for which $n'' = 0$, this reduces to

$$\bar{\nu}(n', 0) = n'\bar{\omega} - x\bar{\omega}n'(n' + 1).$$

For $n' = 1, 2, 3, \cdots$ we obtain the wave numbers

$$\bar{\omega}(1 - 2x),\ 2\bar{\omega}(1 - 3x),\ 3\bar{\omega}(1 - 4x).^{[1]}$$

The theory predicts, therefore, that the centers of the rotation-vibration bands should be nearly, but not exactly, multiples of a constant $\bar{\omega}$. The missing lines for the 3.46 and 1.76μ bands of HCl have the wave numbers 2,886.07 and 5,667.0. From these it is possible to calculate $\bar{\omega}$ and $x\bar{\omega}$, for

$$\bar{\omega} - 2x\bar{\omega} = 2,886.07 \text{ and } 2\bar{\omega} - 6x\bar{\omega} = 5,667.0.$$

By solving these equations simultaneously for $\bar{\omega}$ and $x\bar{\omega}$, they give

$$\bar{\omega} = 2,991.3,\ x\bar{\omega} = 52.6.$$

The energy levels represented in Fig. 5 have been calculated by substituting the values of the constants obtained above in equation (30). The vibration levels are nearly equally spaced, while the spacing of the rotational levels increases with increasing j. The latter are shown on a scale ten times as great as that for the vibration levels. The wave number of the light absorbed, during a transition indicated by an arrow, is plotted immediately below it. The missing lines are shown at the middle of the bands and the corresponding forbidden transitions immediately above them. At the left, we see the transitions for the rotation bands which form an R branch without a P branch. The effect of the small terms in the energy proportional to x, α, and u^2 is to depress each of the energy levels below the value given by the larger terms alone; the small terms also bring the lines of the R branch closer together, and cause those of the P branch to draw farther apart, as j increases.

[1] These differ from the formulas given by Kratzer, which are widely quoted. Kratzer gave $\nu(1, 0) = \omega(1 - x)$, $\nu(2, 0) = 2\omega(1 - 2x)$, etc. The difference is due to the changes made necessary by the use of $(n + \tfrac{1}{2})$ instead of n, i.e., the use of half-integral instead of integral numbers. Only the data of Imes (Sec. **3**) were available when Kratzer developed his theory.

Though no absorption should be observed at ordinary temperatures for bands which have n'' greater than zero, we may expect such absorption at higher temperatures. At $600° K$, about one molecule in a thousand will be in the first vibrational state. Five weak lines of a band involving this level were observed by Colby, Meyer, and Bronk[1] at this temperature. They fit well into the formula ($34b$) for $\bar{\nu}(2, 1; j - 1, j)$ obtained by using the constants we have just derived in equation (36), provided we make j equal to the integers 9 to 13, inclusive.

Table 1 gives the values of the fundamental constants of the hydrogen halides as derived from their infra-red spectra. The moment of inertia is given by the relation, $I = h/8\pi^2Bc = 27.66 \cdot 10^{-40}/B$ and the equilibrium distance between the nuclei is then secured from the relation $I = \mu r^2$, where μ is the reduced mass. u may be found from spectroscopic data, as in equation (36), and may also be obtained from the relation, $u = 2B/\bar{\omega}$. $\bar{\omega}$ for HI has been calculated from this relation together with the observed value of u.

TABLE 1[1]

Molecule	$I \cdot 10^{40}$	u (observed)	u (calculated)	$r \cdot 10^8$	$\bar{\omega}$	$x\bar{\omega}$
HF...................	1.348	0.0120	0.0102	0.929	4,037	50
HCl..................	2.658	0.00659	0.00697	1.282	2,991.3	52.6
HBr..................	3.316	0.00660	0.00631	1.421	2,647	44
HI...................	4.3146	0.00565	......	1.6170	~2,270	

[1] The values for I, u (observed), and r for HF, HCl, and HBr and $\bar{\omega}$ for HCl listed in this table are calculated from the data of CZERNY, Z. Physik, **45**, 476 (1927). The remaining values are taken from BIRGE, "International Critical Tables," Vol. 5, corrected as he directs for the normalization of quantum numbers used here.

Schäfer and Thomas[2] have observed the higher harmonics of HF, HCl, and HBr. The wave numbers of the missing lines of the hydrogen halide bands from all sources are listed in the following table:

	$\bar{\omega}(1 - 2x)$	$2\bar{\omega}(1 - 3x)$	$3\bar{\omega}(1 - 4x)$
HF......................	3,962.6	7,880	
HCl.....................	2,886.2	5,667	8,400
HBr.....................	2,559.1		
HI......................	2,270 (calculated)		

7. THE EFFECT OF ISOTOPY ON THE VIBRATIONAL AND ROTATIONAL ENERGY OF DIATOMIC MOLECULES

The change in the energy of a diatomic molecule produced by alterations in the masses of its nuclei can be seen at once from equation (25) or (27). These equations contain the nuclear masses implicitly, through

[1] Astrophys. J., **58**, 303 (1923); loc. cit.

[2] Z. Physik, **12**, 330 (1923).

the presence of the reduced mass μ, and, therefore; the emission and absorption frequencies of molecules containing different isotopic nuclei will not be identical. Now x, u, and α are small quantities and the percentage of change in them due to differences in the nuclear mass is also small, so the terms in which they occur may be neglected in making comparisons of the frequencies due to isotopic molecules. Then equation (29) becomes

$$E = \left(n + \frac{1}{2}\right)h\left(\frac{k}{4\pi^2\mu}\right)^{\frac{1}{2}} + \frac{h^2}{8\pi^2\mu r_0^2}j(j + 1), \qquad (38)$$

where $\mu = \dfrac{M_1 M_2}{M_1 + M_2}$, and $\left(\dfrac{k}{4\pi^2\mu}\right)^{\frac{1}{2}} = \omega_0$. While μ is different for chemically identical molecules which contain different isotopes of the same element, r_0 and k are the same for all such molecules, for the equilibrium distance and the force binding the atoms together depend only on the electric forces between the nuclei and the electrons, and may be considered the same for all atoms having the same atomic number.

It is convenient to discuss the rotational and vibrational isotope effects separately. Let us consider the simplest case, in which the molecule consists of one pure element and one with two isotopes—for example hydrogen chloride, which consists of the molecules HCl^{35} and HCl^{37}. Let the reduced masses for the two molecules be μ_1 and μ_2 with $\mu_2 > \mu_1$ and let $\rho = (\mu_1/\mu_2)^{\frac{1}{2}}$. The rotational energies of the two molecules will be

$$E_{1r} = \frac{h^2}{8\pi^2\mu_1 r_0^2}j(j + 1), \quad E_{2r} = \frac{h^2}{8\pi^2\mu_2 r_0^2}j(j + 1) = \frac{h^2}{8\pi^2\mu_1 r_0^2}j(j + 1)\rho^2. \,(39)$$

The wave number emitted in a change from j' to j'' is

$$\tilde{\nu}_{1r} = B_1' j'(j' + 1) - B_1'' j''(j'' + 1)$$

for the first type of molecule. For the second, it is $\tilde{\nu}_{2r}$ where

$$\tilde{\nu}_{2r} = \rho^2 \tilde{\nu}_{1r}, \qquad (40)$$

so that

$$\tilde{\nu}_{1r} - \tilde{\nu}_{2r} = \Delta\tilde{\nu}_r = (1 - \rho^2)\tilde{\nu}_{1r}. \qquad (41)$$

Similarly, the vibrational energies will be,

$$E_{1v} = \left(n + \frac{1}{2}\right)h\left(\frac{k}{4\pi^2\mu_1}\right)^{\frac{1}{2}}, \quad E_{2v} = \left(n + \frac{1}{2}\right)h\left(\frac{k}{4\pi^2\mu_2}\right)^{\frac{1}{2}} =$$
$$\left(n + \frac{1}{2}\right)h\left(\frac{k}{4\pi^2\mu_1}\right)^{\frac{1}{2}}\rho, \quad (42)$$

so that

$$\tilde{\nu}_{2v} = n'\left(\frac{k}{4\pi^2\mu_2}\right)^{\frac{1}{2}} - n''\left(\frac{k}{4\pi^2\mu_2}\right)^{\frac{1}{2}} = \rho\tilde{\nu}_{1v}, \qquad (43)$$

and

$$\tilde{\nu}_{1v} - \tilde{\nu}_{2v} = \Delta\tilde{\nu}_v = (1 - \rho)\tilde{\nu}_{1v}. \qquad (44)$$

From equation (41) it can be seen that the wave-length differences due to isotopy in rotation spectra are beyond the limit of detection with apparatus of the kind used up to the present. Equation (44) predicts that it should be possible to detect it in rotation-vibration spectra, and in fact it has been observed in the 1.76μ band of HCl. On the long wave-length side of each prominent peak of the absorption curve of Fig. 6 Imes found a smaller peak or hump in the curve. Independently, Loomis[1] and Kratzer[2] pointed out that this small break could be explained as due to the molecule HCl^{37}. The weaker peak should be due to the isotope present in smaller amount (i.e., the heavier one in this case, since the atomic weight of chlorine is 35.46) and should have a larger wave length than the main peak. According to equation (44), $\Delta\bar{\nu}_v/\bar{\nu}_v =$

$$1 - \rho = 0.0007715 \text{ and } \Delta\lambda = \frac{-\Delta\bar{\nu}\lambda}{\bar{\nu}} = -13.5 \text{ Å.}$$ The experimental value is 14 ± 1 Å.

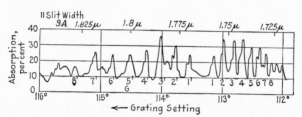

Fig. 6.—The 1.76μ band of HCl.   (*After Imes. Reprinted by permission of the University of Chicago Press.*)

Meyer and Levin[3] have also resolved the lines of the fundamental HCl band at 3.46μ into close doublets and find that the separation and relative intensities are those expected from the theory and the atomic weight of chlorine.

Mulliken[4] first applied the development given here to electronic bands, in the case of the molecule BO. Some very striking results came from this study: these bands were definitely shown to be due to BO, and not to BN as was previously supposed; it was found that the vibration quantum number must be half integral as in equation (27) and not integral as in equation (25), and that in the lowest vibrational state the energy is $h\omega/2$. The calculated value of $1/\rho$ for $B^{10}O$ and $B^{11}O$ is 1.0292, while for $B^{10}N$ and $B^{11}N$ it is 1.0276; the value determined from the spectra is 1.0291 ± 0.0003, in definite agreement with the former. The question of half-integral quantum numbers will be discussed later.

[1] *Nature*, **106**, 179 (1920); *Astrophys. J.*, **52**, 248 (1920).

[2] *Z. Physik*, **3**, 460 (1920); **4**, 476 (1921).

[3] *Phys. Rev.* **34**, 44, (1929).

[4] *Phys. Rev.* **25**, 259 (1925).

B. ELECTRONIC BANDS

8. DEFINITIONS OF ELECTRONIC, VIBRATIONAL, AND ROTATIONAL ENERGIES

In order to explain visible and ultra-violet bands, we are led to the assumption that they are due to changes in the electronic quantum numbers of the molecule. The structure of the individual electronic bands is similar to that of the infra-red rotation-vibration bands, and the frequency differences between the many bands of a related group (or so-called "band system") are of the same order of magnitude as the infra-red vibration frequencies. Thus, even the gross structure of such systems indicates that at least three quantum numbers must change simultaneously in the emission of one line, namely, the electronic quantum number (or in many cases several electronic quantum numbers), the vibration quantum number, and the rotation quantum number. We have tacitly assumed that the energy of vibration and rotation can be fixed by the quantum numbers n and j, introduced above, and that this energy is independent of the electronic energy of the molecule. Strictly, it is impossible to speak of electronic, rotational, or vibrational energy, for the total energy of the molecule is a function of all its quantum numbers and it is impossible to localize energy in the various degrees of freedom. Thus the energy of rotation and vibration of the molecule is a function of n and j, and of certain constants, such as the moment of inertia and the characteristic frequency of vibration for small amplitudes. These constants are functions of the electronic quantum numbers and it would be just as correct to refer to this energy as electronic. For convenience, however, it is arbitrarily separated into electronic, vibrational, and rotational energy, and so we must carefully define these terms.

We represent the total energy of the molecule as

$$E = E(e, n, j), \qquad (45)$$

where e represents all the electronic quantum numbers, n, the vibrational numbers, and j, the rotational numbers. (There are several n's and j's in the case of polyatomic molecules.) The electronic energy is *defined* as the value of $E(e, n, j)$ when j is zero and n is $-\frac{1}{2}$, thus,

$$E_e = E(e, -\frac{1}{2}, 0). \qquad (46)$$

The vibrational energy is then defined as

$$E_n = E(e, n, 0) - E_e \qquad (47)$$

and the rotational energy as

$$E_j = E(e, n, j) - E_e - E_n. \qquad (48)$$

According to these definitions, the energy of rotation of the diatomic molecule as given in equation (29) is

$$E_j = \frac{h^2}{8\pi^2 I} j(j + 1) - u^2 \frac{h^2}{8\pi^2 I} j^2(j + 1)^2 - \alpha h n j(j + 1), \qquad (49)$$

and the vibrational energy is

$$E_n = (n + \tfrac{1}{2})h\omega - xh\omega(n + \tfrac{1}{2})^2. \tag{50}$$

The term $\alpha h n j(j + 1)$ is treated as part of the rotational energy although it contains the vibration quantum number n.

Kratzer's formula was derived by assuming that I, α, ω, x, and u are constants for all vibrational and rotational states as long as the molecule is in its normal electronic state; but, obviously, these assumptions should be equally valid for any electronic steady state and we may expect that his formula will hold for the rotational and vibrational energy in both the initial and final states involved in the emission of electronic bands. Only one modification need be considered, namely, the changes necessary if the electron system has a resultant angular momentum when the nuclei are not rotating; this alters the rotational energy states of the molecule by changing the form of E_j and also by limiting the possible values of j as will be shown later.

9. BAND SYSTEMS AND VIBRATION TRANSITIONS

It is easy to recognize from experimental evidence that certain large groups of bands are very closely related to each other. Thus, either the entire group or a large part of it appears under given experimental conditions or none of it appears, and the relative intensities of different bands are approximately the same for different methods of excitation, or vary in a regular way. Deslandres made the first attempts at classification of such band groups, which are now usually called "systems." A system is the aggregate of bands emitted in transitions having common initial and final electronic states, including under this term all the electronic states corresponding to a multiplet in atomic spectra. Each *system* will consist of many *bands*, such as those discussed under infra-red spectra, whose positions are determined by the changes in vibrational quantum number, and each band will consist of many sharp lines, whose spacings are determined primarily by changes of the rotational quantum number. The electronic energy differences and therefore their contributions to the frequencies are usually much larger than those of the vibrational energy changes and these, in turn, are much larger than the changes in rotational energy. The general position of the system is therefore determined by the electron transition. The systematization of the electronic levels is not thoroughly understood at present. Usually, attention is directed toward finding the quantum numbers of the electronic levels, which are similar in some respects to the atomic azimuthal and inner quantum numbers. This is accomplished by studying the rotational structure of the individual bands. The electronic levels and transitions will be discussed, therefore, after we have treated the detailed structure of the bands.

We begin with the gross structure of the band systems as determined by the vibrational quantum changes. The individual bands, in most cases, have not been resolved into their individual lines and thus the position of the origin of the band, *i.e.*, the missing line of the vibration-rotation bands, is unknown. For most systems only the frequencies of the band heads are known, and these have been used to secure the vibration levels of the initial and final electronic levels. Deslandres first showed that it is possible to arrange the band heads in *progressions*, such that in a given progression the heads are approximately equally spaced in the frequency scale, and such that the frequency differences between the bands of one progression will be almost exactly equal to the differences of other progressions. Further, he showed that the wave numbers in a progression may be represented rather closely by the formula,

$$\tilde{\nu} = a + bn + cn^2, \qquad (51)$$

where n may take integral values either positive or negative, and a, b, and c are constants. Such progressions in any band system can be selected in two ways; in one, the frequency interval between bands increases toward the violet, and in the other, toward the red. Deslandres designated these as first and second progressions, respectively. The quantum theory of band systems leads to a clear understanding of these empirical relationships.

For brevity, we shall neglect the rotational energy at first and shall say that an electronic band system is emitted in transitions between electronic levels, each consisting of a series of vibration levels of the same kind as those necessary to account for the infra-red bands of HCl, etc. (see Fig. 5). The simplified energy diagram we shall employ consists of two groups of vibration levels with different spacings, which may or may not overlap. Figure 7 shows such an energy diagram, with arrows indicating the transitions. A group of transitions from one of the vibration levels of the higher electronic level B to the different vibration levels of the lower electronic level A is called an "n'' progression"; and a group of transitions from different vibration levels of B to one vibration

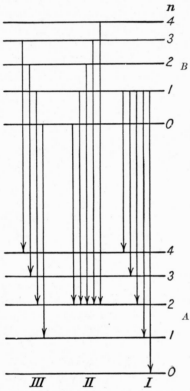

Fig. 7.—Progressions and a sequence. I is a first progression, II a second progression, and III a sequence.

level of A is called an "n' progression." Such progressions are shown under I and II of Fig. 7. Since there are many progressions of each kind, we may specify each n'' progression by the number of its common initial level, and each n' progression by the number of its common final level. It is immediately evident that the differences in frequency of the transitions of any n'' progression, multiplied by h, will be the energy-differences of the vibrational levels belonging to A, and similarly such differences in any n' progression, multiplied by h, will be the energy-differences of B. It is further evident that the differences for the various n'' progressions must be equal, and those for the n' progressions must be equal. In all cases where the band origins have been exactly located and have been used in place of the band heads, this is found to be true within the limits of experimental error. The transitions for which

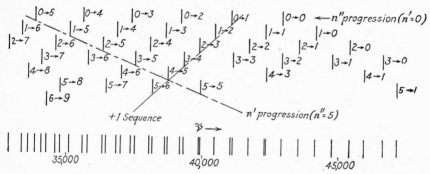

Fig. 8.—The progressions and sequences of the β $B^{11}O$ bands.

$n'' - n'$ is a constant are called "sequences." The sequence $n' - n'' = 1$ is illustrated in the energy diagram of Fig. 7. The appearance of such sequences as observed in the spectrum can be seen from Fig. 1 for the case of the β NO bands.

The problem of the spectroscopist is to arrange the bands in progressions and to assign the proper values to initial and final quantum numbers for each band. The relations of progressions and sequences are illustrated by Fig. 8, which shows the band heads of the β band system of $B^{11}O$ arranged according to progressions.[1] The n'' progressions are arranged in horizontal rows, the diagonal broken line shows an n' progression for $n'' = 5$, and the diagonal solid line shows the sequence, $+1$. The numbering of the transitions is fixed by the position of the $0 \rightarrow 0$ transition, which occupies a unique position in the scheme, and by the equal differences of the progressions. These transitions having been classified, the energy diagram can be constructed by taking the frequency of the $0 \rightarrow 0$ transition as the difference in the electron levels of the molecule, the differences of the n'' progressions as the intervals between vibration levels of

[1] Mulliken, *Phys. Rev.*, **25**, 259 (1925).

A, the lower electron level, and those of the n' progressions as the intervals of B.

The vibrational energy levels belonging to a given electronic level, as defined in the preceding paragraph, will obey a formula of the type of equation (50), approximately. Writing this formula with different constants for the initial and final states, we have

$$E' = E_e' + (n' + \tfrac{1}{2})h\omega' - x'h\omega'(n' + \tfrac{1}{2})^2,$$

and

$$E'' = E_e'' + (n'' + \tfrac{1}{2})h\omega'' - x''h\omega''(n'' + \tfrac{1}{2})^2, \qquad (52)$$

and the wave number of the light emitted in a typical transition will be

$$\tilde{\nu} = \frac{E' - E''}{hc} = \tilde{\nu}_e + \left[\left(n' + \frac{1}{2}\right)\tilde{\omega}' - x'\tilde{\omega}'\left(n' + \frac{1}{2}\right)^2\right]$$
$$- \left[\left(n'' + \frac{1}{2}\right)\tilde{\omega}'' - x''\tilde{\omega}''\left(n'' + \frac{1}{2}\right)^2\right], \quad (53)$$

where $\tilde{\nu}_e = (E_e' - E_e'')/hc$. If n'' is held constant, equation (53) gives the formula for an n' progression and, if n' is held constant, the formula for an n'' progression. These formulas are:

$$\tilde{\nu} = A' + B'n' - C'n'^2, \qquad (54)$$

where

$$A' = \tilde{\nu}_e + \tfrac{1}{2}\tilde{\omega}' - \tfrac{1}{4}x'\tilde{\omega}' - [(n'' + \tfrac{1}{2})\tilde{\omega}'' - x''\tilde{\omega}''(n'' + \tfrac{1}{2})^2],$$
$$B' = \tilde{\omega}'(1 - x'), \ C' = x'\tilde{\omega}',$$

and

$$\tilde{\nu} = A'' - B''n'' + C''n''^2, \qquad (55)$$

where

$$A'' = \tilde{\nu}_e - \tfrac{1}{2}\tilde{\omega}'' + \tfrac{1}{4}x''\tilde{\omega}'' + [(n' + \tfrac{1}{2})\tilde{\omega}' - x'\tilde{\omega}'(n' + \tfrac{1}{2})^2],$$
$$B'' = \tilde{\omega}''(1 - x''), \ C'' = x''\tilde{\omega}'',$$

respectively, and are of the form of equation (51). The n' progressions extend toward the violet and the bands become closer together in the wave-number scale as n' increases, so that if n' becomes sufficiently large, $B'n' - C'n'^2$ would reach a maximum and then decrease. The n'' progressions extend toward the red with decreasing distance between bands as n'' increases, and $-B''n'' + C''n''^2$ would reach a minimum value and then increase. The n' progression is therefore similar to the Deslandres' "second progression," and the n'' progression to his "first progression."[1] The maximum and minimum values for these progressions are approached in only a few cases; the extension of the progression beyond these values has never been observed and is theoretically impossible, because the molecule dissociates if it has more energy than the amount corresponding to either of them, as will appear later. The formula (51)

---

[1] For a detailed discussion of the relations between these progressions see Birge, "Molecular Spectra," p. 73.

TABLE 2.—B¹¹O BAND HEADS

n'' \\ n'	0	1	2	3	4 to 11 →	Δn'	Average Δ₁(n'+½) = 2C'
0	42,880.8 (1,860.9)	41,019.9 (1,837.5)	39,182.4 (1,814.0)	37,368.4 (1,790.4)	35,578.0	1-0	1,257.6 ⟩ 19.9
	(1,260.3)	(1,259.8)	(1,258.4)	(1,259.9)	(1,259.7)	2-1	1,237.7 ⟩ 20.5
1	44,141.1 (1,864.4)	42,279.7 (1,838.9)	40,440.8 (1,812.5)	38,628.3 (1,790.6)	36,837.7	3-2	1,217.2 ⟩ 18.7
	(1,237.9)	(1,238.0)	(1,238.8)	(1,237.2)	(1,237.0)	4-3	1,198.5 ⟩ 18.6
2	45,379.0 (1,861.3)	43,517.7 (1,838.1)	41,679.6 (1,814.1)	39,865.5 (1,790.8)	38,074.7	5-4	1,179.9 ⟩ 19.7
	1,218.2	(1,218.1)	(1,217.4)	(1,217.7)	(1,217.8)	6-5	1,160.2
3 to 6 ↓	46,597.2 (1,861.4)	44,735.8 (1,838.8)	42,897.0 (1,813.8)	41,083.2 (1,790.7)	39,292.5		
	....				....	9-8	1,671.7
						10-9	1,647.5
							24.2

Δn'': 1-0   2-1   3-2   4-3   4-3   9-8

Average Δ₁(n''+½): (1,861.2)   (1,838.3)   (1,813.6)   (1,790.6)   (1,790.6)   1,671.7

Δ₂(n'') = 2C'': 22.9   24.7   23.0   24.2

would hardly be expected to be valid for large values of the vibration quantum number, since it was derived on the assumption of small vibrations, though it does hold quite accurately over a large range for many electronic steady states. By using a graduated scale the reader can see that the bands of the $B^{11}O$ progressions shown in Fig. 8 do become closer together in the way described.

How closely the parabolic equations (54) and (55) are followed can be seen from Table 2, where the wave numbers of the $B^{11}O$ bands are listed. The first differences are given in parentheses between the wave numbers of the bands. At the right and bottom the averages of these first differences are listed, together with the differences of these averages, *i.e.*, the second differences. According to equation (54) the first and second differences for the n' progressions are

$$\Delta_1(n' + \tfrac{1}{2}) = \bar{\nu}(n' + 1) - \bar{\nu}(n') = B' - C'(2n' + 1),$$
$$\Delta_2(n') = \Delta_1(n' + \tfrac{1}{2}) - \Delta_1(n' - \tfrac{1}{2}) = -2C'$$

and for the n'' progressions, from equation (55), we have

$$\Delta_1(n'' + \tfrac{1}{2}) = \bar{\nu}(n'' + 1) - \bar{\nu}(n'') = -B'' + C''(2n'' + 1),$$
$$\Delta_2(n'') = \Delta_1(n'' + \tfrac{1}{2}) - \Delta_1(n'' - \tfrac{1}{2}) = 2C''.$$

Thus, if equations (54) and (55), and therefore equation (51), are correct, the second differences should be constant and equal to $-2C'$ and $2C''$, respectively. The values in Table 2 show that they are very nearly constant as the formula requires, even for fairly large values of n' and n''. This is also true for a majority of known electronic levels, but there are a few very definite exceptions. In these cases the differences between the band frequencies or, what is the same thing, the differences between the vibrational energy levels, decrease more rapidly than the parabolic law (equation (51)) requires. This behavior seems to be associated with an instability of the molecule.

10. HEATS OF DISSOCIATION OF DIATOMIC MOLECULES DETERMINED FROM THEIR VIBRATIONAL LEVELS

Kratzer's theory of the diatomic molecule (Sec. **4**) is limited in application to small displacements from the equilibrium position. Such a theory cannot be used to discuss displacements which are so large that the molecule approaches the dissociated state, and, therefore, it is necessary to reconsider the problem, with special attention to large values of the rotational and vibrational quantum numbers and the transition of the molecule into two isolated atoms.

This problem has been considered by Born and Franck[1] using classical mechanics, which furnishes an especially good approximation in this region of large quantum numbers. If two atoms, A and B, are brought

[1] *Z. Physik*, **31**, 411 (1925).

to a definite distance from each other and thought of as stationary, the energy of the system will contain terms due to the action of the field of each atom on the electron motions of the other, an effect which will resemble the ordinary Stark effect to a marked degree, since the atomic fields are largely electrical in origin. This energy of the system will be a function of the distance between the atom centers, say $V(r)$. This may be considered as the potential energy for the displacement of the atoms relative to each other. The general behavior of this function can be seen from general considerations. At $r = \infty$, V is equal to the total energy of the two isolated atoms, which may be set equal to zero since

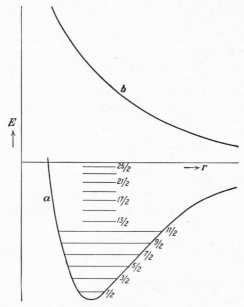

Fig. 9.—Potential energy curves for two atoms: (a) the atoms attract at large distances and repel at small distances; (b) the atoms repel each other at all distances.

we are interested only in the changes of energy in the process of molecule formation or of dissociation. In general, two atoms at a fairly large distance apart will attract each other, though it is also possible that they may repel each other at all distances.[1] At small distances the forces will always be repulsive. If the force at large distances is one of attraction, there must be a distance r_0 at which there is neither attraction nor repulsion, and this is the equilibrium distance of the two atoms; and since the radial force between them is $-\partial V/\partial r$, we see that V must always decrease as r increases, over the region of repulsive force, so that it must have a minimum at r_0. On the other hand, if the force is repulsive at all

[1] It seems likely that all atoms attract each other at least slightly at large distances due to van der Waals forces.

distances, the curve $V(r)$ falls continuously as r increases. These two cases are illustrated by the curves a and b of Fig. 9. In the second case, a molecule cannot be formed, while in the first, a molecule may exist having an energy of dissociation equal to the difference of the values of V at $r = \infty$ and $r = r_0$.

In polar coordinates, the Hamiltonian function for the motion of 2 atoms relative to each other, either in collision or as a permanent molecule is,

$$H = \frac{p_r^2}{2\mu} + \frac{p_\varphi^2}{2\mu r^2} + V. \tag{56}$$

The quantized energy levels for the undissociated molecule can be secured in the usual way, if V is known as a function of r. Kratzer's calculations in Sec. 4 accomplish this for the special case of small oscillations in the neighborhood of $r = r_0$, and for low rotational energies. Also, the problem of two ions revolving in large orbits with respect to each other is almost exactly the same as that of the hydrogen atom, the largest term in the energy being

$$E = -\frac{2\pi^2\epsilon^4\mu}{(n + j)^2 h^2} + \text{a constant}, \tag{57}$$

where ϵ is the charge on one ion, μ the reduced mass, and n and j the radial and angular quantum numbers, respectively; thus the energy becomes zero only when $n + j$ is infinite. The general case cannot be handled in any simple way, but Kratzer[1] has shown that the following statement holds true for the vibrational states without rotation: if V is an inverse power series, and the largest term is the inverse first or second power in the region of large values of r the energy reaches the dissociation value only when n becomes infinite (see equation (57)); but if the most prominent term for large r is the inverse third, or a higher power, the energy becomes sufficient for dissociation at a finite value of n, let us say n_0. The way the vibration energy levels may be expected to run as a function of n is shown by Fig. 9, for the atomic type of binding. The horizontal lines represent the energies of the vibrational states for the values of n given at the right. The curved line represents V, and the points of intersection of V and the horizontal lines give the values of r when $E = V$, or when the kinetic energy is zero, so that the intersections of these lines with the curve V are the limits of oscillation. In Fig. 9 the horizontal lines become closer together as n increases, but at n_0, which is finite, they are separated by finite differences of energy. Without knowing the detailed law of force between the atoms it is possible to secure the energy of dissociation from empirical band spectrum data. Thus, consider the problem of the molecule solved and the energy

[1] Z. Physik, **26**, 40 (1924).

expressed as a function of the rotational and vibrational quantum numbers,

$$E = E(n, j). \tag{58}$$

The molecule will be considered as dissociated if the two atoms are at rest relative to each other or are moving with respect to each other at infinity. These conditions will be met when the frequency of vibration of the non-rotating molecule is zero, for then the period is infinite, corresponding to a fall of the atoms from rest at infinity, a collision and a return to an infinite distance. Thus, the condition for dissociation is

$$\frac{1}{h}\frac{\partial E}{\partial n} = \omega_v(n) = 0, \tag{59}$$

and knowing E as a function of n from the empirical band formula it is possible to solve equation (59) for n, substitute in equation (58) and thus secure the energy of dissociation. In some cases a plot of $\omega_v(n)$ against n is more useful; the energy of dissociation is then taken to be

$$h \int_0^{n_0} \omega(n)dn = D, \tag{60}$$

which is the area under the curve from $n = 0$ out to the abscissa of the maximum n_0.

Essentially, this method was used by Hulthén[1] for the normal state of the HgH molecule. Franck[2] and Dymond[3] also used it in securing the energy of dissociation of the I_2 molecule from the absorption spectrum. The absorption bands of I_2, the energy diagram of the molecule and the transitions giving these bands are shown in Fig. 10. All the bands of the figure are produced in transitions from the lowest vibration level of the normal electronic state to the vibration levels of the first excited electronic state; they are the n' progression with $n'' = 0$. The bands approach a limit at the broken line where $\partial\bar{\nu}/\partial n'$ becomes equal to zero. Beyond this the spectrum is continuous. This limit corresponds to an energy of 2.47 volts which is evidently too high for the dissociation energy of the iodine molecule into two normal iodine atoms in the $^2P_{3/2}$ state. Franck explained this by assuming that one iodine atom is left in the metastable $^2P_{1/2}$ state having an energy of excitation of 0.94 volt.[4] This gives 1.53 volts for the energy of dissociation into normal atoms which is in fair agreement with the thermochemical value of 1.6 volts.

This excited iodine atom cannot be detected by the emission of characteristic lines since the transition $^2P_{1/2} \rightarrow {}^2P_{3/2}$ does not occur, in accordance with the selection rules. Turner[5] found that atomic iodine

[1] *Z. Physik,* **32,** 32 (1925).
[2] *Trans.* Faraday Society, **21,** Part 3 (1925).
[3] *Z. Physik,* **34,** 553 (1925).
[4] TURNER, *Phys. Rev.,* **27,** 397 (1926).
[5] *Phys. Rev.,* **31,** 983 (1928).

lines whose lower energy state is $^2P_{3/2}$ are absorbed by strongly illuminated iodine vapor, but found no evidence of absorption by atoms in the $^2P_{1/2}$ state under these conditions. The excited iodine atoms in this latter state must quickly revert to the $^2P_{3/2}$ state by collisions of the second kind (Chap. XIV). Urey, Dawsey, and Rice[1] have found that the absorption of hydrogen peroxide vapor is entirely continuous so that in this case dissociation of the molecule must always occur. Light in the range 2,100 to 2,200 Å. has sufficient energy to dissociate the molecule

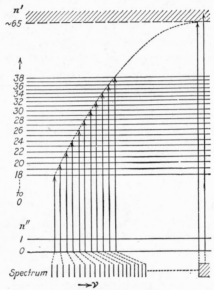

FIG. 10.—The absorption bands and corresponding transitions of iodine; the n'-progression with $n'' = 0$.[2]

into two normal OH molecules and simultaneously to excite one of these to its $^2\Sigma$ state, which is the initial state for the emission of the 3,064 Å. water band. This actually occurs, for the band was obtained in fluorescence when H_2O_2 vapor at low pressures was so illuminated. Thus evidence for dissociation of this halogen-like molecule by light has been secured.

This method of determining dissociation energies was also applied by Birge and Sponer[3] to a number of compounds of oxygen, nitrogen, and carbon in different states of excitation. One of the most striking features of this work is the fact that $\omega(n)$ is almost a linear function of n, even for large values of n, for nearly all molecules with atomic binding, and especially is this true for their normal states. This is exactly the require-

[1] *J. A. C. S.*, **51**, 1371 (1929).
[2] From the data of MECKE, *Ann. Physik*, **71**, 108 (1923).
[3] *Phys. Rev.*, **28**, 259 (1926).

ment of Kratzer's equation (50) for the energy. Although his theory was derived only for small oscillations, it proves to be a very good approximation over a considerable range for this class of molecules.

The O_2 and O_2^+ molecules in their normal and excited states furnish very neat examples of this method of determining dissociation energies. The known electronic vibration levels of these molecules are illustrated in Fig. 11, taken from Birge and Sponer.[1] Since only a few of the vibration levels of the A electronic state are known, any calculations based on it will be inaccurate, and therefore we omit all discussion of this state. The vibration levels of the normal O_2 molecule (X state) can be represented over the known experimental range by the equation

$$\bar{\nu} = 1,565.37n - 11.37n^2. \qquad (61)$$

Applying the condition of equation (59) for determining n_0, the value of n for which $\partial E/\partial n = 0$, we have,

$$\frac{\partial \bar{\nu}}{\partial n} = 1,565.37 - 22.74n_0 = 0; \; n_0 = 68.81. \qquad (62)$$

Substituting this in equation (61), the wave number corresponding to the dissociation energy is

$$\bar{\nu} = 53,856 \text{ cm.}^{-1},$$

which is equivalent to 6.65 volts or 153,280 calories per gram molecule. As we see from Fig. 11 the assumption of the linearity of $\partial \bar{\nu}/\partial n$ over the entire range to dissociation represents a very great extrapolation and the calculation based on this assumption may be expected to be in error by a rather large amount. The dissociation energy may also be secured by using the vibration levels of the B electronic state. These levels do not follow a parabolic equation such as equation (61), so that $\partial \bar{\nu}/\partial n$ is not linear. By plotting the values of $\partial \bar{\nu}/\partial n$ against n it is found that the known vibration levels extend to values of n very close to the limiting value n_0 for dissociation. The value of the dissociation energy is secured by taking the integral of equation (60) graphically. The value so secured is 0.96 ± 0.01 volts. The difference between the X and B levels, with $n = 0$ in each case, is known to be 6.09 volts, from the ultra-violet bands of oxygen. The sum of the energy of excitation to the B level with $n = 0$ and the dissociation energy of the O_2 molecule in the B state

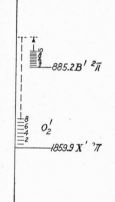

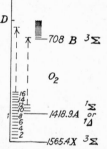

Fig. 11.—The energy levels of O_2 and O_2^+. (*After Birge and Sponer.*) The symbols for the levels are those assigned by Mulliken (*Phys. Rev.* **32**, 206 (1928)).

---

[1] *Loc. cit.* For references to the original literature on the bands from which the energy levels are derived, as well as the numerical values quoted in the following paragraphs, the reader should refer to this article.

is thus $6.09 + 0.96 = 7.05$ volts. This is in fairly good agreement with the value 6.65 volts secured by extrapolating from the vibration levels of the normal molecule, and indicates that the products of dissociation by the two ways must be very nearly identical in energy content. The normal state of the O-atom is a ^3P level with the separations 0.01 and 0.02 volts[1] and the next level (^1D or ^1S) lies a few volts higher on the energy diagram. It is evident, therefore, that the normal and excited oxygen molecules both separate into atoms which differ at most by only 0.01 to 0.03 volt of energy, and the disagreement between the two values secured for D must be due to the error in extrapolating from the vibration levels of the normal electronic level and the better value for the energy of dissociation is that secured by using the data on the excited state of the molecule. It is uncertain whether 7.05 volts is the energy of dissociation of the molecule into two normal atoms or into atoms either or both of which are excited. If both are excited, this energy of excitation is at most 0.06 volt ($2 \cdot 0.03$ volt), so that the energy of dissociation into two normal atoms may be as low as $7.05 - 0.06 = 6.99$ volts. Birge and Sponer give 7.02 ± 0.05 volts as the best value.

The vibrational levels of the O_2^+ molecule are given accurately over the experimental range, by the parabolic formulas,

$$\bar{\nu}(X') = 1{,}859.86n - 16.53n^2, \tag{63}$$

and

$$\bar{\nu}(B') = \phantom{1{,}}885.23n - 13.7n^2. \tag{64}$$

The corresponding values of n_0 are 56.26 and 32.31, and the dissociation energies, calculated as above, 6.46 and 1.76 volts, respectively. Adding the excitation energy of the B' level, 4.73 volts, to 1.76 volts, we get 6.49 volts, which agrees closely with the value 6.46 volts secured from the normal X' level. Again, it appears that an excited molecule may dissociate into normal atoms or atoms with only small amounts of energy.[2] These results may be in error by several tenths of a volt because of the large extrapolation used (Fig. 11).

Note added in proof: Birge[3] has recently revised the value 6.65 volts for the energy of dissociation of O_2 calculated from the vibration levels of the lowest electronic state and concludes that the energy of dissociation into two normal atoms is certainly less than 7 volts and gives 6 volts as the most likely value. Thus 7.02 volts is the energy required to dissociate the molecule into one normal and one excited atom.

Attempts have been made to determine the energy of dissociation of diatomic molecules by applying similar methods to the rotational

[1] HOPFIELD, *Astrophys. J.*, **59**, 114 (1924).

[2] This conclusion is not in accord with theory and may be wrong. See MULLIKEN, *Phys. Rev.*, **32**, 210 (1928).

[3] *Phys. Rev.*, **34**, 1062 (1929).

states.[1] However, the coupling of vibrational and rotational energy and other complications are involved in any complete discussion of the problem, and it will be best to omit further discussion in the present uncertain state of the subject.

11. INTENSITIES IN BAND SYSTEMS

Birge[2] has pointed out that for many band systems the bands of each progression have two maxima of intensity with a minimum between them; there are thus two especially favored transitions from each higher or lower vibration energy level. In other cases there is only one maxi-

n'' \ n'	0	1	2	3	4	5	6	7	8	9	10	11
0	8	5	1	x								
1	7	4	6	2	x							
2	2	6	2	6	3	x						
3	x	4	5	1	4	4	x					
4	x	x	5	4		3	4	x				
5		x	x	4	3		3	3	x			
6			x	x	3	2		2	2	x		
7				x	x	3	1		1	1	x	
8					x	x	2	1		x	x	
9						x	x	1	x		x	x
10							x	x	1	x		x
11								x	x	x	x	

FIG. 12.—Intensities of the AlO bands. (*After Birge.*)

mum which may be regarded as a superposition of two maxima lying very close together; and in yet other cases only one maximum is observed, which, from the general distribution of intensity, seems to be due to the two maxima being very widely separated so that only one of them falls in the observable region. The intensity distributions for AlO, SiN, and I_2 are typical illustrations of these intensity relations.

Figure 12 is a square array of the bands of AlO with intensities given in place of the wave numbers. Otherwise, the arrangement is the same as that of Table 2 for the $B^{11}O$ bands. The rows are the n'' progressions and the columns the n' progressions. The n'' progression with $n' = 0$ and the n' progression with $n'' = 0$ have only one maximum in intensity, namely the (0, 0) band, but all other progressions have two maxima. The zero sequence is very nearly at the minimum intensity, with two maxima on each side. Many other band systems show similar distributions, but are not usually so symmetrical as the AlO bands.

[1] BORN and FRANCK, *loc. cit.*; LUDLOFF, *Z. Physik*, **39**, 528 (1926).

[2] BIRGE, *Phys. Rev.*, **25**, 240 (1925).

The bands of the SiN system ($\bar{\nu}_e = 24{,}234.2$) have one region of maximum intensity in the neighborhood of the zero sequence, while the iodine bands ($\bar{\nu}_e = 15{,}598.29$) have an unusual distribution (Fig. 13). Still other molecules, such as the hydrogen halides, show only continuous emission and absorption. The absorption spectrum of HCl is continuous with no evidence of a band structure. There are regions of maximum absorption, however, which lie at $2{,}150 - 1{,}850$ Å., $1{,}750 - 1{,}650$ Å., $1{,}580 - 1{,}290$ Å. and in the region from $1{,}270$Å. to a point beyond the region of observation; these are probably due to different electron transitions.[1]

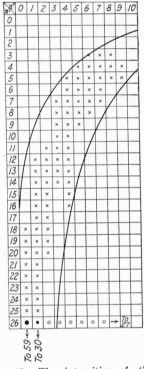

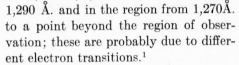

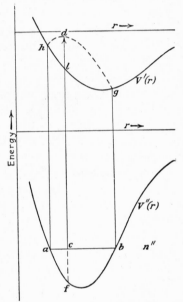

FIG. 13.—The intensities of the I_2 bands. (*Adapted from Birge.*)   FIG. 14.—Illustrating the Franck-Condon theory.

The explanation of these intensity distributions was first given by Franck,[2] who applied his theory primarily to transitions causing the dissociation of the molecule. Condon[3] extended Franck's ideas to explain the intensity distributions in band spectra. It is assumed that in the process of absorption the light acts for the most part on the electron system of the molecule and only to a small extent on the nuclei. Therefore, the action of the light quantum is to raise the electron system to a higher energy level, but not to change the position of the nuclei nor

[1] LEIFSON, *Astrophys. J.*, **53**, 73 (1926).

[2] *Trans. Faraday Soc.*, **21**, Part 3 (1925).

[3] *Phys. Rev.*, **28**, 1182 (1926).

their velocities relative to each other. In the excited state, the nuclei find themselves acted on by different forces and so oscillate with frequency and amplitude different from those characteristic of the lower energy state, *i.e.*, they are brought to a state with a different vibrational quantum number. The change in the vibrational quantum number is determined by the relative shapes of the two potential energy curves for the displacement of the nuclei relative to each other in the initial and final electronic levels. The curves V' and V'' of Fig. 14 represent two such potential energy curves. The energies E_e'' and E_e' are the electronic energies for the two steady states having zero vibrational energy. The solid horizontal line represents one vibrational energy level for the lower electronic state. The curves V' and V'' approach two horizontal lines at large values of r, which represent the energies of the system when dissociated in two independent ways—firstly, into two normal atoms and, secondly, into a normal and an excited atom. We consider the absorption of light by a molecule in the vibration state indicated by n''. The nuclei oscillate with respect to each other in such a way that r oscillates between the limits a and b. At any point r it has kinetic energy equal to the difference between the ordinates of the line ab and the curve V''. Now, when the nuclear separation corresponds to the point c, a quantum of light is absorbed, which for the instant does not change the kinetic energy of the nuclei, nor the value of r, and so the system will be carried to a point d on the energy diagram, where dl is equal to cf, *i.e.*, the kinetic energy remains the same as in the lower state. The molecule will then be in a state (not a quantized energy level) having energy equal to the ordinate of d. In this way the curve gdh can be traced, giving the locus of the energies of the molecule after the absorption of light by a molecule in the n'' state. Since the nuclei remain in the neighborhood of a and b for comparatively longer times than at points between these, the transitions to the region of g and h will be more probable than to other points on the curve gdh. Another maximum in the probability curve for the transitions may be present near the point d, for though the molecule spends less time in the neighborhood of c than near a and b, yet for a considerable distance on either side of c it will be transferred to the same quantum states near d, because of the flatness of the curve gdh at this point. Thus the theory predicts that there will be two very probable transitions, or in certain cases three, if there is a maximum in the curve gdh. In general, the transitions arrived at by using classical mechanics are not quantized states, and, therefore, we must content ourselves with assuming that the actual changes of the vibration quantum number lie in the neighborhood of the unquantized ones required by the above discussion.

The theory as developed does not take into account the distribution of molecules in the various excited electronic and vibrational states, which depends on the mode of excitation of the gas and therefore will vary with the experimental conditions, such as pressure, velocity of the exciting electrons, etc.[1] For this reason the comparison of the theory with bands observed in discharge tubes can only be qualitative.

The general types of intensity distribution in band systems can be accounted for by the different possible shapes of the potential energy curves V' and V''. If these curves were of exactly the same shape and the values of r_0' and r_0'' were the same, the vibration number would not change. This condition is approached in the case of the SiN band system, as can be seen from the values of the moments of inertia and frequencies of vibration in the two states:

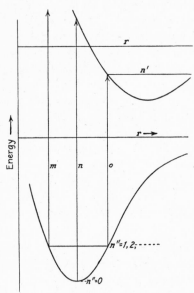

Fig. 15.—Approximate potential energy curves of the Cl₂ type.

$\bar{\omega}' = 1,016.3$, $\bar{\omega}'' = 1,145.0$, $I' = 38.0 \cdot 10^{-40}$, $I'' = 37.4 \cdot 10^{-40}$.

In the case of the AlO band system, the curves do not differ greatly in shape, but the equilibrium distances between the nuclei are different in the two states, thus accounting for the two maxima of intensity in the progressions. The constants for these bands are:

$\bar{\omega}' = 864.4$, $\bar{\omega}'' = 970$, $I' = 46.02 \cdot 10^{-40}$, $I'' = 43.38 \cdot 10^{-40}$.

The constants for the iodine band system are in agreement with its unusual intensity distribution:

$\bar{\omega}' = 127.5$, $\bar{\omega}'' = 213.67$, $I' = 951.6 \cdot 10^{-40}$, $I'' = 742.6 \cdot 10^{-40}$.

In this case, both the shape of the V' and V'' curves and the values of r_0' and r_0'' are very different for the two states.

The relations of the potential energy curves for Cl₂ are certainly of the type shown in Fig. 15. In this case, discontinuous absorption bands involving the normal state of the molecule are unknown,[2] though absorption bands for transitions from the first vibration state have been observed. How this may occur is indicated by the arrows m, n, and o. The transitions from the normal state will transfer the molecule to the continuous energy levels in the neighborhood of the arrow n, while transitions from the first or higher vibration levels may go to the quantized higher vibration levels, as shown by the arrow o, or to the continuous

[1] Herzberg, Z. Physik, **49**, 761 (1928).

[2] Kuhn, Z. Physik, **5**, 130 (1921); **39**, 77 (1926).

region, as indicated by the arrow m. This is certainly a possible mechanism for the photochemical decomposition of some molecules. The reverse process in which two atoms combine to form a molecule with the emission of light should also be possible. The recombination spectra of the halogens have been observed by Kondratjew and Leipunsky[1] and by Urey and Bates.[2] Not every collision between two suitable atoms should result in the formation of a molecule with the emission of light. The probability per sec of such a transition taking place will be about 10^7 at the most, but the duration of a collision is only about 10^{-11} seconds, so that only one collision in 10,000 should result in recombination.

The shape of the V' curve for the excited state of the HCl type of molecule (such as the halogen hydrides and alkali halides) is unknown, since no vibration levels of these molecules in excited states have ever been detected. It may be that it is similar to that of Fig. 15, but with its minimum displaced to a larger value of r relative to r_0 for the lower electronic level. But since only continuous absorption spectra are known for these molecules,[3] it may be that the V' curve for these molecules has no minimum and therefore approaches the horizontal line from the high energy side. In this case both absorption and emission spectra will be continuous, with no possibility of a band spectrum, which agrees with the known experimental facts.

12. THE APPROXIMATE ROTATIONAL STRUCTURE OF AN ELECTRONIC BAND

The structure and gross appearance of an electronic band differ considerably from those of the infra-red bands such as those of HCl. The differences are due principally to two effects: (1) the distance between the nuclei of the molecule may be quite different in the initial and final states, because of the different electron structure of the two states; and (2) the molecule in either or both states may have a resultant angular momentum due to orbital motion of the electron or the electron spins. The first of these influences the gross structure and appearance of all electronic bands and will be discussed in this paragraph, while the latter affects the formulas for the energy levels, the possible values of the rotational quantum number, and the selection rules.

Consider a molecule which has moments of inertia I' and I'' in the states of larger and smaller energy, respectively. If higher terms in j are neglected, and effects due to electronic angular momenta are not

---

[1] *Z. Physik*, **50**, 366 (1928).

[2] *Phys. Rev.*, **33**, 279 (1929); Dec. (1929).

[3] See FRANCK and KUHN, *Z. Physik*, **43**, 164 (1927); **44**, 607 (1927); FRANCK, KUHN, and ROLLEFSON, *ibid.*, **43**, 155 (1927); HOGNESS and FRANCK, *ibid.*, **44**, 26 (1927); DYMOND, ibid., **34**, 553 (1925); GIBSON and RAMSPERGER, *Phys. Rev.*, **30**, 598 (1927).

included, then from equation (5), the rotational energies for the two steady states will be,

$$E_r' = \frac{h^2}{8\pi^2 I'} j'(j' + 1) = B'chj'(j' + 1).$$

and

$$E_r'' = \frac{h^2}{8\pi^2 I''} j''(j'' + 1) = B''chj''(j'' + 1). \tag{65}$$

Accordingly, the wave numbers of the lines emitted will be

$$\bar{\nu} = \frac{(E' - E'')}{hc} = \bar{\nu}_e + \bar{\nu}_n + B'j'(j' + 1) - B''j''(j'' + 1), \tag{66}$$

where $\bar{\nu}_e$ and $\bar{\nu}_n$ are the contributions to the wave number due to the changes in electronic and vibrational energy. In many electronic bands j may change by 0 as well as by ± 1. The wave numbers corresponding to the three possible values of Δj are as follows:

$$R(j) = \bar{\nu}_e + \bar{\nu}_n + (B' - B'')(j + 1)^2 + (B' + B'')(j + 1);$$
$$\Delta j = -1; j = 0, 1, 2 \cdots, \tag{67}$$

$$Q(j) = \bar{\nu}_e + \bar{\nu}_n + (B' - B'')j^2 + (B' - B'')j;$$
$$\Delta j = 0; j = 0, 1, 2 \cdots, \tag{68}$$

$$P(j) = \bar{\nu}_e + \bar{\nu}_n + (B' - B'')j^2 - (B' + B'')j,$$
$$\Delta j = +1; j = 1, 2, 3, \cdots, \tag{69}$$

where now *in each case j is the quantum number of the final rotational state, i.e., j''*. This convention is used throughout this chapter. The possible values of j in equations (67), (68), and (69) are limited by the condition that neither j' nor j'' can become less than 0. The sets of lines described by these formulas are called the R, Q, and P branches, respectively. It is convenient to rewrite them in the forms

$$R(j) = A + 2B(j + 1) + C(j + 1)^2, \tag{70}$$
$$Q(j) = A + Cj + Cj^2, \tag{71}$$
$$P(j) = A - 2Bj + Cj^2, \tag{72}$$

where

$$A = \bar{\nu}_e + \bar{\nu}_n, \ 2B = B' + B'', \ C = B' - B''.$$

If B' and B'' were equal, so that C would be zero, the formulas for the R and P branches would not have the quadratic term and $Q(j)$ would reduce to $\bar{\nu}_e + \bar{\nu}_n$, so that the Q-branch would consist of a single line. Figure 16 shows the wave numbers for the three branches plotted against the values of j for this simple case. Such a plot is known as a "Fortrat diagram." The continuous straight lines joining the points serve only to guide the eye in following the diagram. The R branch is similar to the rotation bands in arrangement and in numbers of initial and final states, but the P branch has no counterpart in the rotation spectrum, since energy cannot be emitted by an increase in the rotational quantum number alone.   A P branch is possible only when either the vibrational or the vibrational and electronic numbers also change.

Figure 17 is the Fortrat diagram for the P, R, and Q branches when C is negative, *i.e.*, $I' > I''$.   The relations are similar to those of the preceding case, except that the spectral lines are no longer equally spaced, and there is a genuine Q branch.

The curves for the P and R branches, shown in the figure and given by equations (70) and (72), intersect at $j = -\frac{1}{2}$, and those for the P and Q branches at $j = 0$; there is no P branch line for which $j = 0$, since this would mean that j would be minus 1 in the initial state.   The R and Q branches intersect at $j = -1$.   The curve for the Q branch is a parabola whose slope is zero at $j = -\frac{1}{2}$.[1]   The P branch lines draw

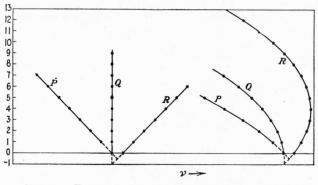

FIG. 16.—Fortrat diagram   FIG. 17.—Fortrat diagram
 in case $I' = I''$.   in case $I' > I''$.

further apart as j increases; the R branch lines draw closer together until $2B(j + 1) + C(j + 1)^2$ becomes a maximum and then draw apart again.   After the maximum is passed, the wave number decreases with increasing j.   This doubling back of the R branch causes an increased density of lines near the maximum and accounts for the existence of the band head on the high-frequency side.   Formerly, the lines were numbered from this point instead of from the band origin at $\tilde{\nu} = A$ as we do at present.   If C is positive, this doubling back will occur in the P branch when $- 2B'j + Cj^2$ is a minimum and the head will lie on the low frequency side.   Bands having the *head on the violet side* are said to be *degraded to the red*, and those having the *head on the red side to be degraded to the violet*.   Visible and ultra-violet bands may be degraded either way for changes in the electron configurations and vibration numbers may be such that C is either positive or negative. C is always negative for the infra-red bands, since it equals $-\dfrac{\alpha}{c}(n' - n'')$, as can be seen from

---

[1] The shape of these curves is modified if the molecule possesses electronic angular momentum, as we can see from Fig. 23, for example.

equations (34a) and (34b), and n' must always be larger than n''. However, C is small for these bands and the doubling back of the R branch would occur only at large values of j. For this reason none of the infra-red bands so far studied have observable heads.

13. THE RIGID GYROSCOPIC DIATOMIC MOLECULE; KRAMERS-PAULI MODEL

The problem of determining the rotational energy states of a diatomic molecule which has a resultant electronic angular momentum even for zero rotation of the nuclei has been considered by Kramers and Pauli,[1] Kratzer[2] and Kemble[3] using the old mechanics, and recently by Hill and Van Vleck,[4] using wave mechanics. By means of the formulas they have developed it appears possible to account for the structure of all known rotational energy levels.

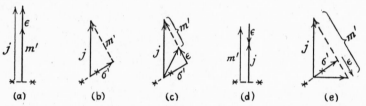

FIG. 18.—Vector combinations of the gyroscopic diatomic molecule—Kramers-Pauli model.

Kramers and Pauli assumed that a diatomic molecule may have a resultant electronic angular momentum vector, rigidly oriented with respect to the line of nuclei at an arbitrary angle, which is supposed to be the same for all rotational states. The components of this angular momentum parallel and perpendicular to this line are represented by $\sigma'h/2\pi$ and $\epsilon h/2\pi$, respectively. It is assumed that the electronic angular momentum s, which is equal to $(\sigma'^2 + \epsilon^2)^{1/2}$ in quantum units, and the total angular momentum of the molecule j, are quantized. In the rotation of this molecule, the vector s lies in a plane determined by the line of nuclei and the direction of j.

The vector diagram for such a molecule is shown in Fig. 18c. Since j is the resultant of σ', ϵ, and m', we have

$$j^2 = \sigma'^2 + (m' + \epsilon)^2.$$

Therefore,

$$m' = (j^2 - \sigma'^2)^{1/2} - \epsilon,$$

[1] Z. Physik, 13, 351 (1923).
[2] Ann. Physik, 71, 72 (1923).
[3] "Molecular Spectra," p. 318; Phys. Rev., 30, 387 (1927).
[4] Phys. Rev., 32, 250 (1928).

and so the angular momentum of the nuclear rotation, $mh/2\pi$, is not ordinarily an integer. The energy may still be written in the same form as for the non-gyroscopic molecule, namely

$$E = \frac{m'^2 h^2}{8\pi^2 I_0} = \left(\frac{h^2}{8\pi^2 I_0}\right)[(j^2 - \sigma'^2)^{\frac{1}{2}} - \epsilon]^2. \tag{73}$$

In the special cases $\sigma' = 0$ and $\epsilon = 0$, this becomes

$$E = \frac{h'^2}{8\pi^2 I_0}(j - \epsilon)^2 \text{ and } E = \frac{h^2}{8\pi^2 I_0}(j^2 - \sigma'^2), \tag{74}$$

respectively. To secure the formulas required by the quantum mechanics it is only necessary to replace j^2 by $j(j + 1)$ and $(j - \epsilon)^2$ by $(j - \epsilon)$ $(j - \epsilon + 1)$ in equations (74). Figure 18, *abc*, shows the arrangement of the vectors for these two special cases and the general case, respectively. The arrangements of vectors shown in Fig. 18*de* were excluded by Kramers and Pauli, since they are dynamically unstable, in the sense that a slight displacement of the vectors would cause a rearrangement into one of the first three types. They were included by Kratzer, however, because they are necessary to account for the number of observed energy levels. We secure the additional formulas for the energy in cases *d* and *e* by using the ambiguous sign before ϵ in equations (73) and (74), and shall always consider ϵ as a positive quantity.

Kratzer introduced an additional term in the energy proportional to the first power of m'. Its theoretical justification has been given by Hund[1] and Hulthén.[2] For simplicity consider the arrangements shown in Fig. 18*a* and *d*, and let the electronic angular momentum ϵ be due to the spin of a single electron, so that $\epsilon = s = \frac{1}{2}$, and the magnetic moment is one Bohr magneton. Further, assume that the nuclei have the same charge and mass. The rotation of the nuclei with m' units of angular momentum will produce a magnetic field at the center of mass equal to $\dfrac{Ze}{\mu c r^3} \dfrac{h}{4\pi} m'$, where Ze is the effective. charge of either nucleus, r the distance between them, and μ the reduced mass. The mutual magnetic energy, due to the coupling of an electron with magnetic moment $eh/4\pi m_0 c$ with the magnetic field will be,

$$E_M = \pm\left(\frac{e}{m_0 c}\frac{h}{2\pi}\right)^2 \frac{m_0}{4\mu} \frac{Z}{r^3} m'.$$

This neglects the magnetic field due to the rotation of the electrons along with the nuclei; this field is opposite to that due to the rotation of the nuclei. Therefore, the expression for E_M should be replaced by a summation which includes the term due to the nuclei and others

[1] *Z. Physik*, **42**, 93 (1927).

[2] *Z. Physik*, **45**, 331 (1927).

due to the magnetic fields produced by the rotation of the individual electrons. This summation will not be zero in general because of the different values of r for the nuclei and electrons and will be equal to a constant multiplied by m'. The additional term in the energy may be positive or negative for either orientation of m' and s, and examples of both cases are known. Using the ambiguous sign before ϵ in equation (73), and adding a term proportional to m', and choosing the ambiguous sign before the last term so that the constant δ is *usually* positive, we have

$$E = \frac{h}{8\pi^2 I}[(j^2 - \sigma'^2)^{1/2} \mp \epsilon]^2 \pm 2\delta[(j^2 - \sigma'^2) \mp \epsilon]. \tag{75}$$

The last term, linear in $[(j^2 - \sigma'^2)^{1/2} \mp \epsilon]$, is necessary to account for the number of energy levels observed in many molecules; and the theoretical value of δ, which can be secured by comparison with E_M, above, is of the right order of magnitude. The case of the hydrides is particularly simple for in this case we can consider the rotation of the positive hydrogen nucleus about the heavier atom. The separation of the levels for parallel and antiparallel m' and s is of the order of magnitude expected.

However, the formula (75) does not yield the energy levels of molecules satisfactorily. Some molecules have rotational energy levels which follow approximately but not exactly, the requirements of the theory, as for example the OH molecule.[1] The reasons for this failure are that classical mechanics cannot be expected to give the correct formula, and that the electronic angular momentum vector is not rigidly bound to any orientation in the molecule, but changes its orientation with changing rotation of the molecule. Before taking up these modifications of the theory (Sec. 15), it is well to consider the origin and nature of the electronic angular momentum, which first became possible with the introduction of the spinning electron.

14. SIMILARITIES OF THE ELECTRONIC LEVELS OF ATOMS AND MOLECULES

Mulliken[2] showed that the first excited level of BO and other molecules with 9 outer electrons is a doublet level, with a separation of the order of magnitude to be expected, if the cause of the multiplicity is the same as that of the alkali metal doublets; and Hulthén[3] showed that the doublet separations of the ZnH, CdH, and HgH molecules were of the same order as those of the Zn, Cd, and Hg atoms. Mecke[4] inde-

---

[1] See BIRGE, "Molecular Spectra," for a detailed comparison of the OH bands with this formula.

[2] *Phys. Rev.*, **25**, 259 (1925); **26**, 561 (1925). See also MECKE, *Z. Physik*, **28**, 261 (1924).

[3] *Nature*, **116**, 642 (1925).

[4] *Naturwiss.*, **13**, 698, 755 (1925).

pendently pointed out certain analogies between the alkali metals and BO, CO^+, CN, and N_2^+. He also noted a similar analogy between these metals and the alkaline earth halides. Birge[1] summed up the evidence previously presented and pointed out that quite generally, definite analogies could be drawn between molecules and "corresponding" atoms; that molecular electronic levels are found to follow a Ritz formula and are arranged in multiplets just as in the case of atoms. Examples of the first of these points of similarity are the electronic levels of the hydrogen and helium molecules,[2] which follow a Ritz formula. The A level of N_2 is a triplet with spacings approximately 20 and 42, while those of the 2^3P level of Mg are 41 and 20.[3] Also, in the case of a doublet level of CO^+ the separation is 126, as compared with the separation 91.5 for the 2^2P level of Mg^+. Subsequent work has amply justified Birge's conclusions.

15. VECTOR MODEL OF THE DIATOMIC MOLECULE WITH AN ELASTICALLY BOUND GYROSCOPE

Hund[4] first applied the methods of describing atomic multiplets by the use of the l and s vectors, as given in Chap. VII, to diatomic molecules. In the theory of the Stark effect (Chap. V, Sec. **12**), we find that the quantum numbers n_1, n_2, and m, (where $n_1 + n_2 + m$ equals the total quantum number, n) must be used to fix the steady states of a hydrogen atom, which in the absence of the electrostatic field has the quantum numbers n and k. According to this theory, m may take all integral values from $-k$ to $+k$, except zero. Wave mechanics (Chap. XVI, Sec. **7**) similarly requires the use of three quantum numbers in the presence of the field, but the allowed values of m are all integral values including zero from $-l$ to $+l$. The quantum numbers k of the older theory and l of the new theory lose their original significance because there is no constant angular momentum vector which precesses uniformly about the direction of the electric field.

Two atoms in close proximity will influence each other in a way similar to that in which an electric field acts on an isolated atom, for each atom finds itself in the strong inhomogeneous electric field of the other. (The magnetic field in the neighborhood of an atom having a magnetic moment will be negligible compared to its electric fields, in its effect on the energy states of neighboring atoms.) The effect of the field of one atom on the other is to cause a torque on the electron

---

[1] *Nature*, **117**, 300 (1926).

[2] FOWLER, *Proc. Roy. Soc.*, **91**, 208 (1915); CURTIS and LONG, *ibid.*, **108**, 513 (1925); BIRGE, *Proc. Nat. Acad. Sci.*, **14**, 12 (1928).

[3] The close agreement between these figures is probably not significant.

[4] *Z. Physik*, **36**, 657 (1926); **40**, 742 (1927); **42**, 93 (1927).

system and nucleus of the latter about a line perpendicular to the line joining them. This causes a precession of the electron system of the second atom about the line of nuclei; the second atom causes a similar precession of the first. This means that one of the angle variables of the system is the frequency of precession multiplied by the time. The angular momentum about the line of nuclei is constant and must be quantized. Let this quantum number be λ. Just as in the case of the Stark effect in a strong electric field, where the component of angular momentum parallel to the field may take all integral values from $-l$ to $+l$, so here λ takes the values $-l$, $-l+1$, $\cdots$ $l-1$, l, where l is a hypothetical quantum number which would be the azimuthal number if the two atomic fields were replaced by a central field. The total number of λ values for given l is thus $(2l+1)$. There is no indication from the Stark effect that the electron spin vector is caused to precess with an appreciable angular velocity in the presence of an electric field, and therefore no such precession of s about the line of nuclei is to be expected, and the orientation of s in the non-rotating molecule will depend only on its coupling with λ. If this is zero, it should be free to orient itself in any direction whatsoever. However, when the molecule is rotating, there will be a coupling between the s and λ vectors on the one hand and the magnetic field due to the rotation of the nuclei on the other hand, as described above (Sec. **13**); but since the λ vector is strongly oriented by large electric fields the coupling between it and this weak magnetic field can be neglected. Also, even neglecting this weak magnetic field, there is a coupling between the λ and s vectors and the j vector, arising from the kinetic reactions in a rotating gyroscope, which tend to orient the λ and s vectors parallel or antiparallel to j, as will be shown presently; but in most cases these effects tending to orient λ in the direction of j are much smaller than the effects due to the electrical fields of the atoms. The orientation of λ is therefore practically unaffected by the rotation of the molecule as a whole. This is not true with respect to the orientation of s; the strength of coupling between λ and s may be weaker or stronger than the strength of coupling between the s and j vectors, or approximately equal to it. For this reason Hund distinguishes the cases:

Case a.—The coupling between λ and s is very much stronger than that between j and s, so that the orientation of s depends principally on λ and only slightly on j. The quantum numbers for this case are j, s, λ and σ; σ is the projection of s along the line of nuclei and (in case a) it takes all values from $-s$ to $+s$. We shall denote the vector sum of λ and σ by ι. The meaning of these vectors can be seen from Fig. 19.

Case b.—The coupling between the λ and s is very much weaker than that between j and s. In this case we have the following quantum numbers: λ as before; k, which is the resultant of λ and the rotational number m', (not quantized) as shown in Fig. 19; and j which is the vector sum of k and s.   The s in this case takes quantized orientations with respect to k and is only slightly influenced by λ.

There is also the intermediate case where the strengths of coupling are nearly the same.   Then for low values of j, the rotational states will follow those required for case a, and for large values of j, those required for case b; between these two extremes there will be a transition from case a to case b.   Since the coupling between s and j is always fairly weak, this transition case will not occur unless the coupling between λ and s is weak.   It will be necessary therefore to correlate the arrangements of vectors for case a with those for case b.   The circles of Fig. 19 indicate the precessions of the vectors.   In case a, m' and ι precess about j with the same frequency while in case b, m' and λ precess

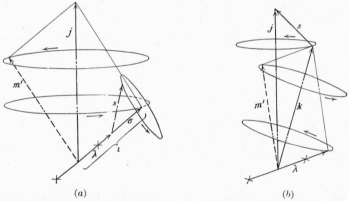

(a) $\qquad\qquad\qquad\qquad\qquad\qquad (b)$

Fig. 19.—Vector combinations and precessions of the gyroscopic diatomic molecule. Hund's cases (a) and (b).

about k with the same frequency. m' is determined by j and ι or by k and λ in these two cases, respectively, and, therefore, is not quantized. It must be understood that we are dealing with a model in which l and s are not directly coupled to form a quantized resultant, as they are in the normal multiplet levels of atoms.   The s vector does not couple with l, which is not a quantum number, but only with λ which has the direction of the line of nuclei in case a, or with k in case b.

The total number of quantized states will be the same for case a and case b.   In case a, the total number of values of σ for a given value of s is $2s + 1$.   Combining this with the total number of λ values, we have $(2s + 1)(2l + 1)$ possible steady states.   For case b, there will be $2l + 1$ possible values of λ, as for case a, and $2s + 1$ possible orientations of s with respect to k and thus a total of $(2s + 1)(2l + 1)$ combinations for each j value, in this case as well.   Some of these levels will have identical energies if the molecule is not rotating.   Changing the sign of both σ and λ in case a, or λ in case b should result in no change of energy if the molecule is of this kind. Simple considerations show that as a consequence the number of levels observed should be $(2s + 1)$ $(l + 1)$. On the other hand, if the molecule has rotational energy, this degeneracy is removed and two steady states with a small energy difference occur if $\lambda \neq 0$ (Chap. XIX, Sec. **9**). This results in the appearance of the full number of levels expected, namely $(2s + 1)$ $(2l + 1)$. They are arranged in close pairs, except that the level for which $\lambda = 0$ is single. It was known that the interpretation of experimental facts required this doubling of the levels before the cause was understood, and the phenomenon was called "σ-type doubling" or, better, using the symbols of this chapter, λ-type doubling. It is always present if λ is not zero. The explanation was first given by Hund,[1] and has been discussed also by Hulthén[2] and Kronig.[3] States for which λ is different will usually be widely separated because of the large "Stark effect" (see Chap. V, Sec. **12** and Chap. XVI, Sec. **7**).

The resultant λ which we have used may be regarded as the vector sum of $\lambda_1, \lambda_2, \lambda_3, \ldots \lambda_r \ldots$, characteristic of the individual electrons. Each of the electrons is influenced by the large inhomogeneous electric field of the two nuclei so very strongly that the coupling between the l's of the individual electrons is broken down and each behaves to a first approximation as though the others were not present and thus,

$$\lambda = \lambda_1 + \lambda_2 + \lambda_3 \cdots \lambda_r + \cdots .$$

These two cases, a and b, occur most frequently and are the only ones discussed in detail in this book, but other ways of combining the l and s vectors may occur. It may occur that the coupling energy of the l vectors among themselves is greater than the energy of the "Stark effect" due to the two nuclei. In this case, the l's will form a quantized resultant l and the s's another resultant s. These two vectors will form a j which will be entirely similar to the atomic j and this will precess about the line of nuclei. Its projection on this line will be ι, which will then combine with the m' to form the resultant j of the molecule. This is Hund's case c.

Again it may happen that the molecule consists of a kernel having only closed shells of electrons and the two nuclei, and one or more "valence" electrons moving at relatively large distances from the kernel. In this case, there will be, first, a rotation of the kernel with a resultant angular momentum and, second, a resultant angular momentum of the outer electron system made up by a vector sum of the l's and s's of the electrons.

[1] *Z. Physik*, **42**, 93 (1927).

[2] *Z. Physik*, **46**, 369 (1927).

[3] *Z. Physik*, **46**, 814 (1928); **50**, 347 (1928). See also Van Vleck, *Phys. Rev.*, **33**, 467 (1929).

Finally, there will be a coupling between these vectors. Several cases may be considered here depending on the way the vectors are coupled. Weizel has shown that this uncoupling of the λ from the line of nuclei occurs in the case of certain He_2 levels.[1]

16. ENERGY OF THE ELASTIC GYROSCOPIC MOLECULE; CORRELATION OF CASES a AND b

Having considered the origin of the resultant electronic angular momentum we wish to secure the formula for the rotational energy and

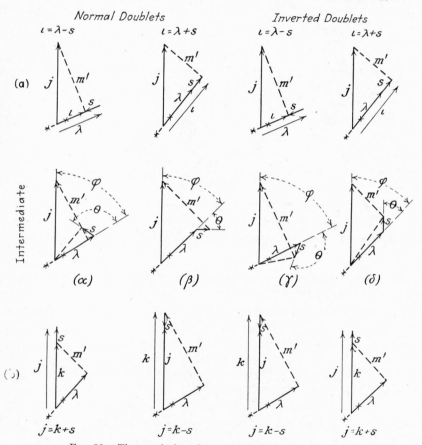

Fig. 20.—The correlation of cases (a) and (b) when $s = \frac{1}{2}$.

to decide how the states of case a are to be correlated with those of case b. In other words, if a molecule belongs to case a and has certain values of the quantum numbers j, λ, σ, and ι for small values of j, and if it becomes a molecule of case b for large j, what will be the values of the quantum numbers j, λ, s and k, which correspond to the values of the

[1] *Z. Physik*, **54**, 321 (1929).

quantum numbers for case a? This correlation is given graphically in Fig. 20 for normal and inverted doublets (where $s = \frac{1}{2}$, so that $\sigma = \pm\frac{1}{2}$). In the normal doublets the higher energy level for no rotation of the nuclei is that for which $\iota = |\lambda| + |\sigma|$, and the lower, that for which $\iota = |\lambda| - |\sigma|$, while the reverse holds for the inverted doublets. Thus, for example, if $\lambda = 1$ and $\sigma = \pm\frac{1}{2}$, $\iota = \frac{3}{2}$, or $\frac{1}{2}$, the molecular states are similar to $^2P_{\frac{1}{2},\frac{3}{2}}$ atomic states, and the rule for normal and inverted doublets is the same. For normal doublets, those states of case a which have λ and σ parallel go into states of case b having k and s antiparallel; and those states of case a having λ and σ antiparallel go into states of case b having k and s parallel. For inverted doublets, parallel λ and σ go over into parallel k and s; and antiparallel λ and σ into antiparallel k and s. One apparent exception to the rule for normal doublets will be discussed later.

The essential features of the argument both for the energy levels and the correlation of the two sets of quantum numbers for the two cases can be understood from the mechanical model considered by Kemble.[1] We shall consider only the special case where $s = \frac{1}{2}$ and therefore $\sigma = \pm\frac{1}{2}$ for small values of j, which is the case of a doublet system of electronic levels. The two possible arrangements of vectors for the case intermediate between cases a and b are given in Fig. 20, with the s slightly displaced from the position parallel or antiparallel to λ in the way expected for normal and inverted doublets. The resultant electronic angular momentum does not lie along the line of nuclei, but it does lie in the plane determined by j and the line of nuclei so that as stated above there is no component of electronic angular momentum perpendicular to this plane. The coordinates θ and φ fixing the position of λ, s, and j relative to each other are shown in the figure. It is assumed as a first approximation at least that the energy of coupling between λ and s is proportional to these numbers and to the angle between them; let this energy be

$$V(\theta) = Ah\lambda s \cos\theta, \tag{76}$$

where A is positive for normal doublets, and negative for inverted doublets. The torque tending to increase θ will be

$$-\frac{\partial V}{\partial \theta} = Ah\lambda s \sin\theta. \tag{76a}$$

This must be equal to the torque due to the precession of the gyroscope about j in a state of steady motion; this is known from the theory of the gyroscope to be equal to the angular velocity of precession multiplied by the component of angular momentum perpendicular to j, and is, therefore,

$$\omega s h \sin(j, s),$$

[1] Phys. Rev., **30**, 387 (1927).

where ω is the frequency of precession of the nuclei about j. Equating this to the right member of equation (76a), we have

$$A\lambda \sin \theta = \sin (\theta \mp \varphi), \tag{77}$$

since the angle $(j, s) = \theta \mp \varphi$ as can be seen from the figure.

These results may be better understood by the following geometrical argument. The torque due to the coupling between s and λ is in a direction to increase the angle θ for the two vector arrangements of Fig. 20 when A is positive, *i.e.*, for normal doublets. This torque if not balanced by an opposing one would cause a rotation of s in the direction of increasing θ. In time dt, it would contribute an additional angular momentum, upward from the plane of the page in (20α) and downward in (20β), equal to the torque times dt. This additional angular momentum is perpendicular to s. In the absence of any coupling with λ, s would keep its orientation in space unchanged. Therefore, s is changed in direction relative to the line of nuclei, by the rotation of the molecule as a whole, at a rate equal to the projection of s on the plane perpendicular to j multiplied by the angular velocity of precession, $2\pi\omega$. This will be downward from the plane of the page in (20α) and upward in (20β), so that these changes due to the rotation of the molecule are always opposite in direction to the angular momenta contributed by the coupling torque. When these two are equal no precession of the s vector about the line of nuclei will occur, and it will be held in kinetic equilibrium at the angle θ. This is the meaning of equation (77). The angle θ decreases with increasing j in (20α) and increases with increasing j in (20β). Finally, s becomes parallel or antiparallel to k, thus proving the correlation of states given for normal doublets. The correlation for inverted doublets is similar; here A is negative so that the direction of the coupling torque is opposite to that for normal doublets and a similar argument applied to the inverted doublets will give the correlation of the cases a and b as before.

The kinetic energy of rotation of the nuclei is

$$T = \tfrac{1}{2}\mu r_0{}^2(2\pi\omega)^2 \sin^2 \varphi = \tfrac{1}{2}I(2\pi\omega)^2 \sin^2 \varphi, \tag{78}$$

where r_0 is the distance between the nuclei, μ the reduced mass, and I the moment of inertia of the molecule. The angular momentum of rotation about a line perpendicular to the line of nuclei and in the plane of j and this line is

$$\mu r_0{}^2(2\pi\omega) \sin \varphi = I(2\pi\omega) \sin \varphi$$

and this must be equal to

$$(j \sin \varphi \mp s \sin \theta)\frac{h}{2\pi},$$

so that

$$\omega = \frac{h(j \sin \varphi \mp s \sin \theta)}{4\pi^2 I \sin \varphi}. \tag{79}$$

Further, from the geometry of the figure, we have

$$j \cos \varphi = \lambda + s \cos \theta. \tag{80}$$

To secure the energy as a function of j, λ and s, we must eliminate φ, ω, and θ from equation (78) by means of equations (77), (79), and (80).

This cannot be done except for the limiting cases of very small and very large values of j. The formulas agree fairly well with the experimental data for the $^2\Pi_{3/2, 1/2}$ state of OH secured from the water band at 2,811 Å., but again we shall make use of the more exact and simpler formula of Hill and Van Vleck[1] secured from matrix mechanics using the matrix analogue of Kemble's model. This formula is

$$E = [(j + \tfrac{1}{2})^2 - \lambda^2 \mp \tfrac{1}{2}\{4(j + \tfrac{1}{2})^2 + \alpha(\alpha - 4)\lambda^2\}^{1/2}]Bhc, \quad (81)$$

where $\alpha = A/Bc$ and $B = h/8\pi^2 Ic$ as used before in this chapter. This formula holds throughout the region of transition from case a to case b for both normal (A positive) and inverted (A negative) doublets and agrees very well with experimental data to be presented in the following paragraphs.

17. NOTATION FOR ELECTRONIC LEVELS AND BANDS[2]

The notation used to describe molecular levels is an outgrowth of the methods of designating atomic levels, but is more complicated because of the greater number of quantum numbers. Undoubtedly, it will be

[1] *Phys. Rev.*, **32**, 250 (1928).

[2] Many symbols have been used for the quantum numbers of molecules and it appears that there may be still further changes. Below we give some of these systems and that used in this book. We list under "Washington" a set adopted by an unofficial group of spectroscopists at the April meeting of the American Physical Society. Prof. R. S. Mulliken tells us that he is using a set somewhat different from this which we list under "Mulliken (revised)." The symbols used in this book are partly chosen because we had used small letters instead of capitals in preparing the book and felt that the labor of changing all our symbols was too great to justify our doing so. Also, we rather prefer small letters because of the greater ease of writing them. We believe the set used is sufficiently similar to the others to make comparison with other works comparatively easy.

Quantum Numbers for Case a.

This book..................... λ_τ	λ	σ	ι	j	m	s
Wigner and Witmer...........	λ	η	ι	j		r
Hund........................ $i_{l\tau}$	i_l	i_s	i	p		s
Mulliken..................... $\sigma_{k\tau}(\sigma_{l\tau})$	$\sigma_k(\sigma_l)$	σ_s	σ	j	m	s
Washington.................. $\lambda(\lambda_\tau)$	Λ	Σ	I	J	M	S
Mulliken (revised)............ $\lambda(\lambda_\tau)$	Λ	Σ	Ω	J	M	S

Quantum Numbers for Case b.

This book..................... λ_τ	λ	k	j	m	s
Wigner and Witmer..............	λ	l	j		r
Hund.......................... $i_{l\tau}$	i_l	p_l	p		s
Mulliken...................... $\sigma_{k\tau}(\sigma_{l\tau})$	$\sigma_k(\sigma_l)$	$j_k(j_l)$	j	m	s
Washington.................... $\lambda(\lambda_\tau)$	Λ	K	J	M	S
Mulliken (revised).............. $\lambda(\lambda_\tau)$	Λ	K	J	M	S

In addition to these, Dennison and Kronig have used n for λ, and Sommerfeld (Ergänzungsband) has used τ for λ. The use of Greek symbols was first introduced by Wigner and Witmer. References to the papers of the authors cited are given throughout the text.

modified in the future, as the subject grows. The detailed symbols introduced by Mulliken,[1] Hund[2] and Wigner and Witmer[3] for electronic levels of molecules will be developed as different types of bands are described and the necessity for them becomes evident. The symbols Σ, Π, Δ, etc., will be used to indicate levels for which $\lambda = 0$, 1, 2, etc., respectively. Bands are indicated by giving the symbols for both the initial and the final electronic states. We now proceed to give illustrations of various types of electronic bands. The selection rules will be derived empirically from the experimental data.

18. BANDS OF THE TYPE $^1\Sigma \to {}^1\Sigma$

The infra-red rotation vibration bands of HCl, discussed in detail in Sec. 6, are examples of this type of band. The rotational energy for both the initial and final states is approximately proportional to $j(j + 1)$, $j = 0$, 1, $\cdots$. The levels are single, which indicates that there is no electronic angular momentum, so that λ and σ are zero. Only P and R branches are known, so that the selection rule is $\Delta j = \pm 1$.

Electronic bands of this type are known, of which the CuH bands at 4,280 Å. are a good example. A least square computation[4] of the best empirical equations for the two branches yields the results,

$$R(M) = 23{,}311.080 + 14.6072M - 1.07834M^2 - 0.001155M^3 +$$
$$0.0000364M^4,$$

and   (82)

$$P(M) = 23{,}310.976 - 14.4439M - 1.09105M^2 + 0.003657M^3 +$$
$$0.0000138M^4,$$

where $M = 1$, 2, $\cdots$. The difference between the constant terms in these two equations is probably not significant, but the differences in the other constants are certainly real. These bands can be accounted for approximately by assuming terms ($\bar{\nu} = E/hc$) given by the equations

$$\bar{\nu}' = \bar{\nu}_e' + \bar{\nu}_v' + F'(j'), F'(j') \cong B'j'(j' + 1),$$
$$\bar{\nu}'' = \bar{\nu}_e'' + \bar{\nu}_v'' + F''(j''), F''(j'') \cong B''j''(j'' + 1), \qquad (83)$$

with j' or $j'' = 0$, 1, $\cdots$ and the selection rule, $\Delta j = \pm 1$. The energy level diagram required for the band is entirely similar to that of the HCl bands (Fig. 5). The arrows showing the transitions for the P and R branches are numbered in accordance with the usual convention by giving the j value of the lower energy state. The first R line is $R(0)$ and the first P line $P(1)$; their wave numbers are given by equation (82) with $M = 1$. Equation (82) can be rewritten, using j instead of the empirical running number M by substituting $M = j + 1$ in $R(M)$

[1] *Phys. Rev.*, **30**, 785 (1927).

[2] *Z. Physik*, **51**, 759 (1928).

[3] *Z. Physik*, **51**, 859 (1928).

[4] Birge and Shea, "Molecular Spectra," p. 87.

and $M = j$ in $P(M)$ in the right hand members so that $R(M)$ and $P(M)$ equal $R(j)$ and $P(j)$ of equations (70) and (72) respectively. The so-called "double differences of the rotational terms," defined as $F(j + 1) - F(j - 1)$ and represented by the symbol $2\Delta F$, can be secured by taking differences between the wave numbers of suitably chosen lines of the P and R branches. From the figure, it is easily seen that these differences are given by the following combinations:

$$2\Delta F'(j) = F'(j+1) - F'(j-1) = R(M) - P(M) = R(j) - P(j) \quad (84)$$
$$= 13.632 + 26.8911j + 0.009463j^2 - 0.004666j^3 + 0.0000226j^4,$$

$$2\Delta F''(j) = F''(j+1) - F''(j-1) = R(M-1) - P(M+1) = R(j-1) - P(j+1)$$
$$= 15.635 + 31.2222j + 0.001656j^2 - 0.004867j^3 + 0.0000226j^4.$$

From these equations we can determine the functions $F'(j)$ and $F''(j)$. Except for an unknown additive constant independent of j, they are,

$$F'(j) = 6.8144j + 6.7239j^2 + 1.5753 \cdot 10^{-3}j^3 - 5.832 \cdot 10^{-4}j^4$$
$$+ 2.26 \cdot 10^{-6}j^5,$$
$$F''(j) = 7.8172j + 7.8068j^2 + 2.685 \cdot 10^{-4}j^3 - 6.084 \cdot 10^{-4}j^4$$
$$+ 2.26 \cdot 10^{-6}j^5. \quad (85)$$

The first two terms on the right of these equations could be replaced by

$$6.7239j(j + 1) + 0.0905j,$$

and

$$7.8068j(j + 1) + 0.0104j, \quad (86)$$

respectively, and thus these equations are approximately, but not exactly, in the form to be expected for a rotating non-gyroscopic diatomic molecule. Kemble[1] has suggested that this deviation is due to an orientation of the electron spin vectors relative to j in such a way that they do not exactly add up to a resultant zero. This would occur because of the kinetic torque due to the rotation and would give a small component of electronic angular momentum parallel to j. The additional term in the energy proportional to j arises for the reasons given in Sec. 13. This deviation is quite frequent in this type of level, but the approximate agreement and the singlet character of the levels lead to the conclusion that neither of the electronic states has any resultant electronic angular momentum. The transition is therefore classified as $^1\Sigma - {}^1\Sigma$.

The CuH molecule has an even number of electrons and 2 of these, one from the copper atom and 1 from the hydrogen atom may form a "valence" group similar to that of the alkaline earths. Thus we may expect the levels to be single and triple, as in these atoms. The known singlet bands are in accord with this expectation; j takes integral values for this level of odd multiplicity, just as the atomic j does in the case of odd atomic multiplets.

---

[1] "Molecular Spectra," pp. 345–346.

19. THE 4,241 Å. BAND OF AlH; A ¹Π → ¹Σ TRANSITION[1]

This band consists of a P, a Q, and an R branch, and, therefore, the first and most obvious assumption to make is that it is emitted in transitions between two sets of single rotational levels, following the selection rule $\Delta j = \pm 1$ or 0. This is not true, for on following through the assumption, we find that a doubling of the levels must be assumed. A doubling of levels is to be expected in accordance with the preceding theoretical discussion for a singlet Π state, for here $\lambda = 1$ and $\sigma = 0$; two states of slightly different energy will be present for each value of j, due to the two possible orientations of λ, which can be explained only by means of the new mechanics (Chap. XIX, Sec. **9**). To see how this doubling is detected in practice, we return to the original erroneous assumption for the present. That is, we assume that the wave numbers of the three observed branches are given by the following differences, omitting for simplicity the contribution to the wave numbers by the change in electronic and vibrational energy,

$$P(j) = F'(j - 1) - F''(j)$$
$$Q(j) = F'(j) - F''(j)$$
$$R(j) = F'(j + 1) - F''(j). \tag{87}$$

Then the first differences designated by $\Delta F(j + \frac{1}{2})$ and defined as $F(j + 1) - F(j)$ are for the two electronic levels,

$$\Delta F'(j + \tfrac{1}{2}) = F'(j + 1) - F'(j) = R(j) - Q(j) = Q(j + 1) - P(j + 1),$$
$$\Delta F''(j + \tfrac{1}{2}) = F''(j + 1) - F''(j) = Q(j) - P(j + 1) = R(j) - Q(j+1). \tag{88}$$

If our assignment of transitions is correct, the two expressions for $\Delta F'$ and similarly the two for $\Delta F''$ should agree. That they do not agree exactly is evident from Table 3. The amount of the discrepancy is known as "the combination defect," and its existence proves that the

TABLE 3

j	$F'(j + 1) - F'(j)$			$F''(j + 1) - F''(j)$		
	$R(j) - Q(j)$	δ'	$Q(j + 1) - P(j + 1)$	$Q(j) - P(j + 1)$	δ''	$R(j) - Q(j + 1)$
0	. . . . .	. . .	. . . . .	. . . . .	. . .	12.8
1	24.1	0.2	23.9	25.1	0.2	25.3
2	36.2	0.3	35.9	37.6	0.3	37.9
3	48.3	0.5	47.8	50.2	0.5	50.7
4	60.3	0.9	59.4	62.3	0.9	63.2
9	107.1	0.9	106.2	112.2	0.9	113.1
10	118.7	1.8	116.9	123.9	1.8	125.7
14	173.5	3.5	170.0	171.2	3.8	174.0
19	220.3	5.5	214.8	227.6	5.6	233.2

[1] ERIKSSON and HULTHÉN, *Z. Physik*, **34**, 775 (1925).

assignment of levels is not quite correct. There are no observed lines for $Q(0)$ or $P(1)$, showing that j for the initial state cannot take a value less than 1.

The combination defect can be satisfactorily accounted for by assuming that the higher energy levels are close doublets. Figure 21 illustrates the first few rotational levels for the two electronic states. According to Mulliken,[1] the lower $^1\Sigma$ levels are designated as A levels and the higher double levels as A and B levels, in such a way that a B level combines with an A level, when $\Delta j = \pm 1$, and an A level with an A level when $\Delta j = 0$. Further cases of this will be met and the more general statement of the selection rule is that

$$B \to A \text{ or } A \to B, \text{ when } \Delta j = \pm 1,$$

and

$$A \to A \text{ or } B \to B, \text{ when } \Delta j = 0.[2] \quad (89)$$

The levels and transitions of Fig. 21 have been drawn so as to be in agreement with this rule and the experimental data of the band.

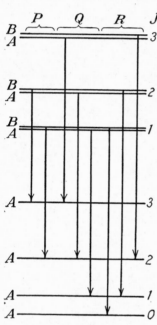

Fig. 21.—Energy levels for the 4,241 Å AlH band.

The three branches are due to the following combinations:

$$P_{BA}(j) = F_B'(j - 1) - F_A''(j),$$
$$Q_{AA}(j) = F_A'(j) - F_A''(j),$$
$$R_{BA}(j) = F_B'(j + 1) - F_A''(j), \quad (90)$$

where the meaning of the subscripts of the F' and F'' is evident, and those of the P, Q, and R indicate the character of the initial and final levels involved. These symbols will be used in the following discussion to indicate levels and transitions, where this so-called "λ-type doubling" occurs. The differences of the second column of Table 3 are really $F_B'(j + 1) - F_A'(j)$, and of the fourth column $F_A'(j + 1) - F_B'(j)$, so that they should not be identical. In the fifth and seventh columns are the differences

$$(F_A''(j + 1) - F_A''(j)) + (F_A'(j) - F_B'(j))$$

and

$$(F_A''(j + 1) - F_A''(j)) + (F_B'(j + 1) - F_A'(j + 1)),$$

respectively, which again should not be identical. The differences δ' and δ'' should be equal to each other in agreement with observation, and equal to

$$(F_B'(j + 1) - F_A'(j + 1)) + (F_B'(j) - F_A'(j)). \quad (91)$$

[1] *Phys. Rev.*, **30**, 785 (1927).

[2] In this type of level j and k are identical.

From these differences, $F_B'(j) - F_A'(j)$ can be secured as a function of j. It appears that it cannot be a linear function of the rotational quantum number and that the B levels lie higher than the A levels as shown in Fig. 21.

By using only the P and R branches, expressions could be secured for $F_B'(j)$ and $F_A''(j)$ as functions of j, by exactly the same methods which were used in discussing the CuH bands above. The differences $F_B'(j + 1) - F_B'(j - 1)$ are found to follow a fairly smooth formula of the type $4B(j + \frac{1}{2})$, which shows that $F_B'(j) = B'j(j + 1)$. Because the lines $Q(0)$ and $P(1)$ are missing, the level for $j = 0$ must be absent. The lower levels follow a formula of the form $F_A''(j) = B''j(j + 1)$ with $j = 0, 1, \cdots$, very closely. Thus, the energy diagram meets all the requirements necessary to account for this band.

The initial state is evidently a $^1\Pi$ state with $\lambda = 1$ and $\sigma = 0$. The final level is evidently a $^1\Sigma$ level of the same type as those of the HCl bands or the CuH band; $\lambda = 0$ and one would expect that its rotation levels might behave as either A or B levels and would combine with both these types of levels, which is not the case. The selection rule for this band is that given in equation (89). It is to be noted that j takes integral values for this system of odd multiplicity, as it should.

20. THE B BAND OF CaH; A $^2\Sigma \rightarrow {}^2\Sigma$ TRANSITION

The CaH molecule has an odd number of electrons so that the spin number s must be half integral. If two of the three valence electrons form a closed shell, only one electron is involved in the emission process and we may expect a doublet system of levels similar in some ways to those of the alkalies. In order to avoid confusion, certain points developed in the preceding theory of the gyroscopic molecule may be repeated here. For a Σ level, λ is zero and therefore the s vector, which is $\frac{1}{2}$ in this molecule, will not tend to orient along the line of nuclei at all since electrostatic fields do not influence its orientation. Therefore, it is free to orient itself parallel or antiparallel to k. However, since λ is zero, k is the angular momentum of rotation of the nuclei, and j will be equal to $(k + \frac{1}{2})$ or $(k - \frac{1}{2})$, for the two orientations of s with respect to k. The energy of rotation will therefore be proportional to $k(k + 1)$ for both these orientations, with only a slight difference due to the two orientations of s in the weak magnetic fields produced by the rotation of the nuclei. This effect was discussed in connection with equation (74), and the theoretical formula for this case, neglecting the small magnetic energy, is secured from equation (81) by setting $\lambda = 0$ and $\alpha = 0$. Thus, the terms should follow the formula,

$$F = B[(j + \frac{1}{2})^2 \pm (j + \frac{1}{2})] \pm 2\delta k$$
$$= Bk(k + 1) \pm 2\delta k \qquad (92)$$

where
$$j = k + \tfrac{1}{2}, \text{ or } j = k - \tfrac{1}{2}.$$

(Compare equations (74), (75), and (81).)   The ambiguous sign is chosen so that the energy is maximum when k and s have the same direction. Those terms which have the same k will evidently form close doublet levels whose separation becomes zero for $k = 0$.

The known bands of CaH have been measured by Hulthén[1] and Mulliken[2] and are called the A, B, and C bands.   The B bands are two in number and are probably the zero sequence with vibration numbers $0 \to 0$ and $1 \to 1$.   These bands and also the C bands are to be classed as a $^2\Sigma \to {}^2\Sigma$ transition.   The A bands are a $^2\Pi \to {}^2\Sigma$ transition.   This type will be considered later.   The B bands consist of two R and two P branches, and perhaps two short Q branches.   All of them can be satisfactorily accounted for by assuming two energy levels for each value of j, both for the initial and final electronic states.   The observed lines are given by the combinations,

$$
\begin{aligned}
P_{11}(j) &= \bar{\nu}_e + F_1{}'(j-1) - F_1{}''(j), \\
R_{11}(j) &= \bar{\nu}_e + F_1{}'(j+1) - F_1{}''(j), \\
P_{22}(j) &= \bar{\nu}_e + F_2{}'(j-1) - F_2{}''(j), \\
R_{22}(j) &= \bar{\nu}_e + F_2{}'(j+1) - F_2{}''(j).
\end{aligned}
\tag{93}
$$

The subscripts 1 and 2 of the F's distinguish the two sets of terms for which s is parallel and antiparallel to k, respectively; and the subscripts of the P's and R's indicate the orientation of the s for both the initial and the final states involved in the emission of the line.   The double subscript is unnecessary here since $P_{12}(j)$, $R_{12}(j)$, etc. are not observed in these bands, but the full symbol will be used, because it will be required in more complex band types.   The subscripts A and B are unnecessary

TABLE 4[1]

k	P_{11}	j	R_{11}	P_{22}	j	R_{22}
0		$\tfrac{1}{2}$	15,761.91			
1	15,745.12	$\tfrac{3}{2}$	15,770.73		$\tfrac{1}{2}$	15,773.07
2	36.53	$\tfrac{5}{2}$	79.91	15,737.87	$\tfrac{3}{2}$	83.20
3	28.13	$\tfrac{7}{2}$	89.51	30.86	$\tfrac{5}{2}$	93.75
4	20.70	$\tfrac{9}{2}$	99.54	24.11	$\tfrac{7}{2}$	804.53
5	13.48	$11\tfrac{1}{2}$	809.93	17.78	$\tfrac{9}{2}$	15.73

[1] Hulthén gives lines which would be designated $P_{22}(\tfrac{1}{2})$ and $R_{22}(-\tfrac{1}{2})$ in the present numeration, with wave numbers 15,745.12 and 15,763.17 respectively; but Mulliken, *Phys. Rev.*, **30**, 145 (1927), gives reasons for believing that these should be classified as $Q_{12}(\tfrac{1}{2})$ and $Q_{21}(\tfrac{1}{2})$ lines and they are therefore omitted from the table. See discussion below.

[1] *Phys. Rev.*, **29**, 97 (1927).

[2] *Phys. Rev.*, **25**, 509 (1925).

because $\lambda = 0$, and all the levels are A levels. Both systems of subscripts will be needed when both λ and s are not zero.

The wave numbers of the observed lines are given in Table 4 for small values of the rotational quantum numbers. The j's and k's given are those for the final state in each case.

Using this assignment of the lines to the branches and the interpretation of the branches expressed by equations (93) we can secure the double differences of terms as before.

$$2\Delta F_1'(j) = F_1'(j+1) - F_1'(j-1) = R_{11}(j) - P_{11}(j)$$
$$2\Delta F_1''(j) = F_1''(j+1) - F_1''(j-1) = R_{11}(j-1) - P_{11}(j+1),$$

and there are similar equations for $2\Delta F_2'(j)$ and $2\Delta F_2''(j)$. These differences are given in Table 5.

TABLE 5

k	j	$2\Delta F_1'$	d'	$2\Delta F_2'$	j	j	$2\Delta F_1''$	d''	$2\Delta F_2''$	j
1	3/2	25.61				3/2	25.37			
2	5/2	43.38	−1.95	45.33	3/2	5/2	42.30	0.09	42.21	3/2
3	7/2	61.08	−1.81	62.89	5/2	7/2	59.21	0.12	59.09	5/2
4	9/2	78.84	−1.61	80.47	7/2	9/2	76.03	0.06	75.97	7/2
5	11/2	96.46	−1.50	97.95	9/2	11/2	92.83	0.05	92.77	9/2

For the higher energy state the differences for the F_2 terms are larger than those for the F_1 terms, showing that the F_2 set is more widely spaced than the F_1 set. Thus the F_2 term lies higher in the energy diagram than the F_1 term having the same value of k. The opposite is true for the lower energy state, and this is the more usual order of these two sets of terms for $^2\Sigma$ electronic levels.

The assignment of these branches to the transitions indicated in equation (93), where $F_1(j)$ and $F_2(j)$ are the rotational terms for parallel and antiparallel k and s, respectively, cannot be proved unique from a study of this band alone. Thus we might interchange the two P branches, or the two R branches in Table 4, for the two doubtful lines at 15,745.12 and 15,763.17 (see footnote of Table 4) are known, which may make the number of lines identical, and in this way values entirely different from those of Table 5 would be secured. Moreover, there is no proof for the assignment of the k values to the j's as given in Table 5. The assignment of lines to the combinations given in equation (93) and the assignment of j values given above are proved to be correct by the study of other bands of CaH which are emitted in transitions from other energy levels to the final levels of the B band. The double differences for the lower energy state are the same as those secured from this band and the selection rules require the assignment of $j = k + s$ to the terms $F_1''(j)$, and $j = k - s$ to the terms $F_2''(j)$, in accord with our assignment here.

The energy diagram for this B band of CaH, and the first few transitions for the observed branches, are illustrated in Fig. 22. The separations of the doublet levels are exaggerated in comparison with the rest of the diagram. In addition to the transitions accounting for the observed lines listed in Table 4, there are two transitions indicated by broken lines, which represent the combinations,

$$Q_{12}(j) = \bar{\nu}_e + F_1'(j) - F_2''(j),$$
$$Q_{21}(j) = \bar{\nu}_e + F_2'(j) - F_1'(j), \tag{94}$$

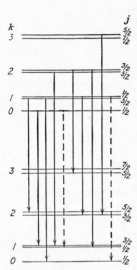

with $j = \tfrac{1}{2}$. Two lines are known, which agree with the positions expected for these lines. From Fig. 22, it is seen that $Q_{12}(\tfrac{1}{2})$ will lie close to $P_{11}(\tfrac{3}{2})$ and $Q_{21}(\tfrac{1}{2})$ close to $R_{11}(\tfrac{1}{2})$, and that higher members of these branches will lie close to the P_{11} and R_{11} branches. For this reason, Hulthén classified these two lines in the P_{11} and R_{11} branches,[1] although Δj is certainly zero for these lines, and strictly they must be called Q branches. To meet this situation, which is encountered also in other molecules, Mulliken[2] has introduced a symbol for branches which must be called Q branches in that $\Delta j = 0$, but which look like P or R branches because of the arrangement of energy levels. The two branches defined by equation (94) are represented by the symbols ${}^P Q_{12}(j)$ and ${}^R Q_{21}(j)$, respectively. The

Fig. 22.—Energy levels for the B band of CaH.

Q in these symbols shows that $\Delta j = 0$, while P and R show the empirical appearance of the branches; the first follows an empirical formula with a negative term proportional to the ordinal number, and the second, one with a positive term. Quite similarly, we may have branches which are designated as ${}^Q R$, ${}^Q Q$, ${}^P P$, etc.

From formula (92) we get for the double term differences,

$$2\Delta F_1(j) = B(4k + 2) + 4\delta,\ j = k + \tfrac{1}{2},$$
$$2\Delta F_2(j) = B(4k + 2) - 4\delta,\ j = k - \tfrac{1}{2}, \tag{95}$$

and so

$$2\Delta F_1(j) - 2\Delta F_2(j) = 8\delta. \tag{96}$$

These differences are listed in Table 5, under d' and d'', for the initial and final sets of levels, respectively, and are very nearly constant as required by the theory. But for the higher energy state, δ is negative

[1] See footnote to Table 4.
[2] *Phys. Rev.*, **30**, 783 (1927).

so that we have here an "inverted doublet." From equation (95) we see that

$$4Bk + 2B = \Delta F_1(j) + \Delta F_2(j),$$

and thus B can be calculated. The values of the constants required to give the best agreement with the empirical data are given by Hulthén and are:

$$B' = 4.400, \quad \delta' = -0.250, \quad r_0' = 1.96 \times 10^{-8} \text{ cm.}$$
$$B'' = 4.225, \quad \delta'' = \quad 0.011, \quad r_0'' = 2.01 \times 10^{-8} \text{ cm.}$$
$$\bar{\nu}_e = 15{,}753.84.$$

The selection rules for the band are:

$\Delta j = \Delta k = \pm 1$, intense lines;
$\Delta j = 0, \Delta k = \pm 1$, weak or forbidden lines;
$\Delta k = 0$ does not occur.   (97)

The CN bands of Fig. 1 are due to a transition of this type, but the separation of the doublet levels for parallel and antiparallel k and s is so small that the two lines with the same k cannot be separated. The unusual intensities of the lines for $k' = 4, 7, 13,$ and 15 are due to some unknown cause associated with their excitation by the action of active nitrogen on organic compounds.

21. THE OH BANDS; A $^2\Sigma \rightarrow$ $^2\Pi$ TRANSITION

In bands of the $^2\Sigma \rightarrow$ $^2\Pi$ type, the $^2\Pi$ levels for small values of j, i.e., for Hund's case a, will have $\lambda = 1, \sigma = \pm\frac{1}{2}$, and also will show the λ-type doubling, depending on the two possible orientations of λ with respect to the two atoms. Four rotational states will therefore be expected for each value of j. The doublet may be called normal or inverted, according as $^2\Pi_{3/2}$ or $^2\Pi_{1/2}$ is the higher energy level. For the region of large values of j, we have the quantum numbers j, k, and λ; j will be equal to $k + \frac{1}{2}$ or $k - \frac{1}{2}$, just as for the $^2\Sigma$ levels.

We select for a detailed example the so-called "water bands"; the higher energy level is a $^2\Sigma$ level similar in every way to the levels of the CaH B band, while the lower level, which is believed to be the ground level, is an inverted $^2\Pi$ level. For small j we are dealing with a case a molecule, and for larger j, the behavior approaches that of a case b molecule. The formula for its energy levels will be given by equation (81) with $\lambda = 1$, if the λ-type of doubling and also the small effect of the magnetic field of the rotating nuclei are neglected; thus,

$$F_i(j) = B[(j + \tfrac{1}{2})^2 - 1 \pm \tfrac{1}{2}\{4(j + \tfrac{1}{2})^2 + \alpha(\alpha - 4)\}^{\frac{1}{2}}], \quad (81a)$$

where $i = 1$ or 2, depending on whether the positive or negative sign is used; i.e., on whether k and s are antiparallel or parallel for large j, or λ and σ are antiparallel or parallel for small j, respectively.

The water bands[1] consist of five bands with the following vibration numbers for the initial and final states: (0, 0), (0, 1), (1, 0), (2, 0), and (2, 1). Thirteen branches have been observed, though the data required for our purpose here are not complete for any one band; those for the (0, 0) band at 3,064 and the (1, 0) band at 2,811 Å. are most nearly complete. In many cases, the structure of these thirteen branches and the first line of each one have been determined from several bands. The reasoning by which the energy levels have been constructed is similar to that used above for the CaH B band, but is more involved because

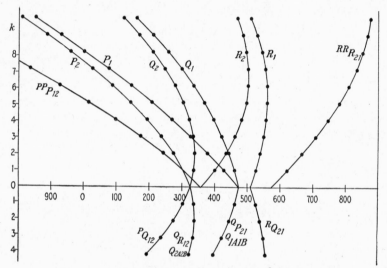

Fig. 23.—The Fortrat diagram of the 2811 Å OH band.

of the more complex structure of these bands; it will not be given here because of the impossibility of briefly summarizing the intricate details. Figure 23 is the Fortrat diagram for the (1, 0) band. The more intense branches known as the main branches are above the line for $k = 0$ and the weaker ones known as satellite branches are below this line. The branches are indicated by Mulliken's symbols which have been described in preceding paragraphs. The reader will see the meaning of these symbols more readily by studying Fig. 24, which is the typical energy diagram for these bands. It is drawn to scale for the (1, 0) band at 2,811 A., except that we have exaggerated the doubling for the F_1 and F_2 levels in the higher electronic state, and the λ-type doub-

[1] We owe the experimental data on these bands to Grebe and Holtz, *Ann. Physik* **39**, 1243 (1912); Fortrat, *J. de Phys.*, **5**, 20 (1924); Watson, *Astrophys. J.*, **60**, 145 (1924); and Jack, *Proc. Roy. Soc.* **115**, 373 (1927) and **118**, 647 (1928) and their theoretical interpretation to Dieke, *Proc. Acad. Sci. Amsterdam*, **28**, 174 (1925); Birge, "Molecular Spectra in Gases,"; Kemble, *Phys. Rev.*, **30**, 387 (1927); Mulliken, *Phys. Rev.*, **32**, 388 (1928); and Hill and Van Vleck, *Phys. Rev.*, **32**, 250 (1928).

ling indicated by the A and B levels for the lower electronic state. The arrows indicate the first lines of observed branches except that $^{PP}P_{12}$ has not been observed. Although it is expected according to the selection rules, it should be weak and hidden by other lines. The j, k, λ, and σ quantum numbers are given for the levels, though k has no real meaning for the $^2\Pi$ levels with small j, nor has σ for the $^2\Pi$ levels with large j.

Kemble has shown that the formula secured by classical mechanics gives approximate agreement with the empirical energy levels for the

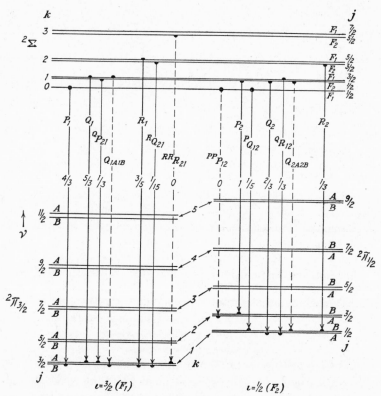

Fig. 24.—Energy diagram of the OH molecule. (*After Mulliken.*)

zero vibrational state, and Hill and Van Vleck have shown that equation (81a) can be made to agree with these levels over the entire range by using $B = 18.58$ and $\alpha(\alpha - 4) = 21.79$ or $\alpha = -3.078$, and adding a small term $-0.00177\ k^4$, to make an approximate correction for the change of moment of inertia with rotation. A slight disagreement for the higher values of j is probably due to neglect of the λ-type doubling, which is not included in the theory, and of the energy contributed by the coupling between s and the magnetic field of the rotating nuclei.

The changes of j and k, the A, B combinations, and the observed branches are listed in Table 6 and from these the empirical selection rules can be stated.

TABLE 6

Δj	Δk	Type of AB combination	Branches
1	1	$A \to B$	R_{1A1B}, R_{2A2B}
-1	-1	$A \to B$	P_{1A1B}, P_{2A2B}
0	0	$A \to A$	Q_{1A1A}, Q_{2A2A}
-1	0	$A \to A$	${}^{Q}P_{2A1A}$
1	0	$A \to A$	${}^{Q}R_{1A2A}$
0	1	$A \to B$	${}^{R}Q_{2A1B}$
0	-1	$A \to B$	${}^{P}Q_{1A2B}$
1	2	$A \to A$	${}^{RR}R_{2A1A}$
-1	-2	$A \to A$	${}^{PP}P_{1A2A}$ (Not yet observed.)
0	0	$A \to B$	Q_{1A1B}, Q_{2A2B}

j may change by 0 or ± 1, and k by 0, ± 1, or ± 2, but the simultaneous changes of these two numbers cannot differ by more than unity; the strong branches are those for which $\Delta j = 0$, ± 1 and $\Delta j = \Delta k$. In addition, $A \to B$, if $\Delta k = \pm 1$, and $A \to A$, if $\Delta k = 0$ or ± 2. The Q_{1A1B} and Q_{2A2B} branches are exceptions to this last rule, though others may actually occur in these bands and not have been observed. The more general form of this selection rule, applicable to bands where λ-type doubling occurs in both states, is that $A \to B$ or $B \to A$, if $\Delta k = \pm 1$, and $A \to A$, or $B \to B$, if $\Delta k = 0$ or ± 2. The values of ι for the lower state and for small values of j can always be secured from the correlation between the states defined by j and k and those defined by j and σ; this correlation for the inverted doublet type is,

$$j = k + s: \iota = \lambda + \sigma,$$

and

$$j = k - s: \iota = \lambda - \sigma.$$

The same selection rules hold for the normal doublet type except that in this case the correlation[1] between the j and k and the j and σ states is

$$j = k + s: \iota = \lambda - \sigma,$$
$$j = k - s: \iota = \lambda + \sigma.$$

The βNO bands[2] illustrated in Fig. 1 are due to a transition between two ²Π states in which the σ and λ are strongly coupled (case a). In this case the selection rules are:

$$\Delta j = 0, \pm 1, \Delta \iota = \Delta \lambda = 0$$

[1] The correlation holds exactly, but the energy of the lowest F_2 states (for which $j = k + s$ when j is large), approaches a value for large doublet separations which places it more naturally in the F_1 set of rotational levels. See MULLIKEN, *Phys. Rev.*, **32**, 388 (1928), particularly Fig. 1, p. 391.

[2] JENKINS, BARTON, and MULLIKEN, *Phys. Rev.*, **30**, 150 (1927).

and the usual selection rule for the A and B states. Since the coupling between the σ and λ is strong, two bands, in which $\iota = \frac{1}{2}$ and $\iota = \frac{3}{2}$, respectively, are widely separated and thus have the appearance of separate bands instead of the complex structure of the OH bands. The values of j given in the figure are for the final electronic state.

22. SYMMETRIC AND ANTISYMMETRIC TERMS AND ALTERNATING INTENSITIES[1]

A review of the examples of electronic bands presented in the preceding paragraphs shows one especially interesting fact, which has not been emphasized. In all the bands studied it is possible to arrange the rotational levels into two sets, such that transitions in which light is emitted always occur between a level of one set, and one of the other. This may be seen from discussions of Hund,[2] Hulthén,[3] Kronig,[4] and Wigner.[5]

Hund first showed that two sets of steady states are to be expected on theoretical grounds for molecules consisting of two like atoms; these two sets are referred to as symmetric and antisymmetric states. Hulthén pointed out that two sets of levels should be expected for all diatomic molecules on the basis of experimental data. Kronig, and also Wigner and Witmer, showed that wave mechanics requires two sets for diatomic molecules consisting of unlike atoms, and that the selection rule stated at the beginning of this paragraph should hold; they may be called the "plus ($\times$) and minus ($|$) sets," respectively. It then became theoretically clear that diatomic molecules with like nuclei should have symmetric and antisymmetric types of levels and that each of these types may be divided into plus and minus sets. Symmetric and antisymmetric terms *never* combine and *plus* terms combine only with *minus* terms, or the reverse. (Chap. XIX, Sec. 9.)

The permitted transitions of the quantum numbers defining the rotational steady states for the types of bands described above, can be shown very clearly by plotting the energies of the rotational steady states horizontally. The two plots for the two electronic states involved are placed one above the other. This has been done in Fig. 25, for all the types of bands discussed here, except in the case of the $^2\Sigma \rightarrow {}^2\Pi$ type, where the $^2\Sigma$ states are placed between the $^2\Pi_{\frac{1}{2}}$ and the $^2\Pi_{\frac{3}{2}}$ states for convenience. The levels are represented by the symbols $\times$ and $|$ for the plus and minus terms, respectively, and the transitions permitted by the above selection rules are indicated by diagonal lines.

[1] See Chap. XIX for a further discussion of this subject.

[2] *Z. Physik.*, **46**, 349 (1928).

[3] *Z. Physik.*, **46**, 814 (1928).

[4] *Z. Physik.*, **50**, 347 (1928).

[5] *Z. Physik.*, **43**, 624 (1927); NEUMANN and WIGNER, *ibid.*, **51**, 844 (1928); WIGNER and WITMER, *ibid.*, **51**, 859 (1928).

There is no irregularity in the energy values as we go from one set of terms to the other, and there is no variation in the intensity of the lines emitted. In fact, there is no known experimental method of differentiating between them. It should be noted from the figure that this classification of levels robs the A and B assigned to the λ-type doublets of any physical meaning, but these letters are still convenient for classifying the experimental data.

In the case of molecules having like nuclei theory requires that the plus and minus states may also be *symmetric* or *antisymmetric* as well. These are well illustrated by the helium bands investigated

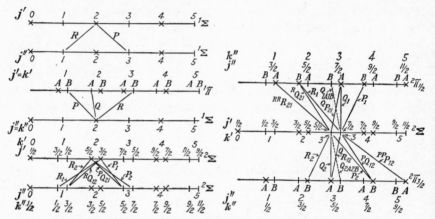

FIG. 25.—The plus (X) and minus (|) terms of diatomic molecules.

by Curtis and Long.[1] Figure 26 illustrates these two types of levels for the $^1\Pi \rightarrow {}^1\Sigma$ transition. The branches observed are similar to those of the AlH bands (Sec. **19**) except that all the transitions involving the symmetric levels are missing, so that only half the lines we should expect to find are present. The resulting spectrum is represented in Fig. 27 where the broken lines indicate the missing lines. Except for these missing lines the structure of the bands and the formulas for the energy levels are exactly similar to those described in the preceding paragraphs. Here we have a case where one set of levels is differentiated from the other by being altogether absent. Mecke was the first to explain this structure of the helium bands by assuming that alternate levels are missing.

The spectrum of the hydrogen molecule investigated by Werner[2] and especially by Hori[3] in the far ultra-violet is similar in some respects

[1] CURTIS, W. E., *Proc. Roy. Soc.*, **101**, 38 (1922); **103**, 315 (1923); CURTIS and LONG, *ibid.*, **108**, 513 (1925).

[2] *Proc. Roy. Soc.*, **113**, 107 (1926).

[3] *Z. Physik*, **44**, 834 (1927).

to the helium bands. Again we expect singlet and triplet electronic levels since it is an even molecule, whose normal state will be $^1\Sigma$. Two ultra-violet band systems are known, which are assigned to $^1\Sigma \rightarrow {}^1\Sigma$ and $^1\Pi \rightarrow {}^1\Sigma$ transitions. Figure 28 is the energy diagram for the Werner bands with broken lines and solid lines to indicate the symmetric and antisymmetric levels, respectively. The doublets of the $^1\Pi$ level are due to λ-type doubling. The permitted transitions are exactly of the type of the AlH band (Sec. **19** and Fig. 21), and only symmetric levels combine with symmetric levels, and antisymmetric levels with antisymmetric levels. There is one very marked difference between the AlH bands and these H_2 bands, namely, that in these bands the spectral lines emitted in transitions between symmetric levels are much

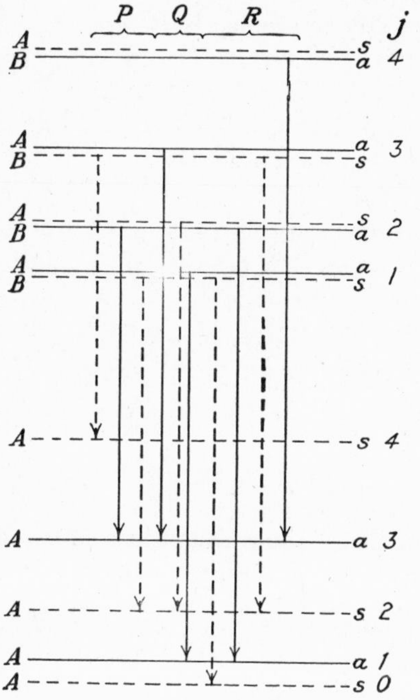

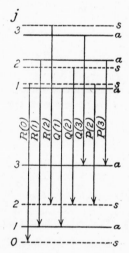

Fig. 26.

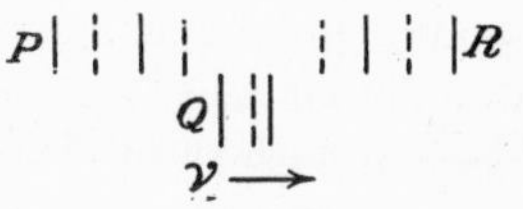

Fig. 27.

Fig. 26.—Energy level diagram for the $^1\Pi \rightarrow {}^1\Sigma$ bands of He₂.

Fig. 27.—The observed lines of the He₂ bands.

Fig. 28.—The transitions of the Werner bands of H_2.

weaker than those due to transitions between antisymmetric levels. It will be noted that this is similar to the behavior of the helium bands. In fact, the latter represent a special case of intensity alternation in which the weaker lines are entirely absent.[1]

[1] See Chap. XIX, Sec. **10**. We really do not know whether it is the symmetric or the antisymmetric levels which are absent in the case of He₂.

There is no irregularity in the energies of the levels, but only a difference in the intensities of the lines emitted. This might be due either to a difference in the number of symmetric and antisymmetric molecules, or to a difference in the probabilities of the transitions. The former postulate is in good agreement with other experimental facts, which will now be presented.

The *a priori* probability of a state of the rotating molecule is given by the number of nondegenerate states into which it splits, when placed in a suitable external field. This is equal to the number of different orientations of the j vector in this field, namely, $2j + 1$. The probabilities for the states with $j = 0, 2, 4, \cdots$ are therefore proportional to 1, 5, 9, $\cdots$ and those for the states with $j = 1, 3, 5, \cdots$ are proportional to 3, 7, 11, $\cdots$, but the relative probabilities of these two sets of states are not one-to-one for otherwise the intensities of the band lines would not alternate as they do. Light is thrown on this question by studies of specific heats. The heat capacity of a diatomic gas due to its rotational energy is given by the formula

$$\frac{C}{R} = \sigma^2 \frac{d^2}{d\sigma^2} lnQ, \tag{98}$$

where

$$\sigma = \frac{h^2}{8\pi^2 IkT}, \ Q = \Sigma P_j \exp\left[-\frac{h^2}{8\pi^2 IkT} j(j+1) \right], \tag{99}$$

and P_j is the *a priori* probability of the jth state. Hund[1] considered the heat capacity of hydrogen, using this formula and adjusting two constants to fit the experimental data; the first of these is the moment of inertia of the hydrogen molecule, unknown at the time but now known from the work of Hori, and the second is the relative probability of the symmetric and antisymmetric rotational states. By equation (99),

$$Q = \beta[1 + 5e^{-6\sigma} + 9e^{-20\sigma} + \cdots] + 3e^{-2\sigma} + 7e^{-12\sigma} + \cdots \tag{100}$$

where β is the ratio of probabilities of the symmetric and antisymmetric states. By taking β equal to 2 and the moment of inertia I equal to $1.54 \cdot 10^{-41}$ g.cm.^{2} he secured fairly good agreement with the experimental heat-capacity curve. The value of the moment of inertia is $4.66 \cdot 10^{-41}$ g.cm.^{2} and no value of β can be chosen so that the heat-capacity curve is even approximated by equation (98) using the above formula for Q; therefore, some modification of the theory is necessary.[2]

The theory used by Hund assumes that symmetric or antisymmetric molecules may be readily changed to the other type in collisions. Dennison[3] made the interesting assumption that this is not true, but that the

[1] *Z. Physik*, **42**, 93 (1927).
[2] See BIRGE and JEPPERSEN, *Nature*, March 22, 1930.
[3] *Proc. Roy. Soc.*, **115**, 483 (1927).

time interval during which a given molecule retains its type is long compared to the time required to determine the heat capacity. If this is true, we have to deal with the heat capacity of a mixture of two gases, whose heat capacities are separately given by the formulas,

$$\frac{C_s}{R} = \sigma^2 \frac{d^2}{d\sigma^2} ln Q_s, \quad Q_s = 1 + 5e^{-6\sigma} + 9e^{-20\sigma} + \cdots ,$$

$$\frac{C_a}{R} = \sigma^2 \frac{d^2}{d\sigma^2} ln Q_a, \quad Q_a = 3e^{-2\sigma} + 7e^{-12\sigma} + \cdots . \tag{101}$$

The measured heat capacity for a gram molecule is that of a mixture of ρ parts of the first gas, to one of the second, namely,

$$\frac{C}{R} = \frac{\rho C_s + C_a}{(1 + \rho)R}. \tag{102}$$

Using these formulas with $\rho = \frac{1}{3}$, the experimental curve is checked very well and the moment of inertia required is $4.64 \cdot 10^{-14}$ in excellent agreement with Hori's value. Hund's original theory requires that at low temperatures all the molecules should be in the symmetric quantum state with $j = 0$. According to Dennison's theory, only one molecule is in this lowest state for every three in the antisymmetric state with $j = 1$. Even collisions with other molecules and with the walls of the containing vessel only slowly change symmetric to antisymmetric molecules, or the reverse.

Further proof of the inability of one set of rotational levels to change to the other set in collisions is given by the work of Wood and Loomis[1] on the fluorescent spectrum of I_2 vapor. When iodine vapor is illuminated with monochromatic light only those states will be excited, whose energy of excitation above one of the low-lying energy levels present in the gas at ordinary temperatures coincides with the frequency of the exciting line within the limits of the Doppler broadening. The transitions from these excited levels to the low-lying levels must conform to the selection rule that $\Delta j = \pm 1$ (the band is a $^1\Sigma \rightarrow {}^1\Sigma$ type), while many changes in the vibration quantum number are permitted. An n'' progression of bands will be emitted with only two lines in each band, one for $\Delta j = 1$ and the other for $\Delta j = -1$. The addition of helium to the iodine gas causes many more lines of these bands to appear, due undoubtedly to molecules losing or gaining rotational energy in collisions with helium atoms, giving rise to other excited states and thus to other transitions for which $\Delta j = \pm 1$. These additional excited rotational states are symmetric states only. By way of illustration, the green mercury line excites the molecule to the state $n' = 26$, $j' = 34$. In the absence of helium, n changes by large amounts but j by only ± 1, and thus the final rotational states have $j'' = 33$ or 35. In the presence

[1] *Phil. Mag.* **6**, 231 (1928).

of helium at a pressure of 0.5 mm. of mercury, fairly strong bands are found for which $n' = 25$ and 27 and weaker bands with $n' = 24$ and 28, in addition to the strong bands with $n' = 26$ so that n' has been changed by ± 1 or ± 2 in collisions. Much larger changes in the j' occur, but lines are found only for *even values of* j' so that collisions carry the molecule from the state, $j' = 34$, to other even (symmetric) states only. It has been assumed that the even numbered rotational states of the excited electronic level are symmetric. If this is also assumed for the normal electronic state and if the transition is $^1\Sigma \rightarrow {}^1\Sigma$, it would be necessary to have transitions between symmetric and antisymmetric terms, contrary to the rule stated above. Wigner and Witmer[1] showed that the symmetric states of Σ electronic levels may be either odd or even numbered. In the case of iodine we do not know which states are symmetric, and which antisymmetric. Loomis and Wood arbitrarily assigned them in the way adopted here.

Though the rate at which the symmetric form of hydrogen changes to the antisymmetric form or vice versa may be very small, it should be finite, and if hydrogen gas is kept at a very low temperature for a sufficiently long time, it should change to the symmetric form. The two varieties of hydrogen should have different boiling and melting points, heat capacities, etc. Giauque and Johnston[2] have found that the triple point pressure for hydrogen which was kept at liquid air temperatures for 197 days was lower than that of hydrogen prepared and kept at room temperature. The two pressures observed were 5.34 and 5.38 $\pm$ 0.01 cm., respectively. This demonstration that two forms of hydrogen exist with different physical properties furnishes convincing proof of the existence of symmetric and antisymmetric diatomic molecules.

Bonhoeffer and Harteck[3] have succeeded in producing large changes in the properties of hydrogen by cooling it to liquid air or liquid hydrogen temperatures in the presence of charcoal. While the equilibrium ratio of symmetric (para) to antisymmetric (ortho) hydrogen at ordinary temperatures is 1:3 at liquid air temperatures this becomes~1:1 and at liquid hydrogen temperatures hydrogen in equilibrium should consist of nearly 100 per cent symmetric molecules. Using charcoal as a catalyst, they prepared mixtures of symmetric and antisymmetric hydrogen varying in composition from 25 per cent to nearly 100 per cent of the symmetric form. Some properties of the two forms and of ordinary hydrogen (the 1:3 mixture) are given in the following table. The properties of the antisymmetric form have been secured by extrapolation from properties of the mixtures.

[1] *Loc. cit.*

[2] *J. A. C. S.*, **50**, 3221 (1928).

[3] *Z. physik. Chemie*, **4B**, 113 (1929); *Naturwis.* **1**, 182 (1929).

	Symmetric	Antisymmetric	Ordinary Hydrogen
Triple point...............	13.83° A	13.99° A	13.95 A
Vapor pressure at 20.39° A...	787 ± 1 mm.	751 mm.	760 mm.

The heat of vaporization of the symmetric hydrogen is 0.65 per cent less than that of the antisymmetric form. Independently Eucken[1] secured an enrichment of the symmetric hydrogen by cooling hydrogen at high pressures to liquid air temperatures and has shown that the heat capacity of different samples so treated differ widely from that of ordinary hydrogen in accordance with Dennison's theory.

Hund suggested that the presence of both the symmetric and antisymmetric levels is to be associated with a spin of the nuclei similar to the spin of the electron. The relative probability of 1 to 3 for symmetric and antisymmetric states is due to the proton having an angular momentum of $\frac{1}{2}$ in quantum units. The relative probabilities of two states, one of which has the two spins in the same direction and the other of which has the two spins in opposite directions, are 3 to 1; for, if the two spins have the same direction, the resultant spin of 1 may orient in an external magnetic field in three directions; but if they have opposite directions, the orientation of the resultant vector zero is indeterminate, and this condition is assigned the probability one. For the symmetric states, the nuclear spins are antiparallel with a resultant of 0 and for the antisymmetric states they are parallel with a resultant of 1. In the case of the helium molecule, we assume that the helium nucleus has no spin and thus there is no orientation of the nuclei relative to each other. Such a case is to be associated with the entire absence of one set of states (Chap. XIX, Sec. 10). In the case of iodine alternating line intensities have not been observed; for some reason the probabilities of the symmetric and antisymmetric states are very nearly equal in this case, due perhaps to a large nuclear spin.

The alternation of line intensities is very characteristic of molecules having like nuclei. The phenomenon is known in the bands of C_2, N_2, N_2^+, O_2, $Cl_{35} - Cl_{35}$ and F_2, in addition to H_2 and He_2, but does not occur in the I_2 and Na_2 bands.

C. Polyatomic Molecules

23. THE INFRA-RED SPECTRA OF POLYATOMIC MOLECULES

Studies have been made on the infra-red rotation-vibration spectra of a number of polyatomic molecules,[2] but none have been investigated with sufficient dispersion to separate the individual lines except methane[3] and ammonia, phosphine and arsine.[4] The latter appear

---

[1] *Naturwis.* **1**, 182 (1929).

[2] See Hettner, *Z. Physik*, **1**, 345 (1920).

[3] Cooley, *Astrophys. J.*, **42**, 73 (1925).

[4] Robertson and Fox. *Proc. Roy. Soc.*, **120**, 128–211 (1928).

to be somewhat irregular, which may be due either to the presence of unresolved double lines or to difficulties of classification. The spectra of such molecules are necessarily more complex than those of diatomic molecules, because of the larger number of degrees of freedom. If we neglect electronic and nuclear spins, there will be $3n$ degrees for an n-atomic molecule. In general, three may be assigned to the translation of the molecule, three to its rotation as a whole, and the remaining $3n - 6$ to its vibrations. Therefore, three rotational and $3n - 6$ vibrational numbers are required to fix the states of the molecule. Thus, for a molecule of five unlike atoms, three rotational and nine vibrational quantum numbers will be required, and the number of energy levels and transitions will be so great that the task of separating the spectral lines in the infra-red becomes almost hopeless. If several atoms are of the same kind

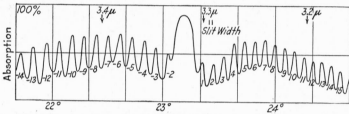

Fig. 29.—The 3.31 μ methane band. (*After Cooley*. Reprinted by permission of the University of Chicago Press.)

so that the molecule has a high symmetry, the molecule may be highly degenerate, so that a much smaller number of quantum numbers will be required. In the case of methane, if we assume the tetrahedral model, only four incommensurable vibrational frequencies should be present, instead of the nine expected for an unsymmetrical non-degenerate molecule.

It is for this reason that detailed work on infra-red rotation-vibration bands has been limited chiefly to symmetrical molecules. Those with small moments of inertia are best for this work, for the moments of inertia appear in the denominator in the equations for the energy, equations (115) and (116), and thus a smaller moment of inertia means a greater separation of the lines of a band. At present, with most infra-red spectrographs, it is impossible to separate lines that are much closer together than those of the halogen hydrides, and for this reason the well-known infra-red bands are practically limited to hydrides and other compounds containing hydrogen.

Cooley[1] observed eight absorption bands of methane and Ellis[2] has extended their number to fifteen. The frequencies of the maxima can all be accounted for by the formula

$$\tau_1 \nu_1 + \tau_2 \nu_2 + \tau_3 \nu_3 + \tau_4 \nu_4 = \nu,$$

where the τ's are integral numbers and $\nu_1 \ldots \nu_4$ are four fundamental frequencies. Two bands, in the neighborhood of 3.31μ and 7.7μ,

[1] *Loc. cit.*

[2] *Proc. Nat. Acad.*, **13**, 202 (1927).

respectively, were partially resolved into lines by Cooley and his absorption curve for the $\lambda 3.31\mu$ band is reproduced in Fig. 29. This curve as well as the one for $\lambda 7.7\mu$, has a structure similar in some respects to the HCl absorption curves of Colby, Meyer, and Bronk (Fig. 3) and of Imes (Fig. 6). There is one marked difference; in the central region of the HCl band the absorption is weak, showing a missing line distinctly, while methane shows strong unsymmetrical absorption in this same region. This appears to be due to an unresolved Q branch. The wave numbers of the P and R branches of these two bands are

$$\bar{\nu} = 1{,}320.4 + 5.409M - 0.0377M^2, \tag{104}$$

and

$$\bar{\nu} = 3{,}019.3 + 9.771M - 0.0351M^2, \tag{105}$$

for the bands at 7.7 and 3.31μ, respectively, where M equals 1, 2, . . . for the R branches and $-2, -3, \cdot\cdot\cdot$ for the P branches. (The lines for $M = -1$ are probably present, but are masked by the intense Q branches.) The peaks in the absorption curve for the 7.7μ band are very regular and symmetrical, but those of the 3.31μ band are somewhat irregular and may not be completely resolved.

24. THE QUANTUM THEORY OF THE HEAVY SYMMETRIC TOP TYPE OF MOLECULE

In order to relate the constants of these empirical equations to the constants of the molecule, it is necessary to consider the rotational energy of the polyatomic molecule. In our study of the rotational levels of diatomic molecules we proceeded as though all the mass of the atoms were located in a mathematical line joining the nuclei; so that the model has two equal principal moments of inertia about two lines perpendicular to each other and to the line of nuclei, and zero moment of inertia about the line of nuclei itself. But when a molecule consists of several atoms, the nuclei usually do not lie in a straight line and thus it is necessary to treat the molecule as a rigid or semirigid body with three principal moments of inertia, usually all different. If the molecule possesses an axis of symmetry, two of the moments will be equal, and for a few molecules, such as the tetrahedral model of methane, all three principal moments may be equal. We consider here the theory of a rigid molecule having two equal moments of inertia, and the third unequal to these, but not equal to zero.

This problem was first solved by Reiche[1] and was further considered by Epstein.[2] Later, a gyroscope, such as a spinning electron, was added to the model.[3] Further it has been considered on the basis of the new

[1] *Physik. Z.*, **19**, 394 (1918).

[2] *Physik. Z.*, **20**, 289 (1919).

[3] KRAMERS, *Z. Physik*, **13**, 343; and KRAMERS and PAULI, *Z. Physik*, **13**, 351 (1923); WITMER, *Proc. Nat. Acad. Sci.*, **12**, 602 (1927).

mechanics by several authors (Chap. XIX, Sec. **5**). Here we shall give a solution in terms of the old mechanics. For convenience, we first obtain the rotational energy states, then the vibrational levels of the non-rotating molecule, and finally the selection rules.

Let A, A, and C be the moments of inertia about the principal axes x', y', and z' fixed in the molecule, and let the components of angular velocity about these axes be p, q, and r. The kinetic energy is given by

$$2T = Ap^2 + Aq^2 + Cr^2$$
$$= \frac{(P^2 + Q^2)}{A} + \frac{R^2}{C} \tag{106}$$

where $P = Ap$, $Q = Aq$, and $R = Cr$. P, Q, and R are the components of angular momentum about x', y', and z', respectively. Instead of these coordinates we shall use the Eulerian angles shown in Fig. 30 and defined as follows: θ is the angle between the fixed z-axis and the axis z'; φ, the

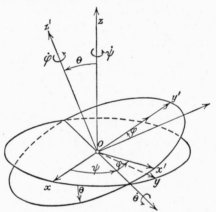

Fig. 30.—The coordinates of the symmetric top.

angle between the x'-axis and the nodal line; and ψ, the angle between the nodal line and an arbitrary line fixed in the nodal plane, which is taken as the fixed x-axis. Then

$$p = \dot{\theta} \cos \varphi + \dot{\psi} \sin \theta \sin \varphi, \quad q = -\dot{\theta} \sin \varphi + \dot{\psi} \sin \theta \cos \varphi$$

and

$$r = \dot{\varphi} + \dot{\psi} \cos \theta. \tag{107}$$

Substituting these in equation (106)

$$2T = A(\dot{\theta}^2 + \dot{\psi}^2 \sin^2\theta) + C(\dot{\varphi}^2 + 2\dot{\varphi}\dot{\psi} \cos \theta + \dot{\psi}^2 \cos^2 \theta), \tag{108}$$

and the momenta conjugate to θ, ψ, and φ are

$$p_\theta = \frac{\partial T}{\partial \dot{\theta}} = A\dot{\theta},$$

$$p_\psi = \frac{\partial T}{\partial \dot{\psi}} = C \cos \theta(\dot{\psi} \cos \theta + \dot{\varphi}) + A\dot{\psi} \sin^2 \theta,$$

$$p_\varphi = \frac{\partial T}{\partial \dot{\varphi}} = C(\dot{\varphi} + \dot{\psi} \cos \theta). \tag{109}$$

On eliminating $\dot{\theta}$, $\dot{\psi}$, and $\dot{\varphi}$ by means of equations (107), using the definitions of P, Q, and R, equations (109) become,

$$p_\theta = P \cos \varphi - Q \sin \varphi,\ p_\psi = R \cos \theta + P \sin \theta \sin \varphi +$$
$$Q \sin \theta \cos \varphi,\ p_\varphi = R. \quad (110)$$

Expressing the kinetic energy in terms of the momenta, equation (109), we have the Hamiltonian,

$$2H = \frac{p_\theta{}^2}{A} + \frac{p_\varphi{}^2}{C} + \frac{(p_\varphi \cos \theta - p_\psi)^2}{A \sin^2 \theta} = 2E. \quad (111)$$

Since φ and ψ do not appear in this equation, p_φ and p_ψ are constants. By choosing the z-axis fixed in space as the invariable axis, *i.e.*, the direction of the resultant angular momentum,

$$J = (P^2 + Q^2 + R^2)^{1/2}, \quad (112)$$

p_θ will be zero. In this case,

$$R = J \cos \theta,\ P = J \sin \theta \sin \varphi,\ Q =$$
$$J \sin \theta \cos \varphi,$$

and substituting these in equation (110), we secure

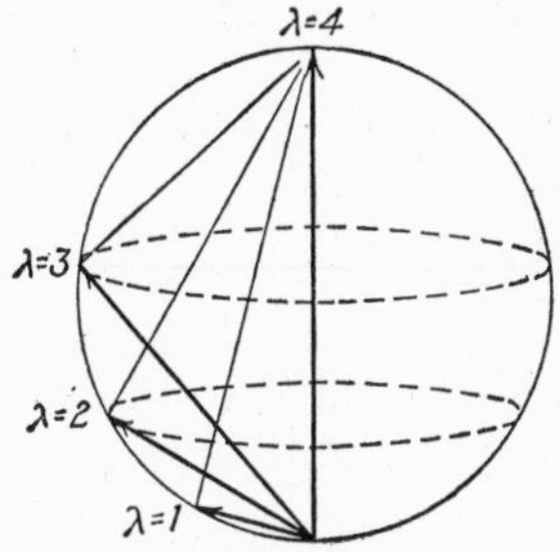

Fig. 31.—The relation between j and λ with $j = 4$.

$$p_\psi = J,\ p_\varphi = J \cos \theta; \quad (113)$$

θ must be constant and the quantum conditions are therefore,

$$\oint p_\theta d\theta = 0;\ \int_0^{2\pi} p_\psi d\psi = 2\pi J = jh;\ \int_0^{2\pi} p_\varphi d\varphi = 2\pi J \cos \theta = \lambda h,$$

and thus

$$\cos \theta = \frac{\lambda}{j}. \quad (114)$$

By substituting these values of J and $\cos \theta$ in equation (113) and then these expressions for p_θ, p_ψ, and p_φ in equation (111), the energy as a function of the quantum numbers j and λ is

$$E = \frac{h^2}{8\pi^2}\left(\frac{j^2}{A} + \left(\frac{1}{C} - \frac{1}{A}\right)\lambda^2\right),\ j = 0, 1, 2, \cdots$$
$$\lambda = 0, 1, \cdots j. \quad (115)$$

Wave and matrix mechanics[1] give a formula which can be obtained by simply replacing j^2 by $j(j + 1)$ in equation (115), except for additive constants (Chap. XIX, Sec. 4). Thus the correct energy formula is

$$E = \frac{h^2}{8\pi^2}\left(\frac{j(j + 1)}{A} + \left(\frac{1}{C} - \frac{1}{A}\right)\lambda^2\right),\ j = 0, 1, 2, \cdots$$
$$\lambda = 0, 1, 2, \cdots j. \quad (116)$$

Figure 31 illustrates the possible λ values when $j = 4$; the broken ellipses show the precession of λ about j.

Since p_ψ and p_φ are constant and p_θ is zero, it follows from equations (109) that $\dot{\psi}$ and $\dot{\varphi}$ are constant and $\dot{\theta}$ is zero. This means that the

[1] Dennison, *Phys. Rev.*, **28**, 318 (1926); Kronig and Rabi, *Phys. Rev.*, **29**, 262 (1927).

motion of the symmetric top is one of uniform rotation about the z'-axis with frequency $\omega_\varphi = \partial E/h\partial\lambda$, together with a uniform precession of z' about z with frequency $\omega_\psi = \partial E/h\partial j$, and thus

$$\psi = 2\pi\omega_\psi t + \delta_\psi, \quad \varphi = 2\pi\omega_\varphi t + \delta_\varphi, \quad \theta = \delta_\theta. \tag{117}$$

If an electric moment P oscillating with frequency ω_v has a component along z' equal to $P_{z'} \cos 2\pi\omega_v t$, and a component perpendicular to z', say along x', equal to $P_{x'} \cos 2\pi\omega_v t$, the components in the directions x, y, and z are

$$P_x = P_{z'} \cos 2\pi\omega_v t \sin\theta \sin\psi + P_{x'} \cos 2\pi\omega_v t(\cos\varphi \cos\psi -$$
$$\cos\theta \sin\varphi \sin\psi),$$
$$P_y = -P_{z'} \cos 2\pi\omega_v t \sin\theta \cos\psi + P_{x'} \cos 2\pi\omega_v t(\cos\varphi \sin\psi +$$
$$\cos\theta \sin\varphi \cos\psi),$$
$$P_z = P_{z'} \cos 2\pi\omega_v t \cos\theta + P_{x'} \cos 2\pi\omega_v t \sin\theta \sin\varphi. \tag{118}$$

Substituting ψ and φ from equation (117), and using trigonometric formulas of the type $2 \sin A \sin B = \cos (A + B) - \cos (A - B)$, we find that P_x and P_y contain sine and cosine terms having the frequencies

$$\omega_v + \omega_\psi, \ \omega_v - \omega_\psi, \ \omega_v + \omega_\psi \pm \omega_\varphi, \ \omega_v - \omega_\psi \pm \omega_\varphi.$$

The first two arise from the coefficients of $P_{z'}$ and the last four from the coefficients of $P_{x'}$. P_z contains

$$\omega_v, \ \omega_v \pm \omega_\varphi,$$

of which the first arises from the coefficient of $P_{z'}$ and the last two from that of $P_{x'}$. If the oscillation is parallel to the figure axis so that $P_{x'} = 0$, only the frequencies ω_v and $\omega_v \pm \omega_\psi$ are present, and the possible changes of the quantum numbers are,

$$\Delta j = 0, \pm 1; \Delta\lambda = 0. \tag{119}$$

On the other hand, if the oscillation is perpendicular to this axis, the active frequencies are $\omega_v \pm \omega_\psi \pm \omega_\varphi$ and $\omega_v \pm \omega_\varphi$, so that

$$\Delta j = 0, \pm 1; \Delta\lambda = \pm 1. \tag{120}$$

25. APPLICATION OF THE THEORY TO THE METHANE BANDS

The selection rules of equation (119) predict a type of spectrum similar to that of the diatomic molecule, except that a Q branch should be present. The methane band at 3.3μ has very sharp and symmetrical absorption peaks and strong absorption slightly to the long wave length side of the center. This simple structure seems to indicate that it arises from transitions following these selection rules. The selection rules of equation (120) would give a more complicated type of band; in place of each line of the simple band required by the rule of equation (119) there would be a complete band with P and R branches corresponding to $\Delta\lambda = \pm 1$, with the possible values of λ limited by the condition $\lambda \leq j$. The structure of the 7.7μ band does not seem to be as complicated as this, but the peaks are not so sharp and symmetrical. The appearance would lead one to suspect that they are composed of unresolved lines and it may be that the selection rule, equation (120), applies to this band. The empirical formulas, equations (104) and (105), show that the spacing of one band is nearly double that of the other so that the moment of inertia in the first case should be about half that in the second. It is difficult to explain this structure on the assumption of a tetrahedral model for methane, where any differences in the principal moments of inertia must be due to the vibration of the nuclei, and for this reason must be small. Most probably the correct explanation of the unequal spacings is not contained in the theory of Sec. **24**. It is possible that the double spacing of the 7.7μ band may be similar to that encountered in the case of symmetrical diatomic molecules such as He_2 (Sec. **22**).

Guillemin[1] and others[2] have proposed that methane has a pyramidal structure with the four hydrogens at the four corners of the base and the carbon at the apex. If it is assumed that the selection rule for the 3.3μ band is

$$\Delta j = \pm 1, 0, \ \Delta \lambda = 0$$

and for the 7.7μ band is

$$\Delta j = 0, \ \Delta \lambda = \pm 1,$$

then from equation (115) and the empirical equations (104) and (105) we see that

$$\frac{h}{4\pi^2 cC} \cong 9.77 \text{ cm.}^{-1}, \text{ and } \frac{h}{4\pi^2 c}\left(\frac{1}{A} - \frac{1}{C}\right) \cong 5.41 \text{ cm.}^{-1}.$$

From these relations the values of A and C and the dimensions of the molecule may be calculated, with the result that the distance between the carbon atom and one hydrogen atom is 1.15×10^{-8} cm. and that between two hydrogen atoms, 1.05×10^{-8} cm. The model, however, is not convincing because of the strong evidence for the symmetrical tetrahedral model.[3]

26. THE VIBRATIONAL STATES OF METHANE

Dennison[4] calculated the vibration frequencies for small amplitudes of the methane molecule assuming, (1) that in the equilibrium positions, the hydrogen nuclei are at the corners of a tetrahedron and the carbon nucleus at its center, (2) that the forces are functions of the distances between the nuclei alone. This assumption may be questioned because the double bond in the unsaturated hydrocarbons can sustain a torque about the line joining the two nuclei; this cannot be explained as due to a force along the line of nuclei.

[1] *Ann. Physik*, **81**, 173 (1926).

[2] See HENRI, V., *Chem. Rev.*, **4**, 189 (1927) for a review of the arguments for the pyramidal model.

[3] See GLOCKLER, G., *J. A. C. S.*, **48**, 2021 (1926), for a review of properties indicating a highly symmetrical structure similar to that of the inert gases.

[4] *Astrophys. J.*, **62**, 84 (1925). Our solution does not follow that of Dennison exactly.

The potential energy V is a function of the four distances from the hydrogen nuclei to the central carbon atom r_1, r_2, r_3, r_4, and of the six distances between the hydrogen nuclei q_1, q_2, $\cdots$ q_6;

$$V = V_1(q_1, \cdots q_6) + V_2(r_1, \cdots r_4). \tag{121}$$

Ten coordinates are used to describe a system having only nine degrees of freedom and, therefore, there must be a relation between V_1 and V_2, which permits the elimination of one of these coordinates. Expanding in the neighborhood of the equilibrium position and neglecting terms above the second degree, we have[1]

$$V = V_0 + \left(\frac{\partial V_1}{\partial q}\right)_0 \sum_1^6 \delta q_i + \left(\frac{\partial V_2}{\partial r}\right)_0 \sum_1^4 \delta r_i + \frac{1}{2}\left(\frac{\partial^2 V_1}{\partial q^2}\right)_0 \sum_1^6 \delta q_i^2 +$$
$$\frac{1}{2}\left(\frac{\partial^2 V_2}{\partial r^2}\right)_0 \sum_1^4 \delta r_i^2. \tag{122}$$

It is necessary to express V as a function of nine independent coordinates and also to select normal coordinates, such that the kinetic energy is a sum of terms proportional to the squares of the velocities and the potential energy a sum of terms proportional to the squares of the coordinates. One such coordinate is the radius of a sphere passing through the four hydrogen nuclei. For displacements of all the hydrogen nuclei toward or away from the carbon nucleus which remains stationary at the center of mass of the four hydrogen nuclei,

$$q = r\frac{4}{\sqrt{6}}, \text{ or } \delta q = \frac{4}{\sqrt{6}}\delta r$$

and therefore

$$V = V_0 + \left[4\sqrt{6}\left(\frac{\partial V_1}{\partial q}\right)_0 + 4\left(\frac{\partial V_2}{\partial r}\right)_0\right]\delta r + \left[8\left(\frac{\partial^2 V_1}{\partial q^2}\right)_0 + 2\left(\frac{\partial^2 V_2}{\partial r^2}\right)_0\right]\delta r^2;$$

but the coefficient of the term in δr must vanish for otherwise the position will not be one of equilibrium; therefore,

$$\frac{\partial V_2}{\partial r} = -\sqrt{6}\frac{\partial V_1}{\partial q}.$$

To simplify our symbols, let

$$K = \left(\frac{\partial^2 V_2}{\partial r^2}\right)_0, \quad \alpha = \frac{(\partial^2 V_1/\partial q^2)_0}{(\partial^2 V_2/\partial r^2)_0}, \text{ and } \beta = \frac{1}{r_0}\frac{(\partial V_2/\partial r)_0}{(\partial^2 V_2/\partial r^2)_0}.$$

Then the expression for the potential energy is

$$V = V_0 + K\left[\beta r_0\left(-\sqrt{6}\sum_1^6 \delta q_i + \sum_1^4 \delta r_i\right) + \frac{1}{2}\alpha\sum_1^6 \delta q_i^2 + \frac{1}{2}\sum_1^4 \delta r_i\right]. \tag{123}$$

[1] Crossed terms of the form

$$\frac{\partial^2 V}{\partial q_i \, \partial q_j} \delta q_i \, \delta q_j$$

are not included in this expression because it is assumed that the force between two particles is not changed by the relative positions of the other particles.

The energy for the mode of vibration in which all the hydrogens move simultaneously toward the carbon atom is

$$E = V_0 + \tfrac{1}{2}(4M_H)\delta\dot{r}^2 + (8\alpha + 2)K\delta r^2,$$

and the frequency is

$$\omega_1 = \frac{1}{2\pi}\left(\frac{K}{M_H}(4\alpha + 1)\right)^{\frac{1}{2}}. \tag{124}$$

The resultant electric moment is zero since the molecule is always symmetrical, and, therefore, the correspondence principle leads us to expect that light of frequency ω_1 will not be emitted.

Another mode of vibration can be described by means of a normal coordinate φ, the angular displacement between two perpendicular planes formed by taking the hydrogen nuclei in pairs and passing planes through each of these pairs and the carbon nucleus. These pairs may be chosen in three ways, and the displacements represent torsional displacements about the three axes, though only two of these are independent

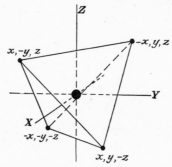

Fig. 32.—The methane molecule and coordinates of the hydrogen nuclei.

since the torsional vibration about the third axis may always be resolved into two components, one about each of the other axes. The potential energy for such a vibration can be obtained by expressing δr and δq in terms of φ and q and substituting in equation (123). It is

$$\frac{1}{2}K\left(\alpha - \frac{\beta}{4}\right)q_0{}^2\varphi^2,$$

where q_0 is the equilibrium value of q. Then,

$$E = \frac{1}{2}(4M_H)\left(\frac{q_0}{2}\right)^2\dot{\varphi}^2 + \frac{1}{2}K\left(\alpha - \frac{\beta}{4}\right)q_0{}^2\varphi^2,$$

and the frequency is

$$\omega_2 = \frac{1}{2\pi}\left(\frac{K}{M_H}\left(\alpha - \frac{\beta}{4}\right)\right)^{\frac{1}{2}}. \tag{125}$$

This mode accounts for two degrees of freedom. It is not active, for the molecule is always symmetrical with respect to the central atom.

There is one mode of vibration in which all four hydrogen atoms move simultaneously in the direction of one axis, say the x-axis, while at the same time the two with positive x-coordinates (see Fig. 32) move *toward* this axis and the two with negative x-coordinates move away from it. There is another mode of vibration, in which all four hydrogen atoms move as before in the direction of increasing x, but the two with positive x-coordinates move *outward* from the axis and those with negative x-coordinates move *toward* it. The same modes of vibration may also occur independently along the y- or z-axes and therefore they account for six degrees of freedom.

The displacement of the hydrogen atoms in the positive x direction is accompanied by a displacement of the carbon atom, $4M_H/M_C$ as great, in the direction of decreasing x. This will be expected to cause the appearance of an isotope effect in these two frequencies in the case of methane-like molecules whose central atom is not a pure element. Also, the unsymmetrical character of these vibrations gives rise to an oscillating electric moment, so that the molecule may be expected to absorb or emit light of these frequencies.

Let the arithmetic sum of the displacements of the carbon atom and the hydrogen atoms along x be p, and the displacement of the hydrogen atoms perpendicular to x be g, where g is positive if away from x, and negative if toward it. By calculating the values of δr and δq in terms of p and g, and substituting in equation (123), the potential energy is found to be

$$V = V_0 + ap^2 + 2bpg + cg^2,$$

where

$$a = K\frac{2}{3}(1 + 4\beta), \; b = K\frac{4}{3\sqrt{2}}(1 + \beta), \; c = K\left(\frac{4}{3} + 4\alpha + \frac{\beta}{3}\right);$$

and the kinetic energy is

$$T = 2\mu \dot{p}^2 + 2M_H \dot{g}^2,$$

where

$$\mu = \frac{M_H M_C}{M_C + M_H}.$$

We form the Lagrangian function L and secure the equations of motion in the usual way. These are

$$\ddot{p} + \frac{a}{2\mu}p + \frac{b}{2\mu}g = 0$$

$$\ddot{g} + \frac{b}{2M_H}p + \frac{c}{2M_H}g = 0, \tag{126}$$

so that

$$p = A \cos 2\pi\omega t \text{ and } g = Af \cos 2\pi\omega t,$$

where f is a quantity now to be determined.

Substituting in equation (126) and solving for f, we find

$$f = -\frac{a}{2b} + \frac{c\mu}{2bM_H} \pm \left[\left(\frac{a}{2b} - \frac{c\mu}{2bM_H}\right)^2 + \frac{\mu}{M_H}\right]^{\frac{1}{2}};$$

these are the two values of the cotangent of the angle between the direction of vibration and the x-axis for the two modes of vibration. The frequencies of vibration are found to be

$$\omega_{3,4} = \frac{1}{4\pi}\left(\frac{K}{M_H}\right)^{\frac{1}{2}}\left[a\,\frac{M_H}{\mu} + c \pm \left\{\left(a\,\frac{M_H}{\mu} - c\right)^2 + 4b^2\frac{M_H}{\mu}\right\}^{\frac{1}{2}}\right]^{\frac{1}{2}}. \quad (127)$$

Substituting M_H/μ, (which equals $\frac{4}{3}$ for the methane molecule) and the values of a, b, c in terms of α, β, and K, this formula becomes

$$\omega_{3,4} = \frac{1}{2\pi}\left(\frac{K}{M_H}\right)^{\frac{1}{2}}\left[\alpha + \frac{5}{9} - \frac{13}{36}\beta \pm \left\{\left(\frac{1}{9} - \frac{19}{36}\beta - \alpha\right)^2 + \frac{8}{27}(1 + \beta)^2\right\}^{\frac{1}{2}}\right], \quad (128)$$

which is equivalent to the formula derived by Dennison.

To summarize, the normal coordinates are: δr; two φ's measuring the torsional displacement about any two axes; three coordinates each of which is measured along a line at an angle to one of the x-, y-, or z-axes, whose cotangent is f using the positive sign; and three coordinates measured along lines making an angle with the axes whose cotangent is f using the negative sign.

The three principal moments of inertia of the molecule will still be equal if the molecule is vibrating with the frequency of equation (124). In the case of the torsional modes of vibration with the frequency of equation (125), the mean moment of inertia about the axis about which the oscillation takes place will differ slightly from the other two and, similarly, the mean moment of inertia about the axis along which the oscillations with frequencies given by equation (127) take place will differ slightly from the other two, but these variations cannot be large enough to explain the very large difference in the spacing of the lines in the two methane bands.

Dennison has found it possible to select the constants α, β, and K in such a way that approximate agreement between the observed and calculated frequencies is secured. Table 7 gives the calculated and observed fundamental wave numbers.

TABLE 7

	Observed wavenumber	Calculated wavenumber	Percentage, error
ω_1.......................	4,217	3,920	−7.1
ω_2.......................	1,520	1,532	+0.8
ω_3.......................	3,014	3,190	+5.9
ω_4.......................	1,304	1,304	0.0

The frequencies 3,014[1] and 1,304 are taken as those of the two frequencies of equation (127) since these bands are much more intense than any of the others and therefore may be expected to correspond to the vibrations with the largest electric moments obtained in our discussion of Dennison's model. The agreement is not very close. This may be due principally to the failure of the assumption that the forces depend only on the distance between the atoms.[2]

27. ELECTRONIC BANDS OF POLYATOMIC MOLECULES

The detailed analysis of the electronic bands of polyatomic molecules has only been begun and progress is slow because of their much greater complexity. In general, the ultraviolet bands of formaldehyde which have been described by Henri and Schou[3] have a structure similar to those of diatomic molecules, with modifications due to the greater number of vibrational degrees of freedom and to the existence of three different moments of inertia. The phenomenon of *predissociation*, as it has been named by Henri, is found in these band spectra. This is a common feature of these bands, which occurs rather seldom in the spectra of diatomic molecules, though it is found in the spectrum of S_2. An excellent example of this is given by the naphthalene bands investigated by Henri and de Làszlò.[4]

These absorption bands may be divided into three parts: the first extends from 3,200 to 2,820 A. and consists of narrow bands with a rotational fine structure; the second, from 2,820 to 2,500 Å., consists of narrow continuous bands with no rotational fine structure; and the third is a continuous spectrum extending further toward the violet. These three parts of the spectrum are due respectively to transitions from the low-lying vibrational and rotational states of the normal molecule (1) to a higher electronic state in which both the vibrational and rotational motions are quantized, (2) to a higher state in which vibrational but not rotational motions are quantized, and (3) to a higher state in which neither vibrational nor rotational motions are quantized, so that to all

---

[1] The wave number 3,014 is that which is observed in all organic compounds in which we have the C-H linkage. (See Ellis, *Phys. Rev.*, **23**, 48 (1924); Marton, *Z. Phys. Chem.*, **117**, 97 (1925), and also Chap. XI, Sec. **5**.) Andrews (*Chem. Rev.*, **5**, 533 (1928)) has shown that the observed heat capacities of a large number of organic compounds containing hydrogen linked to carbon are consistent with this value of a characteristic frequency.

[2] Recently, Dickinson, Dillon and Rasetti (*Phys. Rev.* 34, 582 (1929)) have studied the Raman effect of methane and give reasons for believing that 4217 cm.$^{-1}$ is not a fundamental, but is the sum of 1304 cm.$^{-1}$ and a fundamental of $\sim$2913 cm.$^{-1}$. It is interesting to note that this agrees very closely with the fundamental generally postulated for the C − H bond.

[3] *Z. Physik*, **49**, 774 (1928).

[4] *Proc. Roy. Soc.*, **105**, 662 (1924).

intents and purposes the molecule is dissociated. The first and third of these conditions have been described in connection with the band spectra of diatomic molecules. Henri proposed that the second spectrum is due to the absorption of light in a transition to a molecular state, where the molecule is unstable and dissociates soon after absorption. Kronig[1] showed that the rotational states of a molecule will not be quantized if the molecule has an appreciable probability of dissociating in a time of the order of magnitude of one rotation, but that the vibrational motion will be quantized if the dissociation does not occur within a time sufficient for many vibrations. Since the vibration frequencies are much larger than the rotational frequencies this condition is fulfilled.

References

KEMBLE, E. C., R. T. BIRGE, W. F. COLBY, F. W. LOOMIS and LEIGH PAGE, "Molecular Spectra in Gases," *Bull.* 57 Nat. Res. Coun., **11**, Part 3 (1926).

BIRGE, R. T., "International Critical Tables," **5**, 409, McGraw-Hill Book Company, Inc. (1929).

RAWLINS, F. I. G., and A. M. TAYLOR, "Infra-red Analysis of Molecular Structure," Cambridge University Press (1929).

MECKE, R., *Physik. Z.*, **26**, 217 (1925); MECKE, R., and M. GUILLERY, *Physik. Z.*, **28**, 314 and 479 (1927). An excellent bibliography is given at the end of the last article.

SPONER, H., "Optische Bestimmung Dissociation-wärme von Gasen," Ergebnisse der Exakten Naturwissenschaften, p. 75, Springer (1927).

MECKE, R., "Bandenspektra und ihre Bedeutung für die Chemie," Borntraeger, Berlin, (1929).

[1] *Z. Physik*, **50**, 347 (1928).

CHAPTER XIII

CRITICAL POTENTIALS OF ATOMS AND MOLECULES

The simpler facts in regard to critical potentials have been presented in Chap III, and the present chapter will be devoted principally to recent developments and important results in this interesting field. The existence of a National Research Council Bulletin entitled "Critical Potentials," by Compton and Mohler, and the book by Franck and Jordan, called "Anregung von Quantensprüngen durch Stösse," make it quite unnecessary to give a detailed systematic account of the earlier developments.

In Chap. III, we pointed out the distinction between collisions of the first and second kinds. If, in a collision, between an atom (or molecule) and an electron, the internal energy of the atom is raised at the expense of the relative translational energy of the collision-partners, we are dealing with a collision of the first kind, while if the converse is true, we have a collision of the second kind. We must also consider encounters between excited and unexcited atoms, in which the possibilities are more complicated. Here the collision is of the second kind if the more highly excited atom loses internal energy, whatever the distribution of that energy between translational and internal degrees of freedom may be. If both atoms are excited, this nomenclature is scarcely worth applying, because it does not give an adequate idea of the process. Collisions of the first kind and a few miscellaneous topics form the subject matter of this chapter, while those of the second kind are treated in the following one.

1. ELECTRON SOURCES FOR STUDIES OF CRITICAL POTENTIALS AND RELATED PHENOMENA

The first requisite in nearly all experiments on the collisions of electrons with atoms and molecules is a copious source of electrons, usually of low velocity and having a reasonably narrow range of velocity distribution. Only photoelectric and thermionic sources enter into practical consideration. The use of the former presents many experimental difficulties, for it is necessary to employ noble metals because of the difficulties in removing gases from the more common metals; but the photoelectric ejection of electrons from noble metals requires the use of ultra-violet light since their photoelectric threshold values lie in the ultra-violet and in some cases beyond the limits of transmission by glass, so that it is necessary to construct at least a part of the apparatus of

448

fused quartz. It is usually more convenient to use the electron emission from an incandescent metal strip or filament, and much larger currents can be drawn from such a filament than from a photoelectric source. Under certain conditions, the electrons leaving a hot cathode have velocities distributed according to the Maxwell distribution law. The experiments of del Rosario[1] show that Maxwellian distribution is secured in a high vacuum but not in the presence of a gas or vapor. In correcting for initial velocities of the electrons, the usual procedure is to determine their velocity distribution experimentally. This may be done by varying a retarding potential applied between the hot cathode and a collecting electrode. The electron current which reaches this anode is plotted against the retarding potential. The number of electrons having energies lying between Ve and $(V + dV)e$ is proportional to the slope of this curve at the point with abscissa V. Often, the voltage corresponding to the highest ordinate of the slope curve is applied to the measured voltage as a correction, provided the velocity distribution curve is fairly narrow. There is no theoretical justification for this, but it is usually satisfactory, since great accuracy is not ordinarily sought in critical potential measurements. Another method is to evacuate the apparatus and introduce a gas or vapor of known ionization potential. Often mercury vapor from the diffusion pumps can be used. If the known ionization potential is I, and the value obtained is I', then the quantity $I - I'$ is added to all measured voltages. This method suffers from the objection that the velocity distribution is not the same in the presence of the calibrating gas as in the presence of the gas which is to be studied. In using either method of correction, the contact potential between cathode and anode is automatically eliminated by subtraction.

It is instructive to consider the electron current which flows from a hot cathode to a metal plate in a thoroughly evacuated bulb. Figure 1[2] shows the dependence of this current on the potential V applied between the two electrodes. For low values of the potential the current i is quite accurately proportional to the $\frac{3}{2}$ power of the potential corrected for the initial velocity of the electrons as they leave the hot cathode. As the potential is further increased, the current increases more slowly than the $\frac{3}{2}$ power of the potential and finally approaches a constant value called the "saturation current." The law that i is proportional to $(V - V_0)^{\frac{3}{2}}$ for low values of V was derived theoretically by Child[3] and has been especially studied by Langmuir.[4] It can be derived theoretically, and holds true whatever the geometry of the apparatus may be. At low

[1] *Phys. Rev.*, **27**, 811 (1926).
[2] C. G. FOUND, *Phys. Rev.* **16**, 41 (1920).
[3] *Phys. Rev.*, **32**, 492 (1911).
[4] *Phys. Rev.*, **2**, 450 (1913).

values of the potential the current from the cathode is limited by negative space charge which accumulates in its neighborhood until the potential gradient at its surface is zero. This condition holds because the current flow due to the impressed potential does not remove the electrons from the neighborhood of the cathode as fast as they evaporate from the hot metal. At higher potentials this is no longer the case, and the gradient near the cathode becomes greater and aids the initial emission, although space-charge effects still play a rôle. Finally, the gradient becomes large enough to remove the electrons as fast as they leave the

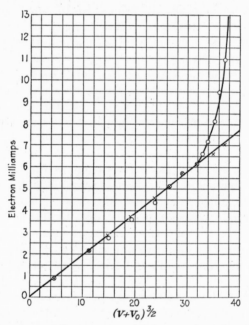

Fig. 1.—The variation of thermionic current with potential. The crosses represent the observations in vacuum and the circles observations with mercury vapor present. (*After Found.*)

metal, and the limiting value of the current is determined by the capacity of the hot filament to emit electrons. The saturation current varies with the temperature according to the empirical formulas,

$$I = aT^2e^{\frac{-b}{T}}, \tag{1}$$

or

$$I = a'T^{\frac{1}{2}}e^{\frac{-b'}{kT}}. \tag{2}$$

Usually, either of these laws can be made to fit the observed points within the experimental error by proper choice of the constants, a, b, a', and b'. The second expression can be reasonably well justified by a simple theory. According to Fowler[1] the current should be given by the equation

$$I = 2A(1 - r)T^2 \exp\left(\frac{-V_0 e}{kT}\right) \tag{3}$$

where

$$A = \frac{4\pi^2 k^2 m e}{h^3};$$

r is the reflection coefficient for electrons which fall on the metal, and V_0 is very nearly equal to the thermionic work function, i.e., the average work required to move an electron from a position of rest inside the metal to a position of rest outside.[2] When the current is in amperes per square centimeter, the value of a in (1) may be taken as about 60 for tungsten, platinum, and molybdenum in a very pure state. The total current from a given material increases with the temperature, and in comparing different metals, the lower V_0 is, the greater the current at a given temperature. V_0 varies from 1.34 volts for cesium to 5.2 ± 0.3 volts for platinum, and increases roughly as the electropositive characteristics of the metal decrease.

The choice of a suitable material for a hot cathode is governed by several factors—the magnitude of the currents required, the possibility of dissociation or catalytic recombination at the filament in studying molecular gases, the effect of the gas on the filament itself (e.g., tungsten should not be used in oxygen), length of time the filament must retain its original properties, etc. The most usual materials are platinum, coated with thin layers of alkaline earth oxides, tungsten, thoriated tungsten, and molybdenum. In the more exact determination of critical potentials, it is important to use electrons which have a narrow velocity distribution. This problem has been partially solved by several methods. Foote and Mohler[3] showed that nickel and platinum surfaces coated with cesium emit electrons copiously at red heat. Kingdon and Langmuir[4] and Williamson[5] then showed that tungsten and platinum surfaces adsorb a monomolecular layer of such metals as the alkalies or thorium, and that such metal surfaces emit electrons in accordance with formula (3), the work function being that of the adsorbed metal.

The retention of an alkali atom on a metal surface is due to the loss of one of its electrons. This will occur if the thermionic work function of the underlying metal is sufficient to remove an electron. Thus, cesium has an ionization potential of 3.87 volts while the thermionic

[1] Proc. Roy. Soc., **117**, 549 (1928).

[2] Warner (Proc. Nat. Acad. Sci., **13**, 56 (1927)) has shown that the thermionic work function of tungsten is very nearly equal to the photoelectric threshold value.

[3] Phil. Mag., **40**, 80 (1920).

[4] Phys. Rev. **21**, 380 (1923).

[5] Phys. Rev. **24**, 127 (1924).

work function of tungsten is 4.7 volts, and, therefore, cesium ions will be held tightly on a tungsten surface. Since the work function of tungsten is 4.7 volts, and that of cesium 1.34 volts, the temperature of a cesiated filament need be only about 1.34/4.7 of the temperature of a bare tungsten filament in order to secure approximately the same current per square centimeter. This low-temperature source yields electrons with a narrow velocity distribution. A mixture of alkaline earth oxides has a similar effect on the work function and is very often used to increase the electron emission from platinum filaments.

In addition to the natural energy-distribution of thermionic electrons, we must consider the distribution due to the potential drop along the filament, which may amount to several volts. Hertz and Kloppers[1] have used an equipotential source made by fusing a small nickel body to the middle of a tungsten filament. Due to its high electrical conductivity, the potential drop across it is very small. When covered with alkaline earth oxides the nickel body emits electrons much more copiously than the filament. A third wire attached to the nickel is used to apply accelerating potential. This method is a variation of the old scheme of covering a small spot on a platinum strip with a mixture of oxides.

Lawrence[2] used the method of magnetic resolution (Chap. II, Sec. 10) to select electrons of a given velocity from an inhomogeneous beam. In this way he secured a beam of electrons with velocities having a sharp upper limit, and determined the ionization potential of mercury with high precision. His value is 10.40 ± 0.04 volts, while the spectroscopic value is 10.392.

2. METHODS FOR DETERMINING CRITICAL POTENTIALS

The electrode arrangements which have been used in critical potential work are very numerous and we must refer to the treatises of Franck and Jordan and of Compton and Mohler for detailed discussion. Here we shall content ourselves with a brief statement of the principles underlying the more usual methods, and with descriptions of a few arrangements which possess special interest.

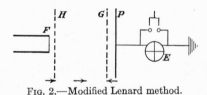

FIG. 2.—Modified Lenard method.

I. **Lenard's Method and Its Modifications.**—This method has been described in Chap. III, Sec. 10. In the simple arrangement of Fig. 4 (Chap. III) collisions between electrons and atoms occur throughout the space between the filament and first gauze. The energy of the electron depends on the potential through which it has fallen and thus varies from zero to the full accelerating potential, depending on the point

---

[1] Z. Physik, **31**, 463 (1925).

[2] Phys. Rev., **28**, 947 (1926).

at which the collision occurs. It is possible to remedy this defect by the use of an additional gauze H, mounted close to the filament as shown in Fig. 2. The accelerating potential is applied between the filament and this gauze so that the electrons enter the space HG at full potential and here collide with atoms in a nearly field-free space. It is usually advantageous to maintain a potential of a few tenths of a volt between H and G. A negative space charge due to the electrons applies a retarding field to the electrons entering this space. A small accelerating potential between H and G reduces this space charge and removes positive ions and slow electrons so that secondary effects such as inelastic collisions between ions and fast electrons are decreased. This arrangement was used by Franck and Einsporn[1] and many subsequent workers in this field.[2]

II. The Method of Franck and Hertz and Its Modifications.—This is also described in Chap. III, Sec. **10**, and can be improved by adding a gauze in the neighborhood of the filament, just as described in the case

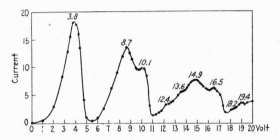

FIG. 3.—Critical potentials of mercury. (*After Einsporn.*)

of the Lenard method. In Fig. 6 of Chap. III, we gave a curve obtained with the three-electrode arrangement in mercury vapor at such a pressure that each bombarding electron makes many collisions in traversing the apparatus. At the pressures used all but a small fraction of the electrons will collide with a mercury atom before acquiring much more than 4.9 volts energy. If the pressure is decreased this will no longer be true. Figure 3 shows a curve secured by Einsporn[3] under such conditions, using mercury. The peaks on this curve occur at spacings which agree very well with the hypothesis that they are combinations of two potentials, 4.9 volts and 6.7 volts. It is possible to interpret some of these critical potentials, however, as due to combinations of other resonance potentials of the mercury atom.

Table 2 shows the agreement between the observed peaks and the calculated values, using the combinations shown in the second column.

[1] *Z. Physik*, **2**, 18 (1920).
[2] See FOOTE and MOHLER, "Origin of Spectra," p. **137**. *Chem. Cat. Co.*, New York (1922).
[3] *Z. Physik*, **5**, 208 (1921).

In the first column, a correction of 1.1 volts has been added to the experimental values because of the mean energy with which the electrons leave the cathode.

TABLE 1

Observed voltage (corrected for initial velocities)	Combination of $a = 4.9$ volts and $b = 6.7$ volts		Difference between calculated and observed values
4.9	a	$= 4.9$	0
	b	$= 6.7$	
9.8	$2a$	$= 9.8$	0
11.2	$a + b$	$=11.6$	-0.4
13.5	$2b$	$=13.4$	$+0.1$
14.7	$3a$	$=14.7$	0
16.0	$2a + b$	$=16.5$	-0.5
17.6	$a + 2b$	$=18.3$	-0.7
19.3	$4a$	$=19.6$	$+0.3$
20.2	$3b$	$=20.1$	$+0.1$
21.2	$3a + b$	$=21.4$	-0.2

III. The Methods of Davis and Goucher and of Compton.—The experimental methods described above do not distinguish between ionization and resonance potentials, since both are associated with loss of

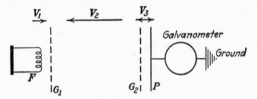

FIG. 4.—The Davis and Goucher apparatus.

energy. Davis and Goucher[1] carried out experiments which distinguished between these two effects, by using an apparatus shown diagrammatically in Fig. 4. Two gauzes were used between the filament F and the plate P with fields V_1, V_2, and V_3 accelerating and decelerating the electrons as shown by the arrows. V_1 is increased by small steps and the current flowing between G_2 and P is measured by a galvanometer for each value of V_1. When atoms are caused to radiate by inelastic impacts of the electrons in the neighborhood of G_1, the light emitted falls on P, and photoelectrons are ejected which are returned to P by the field V_3, contributing nothing to the current through the galvanometer. Any light falling on the side of G_2 nearest to P by reflection, or otherwise, will cause electrons to be emitted from G_2, which will fall to P and register on the galvanometer. If now the potential V_1 is increased until ions are produced near G_1, these will be accelerated toward G_2, and passing through

[1] *Phys. Rev.*, **10**, 101 (1917).

the gauze, will reach P if V_3 is less than V_2. An ion current from G_2 to P will deflect the galvanometer in the sense opposed to that in which it is caused to move by the electron current. If the supply of ions is sufficiently great, the original deflection caused by the light emitted at resonance collisions will be reversed. In the lower curve of Fig. 5, the galvanometer current I obtained under such conditions is plotted against the potential V_1. If the direction of V_3 is now reversed the photoelectrons from P pass to G_2. A negative current flowing from P to G_2 is equivalent to a positive current flowing from G_2 to P. The inelastic collisions producing light will therefore register a current in the same direction as those producing ions. The upper curve of Fig. 5 shows the plot of the galvanometer current I against V for this arrangement of the fields. This experiment was carried out with mercury vapor. The shape of the curves shows clearly that the two critical potentials at 4.9 and 6.7 volts are associated with the production of light following inelastic collisions in which the atom is raised to an excited state. The break at 10.4 volts is associated with the formation of positive ions.

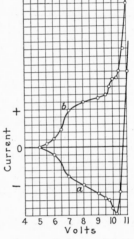

FIG. 5.—The resonance and ionization potentials of Hg. (*After Davis and Goucher.*)

Compton[1] has devised a modification of the Lenard method which makes it possible to distinguish between radiation and ionization potentials. The arrangement of potentials is unchanged, but the receiving electrode is a hollow box, one side of which is covered with metal gauze. The gauze side or the solid side can be turned toward the other electrodes by a magnetic device. On rotating the box, the positive ion current to the electrometer will not change, for the gauze is just as efficient in collecting ions as a solid plate; but the photoelectric current from the box will be smaller when the gauze side is turned toward the other electrodes, because a large part of the radiation passes through the meshes and strikes the inside of the box, from which few photoelectrons escape. Suppose we plot the ratio R of the currents obtained with solid and gauze sides toward the other electrodes, against the accelerating voltage. If we were dealing entirely with positive ion current this ratio would be unity; if with photoelectric current, it would be larger than unity. At a radiation potential we expect an increase of R, and at an ionization potential we expect a decrease.

IV. Hertz' Space Charge Method.—This is adapted to the detection of ionization potentials.[2] Electrons are accelerated through a gauze

---

[1] *Phil. Mag.* **40**, 553 (1920).   [2] *Z. Physik*, **18**, 307 (1923).

into a metal cylinder, where collisions take place. In this cylinder there is a very small filament which is run so hot that the current from it is limited by space charge. A small potential is applied between the filament and the cylinder, for reasons already explained. The galvanometer is connected to one leg of this filament and measures the emission current from it. This remains constant as long as the accelerating voltage is less than the first ionization potential of the gas, but increases greatly as soon as that voltage is passed, because the negative space charge is neutralized. The filament is so small that radiation cannot cause an appreciable photoelectric current from it.

V. Another Method Due to Hertz.—This method is especially adapted for the accurate determination of critical potentials, and minimizes effects due to inelastic impacts occurring at lower voltages. The experimental arrangement used by Hertz[1] is shown in Fig. 6. Electrons of known velocity and having a narrow velocity distribution were shot into a

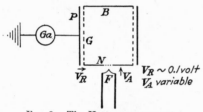

FIG. 6.—The Hertz arrangement.

field-free space containing a helium-neon mixture, where they collided with the atoms and diffused through the gauze sides to the electrode P. Two current measurements were made, one with no field between the cage and the electrode P, and the other with retarding field of 0.2 volts between them. The difference between these two currents is a measure of the number of electrons which have made inelastic collisions and have lost nearly all their energy, so that they cannot move against the small retarding field of 0.2 volts. Hertz took the critical potentials of helium as known from spectroscopic data and determined the potentials of neon relative to these. By way of illustration, Hertz found resonance potentials at 16.65 and 18.45 volts. The first of these corresponds to two resonance lines at 744 and 736 Å., which were discovered spectroscopically by Hertz.[2] The calculated excitation potentials of these lines are 16.58 and 16.77 volts.

In practice, it is often convenient to use a combination of several methods. Thus, we might measure the first resonance potential of a metallic vapor by the Franck-Hertz method, locate the ionization potential by noting the sudden increase in total current which occurs when ionization begins, and study the spectrum of the discharge to determine what lines are emitted just above the resonance voltage. Often it is possible to gain additional information by observing the dependence of line intensities and of breaks in the curve on the current. For example, when the voltage slightly exceeds the first ionization

[1] *Loc. cit.*
[2] *Naturwis.*, **13**, 489 (1925); *Z. Physik*, **32**, 933 (1925).

potential, it is possible for lines of the spark spectrum to appear, due to ionization by one electron and excitation of the ion by another. The intensity of strong lines of the spark spectrum produced in this way should therefore be proportional to the square of the current density. Thus we see the value of using low currents when it is desired to get rid of effects due to successive impacts.

VI. Special Devices Used with Molecular Gases and Vapors.— Special methods must be used for studying the critical potentials of the atoms of elements which are in the molecular form at ordinary temperatures and pressures. In Chap. V, Sec. **3**, we have described the work of Olmstead and Compton on the critical potentials of the hydrogen atom, in which they used a tungsten vacuum furnace to dissociate the gas. Smyth and Compton[1] have used a discharge tube raised to a high temperature in their studies of the critical potentials of the iodine atom.

VII. Kurth's Method for Studying Soft X-ray Potentials of Solids.— In this method radiation is produced at a target bombarded with electrons of controlled energy. This radiation falls on a detecting plate producing a photoelectric current.

An essential feature of Kurth's[2] apparatus consists in an elaborate set of shields, which serve to suppress secondary effects due to ions produced in the residual gas. Studies similar to those carried out by Kurth have been made by Rollefsen,[3] Compton and Thomas[4] and others. Their experiments show that many radiating potentials can be observed in such solid bodies as iron, nickel, copper, and carbon. For the most part, it has been found impossible to arrange these in any systematic order and it seems very probable that future investigations of these soft X-rays will be made principally by using gratings ruled on glass.

3. CONTROLLED EXCITATION OF SPECTRA

As indicated in Chap III, Sec **12** it is often advantageous to supplement our studies of critical potentials by investigations of the light emitted when a gas or vapor is bombarded by low-voltage electrons.

A tube suitable for experiments of this kind is shown in Fig. 7, taken from a paper by Ruark[5] on the step-by-step excitation of the magnesium spectrum. The hot filament is closely surrounded by a spiral, which in turn is surrounded by a concentric cylinder at a relatively great distance. This is often maintained at the same potential as the outer cylinder, but usually a small accelerating voltage—say a few tenths of a volt—may be applied between them with advantage. The main

[1] *Phys. Rev.*, **16**, 501 (1920).
[2] *Phys. Rev.*, **18**, 461 (1921).
[3] *Phys. Rev.*, **23**, 35 (1924).
[4] *Phys. Rev.*, **28**, 601 (1926).
[5] *J. O. S. A.*, 11, **199** (1925).

accelerating potential is applied between the filament and the spiral If the spectrum of a metal is to be studied, a piece is placed inside the cylinder, and the central part of the tube is heated. The pressure is so chosen that relatively few electrons collide with atoms in the space between filament and spiral, while a much greater number undergo collisions in the force-free space between the spiral and the cylinder. In this way, nearly all the electrons reach this space with the energy corresponding to the full potential between filament and spiral. The light from the force-free space is focused on the slit of a spectroscope through the fused quartz window, which is placed a considerable distance away from the discharge, to avoid the deposition of a metal film. The cylinder is nearly closed, to keep the metal where it is wanted. The small tube at the right keeps the direct light of the filament from reaching the

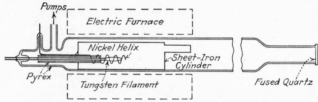

Fig. 7.—Apparatus for the controlled excitation of spectra. (*After Ruark.*)

spectroscope. It also serves to isolate the light coming from regions close to the anode cylinder, where the potential must be nearly that of the anode.

Usually, the current is held constant by varying the temperature of the filament; further, it should be chosen very low, let us say 1 to 3 milliamperes, for the purpose of minimizing effects due to successive excitation of an atom by two or more electrons. Even if these conditions are satisfied, the spectra obtained at different voltages will not be comparable in intensity, for several reasons. First, the percentage of the collisions which are inelastic is a function of the electronic velocity. Second, an electron having 10 volts energy, for example, can undergo two inelastic collisions in a gas having a resonance potential of 5 volts, while an 8-volt electron could excite only one atom. Third, the electronic mean free path and, therefore, the total number of collisions, depends on the velocity. Other factors could be enumerated. For these reasons, the time of exposure is reduced, at constant current, to keep the product of voltage and exposure time constant. With these precautions, spectra are obtained at a number of different voltages. Figure 8 shows magnesium spectra obtained by Foote, Meggers, and Mohler,[1] at voltages from 3.2 to 30. At the first resonance potential, an electron should be carried from the normal level 1^1S_0 to the levels $2^3P_{0,1,2}$. In magnesium,

[1] *Phil. Mag.*, **42**, 1002 (1921); **43**, 639 (1922).

these P levels lie close together and the corresponding resonance potentials cannot be separated electrically. While electrons are carried to all three levels, they cannot return from 2^3P_2 and 2^3P_0 with emission of radiation. These states are metastable, and atoms cannot leave them except by colliding with the walls, with other atoms, or with electrons. As to 2^3P_2, it is higher than 2^3P_1, but spontaneous transitions between these levels will not occur because of the selection principle for the azimuthal quantum number. The result is that only the line $1^1S_0 - 2^3P_1$

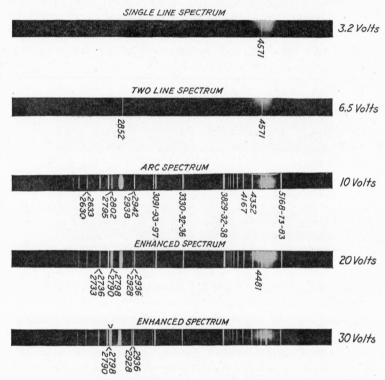

Fig. 8.—Development of Mg Spectrum. (*After Foote, Meggers, and Mohler.*)

at 4,571 Å. should be emitted when the bombarding electrons have voltages slightly higher than the first resonance potential. The minimum voltage required for the excitation of the 4,571 Å. line, should be 2.70 volts, by the relation $Ve = h\nu$. It is recorded at 3.2 volts (Fig. 8) and no other line is found, even when the plate is very much overexposed. The larger value of the observed voltage is due to the fact that the intensity of the light excited at exactly 2.70 volts would be so small that it would be difficult to photograph. The next line to appear should be $1^1S_0 - 2^1P_1$ at 2,853 Å., which requires 4.33 volts for its excitation, and it appears when the energy is increased to 6.5 volts.

Other lines due to the neutral atom appear progressively as the voltage increases. When the ionization potential of 7.61 volts is exceeded, the whole arc spectrum is emitted, as in the 10-volt exposure of Fig. 8. The energy required to ionize the Mg^+ ion corresponds to 14.97 volts and when this is accomplished, the complete Mg II spectrum should be emitted. This spectrum is observed in a low voltage arc run at high currents, at potentials slightly in excess of 15 volts, and is due principally to doubly charged ions produced by the successive impact of two electrons. Now, collisions of singly charged positive ions with the bombarding electrons are proportional in number to the square of the current, and so all spectrum lines produced in this way will decrease in intensity relative to lines produced by single impacts, if the current is made lower. At low currents, therefore, we should expect that the Mg II spectrum

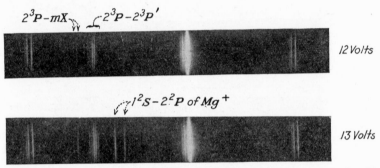

Fig. 9.—The spectrum of Mg^+ excited by single electron impacts. (*After Ruark*.)

would be quite faint until we pass the voltage 22.58 ($= 7.61 + 14.97$) at which two valence electrons may be removed in a single impact. Ruark[1] showed that such is the case, using current densities of the order of 0.1 to 0.2 milliamperes per $cm.^2$ As a typical result, we may consider the excitation of the first principal pair of ionized magnesium, $1^2S_{1/2} - 2^2P_{3/2,1/2}$ at 2,802.7 and 2,795.5 Å. If a singly charged ion is present, these lines could be excited by 4.4-volt electrons, but 7.61 volts are required to produce such ions, and therefore these lines should appear first at the first ionization potential when the current is relatively high; but, if the current is relatively low, these lines should appear at 12.01 volts, due to a type of impact in which one electron is removed and the second is raised to one of the 2^2P levels. The existence of such impacts is proved by the 12- and 13-volt exposures in Fig. 9. While there is no trace of these lines in question at 12 volts, they are strongly developed at 13. The simultaneous excitation of two electrons may also be studied by the same method. If it is possible to raise both valence electrons of magnesium to 3, 1 orbits by a single impact, leaving the atom in one of the $2^3P'$ states, we may expect that the lines $2^3P - 2^3P'$ will be emitted

[1] *Loc. cit.*

as a result. The voltage required for this excitation is 7.14, corresponding to the wave number $1^3S_0 - 2^3P'$. Our expectation is verified, for at low currents the $2^3P - 2^3P'$ lines are absent at 7.5 volts, but present at 7.9. The difference between the theoretical excitation voltage and that observed is attributable to the fact that the initial velocity correction has not been applied. Recently, the hot cathode arc has been used by K. T. Compton, Boyce and Russell[1] in studies of the extreme ultraviolet spectra of neon and argon. In this region, classification is often made difficult by the decreased accuracy of wave-number measurements, and any method of separating successive stages of excitation is very useful.

Very close checks of theoretical potentials have been obtained by Hertz[2] in work on helium, neon, and mercury, by the use of low currents—never greater than 0.1 milliampere. Neon lines which are definitely absent at 19.2 volts are quite strong at 19.6. Later, Hertz and Scharp de Visser[3] made photometric measurements of line intensities as a function of voltage. The curves obtained cut the axis of zero voltage at considerable angles in some cases, and yield quite definite values of the critical voltages for the appearance of these lines.

4. THE DETERMINATION OF IONIZATION POTENTIALS WITH THE MAGNETIC SPECTROGRAPH

A very powerful method for studying the potentials at which various types of ions are first produced has been developed by Smyth[4] and Hogness and Lunn,[5] by combining a hot cathode tube with a magnetic spectrograph like that of Dempster (Fig. 10, Chap. II). The arrangement of electrodes used by Hogness and Lunn is illustrated in Fig. 10. The

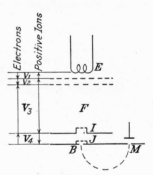

Fig. 10.—Magnetic spectrograph arrangement. (*After Hogness and Lunn.*)

source of electrons is the filament E. The potential V_1 is fixed throughout the experiments and V_2 is varied. The electrons collide with the molecules in the space F producing ions if $V_1 + V_2$ is sufficiently large; these are drawn through the gauze I by a small potential V_3. V_4 is a large variable potential which accelerates the ions through the gauze J and slit B, where they enter the magnetic field. Their paths are bent into a circle and the ions arrive at the slit M and the electrometer

[1] *Proc. Nat. Acad. Sci.*, **14**, 280 (1928); *J. Frank. Inst.*, **205**, 497 (1928); *Phys. Rev.*, **32**, 179 (1928).

[2] *Z. Physik*, **22**, 18 (1924).

[3] *Z. Physik*, **31**, 470 (1925).

[4] *Proc. Roy. Soc.*, **102**, 283 (1922), and later papers.

[5] *Proc. Nat. Acad. Sci.*, **10**, 398 (1924); *Phys. Rev.*, **26**, **786** (1925).

electrode.   In order to bring ions of different ratios of charge to mass to the slit M, it is necessary to vary either V_4 or the magnetic field strength. In practice it is convenient to vary V_4 in order to detect the different ions produced.   By varying the potential V_2, the energy of the exciting electrons can be varied.   Thus, it is possible to observe the exciting potential at which any ion is produced and also the relative numbers of ions of different kinds produced by electrons of any particular energy.

Figures 11a and 11b are plots of electrometer currents against the potential V_4, when the apparatus is filled with N_2, and electrons enter the space F with energies of 23 and 84 volts, respectively. N_2^+ ions

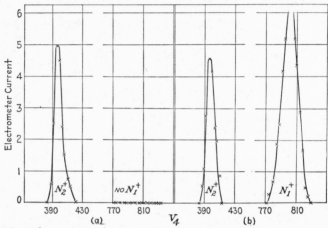

Fig. 11.—Magnetic spectrograph curves; (a)with an accelerating potential of 23 volts; (b) with an accelerating potential of 84 volts. (*After Hogness and Lunn.*)

are present in both cases but N^+ ions only in the latter.   The relative abundance of the ions can be estimated by the heights of the peaks of these curves.   It is found that N_2^+ ions appear first at 17 volts, and in greater numbers at 23 volts; N^+ ions appear above 23 volts, but in small numbers relative to the N_2^+ ions.   Increasing the pressure of nitrogen or the addition of helium gas increases the relative number of N^+ ions; further, the ratio of N^+ to N_2^+ ions approaches zero as the nitrogen pressure approaches zero.   The conclusions that can be drawn are: two types of N_2^+ ions are produced, one at 17 volts and another at 23 volts; the second of these is unstable and at collision with other molecules or helium atoms dissociates into an atom and an atomic ion.

Similar studies have been made with H_2,[1] I_2,[2] HCl,[3] NO,[4] O_2,[5] CH_4[6] and

[1] Smyth, *Phys. Rev.*, **25**, 452 (1925); Hogness and Lunn, *Phys. Rev.*, **26**, 44 (1925); Kallmann and Bredig, *Z. Physik*, **34**, 736 (1925).

[2] Hogness and Harkness, *Phys. Rev.*, **32**, 784 (1928).

[3] Barton, *Phys. Rev.* **30**, 614 (1927).

[4] Hogness and Lunn, *Phys. Rev.*, **30**, 26 (1927).

[5] Hogness and Lunn, *Phys. Rev.*, **27**, 732 (1926).

[6] Hogness and Kvalnes, *Phys. Rev.* **32**, 942 (1928).

H_2O.[1]   A summary of the principal conclusions of these studies is given in Table 2.   The method promises to give further valuable information on the processes of ionization in molecular gases.

TABLE 2

Molecule	Primary process	Excitation potential volts	Secondary and tertiary processes	Negative ions observed
H_2.............	$H_2 \rightarrow H_2^+ + e$	16	$\begin{cases} H_2^+ + H_2 \rightarrow H_3^+ + H \\ H_2^+ \rightarrow H^+ + H \\ H^+ + H_2 \rightarrow H_3^{+*} \end{cases}$	None
N_2.............	$\begin{cases} N_2 \rightarrow N_2^+(17) + e \\ N_2 \rightarrow N_2^+(23) + e \end{cases}$	17 23	$N_2^+(23) \rightarrow N^+ + N$	N_2^-
NO............	$\begin{cases} NO \rightarrow NO^+ + e \\ NO \rightarrow O^+ + N + e \\ NO \rightarrow O + N^+ + e \end{cases}$	9 21 22	....	NO^-, N^-, O^-
O_2.............	$\begin{cases} O_2 \rightarrow O_2^+ + e \\ O_2 \rightarrow O^+ + O + e \end{cases}$	13 20	....	O_2^-, O^-
H_2O....	$H_2O \rightarrow H_2O^+ + e$	13	$\begin{cases} H_2O^+ \rightarrow OH^+ + H\dagger \\ H_2O^+ + H_2O \rightarrow H_3O^+ + OH\dagger \end{cases}$	None
I_2..............	$\begin{cases} I_2 \rightarrow I_2^+ + e \\ I_2 \rightarrow I^+ + I + e \\ I_2 + e \rightarrow I^- + I \end{cases}$	9.3 9.3 <3	$\begin{cases} I^+ + I_2 \rightarrow I_2^+ + I \\ I_2^+ + I_2 \rightarrow I_3^+ + I \\ I^- + I_2 \rightarrow I_2^- + I \\ I_2^- + I_2 \rightarrow I_3^- + I^* \end{cases}$	I, I_2^-, I_3^-
HCl............	$\begin{cases} HCl \rightarrow HCl^+ + e \\ HCl \rightarrow H + Cl\dagger \end{cases}$	13	$Cl + e \rightarrow Cl^{-*}$	Cl^-
CH_4............	$\begin{cases} CH_4 \rightarrow CH_4^+(14.5) \\ \qquad + e \\ CH_4 \rightarrow CH_3^+ + H \\ \qquad + e \\ \qquad \text{or} \\ CH_4 \rightarrow CH_4^+(15.5) \\ \qquad + e \end{cases}$	14.5 15.5 15.5	$CH_4^+ \rightarrow CH_3^+ + H + e$	

* Processes are tertiary.
† Thermal dissociation at the filament.

Somewhat similar methods have been used to separate the spectra of ions from those of neutral molecules.

If an electric field is applied transversely to a beam of canal rays passing through a high vacuum, ions in the beam can be deflected sufficiently to separate them from the neutral particles.   In this way Wien[2] and Kerschbaum[3] obtained a physical separation of the arc and spark spectra of O and N and showed that the second positive bands of N_2 are emitted by the neutral molecule while the negative bands are due to N_2^+.   Wien has also studied the spectra of canal ray beams deflected by magnetic fields.   Brasefield[4] has used this method to separate the spectrum of H_2^+ from that of the neutral molecule.   In this way he has

[1] BARTON and BARTLETT, *Phys. Rev.*, **31**, 822 (1928).
[2] *Ann. Physik*, **69**, 325 (1922); *ibid.*, **81**, 994 (1926).
[3] *Ann. Physik*, **79**, 465 (1926).
[4] *Proc. Nat. Acad. Sci.*, **14**, 686 (1928).

succeeded in finding bands which are characteristic of the ion and has found that they follow a Rydberg series with the changes in the quantum numbers $8 \rightarrow 4$, $9 \rightarrow 4$, $10 \rightarrow 4$, and the Rydberg constant characteristic of singly ionized atoms, namely, $4R_H$. The method is difficult to use because of the low intensity of sources secured in this way, but promises to be a powerful method for separating arc and spark spectra. Maxwell has made studies, of the mercury spectrum with electric deflection, using a tube with a hot cathode, which enables him to obtain much brighter spectra.[1] He finds that the intensity of the arc lines is independent of the electric field, which indicates that recombination of electrons and positive ions contributes very little to these lines.

5. CORPUSCULAR SPECTRA

The first investigation in which a magnetic spectrograph, in the usual sense of the word, was used to bend the paths of charged particles, was that of Danycz[2] who employed this instrument to determine the velocity distribution of β-rays from radioactive substances. Robinson and Rawlinson[3] used this method to determine the velocities of secondary cathode rays produced by X-rays and, Rutherford,[4] in collaboration with these two authors, employed it to investigate the velocities of secondary β-rays produced by γ-rays. De Broglie[5] and Ellis[6] have brought this method to a high state of perfection. A typical arrangement of apparatus is shown in Fig. 12.

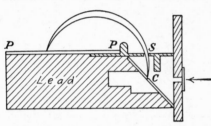

Fig. 12.—Corpuscular spectrograph.

Electrons are ejected from the point C in all directions by X-rays or gamma rays; a magnetic field bends the path of each electron into a circle and those that pass through the slit finally fall on a photographic plate PP. The arrangement of slits is such that all electrons of the same velocity are focused on the same point of PP, those of lower velocity falling nearer to the slit S. The result is a spectrum which is often referred to as a magnetic spectrum.

The energy of the electrons leaving C is determined by the frequency of the rays falling on the target, the photoelectric threshold value, the energy necessary to remove the electron from one of the shells of an

[1] *Phys. Rev.*, **32**, 715 and 721 (1928).

[2] *Compt. Rend.*, **153**, 1066 (1911); *Le Radium*, **9**, 1 (1912).

[3] *Phil. Mag.*, **28**, 277 (1914).

[4] *Phil. Mag.*, **28**, 281 (1914).

[5] *J. de Phys. et Le Rad.*, **2**, 265 (1921).

[6] *Proc. Roy. Soc.*, **99**, 261 (1921); **101**, 1 (1922).

atom and, finally, the loss of energy of the electron as it passes through the substance before it escapes. The photoelectric equation for those electrons which lose no energy by this last method is

$$Ve = h\nu - V_0e - h\nu',$$ (4)

where ν is the frequency of the incident radiation, Ve the energy of the ejected electron, V_0e the photoelectric threshold value and $h\nu'$ the energy necessary to remove the electron from an atom. The latter energy may or may not be zero, depending upon whether the electron was free or was bound in one of the electron shells. The effect of any loss of energy of the electron in passing through the metal will be to decrease Ve. Using X-rays of known frequency and determining Ve from the strength of the magnetic field and the radius of curvature of the electron path, it is a simple matter to deduce the various values of $h\nu'$ from the discontinuities of the blackening on the plate. This method has been

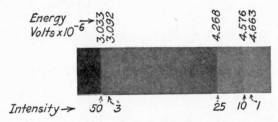

Fig. 13.—Corpuscular spectrum of RaD.   (*After Curtiss.*)

used to determine the K and L energy levels, soft X-ray energy levels, and, when applied to beta rays ejected by gamma rays, the energy levels within the nucleus itself. When studying gamma rays the radioactive material is deposited on a wire which occupies the position of the point C. The electrons, ejected by the gamma rays during the radioactive disintegration process, come from the electron shells of the disintegrating atom itself. It is found that the process of disintegration of radium B and also radium D is first the loss of a β ray from the nucleus, leaving a nucleus of the atomic number 83 which is an isotope of bismuth; then a nuclear rearrangement of this newly formed nucleus takes place with the emission of a gamma ray, and, finally, this gamma ray in passing through the electronic shells of the atom may eject an electron from one of these shells. The result will be a corpuscular spectrum of electrons having the energy $h\nu$ of the gamma-ray quantum, or this energy diminished by that required to remove an electron from one of the X-ray levels of the bismuth atom. It is found that the electrons have velocities corresponding to these energies rather than those to be expected if the electron were ejected from one of the shells of an atom of atomic number 82, which is an isotope of lead. Studies of this kind have been made

on Ra, RaB, RaC, and RaD.[1] Figure 13 is a reproduction of a corpuscular spectrum of RaD taken by Curtiss.

Jones and Whiddington[2] have applied this method of corpuscular
spectra to electrons which have made elastic and inelastic collisions with
molecules. Electrons accelerated by 25 to 150 volts are shot through a
Faraday cage containing hydrogen at a pressure of about 10^{-2} mm. of
mercury where they collide with hydrogen molecules. Some of the
electrons will make elastic collisions and will retain their original energy
while others may make one or two inelastic collisions and thus lose part
of their energy. The result will be that the electrons emerging from
the cage will consist of several groups differing in energy by the amounts
lost in these inelastic collisions. If these electrons are then accelerated
by a fairly high field and passed into a corpuscular spectrograph a
spectrum similar to those described above is secured. The photographic plate shows a fairly sharp line corresponding to electrons which
have made elastic collisions, and others corresponding to those which
have made one or two inelastic collisions. They have investigated at
present only those electrons which after the inelastic collision move on in
nearly the same direction as the original beam.

The distances between the spectral lines show that the electrons have
lost 12.6 volts of energy or approximately double this amount; and, in
addition, there is some evidence for inelastic collisions in which 8 or 9
volts and 14 or 15 volts are lost. The 12.6-volt loss of energy is in
agreement with observations on the resonance potential of hydrogen
made by other methods. The energy changes in the hydrogen molecule
corresponding to the 8- or 9-volt and the 14- or 15-volt loss of energy
are doubtful, though there is reason to believe that the latter loss is due
to the dissociation of the hydrogen molecule. From the relative intensities of the two lines corresponding to the loss of 12.6 volts in one collision,
or twice this amount in two collisions, it is possible to calculate the
probability of excitation by electrons; this has been done for electrons
which are deflected only slightly from their original paths by collisions.
The probability that an electron will make one and only one collision in
traversing the distance d, through the Faraday cage is $(d/\lambda) \exp(-d/\lambda)$,
where λ is the mean free path of the electron in the gas. If p is the
fraction of these collisions which are inelastic, the number of electrons
which have made one inelastic collision will be

$$ I_1 = \text{const.} \left(p\frac{d}{\lambda}\right) \exp\left(\frac{-d}{\lambda}\right). \tag{5} $$

---

[1] ELLIS and co-workers, *Proc. Roy. Soc.*, **99**, 261 (1921); ELLIS, C. D., *Z. Physik*,
10, 303 (1922); ELLIS, C. D., and H. W. B. SKINNER, *Proc. Roy. Soc.*, **105**, 185 (1924);
ELLIS, C. D. and W. A. WOOSTER, **114**, 276 (1927); BLACK, *Proc. Cambridge Phil. Soc.*,
22, 832 (1925); CURTISS, *Phys. Rev.*, **27**, 257 (1926).

[2] *Phil. Mag.*, **6**, 889 (1928).

The probability of an inelastic collision while traversing the path from x to $x + dx$ is $\left(p\dfrac{dx}{\lambda}\right)\exp\left(\dfrac{-x}{\lambda}\right)$; the probability of one and only one encounter in the remaining distance, $d - x$, is $\left[\dfrac{(d-x)}{\lambda}\right]\exp\left[\dfrac{-(d-x)}{\lambda}\right]$ and the probability of this being inelastic is p. Multiplying, and integrating from zero to d, we have for the number of the electrons which have made two and only two inelastic encounters

$$I_2 = \text{const.}\,\frac{p^2 d^2}{2\lambda^2}\exp\left(\frac{-d}{\lambda}\right),\tag{6}$$

and therefore, by equations (5) and (6),

$$p = \left(\frac{2\lambda}{d}\right)\left(\frac{I_2}{I_1}\right).\tag{7}$$

Since each of the quantities on the right of equation (7) can be calculated or measured the probability p can be determined. It was found that 1 or 2 per cent of the collisions of 150-volt electrons with hydrogen molecules are effective in exciting the molecule to the 12.6-volt level. The critical potentials determined in this way are no more precise than those obtained by other methods, but the method can be used for finding the probabilities of inelastic collisions and can be applied to the electrons which leave the molecule in other directions after collision.

6. THE PHOTOELECTRIC AND INVERSE PHOTOELECTRIC EFFECTS IN GASES AND VAPORS

The photoelectric effect for gaseous atoms has been placed on a secure basis only within the past few years because of the great experimental difficulties. The phenomena involved, however, are very much simpler from the standpoint of theoretical interpretation, than those occurring when electrons are ejected from metal surfaces by light. Williamson[1] secured definite evidence of the photoelectric effect in potassium vapor. The chief difficulty in such experiments is the fact that photoelectrons from the walls of any apparatus used are greater in number than those from the gas or vapor, unless extreme precautions are taken. Because of the relatively high vapor pressures of the alkali metals and their low energies of ionization, these metals have been used almost entirely in experiments of this sort. Williamson, by using a jet of potassium vapor which was condensed on a liquid air trap and by illuminating this jet by a beam of light, was able to secure evidence of true photoionization, and found that ionization first began in the neighborhood of the theoretical wave length of 2,856 Å. Samuel[2] used almost precisely the same method and secured the same result, while Kunz and

---

[1] *Phys. Rev.*, **21**, 107 (1923).

[2] *Z. Physik*, **29**, 209 (1924).

Williams[1] determined the photoelectric effect in cesium vapor as a function of the wave length. They took great care in shielding the metal electrodes used for determining the conductivity of the gas from the beam of light which produced the photoionization, and found the long wave-length photoelectric limit of cesium vapor to be very close to 3,180 Å. which is the theoretical limit. Lawrence,[2] using a method similar to that of Williamson, found evidence that no ionization occurred in potassium vapor at wave lengths greater than 2,610 Å., which is considerably smaller than the limit calculated from the known energy of ionization of potassium. He suggested that this was due to the photoionization of the molecule

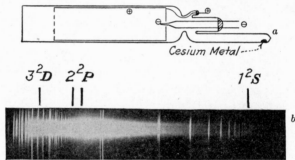

Fig. 14a.—The Foote and Mohler tube for detecting the photoelectric effect; *b*. Recombination spectrum of cesium.   (*After Mohler.*)

K_2 which may be much more sensitive to photoionization than the atom. Recently, Williamson has confirmed this work of Lawrence and has found that a weaker ionization of potassium vapor occurs at wave lengths below about 3,100 A., which also does not agree with the calculated limit. The effect which begins at about 3,100 A. is probably due to ionization of the K_2 molecule without dissociation, while that which begins at about 2,600 A. is probably due to dissociation of this molecule and ionization of one of its atoms. The 2,600 Å. and the 2,856 Å. quanta differ in energy by about 0.4 volt, which agrees fairly well with an estimate of the energy of dissociation of the K_2 molecule made by Carelli and Pringsheim,[3] namely 0.61 volts.

A very sensitive and useful method for studying the effect was devised by Foote and Mohler.[4] The tube used, shown in Fig. 14a, is of the type described by Kingdon[5] and is made of quartz for photoelectric experiments. The filament is very small and is located on the axis of a cylinder which is entirely closed except for a small hole in one end through which the filament leads are inserted. The other end is

[1] *Phys. Rev.*, **22**, 456 (1923).

[2] *Phil. Mag.*, **50**, 345 (1925).

[3] *Z. Physik*, **44**, 643 (1927).

[4] *Phys. Rev.*, **26**, 185 (1925); **27**, 37 (1926).

[5] *Phys. Rev.*, **21**, 408 (1923).

closed by a gauze which permits light to enter. The current from the filament is limited by the space charge in its neighborhood. If a photoelectron is produced in the vapor within the cylinder, the positive ion formed is drawn toward the filament by the electric field. However, if there were no gas present it would not reach the filament, except in the rare case that it had no angular momentum about the filament axis; when it possesses angular momentum relative to the filament it will describe an orbit about the filament and as Kingdon showed it may make several hundred trips around the filament before it falls into it and is neutralized. Because of this long life in the neighborhood of the filament, each positive ion neutralizes the space charge of many electrons and greatly decreases the negative space charge. Thus, a relatively small number of positive ions causes a great increase in the electron current from the filament. The change in current when the light falls into the tube is so great that it can be read on an ordinary microammeter. At the same time, photoelectric emissions from the wall are of no importance, since the electrons are driven back to the walls by the electric field. The tube is sensitive enough to permit the use of light from a monochromator, so that it is possible to study the photoelectric effect as a function of wave length.

The ionization potential of cesium, which was used in these experiments, is 3.88 volts, corresponding to a wave length of 3,183 Å. The simplest possible picture of the effect would lead us to expect that the current would increase sharply when the incident wave length is just inferior to this value. Experiment shows, however, that the increase begins at longer wave lengths; that there are distinct maxima on the long wave-length side of 3,183 Å.; and that the intensity of these maxima grows rapidly as the pressure and temperature of the vapor increase. Moreover, the wave lengths at which the maxima occur coincide with those of the principal series lines of cesium. These facts may be interpreted in the following way: Light having the same wave length as a principal series line excites a cesium atom, and before the energy stored up can be reëmitted as light, the atom makes a collision in which the transfer of translational energy is sufficient to ionize the excited atom. The probability of ionization by this mechanism should increase with the pressure and temperature, as it is observed to do. There are sufficient collisions of this class to account for the observed ionization. The probability of direct photoionization is a maximum at the wave length 3,183 Å. and decreases rapidly as the wave length becomes shorter.

The inverse photoelectric effect in gases has been observed by Mohler,[1] using a tube of the type employed for studying photoionization. In the inverse effect the process which occurs is

$$Cs^+ + e \rightarrow Cs + h\nu;$$

[1] *Phys. Rev.*, **31**, 187 (1928).

that is, an electron falls into a cesium ion, causing the emission of a light quantum whose energy is equal to the relative translational energy of the cesium ion and the electron, plus the energy required to ionize a cesium atom from one of its steady states, which may or may not be the normal state. Since the probability of ionization by a light quantum is a maximum when its energy just exceeds the ionizing potential so that the kinetic energy of the photoelectron is small, it follows from the principle of microscopic reversibility that the probability of combination is greatest when a slow electron collides with an ion.[1]

Mohler looked for the recombination spectrum of cesium in the neighborhood of the small filament of a photoionization tube, the vapor pressure being higher than 0.08 mm. of mercury and the current greater then 70 milliamperes. Under these conditions there should be a very high concentration of ions near the filament. Similar experiments were also performed with potassium. By using these metals it was possible to secure a very large emission of electrons from the filament at low temperatures due to the layer of alkali atoms on the filament and, because the ionizing potentials of these elements are small, comparatively slow electrons could be used to produce the ions. A photograph of the spectrum emitted near the filament is reproduced in Fig. 14b, and shows two distinct continuous bands extending toward the violet from the limits of the subordinate series and the fundamental series. These bands show that the reactions taking place with the emission of this light are,

$$Cs^+ + e \rightarrow Cs(2^2P_{\frac{1}{2},\frac{3}{2}}) + h\nu$$

and

$$Cs^+ + e \rightarrow Cs(3^2D_{\frac{3}{2},\frac{5}{2}}) + h\nu.$$

Mohler and Boeckner[2] have shown that the intensity of these spectra depends on the ion concentration, rather than the ion current. They find that the intensity distribution can be explained on the basis of simple recombination. Further they have studied the relative probability of recombination as a function of electron energy, and find it to be independent of other conditions in the discharge.

Under the conditions of these experiments series lines due to transitions from the higher levels are relatively more intense than they are when excited by other methods, and some higher series lines were observed for the first time. These lines are also more diffuse than they are when excited in other ways. These effects as well as an afterglow lasting for about 10^{-3} seconds were observed by Miss Hayner[3] in mercury vapor, and have recently been found by Kenty[4] in argon. Miss Hayner

[1] For further discussion of a case quite similar to this see Chap. XIV, Sec. 1.
[2] Bureau Standards, *J. Research*, **2**, 489 (1929).
[3] *Z. Physik*, **35**, 365 (1925).
[4] *Phys. Rev.*, **32**, 624 (1928).

explained her observations as due to the recombination of ions and electrons; the afterglow occurs because a finite time elapses before a positive ion can pick up an electron; the prominence of the subordinate and fundamental series points to the existence of large probabilities for recombinations in which the electron goes into orbits of high total quantum number; and broadening results from the perturbing effect of the high ion concentration. Mohler's experiments confirmed these views entirely.

Mohler[1] has used this method of detecting the photoionization of a gas, to determine ionization potentials. His procedure consists in bombarding the gas molecules with electrons of known but variable energy; when the accelerating potential is increased to a value at which ionization occurs sufficient light will be emitted to ionize the gas in a photoionization chamber mounted in one end of the experimental tube. Gauzes are placed between the region in which ionization is produced and the photoionization cell, to prevent the diffusion of ions and electrons to the latter.

In this way he investigated Cs, Rb, K, A, and Ne, and detected ionizing potentials above that corresponding to the removal of the most loosely bound electron. The observed potentials for the alkali metals and the processes which occur at these potentials are given in Table 3. (b) and (e) for potassium and the corresponding values for argon agree very well with values expected for two M levels of the X-ray energy diagram as determined by comparison with the values for neighboring atoms in the periodic system.

TABLE 3

Potentials			Process
Cs	Rb	K	
a. 3.88 (calculated)	4.16 (calculated)	4.32 (calculated)	Removal of the valence electron
b. 13.0 ± .5	16.0 ± .5	19 ± 1	Ionization of rare gas shell, $l = 1$
c. 18.5 ± 1	21.6 ± .5	23.8 ± 1	Ionization and excitation of the ion
d. 21.5 ± .5	25.2 ± .1	31.8 ± 1	Double ionization
e. 39.0 ± 1	....	48.0 ± 1	Ionization of the rare gas shell, $l = 0$

7. CRITICAL POTENTIALS OF MOLECULES

The excitation or ionization of a molecule by electron collision is similar in some ways to excitation or ionization by light. Franck has suggested that the primary effect of excitation is to change the electron

[1] *Phys. Rev.*, **28**, 46 (1926).

configuration without altering the internuclear distance or the kinetic energy of vibration; and this applies to excitation either by the absorption of light or by electron collision.[1]   The reasoning employed in Chap. 12, Sec. **11** applies equally here, and leads to the conclusion that resonance and ionizing potentials will measure the electronic energy changes of molecules only if that part of the potential energy which is a function of the internuclear distance is very closely the same for both the normal and excited states.   If the equilibrium distance between the nuclei in the normal and excited states and the corresponding nuclear vibration frequencies are very different, the molecule will experience a considerable increase of vibrational energy when it is raised to a higher electronic level.   One of the best examples of this case is the hydrogen molecule.

The extreme ultra-violet band systems of hydrogen have been analyzed by Witmer,[2] Dieke and Hopfield,[3] Werner,[4] and Hori[5]; and Birge[6] has deduced the complete energy diagram from these bands and others in the visible and near ultra-violet.   Knowing the equilibrium distances between the nuclei, their vibration frequencies, and the energies of dissociation in the different electronic states, it is possible to construct a curve representing the potential energy as a function of the internuclear distance for each electronic state of the molecule.[7]

Potential energy curves for the $1^1\Sigma$, $2^1\Sigma$, and C states of the hydrogen molecule and the normal state of the hydrogen molecule ion are illustrated in Fig. 15.   Integral vibration quantum numbers are used for reasons of simplicity, since we are interested only in the qualitative validity of the

---

[1] Franck and Jordan, "Anregung von Quantensprüngen durch Stösse," p. 252, Springer, Berlin (1926).

[2] *Proc. Nat. Acad. Sci.*, **12**, 238 (1926).

[3] *Z. Physik*, **40**, 299 (1926).

[4] *Proc. Roy. Soc.*, **113**, 107 (1926).

[5] *Z. Physik*, **44**, 834 (1927).

[6] *Proc. Nat. Acad. Sci.*, **14**, 12 (1928).

[7] The shape of such a curve in the neighborhood of the equilibrium distance between the nuclei is determined by the vibration frequencies of the nuclei, for this frequency is $(k/4\pi^2\mu)^{1/2}$, where μ is the reduced mass.   The potential energy for small displacements is then $V = \frac{1}{2} \cdot k(r - r_0)^2$.   The distance between the minimum of the curve and the horizontal line representing the value of V for the dissociated molecule is obviously the energy of dissociation for the state in question.   The remainder of the curve can be sketched in roughly for we know its general shape.   Its correctness can be tested by applying the quantum condition $\oint p_r dr = nh$, where p_r is equal to $\sqrt{2\mu E - 2\mu V}$.   The first term in this radical is the energy of vibration in some steady state, say the nth, and the second is given by the curve $V(r)$.   We may plot the value of this radical for different values of r, and may perform a graphical integration to determine $\int p_r dr$; the result must then be equal to nh.   Morse (Washington Meeting of the American Physical Society, Apr. 20, 1929) has shown that the vibration energy levels of a diatomic molecule will be of the form $an - bn^2 +$ a constant if the potential energy function has the form

$$-2De^{-2a(r-r_0)} + De^{-2a(r-r_0)}.$$

Franck-Condon theory.   The arrows indicate the only transitions from the normal state of the molecule, namely—the lowest vibration level of the $1^1\Sigma$ electronic state—to the $2^1\Sigma$ and C electronic states for which the distance between the nuclei is nearly unchanged during transition.   Though the energies required to bring the molecule to the lowest vibrational levels of the $2^1\Sigma$ and C states are only 11.1 and 12.23

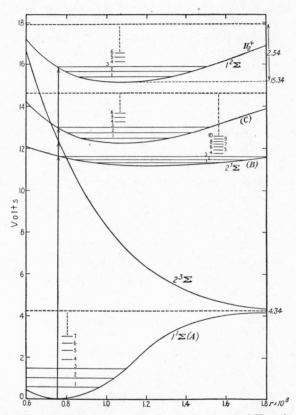

Fig. 15.—The potential energy curves of normal and excited H_2 and of H_2^+.

volts, respectively, the energy changes indicated by the arrows are 11.6 and 12.9 volts, respectively.   The latter value is as close to the observed value of 12.6 volts for the resonance potential as can be expected from the approximate theory.   Direct excitation of the $2^1\Sigma$ state by electron impact does not occur, according to Hori (*loc. cit.*), though according to the reasoning used here this level should be excited by 11.6-volt electrons.

The observed ionization potential of H_2 is 16.1 volts, while the value calculated from the H_2 spectrum is about 15.4 volts.   The arrow in the figure shows that according to the theory this transition should occur at 15.9 volts, which is in close agreement with the observed values.   There is another critical potential of hydrogen at 11.5 volts which seems to be fairly well established. Condon and Smyth[1] assign it to the transition from the $1^1\Sigma$ state to the $2^3\Sigma$ state predicted by Heitler and London.[2] The potential energy curve shown in the figure has no minimum and for large distances between the two atoms the potential energy approaches that of two normal hydrogen atoms. Transitions to this state result in dissociation of the molecule into two normal atoms with a large relative kinetic energy. Evidence for the existence of this process will be presented in Sec. 10.

There is a marked difference in the vibration frequencies and moments of inertia of the I_2 molecule in its normal and excited states (Chap. XII, Sec. 11), and therefore it should exhibit effects similar to those observed for hydrogen. Hogness and Harkness[3] observed such effects in their studies of the ionization of iodine. They find that the I^+ and I_2^+ ions appear at the same critical potential, 9.3 volts, and that they are primary products of the inelastic collision. It is probable that the potential energy curve for the normal I_2 molecule is similar to that of the $1^1\Sigma$ state of hydrogen and that the I_2^+ molecule has one state similar to the $2^1\Sigma$ state of hydrogen. In this case, the energy of vibration would be increased when an electron is removed, and might become so large that the molecular ion would split into a neutral atom and an atomic ion. The probability of an inelastic collision in which an I_2^+ ion with large amounts of vibrational energy is produced appears to be about equal to that of a collision which results in an atom and an atomic ion.

8. THE PROBABILITY OF INELASTIC COLLISIONS

Consider a collision between an atom and an electron, in which the initial values of the energy, momentum and angular momentum are all specified, and the orientation of the atom with respect to the original direction of motion of the electron is given. On the basis of classical mechanics, we expect that every such collision will lead to the same final state, determined by definite values of these same quantities. The statistical interpretation of the new mechanics, however, introduces the possibility that several final states can result from the same initial state (Chap. XVIII). Thus we may speak of the probability of an elastic or an inelastic collision of a 4.9-volt electron with a mercury atom in the 1^1S_0 level. However, this is not the usual sense in which the word probability is used in connection with such problems. So far as the experimental data are concerned, the question of the appearance of pure probability in determining the results of collisions need not be considered, for these data deal with collisions for which the initial and the final states are only partly known. The object is to fix the initial

[1] Proc. Nat. Acad. Sci., **14**, 871 (1928).

[2] Z. Physik, **44**, 455 (1927). See also SUGIURA, Y, ibid., **45**, 484 (1927).

[3] Phys. Rev., **32**, 784 (1928).

and final states as closely as possible and then determine what fraction of the collisions is elastic or inelastic, and to determine how this fraction depends on various circumstances. The determination of such probabilities is of interest in studying the details of the collision process between electrons and atoms.

In some ways the probabilities of inelastic collisions may be expected to parallel the Einstein probabilities B, for the absorption of light quanta. Thus, if an atom can pass from one state to another by the absorption of radiation, its behavior with respect to this transition is similar to that of an oscillating dipole; but if it can not pass from the one state to the other by the absorption of light, it behaves as a quadrupole. Quite similarly it is to be expected that an electron will interact more strongly with an atom to produce a transition if the atom has a dipole character than if it has quadrupole character, and thus the probability of an inelastic collision which excites the atom will be greater for transitions permitted by selection rules than for those which are forbidden. On the other hand, because of its highly inhomogeneous field, the electron can interact with a quadruple more strongly than the light quantum, and thus transitions forbidden by the selection rules will be relatively more probable in electron collisions than in the absorption or emission of light.[1]

In collisions of atoms and electrons, the angular momentum must be conserved, as Blackett[2] has emphasized, and this brings with it the requirement that the probability of excitation must be zero when the relative kinetic energy is equal to the energy of excitation. Consider for example, transitions from a normal 1^1S_0 state, such as that of helium or mercury, which has zero angular momentum, to the 2^1S_0 state by means of an inelastic collision. If the collision is to take place in such a way that the kinetic energy of atom and electron relative to their center of mass is equal to zero after the impact, then their angular momentum after the impact will also vanish. In order to secure this condition the electron and atom must collide head on, so that the angular momentum before collision will be zero. Only an infinitesimal fraction of the collisions will occur in this way and therefore the probability of such a transition is zero when the kinetic energy is just equal to the energy of excitation. Similar considerations hold for the transition to the 2^1P_1 state, for here the relative angular momentum before collision must be exactly $h/2\pi$. In the case of a transition to a triplet state the problem is more complicated, for the spin vectors of the electrons within the atom must change their relative orientations. This case can not be considered simply or precisely by classical mechanics. It appears, however, that the probability of excitation by electrons which have

[1] Franck and Jordan, "Anregung von Quantensprüngen durch Stösse, ' p. 170.
[2] *Proc. Camb. Phil. Soc.*, **22**, 56 (1923).

exactly the necessary energy to induce a transition will be zero in all cases.

It has long been known that in experiments on critical potentials of the type described in this chapter most of the effective collisions take place at potentials fairly close to the critical values; in other words, the probability of such inelastic collisions is relatively high for potentials slightly above the critical values and decreases fairly rapidly with increasing potential. This is shown by the shape of such curves as those secured by Davis and Goucher (Fig. 5). Above 4.9 volts the curve is concave toward the potential axis indicating that the probability of excitation is smaller for electrons of higher energy. The same is observed immediately above the 6.7 volt break in the curve. On the other hand,

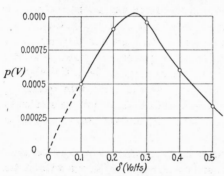

FIG. 16.—The excitation function for the 1¹S→2³S transition of He. (*After Dymond.*)

curves showing the ionizing potential are convex to the voltage axis in the region just above the critical value; this indicates that the probability of ionizing collisions increases, at least until the energy is considerably in excess of the critical value. This is also illustrated by the curve of Fig. 5.

Dymond[1] has determined the probability for the excitation of helium to the $^3S_1$ state by electron impact, as a function of the potential of the exciting electron. This was done by a method similar to that used by Hertz (Sec. 2) for the measurement of excitation potentials. The method consists of shooting electrons of known velocity through a gauze into a Faraday cage (Fig. 6). The electrons make a number of collisions with the helium gas in the field-free space before they diffuse through a gauze at one side. The number of collisions which they make before leaving the cage in this way can be roughly calculated from a knowledge of its dimensions and the mean free path of the electron in helium gas. The electrons which leave through the gauze consist of two groups: those which have made only elastic collisions with the helium atoms and therefore have the original velocity with which they entered the cage, and those which have lost all but a small fraction of their energy due to one inelastic collision. By determining the relative numbers of electrons which leave the cage with velocities corresponding to 0.1, 0.2, . . . volts, and also the distribution of velocities of electrons which have made only elastic collisions with the helium atoms, it is possible to calculate what fraction of the electron collisions of any particular velocity

[1] *Proc. Roy. Soc.* **107**, 291 (1924).

are inelastic. The results secured by Dymond in this way are illustrated in Fig. 16. The probability seems to be zero at the critical potential; it rises very rapidly, reaches a maximum two or three tenths of a volt above the critical value and then decreases rapidly. Moreover, only about 10^{-3} of the collisions are inelastic at the maximum. This low probability is to be expected, for the transition does not occur with the absorption of light. The curve could only be observed to 0.5 volts above the critical potential, because the next critical potential lies only 0.8 volts above the first one. Recently Glockler[1] has reinvestigated this same transition and observes the same general variation of probability of inelastic impact with potential, but finds a maximum probability of 0.002 at 0.18 volt above the critical potential.

The probability of inelastic impact between 150-volt electrons and hydrogen molecules, as determined by Jones and Whiddington (Sec. 5), is considerably larger than that determined by Dymond in the case of helium. The transition of the hydrogen molecule investigated by the former authors may be caused by light absorption. Accordingly we expect that the probability for this transition to occur in collisions with electrons should be greater than the probability for the transition studied by Dymond.

The probability of ionizing collisions has been determined by a number of investigators, for electrons of energy considerably larger than the ionizing potential of the gases investigated.[2] The experiments are in substantial agreement, considering the many experimental difficulties. With increasing electron energy the probability of ionization rises to a maximum value, after which it decreases. The maximum ionization probability varies between 15 and 60 per cent, depending upon the gas. When 100-volt electrons collide with molecules of the commoner permanent gases, several different ionization processes are possible, such as the removal of different electrons, double ionization, or ionization together with excitation of the ion. Because of this the significance of the data is not easily seen.

9. IMPACT POLARIZATION

When radiation is excited by collisions of a unidirectional beam of electrons with gaseous atoms, it may be expected, quite independently of any detailed theory of the excitation process, that the radiation emitted will be polarized either parallel or perpendicular to the electron beam,

[1] *Phys. Rev.*, **33**, 175 (1929).

[2] HUGHES and KLEIN, *Phys. Rev.* **23**, 450 (1924); MAYER, *Ann. Phys.*, **45**, 1 (1914); JESSE, *Phys. Rev.*, **26**, 208 (1925); COMPTON and VAN VOORHUIS, *Phys. Rev.*, **26**, 436 (1925); **27**, 1724 (1926); ANSLOW, *Phys. Rev.*, **25**, 484 (1925); LANGMUIR and JONES, *Science*, **59**, 380 (1924); *Phys. Rev.*, **31**, 357 (1928).

since the excitation is non-isotropic in character. That such polarization should exist was suggested by Kossel and Gerthsen,[1] who investigated the polarization of the sodium D-lines excited in this way with negative results, and independently by Ellett, Foote, and Mohler,[2] who confirmed the negative results of the former authors and secured positive results with the 2,537 Å. resonance line of mercury. On the basis of a simple theory, they expected to find the light partially polarized, with the maximum electric vector parallel to the electron beam, for the electron should be able to increase the angular momentum of the mercury atom in a direction perpendicular to the direction of its motion, and, on the average, such atoms should emit more light polarized parallel to the electron beam than perpendicular to it. They found, however, that the 2,537 A. line was perpendicularly polarized. Skinner,[3] Appleyard,[4] and Quarder[5] have investigated many other lines of the mercury spectrum and have found marked regularities in their results.

The experimental method of all these authors consists in exciting the atoms by a stream of electrons from a heated filament, accelerated through gauzes into a field-free space. The light is usually observed in a line perpendicular to the direction of the electron stream and the polarization parallel or perpendicular to the stream is determined in the usual way. Skinner used a Helmholtz coil to neutralize the earth's field and constructed the filament in such a way as to avoid a magnetic field due to the heating current. Other Helmholtz coils were used to produce magnetic fields parallel and perpendicular to the direction of the electron stream. The percentage of polarization is defined as the intensity of the component polarized parallel to the electron stream minus that polarized perpendicular to this direction, divided by their sum, and multiplied by 100:

$$\Pi = 100 \, \frac{I_1 - I_2}{I_1 + I_2}. \tag{8}$$

This is positive if the net polarization is parallel to the stream, and negative if perpendicular to this direction. For all lines investigated, the percentage of polarization is found to approach zero as the energy of the exciting electrons approaches the energy of excitation; as the energy of the electrons increases, it passes through a maximum or minimum and then, in the cases of most lines, becomes zero again or even changes sign. The general character of these variations in the polarization can be seen from Fig. 17, in which we reproduce four of the curves of Skinner and Appleyard, each illustrating one type of variation of

---

[1] *Ann. Physik*, **77**, 273 (1925).

[2] *Phys. Rev.*, **27**, 31 (1926).

[3] *Proc. Roy. Soc.*, **112**, 642 (1926).

[4] *Proc. Roy. Soc.*, **117**, 224 (1927).

[5] *Z. Physik.*, **41**, **674** (1927).

polarization with the energy of the impacting electron. These four types may be described as follows:

(a) The polarization of the light excited by electrons of low energy is positive, *i.e.*, parallel to the beam; (b) the polarization is negative, *i.e.*, perpendicular to the beam; (c) the polarization is positive when excited by electrons of low energy and does not change sign as the energy of the excited electrons increases; and (d) the line is not polarized at all.

A magnetic field parallel to the direction of the electron stream does not change the polarization, but a magnetic field of a few gauss perpendicular to this direction produces two effects: first, the light is depolarized, the effect being a maximum for the light viewed in the direction of the field, and second, there is a rotation of the plane of polarization about the axis of the field. The theory of these effects is practically

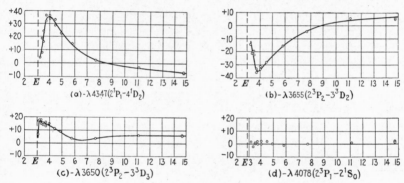

FIG. 17.—The polarization of impact radiation as a function of the electron energy. (*After Skinner and Appleyard.*)

the same as that for the similar phenomena observed in the case of resonance radiation excited in a magnetic field (Chap. XI, Sec. **4**). The influence of a magnetic field in changing the orientation of the excited atoms before they emit the light should be independent of the way in which they are excited, for its only effect is to cause the atoms to precess about the direction of the force-lines during the time between excitation and emission. The apparent rotation of the plane of polarization is given by the equation,

$$\tan 2\Phi = \frac{4\pi gL}{A},\tag{9}$$

and the depolarization by the formula,

$$\frac{\Pi_0{}^2}{\Pi^2} - 1 = \left(\frac{4\pi gL}{A}\right)^2,\tag{10}$$

where Φ is the angle through which the plane of polarization is rotated. A is the probability for spontaneous emission by the excited atom, L the frequency of the Larmor precession, g the Landé factor, and Π and Π_0

the percentages of polarization in the presence and absence of the field, respectively.   The experimental facts confirm these formulas and permit a calculation of A, or its reciprocal τ, which is the mean life of the excited atom.   The mean lives of mercury atoms in the 3^1D_2 and 3^3D_2 states are found to be 2.85 and $2.88 \cdot 10^{-8}$ seconds, from the observed rotation of the plane of polarization and the observed depolarization, respectively; these values are of the order of magnitude found for other atomic states and by other methods.   The magnetic field parallel to the electron beam does not change the polarization because it can only cause a precession of the atoms about this line and thus cannot destroy the symmetry of the excitation process.

A theory of this polarization which explains most of the experimental results qualitatively was proposed by Skinner. Oppenheimer[1] has developed the theory of the process using quantum mechanics, accounting for many features of the effect not explained by the older theory.   Lack of space prevents detailed discussion but the following physical features of Skinner's theory may be pointed out.   The velocity vector of the electron and the nucleus of the atom determine a plane, and the initial relative angular momentum of the two is perpendicular to this plane; likewise, after the collision the velocity vector of the electron and the nucleus of the atom determine a plane and the final relative angular momentum is perpendicular to this plane.   If the collision is elastic,

Table 4

Line	λ	V_0	V_{max}	II, observed, Quarder	II, observed at V_{max}, Skinner and Appleyard	II, calculated, Skinner
$2^1P_1 - 4^1D_2$	4,347	9.5	15	45	35	60
$2^3P_2 - 3^1D_2$	3,663	8.8	14	−45	−41	−100
$2^3P_1 - 4^1D_2$	2,655	9.5	15	50	27	60
$2^3P_1 - 2^1S_0$	4,078	7.9	...	10	0	0
$2^1P_1 - 4^1S_0$	4,108	9.5	...	10	0	0
$2^3P_2 - 3^3D_3$	3,650	8.8	11	15	18	50
$2^3P_2 - 3^3D_2$	3,655	8.8	14	....	−35	−100
$2^3P_1 - 3^3D_2$	3,126	8.8	14	20	28	60
$2^3P_1 - 4^3D_1$	2,654	9.5	...	....	(−17)	−100
$2^3P_0 - 3^3D_1$	2,967	8.8	14	33	25	100
$2^3P_2 - 2^3S_1$	5,461	7.7	...	7	0	14
$2^3P_1 - 2^3S_1$	4,358	7.7	11	15	−12	−100
$2^3P_0 - 2^3S_1$	4,047	7.7	11	33	8	100
$1^1S_0 - 2^3P_1$	2,537	4.9	6.7	−30	−30	100

[1] *Z. Physik*, **43**, 27 (1927).

these two planes coincide and there is no change in the relative angular momentum, but if the collision is inelastic, in general they do not coincide and are not parallel, and there is such a change. In case the electron has just sufficient energy to excite the atom to a certain level, it will have zero velocity after the inelastic collision and the relative angular momentum after the collision will be zero. In this case, the angular momentum transferred to the atom is perpendicular to the velocity vector of the electron before collision, and, therefore, can change the component of angular momentum of the atom perpendicular to the direction of the electron stream, but not the component parallel to it.

If a small magnetic field is present parallel to the electron stream the normal and excited atoms will be space quantized in this field. The mercury atom in its normal state has j equal to zero. Therefore, the magnetic quantum number m is zero, and since the electron cannot increase the component of angular momentum in the direction of the field, all the excited states must also have m equal to zero. In the emission of light the magnetic quantum number may change by zero, in which case the light is polarized parallel to the magnetic field and the electron stream, or by ± 1, in which case the light will be circularly polarized about the direction of the magnetic field and electron stream and will appear perpendicularly polarized when viewed in a direction perpendicular to the magnetic field. Knowing the relative probabilities of these transitions, it is possible to calculate the percentage of polarization to be expected. Similar arguments can be carried through in the case of other lines. Figure 18 illustrates the transitions involved in excitation and emission from the 3^1D_2 state. Only the state with m equal to zero is excited, but three emission transitions are possible; the relative intensities due to these three are given at the top of the diagram and it is easily seen that the percentage of polarization is

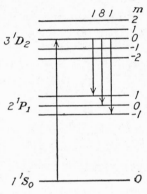

Fig. 18.—Excitation of the 3^1D_2 state of mercury by electron impact.

$$\Pi = 100\frac{8 - 2}{8 + 2} = 60 \text{ per cent.}$$

Table 4 gives the results of measurements for a number of mercury lines and the theoretical polarizations calculated as above. For most of the lines the theory predicts polarization of the correct sign, but the observed polarization is always less than that predicted. In the case of other lines, for all of which the initial state has an inner quantum number equal to 1, the observed polarization is much less than predicted. The observed and predicted polarizations are of opposite sign in the case of the intercombination resonance line, 2,537 Å. These differences, as well as the maximum in the curve of polarization against energy of the bombarding electrons, cannot be accounted for by the simple theory, but are in agreement with the predictions of quantum mechanics.

Before leaving the subject of impact polarization, we shall call attention to a related effect which has not been observed up to the time of writing. Dorfmann[1] suggested that when atoms absorb light from a circularly polarized beam they become oriented in such a way that the medium as a whole should possess a magnetic moment. He has called this phenomenon the "photomagnetic effect." About the same time Rashevsky[2] calculated the magnitude of such an effect on the basis of classical electron theory. He attributed the idea to Fitzgerald, whose work incited Righi to attempt the detection of the magnetic moment produced in NO_2. The experiment did not succeed in spite of the fact that Righi's magnetometer could detect a field of 10^{-6} gauss. It appears that the moment produced should be proportional to the intensity of the light and that it should be a maximum at an absorption wave length. For cesium vapor under favorable conditions, the predicted ratio of the moment to the intensity is 10^{-15}, using CGS units. Of course it would be much larger for a liquid or a solid, and it seems not improbable that the effect could be detected in a favorably chosen case. Ruark and Urey[3] have discussed the possibility that the light-quantum may have an intrinsic impulse moment. The existence of such a moment appears to be easily amenable to test, but so far the necessary experiments have not been performed. In case it does exist, the theory of the photomagnetic effect would have to be modified.

10. CHEMICAL ACTIVATION BY ELECTRON IMPACT

That hydrogen molecules are dissociated by electron impact has been proved by the experiments of Hughes and Skellett[4] and of Glockler, Baxter, and Dalton.[5] The former authors studied the pressure change in a tube containing hydrogen, so arranged that the gas was bombarded with electrons and the hydrogen atoms produced were condensed on a glass wall cooled with liquid air. The pressure ffrst decreases when the electrons have an energy of 11.5 volts and the rate of decrease is proportional to the pressure of the hydrogen. The latter authors found that hydrogen bombarded in this way reacts with copper oxide, resulting in the formation of water, and that this first occurs with 11.4-volt electrons. This value agrees with the first critical potential in hydrogen and might be explained either as due to the formation of an excited

[1] Z. Physik, 17, 98 (1923).
[2] Z. Physik, 20, 191 (1923).
[3] Proc. Nat. Acad. Sci, 13, 763 (1927).
[4] Phys. Rev., 30, 11 (1927).
[5] J. A. C. S., 49, 58 (1927).

hydrogen molecule which then dissociates into atoms spontaneously, or to the formation of atoms as a direct result of electron impact. As mentioned in Sec. 7, it appears probable that the latter process is the correct one. Glockler, Baxter, and Dalton also found that the amount of atomic hydrogen produced increases with voltage up to the molecular ionizing potential. There is evidence that a second process may become important at these higher potentials. Independently, Blackett and Franck[1] suggested that the continuous hydrogen spectrum, which extends from the visible to the far ultra-violet, is due to the emission of light by excited molecules when they dissociate either into normal or excited atoms. The continuous character of the spectrum is due to the fact that part of the energy of the excited molecule appears as kinetic energy of the dissociated atoms and the remainder is emitted as light, and since the translational energy takes continuous values, the frequency of the light quanta must also vary continuously. That hydrogen atoms with high velocities are produced is shown to be the case by studying the breadth of the $H\alpha$ line, which can only be accounted for by assuming it is due to the Doppler effect of atoms moving with 0.3 to 0.6 volt relative energy. Winans and Stueckelberg[2] show that the distribution of the intensity of this continuous spectrum can be explained by the Franck-Condon theory (Sec. 7) applied to the transition from the higher $2^3\Sigma$ state to the lower $2^3\Sigma$ state (Fig. 15). Excitation to the $2^3\Sigma$ state will occur at 12 or 13 volts. Therefore, at these higher potentials it appears probable that the primary process of the electron collisions may be to produce an excited molecule, which may either dissociate into atoms or emit its energy as light.

Bonhoeffer[3] and Taylor and Marshall[4] have found that atomic hydrogen, produced by collisions of the second kind with excited Hg, does not react with nitrogen to form ammonia. Anderson[5] and Storch and Olson[6] have found that ammonia is not produced below 17 volts when a mixture of hydrogen and nitrogen is bombarded with electrons. At 17 volts N_2^+ ions are first produced. Kwei[7] found that the characteristic ammonia bands do not appear below 23 volts where N^+ and N first appear, but as these bands are now known to be due to NH_1 this does not mean that NH_3 may not be produced below this potential. Lewis[9] has shown that ammonia is not produced in a mixture of active nitrogen

[1] Z. Physik, **34**, 389 (1925).
[2] Proc. Nat. Acad. Sci., **14**, 867 (1928).
[3] Z. Electrochemie, **31**, 521 (1925).
[4] J. Phys. Chem., **23**, 1140 (1925).
[5] Z. Physik, **10**, 64 (1923).
[6] J. A. C. S., **45**, 1605 (1923).
[7] Phys. Rev., **26**, 537 (1925).
[8] HULTHÉN and NAHAMORA, Nature, **119**, 235 (1927).
[9] BERNARD LEWIS J. A. C. S., **50**, 27 (1928).

and molecular hydrogen, nor in a mixture of ordinary molecular nitrogen and atomic hydrogen made by Wood's[1] method; but it is produced when active nitrogen and atomic hydrogen are mixed. It appears that atomic hydrogen and the 17-volt molecular nitrogen ion can react to give ammonia as the final product, and also it reacts with the excited nitrogen molecule or the nitrogen atom present in active nitrogen.

11. ELASTIC COLLISIONS AND THE RAMSAUER EFFECT

The number of collisions which a beam of fast electrons makes with atoms arranged at random in its path is proportional to the number of electrons in the beam and to a quantity which we may call the fraction of the beam area covered by the atoms in its path. If each collision removes an electron from the beam, the number lost per unit area in traversing a distance dx is

$$dI = -IN\pi r^2 dx; \tag{11}$$

in this equation I is the number of electrons passing through unit area perpendicular to the beam each second, N is the number of atoms per cubic centimeter, and r the "effective" radius, so that $N\pi r^2 dx$ is the fraction of the cross-sectional area covered by the atoms in the range dx. Since all the quantities in this equation can be measured, with the exception of r, it is possible to determine the value of r or of πr^2 by experiments on the scattering of electrons by atoms. By equation (11),

$$I = I_0 \exp(-xN\pi r^2). \tag{12}$$

Lenard[2] first used these equations in studies of the scattering of cathode rays by atoms, and showed that r steadily decreases as the velocity of the electrons increases. For very high speed electrons, the value of r was found to be much less than the value deduced from the kinetic theory of gases, while for slow electrons, it was of the same order of magnitude as the gas-kinetic value. The experimental method used by Lenard has been improved by Mayer.[3] His apparatus consists of a suitable arrangement for accelerating electrons from a hot cathode into a field-free space.

In this space the electrons may make collisions with gas molecules. Those which do not collide pass through two gauzes, between which there is a retarding potential equal to the potential through which the electrons fell before entering the field-free space. Those electrons which have not been deflected by gas molecules will be able to move against this retarding field and register on an electrometer electrode. The two gauzes and the detecting electrode can be moved as a unit, nearer to or farther from the point at which the electrons enter the field-free space, and thus the variable x of equation (12) can be varied

[1] *Phil. Mag.*, **42**, 729 (1921).

[2] *Ann. Physik*, **2**, 359 (1900); **8**, 149 (1902); **12**, 449, 714 (1903).

[3] *Ann. Physik*, **64**, 451 (1921).

at will. By determining the current to the electrode for different values of x, it is possible to calculate the value of r or of πr^2 for the gas. This method is particularly useful in studying corrosive gases. Nettleton[1] also studied the ionization in a number of gases, using voltages between 100 and 1,400. He concluded that in this range the effective radius for the ionization processes varies inversely as the velocity in accordance with a formula due to Rutherford.

Ramsauer[2] has introduced an especially effective method for determining the decreasing intensity of a beam of electrons, and independently the number of electrons scattered from the beam while passing through a

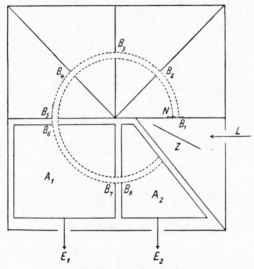

Fig. 19.—Ramsauer's apparatus.

short section of its path. The essential features of his apparatus can be seen from Fig. 19. Photoelectrons are ejected from the plate Z and accelerated by an electric field to the slit B_1. A magnetic field perpendicular to the plane of the paper bends the beam of electrons into a circle passing through the slits B_1 to B_8. Only those electrons whose velocities are connected with the radius of this circle and the magnetic field strength by the relation $v = (e/m)Hr$ will be able to pass through this slit system, and then only if the electrons are not deflected from their path by collisions; the magnetic field strength and the potential V between the plate Z and the slit B_1 must be varied together in order to study electron beams of different velocities. A_1 and A_2 are Faraday cages connected to the electrometers E_1 and E_2. The whole apparatus is filled with gas and by varying the pressure the number of molecules per

[1] *Proc. Nat. Acad. Sci.*, **10**, 140 (1924).

[2] *Ann. Physik*, **64**, 513 (1921); **66**, 546 (1921); **72**, 345 (1923); *Jahrb. d. Radioakt. u. Elektronik*, **19**, 345 (1922).

cm.[3] is adjusted to any desired value.   The slits B_1 to B_5 serve to define a narrow beam of electrons.   The electrons scattered in the path from B_6 to B_7 are measured by the electrometer E_1 and those passing beyond this region by E_2.   In this way I_0 of equation (12) is given by the sum of the currents measured by E_1 and E_2, and I, the intensity after traversing the path B_6 to B_7, by the current measured by E_2.   Only those electrons which have not been deflected and have not had their velocities appreciably changed by collisions with gas molecules will be able to reach the Faraday cage A_2.

The effective cross-sectional areas of molecules secured by Ramsauer, using this method for electrons of high velocity, agree very well with

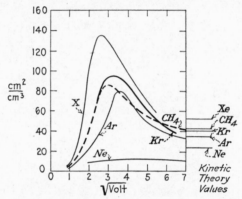

FIG. 20.—Variation of effective cross-sectional area of the inert gases with electron velocity.
(*After Ramsauer and Brüche.*)

those secured by Lenard, but with electrons of lower velocity the effective area is found to pass through one or more maxima and for still lower velocities it approaches a very small value, even less than that of the gas-kinetic area; in fact, it appears to approach zero.   Mayer, using the modified method of Lenard, has secured similar results.   The experimental data on this subject have been very much extended by Brode[1] and Brüche.[2]

There is considerable variation in the shape of the curves giving the effective cross-sectional area as a function of velocity and any general classification at present is impossible.   The inert gases were investigated by Ramsauer.   For electrons of very low velocity, the effective cross-sectional area of these atoms is small and appears to approach zero with the electron velocity; with electrons of higher velocity this area becomes a maximum which is several times the value calculated from kinetic theory and for still higher velocities decreases slowly without limit. Figure 20 shows the curves for these gases as determined by Ramsauer

[1] *Phys. Rev.*, **23**, 664 (1924); **25**, 636 (1925); *Proc. Roy. Soc.*, **109**, 397 (1925).

[2] *Ann. Physik*, **81**, 537 (1926); **82**, 912 (1927); **83**, 1065 (1927); *Physik. Z.*, **29**, (1928).

and also that for methane, where effective cross-sectional area in cm.^{2} per cubic centimeter of the gas at 0°C. and 1 mm. of mercury pressure is plotted against the square root of the voltage, which is proportional to the electron velocity. The curve for helium is similar to that of neon but reaches a maximum at 20 cm.^{2}/cm.^{3} and at $\sqrt{\text{volts}} = 1.6$. The curves for other gases (CO_2, N_2O, N_2, CO) have two maxima, one of which is very sharp, and those for yet other gases (O_2, NO) are quite irregular. Brode has shown that the effective cross-sectional areas of Zn, Cd, and Hg increase indefinitely as the velocity of the electrons decreases, but that these areas for the alkali metal vapors have one maximum in the neighborhood of 2 or 3 volts, and a minimum at less than 1 volt. He

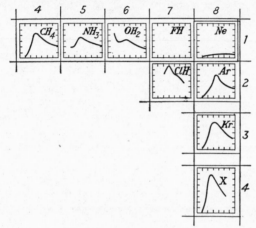

FIG. 21.—The effective cross-sectional areas of the inert and pseudo-inert gases. (*After Brüche.*)

has further shown that the shapes of his curves agree with those expected for hydrogen atoms calculated by means of the new wave mechanics.[1] Brüche has investigated the effective cross-sectional areas of a number of hydrides having inert gas configurations and has found regular modifications of the curves due to the presence of the hydrogen nuclei in the electron shells. These regularities are easily seen from the curves of Fig. 21. It is interesting to note that the curve for methane is of the same general shape as those for inert gases, and that it agrees almost quantitatively with that of krypton. The evidence indicates that an electron of very low velocity in some cases may penetrate the electron shells of atoms and molecules and pass through without exchange of either energy or momentum, *i.e.*, the electron is undeflected. Electrons of somewhat higher velocities find the collisional areas of these same molecules to be higher than those expected from gas kinetic considerations; they are deflected even if they pass within a distance from the atom or molecule equal to several times its gas-kinetic radius. For electrons of still higher

[1] Washington Meeting of the American Physical Society (1929).

velocity the effective collisional area decreases without limit as the electronic velocity increases.

Dempster[1] has investigated the free paths of protons, hydrogen molecule ions, and helium ions in helium gas by means of his apparatus for separating isotopes, which is described in Chap. II, Sec. 10 and is somewhat similar to the Ramsauer apparatus. He has found that protons which have fallen through a field of 14 to 900 volts have a mean free path seventeen times as great as may be expected from the gas-kinetic free path. The 900-volt hydrogen molecule ion has a mean free path in helium about nine times the gas-kinetic value, but the mean free path of the helium ion is very nearly the same as that calculated from kinetic theory. This is equivalent to saying that the effective radius of the helium atom is about equal to the kinetic theory value multiplied by the factors $\frac{1}{4}$, $\frac{1}{3}$, and 1, for collisions of protons, hydrogen molecule ions, and helium ions, respectively. The velocities of the protons used in these experiments vary from $5.3 \cdot 10^6$ to $44 \cdot 10^6$ cm. per second and are of the same order of magnitude as those acquired by electrons which have fallen through 0.01 to 0.5 volts. Thus, helium atoms are easily penetrated by electrons, protons, and hydrogen molecule ions of low velocity. Aich[2] has found by a different method that hydrogen molecules bombarded by 25-volt protons have an effective cross-section very nearly equal to the kinetic theory value.

Ramsauer and Beeck[3] have investigated the effective cross-sectional areas of a number of gases, including He, Ne, A, H_2, O_2, and N_2 relative to the alkali metal ions, as a function of the velocity of the ions. The ions were accelerated by fields from 1 to 30 volts. It was found that the effective cross-sections for all combinations of ions and gases increased as the potential was decreased from 30 volts, slowly at first and then very rapidly between 2 and 1 volts. As yet, there is no evidence that these cross-sectional areas become zero at low velocities.

At the present writing, little can be said with certainty with regard to the theory of the Ramsauer effect. Classical theories were developed by Hund[4] and Zwicky.[5] The latter author lays special emphasis on the polarization of an atom by an electron passing near it, and draws many interesting results from detailed consideration of its nature. The wave mechanics furnishes a perfectly definite mathematical apparatus for solving the problem, but the computations are difficult. The methods used are explained by Wentzel[6] in a general article on aperiodic phenomena in the new mechanics.

[1] *Proc. Nat. Acad. Sci.*, **11**, 552 (1925); **12**, 96 (1926)
[2] *Z. Physik*, **9**, 372 (1922).
[3] *Ann. Physik*, **87**, 1 (1928).
[4] *Z. Physik*, **13**, 241 (1923).
[5] *Physik. Z.*, **24**, 171 (1923).
[6] *Physik. Z.*, **29**, 321 (1928).

CHAPTER XIV

COLLISIONS OF THE SECOND KIND[1]

1. THE RELATION BETWEEN COLLISIONS OF THE FIRST AND SECOND KINDS

The laws of mechanics show that there are certain very general classes of interaction processes of individual atoms and molecules, such that the reverse processes also represent possible motions of the system. What we mean by the reverse of a given motion may be clearly understood from a simple illustration. If we take a moving picture of the motion, and then run the film backward through the projector, we shall see the reverse motion on the screen. In the kinetic theory of gases and in statistical mechanics, it is often very useful to focus attention on a certain type of motion and its reverse. Thus, we may consider a type of collision in which two atoms with vector velocities v_1 and v_2 emerge from the encounter with velocities v_3 and v_4, together with the type in which atoms with velocities $-v_3$ and $-v_4$ emerge with velocities $-v_1$ and $-v_2$. Similar examples can be given for other variables, such as energy, and angular momentum. The principle that to every microscopic process there is a corresponding possible reverse process is known as the "principle of microscopic reversibility." Stated in this simple form, it cannot be correct. Bridgman[2] has suggested an alternative formulation, while Tolman[3] has discussed the conditions under which the principle may be valid in the form given above. Exceptions arise if the Lagrangian function for the motion (Chap. IV, Sec. 3) or the external forces contain odd powers of the velocity. The case where a uniform magnetic field is present furnishes a good illustration.[4] On reversing the velocity of a particle, the direction of the Larmor precession is not reversed, and the original path will not be retraced.

In statistical problems where the principle of microscopic reversibility can be legitimately applied, we can use it to find the equilibrium state, for at equilibrium the numbers of direct processes and of reverse processes taking place in unit time are equal. Klein and Rosseland[5]

---

[1] This chapter was prepared with the collaboration of Dr. Richard Vollrath, to whom we are much indebted for his aid.

[2] *Phys. Rev.*, **31**, 101 (1928).

[3] "Statistical Mechanics with Applications to Physics and Chemistry," D. Van Nostrand Company, Inc., New York (1927).

[4] EINSTEIN and EHRENFEST, *Z. Physik*, **19**, 301 (1923).

[5] *Z. Physik*, **4**, 46 (1921).

used this argument to show that if a collision between a fast electron
and an atom or molecule may result in a slow electron and an excited
atom, then we must expect that a fast electron and a normal atom may
be produced when a slow electron collides with an excited atom or molecule. These two types of inelastic collisions are called "collisions
of the first and second kinds," respectively.

Consider a gas at some high temperature, so that not only the normal
unexcited atoms but also ions, free electrons, and excited atoms are
present. The numbers of atoms in two quantum states, which may
be designated by the subscripts 1 and 2, respectively, are:

$$n_1 = cp_1 e^{-E_1/kT}, \text{ and } n_2 = cp_2 e^{-E_2/kT}; \tag{1}$$

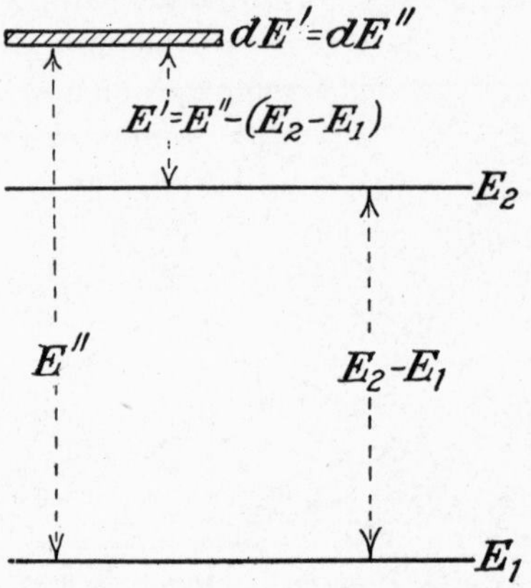

Fig. 1.—Illustrating Klein and Rosseland's argument.

p_1 and p_2 are the *a priori* probabilities, and E_1 and E_2 the energies of
the two states, and c is a constant proportional to the total number
of atoms present. By the Maxwell-Boltzmann distribution law, the
number of electrons, dN, with energy between E and $E + dE$ is given
by

$$\frac{dN}{N} = \frac{2}{\pi^{1/2}(kT)^{3/2}} \exp\left(\frac{-E}{kT}\right) E^{1/2} dE,$$

where N is the total number of electrons under consideration. Writing
A in place of $\dfrac{2}{\pi^{1/2}(kT)^{3/2}}$ we define a probability, $S_{12}(E'')$, such that

$$S_{12}(E'') n_1 A \exp\left(\frac{-E''}{kT}\right)(E'')^{1/2} dE'' \tag{2a}$$

is the number of atoms going from state 1 to state 2 per second, due to
collisons with electrons having energy between E'' and $E'' + dE''$; the
energy of each electron is reduced to a value in the range,

$$E' \text{ to } E' + dE',$$

where

$$E'' - E' = E_2 - E_1,$$

as shown in Fig. 1.   Further, we define a probability $S_{21}(E')$, such that

$$S_{21}(E')n_2 \, A \, \exp\left(\frac{-E'}{kT}\right)(E')^{1/2}dE' \tag{2b}$$

is the number of atoms going from state 2 to state 1 per second, due to collisions with electrons having energy between E' and $E' + dE'$, the electrons being left with energies in the range E'' to $E'' + dE''$. According to the experiments on resonance potentials (Chap. XIII, Sec. 8), the probability, $S_{12}(E'')$, is zero unless E'' is at least equal to $E_2 - E_1$, but reaches fairly large values when E'' is only slightly greater than this.   In the equilibrium state, the number of collisions of the first kind given by equation (2a) must be equal to the number of collisions of the second kind given by equation (2b), so that

$$n_1 S_{12}(E'') \, \exp\left(\frac{-E''}{kT}\right)(E'')^{1/2} \; = \; n_2 S_{21}(E') \, \exp\left(\frac{-E'}{kT}\right)(E')^{1/2},$$

or using equation (1),

$$p_1 S_{12}(E'') \cdot (E'')^{1/2} = p_2 S_{21}(E') \cdot (E')^{1/2}. \tag{3}$$

This holds for all values of E' and E'' such that their difference is equal to $E_2 - E_1$ and such that E'' is not less than $E_2 - E_1$ or, what is the same thing, E' is not less than zero.   Since $S_{12}(E'')$ is fairly large when E'' is only slightly greater than $E_2 - E_1$ it follows from equation (3) that a collision of the second kind between an atom in state 2 and a slow electron (E' small) must be very probable, for

$$S_{21}(E') = \frac{p_1}{p_2}\left(\frac{E''}{E'}\right)^{1/2} S_{12}(E''). \tag{4}$$

Since $E'' >> E'$, and $p_1 \cong p_2$, $S_{21}(E') >> S_{12}(E'')$.   This is to be expected, for a slow electron will remain in the neighborhood of a molecule longer than a fast electron, and the probability of an energy exchange will be greater.   In fact the probabilities S_{12} and S_{21} are inversely proportional to the square root of the energy, that is, to the velocity, and, therefore, directly proportional to the time of the collision.   So far, there has been no experimental confirmation of this type of collision of the second kind.   In experiments with iodine vapor Smyth[1] found evidence which pointed to such increases of energy.   However, he states that the experiments were not conclusive because of experimental difficulties.   Later, he found much more definite evidence in favor of collisions of a somewhat different type.[2]

In a vessel containing ozone decomposing into oxygen, electrons were accelerated by a small potential into a space between a grid and a plate, where a retarding potential was applied.   If electrons attain high speeds by collision with an ozone molecule in a condition to decompose, then

[1] *Proc. Nat. Acad. Sci.*, **11**, 679 (1925).

[2] *Phys. Rev.*, **27**, 108 (1927).

some of them should reach the plate, even though the retarding potential is sufficient to stop them in the absence of ozone. The nature of the curve of plate current against retarding potential led Smyth to conclude that such electrons are present.

The argument used by Klein and Rosseland can be applied to other types of collisions which will now be discussed, to the absorption and emission of light, and to the photoelectric effect in gases and its inverse (Chap. XIII, Sec. 6).

Franck[1] extended the suggestions of Klein and Rosseland to collisions between excited and unexcited atoms. The spectra of atoms and molecules are excited in flames and furnaces.[2] From this fact and other evidence of a similar kind, we know that collisions between two atoms in which the relative energy is sufficiently great may cause the excitation of one of the collision partners. It follows that the reverse process is possible, in which an excited atom colliding with an unexcited one may lose its energy of excitation, while the relative kinetic energy of the atoms is increased. This suggests the possibility of collisions between an excited atom or molecule and another, in which the latter is raised to a higher energy state and the former loses energy. Experiment shows that such collisions actually occur. All these types of collisions are called "collisions of the second kind." As Franck showed, they are readily detected by their effect in quenching resonance radiation, and therefore many of the experiments to be described deal with this subject.

2. THE QUENCHING OF RESONANCE RADIATION

Wood[3] discovered that the resonance radiation of iodine, bromine, and mercury is quenched by the addition of foreign gases. According to the views of Franck, the mechanism of the quenching is as follows: Excited atoms collide with other atoms or molecules before radiating their energy of excitation. A certain fraction of these collisions results in a conversion of the energy of excitation into relative kinetic energy of the atoms, whereas in the absence of a collision the energy of excitation would have been lost by the emission of radiation. The kinetic energy is distributed between the collision partners, so that momentum is conserved. Since the length of time the atom remains in an excited state has been fairly well established in a number of cases (Chap. XI, Secs. 4, 7, and Chap. XIII, Sec. 9), the number of collisions of the excited atom during its life can be determined from the kinetic theory of gases. A comparison of this with the experimentally determined number of

---

[1] Z. Physik, **9**, 259 (1922).

[2] King, A. S., Astrophys. J., **27**, 353 and **28**, 300 (1908); and many more recent publications in this journal and elsewhere.

[3] Verh. d. D. phys. Ges., **13**, 72 (1911); Phil. Mag., **21**, 309 and **22**, 469 (1911); Physik Z., **12**, 1204 (1911) and **13**, 353 (1912).

collisions necessary to bring about quenching gives us quantitative information about the effectiveness of various atoms or molecules in producing quenching, and thus the probability that the collisions will be inelastic.

Aside from quenching the resonance radiation the added gas may have the effect of broadening the absorption line. If all of the radiating atoms of a gas are stationary, the spectrum of the radiation would consist of very narrow lines having a natural width of about 0.00012 Å.[1] But if the atoms are in motion the radiation from those atoms approaching the observer is of shorter wave length, according to Doppler's principle, while that of the atoms leaving the observer is of longer wave length. The result of this is to broaden the original narrow spectrum line in both directions. The width of the line due to Doppler effect alone, measured from the points where the intensity has fallen to one-half the maximum intensity at the center of the line, is

$$\Delta\nu = \nu\sqrt{\frac{4kT}{mc^2}ln2,}$$

and thus the width increases as the square root of the temperature.

In addition to this, the Stark effect due to intermolecular fields broadens a spectrum line and this effect increases with pressure. Also many spectrum lines have a complicated structure (Chap. XI, Sec. 4), *e.g.*, the Hg line at 2,536.7 Å., with which we shall be mainly concerned, consists of a group of five approximately equidistant lines separated by about 0.01 Å.[2]

The wave length absorbed by an atom also depends upon the temperature and pressure, so that low temperature and pressure favor the absorption of a narrow band of wave lengths, that is, a sharp line. In his study of the quenching of mercury resonance radiation, Wood used a hot mercury arc to excite resonance in cold mercury vapor. The arc emitted a very broad resonance line while the cold mercury vapor absorbed only the center of each of the five components composing the 2,536.7 Å. line. The broadening of the absorption line produced by adding more and more foreign gas enables the mercury vapor to absorb more and more of the outlying portions of the broad exciting line, and, consequently, to emit increasing amounts of resonance radiation. Whether quenching or enhancement is observed depends upon the relative magnitude of the two effects. This consideration enabled Wood[3]

---

[1] On the classical theory the natural width was thought of as due to the emission of a damped wave train by an oscillating electron, due to the reaction of its own radiation. See Planck, "Wärmestrahlung," 5th ed., or Jauncey, *Phys. Rev.*, **19**, 641 (1922). The harmonic analysis of such a damped train yields a spectral line having a half width of $4\pi e^2/3mc^2 = 0.00012$ Å.

[2] Wood, *Phil. Mag.*, **50**, 761 (1925).

[3] *Phil. Mag.*, **44**, 1107 (1922).

to account for a remarkable four-fold increase of resonance radiation
resulting from the introduction of helium at a pressure of 330 mm. of
mercury. In quantitative investigations on quenching it is therefore
necessary to use a source of light emitting a very narrow exciting line.
To secure this, the mercury vapor emitting the light must be maintained
at a low temperature and pressure. This is ordinarily accomplished by
using a vertical type of arc with its lower end immersed in a vessel of
running water. The portion of the arc just above the water surface is a
strong emitter of a resonance line having the desired properties.

Cario[1] excited resonance radiation in mercury vapor by means of
electron bombardment, keeping the energy of the electrons low enough
to excite the resonance state exclusively. In this way he obtained a
monochromatic ultra-violet lamp emitting 2,536.7 Å. radiation of great
intensity. The intensity of radiation from the lamp was measured
first in the absence of any foreign gas and then with varying amounts
of argon and of a helium-neon mixture added to the mercury vapor.
The first additions of argon brought about an increase in emission of the
2,537 Å. line. This apparently was due to an increase in the number of
collisions between mercury atoms and electrons caused by the zig-zag
path of the electrons through the argon as they fell through the accelerating field. Quenching took place upon further addition of argon.
The results of the measurements indicated that practically every collision
between excited mercury and foreign gas atoms resulted in quenching,
provided the gas-kinetic radius of the excited mercury atoms is assumed
to be greater than the radius of the normal atom.

We must assume that the radius of the excited atom is three times
greater than the normal radius in order to explain the results for a helium-
neon mixture, and five and one-half times greater in the case of argon.
This method does not claim great accuracy because it is difficult to maintain a constant rate of production of excited mercury atoms as the foreign
gas is added.

Stuart[2] employed the very elegant method of secondary resonance
due to Wood. Light from a water-cooled mercury arc L is focused by
quartz lenses on mercury vapor contained in a large glass bulb R_I,
fitted with a quartz window (Fig. 2). The resonance radiation emitted
by the Hg vapor in R_I is in turn focused on mercury vapor, contained
in a similar vessel R_{II} which could be filled with the gas under investigation. Since the bulb R_I contained only pure Hg vapor at a low temperature and pressure, the resonance line emitted from it was extremely
narrow owing to the absence of the broadening discussed above. The
secondary resonance from vessel R_{II} was photographed on a plate P,
together with a part of the primary radiation reflected by a quartz

[1] Z. Physik, **10**, 185 (1922).
[2] Z. Physik, **32**, 262 (1925).

plate S. The purpose of the latter was to correct for considerable fluctuations in the intensity of the primary radiation. The measurements consisted in photographing the resonance radiation emitted by R_{II} in the absence of any foreign gas and in presence of various pressures of the added gas, each time simultaneously photographing the portion

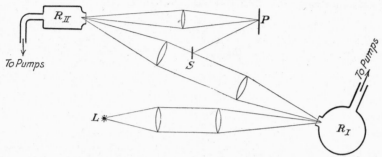

Fig. 2.—Stuart's apparatus for resonance radiation.

reflected by S. Blackening of the photographic plate, as measured by a microphotometer was taken as a measure of the intensity of the radiation. The quenching curves in Fig. 3 show the intensity of the secondary radiation as a function of the pressure of the added gas. These curves enable us to calculate how many collisions the excited mercury atom makes before a collision of the second kind occurs.

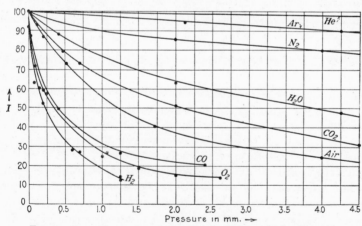

Fig. 3.—Quenching curves of resonance radiation.   (*After Stuart.*)

Stern and Volmer[1] showed that the resonance radiation should be reduced to one-half intensity, when the time between two inelastic collisions is equal to the mean life of the radiating atom. When the steady state is reached, the number of atoms activated per second by the incident light is equal to the number deactivated per second by

[1] *Physik. Z.* **20**, 183 (1919).

spontaneous radiation and collisions of the second kind. The number activated is independent of the pressure of foreign gas mixed with the mercury vapor, and for constant pressure of mercury vapor will be constant. Let the number of excited atoms be n_0, if no foreign gas is present, and n, if foreign gas is present, and let K be the number of excited atoms produced each second. Then,

$$K = k_1 n_0 = (k_1 + k_2)n,$$

where k_1 is the probability of spontaneous emission of light and k_2 is the probability of an inelastic collision. Then, since the intensity of light emitted is proportional to the number of excited atoms present,

$$\frac{n}{n_0} = \frac{k_1}{k_1 + k_2} = \frac{I}{I_0}, \tag{5}$$

where I and I_0 are the intensities of the resonance radiation in the presence and absence of a foreign gas, respectively. Now k_1 is equal to the reciprocal of the mean life τ and k_2 is proportional to the number of collisions. We have,

$$k_2 = P \cdot 2Nr^2(2kT\pi)^{\frac{1}{2}}\mu^{-\frac{1}{2}}; \tag{6}$$

in this equation k is Boltzmann's constant and T the absolute temperature; r is the distance of nearest approach of the excited atom and the foreign gas molecule, N the number of foreign gas molecules per cubic centimeter (always much larger than the number of mercury atoms); μ is the reduced mass, $\dfrac{m_1 m_2}{m_1 + m_2}$, and P is the probability that a collision will be inelastic, which may be called the "quenching efficiency." The reciprocal of k_2 is the mean time t, between two inelastic collisions and is inversely proportional to the pressure. From equation (5) we get

$$\tau = t\frac{I_0 - I}{I}, \tag{7}$$

and thus if $I = I_0/2$, $\tau = t$. Substituting $1/t = ap$ in equation (7), we get

$$I = I_0\frac{1}{1 + a\tau p} = I_0\frac{1}{1 + bp}, \tag{8}$$

p being the pressure. The pressure at which the intensity of resonance radiation is reduced by one-half can be determined experimentally and the value of N corresponding to this pressure can be substituted in equation (6). Also we know that for this pressure t can be set equal to τ which is known from other measurements and thus the only unknown quantities in equation (6) are P and r.

In the case of oxygen, the pressure at which the intensity is reduced to one-half, and which is conveniently represented by $p_{\frac{1}{2}}$, is 0.35 mm. Assuming that $P = 1$, i.e., that every collision is a collision of the second kind, and using the gas kinetic values for the radii, the life of the excited mercury atom is found to be $5.7 \cdot 10^{-7}$ seconds. But the mean life of the 2^3P_1 state of mercury is known to be $1 \cdot 10^{-7}$ seconds.[1]   Since P cannot be greater than 1, the distance between the atoms at nearest approach for an excited mercury atom and the gas molecule, r, must be greater than the mean distance of approach of the normal mercury atom and the gas molecule.   Stuart therefore concludes that the collision radius of the excited mercury is 3.4 times that of the normal mercury atom. If it is assumed that in oxygen each collision quenches, there can be no gas with higher quenching efficiency than oxygen.   The quenching efficiencies calculated by assuming that the radius of the excited mercury atom is always 3.4 times the radius of the normal atom, in collisions with other molecules, are collected in Table 1.

TABLE 1

Gas	$p_{1/2}$ (mm.)	P (Stuart)	k_2 at 1 mm. $\times 10^{-7}$	$r \times 10^{+8}$ cm.	P (Caviola)
H_2.........	0.2	0.7	2.7	5.5	1.0^1
O_2.........	0.35	1.0^1			
CO.........	0.4	0.8	3.0	2.91	1.0^1
CO_2........	2.0	0.2			
H_2O........	4.2	0.1	0.64	1.80	0.4
N_2.........	30.0	0.013	0.6	1.80	0.2
A..........	240	0.002	0.5	1.80	0.05
He.........	760	0.0003	1.4	1.80	0.006
Air........	1.2				
Hg.........	120				

[1] Assumed.

Gaviola[2] has recalculated these quenching efficiencies obtained from Stuart's data taking secondary factors into account.   Before a quantum of resonance light escapes from the vessel it may be reabsorbed and reemitted several times and this effect is quite appreciable in Stuart's experiments.   Moreover, in order to avoid the complicating factor that collisions of the first kind may raise metastable mercury atoms in the 2^3P_0 state to the resonance state, 2^3P_1, it is necessary to extrapolate the quenching curves to zero pressure and calculate the quenching efficiency at this pressure.   When the data are recalculated in this way, it is found that the effective radius of the excited atom, Hg′, is 1.62 times larger than the gas kinetic radius of the normal atom, if the efficiency of quenching by hydrogen is taken as 1.   Using this radius for Hg′, the quenching efficiency of CO is found to be 250 per cent.   This shows that the effective radius of Hg′ cannot be taken the same for all gases.

As Gaviola points out, the only quantity which can be determined from the experiments is the product of the number of collisions and the

[1] "Handbuch der Experimentalphysik," **14**, (1928), Akad Verlagsgesellschaft, Leipzig.
[2] *Phys. Rev.*, **33**, 309 (1929).

quenching efficiency. His calculated values for the numbers of these collisions for different gases are given in the fourth column of Table 1. The last two columns give assumed radii for Hg' and the efficiency. Gaviola assumed the gas kinetic radius of the normal mercury atom for the Hg' atom, in cases where this did not lead to quenching efficiencies greater than 1; if this assumption gave a greater efficiency than 1, he assumed an efficiency of 1 and calculated an effective radius for the Hg' atom.

The high quenching efficiency of H_2 is due to the fact that its energy of dissociation (4.34 volts) is less than the energy of excitation of mercury in the 2^3P_1 state so that the energy is expended in dissociating the molecule. The energies of dissociation of the other molecules listed in Table 1 are greater than the excitation energy of the mercury atom and therefore their high quenching efficiencies must be due to other factors. Mitchell[1] has shown that O_2 has a vibration level 4.86 volts above its normal level so that almost exact resonance between the O_2 molecule and the mercury atom exists. Under such conditions the transfer of energy from one to the other should be very probable (Sec. 5). Also it may be that chemical reaction takes place between O_2 and Hg', since HgO appears in the resonance vessel under proper experimental conditions. The effect of the N_2, H_2O, and CO molecules is to transfer Hg' from the 2^3P_1 state to the metastable 2^3P_0 state. Cario and Franck[2] found that no quenching by N_2 occurs if the temperature of the resonance vessel is raised to 750°C. At this temperature metastable mercury atoms initially produced by collisions with the N_2 molecules are raised again to the resonance state by a collision of the first kind with a high velocity nitrogen molecule, so that they are again in a condition to radiate. When argon is present instead of nitrogen, raising the temperature of the vessel to 750°C. does not destroy the quenching effect and therefore argon must transfer the excited mercury atom to the normal state.[3] Gaviola and Wood have shown that water vapor greatly increases the concentration of mercury atoms in the 2^3P_0 state and that it is about 10^3 times as effective as nitrogen in this respect (Sec. 6). Oldenberg has pointed out that the high efficiency of N_2 and CO in causing this transfer to the 2^3P_0 state is probably due to the fact that these molecules can take up 0.19 volt of energy from the mercury atom almost entirely by a transition in their vibrational energy states. This may also be true in the case of H_2O.

Mannkopf[4] studied the quenching of the resonance radiation of sodium by nitrogen, hydrogen, and by a neon-helium mixture. Nitrogen

[1] *J. Frank. Inst.*, **206**, 817 (1928).

[2] *Z. Physik*, **17**, 202 (1923).

[3] OLDENBERG, *Z. Physik*, **49**, 609 (1928).

[4] *Z. Physik*, **36**, 315 (1926).

quenches this radiation most effectively. Calculation of the quenching efficiency again requires the use of abnormal radii and Mannkopf finds the radius of excited sodium to be 4.3 times the gas-kinetic value. Wood[1] has found that iodine resonance radiation is quenched by foreign gases and by iodine itself. Table 2 gives the values of the half pressures for various gases for this case.

TABLE 2

Gas..................	A	He	Air	CO_2	Ether	Cl_2	I_2
$p_{1/2}$ (mm.).............	7	6	2.1	1.2	0.3	0.2	0.2

3. SENSITIZED FLUORESCENCE

Cario and Franck,[2] developing the logical consequences of the principle of Klein and Rosseland, pointed out that the excitation energy of an atom or molecule should be available for the excitation of a quantum transition of lower energy in a colliding atom or molecule. This view could be supported by a number of experimental results. For example, it had been known since 1873[3] that a photographic plate insensitive to certain wave lengths could be made sensitive to them by impregnating the gelatine layer with a suitable dye. According to our present views, this dye absorbs the energy of the inactive wave lengths and transfers it to the photosensitive silver in the layer by collision. Also, it had been observed[4] that a dye such as eosine or rhodamine adsorbed on a mass of siloxene[5] emits the fluorescent bands characteristic of the dye, while the siloxene is being oxidized. The dye itself emits no light upon oxidation. Apparently, the energy of oxidation of siloxene is transferred by collision to the dye, which is thereby excited and emits light.

If an atom A is excited by the absorption of light, and transfers its energy to an atom B during a collision, the atom B may then emit light which is known as sensitized fluorescence. It will be observed if the following conditions are fulfilled: the energy of excitation of the atoms absorbing the light must be equal to or greater than the energy of the first excited state of those atoms in the mixture which are to exhibit the sensitized fluorescence; and the pressures must be such that the mean time between two collisions is less than or equal to the order of magnitude of the mean life of the excited atom. The latter condition insures that

---

[1] *Phil. Mag.*, **21**, 392 (1911).
[2] CARIO, *Z. Physik*, **10**, 185 (1922); CARIO and FRANCK, *loc. cit.*
[3] VOGEL, *Ber.*, **6**, 1305 (1873).
[4] KAUTSKY and ZOCHER, *Z. Physik*, **9**, 267 (1922); **31**, 60 (1925).
[5] Siloxene is a highly reactive silicon compound of the formula $Si_6H_6O_3$.

most of the optically excited atoms will collide with and excite the atoms which emit the sensitized fluorescence.   In order to secure observable intensities of fluorescent light it is necessary that the monochromatic light producing the primary excitation be intense and that it be strongly absorbed.   All spectrum lines of the non-absorbing component of the gas mixture should appear, whose energy of excitation is less than the energy of the monochromatic exciting or primary radiation.

Suppose we have a mixture of two gases A and B of atomic weights m_1 and m_2, and let the gas A have a resonance line of frequency ν, while B has one of frequency ν'.   The excitation energies of the atoms A and B corresponding to the frequencies ν and ν' are shown in the energy level diagram of Fig. 4.   Now if we illuminate the gas A with light of frequency ν we obtain the reemission of the same frequency or simple resonance. If we illuminate gas B with light of the same frequency ν, no resonance or fluorescence will appear because this frequency is not absorbed by the

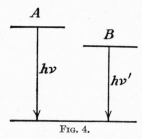

FIG. 4.

gas B.   But if we illuminate the mixture of the two gases with light of frequency ν, we obtain the emission of both ν and ν'.   An atom A, excited by absorption of a quantum $h\nu$, collides with an atom B and excites it to the quantum level with energy $h\nu'$. B then radiates light of frequency ν'.   Some of the atoms A emit their characteristic frequency before colliding with B, and this accounts for the appearance of both frequencies in the fluorescence.   The difference in energy between $h\nu$ and $h\nu'$ appears as relative kinetic energy of A and B.   If the temperature is low, we can neglect the thermal kinetic energy.   The atom B receives kinetic energy which we can calculate from the requirement that the conservation of energy and momentum must hold for the process. Assuming the initial velocities to be very small and letting the final velocities be v_1 and v_2, we have,

$$\tfrac{1}{2}m_1v_1{}^2 + \tfrac{1}{2}m_2v_2{}^2 = h\nu - h\nu',$$

and

$$m_1v_1 = m_2v_2,$$

from which

$$\frac{1}{2}m_1v_1{}^2 = (h\nu - h\nu')\frac{m_2}{m_1 + m_2}, \tag{9}$$

and

$$\frac{1}{2}m_2v_2{}^2 = (h\nu - h\nu')\frac{m_1}{m_1 + m_2}.$$

When $h\nu - h\nu'$ is large, the excited atom B secures a high kinetic energy and consequently moves with high velocity.   When the rapidly moving excited atom emits light, the frequency observed will be different from ν' because of the Doppler effect, except when the atom moves at right angles to the line of vision. The frequency observed, ν'', is related to ν' by the equation,

$$\nu'' = \nu'\left(1 + \frac{v_2}{c}\cos\varphi\right),$$

where φ is the angle between the direction of motion and the line of vision. These predictions were brilliantly confirmed by Cario's experiments.[1] The arrangement of Fig. 5 was employed. A quartz tube containing a

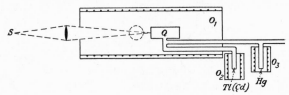

FIG. 5.—The Cario-Franck apparatus.

globule of thallium metal was heated in an electric oven to a temperature of 800°C., at which the vapor pressure of thallium is 2 mm. of Hg. The quartz tube was connected through a side tube to a bulb containing mercury, which could be heated to about 100°C. in a separate and smaller oven. A quartz lens focused the light of a quartz mercury arc at a point just inside the tube containing the mixture of thallium and mercury vapor. The mercury was thereby excited to the resonance state, 2^3P_1. The pressure of the mercury vapor was high enough to confine the resonance to a narrow region near the place of entrance of the exciting light, the purpose being to secure a strong fluorescence concentrated in a small region. A spectrogram of the light scattered from this region showed the presence of a number of thallium lines in addition to the 2,536.7 Å. line of mercury. When the 2,536.7 Å. line was cut off by interposing a sheet of glass, all thallium lines disappeared, and when the tube was illuminated with the 2,536.7 Å. line while the mercury vapor was frozen out no thallium lines appeared. We can see the energy rela-

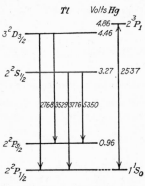

FIG. 6.—Energy level diagrams of Hg and Tl.

tions involved from Fig. 6. The 2,768 line of Tl, which differs in energy from the 2,537 line of Hg by only 0.4 volt, was found to be very weak, due to absorption in the excess thallium vapor. On the other hand, the 3,776 line is excited by 1.6 volts less energy than 2,537, and was found to be emitted very strongly. In this case, the emitting thallium atoms have a high velocity, due to the large energy excess of 1.6 volts, hence

[1] Z. Physik, 10, 185 (1922); 17, 202 (1923).

the Doppler shift is large enough to prevent the relatively cold thallium vapor from absorbing the broadened 3,776 line.

4. COLLISIONS INVOLVING METASTABLE ATOMS

Donat,[1] and later Loria,[2] studied the fluorescence of thallium sensitized by mercury in the presence of certain gases such as nitrogen and argon. Since the resonance radiation of mercury is quenched by nitrogen, it is to be expected that the addition of this gas to the thallium-mercury mixture should diminish the sensitized fluorescence of thallium. On the contrary, it was actually found to be increased. This can be explained in the following way. The mercury atoms absorbing the wave length 2,537 are raised to the 2^3P_1 state, and collide with a nitrogen molecule to which a part of their energy is transferred, and drop to the $^3P_0$ state with 0.19 volt less energy. The $^3P_0$ state has a life of about 10^{-2} seconds as compared to 10^{-8} seconds for $^3P_1$. Therefore, the mercury atom in the $^3P_0$ state is much more likely to collide with a thallium atom during its life than an atom in the $^3P_1$ state. Of course, the energy of the excited mercury atoms can be used to excite thallium more effectively in the absence of any foreign gas by increasing the pressure of the thallium vapor and thereby increasing the number of collisions. This would require very high temperatures because of the low vapor pressure of thallium. Addition of nitrogen has the same effect as increasing the vapor pressure of thallium, for, if the pressure of the nitrogen is sufficiently high, every excited mercury atom produced by absorption of the 2,537 line is brought into the long-lived metastable state which persists until a collision with a thallium atom occurs.

The effect of foreign gases in bringing mercury atoms in the $^3P_1$ state into the metastable state by collisions of the second kind was clearly demonstrated by Wood.[3] The metastable atom can absorb two series of lines, namely, the series $2^3P_0 - m^3S_1$, and the series $2^3P_0 - m^3D_1$. The lines at 4,047 Å. and 2,967 A. corresponding to the first member of each of these two series must be particularly strongly absorbed and therefore reversed by mercury vapor containing a considerable concentration of mercury atoms in the 2^3P_0 state. Absorption of these wavelengths is therefore an indication of the presence of metastable atoms. Wood illuminated mercury vapor with the resonance line and studied the absorption in the presence of varying amounts of N_2, He, and CO. Nitrogen was found to be particularly effective in causing the absorption of subordinate series lines. Absorption of the line at 4,047 Å. is already noticeable when the partial pressure of nitrogen is 0.1 mm. and at 2 mm. it is extraordinarily strong, indicating that a high concentration of

[1] Z. Physik, **29**, 345 (1924).

[2] Phys. Rev., **26**, 576 (1925).

[3] Proc. Roy. Soc., **106**, 679 (1924); Phil. Mag., **50**, 774 (1925).

metastable atoms has been built up. Wood and Gaviola[1] have recently found that water vapor is more effective than nitrogen in bringing mercury atoms from the resonance state into the metastable state. Only 0.005 mm. of water vapor is sufficient to cause reversal of the 4,047 Å. line in excited mercury, while 0.5 mm. of nitrogen is necessary to accomplish the same result.

Orthmann and Pringsheim[2] found that the formation of metastable mercury atoms was favored in the absence of foreign gases by increasing the vapor pressure of mercury. The sensitized fluorescence of thallium was studied in mercury vapor at high pressure. The resonance radiation in pure mercury vapor at a pressure corresponding to 250°C. is practically completely quenched, but the fluorescence of admixed thallium vapor is still very strong. Even in mercury vapor at one atmosphere (350°C.) the 3,776 Å. line of thallium has lost none of its original intensity. Under the conditions of the experiment an excited mercury atom collides on the average with 10^4 other mercury atoms before colliding with a thallium atom, indicating that the fluorescence must be due to collisions of the second kind between metastable mercury atoms and thallium.

Meyer[3] found that the yield of atomic hydrogen by photochemical dissociation with the aid of mercury can be increased, when the partial yressure of hydrogen is low, by the addition of argon. Argon also makes inelastic collisions with mercury in the 2^3P_1 state, causing a transfer to the 2^3P_0 state, which then persists long enough to collide with a hydrogen molecule, though there are reasons to believe that argon also causes a transfer of Hg′ atoms to the normal state (Sec. 2).

5. RESONANCE IN COLLISIONS OF THE SECOND KIND

Merton and Pilley[4] found that it was possible to excite the atomic nitrogen spectrum, which is difficult to secure by other methods, by passing a discharge through a mixture of an inert gas and nitrogen, the former being present in excess.

When a discharge is sent through this mixture there is small probability that an electron will gain energy greatly in excess of the first resonance potential of the rare gas, provided the pressure is sufficiently high. If the concentration of the nitrogen is small, the probability of an electron exciting this gas is small. But since the rare gas is present in excess, most of the excitation will be due to collisions of the second kind between excited rare gas atoms and the nitrogen molecules. In this way the spectrum will be excited by a definitely known energy. Evidently, nitrogen molecules are first dissociated by collisions of the

[1] *Phil. Mag.*, **5**, 271 (1928).
[2] *Z. Physik*, **35**, 626 (1926).
[3] *Z. Physik*, **37**, 639 (1926).
[4] *Proc. Roy. Soc.*, **107**, 411 (1925).

second kind with excited rare gas atoms, and then the resulting atoms are excited by inelastic collisions with electrons or excited rare gas atoms. McLennan[1] found that a characteristic green line appearing in the aurora is excited strongly in a discharge tube containing a mixture of helium and oxygen while it is very difficult to obtain in pure oxygen.

The band spectra of H_2, N_2, CO, CN, and other molecules are much simplified when excited in presence of an excess of the rare gases. The best known example of this is the excitation of the Lyman bands (a progression of the Dieke-Hopfield bands) which appear in great intensity when a discharge is passed through argon at 2 or 3 mm. pressure containing a trace of hydrogen. The bands excited in this way arise from transitions from the B_3 state of Dieke and Hopfield,[2] which is the third vibrational level of the $2^1\Sigma$ state of the hydrogen molecule. This combines with the different vibration levels of the normal $1^1\Sigma$ state to give an n'' progression of bands. Since these bands are not excited by direct electron impact,[3] the excitation probably occurs by collisions of the second kind between excited argon atoms and the hydrogen molecule in its lowest vibrational state and its lower rotational states,[4] and after a very careful theoretical investigation Beutler[5] concluded that this view was correct.

That close "resonance" between two atoms or molecules is of importance for the transfer of energy between the two was first noticed by Beutler and Josephy[6] in the case of the sensitized fluorescence of sodium when excited by mercury atoms. When a mixture of the two gases at low pressures was illuminated by the 2,537 Å. line of mercury the $2P - 7S$ line of sodium appeared with great intensity. The addition of foreign gas caused the appearance of the $2P - 5S$ line of sodium. The excitation energies of the $7S$ and $5S$ levels of sodium are very nearly the same as the excitation energies of the 2^3P_1 and 2^3P_0 states, respectively. Evidently, the foreign gas in the second case caused a transfer of mercury atoms in the 2^3P_1 state to the 2^3P_0 state and atoms in each of these states transfer their energy to sodium atoms with greatest probability

[1] At the high altitudes where the aurora is excited, probably by electrons from the sun, the concentration of helium atoms relative to oxygen molecules will be much higher than at the earth's surface so that the laboratory conditions partly duplicate those occurring in nature.

[2] Z. Physik, **40**, 299 (1926); Phys. Rev., **28**, 1223 (1927).

[3] HORI, Z. Physik, **44**, 834 (1927).

[4] This was first suggested by FRANCK and JORDAN, "Anregung der Quantensprüngen durch Stösse," p. 266. WORTHING (Washington Meeting of the American Physical Society, Apr. 19, 1929) has found an altered intensity distribution of the active nitrogen bands when the nitrogen contains about 1 per cent of argon, and suggests that this is probably due to the excitation of the nitrogen molecule by collisions of the second kind between nitrogen molecules and excited argon atoms.

[5] Z. Physik, **50**, 581 (1928).

[6] Naturwiss., **15**, 540 (1927).

only if the excitation energy of the sodium atoms is very nearly equal to that of the excited mercury atoms.   This case has been further studied by Webb and Wang[1] who introduced sodium vapor into a stream of mercury vapor which had been excited by an arc.   They compared the relative intensities of sodium lines when excited by an arc and when excited by the transfer of energy from the excited mercury atoms. Experimental conditions were arranged so that excited atoms were much more effective in exciting the sodium atoms than any ions present.   The results are shown in Table 3.

TABLE 3

Excitation energy of Hg	Sodium series lines	Excitation energy of Na, cm.$^{-1}$	Intensity of Na lines excited by:	
			(a) Hg atoms	(b) an arc
	$1^2S\ -2^2P$	16,964	0.63	2.40
	$2^2P\ -3^2S$	33,199	0.03	1.70
	$2^2P\ -4^2D$	34,547	0.05	1.38
	-4^2S	36,371	0.04	0.26
	-5^2D	37,033	0.20	0.41
2^3P_0 37,645				
	-5^2S	38,010	0.67	0.07
	-6^2D	38,382	0.44	0.11
	-6^2S	38,963	0.00	0.00
	-7^2D	39,200	0.15	trace
2^3P_1 39,413				
	-7^2S	39,572	0.15	0.00
	-8^2D	39,725	0.07	0.00

Decided maxima in intensity occur in both the sharp and diffuse series when excited by collisions with mercury atoms.   The wave-number differences between the excitation energy of the 2^3P_0 state and that of the 5^2D, 5^2S, and 6^2D states of sodium are 612, -365, and -737 cm.$^{-1}$, respectively, and the differences between that of 2^3P_1 and the 7^2D, 7^2S, and 8^2D are 213, -159, and -312 cm.$^{-1}$, respectively.   Since the 6^2S state is evidently not excited by the mercury in the 2^3P_1 state, the probability of a transfer of energy between the two atoms in which these particular states are involved with an energy difference of only 450 cm.$^{-1}$ ($\sim$ 0.05 volt) must be quite small.   The same lines excited in the arc are less intense than when excited by collisions of the second kind though the reverse is true in the case of the $1^2S - 2^2P$ lines.   This supports the view that collisions of the second kind are responsible for the excitation of the lines as given in column 4 and that in this particular case close

[1] *Phys. Rev.*, **33**, 329 (1929).

resonance between two atoms is necessary if there is to be a high probability of energy transfer.[1]

An interesting method of exciting the spectra of metals which promises to be of importance has been employed by Paschen and Frerichs.[2] If the vapor of a metal is present in a rare gas excited by electrical discharge, the spectrum of the metal is excited intensely. It is found that the excitation of the metal is due in the main to collisions of the second kind with metastable rare gas atoms. All terms whose energy is less than that of the metastable atom which excites them are present in the spectrum. Excitation of metal spectra was also found to take place in a side arm branching off from the discharge tube, although the discharge does not penetrate into the side tube. The presence of metastable atoms here can be demonstrated by absorption measurements similar to those used by Meissner in determining the life of metastable neon atoms.

6. COLLISIONS BETWEEN IONS AND NEUTRAL ATOMS

If we consider the ionized state of an atom as one of its excited states, the possibility immediately suggests itself that an ion can remove an electron from an atom of lower ionizing potential as a result of a collision of the second kind. Experimental evidence of this was found by Hogness and Lunn[3] and by Harnwell.[4] They produced ionization in a mixture of gases by bombarding them with electrons of energy well above their ionizing potentials and determined the relative numbers of ions as a function of the total pressure by means of the magnetic spectrograph (Chap. XIII, Sec. 4). Harnwell observed the number of ions produced in a pure inert gas as a function of the pressure and found that the curves were of exactly the same shape for all the gases investigated, so that one could be superimposed on the other by changing the scale on which the number of ions produced was plotted. This means that, in a mixture of these gases, the ratio of the numbers of ions produced should be independent of the pressure, if no collisions of the second kind occur. Experimentally, it is found that the ratios of the numbers of ions, He^+/Ne^+, Ne^+/A^+, and He^+/A^+ decreased with increasing pressure, and that this decrease was most rapid for the first and slowest for the last of these combinations. The following inelastic collisions must occur in the ionizing space:

$$He^+ + Ne \rightarrow He + Ne^+, \quad Ne^+ + A \rightarrow Ne + A^+, \quad He^+ + A \rightarrow He + A^+.$$

[1] The high quenching efficiency of O_2 gas in the case of Hg' in the $2\,^3P_1$ state is probably due to close resonance. However, close resonance is not necessary for collisions of the second kind to occur (see Sec. **2**).

[2] PASCHEN, *Sitz. ber. d. Preuss. Akad. Wiss.*, Oct. 20, 1927; FRERICHS, *Ann. Physik*, **85**, 257 (1928).

[3] *Phys. Rev.*, **28**, 849 (1926); **30**, 26 (1927).

[4] *Phys. Rev.*, **29**, 683, 830 (1927).

All these processes will result in an increased number of ions of the atom of lower ionizing potential at the expense of the atomic ions of higher ionizing potential. The rate of change of the ratios indicates that the first reaction occurs most readily and the last least readily.

Experiments of this kind have been made using quite a number of pairs of gases.[1] The results show that the following generalizations can be made: (1) this type of collision will not occur unless the ionizing potential of the primary ion is greater than that of the ion to be produced, so that part of the energy of ionization of the first atom is converted into relative kinetic energy of the two collision partners; (2) the nearer the two ionizing potentials are to each other the more probable is the inelastic collision. An excellent example of this is given by the experiments on the inert gases described above. Table 4 gives the reactions in the order of decreasing probability and the differences in ionizing potentials of the atoms.

TABLE 4

Reaction	$V_1 - V_2 = V$
$He^+ + Ne \rightarrow He + Ne^+$ $\cdots$	$24.5 - 21.5 = 3.0$
$Ne^+ + A \rightarrow Ne + A^+$ $\cdots$	$21.5 - 15.7 = 5.8$
$He^+ + A \rightarrow He + A^+$ $\cdots$	$24.5 - 15.7 = 8.8$

An excellent example of this is the ionization of N_2 by He^+. Nitrogen has an ionizing potential at 23 to 25 volts, while that of He is 24.5 volts and the experiments show that the ionization of N_2 by He^+ by a collision of the second kind is very probable.

7. PHOTOSENSITIZED REACTIONS

Franck further suggested that the energy of an excited atom could be utilized in producing a chemical reaction. He proposed as a very simple case of such a reaction the photochemical dissociation of the hydrogen molecule, which is particularly suitable because it can dissociate in only one way, while a more complicated molecule might dissociate in several ways. Hydrogen does not absorb light of a wave length corresponding to its heat of dissociation. Its heat of dissociation has been determined most exactly from its band spectrum[2] and is 4.34 volts. (Burrau's[3] theoretical value is 4.42 ± .03 volts.)

The energy of a quantum of light of wave length 2,537 Å. is 4.86 volts. Consequently, excited mercury atoms produced by absorption

---

[1] HOGNESS and LUNN, loc. cit.; HARNWELL, loc. cit.; SMYTH and STUECKELBERG, Phys. Rev., **32**, 779 (1928).

[2] WITMER, Proc. Nat. Acad. Sci., **12**, 238 (1926); DIEKE and HOPFIELD, Phys. Rev., **30**, 400 (1927). See also LANGMUIR, J. A. C. S., **36**, 1708 (1914); **37**, 417 (1915); HERZFELD, Ann. Physik, **59**, 635 (1919); BICHOWSKY and COPELAND, J. A. C. S., **50**, 1315 (1928).

[3] Naturwiss., **15**, 16 (1927); Kong. Danske Vid. Selsk. Math-fys. Medd., **14**, 7, (1927).

of this wave length should be capable of dissociating H_2 molecules. The occurrence of such dissociation was established by a very simple experiment due to Cario and Franck.[1] A small boat filled with copper oxide, which is reducible by atomic hydrogen, was placed in a quartz tube containing hydrogen and some liquid mercury. The tube was connected to a liquid air trap followed by a Macleod gage. When the radiation of a quartz mercury arc was focused on the tube, the copper oxide was reduced as evidenced by the appearance of the characteristic reddish color of metallic copper on the surface of the mass of copper oxide. At the same time, the Macleod gage showed a decrease of pressure owing to the fact that water formed in the reduction of the copper oxide condensed in the trap. No reduction took place when mercury vapor was not present. Mercury vapor alone in absence of hydrogen caused no reduction. Furthermore, it was shown that the effect occurred only when the mercury arc was kept cool so that the 2,537 line was not self-reversed; this is due to the fact that the cold mercury vapor could absorb only the center of the line. The process taking place in the quartz tube is

$$Hg + h\nu \rightarrow Hg',$$
$$Hg' + H_2 \rightarrow Hg + 2H.$$

It is now clear why hydrogen is so very effective in quenching the resonance radiation of mercury. Practically every collision between an excited mercury atom and a hydrogen molecule leads to a transfer of energy from the excited mercury atom to the hydrogen molecule and causes its dissociation.

This extremely convenient method of producing monatomic hydrogen has some very interesting applications. When a mixture of hydrogen, oxygen, and mercury vapor is illuminated with the 2,537 line, water is formed at a measurable rate.[2] Hydrogen atoms produced by the same method in a mixture of ethylene, hydrogen, and mercury vapor react with the ethylene and form ethane. It was noted that this reaction occurred to a much greater extent than could be accounted for by the number of quanta absorbed. This is due to reaction chains initiated by the primary hydrogen atoms, which behave as follows:

$$C_2H_4 + H \rightarrow C_2H_5,$$
$$C_2H_5 + H_2 \rightarrow C_2H_6 + H.$$

The hydrogen atom produced by the second reaction may then react again in accordance with the first equation, and the chain continues until terminated by combination of two hydrogen atoms. A similar reaction chain was discovered in the photosensitized formation of hydrogen

[1] *Z. Physik*, **11**, 161 (1922).
[2] Dickinson, *Proc. Nat. Acad. Sci.*, **10**, 409 (1924).
 Mitchell, *Proc. Nat. Acad. Sci.*, **11**, 458 (1925).

peroxide[1] from hydrogen and oxygen, mercury being the sensitizer. The mixture passed in a rapid stream through the illuminated reaction vessel giving almost 100 per cent yields of hydrogen peroxide, and each quantum absorbed gave 4 molecules of H_2O_2. Taylor suggested the mechanism,

$$Hg + h\nu \rightarrow Hg',$$
$$Hg' + H_2 \rightarrow 2H + Hg,$$
$$H + O_2 \rightarrow HO_2,$$
$$HO_2 + H_2 \rightarrow H_2O_2 + H \text{ etc.}$$

Dickinson and Sherrill[2] illuminated a mixture of oxygen and mercury vapor with the 2,536.7 Å. line and found that ozone was formed. Since the energy of dissociation of the oxygen molecule is considerably greater than that of the excited mercury atoms, excited oxygen molecules must be formed by collisions of the second kind between excited mercury atoms and oxygen molecules. It was also found that considerable oxidation of the mercury vapor took place. This partially accounts for the effectiveness of oxygen in quenching mercury resonance (Sec. 2).

An interesting variety of photosensitized decompositions were discovered by Bates and Taylor.[3] The vapors of H_2O, NH_3, and of organic compounds saturated with mercury vapor were passed through a quartz tube strongly illuminated by the radiation of a cooled mercury arc. In most cases decomposition into gaseous products occurred even in the absence of mercury vapor, but in general the products formed when the reaction was photosensitized were enormously greater in amount than those obtained from the unsensitized reaction.

In such reactions we are by no means limited to the use of mercury vapor, but since a further discussion of this interesting field is beyond the scope of this book, the reader is referred to an excellent summary by Kistiakowsky.[4]

8. CHEMILUMINESCENCE AND COLLISIONS OF THE SECOND KIND IN FLAMES

It has been known for a long time that many chemical reactions are accompanied by the emission of light although the temperature of the reacting mixture is far below that necessary for the appearance of visible temperature radiation. For example, flames, such as those appearing during the combustion of sulfur vapor and carbon bisulfide, are known to have a temperature less than 200°C. but nevertheless emit a complicated spectrum in the blue. The mean translational energy of gas molecules at 200°C. is somewhat less than 0.06 volt while the energy

[1] MARSHALL, *J. Phys. Chem.*, **30**, 34 (1926); BONHOEFFER and LOEB, *Z. physik. Chem.*, **119**, 474 (1926); TAYLOR, *Trans. Far. Soc.* **21**, 560 (1925).

[2] *Proc. Nat. Acad. Sci.*, **12**, 175 (1926).

[3] *J. A. C. S.*, **49**, 2438 (1927).

[4] "Photochemical Processes," p. 125, Chemical Catalogue Co., New York (1928).

corresponding to a quantum of blue light, say of wave length 4,000 Å., is about 3 volts. As an extreme case we might mention the luminescence of certain living organisms due to reactions involving complicated organic molecules. Obviously, the light cannot be due to temperature radiation. In general, the emission of light during chemical reactions is due to quantum processes taking place before the reacting system has reached equilibrium.

Spectral analysis of the light emitted during a reaction should enable us to gain insight into the details of the process. However, the spectrum emitted in most cases of chemiluminescence is so complicated that it is impossible at present to determine the primary processes taking place. Also, the quantity of light emitted is far less than that expected from Einstein's photochemical equivalence law on the assumption that each newly formed molecule emits a quantum. This indicates that secondary processes are probably responsible for the emission of light.

A notable advance in this field was made in the study of "cold" flames emitting a line spectrum of known origin. Haber and Zisch[1] allowed sodium vapor highly diluted with nitrogen to stream into Cl_2, Br_2, I_2, or oxygen gas where reaction took place between the sodium and the gas. The purpose of the nitrogen is to keep the temperature of the reacting mixture below that at which the eye perceives the black-body radiation corresponding to the temperature of the gas. In spite of the fact that no thermal emission of light could occur, the D-lines of sodium were emitted strongly, and it was found that the number of quanta emitted was very much less than the number of NaCl molecules formed. Consequently, the light emission is due to some secondary process, such as a collision of the second kind between a newly formed excited NaCl molecule and a sodium atom, resulting in an excited sodium atom and a normal sodium chloride molecule. This reaction and similar ones have been investigated by Polanyi[2] and his coworkers who have proved that the reaction consists of the primary process,

(a) $Na + Cl_2 = NaCl + Cl + 35$ Cal,

and the secondary processes,

(b) $Na + Cl = NaCl + 93.4$ Cal.

(c) $Na_2 + Cl = NaCl + Na + 75$ Cal.

(d) $Cl + Cl = Cl_2 + 58.5$ Cal.

The reaction (a) takes place in the gaseous phase but the energy liberated is insufficient to excite the sodium D-lines, namely 48.3 Cal. The reactions (b) and (d) take place on the walls and the energy is dissipated as heat. The reaction (c) takes place in the gas space and is responsible for the excitation of the sodium lines. One might expect that the sodium

[1] Z. Physik, 9, 302 (1922).
[2] Zeit. Phys. Chem., B. 1, 3–73 (1928).

atom liberated in this reaction would be excited directly, but this is proved not to be the case by the quenching effect of nitrogen gas. The nitrogen pressure required to quench the sodium resonance to one-half its original intensity (the so-called half-pressure) is about 20 mm., but here at a pressure of a few millimeters of nitrogen the D-lines are reduced to a fraction of their intensity. The quenching of the excited NaCl molecules by nitrogen must be greater than the quenching of the sodium resonance radiation by this gas. Therefore, the NaCl molecule produced in this reaction (c) probably retains the energy of the reaction as energy of excitation, which it then transfers to a Na atom by a collision of the second kind. Experiments on the yields of these reactions showed that every collision between a Na atom and a Cl_2 molecule as well as between a Cl atom and a Na_2 molecule resulted in reaction. Only about one collision out of 10^4 between Na and Cl atoms in the gas phase results in reaction according to (c) accompanied by emission of light. This low efficiency is to be expected, for the probability of a quantum transition may be estimated at 10^7 in accordance with the observed values for other atoms and molecules; but the time of a collision is about 10^{-11} seconds, so that the probability that the emission will occur during any one collision is only 10^{-4}.[1] Heating the reaction zone decreases the intensity of the light emitted and assuming that this is due to dissociation of the Na_2 molecule, the heat of dissociation is calculated to be 18 $\pm$ 2 Cal. Under suitable conditions between 70 per cent and 100 per cent of all reactions of the type (c) result in the excitation of a sodium atom. The reactions of Na vapor with the other halogens and with $HgCl_2$ have been investigated in a similar way. From these studies and numerous others[2] of a similar character, it is evident that collisions of the second kind play an important part in the excitation of light in flames and very probably an important part in the "dark" reactions taking place in flames, though of course this is not so easily investigated.

A comparatively simple chemiluminescence accompanies the recombination of atomic hydrogen in the presence of metallic vapors.[3] These spectra are probably excited by the recombination of two hydrogen atoms in a three-body collision, in which the third body is the metallic atom excited, so that the energy of recombination of the hydrogen supplies the energy for excitation. Moreover, Kaplan[4] showed that those atomic lines are most readily excited for which the energy of recombination of two hydrogen atoms to form a molecule in one of its vibrational steady

---

[1] See Urey and Bates, *Phys. Rev.*, **33**, 279 (1929); Dec. (1929).

[2] For example, Fränz and Kallman, *Z. Physik*, **34**, 924 (1925); Bonhoeffer and Haber, ibid., **137**, 263 (1928).

[3] Bonhoeffer, *Z. phys. Chem.*, **113**, 199 (1924); **116**, 391 (1925); **119**, 385 (1926); Mohler, *Phys. Rev.*, **29**, 419 (1927).

[4] *Phys. Rev.*, **31**, 997 (1928).

states agrees closely with the energy required for excitation of the atom to one of its steady states. Table 5 gives a list of the atoms and of those spectral lines which we may expect to be excited in this way. The energy required for excitation and the energy which can be supplied when two hydrogen atoms combine to give a molecule in one of its vibration states are also listed. These energies of recombination are designated as R_n, where n is the vibration quantum number of the molecule formed. The data indicate that unless the energy of excitation and energy of recombination agree within a few hundredths of a volt, excitation of the atom does not occur. The 2,537 line of Hg is excited though its excitation potential is greater than R_0; this is probably due to the formation of an excited HgH molecule, whose bands are also emitted, followed by a collision of this excited molecule with a hydrogen atom. If this collision results in the formation of a hydrogen molecule and a mercury atom, the energy liberated should be ample to excite the atom to the 2^3P_1 state.

TABLE 5

Element	λ	Transition	Excitation potential	Intensity	Nearest R	Difference
Na. . . . . {	5,890	$1^2S - 2^2P$	2.09	Strong	$R_5 = 2.06$	0.03
	6,183	$2^2P - 3^2D$	3.6	Absent	$R_1 = 3.83$	0.23
	3,302	$1^2S - 3^2P$	3.7	Absent	$R_1 = 3.83$	0.13
K. . . . . {	7,665	$1^2S - 2^2P_{1/2}$	1.61	Weak	$R_6 = 1.68$	0.07
	4,044	$1^2S - 3^2P$	3.0	Absent	$R_3 = 2.87$	0.13
Cs. . . . . {	8,943	$1^2S - 2^2P_{3/2}$	1.38	Absent(?)	$R_7 = 1.35$	0.03
	. . . . .	1^2S	3.87	Absent	$R_1 = 3.83$	0.04
Mg.	4,571	$1^1S - 2^3P_1$	2.70	Absent	$R_3 = 2.87$	0.17
Cd.	3,261	$1^1S - 2^3P_1$	3.78	Strong	$R_1 = 3.83$	0.05
Zn.	3,076	$1^1S - 2^3P_1$	4.01	Absent	$R_1 = 3.83$	0.18
Tl.	5,350	$2^2P_{3/2} - 2^2S$	3.26	Absent	$R_2 = 3.34$	0.08

Active nitrogen has also been used to excite spectra by collisions of the second kind. This modification of nitrogen was discovered by E. P. Lewis[1] and has been studied by a number of investigators. The early work of Strutt[2] and of Strutt and Fowler[3] was especially extensive. When nitrogen is passed through a discharge tube, the gas flowing out shows a bright yellow afterglow which may persist from a few seconds to several minutes, depending on conditions. The spectrum consists of a selection of the bands of the neutral nitrogen molecule, lying in the red, yellow, and green. The initial states for the emission of these bands are the tenth, eleventh, and twelfth vibrational levels of the B electronic

[1] *Astrophys. J.*, **12**, 8 (1900).

[2] *Proc. Roy. Soc.*, **85**, 219 (1911) and many subsequent papers.

[3] *Proc. Roy. Soc.*, **85**, 377 and **86**, 105 (1911).

state of the molecule. If other gases or vapors are introduced into the stream of active nitrogen coming from the discharge tube, they are also caused to emit light. Saha and Sur[1] suggested that these spectra were due to collisions with metastable nitrogen molecules. Birge[2] showed that the eleventh state has an energy of about 11.4 volts, which is in agreement with the later estimate of Sponer.[3] It now appears most probable that active nitrogen is a mixture of atomic nitrogen, both unexcited and metastable, and of nitrogen molecules in metastable states with of course a large admixture of ordinary nitrogen.

Some investigators are of the opinion that the excited molecules responsible for the emission of the yellow afterglow are produced in a three-body collision of two atoms with a normal molecule. On the other hand, Knauss[4] has put forward the view that the nitrogen atoms recombine to form an excited molecule without the aid of a three-body collision. It seems very likely that both processes occur and possibly others are involved. On the hypothesis of triple collisions, the energy of the excited molecule would be equal to the heat of association of two atoms. It was formerly believed that the heat of association of two unexcited atoms is about 11.4 volts, in good agreement with the energy of the molecule emitting the yellow bands. Recently, Gaviola[5] and Birge and Hopfield[6] have given good reasons for believing that the heat of association is 9.5 volts and this appears at first sight to render the triple-collision hypothesis untenable. It must be remembered, however, that the nitrogen atom has a metastable state at 2.4 volts, and it may prove to be necessary to consider triple collisions of an unexcited atom, a metastable atom, and an N_2 molecule. In such a collision, the energy made available by the association of the atoms is about 11.5 volts, which agrees very well with that required to excite the yellow bands.

Another possibility, suggested by Kaplan and Cario,[7] is that of a triple collision between a metastable molecule in the A level and a metastable atom having 3.56 volts energy. Let us now consider the hypothesis that two unexcited atoms or one metastable and one unexcited atom, may combine without a three-body collision. In order for this to occur, the energy of association, plus the relative kinetic energy of the two atoms, must be very nearly equal to the energy of the molecule in one of its excited states. The recombination would be slow because these conditions will be fulfilled only in a small fraction of the collisions. At the time of writing it appears difficult to distinguish between these views on the basis of existing experiments.[8] Bonhoeffer and Kaminsky[9] performed experiments which they interpreted as being in contradiction with the triple-collision hypothesis. Keeping the partial pressure of active

[1] *Phil. Mag.*, **48**, 421 (1924).

[2] Nature, **114**, 642 (1924).

[3] *Z. Physik*, **34**, 622 (1925).

[4] *Phys. Rev.*, **32**, 417 (1928).

[5] *Nature*, **122**, 313 (1928).

[6] *Astrophys. J.*, **68**, 257 (1928).

[7] *Nature*, **121**, 906 (1928).

[8] ANGERER, *Physik. Z.* **22**, 97 (1921), and RUDY, *Phys. Rev.*, **27**, 110 (1926), have measured the rate of decay of the afterglow. Both found a brightness-time curve which could be explained on the assumption that two activated entities are involved in each elementary process of light emission. Since two excited entities are involved in all the above processes these experiments do not bear on the question.

[9] *Zeits. f. Elektrochemie*, **32**, 536 (1926).

nitrogen constant, they admitted unexcited N_2 to the experimental tube. The luminosity decreased, instead of increasing as required by the triple-collision theory. However, Kneser[1] made similar experiments under somewhat different conditions and found the expected increase.

It may be well to point out that the question as to the existence of unexcited atoms in active nitrogen could be settled by obtaining its absorption spectrum in the far ultra-violet, where the resonance lines of the atom are found.

The final level for the emission of the afterglow bands is the A electronic level, and is metastable, so that molecules with energies from 9.0 to 9.5 volts will persist for a comparatively long time. It appears that these metastable molecules play a major part in exciting the spectra of substances mixed with the nitrogen. For example, the far ultra-violet spectra of NO and CO are excited,[2] but the highest lying level is at about 9 volts. The far ultra-violet bands of hydrogen requiring 11.1 volts are not excited. However, Ruark, Foote, Rudnick, and Chenault,[3] recorded mercury lines which have an excitation potential of 10.0 volts, using a very long exposure time. Okubo and Hamada,[4] using different experimental conditions, did not obtain any lines coming from levels higher than $4D$, with an excitation potential of 9.51 volts. This contradiction, as well as many others encountered in the papers on active nitrogen, is not surprising, for its phenomena are complicated, and secondary processes may play a more prominent part under some conditions than they do under others. Since processes occur in which a nitrogen molecule receives over 11 volts energy, we should anticipate that a larger amount than 9.5 volts could be transferred to a metal atom, as, for example, in a triple collision of a metal atom with one metastable and one unexcited nitrogen atom.

Bernard Lewis[5] has considered the influence of surfaces on the afterglow in both nitrogen and oxygen, and has investigated the afterglow in a mixture of these gases. He finds, among other very interesting results, that water vapor prevents recombination on the walls and, therefore, increases the intensity of the afterglow.

We conclude this section with a brief discussion of the phenomena occurring in ordinary flames. In spite of the fact that chemiluminescence must play an important part in such flames, it appears that thermal and chemical equilibrium is nearly attained in many cases. It is possible to make measurements of flame temperatures which have a definite meaning, even though we are not dealing with stationary conditions. Many of the early measurements are faulty, since they depended on the introduction of a thermometric device into the flame. This is not the case with the measurements of Loomis and Perrott,[6] who employed the method of Kurlbaum.[7] Light from a tungsten strip lamp is focused on a flame, colored with an alkali salt, and the light of both flame and lamp is then focused on the slit of a spectrometer. It has been proved repeatedly that the reflective power of such a flame is zero, and we have strong evidence that Kirchhoff's law applies to the emission and absorp-

[1] Ann. Physik, **87**, 717 (1928).

[2] KNAUSS, loc cit.

[3] J. O. S. A., **14**, 17 (1927).

[4] Phil. Mag., **5**, 372 (1928).

[5] J. A. C. S., **50**, 27 (1928); **51**, 654 and 665 (1929).

[6] J. Ind. Eng. Chem., **20**, 1004 (1928).

[7] Physik. Z., **3**, 187, 322 (1902).

tion of resonance radiation of the salt carried by the flame.   Under these circumstances, the resonance line will have the same brightness as the background of continuous radiation if the emissive power of the flame at this wave length is equal to the emissive power of the lamp multiplied by the absorption coefficient of the flame.   In symbols, we must satisfy the condition

$$E_F = E_R A_F.$$

If this condition is not satisfied, the spectral line from the flame will either be brighter than the background, or will be reversed against it. In practice, conditions are adjusted so that the line is just reversed, and then the brightness temperature of the tungsten lamp is read with an optical pyrometer.   Knowing the emissive power of tungsten, the true temperature is then determined by calculation, and is taken as the flame temperature.   This method may be applied to the study of the processes occurring in internal combustion engines.   Semenoff[1] has developed a theory of detonation in which collisions of the second kind play an important rôle.

[1] *Z. Physik*, **46**, 109 (1927) and **48**, 571 (1928); *Z. phys. Chem.* **B. 2**, 161 and 169 (1929).

CHAPTER XV

WAVE MECHANICS

1. DE BROGLIE'S THEORY OF MATTER WAVES

The methods of quantizing atomic systems due to Bohr and Sommerfeld are of great service because they yield approximate numerical results by the use of fairly simple models, but they seem destined to be superseded by other avenues of attack which are in better agreement with experiment. For some years, prior to 1925, evidence to this effect was accumulating, for example, the older theory failed to yield correctly the energy levels of neutral helium. There were many attempts to construct a theory in better accord with experiment. This might be done by altering the quantum conditions, the expression for the force between moving charges, the equations of motion, or by many other devices. In the face of possibilities so numerous, little progress could be made until some guiding principles were obtained.

Two theories of quantum dynamics were initiated by de Broglie in 1923 and Heisenberg in 1925, respectively. The theory of de Broglie has been greatly improved and extended by Schrödinger. The theories of Heisenberg and Schrödinger won instant favor, because their fundamental postulates are reasonable and because they are remarkably fruitful. They were developed independently, and seem at first sight to have little in common, but Schrödinger has proved them to be equivalent; they are different mathematical formulations of the same physical relations.

Because it is easier to understand, we first describe the Schrödinger theory, known as "wave mechanics." It arose from the ever-increasing evidence that in many cases the behavior of a light quantum can be predicted by treating it as a particle. The conviction grew that the similarity of material particles and of atomic packets of radiant energy was something more than a coincidence. The question is, if a particle moves with a velocity nearly equal to c, will it have properties such that it is convenient and natural to associate with it a characteristic frequency? Long before the spinning electron was introduced into the theory of spectra, there were sporadic suggestions that the electron might have an internal motional frequency given by the equation

$$h\nu = \frac{m_0 c^2}{(1 - \beta^2)^{1/2}} = \frac{h\nu_0}{(1 - \beta^2)^{1/2}}, \tag{1}$$

where $\beta = v/c$ and v is the velocity of the electron. This was mere speculation; but L. de Broglie[1] showed that great advantages are gained by postulating that a *wave* of frequency ν as given by equation (1) accompanies the electron in its motion. We shall call such waves "de Broglie waves" (To the term, "matter-wave" we give a different significance, Sec. 2). In de Broglie's theory it is found convenient to make the phase velocity

$$u = \frac{c}{\beta}. \tag{2}$$

This relation is really a dispersion equation, because β can be expressed as a function of ν. Let us study the properties of a group of superposed wave trains, having frequencies very close to ν. Since the component trains have slightly different phase velocities they continually slide over each other, and the point of maximum disturbance will generally travel with a velocity different from that of any of the component waves. This velocity is called the "group velocity," and in many cases it is the velocity with which energy is transmitted. In Appendix III we prove that the group velocity is $\dfrac{d\nu}{d\left(\dfrac{\nu}{u}\right)}$. Substituting from equations (2) and (1), we find that the velocity of the group accompanying the electron is βc, which certainly should be the velocity of transmission of its energy. In the case of a light quantum, the phase velocity c is identical with the group velocity. Electromagnetic waves are considered in this theory as a special case of the de Broglie waves. These ideas opened up the possibility of a *unification of quantum dynamics and of optics, which gives a natural, plausible interpretation of the existence of stationary states.*

While de Broglie's[2] original treatment of these matters is in some ways superseded, his reasoning is of great interest. It is as follows: While the frequency of the wave accompanying an electron is given by equation (1), an observer will assign to the internal periodic motion a different frequency,

$$\nu_1 = \nu_0(1 - \beta^2)^{\frac{1}{2}},$$

due to the relativity change of time-scale. That is, some quantity connected with the motion varies as $\sin 2\pi\nu_1 t$. At time zero, let the electron be at the origin, and let the phase of its internal motion coincide with the phase of the wave at that point. Then we can prove the theorem, that the phase of the internal motion will always be in agreement with the phase of the wave at the position of the electron. For at time t the electron

---

[1] Thesis presented to the faculty of the University of Paris (1924). *Ann. de Phys.* (**10**) 3, 22 (1925). The whole subject is summarized in his book "Ondes et Mouvements," Gauthier-Villars, Paris (1926).

[2] *Phil. Mag.*, **47**, 446 (1924).

has moved to the point $x = \beta ct$, and is characterized by $\sin 2\pi \nu_1 \dfrac{x}{\beta c}$. The wave is given by $\sin 2\pi \nu \left(t - \dfrac{\beta x}{c} \right) = \sin 2\pi \nu \left(\dfrac{x}{\beta c} - \dfrac{\beta x}{c} \right)$, which agrees with the previous expression provided $\nu_1 = \nu(1 - \beta^2)$. This is actually the case, by virtue of the definitions of ν and ν_1. To apply this resonance relation in the interpretation of the quantum conditions, we must show that *the possible paths of the electron are rays of the phase waves.* Since the new theory is to contain optics as a special case, the laws governing the phase waves are chosen as nearly as possible like those of optics. The assumption is made that the rays are determined by Fermat's principle,

$$\delta \int \frac{\nu}{u} ds = \delta \int \frac{m_0 \beta c}{h(1 - \beta^2)^{1/2}} ds = 0 \tag{3}$$

and this is identical with the principle of least action, ds being an element of path. While this is proved here only for the case of a particle moving with uniform velocity, de Broglie ascribes general validity to the principle. Consider an electron on a circular orbit of the hydrogen atom; it is supposed to be accompanied by a wave system such that the amplitude of the wave varies sinusoidally along the electron orbit. In order that the wave system may be permanent, an integral number of wave lengths must occur in the length of the orbit. In de Broglie's words, "The motion can only be stable if the phase wave is tuned with the length of the path." If T be the period, and we integrate over one revolution, the number of wave lengths contained in the path must be

$$\int \frac{ds}{\lambda} = \int \frac{\nu}{u} ds = \int_0^T \frac{m_0 \beta^2 c^2 \, dt}{h(1 - \beta^2)^{1/2}} = n, \ n = 1, 2 \cdots \tag{4}$$

This is obtained by putting $ds = \beta c \, dt$ in equation (3), and is *identical* with the quantum condition $\Sigma \oint p_k dq_k = nh$, since the sum of the phase integrals is

$$\int_0^T \frac{m_0 v^2 dt}{(1 - \beta^2)^{1/2}}.$$

Even prior to the papers of de Broglie it was realized that the quantum conditions probably have their origin in some resonance property of the atomic motions, but the difficulty was to find a suitable formulation of the facts. An example will show that in ordinary physical problems dealing with stationary waves, we are often confronted with a series of integers which play a rôle similar to that of quantum numbers. If we write the differential equation for the transverse vibrations of a string,

$$v^2 \frac{\partial^2 y}{\partial x^2} = \frac{\partial^2 y}{\partial t^2}, \tag{5}$$

there is a general solution[1]

$$y = f\left(t - \frac{x}{v} \right) + F\left(t + \frac{x}{v} \right). \tag{6}$$

[1] See Webster's "Dynamics," p. 170.

Nothing more can be said until boundary conditions and initial conditions have been imposed. For example, let us fix the string at the points $x = 0$ and $x = d$. That is, we impose the boundary conditions, $y = 0$ at $x = 0$ and $x = d$, for all values of t. Then the motion must be of the form,

$$y = \sum_n A_n \sin \frac{\pi n x}{d} \cdot \cos \left(\frac{\pi n v t}{d} - \alpha_n \right). \tag{7}$$

The constants A_n and α_n are determined by specifying the values of y and $\partial y / \partial t$ as functions of x at a given time t_0. The motion of the string is made up of stationary sinusoidal vibrations having one, two, three, etc. loops in the length d, but never a fractional number of loops, simply because of the boundary conditions. This point deserves emphasis, for it is closely analogous to the appearance of quantum numbers in Schrödinger's mechanics.

This is only a single instance of the "explanatory" power of de Broglie's theory. In generalizing the above interpretation of the quantum conditions to a system with n degrees of freedom, Schrödinger is led to an equation which is most naturally visualized as an equation of wave propagation in n-dimensional space. Thus *the waves which are used in Schrödinger's scheme of atomic dynamics are not three dimensional except in the case of a system having three degrees of freedom.* We shall refer to these n-dimensional oscillations as *matter waves*, or *Schrödinger waves*.

The essence of Schrödinger's discovery is this: He has found a partial differential equation to govern the changes of a new and important quantity ψ, ordinarily called the amplitude of the matter waves, together with boundary conditions which, in the case of conservative atomic systems, limit the allowed solutions to a definite set, each one being characteristic of an energy level of the atom. (When the energy levels are continuously distributed, so also are the wave functions.) Schrödinger noted the important fact that the product of ψ and its complex conjugate ψ^* (*i.e.*, ψ^2, if ψ is real) obeys an equation identical with the equation of continuity. Accordingly, he interpreted $\psi \psi^*$ as proportional to electric charge density. On the other hand, Born[1] advanced cogent reasons for believing that the function ψ is not a definite property of the individual atom, but that it determines the average behavior of the atom. The prevailing view is that

$$\psi(q_1, \cdots q_n)\psi^*(q_1, \cdots q_n)dv$$

measures the probability that the coordinates describing the structure of the atom shall lie between q_1 and $q_1 + dq_1$, q_2 and $q_2 + dq_2$, etc. In this expression, dv is a differential volume element and may be written in the form $\rho(q_1 \ldots q_n)dq_1 \ldots dq_n$. For example, in the case of plane polar coordinates, $dv = r dr d\theta$ and ρ is simply r. This interpretation

---

[1] *Z. Physik*, **38**, 803 (1926) and **40**, 167 (1927).

has led to a generalization of the Schrödinger theory, commonly referred to as the operator theory or transformation theory of quantum dynamics. Discussion of this theory is postponed to Chap. XVIII.

2. THE ANALOGY BETWEEN DYNAMICS AND OPTICS

We shall now amplify the suggestion made in Sec. 1, that Fermat's principle and the principle of least action have a common basis. About a century ago Hamilton showed that there is a close similarity between the laws of geometrical optics and those governing a particle in a conservative field of force. Let T, V, and E be the kinetic, potential, and total energies of the particle. Then, if we agree to consider only those motions, actual or imaginary, for which E is the same, the actual motion will be that for which

$$\int (E - V)^{\frac{1}{2}} ds \tag{8}$$

is a maximum or minimum. (More accurately, the integral is stationary.) This form of the general principle governing the motion of a particle is exactly similar to Fermat's principle of least time in geometrical optics, namely, the actual ray between two fixed points is such that the time of passage of the light is an extreme. If ds is an element of the path of a light ray and $\mu(x, y, z)$ is the refractive index of the medium, the velocity at x, y, z is c/μ and an element ds is traversed in the time $\dfrac{ds}{c/\mu}$. The total time is obtained by integration and Fermat's principle is stated by the equation

$$\delta \int \frac{\mu ds}{c} = 0. \tag{9}$$

From equation (9) we can easily arrive at differential equations in the Hamiltonian form, to determine the path of a ray, just as Hamilton's equations in dynamics determine the path of a particle. In Hamilton's day it was customary to consider Fermat's principle as an expression for the equations of motion of light corpuscles and to think of this principle as a mechanical explanation of geometrical optics.

The ray method of geometrical optics breaks down when we deal with distances comparable with the wave length. Schrödinger introduced the idea that the failure of ordinary mechanics when applied to atomic systems is due to a similar cause; namely, our habit of thinking about the *paths* of electrons and nuclei, when perhaps we should focus our attention on wave fronts associated with those paths. As long as the path predicted by mechanics has a radius of curvature large in comparison with the size of an atom we can rely on the results, but when this is not the case a new law must govern the phenomena. Such deviations from mechanics are analogous to diffraction in optics.

Now the Hamiltonian equations for a system having n degrees of freedom differ from those for a single particle only through the fact that there are more equations, two for each coordinate, and the optical analogue would be the propagation of a wave in space of n dimensions. Suppose we are dealing with a system of particles, $n/3$ in number, having masses $m_1, m_2 \ldots$ and Cartesian coordinates x_1, x_2, x_3 for the first particle; x_4, x_5, x_6 for the second; and so on. It is convenient to adopt new coordinates $X_1, X_2, \ldots$, such that

$$m_1^{1/2} x_1 = X_1, \cdots \tag{10}$$

We shall refer to the space in which the X's are Cartesian coordinates as the *coordinate space* or the Schrödinger space. The square of the element of length in this space is

$$ds^2 = \Sigma dX_i^2 = m_1 \left(\frac{dx_1}{dt}\right)^2 dt^2 + m_1 \left(\frac{dx_2}{dt}\right)^2 dt^2 + \cdots = 2T dt^2. \tag{11}$$

The dynamical analogue of a light ray in this space is the path of a fictitious point having coordinates $X_1, \ldots X_n$, the so-called "representative point" of a given dynamical system. The n-dimensional velocity vector of this point has the components

$$\dot{X}_1 \cdots \dot{X}_n, \tag{12}$$

and its equations of motion are

$$\frac{dX_i}{dt} = \frac{\partial H}{\partial P_i}, \quad \frac{dP_i}{dt} = -\frac{\partial H}{\partial X_i},$$

where $P_i = \dot{X}_i$. As we showed in Chap. IV, Sec. **10**,

$$P_i = \frac{\partial W}{\partial X_i}, \quad -E = \frac{\partial W}{\partial t}, \tag{13}$$

where W is Hamilton's principal function, defined by the equation

$$W = -Et + S(X, \alpha), \tag{14}$$

S being the action function. By equations (12) and (14), we see that the velocity is parallel to the normal to the surface, $W = $ constant, for the direction cosines of the normal to this surface are proportional to $\partial W/\partial X_1$, $\partial W/\partial X_2$, etc. It is natural, therefore, to suppose that surfaces over which W is constant can be utilized as wave surfaces for the matter waves. Since W depends on t, these surfaces are in motion, and their velocity in the coordinate space is taken as the phase velocity of the matter waves. We prove in Sec. **3** that this velocity is

$$u = \frac{E}{[2(E - V)]^{1/2}}. \tag{15}$$

The proof is rather complicated and at this stage the reader will do well to pass at once to Sec. **4**.

3. DETERMINATION OF THE PHASE VELOCITY

It is necessary to consider in more detail the nature of the action function S in equation (14). It depends on the coordinates and on n constants of integration, $\alpha_1 \ldots \alpha_n$; for brevity, we indicate this by writing $S(X, \alpha)$, where X stands for the whole group of variables and α represents all the constants of integration. When we choose a set of α's, we restrict ourselves to the consideration of a certain set of related paths in the X space, and of the surfaces normal to them. To make the situation clear, we consider the free motion of a *single particle* in ordinary space. The matter waves belonging to the particle are assumed to extend through the whole of a three-dimensional coordinate-space, in which each state of the particle corresponds to a certain position of the representative point. In this illustration, the position of the representative point is the *same* as that of the actual particle, so we may as well talk of the representative point as a fictitious particle of unit mass. We take as rays the paths of a number of such particles, all moving parallel to each other with the same velocity. The wave-front surfaces for these paths are planes perpendicular to them. The "energy" of one of the fictitious particles is

$$H = \tfrac{1}{2}(p_X{}^2 + p_Y{}^2 + p_Z{}^2),$$

for there is no potential energy. The action is obtained by solving the Hamilton-Jacobi equation

$$\left(\frac{\partial S}{\partial X}\right)^2 + \left(\frac{\partial S}{\partial Y}\right)^2 + \left(\frac{\partial S}{\partial Z}\right)^2 = 2E. \tag{16}$$

Writing

$$2E = \alpha_X{}^2 + \alpha_Y{}^2 + \alpha_Z{}^2,$$

we find,

$$S = \alpha_X X + \alpha_Y Y + \alpha_Z Z + \text{const.},$$
$$W = -Et + S(X, Y, Z, \alpha). \tag{17}$$

For a fictitious particle which has coordinates $X_0,\ Y_0,\ Z_0$ at time t_0, the W value will be

$$W(X_0,\ Y_0,\ Z_0,\ \alpha_X,\ \alpha_Y,\ \alpha_Z,\ t_0) = W_0. \tag{18}$$

We now agree to consider a class of fictitious particles which have identical values of the α's, for example, those for which $\alpha_X = a,\ \alpha_Y = b,\ \alpha_Z = c$; and further, we restrict ourselves to those particles which have a common value of W, say W_0. The locus of all such particles at time t_0 is

$$W(X, Y, Z, a, b, c, t_0) = W_0. \tag{19}$$

Varying W_0, we obtain a family of planes, over each of which W is constant, and all of them are perpendicular to a bundle of paths characterized by common values of the α's. As time goes on, these surfaces of constant W move; at any time t the surface for which $W = W_0$ is given by

$$W(X, Y, Z, a, b, c, t) = W_0, \tag{20}$$

and it is still normal to all the paths considered, for the relations of equation (13) are always true. The surfaces thus selected are entirely satisfactory to serve as wave fronts of the matter waves.

The argument given above applies almost verbatim to the general case. Given the function $W(X, \alpha, t)$, we assign particular values to the α's, say $\alpha_{10},\ \alpha_{20},\ \dots$ etc. Then the equation,

$$W(X, \alpha_0, t) = W_0,$$

where W_0 is a constant, represents a moving locus of $n - 1$ dimensions. At any instant it is "perpendicular" to the paths of all representative points whose momenta are given by the relations,

$$P_i = \frac{\partial W(X, \alpha_0, t)}{\partial X_i}.$$

The generalization to non-Cartesian coordinates is easily made by writing q_i in place of X_i. In this case, however, it is important to note that the p's may not denote velocity components, but may represent angular momenta, for example. While the surfaces of constant W remain always perpendicular to the trajectories of the representative points, they do not always contain the same fictitious particles; for the particles themselves are moving at velocities different from those of the surfaces. The velocity of movement of the surfaces $W(X, \alpha_0, t)$ is obtained as follows. The equation,

$$\frac{1}{2}\left[\left(\frac{\partial W}{\partial X_1}\right)^2 + \cdots + \left(\frac{\partial W}{\partial X_n}\right)^2\right] + V - E = 0,$$

may be written

$$|\text{grad } W| = \left[\left(\frac{\partial W}{\partial X_1}\right)^2 + \cdots + \left(\frac{\partial W}{\partial X_n}\right)^2\right]^{1/2} = [2(E - V)]^{1/2}. \tag{21}$$

Consider the state of affairs when $t = t_0$, fixing attention on the surface $W = W_0$. Starting from a given point of this surface, and passing a distance dn along the normal in the direction of increasing W we arrive at a point characterized by the value

$$W = W_0 + dW_0$$

where

$$dW_0 = |\text{grad } W| \cdot dn = [2(E - V)]^{1/2}dn, \tag{22}$$

and the locus of such points is the surface $W_0 + dW_0 = W$. But from equation (17), after a time dt_0, given by

$$E dt_0 = dW_0$$

the value of W at every point of the surface will have decreased to W_0. In other words, the surface $W = W_0$ has moved perpendicular to itself with a velocity at any point given by

$$u = \frac{dn}{dt_0} = \frac{E}{[2(E - V)]^{1/2}}. \tag{23}$$

It is important to remember that the potential energy of the system is supposed to be a function only of the coordinates. When we pass to the consideration of the coordinate space, V may be considered as the "potential energy" of a "representative n-dimensional particle." Now this is the same for all representative particles of a given total energy E, regardless of the direction from which they come. Therefore, u is the same for all wave fronts associated with systems of given energy E, at a given point, regardless of their orientation.

4. THE EQUATION OF PROPAGATION OF MATTER WAVES

In setting up the equation to determine the amplitude of the matter waves, we naturally utilize the familiar propagation equations of classical physics. For electromagnetic waves in free space, for sound waves when energy losses are neglected, or in a host of other cases, we meet with an equation of the type

$$\frac{\partial^2 \varphi}{\partial x^2} + \frac{\partial^2 \varphi}{\partial y^2} + \frac{\partial^2 \varphi}{\partial z^2} - \frac{1}{u^2}\frac{\partial^2 \varphi}{\partial t^2} = 0, \tag{24}$$

u being the constant phase velocity of the waves. Equation (24) has broad possibilities. It may happen that φ bears little resemblance to the usual idea of a "wave"; for example, it may be zero at a given point until time t, and unity thereafter. But in general, equation (24) describes a *propagation* of the quantity φ. Thus it has the solutions.

$$\varphi = f(\alpha x + \beta y + \gamma z \pm ut)$$

where $\alpha^2 + \beta^2 + \gamma^2 = 1$ and the function f may be chosen *ad libitum*. This represents a disturbance moving along the line whose direction cosines are α, β, γ. Still more important, the equation has solutions which may be described as *standing waves*, formed by superposing two or more solutions which represent propagation in opposite directions. (Example, $\varphi = \sin (x - ut) + \sin (x + ut) = 2 \sin x \cos ut$.)

Suppose that u is a function of the coordinates and possibly of time. If u does not change too rapidly when the coordinates or the time vary, it will be appropriate to speak of the state of affairs described by equation (24) as a propagation in an *isotropic* but *inhomogeneous* medium, that is, one in which the wave velocity varies from point to point but is the same for all directions at a given point. Generalizing to represent matter waves in the n-dimensional space of X's, we shall *assume* the following wave equation:[1]

Assumption I:

$$\frac{\partial^2 \Psi}{\partial X_1{}^2} + \cdots + \frac{\partial^2 \Psi}{\partial X_n{}^2} - \frac{1}{u^2} \cdot \frac{\partial^2 \Psi}{\partial t^2} = 0. \tag{25}$$

Substituting the value of u into equation (25) we have

$$\sum_1^n \frac{\partial^2 \Psi}{\partial X_i{}^2} - \frac{2(E - V)}{E^2} \frac{\partial^2 \Psi}{\partial t^2} = 0. \tag{25'}$$

5. ELEMENTARY SOLUTIONS OF THE WAVE EQUATION

The question is, what is the relation between the amplitude Ψ and the phase W? There are solutions of equation (25') of the form

$$\Psi = \cos 2\pi \frac{W}{h} \text{ or } \Psi = \sin 2\pi \frac{W}{h},$$

and more complicated solutions may be constructed by forming a trigonometric series composed of such terms. Then W/h is analogous to the phase of monochromatic light and Ψ resembles an amplitude. (Here h is simply a constant having the same dimensions as W, namely those of action, introduced to make the argument of the cosine a pure number.) However, it is usually more convenient to use the solution,

Assumption II:

$$\Psi = \exp \left(2\pi i \frac{W}{h} \right) = \psi(x) \exp \left(-2\pi i \frac{Et}{h} \right). \tag{26}$$

In this equation we may write

$$\psi = \exp \left(2\pi i \frac{S}{h} \right),$$

so that $W = -Et + S$, but it must be understood that S is determined by solving the differential equation, and is not usually identical with the

[1] More general wave equations will be introduced in Secs. 12, 19, and 20.

action function of classical mechanics. Many authors use instead the relations

$$\Psi = \exp\left(-2\pi i \frac{W}{h}\right), \quad \psi = \exp\left(-2\pi i \frac{S}{h}\right).$$

The real part of both solutions is the same, but we shall consistently use the former.

6. SCHRÖDINGER'S AMPLITUDE EQUATION

Substituting equation (26) in equation (25') and removing the factor $\exp\left(-2\pi i \frac{Et}{h}\right)$, we obtain

$$\frac{\partial^2 \psi}{\partial X_1{}^2} + \frac{\partial^2 \psi}{\partial X_2{}^2} + \cdots + \frac{8\pi^2}{h^2}(E - V)\psi = 0. \tag{27}$$

This is often referred to as the Schrödinger wave equation. It is fundamental for all that follows. In the coordinates $x_1, \ldots,$ equation (27) becomes

$$\frac{1}{m_1}\left(\frac{\partial^2 \psi}{\partial x_1{}^2} + \frac{\partial^2 \psi}{\partial y_1{}^2} + \frac{\partial^2 \psi}{\partial z_1{}^2}\right) + \frac{1}{m_2}\left(\frac{\partial^2 \psi}{\partial x_2{}^2} + \frac{\partial^2 \psi}{\partial y_2{}^2} + \frac{\partial^2 \psi}{\partial z_2{}^2}\right) + \cdots$$

$$+ \frac{8\pi^2}{h^2}(E - V)\psi = 0 . \tag{28}$$

In problems dealing with only one electron, we write this in the form

$$\Delta\psi + \frac{8\pi^2 m}{h^2}(E - V)\psi = 0, \tag{29}$$

where $\Delta\psi$ means $\dfrac{\partial^2 \psi}{\partial x^2} + \dfrac{\partial^2 \psi}{\partial y^2} + \dfrac{\partial^2 \psi}{\partial z^2}$, and is read "Laplacian ψ."

Assumption III.—*Since ψ is supposed to represent a physical quantity which, in principle at least, can be measured, it must be finite, continuous, and single valued for all values of its variable which can actually occur in nature.*[1]

It seems very reasonable, and indeed almost naïve, to say a physical quantity cannot become infinite and must not experience discontinuous jumps in value. The requirement of *single valuedness* or *uniformity* means that ψ cannot be a function like $x^{1/2}$, with two values for each value of x, or $\sin^{-1} x$, with an infinite number of values. Of course, the positive value of $x^{1/2}$ is single valued and could be used as a possible form for ψ. This requirement seems obvious too. However, Assumption III is of the utmost importance, for we shall find that ψ *can be finite, continuous, and single valued when, and only when, the energy E has the quantized values actually occurring in nature.* When these conditions are satisfied we shall speak of ψ as an *acceptable* function.

[1] Strictly speaking, it is $\psi^*\psi$ which can be measured. See Sec. **16.**

Assumption III replaces the Wilson-Sommerfeld quantum conditions. While these older quantum conditions were arbitrary, assumption III appears in a natural way, we might even say a necessary way, being analogous to the boundary conditions in the problem of the vibrating string. It is surprising but true that the mere requirements of finiteness, continuity, and uniformity for ψ determine uniquely the distribution of ψ, corresponding to each allowed value of E. The actual numerical values of ψ are not specified, for if S is an acceptable solution of the wave equation, cS is also a solution, c being a constant. The *size* of ψ will be determined by an arbitrary convention in Sec. **13**. In the problem of hydrogen we shall find that ψ will be acceptable if E takes the negative values $-Rhc/n^2$, or any positive value whatsoever. The negative values of E correspond to the elliptic orbits of the older theory; positive values, to the hyperbolic orbits. This illustration shows that the values of E which give rise to acceptable ψ functions may be distributed either discretely or continuously. Such an aggregate of E values is often referred to as a "spectrum of characteristic values," or "proper values," its parts being called the "discrete" (or "discontinuous") and the "continuous spectrum." Either part may be missing, depending on the nature of the problem.[1]

We must note an important special case of assumption III. If the system is periodic, the requirement of uniformity means that *when it returns to its original configuration, ψ must return to its original value.* This suggests a way of avoiding a certain inconsistency. It may be objected against assumption III that an angular coordinate can assume infinite values, although the corresponding configuration remains finite and therefore measurable. In such a case, we simply require that ψ is repeated when the configuration is repeated. Again, the Cartesian coordinate x may have infinite values; why should ψ be restricted to finite size? The reason is that $|\psi^2|$ represents a measurable physical property; while x does not when values approaching infinity are considered.[2]

7. THE RIGID ROTATOR WITH ONE DEGREE OF FREEDOM

If φ is the azimuthal angle of a body rotating about a fixed axis, the moment of inertia being I, then

$$T = \tfrac{1}{2}I\dot{\varphi}^2$$

[1] The German word for characteristic value is Eigenwert; the characteristic function ψ_n belonging to the Eigenwert E_n is called an "Eigenfunktion." We shall often use these words in English sentences without apologetic quotation marks.

[2] It is interesting to note that Korn (Résumé and bibliography in Z. *Physik*, **44**, 745 (1927)) was led to consider equations of the same general type as those used by Schrödinger, in connection with his hydrodynamical theories of gravitation and electromagnetic phenomena, many years before the application of such equations to atomic structure was undertaken.

and the element of length in the q space is

$$ds^2 = 2T dt^2 = I d\varphi^2. \tag{30}$$

Let $I^{\frac{1}{2}}\varphi$ be a new variable of dimensions $M^{\frac{1}{2}}L$, with respect to which the differentiations are carried out in forming $\Delta\psi$. Since there is no potential energy, the wave equation is

$$\frac{d^2\psi}{d(I^{\frac{1}{2}}\varphi)^2} + \frac{8\pi^2 E\psi}{h^2} = \frac{1}{I}\frac{d^2\psi}{d\varphi^2} + \frac{8\pi^2 E\psi}{h^2} = 0. \tag{31}$$

The solution is

$$\psi = c_1 e^{ia\varphi} + c_2 e^{-ia\varphi},$$

where

$$a^2 = \frac{8\pi^2 EI}{h^2}. \tag{32}$$

If E were negative, the solution would become $c_1 e^{-b\varphi} + c_2 e^{b\varphi}$, where b is real. If this is to be finite when $\varphi = \pm \infty$, we must have $c_1 = 0$ and $c_2 = 0$. Therefore E must not be negative if we are to avoid a trivial solution, and equation (32) can be recast in the form $\psi = A \sin\left(\dfrac{8\pi^2 EI}{h^2}\right)^{\frac{1}{2}}\varphi$, or better,

$$\psi = A \exp\left[i\left(\frac{8\pi^2 EI}{h^2}\right)^{\frac{1}{2}}\varphi \right]. \tag{33}$$

The requirement of single valuedness for ψ means that when the system passes through a cycle and regains its original configuration, ψ must return to its original value. The rotator repeats its configuration when φ increases by 2π; if ψ is to repeat its value the coefficient of φ must be an integer m; so

$$E_m = \frac{m^2 h^2}{8\pi^2 I}, \text{ with } m = 1, 2, \cdots. \tag{34}$$

In the singular case $E = 0$, the solution of equation (31) is $C_1\varphi + C_2$. Since ψ must be finite, even when φ is infinite, we must have $C_1 = 0$, $\psi = C_2$. Therefore, the value $m = 0$ should be added.

In discussing band spectra we have seen that formula (34) for the quantized energy levels of a rotating diatomic molecule is not applicable when m takes integral values; but half-integral quantum numbers are in good agreement with the empirical results. The difficulty arises from treating the problem in only one dimension. It is as though we were to study a problem in the three-dimensional motion of a fluid, on the false assumption that conditions do not vary in a direction parallel to one of the coordinate axes.

8. THE RIGID ROTATOR WITH TWO DEGREES OF FREEDOM

Supposing the rotator to be a "dumbbell" molecule, let θ, φ be polar coordinates of the line joining the two nuclei. If the molecule were not rigid, we should have a problem involving six coordinates r_1, θ_1, φ_1,

r_2, θ_2, φ_2, belonging, respectively, to the nuclei of masses m_1, m_2. But

$$\theta_2 = \pi - \theta_1, \ \varphi_2 = \pi + \varphi_1, \ \dot{r}_1 = \dot{r}_2 = 0,$$

and from the definition of the center of mass, $m_1r_1 = m_2r_2$, it is easy to bring the kinetic energy to the form

$$T = \frac{I(\sin^2 \theta_1 \dot{\varphi}_1{}^2 + \dot{\theta}_1{}^2)}{2}.$$

where I is the moment of inertia, $m_1r_1{}^2 + m_2r_2{}^2$. The coordinates used in calculating the Laplacian are $I^{\frac12}\varphi_1$, and $I^{\frac12}\theta_1$. Dropping subscripts, the wave equation is

$$\frac{1}{\sin \theta} \frac{\partial}{\partial \theta}\left(\sin \theta \frac{\partial \psi}{\partial \theta}\right) + \frac{1}{\sin^2 \theta} \frac{\partial^2 \psi}{\partial \varphi^2} + \frac{8\pi^2 EI \psi}{h^2} = 0. \tag{35}$$

We try the solution $\psi = \Theta\Phi$, where Θ is a function of θ alone, and Φ, of φ alone, and introduce a quantity j, such that $j(j+1) = 8\pi^2 EI/h^2$.[1] Substituting this in equation (35), and dividing by $\Theta\Phi/\sin^2 \theta$,

$$\frac{\sin \theta}{\Theta} \cdot \frac{\partial}{\partial \theta}\left(\sin \theta \frac{\partial \Theta}{\partial \theta}\right) + j(j+1) \sin^2 \theta + \frac{1}{\Phi} \frac{\partial^2 \Phi}{\partial \varphi^2} = 0.$$

The first two terms are a function of θ and the last term depends upon φ alone. The only non-trivial way in which a function of one independent variable can always be equal to a function of another is that each shall be a constant. Suppose that we set the last term equal to $-m^2$. Then,

$$\frac{\partial^2 \Phi}{\partial \varphi^2} + m^2\Phi = 0, \ \Phi = e^{im(\varphi - \alpha_m)}.$$

The amplitude constant is omitted, being unimportant for the present. Φ is finite and continuous as it stands. To make it a single-valued function of position we must make m an integer, or zero. Further, the first two terms of equation (35) must be equal to m^2, and the equation for Θ reduces to

$$\frac{1}{\sin \theta} \cdot \frac{\partial}{\partial \theta}\left(\sin \theta \frac{\partial \Theta}{\partial \theta}\right) + \left[j(j+1) - \frac{m^2}{\sin^2 \theta}\right]\Theta = 0. \tag{36}$$

Solutions which are *single-valued as a function of the position of the molecular axis* are denoted by

$$P_{j,m}(\mu)$$

where $\mu = \cos \theta$. Solutions having this property are obtained if we place $j = 0, 1, 2 \cdots$, and if m is less than or equal to j.

The functions,

$$P_{j,m}(\mu) \cos m\varphi \text{ and } P_{j,m}(\mu) \sin m\varphi$$

are called "tesseral harmonics." The functions, $P_{j,m}(\mu)$ are of the form

$$\sin^m \theta \frac{\partial^m P_j(\mu)}{\partial \mu^m}, \tag{37}$$

---

[1] The method used here is explained in JEANS' "Electricity and Magnetism," 4th ed., p. 237, Cambridge Univ. Press, Cambridge (1920).

where $P_j(\mu)$ is the jth polynomial of Legendre (see Appendix IV). $P_{j,m}(\mu)$ is a polynomial in $\cos \theta$, namely

$$\frac{(2j)!\,\sin^m \theta}{2!(j-m)!}\left\{\cos^{j-m}\theta - \frac{(j-m)(j-m-1)}{2(2j-1)}\cos^{j-m-2}\theta \right.$$
$$\left. + \frac{(j-m)(j-m-1)(j-m-2)(j-m-3)}{2\quad 4\quad (2j-1)\quad (2j-3)}\cos^{j-m-4}\theta \cdots \right\} \qquad (38)$$

It terminates when the exponent of $\cos \theta$ in the last term becomes one or zero.

The solution of equation (35) is, therefore,

$$\psi = \Theta\Phi = P_{j,m}(\mu)e^{im(\varphi-\alpha_m)}, \qquad (39)$$

and is acceptable if j and m are integral numbers and $m \leq j$. In this solution, m plays a rôle similar to that of the equatorial quantum number in the space quantization of the H atom. The purely mathematical requirement that it shall be less than or equal to j is analogous to the concept of the older theory that $mh/2\pi$ is a *component* of the total angular momentum $jh/2\pi$. Further, from the definition of j,

$$E_j = \frac{j(j+1)h^2}{8\pi^2 I}, \qquad (39a)$$

a formula in good agreement with experiment; for we have

$$j(j+1) = (j+\tfrac{1}{2})^2 - \tfrac{1}{4}.$$

This shows that the energy levels obtained in the analysis of a rotational band spectrum are all shifted by a small constant amount from the positions predicted by the older theory on the basis of half-quantum numbers. The constant shift does not affect the frequencies of the lines emitted (see however, Chap. XII, Sec. 4).

This example illustrates a behavior frequently encountered in problems of wave mechanics. It often happens that when we neglect to use the full number of degrees of freedom appropriate to a problem, the quantum numbers change from integral to apparently half-integral values, or *vice versa*. It further illustrates a feature common to systems of rotating particles. If we were to take for Ψ the values $P_{j,m}(\mu)$ $\cos (m\varphi)e^{-2\pi i\nu t}$ or $P_{j,m}(\mu) \sin (m\varphi) e^{-2\pi i\nu t}$, which also satisfy equation (36), the change of Ψ as times goes on would be a vibration rather than a rotation. Physical intuition leads us to use the solution of equation (39), for its real part,

$$P_{j,m}(\mu) \cos (m\varphi - 2\pi\nu t),$$

represents a rotating distribution of the ψ function, except when $m = 0$. In many other problems the wave equation is such that ψ depends on the angular coordinates through the factor $P_{j,m}(\mu)e^{im\varphi}$. We wish to study the values which ψ assumes on the surface of a sphere of arbitrary radius as a function of the polar coordinates θ and φ. In the first place, we note that it will be zero at certain points or along certain curves, known as "nodal points" or "lines." This will occur whenever either $P_{j,m}(\mu)$ or $\cos m\varphi$ is zero. Now $\cos m\varphi$ is zero when $m\varphi = \pi/2, 3\pi/2, \cdots$ and these nodes will lie on great circles of the sphere. There will be 0, 1, 2 · · · such circles for $m = 0, 1, 2 \cdots$, respectively. $P_{j,m}(\mu)$ will be

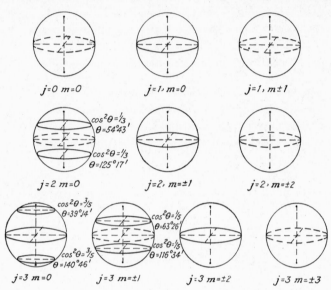

FIG. 1.—Traces of nodal cones of the functions $P_{j,m}(\cos \theta)$.

zero when $\sin \theta = 0$, *i.e.*, for $\theta = 0$ and π and this will occur at the poles of the sphere. It will also be zero at intermediate values of θ

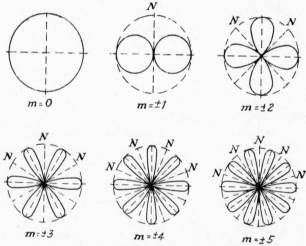

FIG. 2.—Polar graphs of $|\cos m\varphi|$.

dependent on both j and m, as determined by setting the expression in equation (38) equal to zero. We show these nodes for all possible steady states up to $j = 3$ in Fig. 1. The nodal lines are located similarly on the surface of any sphere with center at the origin so that ψ actually vanishes on the *nodal planes*, $m\varphi = \pi/2$, etc., and on the *nodal cones* occurring at values of θ which make $P_{j,m}(\mu) = 0$. To see how the function ψ varies between the nodes we show polar graphs of $|\cos m\varphi|$ for different values of m at an arbitrary value of θ (Fig. 2) and polar graphs of $|P_{j,m}(\mu)|$ for different values of j and m, for an arbitrary value of φ (Fig. 3). These represent the variation of the absolute value of ψ along a circle of longitude and a meridian, respectively. In Fig. 2, the radius vector making angle φ with the horizontal intersects the curve at a distance from the origin proportional to $\cos m\varphi$. Similarly, in Fig. 3, the radius vector making an angle θ with the vertical axis is proportional to $P_{j,m}(\cos \theta)$.

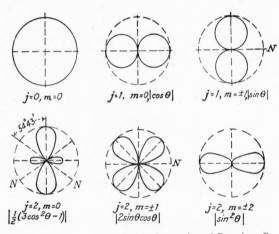

$j=0, m=0$ $j=1, m=0|\cos\theta|$ $j=1, m=\pm 1|\sin\theta|$

$j=2, m=0$
$|\frac{1}{2}(3\cos^2\theta - 1)|$ $j=2, m=\pm 1$
$|2\sin\theta\cos\theta|$ $j=2, m=\pm 2$
$|\sin^2\theta|$

FIG. 3.—Polar graphs of the absolute value of $P_{j,m}(\cos \theta)$.

9. THE LINEAR HARMONIC OSCILLATOR

Let the oscillator have mass μ and let the restoring force be proportional to its distance from the origin, so that its motion is simple harmonic. If the frequency is ν_0, the potential energy is

$$V = 2\pi^2\nu_0^2\mu x^2.$$

The wave equation is

$$\frac{d^2\psi}{dx^2} + \frac{8\pi^2\mu}{h^2}(E - 2\pi^2\nu_0^2\mu x^2)\psi = 0. \tag{40}$$

It is convenient to use a new variable

$$v = 2\pi\left(\frac{\mu\nu_0}{h}\right)^{1/2}x.$$

The equation (40) becomes

$$\frac{d^2\psi}{dv^2} + \left(\frac{2E}{h\nu_0} - v^2\right)\psi = 0. \tag{41}$$

The characteristic values of E are obtained by writing

$$\psi = e^{-v^2/2}H(v) \tag{42}$$

and assuming the solution

$$H = \sum_0^\infty A_n v^n. \tag{43}$$

Negative powers of v are not included because we desire ψ to be finite, continuous, and single valued when $v = 0$. Substituting this series in the differential equation, we obtain the recurrence formula,

$$\frac{A_{n+2}}{A_n} = \frac{2n + 1 - s}{(n + 1)(n + 2)}, \text{ with } s = \frac{2E}{h\nu_0}, \tag{44}$$

to determine the coefficients. We can show that the series begins with either A_0 or $A_1 v$. Suppose that the solution does contain a finite number of negative powers of v. The recurrence formula is not changed but the solution is no longer finite at $v = 0$. Let us seek for a particular value j of the running subscript n such that A_{j+2} is not zero, but all the preceding coefficients, A_{j+1}, A_j, A_{j-1}, . . . are zero. The recurrence formula shows that

$$(j + 1)(j + 2) = 0.$$

Thus the subscript j must be either -1 or -2, and the first non-vanishing coefficient A_{j+2} is either A_0 or A_1. When it is A_1, then from equation (44), $A_2 = 0$, $A_4 = 0$, $\cdots$ When it is A_0, then since A_{-1} is zero by supposition, equation (44) shows that $A_1 = 0$, $A_3 = 0$, $\cdots$. That is, the series for H is either even or odd.

Now the relation, equation (44), is such that $e^{-v^2/2}H$ will not converge when $v \to \infty$, if H contains an infinite number of terms. In order to keep ψ finite, we must choose s in such a way that the series for H comes to an end. This can be done by choosing

$$s = \frac{2E}{h\nu_0} = 1, 3, 5, \cdots.$$

Thus, if $s = 1$, we have

$$\frac{A_2}{A_0} = 0,$$

and the even solution terminates and leads to a finite value of ψ. Quite generally, if s is one of the integers 1, 5, 9, . . . we get an even solution which satisfies all the requirements, and if s is 3, 7, 11, . . . we get an odd solution. Thus the energy levels of the oscillator are

$$E_n = (n + \tfrac{1}{2})h\nu_0. \tag{45}$$

This formula deviates from that obtained by the old quantum mechanics, and shows that the oscillator possesses energy when in its lowest quantized state. Corresponding to each value E_n, there is an appropriate ψ function, ψ_n. If we think of ψ_n as a wave amplitude, an oscillator in the nth quantum state is represented by a stationary wave extending along the v-axis from $-\infty$ to $+\infty$. The graph of its amplitude at any time is obtained by multiplying every ordinate of the curve $\psi_n(v)$ by $\cos 2\pi\nu t$, where $\nu = (n + \frac{1}{2})\nu_0$. The formula for the characteristic functions is,

$$\psi_n(v) = e^{-v^2/2} \cdot H_n(v) = e^{-2\pi^2\mu\nu_0 x^2/h} \cdot H_n(2\pi\sqrt{\mu\nu_0/h} \cdot x). \qquad (46)$$

The polynomial $H_n(v)$ is called the "nth Hermitian polynomial," after its inventor, Ch. Hermite. The values of the first few polynomials are

$$H_0 = 1, \ H_1 = 2v, \ H_2 = 4v^2 - 2, \ H_3 = 8v^3 - 12v,$$
$$H_4 = 16v^4 - 48v^2 + 12, \ H_5 = 32v^5 - 160v^3 + 120v.$$

In general,

$$H_n(v) = (2v)^n - \frac{n(n-1)}{1!}(2v)^{n-2} +$$
$$\frac{n(n-1)(n-2)(n-3)}{2!}(2v)^{n-4} + \cdots$$

The graphs of the functions $\psi_0, \ldots, \psi_4$ are shown in Fig. 4, after Schrödinger.[1] Beyond the range shown, they approach the v-axis.

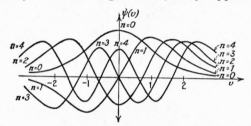

Fig. 4.—Wave functions of the linear oscillator. $\psi_n = \dfrac{1}{\pi^{\frac{1}{4}}2^{n/2}\sqrt{n!}} H(v) \exp(-v^2/2.)$

As plotted, they have been multiplied by the normalizing factor, $\pi^{-\frac{1}{4}}2^{-n/2}(n!)^{-\frac{1}{2}}$. (See however, Chap. XVII, Sec. **21.**)

The result can be extended to two or more coordinates, if the classical frequencies of the separate coordinates are not the same. In place of equation (40) we have

$$\frac{\partial^2\psi}{\partial x^2} + \frac{\partial^2\psi}{\partial y^2} + \frac{8\pi^2\mu}{h^2}(E - 2\pi^2\nu_x^2\mu x^2 - 2\pi^2\nu_y^2\mu y^2)\psi = 0.$$

Letting

$$\psi(x, y) = X(x)Y(y) \text{ and } E = E_x + E_y,$$

we get

$$X'' + \frac{8\pi^2\mu}{h^2} \cdot (E_x - 2\pi^2\nu_x^2\mu x^2)X = 0,$$

and a similar equation for Y, containing E_y, ν_y, y, in place of E_x, ν_x, x. Then the allowed values of E are

$$E_{np} = (n + \frac{1}{2})h\nu_x + (p + \frac{1}{2})h\nu_y, \qquad (47)$$

where n and p equal $0, 1, 2, \ldots$ If

$$v = 2\pi\left(\frac{\mu\nu_x}{h}\right)^{\frac{1}{2}} x \text{ and } w = 2\pi\left(\frac{\mu\nu_y}{h}\right)^{\frac{1}{2}} y, \qquad (48)$$

---

[1] *Naturwiss.*, **14**, 664 (1926).

then corresponding to each *pair* of values of the integers n, p we have a possible state of oscillation with the amplitude,

$$\psi_{np}(x, y) = H_n(v)H_p(w) \exp\left[\frac{-(v^2 + w^2)}{2}\right], \tag{49}$$

and

$$\Psi_{n,p} = \psi_{np} \exp\left(\frac{-2\pi i E_{np} t}{h}\right).$$

As we should expect, there is a double infinity of allowed states, corresponding to the presence of two adjustable parameters E_x and E_y in the equations for X and Y. Difficulties arise if $\nu_x = \nu_y$. In this degenerate case we can obtain a set of values of ψ which differ from equation (49), for the wave equation can be separated in polar coordinates. It is,

$$\frac{1}{r}\frac{\partial}{\partial r}\left(r\frac{\partial\psi}{\partial r}\right) + \frac{\partial}{\partial\theta}\left(\frac{1}{r}\frac{\partial\psi}{\partial\theta}\right) + \frac{8\pi^2\mu}{h^2}(E - 2\pi^2\nu_0{}^2\mu r^2)\psi = 0. \tag{50}$$

Letting $\psi = R(r)\Theta(\theta)$, it is found that

$$\Theta = \exp ik\theta, \quad k = 0, 1, \cdots\cdots$$

The equation for R is

$$R'' + \frac{R'}{r} + \left[\frac{8\pi^2\mu}{h^2} \cdot (E - 2\pi^2\nu_0{}^2\mu r^2) - \frac{k^2}{r}\right]R = 0. \tag{51}$$

Without solving this we can see that the ψ functions derived from it are not identical with equation (49). The loci on which $\psi_{np}(xy)$ is zero are the lines parallel to the y-axis on which $H_n(v)$ vanishes, and those parallel to the x-axis on which $H_p(w)$ vanishes. On the other hand, the real part of Θ vanishes where $\cos k\theta = 0$, *i.e.*, on certain radii through the origin, and $R = 0$ on circles having their centers at the origin. It is interesting to note that each function, $\psi_{np}(xy)$, can be constructed from an infinite number of the solutions $R\Theta$, and *vice versa*.

10. AN EASY RULE FOR OBTAINING THE WAVE EQUATION

In curvilinear coordinates, the expression for $\Delta\psi$ may become quite complicated (Appendix VII), so it is very convenient to have a rule by which the wave equation can be written down at once when we have the Hamilton-Jacobi equation. An examination of this equation (Chap. IV, Sec. 10) and of $\Delta\psi$ shows that the following rule holds true:

In the Hamilton-Jacobi equation, expressed in rectangular coordinates, x_1, x_2, etc., transpose all terms to the left and remove parentheses or irrationalities by performing all indicated operations, so that each term stands by itself. Replace

$$\frac{\partial W}{\partial x_k} \text{ by } \frac{h}{2\pi i}\frac{\partial}{\partial x_k}. \tag{52}$$

The resulting expression is a differential operator. Apply this operator to ψ and set the result equal to zero. This is the wave equation.

The restriction to rectangular coordinates is essential. There has been some confusion in regard to this matter in the literature. Podolsky

(Appendix VII) has discussed and clarified the points at issue and has stated the appropriate procedures for writing out the wave equation in coordinates of any kind whatever.

To illustrate equation (52) we shall apply it to the linear oscillator, for which

$$\left(\frac{\partial W}{\partial x}\right)^2 + 2m(V - E) = 0.$$

We remove parentheses, writing

$$\frac{\partial W}{\partial x} \cdot \frac{\partial W}{\partial x} + 2m(V - E) = 0.$$

We replace $\partial W/\partial x$ by $(h/2\pi i)(\partial/\partial x)$. Of course they are not equal. The replacement is simply an arbitrary method for getting a desired result. Then, applying the operator thus formed to ψ, we get

$$\left(\frac{h}{2\pi i}\frac{\partial}{\partial x}\right)\left(\frac{h}{2\pi i}\frac{\partial}{\partial x}\right)\psi - 2m(E - V)\psi = 0.$$

This means,

$$\frac{h^2}{4\pi^2}\frac{\partial^2\psi}{\partial x^2} + 2m(E - V)\psi = 0,$$

which is the wave equation.

11. ENERGY LEVELS OF HYDROGEN

Ruark,[1] and Vrkljan,[2] independently, have given an easy method for finding the energy levels of hydrogen and the former author has also obtained its Zeeman and Stark effect levels.[3] The virial theorem tells us that in a hydrogenic atom,

$$\overline{T} = \frac{-\overline{V}}{2} = -E, \tag{53}$$

where bars denote time averages. Now for the circular orbits of the atom, the actual kinetic and potential energies are the same as their average values, so

$$\frac{-Ze^2}{2a} = E, \tag{54}$$

a being the radius of the orbit. We use equation (54) to eliminate a from the equation

$$\frac{p_\varphi^2}{2ma^2} = -E, \tag{55}$$

obtaining

$$p_\varphi^2 + \frac{Z^2e^4m}{2E} = 0. \tag{56}$$

[1] *J. O. S. A.*, **16**, 40 (1928); *Phys. Rev.*, **31**, 533 (1928).

[2] *Z. Physik*, **52**, 735 (1928).

[3] The method used can be applied only when we know from other considerations that ψ contains a factor of the type exp $in\varphi$, where φ is an angle variable, and when the problem can be reduced to a single degree of freedom, so that the equation for the part of ψ, depending on φ, has the same form as the wave equation of the one-dimensional rotator. For this reason, the procedure does not give the *complete* expression for ψ, but only the factor which depends on the single independent variable appearing in the wave equation.

This is an equation of Hamilton-Jacobi type, and the wave equation is

$$\frac{d^2\psi}{d\varphi^2} + k^2\varphi = 0,$$

$$k^2 = \frac{2\pi^2 me^4 Z^2}{-Eh^2}. \tag{57}$$

We exclude the value $k = 0$, for if $k = 0$, the energy becomes infinite. The number k is to be regarded as the total quantum number, which happens to be identical with the azimuthal number k of Chap. V when we consider circular orbits. The use of only one degree of freedom leads to the right energy values, but the wave functions are not quite correct. When k is real, but not zero, the solution is $F \exp ik\varphi$, F being the part of ψ which does not depend on φ. In order that ψ may return to its original value when φ increases by 2π, k must be a positive or negative integer. If positive values of the azimuthal number correspond to an atom rotating clockwise about the Z-axis, negative values correspond to counterclockwise rotation, so we see intuitively that a negative k-value must give the same E as the corresponding positive k-value. Therefore, we consider only the positive values of k. These give the Balmer formula, when we solve equation (54) for E. The correction due to motion of the nucleus is easily obtained; equation (56) is replaced by

$$p_\varphi^2 + \frac{Z^2 e^4 \mu}{2E} = 0, \tag{58}$$

where $p_\varphi = \mu a^2 \dot\varphi$, μ is the reduced mass, and a the distance between electron and nucleus. The proof is the same as above, and we obtain the Balmer formula with μ in place of m, in agreement with the results of Chap. 5. Similarly, the energy levels corresponding to elliptic orbits can be obtained by starting with $E = -Rh^3 c/J^2$, in place of equation (56), where J is a momentum variable conjugate to an angle variable w. Then $J = \partial S/\partial w$, and the wave equation is gotten by replacing J with $\frac{h}{2\pi i} \frac{\partial}{\partial w}$. The energy levels corresponding to the circular orbits of an electron with variable mass can be obtained by similar methods. We can show that

$$p_\varphi^2 - \frac{Z^2 e^4}{c^2(1 - A)} = 0, \tag{59}$$

where

$$A \equiv \left(1 + \frac{E}{mc^2}\right)^2. \tag{60}$$

Proceeding as before, the wave equation takes the form of equation (57), where

$$k^2 = \frac{4\pi^2 Z^2 e^4}{h^2 c^2 (1 - A)}, \tag{61}$$

k must be an integer, and on solving for A we find an energy formula which agrees with equation (34) of Chap. V.

To obtain the energy levels in a magnetic field we consider the equation

$$p_\varphi = \frac{\Delta E}{2\pi L}, \tag{62}$$

which is derived in Chap. V, Sec. **11.** ΔE is the alteration of energy due to the field and L the frequency of the Larmor precession, while p_φ is the component of angular momentum parallel to the lines of force, as seen from a system of axes rotating with the angular velocity $2\pi L$. In the old quantum theory we would quantize p_φ at this point to obtain the allowed values of ΔE. In the new theory, we replace p_φ by $\dfrac{h}{2\pi i}\dfrac{\partial}{\partial \varphi}$, and form the wave equation

$$\frac{h}{2\pi i}\frac{\partial \Psi}{\partial \varphi} - \frac{\Delta E \Psi}{2\pi L} = 0. \tag{63}$$

The solution is $F \exp im\varphi$, where $mh = \Delta E/L$. To make this solution have the same period as the corresponding classical motion of the electron, m must be an integer. If $m = 0$, Ψ does not depend on φ, and $\Delta E = 0$. Thus we arrive at energy values identical with those of the classical theory.

12. A GENERALIZATION OF THE WAVE EQUATION

In our illustrations of quantization by wave mechanics, we have used equation (28) which is derived from the more general equation (25') by assuming that its solution is of the form of equation (26). With this restriction, we can obtain an acceptable solution Ψ_1 of equation (25'), if we make $E = E_1$; an acceptable solution Ψ_2 when $E = E_2$; and so on. But of course Ψ_1 will not be an acceptable solution if E takes any value except E_1, Ψ_2 is not an acceptable solution if E is not E_2, and so on. We now attempt to find a linear equation which will be satisfied by all the functions Ψ_n, regardless of the value of E. An equation of this kind can be constructed in a variety of ways but we shall discuss only one of these, devised by Schrödinger. His procedure consists in eliminating E from his wave equation (28), by the use of the equation,

$$\Psi = \psi \exp\left(\frac{-2\pi i E t}{h}\right), \tag{64}$$

which holds when we deal with solutions of the type of equation (26). From equation (64),

$$\frac{\partial \Psi}{\partial t} = -\frac{2\pi i E \Psi}{h}.$$

Substituting E from this relation into equation (28), we have

$$\Delta\Psi - \frac{8\pi^2}{h^2}V\Psi + \frac{4\pi i}{h}\frac{\partial \Psi}{\partial t} = 0, \tag{65}$$

Similarly, the complex conjugate of Ψ obeys the equation.

$$\Delta\Psi^* - \frac{8\pi^2}{h^2}V\Psi^* - \frac{4\pi i}{h}\frac{\partial\Psi^*}{\partial t} = 0. \tag{66}$$

where the independent variables of $\Delta\Psi$ are those used in equation (27). Since equation (65) is independent of E, it holds true whenever equation (28) is satisfied. Of course, if Ψ_n is any *acceptable* solution of equation (28), it retains this characteristic when considered as a solution of equation (65). Further, since equation (65) is linear, a sum of eigenfunktions such as

$$\Psi = \sum_n c_n\Psi_n = \sum_n c_n\psi_n(E_n, x) \exp \frac{-2\pi i E_n t}{h} \tag{67}$$

will also satisfy it, where c_n may be a constant or a function of any parameters, but not a function of the q's, or of t. Because of these broader possibilities, *we take equation* (65) *as fundamental*, replacing equations (25') and (28), and shall consider all of its acceptable solutions as possible value of Ψ. The physical significance of equation (67) is discussed in Secs. **14** and **16**.

13. THE NORMALIZATION OF Ψ

Before proceeding further, we find it convenient to adopt a definite convention in regard to the magnitude of Ψ; for if we multiply any solution of Schrödinger's equation by a constant, the result is also a solution. First we take the case of a single characteristic function, Ψ_m. The convention used is a familiar one in the study of differential equations, namely,

$$\int\psi_m\psi_m^*dv \equiv \int |\psi_m|^2dv = 1, \tag{68}$$

the integral being extended over the whole of the coordinate space specified by equation (11); dv is the element of volume in this space. When this condition is satisfied we say that ψ_m is *normalized*. It will do just as well to write

$$\int\Psi_m\Psi_m^*dv = 1, \tag{68'}$$

for $\Psi_m\Psi_m^* = \psi_m \exp\left(\dfrac{-2\pi i E_m t}{h}\right)\psi_m^* \exp\left(\dfrac{2\pi i E_m t}{h}\right) = \psi_m\psi_m^*.$ That

is, when ψ_m is normalized, Ψ_m enjoys the same property, for the absolute value of the time factor is unity. A simple illustration is the normalization of $\exp im\varphi$, the wave function of the one-dimensional rotator. Let

$$\psi_m = c_m \exp im\varphi \tag{69}$$

where the constant c_m is to be so chosen that equation (68) is true. Then, remembering from equation (30) that

$$dv = I^{1/2}d\varphi,$$

we have

$$I^{1/2}c_mc_m^*\int_0^{2\pi} \exp im\varphi \exp(-im\varphi)d\varphi = 2\pi c_mc_m^*I^{1/2} = 1,$$

so we must have $|c_m|^2 = 1/2\pi I^{\frac{1}{2}}$. Any value of c_m satisfying this will be satisfactory so we take

$$c_m = (4\pi^2 I)^{-\frac{1}{4}}, \psi_m = (4\pi^2 I)^{-\frac{1}{4}} \exp im\varphi. \tag{70}$$

The function (46) must be multiplied by $\pi^{-\frac{1}{4}}2^{-n/2}(n!)^{-\frac{1}{2}}$ in order that it be normalized with respect to v as an independent variable. (However, see Chap. XVII, Sec. **21**.) Thus the functions plotted in Fig. 4 are

$$\psi_n = \frac{1}{\pi^{\frac{1}{4}}2^{n/2}(n!)^{\frac{1}{2}}} H_n(v)e^{-v^2/2}.$$

We now prove that in non-degenerate systems, the ψ-functions belonging to the discrete energy values are *orthogonal* to each other; that is, whenever m is not equal to n,

$$\int \psi_m \psi_n^* dv = 0. \tag{71}$$

Thus, in the example above,

$$\int_0^{2\pi} \exp[i(m-n)\varphi]d\varphi = 0,$$

if $m \neq n$. Multiplying the wave equation for ψ_m by ψ_n^*, we have

$$\psi_n^* \Delta \psi_m + \frac{8\pi^2}{h^2}(E_m - V)\psi_m \psi_n^* = 0$$

and multiplying the equation for ψ_n^* by ψ_m,

$$\psi_m \Delta \psi_n^* + \frac{8\pi^2}{h^2}(E_n - V)\psi_m \psi_n^* = 0.$$

Subtracting, and integrating over the whole coordinate space,

$$\int \left(\psi_n^* \Delta \psi_m - \psi_m \Delta \psi_n^* + \frac{8\pi^2}{h^2}(E_m - E_n)\psi_m \psi_n^* \right) dv = 0. \tag{72}$$

We now transform the first two terms into a surface integral by the aid of Green's theorem.[1] This surface integral vanishes, as we can see from the wave equation. For example, consider a case in which the coordinate space extends to infinity, and in which $V = 0$ at infinity. The nature of the wave function at infinity is ascertained by leaving V out of the wave equation. It behaves like $\exp(-\alpha r)$, where α is real and positive because we have restricted the discussion to the discrete energy spectrum. On carrying out the integration, we find that the surface integral vanishes. In all cases in which this occurs, we have

$$\int (E_m - E_n)\psi_m \psi_n^* dv = 0,$$

and since we are dealing with a non-degenerate system $E_m \neq E_n$, so that equation (71) must be true. The same proof will apply to a degenerate system as long as we deal with energy levels which do not coincide; but when $E_m = E_n$, we proceed as follows: Suppose there are r distinct functions $\psi_{m1} \ldots \psi_{mr}$ which are acceptable solutions of equation (28)

---

[1] JEANS, "Electricity and Magnetism," 4th ed., p. 156, Cambridge Univ. Press, Cambridge (1920).

when $E = E_m$. We introduce r new functions F_{mj} defined by the relations

$$F_{m1} = k_{11}\psi_{m1} + k_{12}\psi_{m2} + \cdots + k_{1r}\psi_{mr}$$
$$F_{mj} = k_{j1}\psi_{m1} + k_{j2}\psi_{m2} + \cdots + k_{jr}\psi_{mr}$$

and seek to determine the k's in such a way that

$$\int F_{mp}F_{mq}{}^* dv = 0 \tag{73}$$

wherever p is not q. The equations (73) are fewer in number than the k's, so they can be satisfied in an infinite number of ways. We shall always suppose this has been done, so that in all problems the ψ's are normal and orthogonal.[1] Sets of normal orthogonal functions which are important in atomic physics are described in Appendix IV.

It is also convenient to normalize the sum of characteristic functions occurring in equation (67). That is, having arranged that equations (68), and (71) hold true for the individual functions Ψ_n, we require that

$$1 = \int \psi\psi^* dv$$
$$= \sum_n \sum_p c_n c_p{}^* \int \Psi_n \Psi_p{}^* dv. \tag{74}$$

Since the last integral is zero unless $n = p$, in which case it is 1, we get

$$\sum_n c_n c_n{}^* = 1. \tag{75}$$

We can easily show that if equation (74) is satisfied at a given instant, it is true at all other times. Multiplying equation (65) by Ψ^* and equation (66) by Ψ, and subtracting, we have

$$-\left(\frac{h}{4\pi i}\right)(\Psi^*\Delta\Psi - \Psi\Delta\Psi^*) = \Psi^*\frac{\partial \Psi}{\partial t} + \Psi\frac{\partial \Psi^*}{\partial t} = \frac{\partial}{\partial t}(\Psi\Psi^*). \tag{76}$$

Integrating,

$$-\left(\frac{h}{4\pi i}\right)\int (\Psi^*\Delta\Psi - \Psi\Delta\Psi^*) dv = \frac{\partial}{\partial t}\int \Psi\Psi^* dv. \tag{77}$$

Transforming the first integral into an integral over the boundaries of the space by Green's theorem, we find it is zero, for the reasons mentioned in connection with equation (72). Now $\int \Psi\Psi^* dv$ is a function of t alone, for the coordinates disappear in the integration; so its partial time derivative is identical with its total time derivative, and it is constant with respect to time.

In writing down the solution, equation (67), of the wave equation (65), we have not included characteristic functions corresponding to energy values which are distributed continuously, for reasons of convenience. We shall say that such characteristic functions lie in the continuous spectrum, meaning by this the "spectrum" of energy values.

---

[1] A method of finding the functions F_{mj} is given in COURANT-HILBERT's "Methoden der mathematischen Physik," Vol. 1, p. 35, Springer, Berlin (1924).

If we write $\psi(E, x)$ for such a function, then $\psi(E, x)dE$ is a solution of the wave equation, where dE is infinitesimal, and the sum of any number of such solutions, each multiplied by an arbitrary function of the energy, $C(E)$, let us say, will also be a solution. Therefore, we must add

$$\int C(E)\psi(E, x)dE \qquad (67a)$$

to the right side of equation (67) in order to get a more general wave function. Ordinarily, we shall use only the solution of equation (67) in the remainder of this chapter, to shorten our equations. In Chap. XVIII, on the other hand, where we are concerned mostly with problems of aperiodic motion, such as that of a free electron, nearly all the formulas will be written without including discrete wave functions.

We must now set up a more comprehensive normalization and orthogonality equation. If ψ_n is a wave function of the discrete spectrum and ψ_E is one belonging to the continuous spectrum, then we can prove that

$$\int \psi_n \left(\int_E^{E+\Delta E} \psi_E{}^* dE \right) dv = 0, \qquad (71a)$$

and that

$$\lim_{\Delta E \to 0} \frac{1}{\Delta E} \int \left(\int_E^{E+\Delta E} \psi_E dE \right) \left(\int_{E'}^{E'+\Delta E'} \psi_{E'}{}^* dE' \right) dv = 1 \text{ or } 0, \qquad (68a)$$

according as ΔE and $\Delta E'$ do or do not overlap. This rule may be replaced by the equation

$$\lim_{\Delta E \to 0} \int \psi^*{}_{E'} \left(\int_E^{E+\Delta E} \psi_E dE \right) dv = \delta(E', \Delta E), \qquad (68b)$$

where $\delta(E', \Delta E)$ equals one if E' lies in ΔE, and equals zero otherwise.

The application of equation (68a) often leads to rather complicated calculations and we shall confine ourselves to one simple example. The wave function for a light quantum moving parallel to the x-axis may be taken as $\psi_E = C \exp\left(\dfrac{2\pi i E x}{hc} \right)$; the element of volume in the q-space reduces to dx, as we can show by considering the definition of ds implied by equation (25). We have,

$$\int_E^{E+\Delta E} \psi_E dE = C \frac{hc}{2\pi i x} \psi_E \left[\exp\left(\frac{2\pi i \Delta E x}{hc} \right) - 1 \right].$$

The integral $\int_E^{E+\Delta E} \psi_E{}^* dE$ is the conjugate of this expression, and their product is

$\dfrac{CC^* h^2 c^2}{2\pi^2 x^2} \left(1 - \cos \dfrac{2\pi \Delta E x}{hc} \right)$. We now integrate this with respect to x, from minus infinity to plus infinity. The result is $CC^* hc \Delta E$. Dividing this by ΔE, we must set the result equal to unity, by equation (68a), so that we have

$$|C|^2 = \frac{1}{hc}.$$

The phase of C is unknown, and may be set equal to zero. Finally,

$$\psi_E = \left(\frac{1}{hc} \right)^{1/2} \exp \left(\frac{2\pi i E x}{hc} \right).$$

[1] Weyl, *Math. Ann.*, **68**, 220 (1910); Fues, *Ann. Physik*, **81**, 281 (1926).

14. SCHRÖDINGER'S INTERPRETATION OF CHARGE AND CURRENT DENSITY IN TERMS OF Ψ

In Sec. 1 we mentioned the theories of Schrödinger and of Born as to the physical interpretation of Ψ. For reasons soon to be explained, we shall refer to these two theories as the *hydrodynamical* and the *statistical* interpretations of quantum dynamics. Schrödinger's idea that ΨΨ* represents charge density, leads easily and directly to methods for computing the polarization and relative intensity of spectral lines, and for this reason we shall use it in some of the illustrations which follow. To avoid complexity, we begin with the problem of one electron, and shall use Cartesian coordinates. Schrödinger's first attempt at a physical interpretation of Ψ^1 was to the effect that $\Psi \partial \Psi^*/\partial t$ is proportional to the electric charge density, and was soon rejected by him. He then found[2] four functions of Ψ and Ψ* which possess a property characteristic of charge density and the three components of current density. If we call these four functions ρ, s_x, s_y, and s_z, then

$$\frac{\partial \rho}{\partial t} + \frac{\partial s_x}{\partial x} + \frac{\partial s_y}{\partial y} + \frac{\partial s_z}{\partial z} = 0, \tag{78}$$

which is the familiar equation of continuity, expressing the fact that electric charge is neither created nor destroyed but simply flows from place to place like a perfect fluid. It is for this reason that Schrödinger's theory is referred to as the hydrodynamical interpretation of wave mechanics. The four functions occurring in equation (78) are

$$\rho = \epsilon \Psi \Psi^* \tag{79}$$

and

$$s_x = \left(\frac{\epsilon h}{4\pi i m}\right)\left(\Psi^* \frac{\partial \Psi}{\partial x} - \Psi \frac{\partial \Psi^*}{\partial x}\right) \tag{80}$$

with similar equations for s_y and s_z; ϵ is the total charge of the particle. To prove that ρ, s_x, etc. can have the forms of equations (79) and (80), we note that equation (76) can be written

$$\frac{\partial}{\partial t}(\Psi \Psi^*) = \frac{-h}{4\pi i m}\left[\frac{\partial}{\partial x}\left(\Psi^* \frac{\partial \Psi}{\partial x} - \Psi \frac{\partial \Psi^*}{\partial x}\right) + \frac{\partial}{\partial y}\left(\Psi^* \frac{\partial \Psi}{\partial y} - \Psi \frac{\partial \Psi^*}{\partial y}\right) + \cdots \right] \tag{81}$$

which is identical in form with equation (78). The introduction of ϵ can be justified as follows: because the attracting center (the nucleus, for example) is assumed to be at rest, its contribution to the Ψ function is suppressed, and $\int \rho dv$ must be equal to the charge of the particle; that is,

$$\epsilon = \epsilon \int \Psi \Psi^* dv,$$

which is verified because Ψ is normalized. It is easily seen that

[1] *Ann. Physik*, **79**, 734 (1926).

[2] *Ann. Physik*, **81**, 109 (1926).

$\Psi^* \dfrac{\partial \Psi}{\partial x} - \Psi \dfrac{\partial \Psi^*}{\partial x}$ is a pure imaginary, for, if we write the first term in the form $a + ib$, the second is $a - ib$. Thus, the components of current density are real, and ρ is also real.

15. SCHRÖDINGER'S THEORY OF RADIATION FROM AN ATOM

Schrödinger assumed that *the radiation from a system with three degrees of freedom is to be obtained by computing the classical field which would be emitted by the charge and current distribution specified in equations (79) and (80)*, in accordance with Chap. VI, Sec. 1. If Ψ is of the form of equation (67), the expression for the electric moment will contain sine or cosine terms which give rise to the emission of frequencies corresponding to quantum jumps between all the states whose eigenfunktions occur in equation (67). Thus, if

$$\Psi = c_1\Psi_1 + c_2\Psi_2,$$

then

$$\Psi\Psi^* = c_1c_1{}^*\psi_1\psi_1{}^* + c_2c_2{}^*\psi_2\psi_2{}^*$$
$$+ c_1c_2{}^*\psi_1\psi_2{}^* \exp\left[-2\pi i(E_1 - E_2)\frac{t}{h}\right]$$
$$+ c_2c_1{}^*\psi_2\psi_1{}^* \exp\left[-2\pi i(E_2 - E_1)\frac{t}{h}\right].$$

Now the coordinates of the electrical center of gravity of the ρ distribution are

$$\bar{x} = \frac{\int x\Psi\Psi^*dv}{\int \Psi\Psi^*dv}, \text{ etc.} \tag{82}$$

By equation (74), the denominator is unity, and so we shall write

$$\bar{x} = \int x\Psi\Psi^*dv, \text{ etc.} \tag{83}$$

Substituting the above expression for $\Psi\Psi^*$ in equation (83), we see that the electric moment will contain constant terms, which contribute nothing to the radiation, and periodic terms with the frequency $\nu(12)$. More generally we have

$$\Psi\Psi^* = \sum_j \sum_k c_j c_k{}^* \exp\left[-2\pi i(E_j - E_k)\frac{t}{h}\right], \tag{84}$$

where j and k both vary from 1 to ∞. The frequencies occurring in the electric moment are therefore given by $E_j - E_k = h\nu(jk)$ so that *the emission frequencies are differences of the motional frequencies of the matter waves*, analogous to beat notes in the case of sound. If Ψ reduces to a single term, let us say

$$\Psi = c_n\Psi_n,$$

which means that only one "overtone" of the matter waves is excited, then we have

$$\rho = \epsilon c_n c_n{}^* \psi_n \psi_n{}^*. \tag{85}$$

In equation (84), $c_j c_k^*$ determines the amplitude of the emission frequency $\nu(jk)$, and c_j and c_k may be thought of as measuring the strength of excitation of components in the ψ waves having frequencies E_j/h and E_k/h, respectively. On this interpretation, however, each atom may radiate several frequencies simultaneously, and the relative intensities of its spectral lines would depend on the values of the c's. Further, the relative intensities of the spectral lines emitted by an aggregate of atoms will depend on averages of the c's, and of products and powers of the c's, for all the atoms, as well as on the phases of the contributions from the individual atoms. If the consequences of this view are consistently followed out, one arrives at results which do not agree with experiment (Chap. XX, Sec. 1), so that we have good reasons for interpreting the c's in another manner introduced by Born. This interpretation forms the basis for the statistical theory of quantum mechanics, and will now be explained.

16. BORN'S INTERPRETATION OF Ψ[1]

In Chap. III, Sec. **13**, we explained that the theory of light quanta and Maxwell's theory of light can be synthesized into a consistent body of truth if we assume that the electromagnetic field serves as a "ghost field" or "guiding field," which determines the probability that a quantum shall take a certain path. In fact, at any point x, y, z, $E^2(x, y, z)dxdydz$ is a measure of the number of quanta which are located in the volume element $dxdydz$. The idea suggests itself that when we are dealing with an assembly of electrons far enough apart so that the interaction is negligible, the function $\Psi\Psi^*(x, y, z)dv$ is equal to the fraction of the electrons which have coordinates lying in the volume element, dv, of the Schrödinger space. As in Sec. **2**, dv equals $m^{3/2}dxdydz$. More generally, if we are dealing with an aggregate of independent systems described by coordinates q_r, it is assumed that $\Psi\Psi^*(q_1 \ldots q_n)\rho dq_1 \ldots dq_n$ *is the fraction of the systems having their coordinates in the ranges q_1 to $q_1 + dq_1$, $\cdots$ q_n to $q_n + dq_n$,* where $\rho dq_1 \cdots dq_n$ is the volume element of the Schrödinger space. This expression is said to be the probability that a given system shall have its coordinates in the range specified. For brevity, we shall often denote it by $P(q)dv$ where q stands for the group of coordinates $q_1 \ldots q_n$, and shall also use the notation,

$$P_{nm} \equiv \Psi_n^* \Psi_m. \tag{86}$$

If Ψ is of the form of equation (67), then in accordance with equation (74) it is so normalized that $\int Pdv$ is unity, as it should be. Further, if N is the number of atoms in the aggregate,

$$N \int Pdv = N \Sigma c_n c_n^* \int \Psi_n \Psi_n^* dv = N \Sigma c_n c_n^*,$$

[1] *Z. Physik*, **37**, 863; **38**, 803; and **40**, 167 (1926).

by equation (75), which we interpret as meaning that the number of atoms in the nth quantum state is

$$Nc_n c_n^*; \tag{87}$$

and further the number in the nth quantum state having coordinates in the element $dq_1 \ldots dq_n$ will be

$$Nc_n c_n^* \Psi_n \Psi_n^* dv. \tag{88}$$

This interpretation of the c's and of Ψ leads easily to a host of interesting results. The function ψ is no longer characteristic of a single atom, but describes the statistical behavior of an assemblage. For example, the electron of the H atom can be *anywhere* with respect to the nucleus, and from equation (88) the probability that it be in a given element dx, dy, dz when the atom is in the nth quantum state is

$$\Psi_n \Psi_n^* dv \equiv P_{nn} dv. \tag{89}$$

It is satisfactory to find that P_{nn} is very small outside the region which we should expect the atom to occupy on Bohr's theory, when it is in the nth state.

17. SELECTION PRINCIPLES, POLARIZATION RULES, AND SPECTRAL INTENSITIES

Whether we speak in the language of Schrödinger or of Born, the *analytical apparatus* for computing the intensity of a spectral line is assumed to be as follows in the one-electron problem:

We calculate a quantity which is analogous to the x-component of the electric moment of an oscillator on the classical theory, namely,

$$M_x(nm) = \epsilon \int x \psi_n^* \psi_m dv \exp 2\pi i \nu(nm)t$$
$$+ \epsilon \int x \psi_n \psi_m^* dv \exp(-2\pi i \nu(nm)t), \tag{90}$$

and similar expressions for $M_y(nm)$ and $M_z(nm)$. $M_x(nm)$ is real because the second term is the conjugate of the first. If it happens that

$$\int x \psi_n^* \psi_m dv = 0, \tag{91}$$

then there is no term in the x-component of the electric moment with frequency $\nu(nm)$, and we should expect no radiation of that frequency polarized parallel to the x-axis; thus we can arrive at a *selection principle* by determining under what conditions equation (91) will vanish. Also the polarization of the line $\nu(nm)$ is determined from the values and relative phases of $M_x(nm)$, $M_y(nm)$, and $M_z(nm)$. According to Schrödinger[1] and Eckart,[2] the intensity of the line $\nu(nm)$ is determined as follows in close analogy to the corresponding computation in classical theory (Chap. VI, Sec. 1). The instantaneous rate of emission of energy with the electric vector parallel to the x-axis is proportional to

$$I_x = \frac{2}{3c^3}[2\pi\nu(nm)]^4 |M_x(nm)|^2. \tag{92}$$

[1] *Ann. Physik*, **79**, 734 (1926).
[2] *Phys. Rev.*, **28**, 711 (1926).

Similar equations hold for the energy radiated with electric vector parallel to the y- and z-axes. We are now prepared to illustrate these equations by applying them to the one-dimensional rotator, which is chosen because it is the simplest example available, although it is not strictly correct to use it in computing radiation intensities in three-dimensional space.

18. SELECTION PRINCIPLE, POLARIZATION RULE, AND INTENSITY COMPUTATIONS FOR THE ROTATOR

For the one-dimensional rotator, by equation (70),

$$\psi_m = (4\pi^2 I)^{-\frac{1}{4}} \exp im\varphi,$$

I being the moment of inertia. We assume that φ is measured positively in the xy plane, so that the z-component of electric moment is zero. Neglecting time factors, the x-component of the center of gravity of the charge consists of terms of the type

$$x(nm) \equiv \int x\psi_n{}^*\psi_m dv = \frac{1}{2\pi}\int x \exp i(m-n)\varphi d\varphi,$$

since $dv = I^{\frac{1}{2}}d\varphi$. Now let the rotator consist of a charge ϵ moving on a circle of radius r. We have

$$x = r \cos \varphi = \frac{r}{2}[\exp i\varphi + \exp(-i\varphi)]$$

$$y = r \sin \varphi = \frac{r}{2i}[\exp i\varphi - \exp(-i\varphi)],$$

so

$$x(nm) = \frac{r}{4\pi}\left[\int \exp(m-n+1)i\varphi d\varphi + \int \exp(m-n-1)i\varphi d\varphi\right], \quad (93)$$

$$y(nm) = \frac{r}{4\pi i}\left[\int \exp(m-n+1)i\varphi d\varphi - \int \exp(m-n-1)i\varphi d\varphi\right]. \quad (94)$$

The integrals extend from 0 to 2π. In equation (93), the first integral vanishes unless

$$m - n + 1 = 0,$$

when it equals 2π; and the second vanishes unless

$$m - n - 1 = 0,$$

when it equals 2π; so we find that

$$x(nm) = \frac{r}{2} \text{ when } n = m \pm 1. \quad (95)$$

Similarly,

$$y(nm) = \frac{r}{2i} \text{ when } n = m + 1$$

and

$$= -\frac{r}{2i} \text{when } n = m - 1. \quad (96)$$

Further, letting $x(mn) = \int x\psi_m{}^*\psi_n dv$, we see that $x(nm)$ and $y(nm)$ are, respectively, the complex conjugates of $x(mn)$ and $y(mn)$. Thus we see that $M_x(nm)$ and $M_y(nm)$ are zero except when $\Delta m = \pm 1$, the selection principle for the rotator.

Let us now study the polarization of its radiation. To do this, we need the values of $M_x(nm)$ and $M_y(nm)$. Referring to equation (90), and using the values given in equation (95), we have

$$M_x (m - 1, m) = \left(\frac{\epsilon r}{2}\right)(e^{-2\pi i \nu(m-1, m)t} + e^{2\pi i \nu(m-1, m)t}) = \tag{97}$$

$$\epsilon r \cos 2\pi \nu(m - 1, m)t,$$

$$M_x(m + 1, m) = \epsilon r \cos 2\pi \nu (m + 1, m)t.$$

Also remembering that $i = e^{\pi i/2}$, we find with the aid of equation (96) that

$$M_y(m - 1, m) = -\epsilon r \sin 2\pi \nu(m - 1, m)t,$$

$$M_y(m + 1, m) = \epsilon r \sin 2\pi \nu(m + 1, m)t. \tag{98}$$

These equations show that the light emitted and absorbed is circularly polarized, for the x- and y-components of the electric moment are equal for each transition. The electric moment components for the transition from $m + 1$ to m show that the light emitted has its electric vector revolving in the same sense as the rotator itself, while the first equations of (97) and (98) represent the absorption of circularly polarized light rotating in the same sense. As to intensities, putting ϵ equal to the electronic charge we have, from equation (92),

$$I_x(m \pm 1, m) = \frac{32\pi^4 e^2}{3c^3} \nu(m \pm 1, m)^4 r^2 \cos^2 2\pi \nu(m \pm 1, m)t, \tag{99}$$

and there is a similar expression for $I_y(m \pm 1, m)$. The subject of spectral intensities is developed in detail in Chap. XX. We now turn our attention to generalizations of the wave equation and to perturbation methods.

19. THE RELATIVISTIC WAVE EQUATION

The wave equation is easily modified to take account of the variation of mass with velocity. Just as in Sec. **2**, the principle of least action for the dynamical system is interpreted as a principle of least time, like that of Fermat, to determine the rays of the matter waves. We proceed to study the motion of the W surfaces, the wave fronts, using the Hamilton-Jacobi equation in the form appropriate to relativity mechanics. Confining our remarks to the case where no magnetic forces act on the particle, this is (Appendix VIII, Sec. **2**),

$$\left(\frac{\partial W}{\partial x}\right)^2 + \left(\frac{\partial W}{\partial y}\right)^2 + \left(\frac{\partial W}{\partial z}\right)^2 - \left(\frac{\mathcal{E} - V}{c}\right)^2 + m^2 c^2 = 0. \tag{101}$$

where $\mathcal{E} = mc^2 + E = mc^2 + T + V$, T and V being the kinetic and potential energies, respectively. Now the velocity of the W surfaces is obtained exactly as it was in Sec. **3**, the result being

$$u = \frac{\text{Energy}}{\text{Momentum}} = \frac{c\mathcal{E}}{[(\mathcal{E} - V)^2 - m^2 c^4]^{\frac{1}{2}}}, \tag{102}$$

and the wave equation is

$$\Delta\Psi - \frac{(\mathcal{E} - V)^2 - m^2c^4}{c^2\mathcal{E}^2}\frac{\partial^2\Psi}{\partial t^2} = 0. \tag{103}$$

Writing

$$\Psi = \psi\exp\left(\frac{-2\pi i\mathcal{E}t}{h}\right)$$

we get

$$\Delta\psi + \frac{4\pi^2}{h^2c^2}[(\mathcal{E} - V)^2 - m^2c^4]\psi = 0. \tag{104}$$

This reduces to the non-relativistic wave equation (28), as it should, when E/mc^2 is small, for we have

$$(\mathcal{E} - V)^2 - m^2c^4 = (mc^2 + E - V)^2 - m^2c^4 \cong 2mc^{\text{L}}(E - V).$$

Substituting this in equation (104), we get the old form of the wave equation.

If we take the energy of the nucleus Mc^2 into account, the total energy of the atom is $E + (m + M)c^2$, and the frequency of the waves is seen to be equal to this energy divided by h. Except in the case of the free electron, the frequency of the waves lies beyond the gamma-ray region. For the hydrogen atom, the frequency Mc^2/h corresponds to a wave length of 1.3 10^{-5} Å. This must not be confused with the wave length h/Mv of the matter waves associated with an atom having velocity v.

20. THE GENERAL WAVE EQUATION FOR A SINGLE PARTICLE

In obtaining this equation we introduce a method which makes use of a variational principle. The result is very convenient in practice for it enables us to establish the following generalization of the rule given in Sec. **10.**

In the Hamilton-Jacobi equation, written out in full, using Cartesian coordinates, replace

$$\frac{\partial W}{\partial x} \text{ by } \frac{h}{2\pi i}\frac{\partial}{\partial x}, \text{ etc., and } -E, \text{ or } \frac{\partial W}{\partial t} \text{ by } \frac{h}{2\pi i}\frac{\partial}{\partial t}. \tag{105}$$

Apply the operator thus formed to Ψ, *and the result is the wave equation.*

We use a method, due to Fock,[1] starting with a simple example. In the Hamilton-Jacobi equation for a single particle in a conservative force field,

$$\left(\frac{\partial W}{\partial x}\right)^2 + \left(\frac{\partial W}{\partial y}\right)^2 + \left(\frac{\partial W}{\partial z}\right)^2 + 2m\left(V + \frac{\partial W}{\partial t}\right) = 0, \tag{106}$$

we introduce a new dependent variable, Ψ, such that

$$W = f(\Psi).$$

Then if q_i denotes any one of the variables, and $f' = df/d\Psi$,

$$\frac{\partial W}{\partial q_i} = f'\frac{\partial\Psi}{\partial q_i}, \frac{\partial W}{\partial t} = f'\frac{\partial\Psi}{\partial t} = -E. \tag{107}$$

[1] *Z. Physik*, **38**, 242 (1926), and **39**, 226 (1926).

We use the last of these relations to eliminate f' from the others, and then

$$\frac{\partial W}{\partial q_i} = -E\frac{\partial \Psi/\partial q_i}{\partial \Psi/\partial t}. \tag{108}$$

After multiplication by $\dfrac{1}{E^2}\left(\dfrac{\partial \Psi}{\partial t}\right)^2$, equation (106) becomes

$$\sum\left(\frac{\partial \Psi}{\partial q_i}\right)^2 + \frac{2m(V-E)}{E^2}\left(\frac{\partial \Psi}{\partial t}\right)^2 = 0. \tag{109}$$

Let us call the left side of this relation F. The equation $F = 0$ is practically[1] equivalent to equation (106).

Now, instead of requiring that $F = 0$, which leads to the results of the old mechanics, *we introduce a new assumption as a basis for wave mechanics, namely,*

$$\delta \int F dx dy dz dt = 0. \tag{110}$$

The integral is to be taken over the whole range of the space and time variables. The method for determining F by the calculus of variations is given in Appendix VI. It is assumed in solving the problem that for infinite values of the variables, Ψ and its derivatives behave in such a way that the "surface" integral arising in the variation problem is zero. The differential equation which F must obey in order to satisfy equation (110) is,

$$\frac{\partial}{\partial x}\left(\frac{\partial F}{\partial(\partial \psi/\partial x)}\right) + \cdots + \frac{\partial}{\partial t}\left(\frac{\partial F}{\partial(\partial \psi/\partial t)}\right) - \frac{\partial F}{\partial \psi} = 0.$$

Writing this out in full, we obtain equation (25').

The generalization for a particle with charge ϵ moving in any type of electromagnetic field, using relativity mechanics, is evident. From Appendix VIII Sec. **2,** the Hamilton-Jacobi equation takes the form

$$\sum\left(p_j - \frac{\epsilon}{c}A_j\right)^2 - \left(\frac{\mathcal{E}}{c} - \frac{\epsilon\Phi}{c}\right)^2 + m^2c^2 = 0. \tag{111}$$

Using equation (108) and multiplying by $\dfrac{(\partial \Psi/\partial t)^2}{\mathcal{E}^2}$, the form F corresponding to equation (109) in the problem just solved is

$$\sum_j\left(\frac{\partial \Psi}{\partial x_j} - \frac{\epsilon}{c}\frac{A_j}{\mathcal{E}}\frac{\partial \Psi}{\partial t}\right)^2 - \left(\frac{1}{c}\frac{\partial \Psi}{\partial t} - \frac{\epsilon}{c}\frac{\Phi}{\mathcal{E}}\frac{\partial \Psi}{\partial t}\right)^2 + \frac{m^2c^2}{\mathcal{E}^2}\left(\frac{\partial \Psi}{\partial t}\right)^2.$$

The variation problem for this form is solved in detail in Appendix VI, and yields the wave equation,

$$\Delta\Psi - \frac{1}{c^2}\frac{\partial^2\Psi}{\partial t^2} + \frac{2\epsilon}{c\mathcal{E}}\left(\sum A_j\frac{\partial^2\Psi}{\partial x_j\partial t} + \frac{\Phi}{c}\frac{\partial^2\Psi}{\partial t^2}\right) +$$
$$\frac{1}{\mathcal{E}^2}\frac{\partial^2\Psi}{\partial t^2}\left[m^2c^2 + \frac{\epsilon^2}{c^2}(\Sigma A_j^2 - \Phi^2)\right] = 0. \tag{112}$$

---

[1] We use this expression because it may occur that $f(\Psi)$ is a many-valued function; or, it may be indeterminate when Ψ takes certain forms.

Assuming that

$$\Psi = \psi e^{-2\pi i \epsilon t/h}, \tag{113}$$

we eliminate ϵ from equation (112) to get an equation valid for all values of ϵ, possessing all the advantages of equation (65). It is,

$$\Delta\Psi - \frac{1}{c^2}\frac{\partial^2\Psi}{\partial t^2} - \frac{4\pi i\epsilon}{hc}\left(\sum A_j\frac{\partial\Psi}{\partial x_j} + \frac{\Phi}{c}\frac{\partial\Psi}{\partial t}\right) -$$
$$\frac{4\pi^2\Psi}{h^2}\left[m^2c^2 + \frac{\epsilon^2}{c^2}(\Sigma A_j{}^2 - \Phi^2)\right] = 0. \tag{114}$$

This is the general wave equation proposed independently by a number of physicists.[1]

The complex conjugate of Ψ will satisfy an equation which is identical with equation (114) except that i is changed to $-i$ in the coefficient $4\pi i\epsilon/hc$. The simple rule for passing from the Hamilton-Jacobi equation to the wave equation, given at the beginning of this section, is verified directly by applying it to equation (111).

21. EXPANSION OF A FUNCTION IN A SERIES OF Ψ FUNCTIONS

When it is difficult to obtain an exact solution of the wave equation, we are forced to treat it by perturbation methods. As we shall see in the following sections, the solution is usually obtained as a series of acceptable functions. Thus, in a problem involving a single coordinate x, the series representing a function $f(x)$ will be

$$f(x) = \sum_n f_n \psi_n. \tag{115}$$

The constants f_n are called "development coefficients." This is to be considered as a simple generalization of a Fourier series, for the set of functions

$$\sin 2\pi\nu t, \sin 4\pi\nu t, \cdots \cos 2\pi\nu t, \cos 4\pi\nu t, \cdots$$

form a normal orthogonal system, just as the ψ functions do. This property of the functions ψ_n makes it possible to determine the coefficients f_n by the method used for Fourier series. To obtain f_m, for example, we multiply equation (115) by $\psi_m{}^*$ and integrate over the complete range of x; or, if x is a cyclic variable, over a complete cycle of its values. Thus,

$$\int f\psi_m{}^* dx = \sum_n f_n \int \psi_n \psi_m{}^* dx.$$

Because the ψ's are orthogonal, all integrals on the right will vanish except the one for which $n = m$, which equals unity, by equation (68): so

$$f_m = \int f\psi_m{}^* dx. \tag{116}$$

(Just as in the case of Fourier series, the properties of the function f and of the ψ's must be restricted somewhat in order that equations (115) and (116) may be correct. Suppose the function f and its first derivative have

[1] For detailed references see Brillouin, *J. de Phys. et Le Radium*, **8**, 74 (1927).

only a finite number of discontinuities, and do not become infinite.   Then we may be sure that equations (115) and (116) are valid if the series converges for all values of x in the interval of integration and if it represents a function having the properties we have just attributed to f.[1] When the energy spectrum has both discrete and continuous ranges, the characteristic functions ψ_n and ψ_E taken together form a complete orthogonal system, in terms of which an arbitrary function can be expanded.   That is, we have

$$f = \Sigma f_n \psi_n + f_E \psi_E dE. \qquad (115a)$$

We find that $f_n = \int f \psi_n{}^* dx$, just as in the case where all the characteristic functions are discrete.   To get f_E, we multiply equation (115a) by $\left(\int_E^{E+\Delta E} \psi_E{}^* dE \right) dx$ and integrate, with the result that

$$f_E = \int f \psi_E{}^* dx. \qquad (116a)$$

22. SCHRÖDINGER'S PERTURBATION THEORY FOR THE WAVE EQUATION

Especially useful perturbation theories have been devised by Schrödinger, Born, and Brillouin.   We begin with Schrödinger's method,[2] and shall deal first with a non-degenerate system of one degree of freedom which has potential energy $V(x)$ when unperturbed.   Let it be perturbed by forces which add a term $\lambda F(x)$ to V, λ being a small constant, so that the wave equation is

$$\Delta \psi + C(E - V - \lambda F)\psi = 0. \qquad (117)$$

C is an abbreviation for $8\pi^2/h^2$, and x a coordinate in the Schrödinger space.   Suppose the unperturbed problem is solved, and that E_{0k}, and ψ_{0k} are a typical energy value and its corresponding eigenfunktion, respectively, satisfying the equation

$$\Delta \psi_{0k} + C(E_{0k} - V)\psi_{0k} = 0. \qquad (118)$$

We seek for the energy constant and acceptable solution of equation (117) which reduce to E_{0k}, and ψ_{0k} when λ is placed equal to zero.   Let them be

$$E_k = E_{0k} + \lambda \epsilon_k + \cdots, \psi_k = \psi_{0k} + \lambda v_k + \cdots. \qquad (119)$$

Neglecting powers of λ higher than the first in equation (119), and substituting in equation (117), we have

$$\Delta \psi_{0k} + \lambda \Delta v_k + C(E_{0k} + \lambda \epsilon_k - V - \lambda F)(\psi_{0k} + \lambda v_k) = 0.$$

Taking account of equation (118), dropping terms in λ^2, and dividing by λ, we get

$$\Delta v_k + C(E_{0k} - V)v_k = C(F - \epsilon_k)\psi_{0k}. \qquad (120)$$

From this inhomogeneous linear equation containing the energy constant E_{0k} belonging to the equation (118), we wish to determine an acceptable

---

[1] For a detailed discussion see COURANT-HILBERT'S "Methoden der Mathematischen Physik," Vol. 1, Chap. 2.

[2] *Ann. Physik*, **80**, 437 (1927), and "Abhandlongen," p. 88.

value for v_k in order that ψ_k may also be acceptable. *An acceptable value of v_k can be found only if the condition*

$$\int (F - \epsilon_k)\psi_{0k}\psi_{0k}{}^* dx = 0, \tag{121}$$

is satisfied.

Proof.—Multiply both sides of equation (120) by $\psi_{0k}{}^*$, multiply the conjugate of equation (118) by v_k, and subtract one equation from the other. We obtain

$$\psi_{0k}{}^* \Delta v_k - v_k \Delta \psi_{0k}{}^* = C(F - \epsilon_k)\psi_{0k}\psi_{0k}{}^*.$$

Integrating both sides over the entire range of the coordinate x, we have on the left the integral

$$\int (\psi_{0k}{}^* \Delta v_k - v_k \Delta \psi_{0k}{}^*) dx. \tag{122}$$

On integrating by parts, we obtain two terms which vanish at the boundaries, provided v_k is acceptable, so that if these conditions are met, equation (121) is true. Usually, if equation (121) is true, v_k must be acceptable in order that equation (122) may vanish. (Trivial special cases can be constructed in which this is not true.) For a proof based on the theory of linear integral equations, see Courant-Hilbert, "Methoden der Mathematischen Physik, I," p. 277. Springer, Berlin (1924).

From equation (121), we can immediately obtain the value of ϵ_k. Since

$$\epsilon_k \int \psi_{0k}\psi_{0k}{}^* dx = \epsilon_k,$$

ψ_{0k} being normalized, we have

$$\lambda \epsilon_k = \int \lambda F \psi_{0k}\psi_{0k}{}^* dx. \tag{122}$$

Referring to the consideration in Sec **16,** we see the meaning of equation (122). *The change of the energy is equal to the average of the perturbing term in the potential energy, taken over the undisturbed motion,* just as in classical theory. To determine v_k, we assume that it is expressible as a series of the unperturbed eigenfunktions:

$$v_k = \sum_i v_{ki}\psi_{0i}, \tag{123}$$

where the v_{ki} are constants to be determined from equation (120). We also expand the known function $(F - \epsilon_k)\psi_{0k}$ by the method of Sec. **21,** obtaining

$$(F - \epsilon_k)\psi_{0k} = \sum_i c_{ki}\psi_{0i} \tag{124}$$

where

$$c_{ki} = \int (F - \epsilon_k)\psi_{0k}\psi_{0i}{}^* dx. \tag{125}$$

By equation (121),

$$c_{ki} = 0 \text{ when } i = k,$$

and

$$c_{ki} = \int F\psi_{0k}\psi_{0i}{}^* dx \text{ when } i \neq k,$$

since the ψ_0's are orthogonal functions. Putting these expressions into equation (120), we obtain

$$\Sigma v_{ki}\Delta\psi_{0i} + \Sigma v_{ki}C(E_{0k} - V)\psi_{0i} = C\Sigma c_{ki}\psi_{0i}. \tag{126}$$

Now for every value of i,

$$\Delta\psi_{0i} + C(E_{0i} - V)\psi_{0i} = 0$$

and so

$$\Sigma v_{ki}[\Delta\psi_{0i} + C(E_{0i} - V)\psi_{0i}] = 0.$$

The result of subtracting this from equation (126) is

$$\Sigma v_{ki}C(E_{0k} - E_{0i})\psi_{0i} = C\Sigma c_{ki}\psi_{0i}. \tag{127}$$

The coefficients of ψ_{0i} must be the same on both sides, so the equations to determine the coefficients in the expansion of v_k are

$$v_{ki} = \frac{c_{ki}}{(E_{0k} - E_{0i})_j}. \tag{128}$$

The right side becomes indeterminate when $k = i$, so v_{kk} must be found in another way. This is done by so choosing v_{kk} that the perturbed eigenfunktion ψ_k is normalized. This process leads to the result

$$v_{kk} = 0. \tag{128a}$$

Finally, we have,

$$\psi_k = \psi_{0k} + \lambda\sum_i{}'\psi_{0i}\frac{\int F\psi_{0k}\psi_{0i}{}^*dx}{E_{0k} - E_{0i}}, \tag{129}$$

where the prime denotes the omission of the term $i = k$ from the summation.

For the extension of this method to systems with several degrees of freedom we refer the reader to Schrödinger's original paper or to his "Abhandlungen." The method is nearly the same as above for non-degenerate systems, except that multiple summations replace the single-fold summations. When degenerate systems are studied, however, new phenomena are encountered. If the r distinct ψ functions

$$\psi_{j1}, \ldots \psi_{jr}$$

belong to the energy value E_j, then in the perturbed system we encounter r new energy values and r new ψ functions corresponding to them. In Chap. XIX this perturbation method is applied to the problem of finding the energy levels of the diatomic molecule. The reader desirous of other illustrations may examine Schrödinger's treatment of the Stark effect of hydrogen, and of dispersion.[1]

23. BORN'S PERTURBATION METHOD

The procedure discussed above is not suitable for the study of perturbations which depend on the time. We shall describe a method devised by Born[2] which avoids this difficulty. The wave equation for the perturbed system is taken in the form of equation (65):

$$\Delta\Psi - C(V + \lambda F)\Psi + \left(\frac{4\pi i}{h}\right)\cdot\frac{\partial\Psi}{\partial t} = 0. \tag{130}$$

[1] *Ann. Physik,* **80,** 437 (1926) and **81,** 109 (1926).

[2] *Z. Physik* **40.** 167 (1926).

Suppose the solution is

$$\Psi_0(x, t) = \Sigma c_k \Psi_{0k}(x, t), \tag{131}$$

where

$$\Psi_{0k}(x, t) = \psi_{0k}(x) \exp\left(-\frac{2\pi i E_k t}{h}\right), \tag{132}$$

when the perturbing force is absent. To obtain the solution for the perturbed system, we need only consider the change in one of the acceptable functions, let us say $\Psi_{0k}(x, t)$; for, if this function is altered to $\Psi_k(x, t)$, then the solution of equation (131), as a whole, takes the form

$$\Psi(x, t) = \Sigma c_k \Psi_k(x, t), \tag{133}$$

because the wave equation is linear. Accordingly, we take up this simplified problem, and begin by expanding the perturbed acceptable function $\Psi_k(x, t)$ in a series proceeding by ascending powers of λ:

$$\Psi_k = \Psi_{0k} + \lambda \Psi_{1k} + \lambda^2 \Psi_{2k} + \cdots \tag{134}$$

Now the expression obtained by substituting this in the wave equation must be zero for all values of λ, so the coefficient of each power of λ must vanish. Setting these coefficients equal to zero gives us the following approximation equations:

$$\Delta\Psi_{0k} - CV\Psi_{0k} + \left(\frac{4\pi i}{h}\right) \cdot \frac{\partial \Psi_{0k}}{\partial t} = 0,$$

$$\Delta\Psi_{1k} - CV\Psi_{1k} + \left(\frac{4\pi i}{h}\right) \cdot \frac{\partial \Psi_{1k}}{\partial t} = CF\Psi_{0k}, \tag{135}$$

$$\Delta\Psi_{pk} - CV\Psi_{pk} + \left(\frac{4\pi i}{h}\right) \cdot \frac{\partial \Psi_{pk}}{\partial t} = CF\Psi_{p-1,k}.$$

The solution of the first equation is equation (132). To obtain Ψ_{1k}, we expand it in the form

$$\Psi_{1k} = \sum_j f_{1kj}(t)\psi_{0j}(x) \exp\left(-\frac{2\pi i E_j t}{h}\right) \tag{136}$$

and also expand the function $F(x, t)\psi_{01k}(x)$, by a slightly different method, as follows:

$$F(x, t)\psi_{0k}(x) = \sum_j F_{kj}(t)\psi_{0j}(x).$$

Then we have

$$F\Psi_{0k} = \left\{\sum_j F_{kj}(t)\psi_{0j}(x)\right\} \exp\left(-\frac{2\pi i E_k t}{h}\right). \tag{137}$$

Substituting equations (136) and (137) in the differential equation for Ψ_{1k}, we have

$$\sum_j f_{1kj}(t) \exp\left(\frac{-2\pi i E_j t}{h}\right) \cdot \{\Delta\psi_{0j} - CV\psi_{0j} + CE_j\psi_{0j}\}$$

$$+ \left(\frac{4\pi i}{h}\right)\sum_j \frac{df_{1kj}}{dt}\psi_{0j} \exp\left(-\frac{2\pi i E_j t}{h}\right) = C\left(\sum_j F_{kj}(t)\psi_{0j}\right) \exp\left(-\frac{2\pi i E_k t}{h}\right).$$

Each term in the first line of this equation vanishes, because each function ψ_{0j} is a solution of the wave equation (28), so that the term in curved brackets is zero for each value of j; and in the second line, the coefficient of ψ_{0j} on the left side must be the same as its coefficient on the right side. Therefore, we can write an equation of the following type for each value of j:

$$\left(\frac{h}{2\pi i}\right)\frac{df_{1kj}}{dt} + F_{kj}(t) \exp\left[-2\pi i\nu(kj)t\right] = 0. \tag{138}$$

Let us now assume that the system is initially unperturbed, and let us choose the time origin at the instant when the disturbance begins. This means that we should seek the solution of equation (138) which vanishes when $t = 0$, so that Ψ_{1k} will be zero when $t = 0$. This solution is

$$\left(\frac{h}{2\pi i}\right)f_{1kj} + \int_0^t F_{kj}(a) \exp\left[-2\pi i\nu(kj)a\right]da = 0, \tag{139}$$

a being simply a variable of integration introduced to avoid confusion with t. This gives us all the material needed to find Ψ_{1k} from equation (136). The procedure for getting higher approximations is similar. We expand Ψ_{pk}, obtaining

$$\Psi_{pk} = \sum_j f_{pkj}(t)\psi_{0j}(x) \exp\left(-\frac{2\pi i E_j t}{h}\right), \tag{140}$$

and also expand $F\Psi_{p-1,k}$ according to the plan used above for $F\Psi_{0k}$. The result, analogous to equation (139), is

$$\left(\frac{h}{2\pi i}\right)f_{pkj} + \int_0^t \sum_s f_{(p-1),ks}(a)F_{sj}(a) \exp\left[-2\pi i\nu(sj)a\right]da = 0, \tag{141}$$

from which we can construct Ψ_{pk}.

24. THE RELATION OF WAVE MECHANICS AND ORDINARY MECHANICS

By a change of the dependent variable, the wave equation can be brought to a form which we recognize as a generalization of the Hamilton-Jacobi equation. To show this, let us consider the Hamilton-Jacobi equation in the form of equation (109). The wave equation corresponding to it is (25′), and assuming that we are dealing with solutions of the form (26), we may replace equation (25′) by equation (28).

It must be understood that the value of Ψ found from the wave equation (28) is not the same as that which would be found by solving the transformed Hamilton-Jacobi equation (109). To avoid confusion, it will be convenient to call the classical Hamiltonian function W_0. Then the variable Ψ_0 which occurs in equation (109) is defined by $W_0 = f(\Psi_0)$; on the other hand, Ψ is determined from the wave equation, and a generalized Hamiltonian function W can then be defined by the relation

$$W = f(\Psi). \tag{142}$$

We must now demonstrate that Ψ reduces to Ψ_0, and W to W_0, when we deal with systems so large or quantum numbers so great that terms containing h can be neglected. This means that the results of wave mechanics approach those of ordinary mechanics if we allow h to approach zero. This proof can be carried out by changing the dependent variable in the wave equation (28) from Ψ to W, by the aid of equation (142). For simplicity, we shall take the wave equation in Cartesian coordinates and shall deal with only a special case of equation (142), namely

$$W = \frac{h}{2\pi i} \log \Psi,$$

which is by far the most usual transformation considered.[1] The result is,

$$\left(\frac{\partial W}{\partial x}\right)^2 + \left(\frac{\partial W}{\partial y}\right)^2 + \left(\frac{\partial W}{\partial z}\right)^2 + 2m(V - E) + \frac{h}{2\pi i}\Delta W = 0. \quad (143)$$

Obviously, when h approaches zero, this reduces to the ordinary Hamilton-Jacobi equation, and the solution W must reduce to W_0. This brings out clearly the fact that *wave mechanics is a rational generalization of ordinary mechanics.*[2]

Considerable light can be thrown on the nature of the wave equation, by using a series solution for W. Let us assume that

$$W = W_0 + \frac{h}{2\pi i}W_1 + \left(\frac{h}{2\pi i}\right)^2 W_2 + \cdots \quad (144)$$

The result of substituting this into equation (143) is

$$\left(\frac{\partial W_0}{\partial x}\right)^2 + \cdots + 2m(V - E)$$

$$+ \frac{h}{2\pi i}\left[2\left(\frac{\partial W_0}{\partial x}\frac{\partial W_1}{\partial x} + \frac{\partial W_0}{\partial y}\frac{\partial W_1}{\partial y} + \frac{\partial W_0}{\partial z}\frac{\partial W_1}{\partial z}\right) + \Delta W_0\right]$$

$$+ \left(\frac{h}{2\pi i}\right)^2\left[\left(2\frac{\partial W_0}{\partial x}\frac{\partial W_2}{\partial x} + \frac{\partial W_1}{\partial x}\frac{\partial W_1}{\partial x} + \cdots \right) + \Delta W_1\right] + \text{etc.}$$

$$+ \left(\frac{h}{2\pi i}\right)^n\left[\sum_{j=o}^{j=n}\left(\frac{\partial W_j}{\partial x}\frac{\partial W_{n-j}}{\partial x} + \frac{\partial W_j}{\partial y}\frac{\partial W_{n-j}}{\partial y} + \frac{\partial W_j}{\partial z}\frac{\partial W_{n-j}}{\partial z}\right) + \right.$$

$$\left. \Delta W_{n-1}\right] + \text{etc.} = 0. \quad (145)$$

This equation holds true for all values of h, so that the coefficient of every power of h must vanish. Setting the coefficient of the zero

---

[1] This treatment is modelled on that of Brillouin, C. R., **183**, 24 (1926), and Debye, *Physik. Z.*, **28**, 170 (1927).

[2] Bramley (*J.* Franklin Institute, **206**, 605 (1928)) has obtained the exact solution of the wave equation (143) in several problems involving a single electron. He has pointed out in some detail the properties of the function, $p = \partial W/\partial x$, which reduces to the x-component of momentum, when h approaches zero.

power of h equal to zero gives the Hamilton-Jacobi equation for the corresponding classical system. Having solved it for W_0, we get W_1 from

$$2\left(\frac{\partial W_0}{\partial x}\frac{\partial W_1}{\partial x} + \frac{\partial W_0}{\partial y}\frac{\partial W_1}{\partial y} + \frac{\partial W_0}{\partial z}\frac{\partial W_1}{\partial z}\right) + \Delta W_0 = 0. \qquad (146)$$

W_0 is real; imaginaries do not enter in the perturbation equations. so all the other W_n's may be taken as real.   To a first approximation, the wave function takes the form

$$\Psi = e^{2\pi i W_0/h}e^{W_1} \qquad (147)$$

so that W_0 determines the phase of the waves and W_1 their amplitude. As an illustration, let us construct the function Ψ for a particle having one degree of freedom.   By equation (146),

$$\frac{dW_1}{dx} = \frac{-\dfrac{d^2W_0}{dx^2}}{2\dfrac{dW_0}{dx}},$$

and

$$W_1 = \text{Const. log}\left(\frac{dW_0}{dx}\right)^{-\frac{1}{2}},$$

but

$$\frac{dW_0}{dx} = [2m(E - V)]^{\frac{1}{2}}, \text{ from equation (145)},$$

and therefore,

$$e^{W_1} = \frac{\text{const.}}{[2m(E - V)]^{\frac{1}{4}}}. \qquad (148)$$

This tells us, in an approximate way, how the amplitude of the waves changes from point to point in space.   Now $[2m(E - V)]^{\frac{1}{4}}$ is equal to $p^{\frac{1}{2}}$, where p is the momentum which the particle would have in the corresponding classical motion, and so

$$\Psi\Psi^* = e^{2W_1} = \frac{\text{const.}}{p}. \qquad (149)$$

The probability Pdx that the particle is in the range x to $x + dx$ is proportional to $\Psi\Psi^*dx$, so we have

$$Pdx \sim \frac{dx}{m\left(\dfrac{dx}{dt}\right)} \sim dt. \qquad (150)$$

This relation states that in an assembly of particles the number which are found in the range dx is proportional to the time which one of the particles would spend in that element according to the classical theory.   This result is modified, of course, when we use higher approximations in determining Ψ.   It is worth noting that the next two approximations to Ψ introduce the factors $e^{W_2h/2\pi i}$ and $e^{W_3(h/2\pi i)^2}$ on the right of equation

(147).   The first of these does not alter the validity of equation (150). The importance of the second is determined by the magnitude of $W_3 h^2 / 4\pi^2 W_1$. This term is often so small that equation (150) is an excellent approximation.

References

BIRTWISTLE, G., "The New Quantum Mechanics," Cambridge University Press (1928).

BORN, MAX, "Problems of Atomic Dynamics," Massachusetts Institute of Technology, Cambridge, Mass. (1926).

DE BROGLIE, L., "Ondes et mouvements," Gauthier-Villars, Paris (1926).

DARROW, K. K., "Introduction to Wave Mechanics," *Bell System Technical Journal*, **6**, 653–701 (1927).

HAAS, ARTHUR, "Materiewellen und Quantenmechanik," Leipzig (1928).

A number of SCHRÖDINGER's original papers have been published as a volume entitled "Abhandlungen zur Wellenmechanik," Barth, Leipzig.   The following are in *Ann. der Physik:*

"Quantisierung als Eigenwertproblem," Parts I, II, III, and IV, **79**, 361 and 489; **80**, 437, and **81**, 109; "Uber das Verhältnis der Heisenberg-Born-Jordanschen Quantenmechanik zu der meinen," **79**, 734; See also a general summary in *Phys. Rev.*, **28**; 1049 (1926).

CONDON and MORSE, "Quantum Mechanics," McGraw-Hill Book Company, Inc., New York (1929).

CHAPTER XVI

HYDROGENIC ATOMS IN WAVE MECHANICS

The study of the hydrogenic atom in wave mechanics is important because it furnishes us with a series of exact solutions of the wave equation which are suitable as starting points for investigating other atoms by perturbation methods, and because it enables us to test accurately the agreement of wave mechanics and the results of experiment. In this chapter we shall be concerned solely with the energy values and acceptable functions, except that selection principles are discussed. Intensity questions are postponed to Chap. XX.

1. ENERGY VALUES, NEGLECTING RELATIVITY

The solution of the problem of the hydrogenic atom in wave mechanics is as follows: The wave equation is separable in polar coordinates, and also in parabolic coordinates. In polar coordinates, it is

$$\frac{1}{r^2}\frac{\partial}{\partial r}\left(r^2\frac{\partial\psi}{\partial r}\right) + \frac{1}{r^2}\left[\frac{1}{\sin\theta}\frac{\partial}{\partial\theta}\left(\sin\theta\frac{\partial\psi}{\partial\theta}\right) + \frac{1}{\sin^2\varphi}\frac{\partial^2\psi}{\partial\varphi^2}\right]$$
$$+ \frac{8\pi^2 m}{h^2}\left(E + \frac{Ze^2}{r}\right)\psi = 0. \quad (1)$$

The solution will be of the form

$$\psi = R(r)S(\theta, \varphi).$$

Substituting in equation (1) and dividing by RS, the equation falls into two parts, one of which contains only r while the other contains only θ and φ. These two parts are set equal to $l(l + 1)$ and $-l(l + 1)$, respectively. Then,

$$\frac{1}{\sin\theta}\cdot\frac{\partial}{\partial\theta}\left(\sin\theta\frac{\partial S}{\partial\theta}\right) + \frac{1}{\sin^2\varphi}\frac{\partial^2 S}{\partial\varphi^2} + l(l + 1)S = 0; \quad (2)$$

$$\frac{d^2 R}{dr^2} + \frac{2}{r}\frac{dR}{dr} + \left(\frac{8\pi^2 mE}{h^2} + \frac{8\pi^2 mZe^2}{h^2 r} - \frac{l(l + 1)}{r^2}\right)R = 0. \quad (3)$$

The reason for using the constant $l(l + 1)$ is that it must be of this form with

$$l = 0, 1, 2, 3, \cdots$$

if S is to be an acceptable function. Equation (2) was solved in Chap. XV, Sec. 8 with the result that

$$S = e^{im\varphi}P_{l,m}(\cos\theta),$$

where $l \geqq m$. The instantaneous distribution of the ψ function over the surface of any sphere r = constant, is illustrated by Figs. 1 to 3 in the preceding chapter. The numbers, $l + 1$ and $m + 1$, correspond to the azimuthal and equatorial quantum numbers k and k_1 of the treatment in terms of the old mechanics. To obtain finite, single-valued continuous solutions of equation (3), we transform to new variables x and $L(x)$, such that

$$x = 2r\left(\frac{-8\pi^2 mE}{h^2}\right)^{1/2}, \ R = r^l \exp\left(\frac{-x}{2}\right) \cdot L(x). \tag{4}$$

(The variable x is dimensionless and is introduced to simplify the coefficients of the equation for L; when E assumes the values given by the Balmer formula, we get $x = 2Zr/na$, n being the total quantum number and a the radius of the first orbit in hydrogen.) The transformed equation is

$$xL'' + [2(l + 1) - x]L' + \left[\left(\frac{2\pi^2 me^4 Z^2}{-h^2 E}\right)^{1/2} - l - 1\right]L = 0$$

or

$$xL'' + (A - x)L' + BL = 0, \tag{5}$$

where $A - x$ and B are abbreviations for the coefficients of L' and L, respectively. The advantage of using equation (5) instead of equation (3) is that when equation (5) is solved by using a power series the recurrence formula for the coefficients is extremely simple. If we let

$$L = \sum_{-\infty}^{\infty} a_p x^p,$$

equation (5) becomes

$$\sum_{-\infty}^{\infty} a_p p(p - 1)x^{p-1} + (A - x)\sum_{-\infty}^{\infty} a_p p x^{p-1} + B\sum_{-\infty}^{\infty} a_p x^p = 0. \tag{6}$$

To satisfy this equation for all values of x, the coefficient of each power of x must vanish. Applying this requirement to the coefficient of x^p, where p is any integer or zero, we obtain

$$a_{p+1}(p + 1)(p + A) - a_p(p - B) = 0. \tag{7}$$

Now we can find the properties which the coefficients a_p must possess if R is to be finite for all positive values of r from zero to infinity. Two cases are considered, corresponding, respectively, to elliptic and hyperbolic orbits of the older theory:

(1) E negative, *i.e.*, x real; (2) E positive, *i.e.*, x pure imaginary.

(1) E **Negative, x Real and Positive.**—Consider the behavior of the series for L when x equals zero. It will not converge if negative powers of x are present, and R will take an infinite value. For this reason we wish to avoid a solution in which negative powers appear. The question is, can the equation for L be satisfied if this is done? Let us assume that

the series does not extend to $p = -\infty$, so that there is a first term, say $a_{j+1}x^{j+1}$. Then, by equation (7),

$$a_{j+1}(j + 1)(j + 2l + 2) - a_j(j - B) = 0. \tag{8}$$

But by hypothesis $a_j = 0$, and to keep a_{j+1} finite, j must be either -1, or $-2l - 2$. By taking $j = -1$, then, it is possible to obtain a value of L beginning with the coefficient a_0, so that

$$L = \sum_0^\infty a_p x^p. \tag{9}$$

In equation (9), the absolute ratio of two neighboring terms is

$$\left|\frac{a_{p+1}x}{a_p}\right| = \frac{(p - B)x}{(p + 1)(p + 2l + 2)}. \tag{10}$$

So long as x remains finite, then no matter what finite values A and $2l + 2$ may take, we can make this ratio less than 1 (or indeed as small as we please) by choosing p sufficiently large. Therefore, the series for L converges for any *finite* value of $x;$ indeed, the series formed of the absolute values of its terms converges. However, if R is to be finite when $r = \infty$, the series for L must contain only a finite number of terms. Let $a_{n'}$ be the last non-zero coefficient. Then $a_{n'+1}$ must be zero and equation (7) tells us that

$$n' - B = 0,$$

or, by equation (5),

$$n' + l + 1 - \left(\frac{2\pi^2 m e^4 Z^2}{-h^2 E}\right)^{\frac{1}{2}} = 0. \tag{11}$$

Putting $n' + l + 1 = n$, we get the Balmer formula,

$$E_n = \frac{-2\pi^2 m e^4 Z^2}{n^2 h^2}. \tag{12}$$

It is easily seen that ψ is continuous and single valued, so it will be an acceptable function if E takes the values specified by equation (12); n' is analogous to the radial quantum number of the earlier theory. It takes the values

$$n' = 0, 1, 2, \cdots.$$

(2) *E* **Positive,** *x* **Pure Imaginary.**—As long as x is finite, the remarks made in (1) for the case of finite x hold true for case (2) without alteration, but when x approaches infinity, we must study the behavior of $L(x)$ in more detail. To do this, we note that in equation (3), the last two terms of the coefficient of R can be neglected, when r is very large. The equation obtained by dropping them is a Bessel equation and has the solutions $R = \sin(\alpha r)/r$ and $R = \cos(\alpha r)/r$, where $\alpha^2 = 8\pi^2 m E/h^2$.

These, and linear combinations of them, are obviously finite for all positive valves of E, a fact which corresponds to the existence of a continuous set of hyperbolic orbits in the older theory.

2. ACCEPTABLE FUNCTIONS FOR THE HYDROGEN ATOM

Corresponding to each value of n, there are n characteristic functions $R(n, l)$ corresponding to the values $l = 0, \cdots (n - 1)$. To calculate these functions we put $B = n'$ and $A = 2(l + 1)$ in equation (7). Giving an arbitrary value to a_0, we compute the coefficients a_p; and find, aside from an arbitrary constant factor, the formula

$$R(n, l) = x^l e^{-x/2}[-(n + l)!] \sum_{p=0}^{p=n-l-1} (-1)^p \frac{x^p}{p!} C_{n-l-1-p}^{n+l}, \quad (13)$$

where $x = 2r(-8\pi^2 mE/h^2)^{1/2}$ and n, l, n' are, respectively, the total quantum number, the azimuthal number minus one, and the radial number. The symbol $C_b{}^a$ stands for $\dfrac{a!}{b!\,(a - b)!}$, and is the $(b + 1)$th coefficient in the expansion of a binomial raised to the ath power; therefore,

$$C_{n-l-1-p}^{n+l} = \frac{(n + l)!}{(n - l - 1 - p)!(2l + 1 + p)!} \quad (14)$$

The series in equation (13) is related to a set of functions known as "Laguerre polynomials." The more important properties of these polynomials are collected in Appendix IV. Here we need only the definition

$$L_s(x) \equiv e^x \frac{d^s(x^s e^{-x})}{dx^s} \equiv \sum_{p=0}^{s} (-1)^p C_p{}^s s(s - 1) \cdots (p + 1)x^p. \quad (15)$$

Thus,

$$L_0(x) = 1, L_1(x) = -x + 1, \text{ etc.}$$

Now, aside from a constant factor, c, the summation in equation (13) is identical with

$$\frac{1}{[-(n + l)!]} \frac{d^{2l+1}L_{n+l}(x)}{dx^{2l+1}}.$$

Denoting this derivative by $L_{n+l}^{2l+1}(x)$, we rewrite equation (13) in the form

$$R(n, l) = x^l e^{-x/2}L_{n+l}^{2l+1}(x). \quad (16)$$

To obtain an idea of the ψ functions and the charge distribution for this simplest of all atoms, we begin by writing out in Table 1 the values of L_{n+l}^{2l+1} for small values of l and n, remembering that l is less than n.

TABLE 1

n	l	L_{n+l}^{2l+1}
1	0	$L_1{}^1 = -1$
2	0	$L_2{}^1 = 2x - 4$
	1	$L_3{}^3 = -3!$
3	0	$L_3{}^1 = -3x^2 + 18x - 18$
	1	$L_4{}^3 = 24x - 96$
	2	$L_5{}^5 = -5!$
4	0	$L_4{}^1 = 4x^3 - 48x^2 + 144x - 96$
	1	$L_5{}^3 = -60x^2 + 600x - 1,200$
	2	$L_6{}^5 = 720x - 5,760$
	3	$L_7{}^7 = -7!$

Attention must be paid to the fact that x has a different significance in each row of the table, for $x = 2Zr/na$, as mentioned in connection with equation (4). It can be shown that the normalized functions $\psi(n, l, m)$, are as follows:

$$\psi(n, l, m) = \frac{e^{im\varphi}}{(2\pi)^{1/2}} \cdot \left[\frac{(2l + 1)(l - m)!}{2(l + m)!} \right]^{1/2} P_{l,m}(\cos \theta) \, .$$

$$\left[\frac{(n - l - 1)!}{(n + l)!^3 2n^4} \left(\frac{2}{a}\right)^3 \right]^{1/2} x^l e^{-x/2} L_{n+l}^{2l+1}(x),$$

where $n = 1, 2, 3 \cdots , l = 0, \cdots (n - 1)$, and m takes all values between $-l$ and $+l$, including zero. The ψ functions belonging to a given value of n are n^2 in number. That is, the statistical weight of the nth quantum state is n^2, just as in the older theory.

3. THE DISTRIBUTION OF THE FUNCTIONS ψ AND $\psi\psi^*$

It is useful to study the way in which ψ depends on r in a few simple cases. Whenever $n = l + 1$ (circular orbits), the function L_{n+l}^{2l+1} becomes L_{n+l}^{n+l} and is a constant. For all such orbits, the part of ψ depending on x is essentially

$$X = x^l e^{-x/2}. \tag{18}$$

It is interesting to note that the maximum of X occurs at $x = 2n$, so that the corresponding value of r is

$$r_{\max} = \frac{n^2 a}{Z},$$

which is the radius of an n-quantum circle on Bohr's theory; but this is a chance agreement, for there seems to be no simple relation between orbital shape and the properties of the ψ function for elliptic orbits. The rapid decrease of equation (18) for values of x greater than that corresponding to the maximum shows that the region, in which ψ (or $\psi\psi^*$)

has an appreciable value, has a radius comparable with that of the corresponding circular orbit. Since L_{n+l}^{2l+1} is a polynomial, the value of $R(n, l)$ for an elliptic orbit is a superposition of the R's for several circular orbits, with relative weights determined by the coefficients of L_{n+l}^{2l+1}. Writing C for the nomalization factor immediately preceding $R(n, l)$, in equation (17), let us examine a few of the curves $R(n, l)$ for the case $Z = 1$. If we write $\rho = r/a$, or $x = 2Z\rho/n$, which amounts to choosing the radius of the first Bohr orbit as the unit of length, we have the following table:

n	l	$R(n, l)$	$R(n, l)$	$\left(\dfrac{a}{2}\right)^{3/2} C$
1	0	$-\exp\left(\dfrac{-x}{2}\right)$	$-\exp\left(-\rho\right)$	$\dfrac{1}{2^{1/2}}$
2	0	$(2x - 4) \cdot \exp\left(\dfrac{-x}{2}\right)$	$(2\rho - 4) \cdot \exp\left(\dfrac{-\rho}{2}\right)$	$\dfrac{1}{16}$
2	1	$-6x \cdot \exp\left(\dfrac{-x}{2}\right)$	$(-6\rho) \exp\left(\dfrac{-\rho}{2}\right)$	$\dfrac{1}{24.12^{1/2}}$
3	0	$3(-x^2 + 6x - 6) \exp\left(\dfrac{-x}{2}\right)$	$3\left(-\dfrac{4}{9}\rho^2 + 4\rho - 6\right) \cdot \exp\left(\dfrac{-\rho}{3}\right)$	$\dfrac{1}{9 \cdot 6^{3/2}}$
3	1	$24x(x - 4) \exp\left(\dfrac{-x}{2}\right)$	$24\left(\dfrac{2}{3}\rho\right)\left(\dfrac{2}{3}\rho - 4\right) \cdot \exp\left(\dfrac{-\rho}{3}\right)$	$\dfrac{1}{9 \cdot 2^{1/2} \cdot 24^{3/2}}$
3	2	$-120x^2 \exp\left(\dfrac{-x}{2}\right)$	$-120\left(\dfrac{4}{9}\rho^2\right) \exp\left(\dfrac{-\rho}{3}\right)$	$\dfrac{1}{9 \cdot 2^{1/2} \cdot 120^{3/2}}$

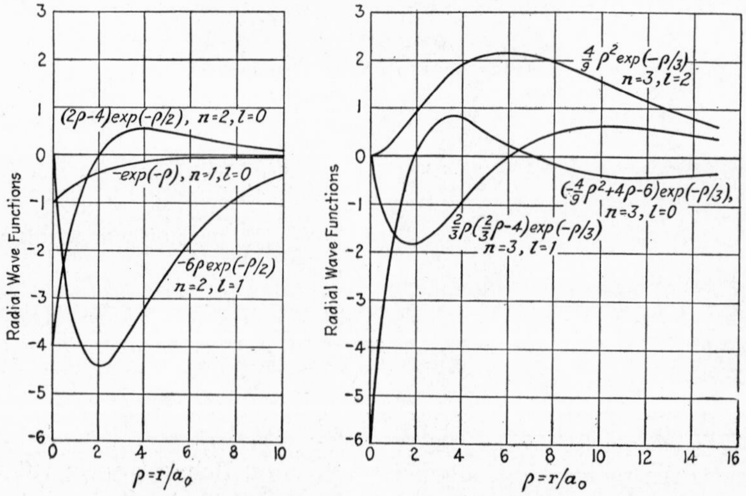

FIG. 1.—Radial wave functions of the hydrogen atom.

If Z is not unity, the values of $R(n, l)$ in terms of x are not altered, but we must put $Z\rho$ in place of ρ throughout the table. A few of the curves $R(n, l)$ are shown in Fig. 1.

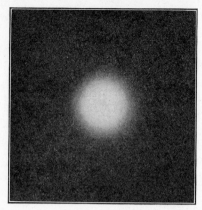

Hydrogen 1²S

Helium 1¹S

Hydrogen 2²S

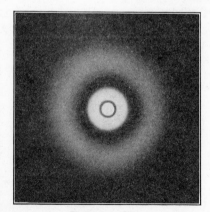

Hydrogen 3²S

Hydrogen 3²S

FIG. 2.—Distribution of the function $\psi\psi^*$ for certain states of hydrogen and helium. (*After Langer and Walker.*)

The spatial distribution of the normalized functions $\psi\psi^*$ is beautifully shown in Figs. 2, which were kindly supplied by Dr. R. M. Langer and Miss Geraldine Walker. All of them are for energy levels in which the quantum numbers l and m are zero so that the distribution of $\psi\psi^*$ is spherically symmetrical. At any point in the diagram, the brightness is proportional to the value of $\psi\psi^*$. In the original photograph for the state $1S$, that is, the normal state, for which $n = 1$, $l = m = 0$, distances are proportional to r/a_0, the radius of the first hydrogen orbit being represented as 3 cm. The scales for the states 200 and 300 are five times and ten times smaller, respectively. The intensity in the photograph of $2S$ is multiplied by 50 in comparison with $1S$; the intensity scale in the brighter diagram for $3S$ is 500 times that of $1S$, while the other diagram for $3S$ is a much lighter print which gives a better idea of the smallness of $\psi\psi^*$ in comparison with the values for $1S$. The $2S$ distribution serves also as an approximate representation of $\psi\psi^*$ for the lowest term of lithium, taking only the valence electron into account. Similarly, the $3S$ distribution is similar to the normal state of sodium. The diagram for the normal state of neutral helium, which also possesses spherical symmetry, is included for the sake of comparison with $1S$ of hydrogen. The length scale is about the same in these two diagrams, but the intensity at the center of the helium distribution should be nearly 100 times as great as in the diagram for $1S$. At $r = 1.5a_0$, the two are about equal, which shows that the radial rate of decrease of $\psi\psi^*$ is very rapid for helium, corresponding to its small external field and inert chemical nature.

4. THE RELATIVISTIC HYDROGEN ATOM

The energy levels of the relativistic H atom have been found by Schrödinger,[1] Fock,[2] and Epstein.[3] The formula obtained is similar to that of Sommerfeld except that the azimuthal quantum number takes half-integer values, due to the neglect of electron spin. We shall give a treatment similar to the derivation given by Epstein. From Chap. XV, equation (104), the amplitude equation is

$$\Delta\psi - \frac{4\pi^2}{c^2h^2}\left[m^2c^4 - \left(\mathcal{E} - \frac{Ze^2}{r} \right)^2 \right]\psi = 0, \tag{19}$$

with $\mathcal{E} = mc^2 + E$. The solution is exactly like that for the non-relativistic case, except that the coefficients are altered in the equation for the factor in ψ which depends on r, namely,

$$\frac{d^2R}{dr^2} + \frac{2}{r}\frac{dR}{dr} + \left[\frac{4\pi^2}{h^2c^2}(\mathcal{E}^2 - m^2c^4) + \frac{8\pi^2Ze^2\mathcal{E}}{h^2c^2r} + \frac{Z^2\alpha^2 - l(l+1)}{r^2} \right]R = 0. \tag{20}$$

[1] "Abhandlungen," 12 and 87.
[2] Z. Physik, **38**, 411 (1926).
[3] Proc. Nat. Acad. Sci., **13**, 94 (1927).

α^2 is Sommerfeld's fine-structure constant (Chap. V, equation (30)). We treat equation (20) in the same way as equation (3), using the substitutions

$$x = 2r\left[-\frac{4\pi^2}{h^2c^2}(\mathcal{E}^2 - m^2c^4) \right]^{\frac{1}{2}}, \tag{21}$$

and

$$R = x^\lambda e^{-x/2} F(x),$$

where the exponent λ is $-\frac{1}{2} + [(l + \frac{1}{2})^2 - Z^2\alpha^2]^{\frac{1}{2}}$. The equation to determine F is of the same form as equation (5) if we write $A = 2(\lambda + 1)$, and

$$B = \frac{4\pi^2 Z e^2 \mathcal{E}}{h^2 c^2}\left[-\frac{4\pi^2}{h^2 c^2}(\mathcal{E}^2 - m^2 c^4) \right]^{\frac{1}{2}} - \frac{1}{2} - \left[\left(l + \frac{1}{2}\right)^2 - Z^2\alpha^2\right]^{\frac{1}{2}} = n'.$$

As before, n' must be an integer or zero, and, finally, the energy values are given by

$$1 + \frac{E}{mc^2} = \left[1 + \alpha^2 Z^2\left(n' + \frac{1}{2} + \sqrt{\left(l + \frac{1}{2}\right)^2 - \alpha^2 Z^2}\right)^{-2} \right]^{-\frac{1}{2}}. \tag{22}$$

This agrees in form with Sommerfeld's empirically verified equation, but the combinations $n' + \frac{1}{2}$ and $l + \frac{1}{2}$ appear in place of his n' and k. The denominator of the first term in E corresponding to the Balmer formula, is $n' + l + 1 = n$ which takes the values 1, 2, $\cdots$, just as it should, but the first-order relativity correction of a spectral term is

$$\frac{RZ^4\alpha^2}{n^4}\left(\frac{n}{l + \frac{1}{2}} - \frac{3}{4}\right). \tag{23}$$

The correction for the effect of electron spin was carried out by Heisenberg and Jordan and also by Richter. Their result for the first-order correction was given in Chap. V, Sec. **17.**

Richter solved the problem by perturbation methods, using wave mechanics. The unperturbed motion corresponds to a spherical electron moving about the nucleus and simultaneously rotating, the two motions not affecting each other. Thus, an acceptable function can be obtained for this unperturbed problem by taking the product of a ψ function for the simple H atom (Sec. **2**) and a ψ function for a rotating rigid body. The first-order perturbation of the energy can be obtained by the method of Chap. XV, Sec. **22.**

Darwin and Gordon[1] have obtained the general formula for the hydrogen energy levels on the basis of Dirac's theory of the electron.[2] The result is identical with Sommerfeld's formula, given in equation (34) of Chap. V. The radial number can assume the values 0, 1, 2, $\ldots$ The azimuthal number k of Sommerfeld's theory is replaced by $l + 1$, where $l = 0$, 1, 2, $\cdots$ $n - 1$, n being the total quantum number.

[1] *Proc. Roy. Soc.*, **118**, 654 (1928); *Z. Physik*, **48**, 11 (1928).

[2] *Proc. Roy. Soc.*, **113**, 621 (1927).

A quantum number corresponding to the electron spin does not appear explicitly in this formula, so that it does not predict the complete scheme of X-ray energy levels.

5. THE ZEEMAN EFFECT OF HYDROGEN

We have already found the energy levels of the normal Zeeman effect in Chap. XV, by a very simple method. That method is unsuited for the study of the acceptable functions and for obtaining higher approximations, so we shall attack the problem here *ab initio*. It is one which has received much attention. Heisenberg and Jordan[1] obtained the g formula by means of matrices. Epstein[2] treated the problem of the normal effect by obtaining the energy of a system composed of the atom and the apparatus which produces the field. This procedure is advantageous, for it is capable of showing the nature of the interaction between the atom and the magnetic field. For example, it is well known that when a quantum jump occurs there may be an exchange of angular momentum between the atom and the field producing mechanism, as well as a contribution of angular momentum to the radiation field. This indicates that we might expect a difference between the energy of a quantum and the decrease of energy of the emitting atom, because of a possible interchange of energy between the atom and the magnet. The calculation of Epstein shows that the correct result is the same as that obtained by neglecting the reaction of the atom on the field—that is, by treating the field strength H as quite independent of the behavior of the emitting atom. Brillouin[3] has also treated the problem in wave mechanics, and we shall give a derivation not very different from his. Although we speak of the hydrogen atom, the method can be applied to any atom if we neglect electron spin. In the wave equation (114) of Chap. XV, we substitute the values of the vector potential components for the case of a uniform magnetic field parallel to the z-axis, as derived in Appendix VIII, Sec. **1**. They are

$$A_x = -\frac{Hy}{2}, \; A_y = \frac{Hx}{2}, \; A_z = 0,$$

and we easily find that equation (114) reduces to

$$\Delta\Psi - \frac{1}{c^2}\frac{\partial^2\Psi}{\partial t^2} + \frac{4\pi i e}{hc}\left(\frac{H}{2}\frac{\partial\Psi}{\partial\varphi} + \frac{\Phi}{c}\frac{\partial\Psi}{\partial t}\right) - \frac{4\pi^2}{h^2}\left(m_0{}^2c^2 - \frac{e^2\Phi^2}{c^2}\right)\Psi = 0. \quad (24)$$

(We have neglected $\Sigma A_j{}^2$ in the last term because we only wish a result correct to the first power of H. This corresponds to the assumption used in the classical theory of the Zeeman effect, that the force due to the

[1] *Z. Physik*, **37**, 263 (1926).

[2] *Proc. Nat. Acad. Sci.*, **12**, 634 (1926).

[3] BRILLOUIN, *J. de Physique*, **8**, 74 (1927).

magnetic field is small compared with the Coulomb attraction between electron and nucleus.) We now assume that

$$\Psi = \psi e^{-2\pi i \mathcal{E} t/h}, \quad \mathcal{E} = m_0 c^2 + E$$

and use these relations to remove the time from equation (24). Further, we drop all terms which arise from the variable mass of the electron, arriving at the equation

$$\Delta\psi + \frac{4\pi i e}{hc}\frac{H}{2}\frac{\partial\psi}{\partial\varphi} + \frac{8\pi^2 m_0}{h^2}(E - V)\psi = 0. \tag{25}$$

This can be satisfied by a wave function which depends on φ through a factor $\exp im\varphi$, just as in the absence of the field, so $\partial\psi/\partial\varphi = im\psi$. Also, by Larmor's theorem the only change in the Ψ distribution when the field is applied consists in a uniform precession L which makes it go faster or slower, according to its sense of rotation. Only the time factor in Ψ is altered, so ψ must remain unaltered. Let E_0 be the energy in the absence of the field, and let $E = E_0 + \Delta E$. Then equation (25) reduces to

$$\Delta\psi + \left(\frac{8\pi^2 m_0}{h^2}\right)(E_0 - V)\psi - \left(\frac{2\pi e m H}{hc} - \frac{8\pi^2 m_0}{h^2}\Delta E\right)\psi = 0. \tag{25a}$$

The first two terms vanish because ψ is the wave function for the unperturbed atom, so the remaining two terms must also vanish, which will occur if

$$\Delta E = me\frac{Hh}{4\pi m_0 c} = mLh \tag{26}$$

in exact agreement with the result of the older theory. Finally, we have for the wave function in the presence of the field

$$\Psi = \Psi_0 e^{-2\pi i m L t}. \tag{27}$$

If relativity modifications are taken into account,[1] equation (27) is replaced by

$$\Delta E = mLh\left(1 + \frac{E}{m_0 c^2}\right), \tag{26a}$$

which agrees with a result of Pauli[2] obtained by the use of ordinary mechanics. Terms in H^2 have been calculated by Hill and Van Vleck.[3]

6. SELECTION PRINCIPLES

Consider two states of the hydrogen atom, having the quantum numbers n_2, l_2, m_2, and n_1, l_1, m_1, respectively. Let the frequency which is emitted in a transition between these terms be ν_{21}. In order that the intensity of the line ν_{21} shall vanish, the terms in the components of the electric moment having this frequency must be zero. We neglect the motion of the nucleus and treat the problem by equation (90) of Chap.

[1] Ruark, Phys. Rev., **31**, 533 (1928).

[2] Z. Physik., **31**, 373 (1925).

[3] Phys. Rev., **31**, 715 (1928).

XV, together with two similar equations for the y- and z-components of the electric moment. Writing M_x, M_y, and M_z for the terms which concern us, and neglecting the exponential time factors, we have

$$M_x = -e\int x\psi(n_2l_2m_2)\psi^*(n_1l_1m_1)dv - e\int x\psi(n_1l_1m_1)\psi^*(n_2l_2m_2)dv. \quad (28)$$

Remembering that $x = r \sin\theta \cos\varphi$, we find that M_x is proportional to the real part of

$$\int\int\int R_2(r)P_{l_2,m_2}(\cos\theta)e^{im_2\varphi}R_1(r)P_{l_1,m_1}(\cos\theta)e^{-im_1\varphi}(r\sin\theta\cos\varphi)$$
$$r^2 \sin\theta dr d\theta d\varphi, \quad (28a)$$

where the limits are such that the integral extends over the whole q space. We write down similar expressions for M_y and M_z, and proceed to consider the integration with respect to φ. The three integrals for the x, y, and z coordinates are, respectively,

$$\int_0^{2\pi} \exp\left[i(m_2 - m_1)\varphi\right] \cdot \begin{Bmatrix} \cos\varphi \\ \sin\varphi \\ 1 \end{Bmatrix} d\varphi. \quad (29)$$

The first two were treated in Chap. XV, Sec. **18,** and give rise to a finite result only if $\Delta m = \pm 1$. The third vanishes except when $\Delta m = 0$. Now if $\Delta m = \pm 1$, on carrying out the integrations over θ and r in equation (28a) we arrive at values similar to those of Chap. XV except that ϵr is replaced by another expression dependent on the quantum numbers, and $M_z = 0$. Therefore, the radiation emitted will be circularly polarized with the axis of polarization along OZ. On the other hand, when $\Delta m = 0$, only M_z has a finite value and the radiation is linearly polarized with electric vector parallel to OZ. Thus, we have derived the selection rule for m and the polarization rule, in agreement with the results of Chap. V.

Now we consider the integration with respect to θ, restricting ourselves to the cases in which $\Delta m = \pm 1$ or 0. There are two integrals to be considered, corresponding to the x- or y- and to the z-component of the electric moment, respectively. They are,

$$\int P_{l_2m_2}(\cos\theta)P_{l_1m_1}(\cos\theta) \begin{Bmatrix} \sin^2\theta \\ \sin\theta\cos\theta \end{Bmatrix} d\theta. \quad (30)$$

Eckart[1] has shown that these integrals lead to the selection principle $\Delta l = \pm 1$.

7. THE FIRST-ORDER STARK EFFECT

The problem of the first-order Stark effect, neglecting relativity, has been solved independently by several physicists.[2] Schrödinger has given two proofs, one by a separation-of-variables method, and the

[1] *Phys. Rev.*, **28**, 927 (1926).

[2] EPSTEIN, *Phys. Rev.*, **28**, 695 (1926); FOCK, *Z. Physik*, **38**, 242 (1926); SCHRÖDINGER, *Ann. Physik*, **80**, 437 (1926); WENTZEL, *Z. Physik*, **38**, 518 (1926); EPSTEIN and WENTZEL obtain also the second order terms.

other by a method similar to that of Bohr.   We shall follow the former procedure.   The wave equation is

$$\Delta\psi + \left(\frac{8\pi^2 m_0}{h^2}\right) \cdot \left(E + \frac{Ze^2}{r} - eFz\right)\psi = 0, \tag{31}$$

if the field is directed along the positive z-axis.   We transform to parabolic coordinates[1] λ_1, λ_2, φ, such that

$$x = \sqrt{\lambda_1\lambda_2} \cos\varphi, \; y = \sqrt{\lambda_1\lambda_2} \sin\varphi, \; z = \frac{(\lambda_1 - \lambda_2)}{2}. \tag{32}$$

After multiplication by $(\lambda_1 + \lambda_2)/4$, equation (31) takes the form

$$\frac{\partial}{\partial\lambda_1}\left(\lambda_1\frac{\partial\psi}{\partial\lambda_1}\right) + \frac{\partial}{\partial\lambda_2}\left(\lambda_2\frac{\partial\psi}{\partial\lambda_2}\right) + \frac{1}{4}\left(\frac{1}{\lambda_1} + \frac{1}{\lambda_2}\right)\frac{\partial^2\psi}{\partial\varphi^2}$$

$$+ \left(\frac{2\pi^2 m_0}{h^2}\right) \cdot \left[E(\lambda_1 + \lambda_2) + 2Ze^2 - \frac{1}{2}eF(\lambda_1{}^2 - \lambda_2{}^2)\right]\psi = 0. \tag{33}$$

Assuming the solution,

$$\psi = X(\lambda_1)Y(\lambda_2)\Phi(\varphi), \tag{34}$$

we find that

$$\Phi = \exp(im\varphi), \; m = 0, 1, 2, \cdots, \tag{35}$$

and that the equations for X and Y are

$$\frac{\partial}{\partial\lambda_1}\left(\lambda_1\frac{\partial X}{\partial\lambda_1}\right) + \left(\frac{2\pi^2 m_0}{h^2}\right) \cdot \left(-\frac{eF\lambda_1{}^2}{2} + E\lambda_1 + Ze^2 - \beta - \frac{m^2 h^2}{8\pi^2 m_0\lambda_1}\right)X = 0, \tag{36}$$

$$\frac{\partial}{\partial\lambda_2}\left(\lambda_2\frac{\partial Y}{\partial\lambda_2}\right) + \left(\frac{2\pi^2 m_0}{h^2}\right) \cdot \left(\frac{eF\lambda_2{}^2}{2} + E\lambda_2 + Ze^2 + \beta - \frac{m^2 h^2}{8\pi^2 m_0\lambda_2}\right)Y = 0. \tag{37}$$

β is a constant introduced by the process of separating variables, and our problem is to determine pairs of values of E and β which will make X and Y acceptable functions.   The last two equations both have the form

$$\frac{\partial}{\partial y}\left(y\frac{\partial f}{\partial y}\right) + \left(Dy^2 + Ay + 2B + \frac{C}{y}\right)f = 0, \tag{38}$$

where

$$D = \mp\frac{\pi^2 m_0 eF}{h^2}, \; A = \frac{2\pi^2 m_0 E}{h^2}, \; B = \frac{\pi^2 m(Ze^2 \mp \beta)}{h^2}, \; C = -\frac{m^2}{4}.$$

The upper signs refer to the equation for X, and the lower to the equation for Y.   We commence our study of equation (38) by solving the wave equation for the unperturbed atom, obtained by letting $D = 0$.   We transform to new variables L, x, such that

$$x = 2y\left(-\frac{2\pi^2 m_0 E}{h^2}\right)^{\frac{1}{2}}, f = e^{-x/2}y^{m/2}L(x), \tag{39}$$

---

[1] These definitions are adopted in agreement with Schrödinger, instead of those used in Chap. V, Sec. **12**, because the computation of the energy perturbation is simpler in terms of λ_1 and λ_2; $\lambda_1 = \xi^2$, $\lambda_2 = \eta^2$.

and find that L obeys the equation

$$xL'' + [(m + 1) - x]L' + \left[\frac{B}{(-A)^{\frac{1}{2}}} - \frac{(m + 1)}{2} \right]L = 0, \quad (40)$$

which is identical in form with the equation (5) for the unperturbed H atom, although the meaning of the variables and the coefficients is quite different. Just as before, we seek for the values of the coefficient of L which make f an acceptable function. If we write

$$\frac{B}{(-A)^{\frac{1}{2}}} - \frac{(m + 1)}{2} = k, \quad (41)$$

then we must make $k = 0, 1, 2, \cdots$ in order that f may be an acceptable function. When k takes one of these values, then L is the mth derivative of the $(m + k)$th Laguerre polynomial (Appendix IV, Sec. 7), which is represented by the symbol $L^m_{m+k}(x)$. To see the significance of k we give B the value appropriate to equation (36), and put $k = k_1$, obtaining,

$$\frac{\pi^2 m_0 (Ze^2 - \beta)}{h^2(-A)^{\frac{1}{2}}} = k_1 + \frac{(m + 1)}{2}. \quad (42)$$

Again, we give B the value which it has in equation (37), and put $k = k_2$, with the result

$$\frac{\pi^2 m_0 (Ze^2 + \beta)}{h^2(-A)^{\frac{1}{2}}} = k_2 + \frac{(m + 1)}{2}. \quad (43)$$

Adding, and solving for the energy constant which appears in A, we have

$$E = -\frac{Rhc}{(k_1 + k_2 + m + 1)^2}. \quad (44)$$

It is found that k_1 and k_2 take the same range of values as the parabolic quantum numbers introduced in equation (65), Chap. V, while the $m + 1$ of this computation plays a rôle similar to that of the equatorial quantum number of equation (65). According to equation (35), the zero value of $m + 1$, which is analogous to the equatorial number in the older quantum theory, is automatically excluded in wave mechanics, although a special consideration was required in order to obtain this result by the old mechanics.

We now determine the change of E when the field F is applied, which results in changing equation (40) to the form,

$$xL'' + [(m + 1) - x]L' + \left[\frac{B}{(-A)^{\frac{1}{2}}} - \frac{(m + 1)}{2} + \frac{Dx^2}{8(-A)^{\frac{3}{2}}} \right]L$$
$$= 0. \quad (45)$$

The first step is to determine the change in the value of $B/(-A)^{\frac{1}{2}}$ which results from the addition of the term containing F. Since we know experimentally that the contribution of this term to E will be small compared with E itself, we use the approximate value of $-A$ obtained from equations (42) and (43) in evaluating the perturbation term, with the result,

$$\frac{Dx^2}{8(-A)^{3/2}} = \mp x^2 F\left(\frac{n^3 h^4}{64\pi^4 m_0{}^2 Z^3 e^5}\right) = \mp cFx^2; \qquad (46)$$

n is the total quantum number and c is an abbreviation for the quantity in parentheses. The ambiguity of sign arises from equation (38). The addition of this term changes the allowed values of $B/(-A)^{1/2}$, and the magnitude of the change may be determined by applying the perturbation theory of Chap. XV, Sec. 22 to equation (45). Before doing so, it is convenient to multiply equation (45) by $e^{-x}x^m$. $B/(-A)^{1/2}$ then corresponds to the energy E of Chap. XV, Sec. 22, while the term, $\mp cFx^2$, replaces the perturbation of the potential energy, which was denoted by λF in equation (117) of that section. If S_k is the perturbation of $B/(-A)^{1/2}$, corresponding to $\lambda \epsilon_k$ in Chap. XV, then in place of equation (41) we have

$$\frac{B}{(-A)^{1/2}} = \frac{m+1}{2} + k + S_k. \qquad (41a)$$

Then by equation (122) of Chap. XV, we have

$$S_k = \pm cF \frac{\displaystyle\int_0^\infty e^{-x} x^{m+2} [L^m{}_{m+k}(x)]^2 dx}{\displaystyle\int_0^\infty x^m e^{-x} [L^m{}_{m+k}(x)]^2 dx}. \qquad (47)$$

Schrödinger shows that the result of integration is

$$S_k = \pm cF(m^2 + 6mk + 6k^2 + 6k + 3m + 2). \qquad (48)$$

Just as before, we write down equation (41a) two times, putting $k = k_1$ and k_2, and $B = \pi^2 m_0 (Ze^2 \mp \beta)$. Solving these two equations for E, the result is

$$E = \frac{-2\pi^2 m_0 Z^2 e^4}{n^2 h^2} - \left(\frac{3h^2 F}{8\pi^2 meZ}\right) n(k_1 - k_2) \qquad (49)$$

in exact agreement with the Epstein-Schwarzschild formula.

The above calculations give us a second form for the acceptable functions of the unperturbed hydrogen atom, which is not identical with equation (17). This ambiguity arises from our neglect of the relativity correction, which makes the unperturbed atom degenerate. Using the Balmer formula for E in equation (39) we have

$$x = \frac{\lambda_1}{na} \text{ or } \frac{\lambda_2}{na},$$

as the case may be, where a is the radius of the first Bohr orbit. With this notation, we find from equation (34) that the acceptable functions (not normalized) are,

$$\psi(k_1, k_2, m) = (\lambda_1 \lambda_2)^{m/2} \exp\left[\frac{-(\lambda_1 + \lambda_2)}{2na}\right] L^m{}_{m+k_1}\left(\frac{\lambda_1}{na}\right) L^m{}_{m+k_2}\left(\frac{\lambda_2}{na}\right)$$
$$\exp(im\varphi). \qquad (50)$$

CHAPTER XVII

MATRIX MECHANICS

1. THE VIEWPOINT OF MATRIX MECHANICS

In the search for the true laws of atomic dynamics, Heisenberg[1] introduced a new method of attack. Instead of attempting to find models operating in accord with Newtonian dynamics which would yield the correct energy levels, he abandoned all idea of atomic models, and sought to obtain general postulates which would lead to known relationships between quantities which can be observed. It seems useless to speak of the amplitude or the phase of the motion of an electron within the atom. Essentially, the amplitude, phase, state of polarization, and frequency of the emitted light are representative of the type of quantities which should be the subject matter of a reasoned atomic theory, for predictions about them can be tested directly. The reader will understand that the adoption of such a viewpoint does not deny the usefulness of models as an aid in research. In the last analysis, the atom must be described in terms of space and time, if it is described at all. The new theory indicates that we need not trouble to describe it, and furnishes rules for calculating the *observable* quantities characteristic of the atom without bothering about the coordinates and velocities of its particles as functions of the time. In principle, such a program can be carried through. In practice, the mathematical difficulties are often great, for the calculations are not carried out with ordinary algebra. The equations of the theory consist of relations between sets of numbers called "matrices" instead of *single numbers*. We have said that the results of Schrödinger's theory are identical with those of Heisenberg's—a fortunate circumstance, because it means that the numbers forming the matrices for an atomic system can be obtained by simple integration, if we have quantized the atom by means of wave mechanics.

2. TWO-DIMENSIONAL MATRICES

In beginning our study of Heisenberg's theory, we shall consider systems with one degree of freedom. We saw in Chap. VI, using the old dynamics, that the intensities of spectral lines yield us relative values of the amplitudes of the various harmonics in the electric moment of the atom. Often it is convenient to deal with these amplitudes q_1,

[1] *Z. Physik*, **33**, 879 (1925).

q_2, . . . as though they were the amplitudes of ideal virtual oscillators associated with the atom. Now, consider the classical problem of the radiation from an oscillator having one frequency and a single coordinate q expressed by a Fourier series,

$$q = \Sigma A_k e^{2\pi i\nu kt + i\delta_k} \tag{1}$$

where the A's are supposed to be complex quantities of such a character that the whole series is a real quantity. Such will be the case if

$$A_{-k} = A_k{}^*, \ \delta_{-k} = -\delta_k, \tag{2}$$

for then the sum of the two terms,

$$A_k e^{2\pi i\nu kt + i\delta_k} \text{ and } A_{-k} e^{2\pi i\nu(-k)t + i\delta_{-k}}, \tag{3}$$

is real.

Similarly, if we study the radiation from an aggregate of quantized systems, we may consider each monochromatic spectrum line as coming from oscillators each of which is characterized by an amplitude, a phase, and a factor containing the frequency. Let the energies of the stationary states, as yet unknown, be E_1, E_2, etc., and let $\nu(nm)$ denote the frequency emitted in the transition from the nth to the mth state, calculated from the relation $E_n - E_m = h\nu(nm)$. Let $A(nm)$ be the corresponding amplitude, which is assumed to be constant, and $\delta(nm)$ the phase. Then, wherever we would deal with the quantities of equation (2) in the corresponding classical problem, we shall need the quantities

$$A(nm)e^{2\pi i\nu(nm)t + i\delta(nm)} \tag{4}$$

in Heisenberg's theory. We leave the question open whether the sum of these quantities is useful in studying the atom, for the theory deals only with the set of quantities (4), and not with their sum. It will be convenient to write

$$q(nm) \equiv A(nm)e^{i\delta(nm)}$$

whence,

$$q(mn) \equiv A(mn)e^{i\delta(mn)}. \tag{5}$$

In analogy to equation (2) we *assume* that

$$A(mn) = A^*(nm),$$
$$\delta(mn) = -\delta(nm). \tag{6}$$

Then,

$$q(mn) = q^*(nm). \tag{7}$$

Further,

$$h\nu(nm) = E_n - E_m, \tag{8}$$

so that

$$\nu(nm) = -\nu(mn). \tag{9}$$

The absolute value of $q(nm)$ is equal to the absolute value of $q(mn)$, and therefore,

$$|q(nm)|^2 = q(mn)q^*(mn) = q(nm)q^*(nm).$$

Now, it is convenient to order the quantities

$$q(nm)e^{2\pi i\nu(nm)t}$$

in a square array, having an infinite number of rows and columns, which is called the matrix q. This is expressed by writing

$$\left\| \begin{matrix} q(11)e^{2\pi i\nu(11)t} \ q(12)e^{2\pi i\nu(12)t} \ \cdots \\ q(21)e^{2\pi i\nu(21)t} \ q(22)e^{2\pi i\nu(22)t} \ \cdots \\ \cdots\cdots\cdots\cdots\cdots\cdots\cdots\cdots\cdots \end{matrix} \right\| \equiv q. \tag{10}$$

A matrix is not a single quantity, like a determinant, but simply a set of quantities. The array is often referred to as the coordinate q, because it may be considered as a generalization of the set listed in (3), which gives us the means of calculating the classical coordinate q. As we have said, however, matrix theory does not deal with the sum of the matrix elements of equation (5), so the application of the name "coordinate" to the matrix must be regarded as a convention. Corresponding to any other variable encountered in classical theory, such as a momentum p we shall need to introduce a matrix p, which is an array of the type

$$\left\| \begin{matrix} p(11)e^{2\pi i\nu(11)t} \ p(12)e^{2\pi i\nu(12)t} \ \cdots \\ p(21)e^{2\pi i\nu(21)t} \ p(22)e^{2\pi i\nu(22)t} \ \cdots \\ \cdots\cdots\cdots\cdots\cdots\cdots\cdots\cdots\cdots \end{matrix} \right\| \equiv p. \tag{11}$$

For brevity, it is customary to omit the exponential factors in these matrices, and to refer to the quantities $q(nm)$ or $p(nm)$ as the elements of the matrices. The matrix q is usually written as the square array of the quantities $q(nm)$, and it must be understood that this is *always* an abbreviation. The same is true for other matrices.

A matrix is called "Hermitian," after the French mathematician, Hermite, if the element in the nth row and mth column is the complex conjugate of the element in the mth row and nth column. The matrices considered in atomic theory have this property, by virtue of equations (5) to (9). The requirement that a matrix shall be Hermitian is somewhat analogous to the requirement that a physical quantity shall be real in ordinary mechanics.

3. MATRIX EQUATIONS

Heisenberg's guiding thought was that *the separate elements of these matrices are to play a rôle in atomic dynamics analogous to that played by the separate terms of the corresponding Fourier series in ordinary mechanics.* The question is, what are the dynamical laws by which these elements can be calculated? Before answering this, we must examine the nature of the equations occurring in ordinary physical theory. These equations consist of relations between numbers expressing the magnitudes of physical quantities. When we write $q = f(t)$, we mean that on putting a particular value of t in $f(t)$ we obtain a number which is the value of the coordinate q at that time. We are just as well off if we proceed in a more general way, as follows: To every physical quantity we assign an auxiliary quantity, or parameter, or, more generally, a group of parameters. The parameters belonging to t will be T_1, T_2, etc., and those belonging to q will be Q_1, Q_2, etc. These parameters need not have the slightest resemblance to the values of t or q, but there is to be a set of equations

$$f_1(Q_1, \cdots T_1, \cdots) = 0, f_2(Q_1, \cdots , T_1, \cdots) = 0, \text{etc.}$$

sufficient in number to give us the values of all the Q's when all the T's are specified, and such that on using the T's appropriate to a given value of t, the Q's we calculate will be those we have correlated with the value of q at that time. The equations of atomic dynamics are of this kind. The concept of an electronic coordinate is replaced by the set of elementary oscillations of equation (10), but we do not write down equations which contain explicitly the elements of the coordinate matrix of equation (10) and of other matrices. The equations are connections between matrices, between sets of numbers considered as entities. Of course, they *imply* relations between the individual elements, but the passage to these relations is analogous to the arbitrary way in which we pass from the Q's to the value of q in the illustration above. Often it is said that a matrix is a generalized coordinate; that somehow we have been wrong in our microscopic theories when we suppose that the state of a physical variable can be specified by assigning a single number to it. It is more general to consider a matrix simply as a symbol belonging to a physical variable. Then it is not surprising when we find that the discussion of relations between matrices requires the use of a generalized algebra. The reason for this will become fully comprehensible to the reader only after he has had a little practice in dealing with this algebra, and has studied the connection between wave mechanics and the mechanics of matrices. Then it will be seen that every matrix equation—at first sight so artificial—is really an expression of a definite, easily understandable physical law.

4. THE LAWS OF MATRIX ALGEBRA[1]

1. Equality of Matrices.—By equality of two matrices we mean that each element of one is equal to the corresponding element of the other.

$$a = b \text{ implies that } a(11) = b(11), a(nm) = b(nm), \text{etc.} \quad (12)$$

2. Addition.—The sum of two matrices a and b is a matrix whose elements are the sum of the corresponding elements of a and b.

$$a + b = c \text{ implies that } a(11) + b(11) = c(11), a(nm) + b(nm) = c(nm). \quad (13)$$

[1] The word "matrix" is used by mathematicians in a broader sense than that in which it is used here. The elements do not necessarily contain an exponential factor, and the arrays considered are generally taken to be rectangular instead of square.

The reason for this convention is plain. Given two Fourier series,

$$a = \Sigma a_k e^{2\pi i\nu kt}, \quad b = \Sigma b_k e^{2\pi i\nu kt},$$

the typical term in their sum has the coefficient $a_k + b_k$, so the same rule is assumed for matrices. The law of subtraction is similar.

3. Multiplication.—In setting up the law of multiplication we are guided by the fact that the product of two Fourier series having the same fundamental frequency is also a Fourier series.

For example, the product of the series a and b above is

$$c = \Sigma c_r e^{2\pi i\nu rt}$$

where we easily verify that

$$c_r = \Sigma_k a_k b_{r-k}, \quad k = -\infty, \cdots + \infty,$$

for each product term such as $a_k e^{2\pi i\nu kt} b_{r-k} e^{2\pi i\nu(r-k)t}$ reduces to $a_k b_{r-k} e^{2\pi i\nu rt}$. It is essential in atomic theory to retain this property for the products of matrices. We can arrange to do so by making the rule for multiplying two matrices the same as that for multiplying two determinants, rows by columns. The symbol for the product of a and b is ab and the typical element of such a matrix is $ab(nm)$. The equation,

$$ab = c, \text{ implies that } ab(nm) = c(nm) = \sum_{k=1}^{k=\infty} a(nk)b(km) =$$

$$a(n1)b(1m) + a(n2)b(2m) + \cdots \quad (14)$$

The time factor multiplying $c(nm)$ is $e^{2\pi i\nu(nm)t}$; for if the right side of equation (14) were written out with time factors included, the typical term would be

$$a(nk)e^{2\pi i\nu(nk)t}b(km)e^{2\pi i\nu(km)t}.$$

This reduces to

$$a(nk)b(km)e^{2\pi i\nu(nm)t}$$

by virtue of the combination principle, which is assumed in this theory

For the sake of thorough understanding let us illustrate further. The matrix a is:

$$
\begin{array}{llll}
a(11) & a(12) & \cdots a(1k) & \cdots \\
a(21) & a(22) & \cdots a(2k) & \cdots \\
\\
a(n1) & a(n2) & \cdots a(nk) & \cdots
\end{array}
$$

The matrix b is

$$
\begin{array}{llll}
b(11) & b(12) & \cdots b(1m) & \cdots \\
b(21) & b(22) & \cdots b(2m) & \cdots \\
\\
b(k1) & b(k2) & \cdots b(km) & \cdots
\end{array}
$$

The element of c standing in the nth row and the mth column is obtained by picking out the nth row of a and the mth column of b. Write their elements in two lines as follows:

$$
a(n1)\ a(n2)\ \ldots\ a(nk)\ \ldots \\
b(1m)\ b(2m)\ \ldots\ b(km)\ \ldots
$$

Then the nth, mth element of c is obtained by multiplying each pair in these lines, and forming the sum of the products as shown in equation (14). In summations of the type indicated in equation (14) we shall not indicate the range of values assumed by k, whenever it extends from 1 to ∞.

By equation (14), the typical element of the matrix ba is

$$\Sigma b(nk)a(km)$$

and this is *not* identical with the typical element of ab, so that in general $ab \neq ba$. This is expressed by saying that *the commutative law of multiplication does not hold for matrices*. If it happens that $ab = ba$, than a and b are said to be interchangeable or commutable (German, *vertauschbar*).

4. Associative Law of Multiplication.—In forming the product abc it makes no difference whether we first obtain bc and then abc, or ab and then abc. Expressed in symbols,

$$[ab]c = a[bc]. \tag{15}$$

The truth of this is seen at once if we write out the product abc. Its typical element is

$$\sum_{k}\sum_{j} a(nk)b(kj)c(jm)$$

which can be written in either one of two ways: ·

$$\sum_{k} a(nk)bc(km), \text{ where } bc(km) = \sum_{j} b(kj)c(jm)$$

or

$$\sum_{j} ab(nj)c(jm) \text{ where } ab(nj) = \sum_{k} a(nk)b(kj).$$

The reader should practice writing out such products until he can recognize at a glance the type of summation involved in any product. The principle used in the proof of the associative law is quite generally useful. It is simply the application of the fact that when we carry out a multiple summation, the final result is independent of the order of summation.

5. Distributive Law of Multiplication.—Obviously,

$$a(b + c) = ab + ac. \tag{16}$$

6. The Reciprocal of a Matrix; Matrix Division.—Division by a matrix is defined as multiplication by its reciprocal. To define the reciprocal we shall need a very important matrix called the "unit matrix," and denoted by the symbol, 1. It is composed entirely of zeros, except for the elements of the principal diagonal, which are all unity. It is convenient to call the typical element δ_{nm}, where δ_{nm} is Kronecker's symbol, which has the value zero if $n \neq m$, and the value 1 if $n = m$. The unit matrix is such that

$$a\,1 = a, \text{ and } 1a = a; \tag{17}$$

for, $a1(nm) = \Sigma a(nk)1(km) = \Sigma a(nk)\delta_{km}$. The only term which survives in this sum is that for which $k = m$, namely $a(nm)$. The proof of the second equation is similar. The reciprocal of the matrix a is a matrix a^{-1} such that

$$a^{-1}a = 1. \tag{18}$$

If this equation is fulfilled then also

$$aa^{-1} = 1. \tag{19}$$

In other words, the matrices a and a^{-1} can be commuted. This follows if we multiply both sides of equation (18) by a^{-1}, obtaining

$$a^{-1}aa^{-1} = 1a^{-1}.$$

By equation (17) the right member is a^{-1}, so that the product of the last two factors on the left must be the unit matrix.

7. The Time Derivative of a Matrix.—$\dot{q}$ is the matrix whose elements are the time derivatives of the elements of q. A similar statement holds for differentiation with respect to any parameter. By definition, the matrix $\dot{q}$ has the typical element

$$\frac{d}{dt}[q(nm)e^{2\pi i\nu(nm)t}] = 2\pi i\nu(nm)q(nm)e^{2\pi i\nu(nm)t}.$$

In accord with our usual convention we leave out the time factor. The remainder of the expression is denoted by $\dot{q}(nm)$ which is purely conventional and does not imply that the constant $q(nm)$ has a time derivative. We have then

$$\dot{q}(nm) = 2\pi i\nu(nm)q(nm). \tag{20}$$

It must be noted that this is a property only of the type of matrices specified in equation (10), which contain the time only through the factor $e^{2\pi i\nu(nm)t}$. Further,

$$\frac{d(ab)}{dt} = \dot{a}b + a\dot{b}. \tag{21}$$

Integration with respect to a parameter is the operation inverse to differentiation. Since the matrices discussed in quantum theory contain the time in an exponential factor, it is not possible to frame a definition for a definite integral with respect to time without destroying this characteristic of the matrix elements. There is no reason, however, why we should not consider arrays of indefinite integrals such as

$$\int q(nm)e^{2\pi i\nu(nm)t}dt,$$

if it serves a useful purpose.

8. Derivative of a Matrix with Respect to a Matrix.—The derivative of a matrix y—where y is a function of an independent variable which is also a matrix, x—is defined in exact analogy to the derivative of an ordinary function:

$$\frac{dy}{dx} = \lim_{o \to 0}\frac{y(x + \alpha) - y(x)}{\alpha}, \tag{22}$$

where α is the matrix obtained by multiplying each element of the unit matrix by a constant α. That is, $\alpha(nm) = \alpha\delta_{nm}$. In forming the quotient in equation (22), it is immaterial whether the factor α^{-1} stands before or after the numerator in multiplication; for the typical element of this matrix is

$$\alpha^{-1}(nm) = \frac{\delta_{nm}}{\alpha} \tag{23}$$

and this can be commuted with any matrix. To illustrate equation (22), let $y = x$. Then the typical element of dx/dx is

$$\lim \frac{1}{\alpha}[x(nm) + \alpha\delta_{nm} - x(nm)] = \delta_{nm}, \tag{24}$$

that is, all the elements of this matrix are zero except those on the principal diagonal. Likewise,

$$\frac{dx^2}{dx}(nm) = \lim \frac{1}{\alpha}\left\{ \sum_k [x(nk) + \alpha\delta_{nk}][x(km) + \alpha\delta_{km}] - \sum_k x(nk)x(km) \right\}$$

$$= \lim \frac{1}{\alpha}\left\{ \sum_k x(nk)\alpha\delta_{km} + \sum_k x(km)\alpha\delta_{nk} + \alpha^2\sum_k \delta_{nk}\delta_{km} \right\}.$$

In the first summation, each term is zero except the one in which $k = m$, namely, $x(nm)\delta_{mm}$, or $x(nm)$; and in the second summation each term is zero except that in which $k = n$, namely, $x(nm)\delta_{nn}$. Therefore, the result is $2x(nm)$, and the corresponding matrix equation is

$$\frac{dx^2}{dx} = 2x.$$

The rule for the differentiation of a product is identical with that of ordinary calculus. To prove this we take $y = fg$ in equation (22) and note that the numerator

$$f(x + \alpha)g(x + \alpha) - f(x)g(x)$$

can be rewritten in the form

$$f(x + \alpha)g(x + \alpha) - f(x + \alpha)g(x) + f(x + \alpha)g(x) - f(x)g(x).$$

In passing to the limit the first two terms give rise to $f\dfrac{dg}{dx}$ and the last two to $\dfrac{df}{dx}g$ so that

$$\frac{d(fg)}{dx} = f\frac{dg}{dx} + \frac{df}{dx}g. \tag{25}$$

Since any power of x can be considered as a continued product, we can use this relation to prove the formula

$$\frac{dx^n}{dx} = nx^{n-1}. \tag{26}$$

Applying this rule to the matrix power series representing any function, we see that all the usual derivative formulas hold true for functions which can be represented by such series. The idea of partial differentiation is also formally identical with that of ordinary calculus.

9. Diagonal matrices are those in which all the elements are zero except those along the principal diagonal, such as,

$$
\begin{array}{cccc}
M_1 & 0 & 0 & \cdots \\
0 & M_2 & 0 & \cdots \\
0 & 0 & M_3 & \cdots \\
\vdots & \vdots & \vdots &
\end{array}
\tag{27}
$$

The general element may be written $M_n \delta_{nm}$. A matrix of this kind is analogous to a constant in ordinary dynamics, for it has the property

$$ d\boldsymbol{M}/dt = 0. $$

If a matrix $\boldsymbol{q}$ is such that $d\boldsymbol{q}/dt = 0$, this implies that

$$ 2\pi i \nu(nm) q(nm) = 0 $$

for every pair of values of n and m. If all the energy values E_k are distinct then $\nu(nm)$ cannot be zero unless $n = m$. In this case,

$$ q(nm) = 0, \ n \neq m, $$

so that the matrix $\boldsymbol{q}$ is diagonal. If the energy values are not distinct this may be true, but is not necessarily so. We have proved, therefore, that *if the time derivative of a matrix $\boldsymbol{q}$ is zero in a non-degenerate problem, $\boldsymbol{q}$ is a diagonal matrix.*

Diagonal matrices enjoy many remarkable properties not possessed by matrices in general. The product of two diagonal matrices is also diagonal and the order of multiplication is immaterial, that is, $\boldsymbol{ab} - \boldsymbol{ba} = 0$ if both $\boldsymbol{a}$ and $\boldsymbol{b}$ are diagonal. Further, *if $\boldsymbol{ab} - \boldsymbol{ba} = 0$, and $\boldsymbol{a}$ is diagonal and is not degenerate, then $\boldsymbol{b}$ is also diagonal,* for we have

$$ a(nn)b(nm) - b(nm)a(mm) = 0. $$

Since $\boldsymbol{a}$ is not degenerate, $a(nn)$ is not equal to $a(mm)$ when n is not equal to m; and so $b(nm)$ must be zero, which proves that $\boldsymbol{b}$ is diagonal.

10. An Alternative Expression of the Time Derivative.—Consider the diagonal matrix formed of the energy values E_n, and let $\boldsymbol{q}$ be any other matrix. Then, forming the function

$$ Eq - qE, $$

we have for its nth, mth element, the sum of terms,

$$ \sum_k E_n \delta_{nk} q(km) - \sum_k q(nk) E_k \delta_{km}. $$

In the first sum, the only surviving term is that for which $k = n$ and, in the second, the only survivor occurs when $k = m$, so we obtain

$$ (E_n - E_m)q(nm) = (Eq - qE)(nm), $$

or, by Ritz's principle,

$$ h\nu(nm)q(nm) = (Eq - qE)(nm) $$

so that by equation (20),

$$\left(\frac{h}{2\pi i}\right)\dot{q} = (Eq - qE).\tag{28}$$

Obviously, q can be any matrix whatever, for the proof does not require it to be a coordinate.

11. Alternative Form for Matrix Derivatives.—We now prove that if f is a matrix function of two other matrices p and q, then,

$$fq - qf = \frac{h}{2\pi i}\frac{\partial f}{\partial p},\tag{29}$$

and

$$pf - fp = \frac{h}{2\pi i}\frac{\partial f}{\partial q},\tag{30}$$

provided that p and q satisfy the relation

$$pq - qp = \left(\frac{h}{2\pi i}\right)1.\tag{31}$$

First, we note that equations (29) and (30) are satisfied when f is set equal to either p or q. Now we show that if they are true for any two functions F and G they are true for $F + G$ and FG. The first statement is obvious. As to the second, we write

$$FGq - qFG = F(Gq - qG) + (Fq - qF)G.\tag{32}$$

But by hypothesis

$$Gq - qG = \left(\frac{h}{2\pi i}\right)\frac{\partial G}{\partial p}, \text{ etc.}$$

so that the right side of equation (32) reduces to

$$\left(\frac{h}{2\pi i}\right)\left(F\frac{\partial G}{\partial p} + \frac{\partial F}{\partial p}G\right) = \left(\frac{h}{2\pi i}\right)\frac{\partial FG}{\partial p}.$$

The extension to a product containing any number of factors is accomplished in the same way. Now the only type of matrix functions with which we shall deal is that which can be expanded in series containing terms of the type $q^{a_1}p^{b_1}q^{a_2}p^{b_2} \ldots$, and since we have shown that equation (29) is true when f is a product of this kind, it also holds for a series composed of such products. This completes the proof of equation (29), and that of equation (30) is similar.

12. Some Convenient Rules of Computation.—Assuming equation (31), we obtain by induction the following results:

$$p^n q = qp^n + \left(\frac{h}{2\pi i}\right)np^{n-1},$$

$$q^n p = pq^n - \left(\frac{h}{2\pi i}\right)nq^{n-1}.\tag{33}$$

13. The Permutation Theorem.—A matrix is said to be permuted when its rows are interchanged according to any plan we care to specify, and when the columns are also interchanged in the same way. The permutation theorem is as follows:

Every matrix equation $F(x_1, x_2, \cdots) = 0$ *remains true if all the matrices* $x_1, \ldots$ *are subjected to the same permutation.*

To prove this, we need only show that if a and b go into a' and b' as a result of this permutation, then the results of applying it to $a + b$ and ab will be $a' + b'$ and $a'b'$, respectively. The proof depends on the fact that a permutation can be replaced by a suitable matrix multiplication. Let us agree to replace

$$1, 2, 3, \ldots n, \ldots$$

by the numbers

$$k_1, k_2, k_3, \ldots k_n, \ldots$$

and let us form a permutation matrix, p, such that

$$p(nm) = 1 \text{ if } m = k_n, \text{ and } 0 \text{ otherwise.}$$

The matrix $\tilde{p}$ obtained by interchanging rows and columns is such that

$$\tilde{p}(nm) = 1 \text{ if } n = k_m, \text{ and } 0 \text{ otherwise,}$$

and so the typical element of $p\tilde{p}$ is

$$\sum_j p(nj)\tilde{p}(jm).$$

This will be zero unless $j = k_n \equiv k_m$, that is, unless $n = m$, in which case it is unity, and therefore $p\tilde{p} = 1$, so that $\tilde{p} = p^{-1}$.

Illustration.—Consider the permutation of the numbers 1. 2, 3, defined by

$$k_1 = 3, \quad k_2 = 1, \quad k_3 = 2.$$

Then

$$p = \begin{Vmatrix} 0 & 0 & 1 \\ 1 & 0 & 0 \\ 0 & 1 & 0 \end{Vmatrix} \qquad \tilde{p} = \begin{Vmatrix} 0 & 1 & 0 \\ 0 & 0 & 1 \\ 1 & 0 & 0 \end{Vmatrix}$$

Returning to our theorem, we have

$$pa(nm) = \Sigma p(nj)a(jm)$$

which reduces to the single term

$$p(nk_n)a(k_n m) = a(k_n m).$$

That is, the element of pa standing in the nth row and mth column is the same as the element of a standing in the k_nth row and mth column, so the multiplication has simply carried the k_nth row into the nth row. Similarly,

$$ap^{-1}(nm) = a(nk_m)$$

which means that this multiplication results in carrying the k_mth column into the position of the mth column. Applying both multiplications in succession,

$$a' = pap^{-1},$$

so that

$$a' + b' = p(a + b)p^{-1}.$$

Further,
$$a'b' = pap^{-1}pbp^{-1}.$$
In the center $p^{-1}p = 1$, so the right side is $pabp^{-1}$. This completes the proof of our theorem.

5. THE QUANTUM CONDITION FOR SYSTEMS OF ONE DEGREE OF FREEDOM

We must now study the laws of atomic mechanics discovered by Heisenberg[1] and extended by Born, Heisenberg, and Jordan,[2] which enable us to calculate the values of the quantities $q(nm)$, $p(nm)$, and $\nu(nm)$.

These amplitudes and frequencies are not variables; they are constant quantities, depending only on pure numbers and universal physical constants. They are infinite in number and we may expect that the true laws of atomic mechanics will yield an infinite number of equations for determining them. We may also expect that these laws will reduce to the ordinary dynamical laws in the region of high quantum numbers and small changes of the quantum numbers.

In the old mechanics the amplitudes and phases of an atom are not completely determined by the equations of motion. They appear as constants of integration, and are assigned definite values by applying the quantum conditions. Similarly, in matrix mechanics, we have a set of equations involving the p's, q's, and ν's, together with h, which form a natural generalization of the quantum conditions. Heisenberg's assumption as to the matrix quantum conditions was based on a form of the ordinary quantum conditions used by Thomas[3] and W. Kuhn.[4] If we write

$$p = \Sigma p_j e^{2\pi i \nu j t}, \quad q = \Sigma q_l e^{2\pi i \nu l t}$$

with the summations running from $-\infty$ to $+\infty$, the integral $I = \oint p\,dq$ takes the form

$$I = \int_0^{1/\nu} \sum_j \sum_l 2\pi i \nu l p_j q_l e^{2\pi i \nu (j+l) t} dt.$$

The only terms different from zero are those in which $j = -l$, so that

$$I = 2\pi i \sum_l l p_l q_l. \tag{34}$$

Differentiating,

$$2\pi i \sum_l \frac{l \partial (p_l q_l)}{\partial I} = 1. \tag{35}$$

---

[1] *Z. Physik*, **33**, 879 (1925).

[2] Born and Jordan, *Z. Physik*, **34**, 858 (1925); Born, Heisenberg, and Jordan, *Z. Physik*, **35**, 557 (1925).

[3] *Naturwis.*, **13**, 627 (1925).

[4] *Z. Physik*, **33**, 408 (1925).

For the case where $p = m\dot{q}$, Thomas and Kuhn succeeded in generalizing equation (35) so that it held for all values of the quantum numbers. Their procedure was based on the correspondence principle and consisted in replacing each derivative by a suitable finite difference. Further, Heisenberg was able to construct a matrix function which may be considered as a generalization of the result obtained by Thomas and Kuhn, without any restriction on the form of p. It must be understood that this procedure is purely an assumption, justified by the striking character of its results. The equation adopted by Heisenberg was

$$\frac{h}{2\pi i} = \sum_l [q(n+l, n)p(n, n+l) - q(n, n-l)p(n-l, n)], \quad (36)$$

n being a quantum number. Terms which contain a negative index are to be set equal to zero, for they correspond to transitions involving non-existent terms. Writing $n + l = k$ in the first product and $n - l = k$ in the second, equation (36) becomes

$$\sum_k [p(nk)q(kn) - q(nk)p(kn)] = \frac{h}{2\pi i}. \quad (37)$$

There is an equation of this form for each value of n, and the left members are evidently the diagonal elements of the matrix $pq - qp$. This suggests that we write

$$pq - qp = \left(\frac{h}{2\pi i}\right)1, \quad (38)$$

as the quantum condition of matrix mechanics. This is the *commutation relation* which tells us how much the product pq exceeds qp. It serves as an additional law of computation in matrix algebra, which enables us to obtain definite numerical results.

6. THE ENERGY MATRIX

In Sec. **4** we assumed that the frequencies occurring in the elements of all the matrices of atomic physics obey the Ritz combination law, from which it follows that each frequency can be expressed as the difference of two numbers,

$$E_n - E_m = h\nu(nm).$$

We wish to know how these numbers are related to the elements of the matrix representing the energy. In ordinary mechanics the energy is invariable, so that the Fourier series representing it reduces to a constant term. This constancy is expressed by the vanishing of the time derivative, so by analogy we require in matrix mechanics that $dE/dt = 0$. This means that E is a diagonal matrix, if the energy levels are all distinct, which we shall assume to be the case until further notice. With this clue, we form a diagonal matrix E with the constants

E_n for its non-vanishing elements, and ask, how can we justify our action if we call this the energy matrix? This identification will be satisfactory if we succeed in finding analogues of the canonical equations of motion, involving a matrix function $H(p, q)$ called the "Hamiltonian function," such that when the coordinates are suitably chosen the relations

$$\frac{dH}{dt} = 0, \tag{40}$$

and

$$H = E, \tag{41}$$

are satisfied. The first of these will be referred to as the law of conservation of energy. The second, when proved, yields the Bohr frequency condition,

$$H_n - H_m = h\nu(nm). \tag{42}$$

7. THE MATRIX LAWS OF MOTION; THE THEOREM OF ENERGY CONSERVATION

We are now in a position to discuss the laws of motion. As we shall see, there is a close relation among (1) the quantum conditions; (2) the law $dH/dt = 0$; (3) equation (42); and (4) the laws of motion. Assuming (1) and (3) we can prove (2) and (4); assuming (1) and (4) we can prove (2) and (3), and other combinations are probably possible. Here we shall proceed according to the second plan, and shall begin by stating the equations of motion proposed by Born and Jordan. They are

$$\dot{q} = \frac{\partial H}{\partial p}, \quad \dot{p} = -\frac{\partial H}{\partial q}. \tag{43}$$

These equations are not differential equations; on the contrary, they stand for an infinite number of algebraic equations, each one of which has an infinite number of terms. H is a function of p and q, constructed by matrix multiplication and addition, and is taken as nearly similar to the energy function of classical theory as possible. For example, if the classical energy function is $p^2 + pq$, we take $H = p^2 + \frac{pq}{2} + \frac{qp}{2}$. The last term is split into two terms symmetrical in p and q, because in classical mechanics the product qp stands on an equal footing with pq. This is not true in matrix mechanics and in a certain sense the symmetrization of the term pq serves to restore p and q to an equal footing. General rules for writing the matrix energy function from a knowledge of the classical energy function are given by Born and Jordan. They are rather complicated and since they are often equivalent to the requirement that H be symmetrical in p and q, we shall not pursue the subject further.

We shall now prove equations (40) and (42). By equations (28), (43), and (29), we have

$$\left(\frac{h}{2\pi i}\right)\dot{q} = Eq - qE = \left(\frac{h}{2\pi i}\right)\frac{\partial H}{\partial p} = Hq - qH, \tag{44}$$

and similarly,

$$Ep - pE = Hp - pH,$$

whence,

$$(E - H)q = q(E - H), \; (E - H)p = p(E - H).$$

That is, the matrix $E - H$ commutes with q and p, and therefore with any function of q and p, so that

$$(E - H)H = H(E - H)$$

and

$$EH - HE = 0,$$

but by equation (28), this means that

$$\frac{dH}{dt} = 0,$$

and H is diagonal. A typical element of equation (44) may be written

$$q(nm)(E_n - E_m) = q(nm)(H_n - H_m).$$

From this equation (42) follows at once, unless $q(nm) = 0$.

When this exceptional case occurs, we proceed as in the following example: Let $q(34)$ be the vanishing element. If $q(35)$ and $q(45)$ are not zero, we get

$$H_3 - H_5 = \nu(35), \; H_4 - H_5 = \nu(45),$$

and by subtraction,

$$H_3 - H_4 = \nu(34).$$

A device of this kind will always work if we can find a set of transitions having finite q's which leads us from level 3 to level 4. If such a set cannot be found, the term system obviously splits into two (or more) parts which do not combine.

8. THE HARMONIC OSCILLATOR

The Hamiltonian for the oscillator is

$$H = \frac{p^2}{2\mu} + 2\pi^2\nu_0^2\mu q^2. \tag{45}$$

It is *assumed* that we are dealing with a non-degenerate system—that is, E_n is not equal to E_m unless $n = m$. We have

$$\dot{q} = \frac{p}{\mu}, \; \dot{p} = -4\pi^2\nu_0^2\mu q, \tag{46}$$

just as in classical mechanics, although the meaning of the equations is profoundly different. Let us differentiate the first of equations (46), obtaining $\ddot{q} = \dot{p}/\mu$, and eliminate p, obtaining,

$$\ddot{q} + (2\pi\nu_0)^2 q = 0.$$

This represents a double infinity of equations in square array. The equation in the nth row and mth column involves only the element $q(nm)$ of the coordinate-matrix q. It is

$$\ddot{q}(nm) + (2\pi\nu_0)^2 q(nm) = 0,$$

or,

$$-4\pi^2\nu^2(nm)q(nm) + (2\pi\nu_0)^2 q(nm) = 0,$$

or,

$$\{\nu^2(nm) - \nu_0^2\}q(nm) = 0. \tag{47}$$

From this we conclude that $\nu(nm) = \pm\nu_0$, provided that $q(nm)$ is not zero. In other words, the frequency in the time factor of all non-vanishing elements of q is $\pm\nu_0$. (This information is available only because of the simple character of the problem. At the corresponding stage in the solution of almost all dynamical problems we shall study, no similar conclusions can be drawn.) This is all that can be said about $\nu(nm)$ and $q(nm)$ by use of the equations of motion. The problem comes to a halt in similar fashion if we eliminate q from equation (46) and solve for p. This brings out clearly the rôle of the commutation equation (38) which plays the same rôle as the quantum condition in Wentzel's treatment of Schrödinger's theory (App. V, Sec. 3). It enables us to determine the size of the p's and q's, the result being in exact agreement with the amplitudes obtained by the methods of wave mechanics, introduced in Chap. XV, Sec. **17**. The use of the matrix 1 on the right side of the commutation equation, rather than any other value, is responsible for results equivalent to those which arise from the normalization of Ψ.

In order to utilize equation (38), we substitute the value $\dot{q}\mu$ for p, obtaining

$$\dot{q}q - q\dot{q} = \frac{1 \cdot h}{2\pi i\mu}$$

The typical element of this relation is

$$\sum_k [2\pi i\nu(nk)q(nk)q(km) - q(nk) \cdot 2\pi i\nu(km)q(km)] = \delta(nm)\frac{h}{2\pi i\mu}.$$

That is,

$$\sum_k [\nu(nk) - \nu(km)]q(nk)q(km) = -\frac{h}{4\pi^2\mu} \text{ or } 0, \tag{48}$$

according as n is or is not equal to m. The diagonal elements of equation (48) may be rewritten

$$\sum_k \nu(nk)|q(nk)^2| = -\frac{h}{8\pi^2\mu}, \tag{49}$$

for $-\nu(kn) = \nu(nk)$. This can be simplified at once. By equation (47), all elements in the nth row of the q matrix vanish except two at most, having the frequencies

$$\nu(nn') = \nu_0, \ \nu(nn'') = -\nu_0 = -\nu(nn'). \tag{50}$$

The level n' is below n and n'' above n, because ν_0 is positive. Now equation (49) reduces to the form

$$\nu(nn')|q(nn')|^2 + \nu(nn'')|q(nn'')|^2 = \nu(nn'')\{|q(nn'')|^2 -$$
$$|q(nn')|^2\} = -\frac{h}{8\pi^2\mu} \quad (51)$$

We are now in possession of all the material needed for determining the elements of H. Remembering that $p = \mu\dot{q}$, H may be written

$$\frac{\mu\dot{q}^2}{2} + 2\pi^2\nu_0^2\mu q^2$$

and by the use of equation (20), we obtain

$$H(nm) = 2\pi^2\mu\sum_k q(nk)q(km)[\nu_0^2 - \nu(nk)\nu(km)]. \quad (52)$$

The bracket in equation (52) reduces to $2\nu_0^2$ so that

$$H(nn) \equiv W_n = 4\pi^2\mu\nu_0^2[|q(nn')|^2 + |q(nn'')|^2]. \quad (53)$$

In the nth row of q, one of the two non-vanishing elements lies to the left, and the other to the right of the principal diagonal (if both exist), the first corresponding to emission and the second to absorption. Likewise, each column contains at most two non-zero elements, one above and one below the diagonal. Our knowledge of the Planck oscillator makes us suspect that the non-vanishing elements correspond to transitions in which the quantum number changes by unity, so that for any n, these elements are $q(n, n+1)$ and $q(n, n-1)$. If this is so, the matrix q has the appearance

$$
\begin{array}{cccccc}
0 & q(01) & 0 & 0 & \cdots \\
q(10) & 0 & q(12) & 0 & \cdots \\
0 & q(21) & 0 & q(23) & \cdots \\
0 & 0 & q(32) & 0 & \cdots \\
\cdots & \cdots & \cdots & \cdots & \cdots
\end{array}
$$

Let us assume for the moment that such is the case, and that the energy level numbered zero is the lowest level. Then from equation (51)

$$\nu(01)\{|q(01)|^2 - |q(0,-1)|^2\} = -\frac{h}{8\pi^2\mu}.$$

Now, $q(0, -1)$ must be put equal to zero, because there is no level numbered minus 1, and $\nu(01) = -\nu_0$ so this equation becomes

$$\nu_0|q(01)|^2 = \frac{h}{8\pi^2\mu}.$$

Substituting this value of $|q(01)|^2$ in equation (53), we see that

$$E_0 = \frac{h\nu_0}{2}.$$

Now it is easy to obtain the other levels.   Remembering that $|q(01)|^2 = |q(10)|^2$, it follows from equation (51) that

$$|q(12)|^2 = |q(01)|^2 + \frac{h}{8\pi^2\mu\nu_0} = \frac{2h}{8\pi^2\mu\nu_0}.$$

Similarly,

$$|q(n, n+1)|^2 = |q(n+1, n)|^2 = (n+1)\frac{h}{8\pi^2\mu\nu_0}. \qquad (54)$$

By using these values in equation (53) we find that

$$E_n = (n + \tfrac{1}{2})\, h\nu_0, \qquad (55)$$

in exact agreement with the result obtained by wave mechanics.

To complete our study of the harmonic oscillator, we discuss the values of the amplitudes.   From equation (54), we may write

$$q(n, n+1) = \left[(n+1)\frac{h}{8\pi^2\mu\nu_0}\right]^{\frac{1}{2}} e^{i\delta_n}, \qquad (56)$$

but nothing can be said as to the values of the phase constants.   This is not to be considered a defect of the theory, for just as in the classical theory, the unobservable phase of the oscillator has no influence on its energy or the intensity of its radiation, both of which are to be considered as observable.   The energy depends on the square of the absolute value of q, which does not involve the phase.

It is interesting to compare the elements of the *p*-matrix with the classical p's.   By equation (46),

$$|p(nm)|^2 = 4\pi^2\mu^2\nu(nm)^2|\gamma(nm)|^2. \qquad (57)$$

This is zero except when $m = n \pm 1$, when we have

$$|p(n, n+1)|^2 + |p(n, n-1)|^2 = \mu E_n.$$

This may be compared with the classical relation $2p^2 = \mu E$, while after multiplication by the implied factor $\exp 2\pi i\nu_0 t$, equation (56) is similar to the classical equation

$$q = \left[\frac{J}{8\pi^2\mu\nu_0}\right]^{\frac{1}{2}} \exp\left(2\pi i\nu_0 t + i\delta\right),$$

J being equal to nh.

In our treatment of the oscillator, we assumed that the numbers n', n, and n'' have consecutive values, that is, transitions occur only between adjoining levels. How can we *prove* that such is the case?   First of all, each energy level can be entered in at least one direction, that is, for every level E_n there is at least one level E_m such that $q(nm)$ is not zero; there is at least one non-vanishing element in every column and every row of the q matrix.   For if this were not true in the case of the nth row or column, the (nn) element of $pq - qp$, namely, $\Sigma[p(nk)q(kn) - q(nk)p(kn)]$, would vanish, contradicting the equation (38).

Suppose the situation portrayed in the diagram of the matrix, q, is not correct, so that ν_0 may correspond to a change of the quantum number greater than 1.   Beginning with the lowest level, for there must be a lowest level, we construct a sequence of levels at intervals ν_0. The numbers belonging to the higher levels in this sequence are unknown for the moment, but we suppose at least one pair of them has numbers which are not consecutive. Similarly, there may be another level, (E_2 for example), which is not entered from below, on which we build up another sequence of levels, at intervals ν_0, and so on. Now consider the *lowest* term in one of these sequences. The proof given above shows that its energy is $h\nu_0/2$. But this reasoning applies to the lowest level of any of these sequences, so all of them must lie in the same position on the energy diagram. However, this violates the assumption that no two levels have the same energy, and so only one sequence of levels exists after all. Therefore, ν_0 is the spacing between adjacent levels, which is what we set out to prove.

Further, we assumed that the levels are numbered in the order of increasing energy. If this were not true, we could make it so by permuting rows and columns of all matrices in the same way, until the lowest energy value occurs in the leading position in the E matrix, and so on. By Sec. **4**, Part (13), this does not destroy the meaning of any matrix equations. In the remainder of our work with matrices, we shall suppose this detail attended to.

9. QUANTIZATION OF THE ROTATOR

There is no place in Heisenberg's matrix scheme for the treatment of problems in which the independent variables continually increase; each element of a matrix must be considered as a generalization of a term in a Fourier series, and such a series is naturally fitted to represent an oscillation. Halpern[1] quantized the rotator in matrix theory by the use of a transformation which changes the energy function of the rotator into that of the oscillator. He recognized that the success of this expedient was a lucky chance, and it cannot be employed to reduce the general conditionally periodic system to a system of independent oscillators. In spite of the drawbacks of Halpern's method, it will be of interest to outline his treatment of the rotator.

The Poincaré transformation,

$$q = (2p_\varphi)^{1/2} \cos \varphi, \; p = -(2p_\varphi)^{1/2} \sin \varphi,$$

will carry the function $p_\varphi{}^2/2I$ over into

$$H = \frac{(p^2 + q^2)^2}{8I}.$$

In classical theory this represents the product of the energy function for an oscillator with energy $(2HI)^{1/2}$ and for a system which might be referred to as an "imaginary oscillator," with energy $(-2HI)^{1/2}$. For use in matrix theory, we symmetrize this function, writing it as

$$\frac{(p^4 + p^2q^2 + q^2p^2 + q^4)}{8I}.$$

The solution of this matrix problem is very simple, and yields the energy values $(j + \frac{1}{2})^2 h^2/8\pi^2 I$.

[1] *Z. Physik*, **33**, 8 (1923). See also Tamm, *ibid.* **37**, 685 (1926).

10. SPECTRAL INTENSITIES IN THE MATRIX THEORY

The calculation of the relative intensities of spectral lines in the matrix theory is very similar to the corresponding process of classical theory. The matrix component $q(nm)$ may be considered as the amplitude of a virtual harmonic oscillator of frequency $\nu(nm)$. Multiplying by the electronic charge, we obtain the electric moment, and substitute it into the classical formula for the average rate of radiation by such an oscillator. (Chap. VI, Sec. **1**.) The Einstein probability coefficient for the transition n to m is defined by the relation

$$A_{nm}h\nu(nm) = I, \tag{58}$$

where I is the average rate of emission. This relation gives us a means of comparing the results of the matrix theory directly with experiment.

11. MATRIX MECHANICS FOR SEVERAL DEGREES OF FREEDOM

The extension of matrix mechanics to conservative systems having f degrees of freedom is easily understood, for the underlying physical ideas are nearly identical with those outlined for the case of one degree. Dirac[1] and Born, Heisenberg, and Jordan,[2] independently, discovered the appropriate generalization. A coordinate is expressed in classical mechanics by an f-fold Fourier series, having a typical term

$$q_{k_1}, \cdots {}_{k_f} \exp [2\pi i(k_1\omega_1 + \cdots k_f\omega_f)t].$$

There is an f-fold infinity of such terms. On the other hand, the emission frequencies of a system with f degrees depend on the values of $2f$ quantities, namely, the quantum numbers of the initial state and those of the final state, and therefore may be written

$$\nu(n_1, \ldots n_f; m_1, \ldots m_f).$$

Instead of the f-fold Fourier series, in matrix theory we consider an aggregate of terms,

$$q_r(n_1, \ldots n_f; m_1, \ldots m_f) \exp 2\pi i\nu(n_1, \ldots n_f; m_1, \ldots m_f)t,$$

which form altogether a matrix of $2f$ dimensions. All the laws of Sec. **4** hold without change if we replace the multiplication rule by the following rule involving f-fold summations:

$$(ab)(n_1, \cdots n_f; m_1, \cdots m_f) =$$
$$\sum_{k_1} \cdots \sum_{k_f} a(n_1, \cdots n_f; k_1, \cdots k_f)b(k_1, \cdots k_f; m_1, \cdots m_f). \tag{59}$$

The multiplicity of summations makes the attainment of numerical results more complicated, but general theorems are usually no more complicated than before. This is partly due to the fact that a $2f$-

---

[1] *Proc. Roy. Soc.*, **109**, 642 (1925).

[2] *Z. Physik*, **35**, 557 (1925).

dimensional matrix can be rewritten as a two-dimensional one. For example, the terms of a four-dimensional matrix are drawn up as follows:

$$
\begin{array}{llll}
a(11;11) & a(11;12) \cdots a(11;21) & a(11;22) \cdots \\
a(12;11) & a(12;12) \cdots a(12;21) & a(12;22) \cdots \\
\cdots\cdots\cdots\cdots\cdots\cdots\cdots\cdots\cdots\cdots\cdots \\
a(21;11) & a(21;12) \cdots a(21;21) & a(21;22) \cdots \\
a(22;11) & a(22;12) \cdots a(22;21) & a(22;22) \cdots \\
\cdots\cdots\cdots\cdots\cdots\cdots\cdots \quad \cdots\cdots\cdots
\end{array}
$$

We are dealing with an infinite checkerboard, each square being also an infinite checkerboard. If we have another such board, b, and apply the multiplication rule of equation (14) we see that the single summation involved takes in all the terms of the f-fold summation of equation (59).

The Hamilton equations are identical in form with the classical ones, and the commutation rules are as folllows:

$$p_r p_s - p_s p_r = 0, \tag{60}$$

$$q_r q_s - q_s q_r = 0, \tag{61}$$

$$p_r q_s - p_s q_r = 0, \; r \text{ not equal to } s, \tag{62}$$

$$p_r q_r - q_r p_r = \frac{1h}{2\pi i}. \tag{63}$$

The reader is strongly advised to write out a few terms of the products involved in these quantum conditions, to aid in understanding what they imply.

It is worth noting that the equations of motion and the commutation relations do not suffice to prove the Bohr frequency condition when the system is degenerate. As Born, Heisenberg, and Jordan have proved, the law of energy conservation $dH/dt = 0$ can still be obtained from these equations, but this does not show that H is a diagonal matrix because the system may be degenerate. For example, if we are dealing with a system of two degrees of freedom it may occur that $H(3, 10; 3, 10) = H(3, 12; 3, 12)$, say. Then $\nu(3, 10; 3, 12) = 0$, and there may be a term $H(3, 10; 3, 12)$, for which the exponential time factor reduces to a constant. The time derivative of this term is zero, as it should be, but it does not lie on the principal diagonal of the matrix. This prevents us from proving the frequency condition as we did for systems having one degree of freedom. For this reason, we take as our fundamental equations the quantum conditions (equations (60) to (63)), and the relation

$$H = E = \text{diagonal matrix.}$$

This assures the validity of the frequency condition in all cases.

12. THE MATRIX ANALOGUE OF THE HAMILTON-JACOBI EQUATION

Our matrix calculation of the energy and the coordinates of the harmonic oscillator was made as simple as possible, but it will convince the reader that the study of more complex systems would be very difficult, if attacked by direct methods. In general, we are confronted with an infinite number of algebraic equations having an infinite number of unknowns. It is very important therefore, to introduce methods for simplifying matrix problems by transformation of coordinates. This term must be carefully explained, for the matrices q and p are not really variables, but simply aggregates of algebraic quantities. A transformation is simply a set of matrix equations expressing the q's and p's in terms of an equal number of new coordinates and momenta $Q_1 \ldots P_f$.

For the present we restrict our study to problems of one degree of freedom. We saw in Chap. IV how the action function S serves to define a canonical transformation to new variables P, Q, such that the energy is a function only of the P's, which are constant, while the Q's are angle variables. We now introduce a matrix transformation which enjoys analogous properties, namely,

$$P = SpS^{-1}, \quad Q = SqS^{-1}, \tag{64}$$

where S is any matrix whatever. This transformation has the property that

$$f(PQ) = Sf(pq)S^{-1} \tag{65}$$

where $f(PQ)$ is obtained from $f(pq)$ by replacing p and q with P and Q *without altering the form of the function.* Thus, if

$$H(pq) = \frac{p^2}{2\mu},$$

then

$$H(PQ) = \frac{P^2}{2\mu}.$$

To prove equation (65) we simply note that if it is true for two functions f and g it is true for $f + g$ and fg. Thus,

$$f(PQ)g(PQ) = Sf(pq)S^{-1} \cdot Sg(pq)S^{-1} = Sf(pq)g(pq)S^{-1},$$

since $S^{-1}S$ in the middle is equal to 1. The relation is true for p and q, by hypothesis and so it holds for any function. In particular, it shows that

$$PQ - QP = \frac{1h}{2\pi i} \tag{66}$$

by virtue of equation (38). Any transformation in which equation (38) holds true for both the old and the new variables is called a "canonical transformation." Similarly, in the case of problems of several degrees of freedom, a transformation is said to be canonical if both the old and the new variables obey the commutation rules of equations (60) to (63). Jordan[1] has proved that the most general canonical transformation can be expressed in the form

$$P_k = Sp_kS^{-1}, \quad Q_k = Sq^kS^{-1}.$$

[1] *Z. Physik*, **37**, 383 (1926).

We use equation (64) to solve mechanical problems by a perturbation method. Suppose we have an "unperturbed" problem for which the energy function is $H_0(p_0q_0)$, a diagonal matrix, and that we have found the elements of the matrices p_0 and q_0 which satisfy equation (38). Let the energy function for the perturbed problem be

$$H(p_0q_0) = H_0(p_0q_0) + \lambda H_1(p_0, q_0) + \lambda^2 H_2(p_0, q_0) + \cdots , \quad (67)$$

where $H(p_0q_0)$ is *not* a diagonal matrix. We seek for a transformation

$$p = Sp_0S^{-1}, q = Sq_0S^{-1} \quad (68)$$

such that the new Hamilton function $H(pq)$ will be a diagonal matrix E. It will be understood that although $H(pq)$ is the same function of p, q that $H(p_0q_0)$ is of p_0, q_0, the values of the elements of p, q are different from those in p_0, q_0, and so $H(pq)$ can be diagonal although $H(p_0q_0)$ is not. Our problem is to find S. We begin by assuming that

$$S = 1 + \lambda S_1 + \lambda^2 S_2 + \cdots ,$$
$$E = E_0 + \lambda E_1 + \lambda^2 E_2 + \cdots , \quad (69)$$

where all the E's are diagonal. Multiplying the equation

$$SH(p_0, q_0)S^{-1} = E$$

by S, we have

$$SH(p_0, q_0) = ES, \quad (70)$$

or,

$$(1 + \lambda S_1 + \cdots)(H_0 + \lambda H_1 + \cdots) = (E_0 + \lambda E_1 + \cdots)$$
$$(1 + \lambda S_1 + \cdots).$$

Multiplying out, and equating the coefficients of the various powers of λ on both sides, we have

$$H_0 = E_0 \quad (71)$$

$$S_1H_0 - H_0S_1 + H_1 = E_1, \quad (72)$$

$$S_2H_0 - H_0S_2 + H_0S_1^2 - S_1H_0S_1 + S_1H_1 - H_1S_1 + H_2 = E_2, \quad (73)$$

and, in general,

$$S_rH_0 - H_0S_r + F_r(H_0 \cdots H_r, S_0, \cdots S_{r-1}) = E_r. \quad (74)$$

The equations for several degrees of freedom are similar, except that multiple summations replace the simple summations implied in the relations given.

13. PERTURBATION THEORY FOR A NON-DEGENERATE SYSTEM[1]

H_0 of equation (71) is a known diagonal matrix. Nominally, it is a function of the old coordinates, while we should like to express the final solution of our problem in terms of the new ones. Actually, however, its elements depend only on pure numbers and on universal constants, and H_0 is not changed by a transformation. Thus, the elements of E_0 are not only *equal* to those of H_0, but are *identical* with them. We now

---

[1] We discuss non-degenerate and degenerate systems separately because certain equations are altered when several energy levels coincide.

proceed to equation (72).   Although E_1 is unknown, we have made the hypothesis that it is diagonal, and so the left member of equation (72) is also diagonal.   This means that the diagonal elements of the left member are equal to the quantities $E_1(nn)$, whatever they may be, while the non-diagonal elements vanish.   To find the first-order perturbation terms in the energy we simply write down the equations,

$$\Sigma S_1(nk)H_0(kn) - \Sigma H_0(nk)S_1(kn) + H_1(nn) = E_1(nn). \tag{75}$$

$H_0(nk)$ is zero except when $k = n$, since H_0 is diagonal, and the only terms which survive in the summations are

$$S_1(nn)\,H_0(nn) - H_0(nn)S_1(nn),$$

which cancel, leaving us with the relation,

$$H_1(nn) = E_1(nn). \tag{76}$$

The matrix H_1 is known from the statement of the problem, and so we have complete knowledge of the elements of E_1.   The first-order perturbations of the energy are the diagonal elements of λH_1.   This is strikingly similar to the classical theorem that the first-order perturbation is equal to the average value of the perturbing potential taken over the undisturbed orbit (Chap. VI, Sec. **10**).

We now obtain S_1, in order to use it in equation (73) for determining E_2.   To do this, we write down the general element of equation (72):

$$\Sigma S_1(nk)H_0(km) - \Sigma H_0(nk)S_1(km) + H_1(nm) = E_1(nm). \tag{77}$$

Because H_0 is diagonal, all terms in the summations vanish except those containing $S_1(nm)$.   Thus, we have one linear equation to determine each element of S_1.   Now our previous treatment of the diagonal terms of equation (72) shows that the equation containing an element $S_1(nn)$ fails to determine it, so we may take the elements $S_1(nn)$ equal to zero. When n is not m, equation (77) reduces to

$$S_1(nm)[H_0(mm) - H_0(nn)] + H_1(nm) = 0,$$

whence,

$$S_1(nm) = \frac{H_1(nm)}{h\nu_0(nm)}, \; n \neq m. \tag{78}$$

The method of deriving higher approximations is similar.   We write the diagonal terms of equation (74), namely,

$$\Sigma S_r(nk)H_0(kn) - \Sigma H_0(nk)S_r(kn) + F_r(nn) = E_r(nn),$$

and note that the two summations vanish for the same reasons as in the analogous case above; and so

$$F_r(nn) = E_r(nn). \tag{79}$$

But the matrix F_r is completely known, from the calculations by which preceding approximations were obtained, and so E_r is known, since it is assumed to be diagonal.   This result may be expressed in the form

$$\overline{F}_r = E_r, \tag{80}$$

where $\overline{F_r}$ is formed from F_r by setting all its non-diagonal elements equal to zero. $\overline{F_r}$ is called the time mean of F_r for it is analogous to the constant term of a Fourier series, which is the time mean of the series. The equation for $S_r(nm)$ is obtained in the same manner as that for $S_1(nm)$, and leads to the result

$$S_r(nm) = \frac{F_r(nm)(1 - \delta_{nm})}{h\nu_0(nm)} \tag{81}$$

where δ_{nm} is one if $n = m$ and zero if n is not m.

Now we are able to find p and q by using the values of S and S^{-1} in equation (68). We easily find that

$$S^{-1} = 1 - \lambda S_1 + \lambda^2(S_1^2 - S_2) \cdots , \tag{82}$$

and so, writing q as a series in ascending powers of λ, we get

$$q \equiv q_0 + \lambda q_1 + \cdots = (1 + \lambda S_1 + \cdots)q_0$$
$$[1 - \lambda S_1 + \lambda^2(S_1^2 - S_2) + \cdots].$$

Then q_1, q_2, etc., are equal to the coefficients of λ, λ^2, etc. on the right. We get

$$q_1 = S_1 q_0 - q_0 S_1,$$
$$q_2 = S_2 q_0 - q_0 S_2 + q_0 S_1^2 - S_1 q_0 S_1. \tag{83}$$

The formulas for p, and for any function of p and q, are similar, by virtue of equation (68).

14. SUMMARY OF PERTURBATION FORMULAS

It will be useful to assemble the explicit formulas for the first- and second-order perturbation terms in E, q, and p. By equation (76),

$$E_1 = \overline{H}_1, \quad E_1(nn) = H_1(nn). \tag{84}$$

By equation (78),

$$S_1(nm) = \frac{H_1(nm)(1 - \delta_{nm})}{h\nu_0(nm)}. \tag{85}$$

By equation (83),

$$q_1(nm) = \sum \frac{'H_1(nk)q_0(km)}{h\nu_0(nk)} - \sum \frac{'q_0(nk)H_1(km)}{h\nu_0(km)}, \tag{86}$$

$$p_1(nm) = \sum \frac{'H_1(nk)p_0(km)}{h\nu_0(nk)} - \sum \frac{'p_0(nk)H_1(km)}{h\nu_0(km)}. \tag{87}$$

The prime indicates the omission of the term $k = n$ in the first summation, and $k = m$ in the second, arising from the fact that $S_1(nn) = 0$. By equation (80),

$$E_2 = \overline{H_0 S_1^2} - \overline{S_1 H_0 S_1} + \overline{S_1 H_1} - \overline{H_1 S_1} + \overline{H_2},$$

$$E_2(nn) = \sum_k{}' \Big\{ E_0(nn)S_1(nk)S_1(kn) - S_1(nk)E_0(kk)S_1(kn)$$
$$+ S_1(nk)H_1(kn) - H_1(nk)S_1(kn) \Big\} + H_2(nn).$$

The first, second, and fourth terms cancel, and, therefore,

$$E_2(nn) = H_2(nn) + \sum {}' \frac{H_1(nk)H_1(kn)}{h\nu_0(nk)}. \tag{88}$$

By equation (81), after reductions practically identical with those used in finding E_2,

$$S_2(nm) = \frac{H_2(nm)}{h\nu_0(nm)} + \sum_k {}' \frac{H_1(nk)H_1(km)}{h\nu_0(nm)h\nu_0(km)} - \frac{H_1(nn)S_1(nm)}{h\nu_0(nm)}. \tag{89}$$

By methods which will be understood after reading the next section, J. L. Dunham found that

$$S_2(nn) = \frac{1}{2} \sum_j S_1(nj) S_1(jn). \tag{90}$$

These equations permit the evaluation of q_2 from (83), and formulas for p_2, etc. are obtained on replacing q_0 by p_0, etc.

15. A CONDITION WHICH S MUST FULFILL; $S\tilde{S}^* = 1$

We saw in Sec. 2 that it is important for all the matrices of atomic physics to be Hermitian, a condition which corresponds to the classical requirement that any physical quantity must be real. Therefore, we must ask whether the transformation of coordinates determined by equation (68) is such that the new coordinates will enjoy this property. We have the following theorem:

If a Hermitian matrix x is subjected to the transformation

$$X = SxS^{-1}, \tag{91}$$

then in order that X shall also be Hermitian, S must obey the relation

$$S\tilde{S}^* = 1, \tag{92}$$

where S is called the transposed matrix of S and is the matrix obtained by interchanging the rows and columns of S, so that

$$\tilde{S}(nm) = S(mn).$$

Proof.—In proving this theorem, we need the fact that if $x = yz$, then $\tilde{x} = \tilde{z}\tilde{y}$, which may be shown as follows:

$$\tilde{x}(nm) = x(mn) = \Sigma y(mk)z(kn) = \Sigma \tilde{z}(nk)\tilde{y}(km) = \tilde{z}\tilde{y}(nm). \tag{93}$$

Now, since x is supposed Hermitian,

$$x = \tilde{x}^*;$$

that is, if transposition is followed by change of sign of i wherever it occurs, the matrix is restored to its original form. Similarly, if X is Hermitian, we must have $X = \tilde{X}^*$. By transposition of equation (91) with due respect to equation (93), we see that

$$\tilde{X} = \tilde{S}^{-1}\tilde{x}\tilde{S},$$

and taking the complex conjugate of this we have

$$\tilde{X}^* = \tilde{S}^{-1*}\tilde{x}^*\tilde{S}^* = \tilde{S}^{-1*}x\tilde{S}^*.$$

($\tilde{S}^{-1}$ means the transposed of S^{-1}, not the reciprocal of $\tilde{S}$.)   If this is to be identical with X, as we wish it to be, so that X will be Hermitian, we must have

$$\tilde{S}^{-1}{}^{*}x\tilde{S}^{*} = SxS^{-1},$$

by equation (91).   This will be the case if

$$\tilde{S}^{*} = S^{-1},$$

as the reader will verify; but $SS^{-1} = 1$, and so we must have

$$S\tilde{S}^{*} = 1,$$

which agrees with equation (92).

As to our perturbation problem of Sec. **13**, the proof that equation (92) is satisfied when $S = 1 + \lambda S_1$ is given by Born.[1]   It shows that we must make $S_1(nn)$ equal to zero in order to fulfill this condition.

16. ANHARMONIC OSCILLATOR

The oscillator furnishes an excellent illustration of matrix perturbation methods.   The theory of the oscillator with a small term λq^3 added to its energy function was considered in detail in Heisenberg's original paper on the new mechanics, and also by Born and Jordan.   We write in equation (67)

$$H(p_0 q_0) = H_0(p_0 q_0) + \lambda q_0^3,   \tag{67a}$$

and recollect from equation (56) that

$$|q(n, n - 1)|^2 = Cn   \tag{94}$$

where

$$C = \frac{h}{8\pi^2 \mu \nu_0}.$$

Then, dropping the subscript zeroes,

$$H_1(nm) = q^3(nm) = \Sigma\Sigma q(nj)q(jk)q(km).   \tag{95}$$

Following Birtwistle,[2] we use the diagram below to show the only combinations of values of j, k, m which contribute finite terms to equation (95):

n: n

j: $n-1 \qquad n+1$

k: $n-2 \qquad n \qquad n+2$

m: $n-3 \qquad n-1 \qquad n+1 \qquad n+3$

Since the diagonal terms of H_1 vanish, $E_1 = 0$, and we proceed to compute the second-order perturbation of E from equation (88).   By way of illustration, the only non-zero term in $H_1(n, n + 3)$ is the one for which $j = n + 1$, $k = n + 2$, namely,

$$q(n, n + 1)\, q(n + 1, n + 2)q(n + 2, n + 3).$$

[1] "Problems of Atomic Dynamics," p. 87.
[2] "The New Quantum Mechanics," p. 97.

The term, $H_1(n, n + 3)H_1(n + 3, n)$ in equation (88) is equal to

$$|q(n, n + 1)|^2 |q(n + 1, n + 2)|^2 |q(n + 2, n + 3)|^2,$$

or

$$C^3(n + 1)(n + 2)(n + 3).$$

Similarly, we obtain $H_1(n, n + 1)$, comprising the terms of equation (95) in which

$$j = n - 1, k = n,$$

or

$$j = n + 1, k = n,$$

or

$$j = n + 1, k = n + 2.$$

Continuing in this way and substituting in equation (88), we get

$$E_2(nn) = -\frac{C^3(30n^2 + 30n + 11)}{h\nu_0}$$

and the energy perturbation is

$$\lambda^2 E_2(nn) = -\frac{\lambda^2 h^2(30n^2 + 30n + 11)}{64\nu_0(2\pi^2 m\nu_0)^3}. \tag{96}$$

The result obtained by Bohr's theory does not contain the terms $30n + 11$. The divergence between equation (96) and results of Chap. XIX, Sec. **4,** is due to the use of different potential energy functions in these two cases. Experiment agrees with a formula in which the additional energy is proportional to $(n + \frac{1}{2})^2.$[1]

17. CONSERVATION OF ANGULAR MOMENTUM

Consider a single electron with coordinates and momenta x, y, z, p_x, p_y, p_z. The matrices representing its components of angular momentum are

$$M_x = q_y p_z - p_y q_z, \text{ etc.} \tag{97}$$

while the total angular momentum M is a matrix such that

$$M^2 = M_x^2 + M_y^2 + M_z^2. \tag{98}$$

Under what conditions will M_x say, obey the condition $\dot{M}_x = 0$, so we can state that the x-component of angular momentum is conserved? Suppose H is of the form,

$$H = T(p) + V(q). \tag{99}$$

Then by the Hamilton equations dq_k/dt is a function of the p's alone, and dp_k/dt is a function of the q's alone. But

$$\dot{M}_x = \dot{q}_y p_z + q_y \dot{p}_z - \dot{p}_y q_z - p_y \dot{q}_z \tag{100}$$

and each term in this reduces to a function of the p's alone, or of the q's alone. By equations (60) to (63), all p's commute among themselves and all q's commute among themselves. Now, whenever the torque around the x-axis is such a function of the q's and p's that the right side

[1] MULLIKEN, *Phys. Rev.*, **25**, 259 (1925).

of equation (100) vanishes when considered as a classical equation, it will also vanish, considered as a matrix quantity, for its algebraic behavior is the same as in our ordinary calculations. What we have proved is this: *If H is of the form (99), the conservation of angular momentum holds true under exactly the same conditions as in ordinary mechanics.* The extension of this theorem to a system containing several particles is immediate if we simply write

$$M_x = \sum_k (q_{ky}p_{kz} - p_{ky}q_{kz}),\qquad (101)$$

where the summation runs over all the electrons.

18. SELECTION PRINCIPLE FOR THE AXIAL QUANTUM NUMBER

Consider a non-degenerate system for which one of the components of angular momentum is constant, say $dM_z/dt = 0$. Then M_z is diagonal, and we can prove that for each electron, say the kth, the following relations hold true:

$$q_{kx}M_z - M_zq_{kx} = q_{ky}\frac{h}{2\pi i},$$

$$q_{ky}M_z - M_zq_{ky} = -q_{kx}\frac{h}{2\pi i},$$

$$q_{kz}M_z - M_zq_{kz} = 0.\qquad (102)$$

Example.—To prove the first of these equations write out the left side in full:

$$q_{kx}q_{1x}p_{1y} + q_{kx}q_{2x}p_{2y} \cdots - q_{kx}p_{1x}q_{1y} - q_{kx}p_{2x}q_{2y} - \cdots$$
$$-q_{1x}p_{1y}q_{kx} - q_{2x}p_{2y}q_{kx} + \cdots p_{1x}q_{1y}q_{kx} + p_{2x}q_{2y}q_{kx} + \cdots$$

Any p_y commutes with any q_x, and the q_x's commute among themselves. Thus, the first term in the second line can just as well be written $-q_{kx}q_{1x}p_{1y}$, which cancels the first term in the first line, and so on, until we reach the pair of terms,

$$-q_{kx}p_{kx}q_{ky} + p_{kx}q_{kx}q_{ky},$$

which reduces to

$$(p_{kx}q_{kx} - q_{kx}p_{kx})q_{ky},$$

or, by equation (63),

$$q_{ky}\frac{h}{2\pi i}.$$

The proof of the other equations is similar.

Let us examine the meaning of typical elements of the relations of equations (102). We may single out for attention the particle for which $k = 1$, and shall denote its coordinates by x_1, y_1, and z_1. Then, since M_z is diagonal we have,

$$x_1(nm)[M_z(mm) - M_z(nn)] = y_1(nm) \cdot \frac{h}{2\pi i},$$

$$y_1(nm)[M_z(mm) - M_z(nn)] = -x_1(nm) \cdot \frac{h}{2\pi i},$$

$$z_1(nm)[M_z(mm) - M_z(nn)] = 0.\qquad (103)$$

It will be understood that $M_z(mm)$ is an abbreviation, for the matrix M_z has $6f$ indices, $n_1, \ldots n_{3f}$; $m_1, \ldots m_{3f}$, if the system has f particles. The general element is

$$M_z(n_1, n_2, \ldots ; m_1, m_2, \ldots),$$

and by $M_z(mm)$ we mean $M_z(m_1, m_2, \ldots ; m_1, m_2, \ldots)$. Just as we assume that the elements of the diagonal energy matrix represent the possible energy values of the system, so we *assume* that $M_z(m_1, m_2, \ldots ; m_1, m_2, \ldots)$ is equal to the z-component of angular momentum of the atom when the quantum numbers take the values $m_1, m_2, \ldots$

The third equation tells us that in any quantum jump in which the angular momentum component M_z changes, $z_1(nm) = 0$. This means that the z-component of electric force in the emitted radiation is zero. Further, multiplying the first two equations, we obtain

$$[M_z(mm) - M_z(nn)]^2 = \frac{h^2}{4\pi^2},$$

so that in every allowed quantum jump of the kind under consideration M_z changes by $h/2\pi$. Interchanging the members of the second equation and multiplying it by the first, we find that $x_1 = \pm iy_1$. This means that the radiation is circularly polarized in transitions in which M_z changes its value. Now consider transitions in which M_z is unaltered. The first and second equations show immediately that $x_1(nm) = y_1(nm) = 0$ in these transitions. However, $z_1(nm)$ may be finite, and if so, the radiation is linearly polarized with electric vector parallel to the z_1 axis. The conclusion is that the possible values of the z-component of angular momentum are of the form

$$M_z(nn) = (N + C)\frac{h}{2\pi}, \tag{104}$$

where C is a constant and N is an integer.

It can be shown that

$$\sum M_z(nn) = \left(\frac{h}{2\pi}\right)\sum_N (N + C) = 0 \tag{105}$$

and that the number of values of N is finite when the values of all quantum numbers (except the axial quantum number) are specified. Now equation (105) means that the possible values of $N + C$ form a series symmetrical with respect to zero. This can be the case only if $N + C$ takes the values

$$\cdots -2, -1, 0, 1, 2, \cdots$$

or

$$\cdots -\tfrac{3}{2}, -\tfrac{1}{2}, \tfrac{1}{2}, \tfrac{3}{2}, \cdots$$

so that $N + C$ is identical with the axial quantum number. The proof is complicated and we shall omit it. This investigation is due to Heisenberg, Born, and Jordan[1] who also derived the selection principle for the

[1] *Loc. cit.*

inner quantum number and showed that it is either an integer or a half-integer.

Heisenberg and Jordan[1] investigated the anomalous Zeeman effect by matrix methods, with the result that the Landé g formula and the usual sum rules are obtained.

19. THE HYDROGEN ATOM IN MATRIX MECHANICS

The theory of the hydrogen atom was worked out independently by Pauli[2] and by Dirac.[3] In both investigations the energy levels were found to follow the Balmer formula, furnishing strong support to the underlying theory. The computation of Dirac was based on an extension of matrix mechanics known as the "theory of q numbers." (Secs. **25** and **26**.) The treatment by Pauli, even when simplified by restricting the problem to two dimensions, is too lengthy for inclusion here, but we shall give an outline of his reasoning, which illustrates an important general method of attack on matrix problems.

First, it is assumed that in Cartesian coordinates the energy function is

$$H = \frac{1}{2\mu}(p_x{}^2 + p_y{}^2) - \frac{Ze^2}{(x^2 + y^2)^{\frac{1}{2}}}. \tag{106}$$

The equations of motion are

$$\dot{p}_x = \frac{Ze^2 x}{(x_2 + y^2)^{\frac{3}{2}}}, \quad \dot{x} = \frac{p_x}{\mu}, \text{ etc.} \tag{107}$$

and the variables x, y, p_x, and p_y must satisfy the quantum conditions. It is convenient to introduce the matrix r defined by

$$r^2 = x^2 + y^2, \tag{108}$$

and to prove that r and $m_0\dot{r}$ satisfy the relation

$$p_r r - r p_r = 1 \cdot \frac{h}{2\pi i}. \tag{109}$$

Further, we define the angular momentum by the equation

$$M = x p_y - p_x y. \tag{110}$$

It is apparent that matrix computations will be relatively simple as long as the matrices are diagonal, but when this is not the case, we become involved in a maze of infinite sums. We seek, therefore, to find as many diagonal matrices as possible. In this search we are guided by the fact that such matrices are analogous to constants in ordinary algebra. Therefore, we may expect that any dynamical quantity which is conserved, such as momentum or energy, will be represented

[1] *Z. Physik*, **37**, 263 (1926).
[2] *Z. Physik*, **36**, 336 (1926).
[3] *Proc. Roy. Soc.*, **110**, 561 (1926).

by a diagonal matrix.   Now in the case of the hydrogen atom as treated by ordinary mechanics we know that the angular momentum is constant, and that its components parallel to the three axes are constant, so that we expect the matrix of equation (110) to be diagonal.   Further, Lenz[1] discovered a second vector which is constant in magnitude and direction in this problem.   This is called the axial vector,

$$\mathbf{A} = \left(\frac{1}{Ze^2}\right)[\mathbf{Mv}] + \frac{\mathbf{r}}{r}.$$

That is, the components of **A** are

$$A_x = \left(\frac{1}{Ze^2}\right)(M_y z - M_z y) + \frac{x}{r} \text{ etc.} \tag{111}$$

By direct computation we can verify the fact that the major axis, a, of the Keplerian orbit and the energy can be expressed in the form

$$a = \frac{M^2}{Ze^2\mu}\frac{1}{1 - A^2}, \quad E = -\frac{Z^2e^4\mu}{2M^2}(1 - A^2). \tag{112}$$

M^2 and A^2 denote the squares of the magnitudes of the vectors **M** and **A**. Now, we attempt to carry over this computation into matrix mechanics, remembering that $z = 0$, $p_z = 0$, and that $M_z = M$, since the motion is restricted to the xy plane.   By straightforward processes of non-commutative algebra, we obtain the following relations:

$$A_x M - M A_x = \left(\frac{h}{2\pi i}\right)A_y,$$

$$A_y M - M A_y = -\left(\frac{h}{2\pi i}\right)A_x, \tag{113}$$

$$A_x(m, n; m \pm 1, n) \pm i A_y(m, n; m \pm 1, n) = 0,$$

$$\frac{h}{2\pi i}\frac{2}{Z^2e^4\mu} MH = A_x A_y - A_y A_x,$$

and

$$A^2 - 1 = \frac{2}{Z^2e^4\mu} H\left(M^2 + \frac{h^2}{16\pi^2}I\right).$$

In these relations, the elements of M are known from the conclusions of Sec. **18**; the elements of A_x and A_y can be eliminated, and thus we determine the elements of the energy matrix.   There is little point in going through the calculations, for the elements of any matrix can be computed by integration when the corresponding problem in wave mechanics has been solved, as explained in Secs. **20** to **24**.

In his paper on the H atom, Pauli also determined the effect of magnetic and electric fields, applied both singly and in combination.   It is noteworthy that the selection principles are furnished automatically

[1] *Z. Physik*, **24**, 197 (1924).

by the theory through the vanishing of all components of the q matrix except those corresponding to transitions allowed by the classical selection rules.

Wentzel[1] has used an alternative method to obtain the energy levels of hydrogenic atoms. It consists in searching for matrix variables which are analogous to the angle variables of classical theory. The angle variables w_k and their conjugate momenta J_k must obey the commutation relations and in addition they must be such that the equations of motion take the form

$$\dot{J}_k = 0, \quad \dot{w}_k = f(J_k). \tag{114}$$

Further, the matrices x, y, z corresponding to Cartesian coordinates must be representable as multiple Fourier series in the w_k, with all the periods equal to unity, just as in equation (63) of Chap. IV. A typical term, $\exp 2\pi i \Sigma \tau_k w_k$, in such a matrix series is defined by using the series expansion of the exponential function. The method outlined for finding the angle variables is analogous to the solution of the Hamilton-Jacobi equation (Chap. IV). If the matrix action function is S, it can be shown that when q_k passes around a cycle, the other coordinates being unaltered, the change in S is J_k. Now the change in S can also be expressed in terms of the energy and other constants of integration, just as in ordinary mechanics. Following this plan, Wentzel obtains equations connecting these dynamical quantities with the matrices J_k. Thus, when the J_k's are determined by straightforward methods the values of the energy, angular momentum, etc. can be determined at once.

20. THE CONNECTION BETWEEN WAVE AND MATRIX MECHANICS

The discovery that wave mechanics is mathematically equivalent to the dynamics of Heisenberg, Born, and Jordan must be considered a great advance in the development of quantum dynamics. We owe this advance to Schrödinger[2] and to Eckart,[3] working independently. It clarified the situation by showing that the two rival theories were only different mathematical formulations of the same physical facts; but still more important, it furnished a method of calculating the elements of matrices by simple integration. The complete statement of the connection between the two theories will be much more intelligible if we approach the matter by studying a few simple illustrations. We shall suppose that a system of one degree of freedom—its constitution does not matter—has been quantized by the aid of wave mechanics, and that we know the eigenfunctions of the problem, which are properly normalized in accordance with equation (68) of Chap. XV.

Suppose we wish to construct the elements of the matrix corresponding to any classical function u, which depends only on the coordinate q. We shall find that *the elements of the mth column in the matrix corresponding to u are the coefficients $u(nm)$ which appear in the expansion of $u\Psi_n$,*

[1] *Z. Physik*, **37**, 80 (1926).

[2] *Ann. Physik*, **79**, 734 (1926).

[3] *Phys. Rev.*, **28**, 711 (1926).

in terms of the normal orthogonal functions Ψ_k.   In Chap. XV, Sec. **21** we gave a method for expanding any function in a series of this kind. Briefly, the result was that if we write

$$u\Psi_n = \sum_k u(kn)\Psi_k, \qquad (115)$$

the coefficients $u(kn)$ can be found by a process like that used to evaluate the coefficients of a Fourier series; that is, for any values of n and m we have[1]

$$u(nm) = \int u\Psi_n^*\Psi_m dq. \qquad (116)$$

If x is a Cartesian coordinate, then for the case of a particle of mass m_0, $q = m_0^{1/2}x$, in agreement with the convention of Chap. XV, Sec. **2**. In this integration, and in all others in this chapter for which limits are not given, the summation extends over all physically possible values of q. We see that $u(mn) = u^*(nm)$ provided u is real, so that the array of these elements is Hermitian.

To show that the quantities $u(nm)$ are the elements of the Heisenberg matrix belonging to the function u, we proceed in the following way: For any other function v, we have

$$v\Psi_n = \Sigma v(kn)\Psi_k; \, n = 1, 2, \cdots, \qquad (117)$$

which implies that

$$v(nm) = \int v\Psi_n^*\Psi_m dq. \qquad (118)$$

If it is true that $u(nm)$ and $v(nm)$ are matrix elements, then the laws of matrix addition and multiplication must be verified. That is, the nmth element of the matrix $\boldsymbol{u} + \boldsymbol{v}$ must be $u(nm) + v(nm)$, and also $uv(nm)$ must be equal to $\sum_k u(nk)v(km)$. It is obvious that the first condition is satisfied. As to the second, we may obtain $uv(nm)$ from the equation which defines it, namely,

$$uv(nm) = \int uv\Psi_n^*\Psi_m dq. \qquad (119)$$

In order to evaluate this integral we use the value of $v\Psi_m$ obtained from equation (117). As to $u\Psi_n^*$, we see from equation (115) that

$$u\Psi_n^* = \Sigma u(nk)\Psi_k^*.$$

Substituting in equation (119), we get

$$\sum_k \sum_j u(nk)v(jm)\int \Psi_k^*\Psi_j dq. \qquad (119a)$$

But the last integral is equal to one when $k = j$, and is zero otherwise; therefore, the double summation reduces to a summation over a single

---

[1] This definition of $u(nm)$ agrees with that used by Dirac and is dictated by our convention that $\Psi_n = \psi_n \exp(-2\pi i E_n t/h)$. If we had adopted the positive sign for the exponent in the time factor, equation (116) would have taken the form $u(nm) = \int u\Psi_n\Psi_m^* dq$.

running index, let us say k, and we have $uv(nm) = \sum_k u(nk)v(km)$, which shows that the elements under consideration obey the law of matrix multiplication.

If we can discover a similar method of constructing the matrix corresponding to the classical function p, we shall then be able to find the matrix for any function of q and p, by straightforward addition and multiplication. To do this, we specify that *the characteristic functions used will be those obtained by solving Schrödinger's equation for the dynamical system under consideration.* This restriction is essential to our purpose. For simplicity, we limit the discussion to the problem of a single electron in Cartesian coordinates. It will be proved that the matrix

$$p_x(nm) = \epsilon \int \Psi_n^* \frac{\partial \Psi_m}{\partial x}\, dq \tag{120}$$

satisfies all the conditions of the problem.

Proof.—It is known that

$$\int \left(\Psi_n^* \frac{\partial \Psi_m}{\partial x} + \frac{\partial \Psi_n^*}{\partial x} \Psi_m \right) dq = 0, \tag{121}$$

because this integral is the difference of the values of $\Psi_n^*\Psi_m$ at the upper and lower limits of integration. Each of these is zero by hypothesis, for no part of the system is located at infinity. Therefore, we may write equation (120) in the form

$$p(nm) = \left(\frac{\epsilon}{2}\right) \int \left(\Psi_n^* \frac{\partial \Psi_m}{\partial x} - \Psi_m \frac{\partial \Psi_n^*}{\partial x} \right) dq. \tag{122}$$

This may be simplified by using the wave equations

$$\Delta\Psi_n^* + G(E_n - V)\Psi_n^* = 0;$$
$$\Delta\Psi_m + G(E_m - V)\Psi_m = 0.$$

Multiply the first by $x\Psi_m$ and the second by $x\Psi_n^*$, subtract, and integrate, obtaining

$$\int(x\Psi_m\Delta\Psi_n^* - x\Psi_n^*\Delta\Psi_m)dq = -G(E_n - E_m)\int x\Psi_n^*\Psi_m dq. \tag{123}$$

By partial integration it is found that the difference between the integrands in equations (122) and (123) consists of terms which yield a vanishing contribution on integration. Therefore,

$$p(nm) = m_0\epsilon^{-1}(E_n - E_m)\int x\Psi_n^*\Psi_m dq = 2\pi i\nu(nm)m_0x(nm), \tag{124}$$

in complete agreement with Heisenberg's theory.

The usefulness of Schrödinger's matrices q and p depends on the fact that they obey Heisenberg's quantum condition and satisfy the matrix law of motion (Sec. **23**), so that they are actually identical with the Heisenberg matrices.

21. CALCULATION OF THE MATRICES p AND q FOR THE OSCILLATOR

To obtain the components of the matrix x for the oscillator, we apply equation (116) in the form

$$x(nm) = \int x\Psi_n^*\Psi_m d\gamma. \tag{125}$$

The characteristic functions of the oscillator are derived in Chap. XV, Sec. **9**, and when normalized may be written[1]

$$\psi_n = \left(\frac{4\pi^2 \nu_0}{h}\right)^{1/4} \frac{e^{-v^2/2} H_n(v)}{(2^n n! \pi^{1/2})^{1/2}}.$$

The calculation of equation (125) can be attacked directly with the aid of the expressions for the Hermitian polynomials given in Appendix IV, but it is much easier to use a short cut due to Eckart. As we have seen, aside from the exponential time factor, $x(mn)$ is the coefficient of ψ_m in the expansion of $x\psi_n$. Fortunately, the recursion formula for the functions ψ is

$$x\psi_n = \left(\frac{h}{8\pi^2 \mu_0 \nu_0}\right)^{1/2} [n^{1/2} \psi_{n-1} + (n+1)^{1/2} \psi_{n+1}], \tag{126}$$

which gives us the expansion we desire. Only the coefficients $|x(n, n-1)|$ and $|x(n, n+1)|$ are different from zero, and neglecting the time factor they take the forms

$$|x(n, n-1)| = \left(\frac{nh}{8\pi^2 \mu_0 \nu_0}\right)^{1/2}, |x(n, n+1)| = \left(\frac{(n+1)h}{8\pi^2 \mu_0 \nu_0}\right)^{1/2}, \tag{127}$$

in precise agreement with the results obtained by the calculus of matrices. Since the energy levels of the oscillator are also given by the wave theory, we have all the material needed for computing $p(nm)$ from equation (124). The result agrees with equation (57).

22. SCHRÖDINGER'S METHOD FOR CONSTRUCTING MATRICES

We must now formulate rules for obtaining the matrix of any function $F(p, q)$. First, we rearrange the function, replacing it by what Schrödinger aptly calls a "well-ordered function." Usually, the rearrangement merely consists in making the function symmetric, just as in our treatment of the proper form for the energy in matrix mechanics.[2] For example, the product pq^2 is rewritten in the form

$$\tfrac{1}{2}(pq^2 + q^2 p).$$

From now on, we assume that the function has been so ordered. We expand the well-ordered function F as a series, according to powers of the p's. We need consider only a single term of such a series, for example

$$F = f p_r p_s g p_t h, \tag{128}$$

---

[1] This differs from the normalized function given in COURANT-HILBERT, "Methoden der mathematischen Physik," p. 77, and in Chap. XV, Secs. **9** and **13**, because our variable of integration is $m^{1/2}x$, instead of v.

[2] More general rules for symmetrization have been given by HEISENBERG, BORN and JORDAN, *Z. Physik*, **35**, 557 (1926); and by HILBERT, VON NEUMANN, and NORDHEIM, *Math. Annalen*, **98**, 1 (1927).

where f, g and h are functions only of the q's. It will be remembered (Sec. **20**) that in forming the matrix component $p_x(nm)$ we take the integral of $\Psi_n^*\epsilon\dfrac{\partial}{\partial x}\Psi_m dv$. This form for the integrand of equation (124) was suggested by the fact that we replace p_x by $\epsilon\dfrac{\partial}{\partial x}$ in the energy function H, in order to obtain the wave equation. Similarly, in securing the matrix F, it is natural to construct the *well-ordered operator*

$$F = f\epsilon^2 \frac{\partial^2}{\partial q_r \partial q_s} g \frac{\partial}{\partial q_t} h \cdots . \tag{129}$$

Just as in equation (120), we form the integral

$$F(nm) = \int \Psi_n^* F \Psi_m dv, \tag{130}$$

where $F\Psi_m$ means the result of applying the operator F to Ψ_m. *The Heisenberg matrix corresponding to the function F has the typical element $F(nm)$, given by equation* (130). The proof is given in the following section.

In practice, little difficulty arises from using the symbol F to indicate both the function F and the operator formed from it; but the reader is advised to be on his guard. In forming the function $F\Psi_m$, each differentiation is applied to all terms lying to its right, so that we first take $\dfrac{\partial(h\Psi_m)}{\partial q_t}$, then $\dfrac{\partial}{\partial q_s}\left(g\dfrac{\partial(h\Psi_m)}{\partial q_t}\right)$, and so on.

It must be understood that in any problem of several degrees of freedom, the integral in equation (130) is multiple and that the real meaning of the equation is

$$F(n_1 \cdots n_i; m_1 \cdots m_r) = \int \cdots \int \Psi^*_{n1} \ldots _{nr} F \Psi_{m1} \ldots _{mr} dv. \tag{130a}$$

The differential dv is the element of volume in the q space used by Schrödinger and may be written in the form

$$dv = \rho dq_1 dq_2 \cdots .$$

Thus, in Cartesian coordinates, for the 1-electron problem,

$$dv = m^{3/2} dx dy dz,$$

so that $\rho = m^{3/2}$.

As an illustration of equation (130), we may calculate the elements of the energy matrix for a problem of one degree of freedom. In such a problem, the energy function can always be brought to the form

$$\tfrac{1}{2}p^2 + V(q) = H, \tag{131}$$

by suitable choice of coordinates. This function is already well ordered and the corresponding operator H formed according to equation (129) is

$$-\frac{h^2}{8\pi^2}\frac{\partial^2}{\partial q^2} + V,$$

so that

$$H\Psi_m = -\frac{h^2}{8\pi^2}\frac{\partial^2 \Psi_m}{\partial q^2} + V\Psi_m.$$

Then by equation (130), the elements of the energy matrix are

$$H(nm) = \int \Psi_n^* \left(-\frac{h^2}{8\pi^2} \frac{\partial^2 \Psi_m}{\partial q^2} + V\Psi_m \right) dq. \tag{132}$$

Now Ψ_m is a function of E_m and q, while Ψ_n^* is a function of E_n and q. Substituting their values from the wave equation, and integrating, we obtain $H(nm)$ expressed as a function of E_n and E_m. Fortunately, in this case we can avoid such labor, for by the wave equation, the quantity in parentheses is simply $E_m\Psi_m$, and we have

$$H(nm) = \int E_m \Psi_n^* \Psi_m dq. \tag{133}$$

The Ψ's are normal and orthogonal, so on the right side we have E_n if $n = m$, and zero, if n is not equal to m. That is, $H(nm)$ is a diagonal matrix with the energy values for its non-vanishing elements. A similar proof can be carried out for any conservative system.

23. THE IDENTITY OF SCHRÖDINGER AND HEISENBERG MATRICES

We wish to show that the expressions defined by equation (130) obey the matrix multiplication law. That is, if the matrices of F and G are constructed with the aid of equation (130) and if we also write out the matrix of FG by using equation (130), we wish to verify the equation

$$FG(nm) = \sum_k F(nk)G(km). \tag{134}$$

Written out in terms of integrals, this relation becomes

$$\int \Psi_n^* FG\Psi_m dv = \sum_k \int \Psi_n^* F\Psi_k dv \cdot \int \Psi_k^* G\Psi_m dv, \tag{135}$$

where it is understood that in the first integral $FG\Psi_m$ is the function which results from applying the operator G to Ψ_m, and then operating on the result with F. To prove equation (135) we write

$$G\Psi_m = \sum_k G(km)\Psi_k, \tag{136}$$

where G stands for the operator, not the function, on the left side. We now apply the operator F to both sides, obtaining

$$FG\Psi_m = \sum_k FG(km)\Psi_k.$$

But since the operator F does not affect the constant quantities $G(km)$, this is the same as $\sum_k G(km)F\Psi_k$. Now we expand $F\Psi_k$, arriving at

$$FG\Psi_m = \sum_k G(km) \sum_j F(jk)\Psi_j,$$

and finally,

$$\int \Psi_n^* FG\Psi_m dv = \sum_k G(km) \sum_j F(jk) \int \Psi_n^* \Psi_j dv = \sum_k G(km)F(nk),$$

for all terms of the second sum on the right are zero, except the one for which $j = n$, because the Ψ's are orthogonal. This result is identical with equations (134) and (135).

It remains to be shown that Schrödinger's matrices obey the matrix quantum conditions and the laws of motion (Secs. **5** and **7**) before we can assert their identity with the Heisenberg matrices. Let us consider the quantum condition for a system with a single variable, $pq - qp = \epsilon$.

The operator corresponding to $pq - qp$ is $\epsilon \dfrac{\partial}{\partial q} q - q\epsilon \dfrac{\partial}{\partial q}$. But

$$\frac{\partial}{\partial q}(q\Psi_m) - q\frac{\partial \Psi_m}{\partial q} = \Psi_m,$$

so equation (130) reduces to

$$(pq - qp)(nm) = \epsilon \int \Psi_n{}^* \Psi_m dv,$$

which equals $h/2\pi i$ if $n = m$, and 0 if n is not m. The proof of the quantum conditions for a system having several degrees of freedom is similar.

As to the matrix equations of motion, they can be written in the form

$$\epsilon q = Hq - qH, \quad \epsilon \dot{p} = Hp - pH. \tag{137}$$

It will suffice if we prove that Schrödinger's matrices satisfy the first of these relations, for the proof of the second is similar. Remembering that

$$\epsilon \dot{q}(nm) = (E_n - E_m)q(nm),$$

we see that a typical element of the first equation in equations (137) is

$$(E_n - E_m)q(nm) = (Hq - qH)(nm). \tag{138}$$

From the standpoint of Heisenberg's theory this is obvious, but we wish to prove the corresponding equation for Schrödinger's matrices that is,

$$(E_n - E_m)q(nm) = \int \Psi_n{}^*(Hq - qH)\Psi_m dv. \tag{139}$$

We have,

$$Hq\Psi_m = H\Sigma q(km)\Psi_k = \Sigma q(km)H\Psi_k. \tag{140}$$

The operator H may be placed after the quantities $q(km)$ because they are constant and the operator does not affect them. Now the wave equation states that

$$H\Psi_k = E_k\Psi_k.$$

In other words, the expansion of the function $H\Psi_k$ in terms of the wave functions reduces to a single term. Substituting this in equation (140), we have

$$Hq\Psi_m = \Sigma q(km)E_k\Psi_k.$$

Similarly,

$$qH\Psi_m = qE_m\Psi_m = E_m q\Psi_m,$$

so that the integral in equation (139) takes the form

$$\int \Psi_n{}^* \Sigma q(km)E_k\Psi_k dv - E_m \int \Psi_n{}^* q\Psi_m dv.$$

In the first integral, the only surviving term is that for which $k = n$. It yields a contribution $E_n q(nm)$ to the result, and the second integral is $E_m q(nm)$, so the result is $(E_n - E_m)q(nm)$.

24. THE WAVE MECHANICAL ANALOGUES OF CLASSICAL QUANTITIES

In conclusion, we may note a few applications of equation (130). It furnishes the connecting link between the matrix and wave methods of calculating spectral intensities (Chap. XV, Sec. **17**, and Sec. **10** of this chapter). We see now that in terms of Schrödinger's charge-density interpretation, $eq(nm)$ is the electric moment of a part of the charge-density which oscillates with frequency $\nu(nm)$. Much of Chap. XX will deal with laws governing intensities, obtained with the aid of equation (130). Further, equation (130) enables us to set up expressions which take the place of quantities occurring in classical mechanics. For example, we may write down at once the components of the kinetic energy matrix T. Taking the case of a single particle in rectangular coordinates, the classical value of T is

$$\frac{1}{2M}(p_x{}^2 + p_y{}^2 + p_z{}^2)$$

and the operator T is

$$-\frac{h^2}{8\pi^2 M}\left(\frac{\partial^2}{\partial x^2} + \frac{\partial^2}{\partial y^2} + \frac{\partial^2}{\partial z^2}\right),$$

so that

$$T(nm) = -\frac{h^2}{8\pi^2 M}\int \Psi_n{}^* \Delta\Psi_m dv. \tag{140}$$

By the wave equation, $\Delta\Psi_m$ may be replaced by $-\dfrac{8\pi^2 M}{h^2}(E - V)\Psi_m$, whence

$$T(nm) = \int \Psi_n{}^* E_m \Psi_m dv - \int \Psi_n{}^* V \Psi_m dv.$$

or

$$T(nm) + V(nm) = E_m \text{ if } n = m,$$
$$= 0 \text{ if } n \neq m. \tag{141}$$

This is the analogue of the law of conservation of energy.

More generally, if Ψ is of the form $\Sigma c_n \Psi_n$, we define the kinetic energy in wave mechanics by the relation

$$T_q = -\frac{h^2}{8\pi^2 M}\int \Psi^* \Delta\Psi dv, \tag{142}$$

and the potential energy by

$$V_q = \int \Psi^* V\Psi dv. \tag{143}$$

The subscript q serves to remind us that we are dealing with a quantity calculated by means of quantum dynamics. It is interesting to consider the value of $T_q + V_q$. Using the wave equation (65) of Chap. XV, we find that

$$T_q + V_q = -\epsilon \int \Psi^* \frac{\partial \Psi}{\partial t} dv,$$

and substituting the values of the quantities under the integral,

$$T_q + V_q = \int \left(\sum_k c_k^* \Psi_k^* \right) \left(\sum_j c_j \Psi_j E_j \right) dv.$$

The only non-zero terms in this integral are those for which $j = k$, and so

$$\overline{T} + \overline{V} = \sum_k c_k c_k^* E_k.$$

On the charge-density interpretation $c_k c_k^*$ is a measure of the strength of excitation of Ψ_k in a single atom, and the right side would be the total energy associated with the system of waves. However, on the statistical interpretation, $c_k c_k^*$ is the fraction of the atoms which reside in the kth quantum state, so that either side of equation (32) represents the average energy of an atom.[1]

25. DIRAC'S FORMULATION OF QUANTUM DYNAMICS

Dirac[2] has shown that the quantum mechanics of Heisenberg can be thrown into an especially convenient notation by using generalizations of certain quantities called "Poisson brackets."[3] These brackets make their appearance when we consider a transformation from the variables q, p to the variables Q, P. To simplify the notation, let us consider a single particle with Cartesian coordinates x, y, z. These coordinates are taken as the Q's. Then *the Poisson bracket of x and y is defined as*

$$\sum_{k=1}^{k=3} \left(\frac{\partial \dot{x}}{\partial q_k} \frac{\partial y}{\partial p_k} - \frac{\partial x}{\partial p_k} \frac{\partial y}{\partial q_k} \right). \tag{144}$$

More generally,

$$\sum_{k=1}^{k=n} \left(\frac{\partial F_r}{\partial q_k} \frac{\partial F_s}{\partial p_k} - \frac{\partial F_s}{\partial q_k} \frac{\partial F_r}{\partial p_k} \right) \tag{145}$$

is the Poisson bracket of F_r, F_s and is written $[F_r F_s]$. This notation is incomplete, since it does not indicate the variables with respect to which F_r and F_s are differentiated, and so we shall speak of the Poisson bracket of F_r and F_s with respect to p and q, or with respect to other variables. Now the Poisson brackets of any set of p's and q's with respect to themselves have the following simple properties;

$$[p_r p_s] = 0, \quad [q_r q_s] = 0, \tag{146}$$

$$[q_r p_s] = 1, \text{ when } r = s, \text{ but } 0 \text{ when } r \neq s. \tag{147}$$

These relations are easily verified by the use of equation (145), using the variables p and q in the numerator. They are strikingly similar

---

[1] For other illustrations of the calculation of physical quantities as averages over the $\Psi\Psi^*$ distribution, the reader should refer to Sommerfeld's "Ergänzungsband" pages 283–299.

[2] *Proc. Roy. Soc.*, **109**, 642 (1925).

[3] See Whittaker, "Analytical Dynamics," or Van Vleck, "Quantum Principles and Line Spectra."

to the matrix quantum conditions and lead to the suspicion that the quantum conditions must reduce to them in the region of large quantum numbers. Dirac showed that this is actually the case.[1] We shall content ourselves with indicating the method. Consider the n, m element of the matrix $q_r p_r - p_r q_r$, namely,

$$\sum_k [p_r(nk)q_r(km) - q_r(nk)p_r(km)].$$

$q(km)$ is a measure of the amplitude of the radiation emitted in jumps from the kth state to the mth state. By the correspondence principle it must reduce to the amplitude of the harmonic of order $k - m$ in the classical Fourier series for q, when we pass to the region of high quantum numbers. Similarly, a classical equivalent for $p(nk)$ may be found. The Fourier series referred to are taken in the form

$$\Sigma C_{\tau_1} \ldots \tau_n \exp 2\pi i \, (\tau_1 w_1 + \cdots),$$

where the w's are angle variables, and the C's are functions of the conjugate momenta $J_1, \ldots J_n$. Finally, the sum of all the matrix elements is found to reduce to the form

$$\frac{h}{2\pi i} \sum_k \left(\frac{\partial q_r}{\partial w_k} \frac{\partial p_r}{\partial J_k} - \frac{\partial q_r}{\partial J_k} \frac{\partial p_r}{\partial w_k} \right).$$

Now it is a fact that a Poisson bracket taken with respect to any set of variables is equal to the Poisson bracket of the same quantities taken with respect to any other set of variables, so if we like we may write this bracket as

$$\frac{h}{2\pi i} \sum_k \left(\frac{\partial q_r}{\partial q_k} \frac{\partial p_r}{\partial p_k} - \frac{\partial q_r}{\partial p_k} \frac{\partial p_r}{\partial q_k} \right),$$

and by equation (147), this is equal to $h/2\pi i$, as we should expect from inspection of the matrix quantum conditions. Accordingly, Dirac writes

$$pq - qp = \epsilon[qp] \tag{148}$$

and assumes that in the quantum theory $pq - qp$ must be calculated by using this equation. Further, it is assumed that for any two quantum magnitudes A and B,

$$BA - AB = \epsilon[AB]. \tag{149}$$

The Poisson bracket is supposed to be a function of the quantum p's and q's which is formally identical with the corresponding Poisson bracket in the classical theory. Accordingly, in order to find the quantum analogue of any classical equation, we try to get it into a form which contains Poisson brackets, and then use equation (149).

[1] His proof is reproduced in Birtwistle's "New Quantum Mechanics," p. 70.

For example, if F is any function of the p's and q's,

$$\dot{F} = \sum_k \left(\frac{\partial F}{\partial q_k} \dot{q}_k + \frac{\partial F}{\partial p_k} \dot{p}_k \right),$$

and by Hamilton's equations, this is the same as

$$\dot{F} = \sum_k \left(\frac{\partial F}{\partial q_k} \frac{\partial H}{\partial p_k} - \frac{\partial F}{\partial p_k} \frac{\partial H}{\partial q_k} \right) = [FH]. \tag{150}$$

This is in a form such that it can be taken over directly into the new mechanics, with the understanding that $[FH]$ will then have the meaning explained in equation (148). For example,

$$\epsilon \dot{p} = \epsilon[pH] = Hp - pH,$$

in agreement with equation (28). We therefore write

$$\epsilon \dot{F} = HF - FH. \tag{151}$$

This important relation is often called the "law of motion of F."

26. DIRAC'S THEORY OF q NUMBERS

In Dirac's theory of q numbers, it is assumed that we must work with quantities called q numbers, instead of our usual numbers, which are called c numbers. The essential distinction is that the variables used for the study of a dynamical system do not satisfy the commutative law of multiplication, but obey the matrix quantum conditions. Dirac[1] states that at present no one can form a picture of what a q number is like. We operate with them until we arrive at the value of any dynamical quantity which is desired. A special assumption is then introduced, by which results in terms of c numbers can be derived from results involving both q and c numbers. Only in the case of oscillating systems do the q numbers take the form of matrices. The importance of Dirac's viewpoint is due to the fact that *the matrix quantum conditions and laws of motion can be satisfied by entities of a much more general type than matrices. In fact, the equations themselves define the properties of the q numbers*, and if we were confronted with them we should have no idea that matrices enjoy the properties which they express. In the case of non-periodic motions, the use of q numbers may enable us to solve our problem while the attempt to use calculations in which matrix elements appear would end in failure. We shall not give illustrations at this point, for much of the following chapter is devoted to development of the method of q numbers.

[1] *Proc. Roy. Soc.*, **110**, 561 (1926).

CHAPTER XVIII

GENERAL THEORY OF QUANTUM DYNAMICS

1. HEISENBERG'S PRINCIPLE OF INDETERMINATION

In this chapter we shall be concerned with the so-called transformation theory of quantum dynamics, which was developed independently by Dirac[1] and by Jordan.[2] It represents the most general formulation of the problem which we possess, and includes the previous forms of quantum mechanics as special cases. In order to appreciate the transformation theory and the statistical interpretation (Chap. XV, Sec. 16) which completes it and gives it power to deal with physical problems, we must consider the nature of the questions which we try to answer in a dynamical problem. In classical mechanics, the problem is very definite: given the initial positions and velocities, what will be the state of the system at any later time? Quantum mechanics, on the other hand, proceeds by setting up an equation for a quantity called Ψ, which governs the distribution of Ψ over all space and at all times. The very fact that this equation is usually differential shows that causal law is involved in the determination of Ψ. That is, the conditions at a given instant completely determine the conditions at the next instant. There are no extraneous factors, and there appears to be no room for probabilities or uncertainties. It seems strange, when the work is done, to say that Ψ is not a quantity characteristic of an individual system; that on the contrary $\Psi\Psi^*$ serves to describe the average behavior of a great number of systems. This situation applies to electrodynamics as well as to mechanical problems, for we customarily apply Schrödinger's equation to systems which contain light quanta.

Much light is thrown on this situation by a discussion of the nature of physical measurements which we owe to Heisenberg[3] and Bohr.[4] They consider the question of what meaning can be attached to the position or the velocity of an atom, or of an elementary charged particle, let us say an electron. Now, the x-coordinate of an electron is really *defined* by describing an experiment which we may perform in order to

---

[1] *Proc. Roy. Soc.*, **113**, 621 (1927), and later papers mentioned in the bibliography at the end of this chapter.

[2] *Z. Physik*, **40**, 809 and **44**, 1 (1927).

[3] *Z. Physik*, **43**, 172 (1927).

[4] *Nature*, **121**, 580 (1928); *Naturwissenschaften*, **16**, 245 (1928).

measure it.[1]   For example, we may allow light to fall on the electron, and observe the scattered light with a suitable optical apparatus (Fig. 1).   The smallest length interval which can be distinguished is of the order of the wave length of the scattered light.   If we wish to make our measurement of x highly precise, we must use light of very small wave length; in fact, to illustrate his point, Heisenberg speaks of using a "gamma-ray microscope" for detecting the scattered quanta.   The use of short wave lengths brings with it a limitation of the accuracy with which we can know the x-component of the momentum at the instant when x is measured.   This is due to the recoil of the electron, which becomes greater as the wave length of the light becomes shorter.   Simple

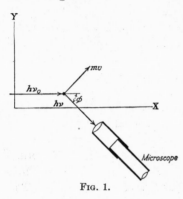

FIG. 1.

formulas derived by considering the Compton effect (Chap. III, Sec. **16**), show that the change in momentum of the electron is of the order h/λ_0, aside from a factor which is of the order of unity, and which depends on the angle of scattering; λ_0 is the wave length of the incident quantum.   This statement must be modified when $h\nu_0/mc^2$ becomes comparable with unity.   If we write $C(p_x)$ for the change of p_x caused by the measurement of x, we have,

$$C(p_x) \cong \frac{h}{\lambda_0}. \tag{1}$$

This quantity is also a measure of the uncertainty Δp_x in our knowledge of the momentum at an instant t, so that

$$\Delta p_x \cong \frac{h}{\lambda_0}. \tag{2}$$

Therefore the product of the uncertainty in our measurement of position, namely λ, and this uncertainty in the momentum is h.

It may be worth noting that in this example we have neglected the uncertainty of our knowledge of the direction from which the scattered quantum came to the microscope.   If α is the angle subtended at the electron by the diameter of the microscope objective, then the smallest resolvable object is of the order $\lambda/\sin \alpha$, rather than λ.   The momentum of the scattered quantum is h/λ and its direction is uncertain by the amount α, so that the possible error of its momentum is of the order $h \sin \alpha/\lambda$.   The product of the two uncertainties is h, as before.

---

[1] This operational point of view has been emphasized by J. S. AMES for many years in his lectures on dynamics, and has been charmingly presented by BRIDGMAN in his book, "The Logic of Modern Physics."

Perhaps the reader will feel that if the dynamics of the collision were investigated in more detail we should be able to follow the value of p_x as a function of the time. The point is that the consequences of such a calculation cannot be checked by any experiment which has been devised up to the present time. We can study the final state of the system, but not the course of the scattering process. Assuming that the collision process occurs over a finite range of the coordinate x and over a finite time, t_1 to t_2, we do not know what point of the range is obtained by our calculation for the value of x, nor do we know at what instant in the interval $t_2 - t_1$ the electron will be at a given point.[1] Further, in connection with equation (2), there is an error involved in speaking of Δp_x as the uncertainty of the momentum at a definite instant, because of the errors inherent in our time measurements.

To sum up, when we measure the x-coordinate of the electron with an error of the order of Δx, the value of p_x is changed by a quantity $C(p_x)$, such that

$$\Delta x \cdot C(p_x) \cong h, \tag{3}$$

and further,

$$\Delta x \cdot \Delta p_x \cong h. \tag{4}$$

It was recognized by Heisenberg that relations similar to equations (3) and (4) must hold true for every measurement which we make, a truth which is referred to as the "uncertainty or indetermination principle," and which may be stated as follows:

If a coordinate q is measured with an error of the order Δq, the uncertainty, Δp, of the conjugate momentum introduced by our measurement is such that

$$\Delta q \cdot \Delta p \cong h; \tag{5}$$

and conversely, if p is measured with an error of the order Δp, as a consequence q is altered by an amount Δq, such that equation (5) is satisfied.

To illustrate the latter statement, let us consider how to measure the momentum mv of an electron moving parallel to the x-axis. This may be done by allowing a light quantum to fall on the electron from the direction of the positive x-axis. Let the quantum be scattered through 180° so that it returns along the positive x-axis. If it is received in a spectrograph, the momentum may be determined by measuring the change in wave length due to the Doppler shift. From the usual equation for the Doppler shift,

$$\frac{\delta\lambda}{\lambda} = -\frac{2v}{c}. \tag{6}$$

---

[1] Indeed, many physicists will go so far as to say that we cannot attach any physical meaning to the instantaneous value of p_x, t, or x during the scattering process. This is justifiable, providing we say that a quantity must be measured in order to have physical significance. The point is, we have no physical method for checking up on our ideas about the details of the collision.

On the theory of light quanta, we may think of the Doppler shift as caused by a change in the energy and momentum of the quantum, due to the recoil of the scattering electron.[1] In the present case, let the electron be at the origin when it encounters the quantum, say at the time $t = 0$, and let their interaction persist for a time τ. If the electron had not suffered collision, it would have been at the position $v\tau$ when $t = \tau$, but due to its recoil it moves with a smaller average velocity, say $v - \Delta v$, where $m\Delta v$ is of the order of $2h\nu/c$, the vectorial change of momentum of the quantum. Therefore, the change of x, or uncertainty of x, due to the collision is

$$\Delta x \cong \frac{h\nu\tau}{mc}. \tag{7}$$

We now consider the error Δv involved in measuring the velocity, which depends on the excellence of our wave-length measurements with the spectrograph. In equation (6), the percentage error of $\delta\lambda$ will be large compared with that of λ, so that $\Delta v/c \cong \Delta(\delta\lambda)/\lambda$. Assuming that the spectrograph has extremely great resolving power, the value of $\Delta(\delta\lambda)$ will be determined by the natural width of the spectrum line. Returning for a moment to the terminology of classical theory, $\Delta(\delta\lambda)/\lambda$ will be equal to the wave length divided by the length of the wave train, that is, to $\lambda/c\tau$. Therefore,

$$\frac{\Delta v}{c} \cong \frac{\lambda}{c\tau},$$

and

$$\Delta(mv) \cong \frac{m\lambda}{\tau} \tag{8}$$

Combining equations (7) and (8), we have $\Delta x \cdot \Delta(mv) \cong h$, in agreement with the uncertainty principle.

Other illustrations of the uncertainty principle have been given by Darwin,[2] Ruark,[3] and Kennard.[4] Further, Ruark[5] proved that in certain types of measurement, at least, there is an upper limit to the accuracy with which an individual coordinate or momentum can be measured. Independently, Flint and Richardson[6] assumed that such an upper limit exists on the basis of certain relativistic considerations. They consider several applications connected with Heisenberg's uncertainty principle, and further, they arrive at the value 98 as an upper limit to the number of the chemical elements.

Ruark's argument depends on the fact that the measuring device is affected by its encounter with the measured object, as Bohr[7] has emphasized, and can be understood from a simple illustration. Let us measure the x-coordinate of an electron by allowing it to scatter a light quantum, at about 90°, the quantum passing to a suitable receiving device. If we wish to have high precision, the wave length of the scattered quantum must be small. To make it small, we decrease the wave length of the incident quantum, but beyond a certain point this procedure will not be effective, for *the scattered wave length cannot be made smaller than the increase in wave length due to the Compton effect*, which is h/mc for the scattering angle 90°. Similarly, if the detecting device is a particle which is allowed to collide with the electron, its de Broglie wave length, h/mv, cannot be made as small as we like after the collision. A detailed examination

[1] Schrödinger, *Physik, Z.*, **23**, 301 (1922); Dirac, *Proc. Camb. Phil. Soc.*, **22**, 432 (1924); Ruark, *Phil. Mag.*, **3**, 1051 (1927).

[2] *Proc. Roy. Soc.*, **117**, 258 (1927).

[3] *Phys. Rev.*, **31**, 311, 709 (1928); *Proc. Nat Acad. Sci.*, **14**, 322 (1928).

[4] *Phys. Rev.*, **31**, 344 (1928).

[5] *Loc. cit., Proc. Nat. Acad. Sci.*

[6] *Proc. Roy. Soc.*, **117**, 637 (1928).

[7] *Trans. of Volta Centenary Congress at Como* (1927); *Nature*, **121**, 580, (1928).

of the problem, using relativistic dynamics, shows that the momentum of the scattered particle cannot be made as large as we please, for reasons similar to those encountered in the case of the light quantum. Electron diffraction effects (Chap. XXI) limit the accuracy of measurement to a quantity of the order h/mv.

On the basis of Newtonian mechanics these effects are not encountered. Doubling the velocity of the incident particle will always double that of the scattered particle, and the wave length of the de Broglie waves can be decreased without limit. Thus, the existence of a limit of accuracy in length measurements is connected with the physical impossibility of velocities greater than that of light, and, therefore, is a consequence of relativistic dynamics, together with the fact that the de Broglie wave length is h/mv.

The smallest interval of time which can be distinguished in experiments on an electron is found to be h/mc^2. The smallest possible uncertainty of a derived quantity such as energy or angular momenum is easily found by using the relations

$$\Delta x_{min} = \frac{h}{mc}, \ \Delta t_{min} = \frac{h}{mc^2}.$$

Heisenberg has pointed out the connection of the indetermination principle with the matrix quantum condition. He states that the inexactness of our measurements expressed by equation (5) makes it possible that pq should be different from qp, so that the quantum conditions may be valid; further, that if it were possible in any way to carry out more accurate simultaneous determinations of p and q than those allowed by equation (5), quantum mechanics would become impossible. His trend of thought is that p and q are to be considered as rational generalizations of the coordinates and momenta, used in classical mechanics, so that we must modify our ideas of the significance of a coordinate, even in the case of large-scale dynamics. According to his view, a coordinate is always a matrix. In large-scale experiments, this fact is concealed from us by the imperfections of our instruments and by the overlapping of energy levels in large systems, due to their natural width. For these reasons we are contented with expressing a coordinate by a Fourier series, rather than a matrix, and the matrix quantum condition goes unnoticed.

These views of the physical meaning of matrices are quite different from those developed in Chap. XVII, Sec. **3**. To many investigators, a matrix is merely a mathematical auxiliary, useful in helping us to get the possible values of a physical quantity, but itself devoid of physical meaning and incapable of appealing directly to our senses. This view has been discussed by Hilbert, von Neumann, and Nordheim.[1] However, the matter need not detain us here. The important point for our present purpose is the aid which Heisenberg's principle gives us in understanding the statistical interpretation of quantum mechanics, already outlined in Chap. XV, Sec. **16**. His treatment of this matter is so helpful that we shall give a rough translation of his remarks. He says,

[1] *Math. Annalen*, **98**, 1 (1927). Especially pp. 1–3.

We do not assume that the quantum theory is an essentially statistical theory, as opposed to the classical, in the sense that only statistical conclusions can be drawn from data which are given exactly. The well-known experiments of Geiger and Bothe speak against such an assumption (Chap. III, Sec. **17**). On the contrary, in all cases in which relations exist in the classical theory between quantities which are exactly measurable, we have correspondingly exact relations in the quantum theory (for example, the laws of conservation of energy and momentum). But in the formulation of the causal law, namely, "If we know the present exactly, we can predict the future," not the conclusion, but the premise, is false. We cannot determine present conditions with the completeness postulated by the classical theory. Therefore, all our observations represent only a selection out of a much broader range of possible observations, which cannot all be carried out simultaneously, and with any desirable accuracy, because of the limitations imposed by the principle of uncertainty.

2. THE FUNDAMENTAL PROBLEMS OF QUANTUM MECHANICS

Consider the motion of a free electron along the x-axis. If we determine its position at time $t = 0$, its velocity is altered by the interaction with the device for measuring position. Since the velocity is indeterminate, the position after the passage of a certain time interval τ is also indeterminate. Let us suppose now that the experiment is repeated with a number of electrons. Due to the uncertainty of our measurements of position, we cannot specify the original position of each electron. However, we can draw a distribution curve, $D_0(x)$ such that $D_0(x)dx$ is the fraction of the electrons for which the measured x-coordinate lies between x and $x + dx$. At time τ, we have another distribution curve $D(x)$. The width of the peak of this curve is due to two causes: (1) the dispersion of the original positions, and (2) the dispersion of velocities. The problem confronting us is this: Given the initial distribution of positions, what will be the final distribution? More generally, we may ask the following question in the case of a system with several degrees of freedom:

When the distribution curve for each of the coordinates is specified at time t_0, what is the probability that the coordinates will lie in the ranges q_1 to $q_1 + dq_1$, q_2 to $q_2 + dq_2$, etc., at a later time t?

The reader who feels disappointed that the information sought in solving a dynamical problem on the quantum theory is statistical, and that the course of the individual system is not followed by our equations, should console himself with the thought that we seldom need any information other than that which is given by the quantum theory. It will not do, however, to close our eyes to the fact that this situation may be altered by the advance of our experimental knowledge.

By comparison with Chap. XV, Sec. **16**, we see that if Born's statistical interpretation is to be upheld, the function D must be identical with $\Psi\Psi^*$. The problem outlined above reduces to the question of solving the wave equation (65) of Chap. XV, and choosing the constants c_n and c_E in the general solution,

$$\Psi = \Sigma c_n \Psi_n + \int c_E \Psi_E dE, \tag{9}$$

in such a way that at time t_0 the solution reduces to the prescribed initial distribution curve $D_0(x_0)$. However, this does not give all the information which we may desire. Often, we wish to know the distribution curves for quantities other than the coordinates—the momenta, for example—and it may happen that we wish to compare these curves, not at different times, but for different values of some other variable or parameter. This leads us to generalizations of the function Ψ and of Schrödinger's equation, which enable us to solve all these problems.

3. PROBABILITY AMPLITUDE FUNCTIONS

Before introducing these more general probability functions it will be well to make a systematic statement as to the statistical interpretation of the Ψ function, equation (9). In Chap. XV, Sec. **16,** we spoke of this function as belonging to an aggregate of independent atoms, or electrons, as the case may be. For example, it was stated that for electrons moving along the x-axis, $\Psi\Psi^* dx$ is a measure of the fraction which lies between x and $x + dx$. However, it is better to think of performing the same experiment a number of times on individual electrons or atoms, just as in the illustration of Sec. **2.** *Strictly, $\Psi\Psi^* dx$ is the fraction of such a group of experiments in which the coordinate lies between x and $x + dx$. The use of the Ψ function to describe the properties of an aggregate of atoms or electrons is justified only when they do not interact.*

In the case of quantized atoms, having the wave function $\Sigma c_n \Psi_n$, we may classify the individual systems not according to position but according to energy, if we like. Following Born, the fraction of the atoms in an aggregate which are in the nth quantum state is proportional to $c_n c_n^*$. As Darwin[1] says, the distinction between the two types of classification is best appreciated by considering the analogy to light. The intensity of light can be regarded in two different ways, either by measuring the density of electromagnetic energy at a point and so giving the intensity at that point, or else by making a spectral analysis, not now at a point but in a region of space, and determining the distribution of energy in the spectrum.

After Pauli, $\Psi_n(E_n, q)$ is called a "probability amplitude," partly because it may be thought of as analogous to the amplitude of the electric vector in an optical problem. Now suppose that any dynamical variable $F_2(p, q)$ is given a fixed value y; what is the probability $P(xy, F_1F_2)$ that another variable $F_1(p, q)$ shall lie between x_0 and $x_0 + dx_0$? In giving the answer to this question, Jordan[2] assumed that *there is*

[1] *Proc. Roy. Soc.*, **117**, 258 (1927).

[2] *Z. Physik*, **40**, 809, and **44**, 1 (1927).

always a function $\varphi(xy, \ F_1 F_2)$, *called the probability amplitude,*[1] *such that*

$$\varphi(xy, F_1 F_2)\varphi^*(xy, F_1 F_2) = P(xy, F_1 F_2). \tag{10}$$

Preparatory to finding the function φ, we shall write down some very reasonable conditions which it is assumed to obey:

I. The first assumption is expressed by equation (10).

II. The probability that for a given value of F_1—let us say x—the function F_2 shall have a value between y and $y + dy$, is given by the same expression, $P(xy, F_1 F_2)$, which was used in equation (10). That is

$$P(xy, F_1 F_2) = P(yx, F_2 F_1). \tag{11}$$

III. If F_1 is identical with F_2, and F_2 is given the specified value y, the probability that x shall equal y must reduce to certainty. That is,

$$\begin{aligned} P(xy, F_1 F_1) &= 1 \text{ if } x = y, \\ &= 0 \text{ if } x \neq y. \end{aligned} \tag{12}$$

IV. We now consider the rule for the composition of probabilities, which is essential to all that follows: Suppose F_1 is given the value x. In addition to the above definitions let us agree that $\varphi(yz, F_2 F_3)$ is the probability amplitude for a value of F_3 between z and $z + dz$, when $F_2 = y$.[2] At first sight we should expect that

$$P(xz, F_1 F_3)dz = [\int P(xy, F_1 F_2)dyP(yz, F_2 F_3)dz. \tag{13}$$

The basis for such an equation would be as follows: When $F_1 = x$, then the probability for F_2 to lie in the range y to $y + dy$ is the first factor in the integrand multiplied by dy; but when y has a value in this infinitesimal range, the probability for F_3 to lie in the range between z and $z + dz$ is the second factor times dz. The probability for both of these conditions to be satisfied should be the product of the two factors if the separate probabilities are independent; and integrating over all possible values of y we should obtain equation (13). However, *the assumption is made in quantum mechanics that the probabilities considered above are not usually independent. (They may be independent in special cases.) Just as we have interference phenomena in optics which make it proper to add the amplitudes rather than the intensities of the individual wave trains making up a natural beam of light, so in quantum theory we must compound the probability amplitudes. Therefore, we replace equation (13) by the relation*

$$\varphi(xz, F_1 F_3) = \int \varphi(xy, F_1 F_2)\varphi(yz, F_2 F_3)dy. \tag{14}$$

V. It is assumed that the probabilities depend only on the functional nature of the quantities $F_1(p \ q)$ and $F_2(p \ q)$, that is, on their kinematic

---

[1] The notation used here is that of Hilbert, von Neumann and Nordheim, *Math. Annalen*, **98**, 1 (1927).

[2] It must be understood that φ does not denote the same function which it did in equation (10). A change of the mechanical variables F inside the parentheses means that we are dealing with a new function.

connection, and not on special properties of the mechanical system under investigation, such as its charge or the form of its energy function.

At this point it is advantageous to simplify the notation somewhat. We write

$$S(F_1, F_2)$$

in place of $\varphi(xy, F_1F_2)$, leaving out the particular values of F_1 and F_2 which are considered. Thus the Schrödinger function $\Psi_n(E_n, q)$ gives the probability distribution of q when E has the value E_n, and is written $S(E_n, q)$; if we wish to indicate the value of Ψ_n at q_0, we write

$$S(E_n, q_0).$$

4. THE PROBABILITY AMPLITUDE $S(p, q)$

We shall illustrate these remarks by considering the probability amplitude $S(p, q)$, where q is a coordinate and p is the conjugate momentum. Let us suppose that p is given a definite value. It was assumed by Jordan that all values of q are equally probable. That is, for any value of p,

$$S(p, q)S^*(p, q)dq = C^2dq, \tag{15}$$

where C is a constant. This equation is to hold for each and every value of q. The value of C is determined by writing an equation which states that some value of q is certainly occupied, that is,

$$\int S(p, q)S^*(p, q)dq = C^2\int dq = 1. \tag{16}$$

This shows that C^2 is the reciprocal of the range of values of q. If the range is infinite, $C = 0$, which means that the probability for q to lie in any finite range is zero. In such a case, this method of normalization must be abandoned.[1] We now write S in the form $A \exp iB$, where A and B are real. We can determine the form of B by considering the special case of a particle moving freely along the x-axis. If the momentum is held constant, the energy is also constant, and $S(p, q)$ must be the same as $S(E, q)$.[2] But $S(E, q)$ is simply the appropriate solution of Schrödinger's equation, $\exp 2\pi ip_x x/h$. Now, by Assumption V in Sec. **3**, the functional form of $S(p_x, x)$ will be the same in any problem,

---

[1] The difficulty is one of our own making. Strictly speaking, quantities which can take infinite values should not be used in physics. See Ruark, *Bull.* Amer. Phys. Soc., **4**, 1, 15 (1929).

[2] This is physically obvious, but can be proved mathematically by considering a special case of equation (14), namely,

$$S(p^2, q) = \int S(p^2, p')dp'S(p', q).$$

$S(p^2, p')$ is zero except when the variable of integration p' is equal to p because when p is sharply determined so also is p^2. Thus the quantity on the right is simply $S(p, q)$, multiplied by some constant.

as long as we do not alter the geometrical significance of p_x or x. Therefore, we write

$$S(p_x, x) = \exp \frac{2\pi i p_x x}{h}, \tag{17}$$

without any restrictions. More generally, it follows from the developments in Sec. **15**, that for any conjugate pair of variables,

$$S(p, q) = \exp \frac{2\pi i p q}{h}. \tag{18}$$

In accord with Assumption II, Sec. **3**, $S(p, q)$ can be interpreted in an alternative way, namely, $S(p_0, q)S^*(p_0, q)dp_0$ is the probability that p shall lie between p_0 and $p_0 + dp_0$, when q is sharply determined.

5. THE UNCERTAINTY THEOREM

We are now in a position to prove a remarkable theorem due to Heisenberg,[1] which expresses a portion of the content of his principle of indetermination. This theorem is not as broad as the principle,

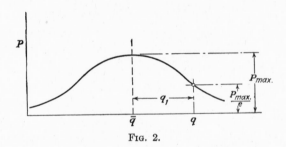

FIG. 2.

for the former deals only with a special type of distribution curve. Suppose we have measured a coordinate q a number of times, and have obtained the value q by taking the mean of the observed values. Let us assume that the probability of the coordinate lying between q and $q + dq$ is

$$Pdq = \exp\left[-\frac{(q - \bar{q})^2}{q_1^2}\right]dq. \tag{19}$$

The error curve P is shown in Fig. 2. If q_1 is the value of $q - \bar{q}$ at which the curve has fallen to $1/e$ times its maximum height, and m is the mean error then $2m^2 = q_1^2$. Following a widespread custom, we shall speak of q_1 as the *precision* of a measurement, although q_1 is really a measure of the lack of precision.

Now, it is convenient to consider a probability amplitude $S(\eta, q)$, such that $SS^* = P$, η being some parameter which is held constant. It will not be necessary to specify the nature of η. S can take the form

$P^{1/2}e^{iR}$, where R is a real function, and guided by our study of matter waves, we choose a value of R which depends on q through a sine (or cosine) factor:

$$S(\eta, q) = c \exp\left[-\frac{(q - \bar{q})^2}{2q_1{}^2} - \frac{2\pi i \bar{p}(q - \bar{q})}{h} \right], \tag{20}$$

where c is a constant and p is a value of p measured with the precision p_1 at the same time as q. Then the general assumption (14) shows that

$$S(\eta, p) = \int S(\eta, q)S(q, p)dq. \tag{21}$$

The uncertainty theorem now to be proved states that

$$p_1 q_1 = \frac{h}{2\pi}. \tag{22}$$

By equations (18) and (20),

$$S(\eta, p) = c \int \exp\left[-\frac{(q - \bar{q})^2}{2q_1{}^2} - \frac{2\pi i \bar{p}(q - \bar{q})}{h} + \frac{2\pi i p q}{h} \right]dq.$$

The factor, $\exp(2\pi i \bar{p}\bar{q}/h)$, is constant and can be included in c. This leaves us with

$$S(\eta, p) = c \int \exp\left[\frac{2\pi i(p - p)q}{h} - \frac{(q - \bar{q})^2}{2q_1{}^2} \right]dq.$$

To bring this to an easily integrable form we multiply by a suitable factor in front of the integral sign, and divide by it inside, obtaining

$$S(\eta, p) = c \exp\left[\frac{2\pi i(p - \bar{p})\bar{q}}{h} - \frac{2q_1{}^2\pi^2(p - \bar{p})^2}{h^2} \right]$$
$$\int \exp\left[-\left(\frac{\sqrt{2}q_1\pi(p - \bar{p})i}{h} - \frac{(q - \bar{q})}{\sqrt{2}q_1} \right)^2 \right]dq.$$

The limits of the integral are $-\infty$ and $+\infty$, so its value does not depend on p, $\bar{p}$, q, or $\bar{q}$. Introducing the quantity p_1, defined by equation (22),

$$S(\eta, p) = \text{const. } \exp\left[-\frac{(p - \bar{p})^2}{2p_1{}^2} + \frac{2\pi i(p - \bar{p})\bar{q}}{h} \right]. \tag{23}$$

Therefore,

$$S(\eta, p)S^*(\eta, p) = \text{const. } \exp\left(-\frac{(p - \bar{p})^2}{p_1{}^2} \right). \tag{24}$$

This shows the significance of p_1; it is the precision of p, which proves our theorem.

6. INTRODUCTION TO THE TRANSFORMATION THEORY

As an approach to the transformation theory of Jordan and Dirac, we take up afresh the problem outlined at the beginning of Sec. 2. At any time t_0, let the coordinate q and the momentum p of a number of typical systems be measured. We shall write q_0 and p_0 for typical values of q and p measured at this time. As a result of the uncertainty involved in determining q_0, $S(\eta, q_0)$ will be appreciable over a certain range of values of q, and, similarly, $S(\eta,\ p_0)$ will be appreciable over a certain range of p values. Of course, these systems are spoiled for further study by the process of measurement, but we are at liberty to suppose that we have a similar aggregate of systems which are not subjected to measurement, but which would give the same values of $S(\eta,\ q_0)$ and $S(\eta,\ p_0)$ if they were measured. At a later time t, systems in this group which may be supposed to have had their representative points in a range q_0 to $q_0 + dq_0$ will have moved to another range, q to $q + dq$. In general, the latter range will be larger than the former, for the uncertainties of the momenta will cause the representative points of the various systems to scatter.

Assuming that $S(\eta,\ q_0)$ is given, our problem is to calculate the value of $S(\eta,\ q)$ at time t. In the case of systems with several degrees of freedom, we begin with the values of a distribution function $S(\eta_1, \eta_2, \ldots ; q_1, q_2, \ldots)$ at time t_0, and desire to find S at a later time t. In general, the region over which the values of S are appreciable will spread out, just as in the one-dimensional problem.[1]

In the following discussion, our equations and terminology will refer to the one-dimensional case, for the extension to a number of degrees of freedom is obvious. We have the equation,

$$S(\eta,\ q) = \int S(\eta,\ q_0)dq_0 S(q_0,\ q),\qquad(25)$$

and everything hinges on our ability to obtain $S(q_0,\ q)$, which is often called a transformation function for reasons now to be explained. It is often convenient to speak of the relation between the initial and final values of a variable or a group of variables as a transformation equation. Thus, if we are dealing with a particle in uniform motion, the relation

$$x = x_0 + v(t - t_0)$$

sets up a correspondence between the initial and final positions. Again, we may transform n variables $x_1, \ldots x_n$, to new values $x_1', \ldots x_n'$, by the equations

$$x_i' = a_{i1}x_1 + a_{i2}x_2 + \cdots a_{in}x_n, \ i = 1 \cdots n.\qquad(26)$$

The aggregate of the quantities a_{ij}, drawn up in square array, is called a "transformation matrix." It is a simple and natural step to introduce the idea of transforming a continuous range or field of values, instead of a finite number of variables. The equation (25) is an illustration. If we write it in the form,

$$S(\eta,\ q) = S(q,\ q_{01})S(\eta,\ q_{01})dq_{01} + S(q,\ q_{02})S(\eta,\ q_{02})dq_{02} + \cdots ,$$

its similarity with equation (26) is quite evident. One such equation can be written for each value of q, so that the scale of values of q replaces the discontinuous scale of values of the subscript i. We may imagine a square field with a vertical scale of q values, and a horizontal scale

---

[1] However, FLAMM, *Physik, Z.*, **29**, 927 (1928), has considered solutions of the wave equation which are propagated without change of form.

of q_0 values. There is a value of $S(q, q_0)$ for each point of the field. The aggregate of these values is quite analogous to that of a_{ij}, and is also called a "transformation matrix." The function $S(q, q_0)$ is a transformation function, for it furnishes the connection between the old and new values of $S(\eta, q)$. There are two essentially different ways to obtain this function. One depends on a generalization of the theory of matrices invented by Dirac,[1] and the other, due to Jordan,[2] is based on the theory of operators.

On both theories, the derivation of the equations for determining transformation functions is rather complex, though not inherently difficult. Considerations of space prevent a detailed treatment by both methods. We shall follow the method of Dirac. The subject matter of the next few sections has many interrelated aspects, and the reader must not be disappointed if he finds that he does not fully appreciate it at a single reading.

7. DEFINITION OF CONTINUOUS MATRICES[3]

Dirac's theory is based on the extension of the idea of a matrix explained in Sec. **6,** which makes it possible to write down a matrix corresponding to a non-periodic coordinate or any other dynamical variable. In general, only periodic (or conditionally periodic) systems have discrete quantized energy values, while non-periodic systems, such as the hydrogen atom with its electron on a hyperbolic orbit, have continuous ranges of energy values. In Chap. XVII matrices were defined only for systems with discrete states, for each row or column of a matrix is associated with a particular value of the quantum integral J, or of the energy, if the system is not degenerate. We may say that the rows and columns are numbered according to the values of J. The rows or columns of such matrices may be said to form a denumerable infinity, for they can be brought into one-to-one correspondence with the integers. It is a natural and easy extension to think of matrices which have a non-denumerable infinity of rows and columns. We suppose there is a row or column for every number in the real continuum or in a portion of that continuum; that is, the rows or columns can be put into one-to-one correspondence with the points of a straight line, or a segment thereof. As before, we may number the rows according to the values of J, which is now a continuous variable. It is also convenient

---

[1] *Proc. Roy. Soc.*, **113,** 621 (1926).

[2] Following earlier work of BORN and WIENER, *Z. Physik*, **36,** 174 (1926), of ECKART, *Phys. Rev.*, **28,** 711 (1926), and of SCHRÖDINGER, *Ann. Physik*, **79,** 734 (1926), the operator theory was developed in full generality by JORDAN, *Z. Physik*, **40,** 809 (1927) and **44,** 1 (1927).

[3] In addition to Dirac's papers, the reader should consult an excellent résumé by KENNARD, *Z. Physik*, **44,** 326 (1927).

to consider matrices, in which a portion of the rows and columns are discrete and the remainder continuous, for, in general, we are confronted with a spectrum of energy values which has both discrete and continuous parts. For example, the q matrix for the hydrogen atom is divided into the domains indicated in Fig. 3. We number the rows and columns according to energy values, rather than values of J, simply for convenience. In A, both rows and columns are discrete. The first row and column belong to the lowest quantum state, the second to the two-quantum state, and so on. The typical element $q(nm) \exp 2\pi i\nu(nm)t$ represents the radiation amplitude due to transitions between the nth and mth orbits. In region B, the initial state lies in the region of hyperbolic orbits, the final, in the quantized orbits; in C, the reverse is the case. In both these regions an element is related to the intensity of the continuous spectrum at the corresponding wave length. Region D belongs to transitions between hyperbolic orbits.[1]

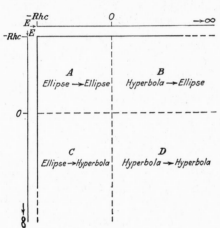

FIG. 3.—Continuous and discrete matrices of the hydrogen atom.

8. GENERALIZED MATRIX ALGEBRA

We must now study the algebraic laws to which generalized matrices are subject, restricting the discussion to one degree of freedom. The definition of the sum of two matrices requires no change. The typical element of $A + B$ is the sum of the typical elements of A and B. As to multiplication, in place of the law

$$AB(nm) = \sum_k A(nk)B(km)$$

we may write

$$AB(J_n J_m) = \sum_k A(J_n J_k)B(J_k J_m). \tag{27}$$

Here J_n stands for the quantum integral having the value nh, and it is assumed that the quantities J_n are the diagonal elements of a diagonal matrix J. This notation makes it clear that each row or column is associated with a particular value of J. In close analogy with equation

---

[1] The reader may be disturbed by the impracticability of writing down all the elements in the continuous or semicontinuous regions of such a matrix, due to the fact that they are infinite in number. We must content ourselves with being able to write a typical element. In some cases even this is impossible, except by the use of special symbols, as we shall see in Secs. **9** and **10.**

(27), the typical element of the product of two continuous matrices is defined as

$$AB(J'J'') = \int A(J'J)dJB(JJ''). \tag{28}$$

In the more general case where there is both a discrete and a continuous spectrum, equation (28) must be replaced by such expressions as

$$AB(J'J'') = \sum_k A(J'J_k)B(J_kJ'') + \int A(J'J)dJB(JJ''). \tag{29}$$

J_k assumes all values in the discrete range and J all values in the continuous range· Ordinarily, we shall write only the integral, with the understanding that every formula can be generalized to include the discrete range as well. Strictly, equation (29) is not dimensionally correct, because of the additional factor dJ in the integral, having the dimensions of action. We get around this by assuming that the integral is always divided by a number having the value unity and possessing the dimensions of action.

9. DIRAC'S δ FUNCTION

In the Heisenberg matrix theory, we often have use for the Kronecker symbol $\delta(nm)$, which is equal to 1 when $n = m$, and otherwise is equal to zero. For example, a typical element of the energy matrix is

$$E(nm) = E_n\delta(nm). \tag{30}$$

The advantage of such a notation is that it combines in a single equation information which otherwise would have to be written out in two separate equations, as follows:

$E(nm) = E_n$ if $n = m$, and 0 if n is not m.

Dirac's δ function is a generalization of the Kronecker symbol. It has the properties

$$\delta(x) = 0 \text{ if } x \text{ is not } 0, \tag{31}$$

and

$$\int_{-\infty}^{+\infty} \delta(x)dx = 1. \tag{32}$$

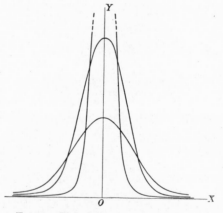

Fig. 4.—Illustrating Dirac's δ function.

For many purposes it is better to consider $\delta(x)$ as the limit of a sequence of even functions $\Phi(x)$, like those shown in Fig. 4, as we allow the symmetrical peak to approach infinite height and narrowness, and all ordinates outside the peak to approach zero, while $\int\Phi(x)dx$ is always equal to 1. Further, we suppose that $\delta(x)$ obeys all relations with other symbols which hold true for $\Phi(x)$ in the limit. The advantage of considering the sequence of functions $\Phi(x)$, is that by their aid we can set up definitions of various functions of $\delta(x)$, and can deduce the properties of these functions. For example, $\delta'(x)$ is defined as the limit of the first derivative of $\Phi(x)$, and so we have the properties

$$\delta(-x) = \delta(x) \tag{33}$$
$$\delta'(-x) = -\delta'(x). \tag{34}$$

If $f(x)$ is any regular function of x, we have

$$\int_{-\infty}^{+\infty} f(x)\,\delta(a - x)dx = f(a); \tag{35}$$

for the only finite contribution to the integral comes from the terms in the neighborhood of $x = a$, the integrand being zero elsewhere. Therefore, the integral may be replaced by

$$f(a)\int \delta(a - x)dx = f(a)\int \delta(x - a)d(x - a) = f(a),$$

as we see from equations (32) and (33). Using integration by parts it is also easy to show that

$$\int f(x)\,\delta^n(a - x)dx = f^n(a). \tag{36}$$

Further, putting $f(x) = \delta(x - b)$ in equation (35), we have

$$\int \delta(a - x)\,\delta(x - b)dx = \delta(a - b). \tag{37}$$

10. THE UNIT MATRIX

Dirac's δ function is indispensable in discussing the properties of continuous matrices. We require it, for example, in setting up the unit matrix. By definition, this matrix must be such that its product (either before or behind) with any matrix A is equal to A. Writing out a typical element of the relation $1A = A$, we require that

$$1A(J'J'') = \int 1(J'J)dJA(JJ'') = A(J'J''). \tag{38}$$

If we put

$$1(J'J) = \delta(J'J) \tag{39}$$

this integral becomes

$$\int \delta(J'J)dJA(JJ'')$$

and by equation (35), this is simply $A(J'J'')$, so that equation (38) is satisfied. If we are dealing with a problem of several dimensions, the argument is similar and we define the unit matrix by the equation

$$1(J_1', J_2', \cdots J_n'; J_1, J_2, \cdots J_n) = \delta(J_1' - J_1)$$
$$\delta(J_2' - J_2) \cdots \delta(J_n' - J_n). \tag{39a}$$

11. INTERPRETATION OF THE ENERGY MATRIX

Let us recall the way in which the quantized energy values were obtained in Heisenberg's matrix theory. The details of the mathematical method are sufficiently explained in Secs. 5 to 7 of Chap. XVII. Briefly, the problem consists in finding Hermitian matrices which satisfy the following conditions:

1. The quantum conditions (Chap. XVII, Sec. 11).

2. The matrix equations of motion.[1]

3. The Hamiltonian function must be represented by a diagonal matrix.

When such matrices are found, an assumption must be made in order to interpret the results. It is natural to consider a matrix element standing in the nth row and nth column as belonging to the nth quantum state. Accordingly, *it is assumed that the diagonal elements of the energy matrix represent the possible values of the energy.*

This idea is carried over almost without change into the theory of continuous matrices. We seek to find a transformation to new variables, such that the conditions above will be satisfied. When such a transformation has been found, the possible energy values are assumed to be the non-vanishing elements of the diagonal energy matrix, which now may be either discrete, or continuous, or a combination of the two. A word of explanation as to condition (3) is necessary. When we say the energy matrix is diagonal we mean that

$$E(J'J'') = E'\delta(J'J''), \qquad (40)$$

where $E' = E(J')$. A similar equation is used in defining any diagonal matrix. This is all very satisfactory, but we wish also to obtain the possible values of other physical quantities, and this requires us to consider transformations which are more general than those used in Chap. XVII.

12. TRANSFORMATIONS OF CONTINUOUS MATRICES

It will be recalled (Chap. XVII, Sec. 12) that when a set of discrete matrices p, q, obey all the conditions mentioned in the preceding section, we may apply the transformation

$$P = SpS^{-1}, \; Q = SqS^{-1},$$

where S is an arbitrary matrix not containing the time, and then the matrices P, Q, will also obey these conditions. Further, if f is any function of p and q, we have from equation (65), Chap. XVII,

$$F = SfS^{-1}, \qquad (41)$$

where F is obtained from $f(pq)$ by replacing p and q with P and Q, leaving the form of the function unaltered. All these theorems hold true for continuous matrices, and we wish to examine the form assumed by a typical element of equation (41). Let us agree that matrices expressed in the old system of variables will be numbered according to the values of an index j. Then we have

$$F(j'j'') = \int\int S(j'j_1)dj_1 f(j_1 j_2)dj_2 S^{-1}(j_2 j''). \qquad (42)$$

---

[1] In Chap. XVII, the equation of motion for a typical variable x was taken to be $\epsilon\dot{x} = Hx - xH$, but if x involves the time, this must be replaced by $\epsilon\left(\dot{x} - \dfrac{\partial x}{\partial t}\right) = Hx - xH.$

The integration variables j_1 and j_2 run over all possible values of j. It would be more elegant to number the matrix F according to the values of the quantity J, defined by the relation

$$J = SjS^{-1}.$$

Now j is a diagonal matrix, by hypothesis, and on working out a typical element of this relation, we find that $J = j$. This means that $J' = j'$, $J'' = j''$, and so on. Therefore equation (42) may be rewritten in the more satisfactory form

$$F(J'J'') = \iint S(J'j_1)dj_1 f(j_1 j_2)dj_2 S^{-1}(j_2 J''). \tag{43}$$

Now as Dirac remarks, this transformation does not go far enough. We can make any permutation of the rows of the new matrices and the same permutation of their columns, without violating any of the conditions in the preceding section. This theorem was proved in Chap. XVII, Sec. 4, Part (13). As a consequence, there is no one-to-one correspondence between the rows or columns of the old and new matrices. It is essential to grasp the broad possibilities of such permutations in the case of continuous matrices—possibilities which are not encountered with discrete matrices.

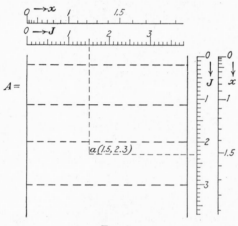

Fig. 5.

To make this clear, let us consider any discrete matrix, A. If we carry out one and the same permutation on the rows and columns of A, the number of elements in a given area of the matrix is unchanged. The situation is not so restricted when we come to continuous matrices. Let one of these be represented by the scheme in Fig. 5, with all positive energy values, as shown by the continuous scales of J values. So long as we avoid duplication, we can shift or distort the system of rows according to any prearranged plan, the columns being treated in exactly the same way, of course. Or, if we prefer, we may shift or distort the scheme of numbering, and arrive at the same result. For example, suppose that we write $J = x^2$. We can write opposite each value of J the corresponding value of x, and then the matrix is said to be numbered according to the variable x. In general, the connection between the two systems of numbering will be much more complicated, for we usually wish to number the matrices according to the values of some quantity X, which is represented by a diagonal matrix when expressed in terms of the new variables P, Q.

Because of this situation, Dirac rewrites the equation (43), so as to make it apparent that the quantity on the left simply denotes the matrix F, numbered in terms of such a variable X. Further, since F is the same function of the new variables which f was of p, q, there is no reason why we should not denote it by f. The result of these changes is that equation (43) takes the form

$$f(X'X'') = \int\int S(X'j_1)dj_1 f(j_1 j_2)dj_2 S^{-1}(j_2 X''), \tag{44}$$
$$= \int\int S(X'J_1)dJ_1 f(J_1 J_2)dJ_2 S^{-1}(J_2 X''). \tag{45}$$

This brings out the fact that the functions $S(X, J)$ and $S^{-1}(J, X)$ are numbered partly according to the values of X and partly according to the values of J. The rows of $S(X, J)$ are numbered on the X scheme, and the columns on the J scheme, for example. We shall speak of such matrices as *mixed matrices*.

In discussing such transformations, there is no reason why we should restrict ourselves to consideration of the functions $S(X, J)$. When we have passed to the X scheme of numbering, we can repeat the process, obtaining matrices which are numbered according to the variable Y, and so on. The general problem is to pass from a scheme where the variable A is a diagonal matrix, whose values are used in numbering both the rows and columns, to another scheme where the matrix X is diagonal, and serves the same purpose. Therefore, we consider equation (45) in the still more general form

$$f(X'X'') = \int\int S(X'\alpha_1)d\alpha_1 f(\alpha_1\alpha_2)d\alpha_2 S^{-1}(\alpha_2 X''). \tag{46}$$

From this point onward, a variable of integration running over all values of A will be denoted by α, and one which covers all values of X by ξ. The principle is that we indicate a variable of integration by a Greek letter analogous to the English letter under consideration.

If we are dealing with a problem having n degrees of freedom, instead of X we have a set of functions $X_1, X_2, \ldots X_n$, all of which are diagonal. The very fact that they are diagonal tells us that they do not involve t, and that they commute with one another. These are the only conditions which need be fulfilled in order that we may consider the X's as canonical coordinates. The momenta belonging to them will be called $Y_1 \ldots Y_n$.

13. MATRIX METHOD FOR OBTAINING THE POSSIBLE VALUES OF ANY PHYSICAL QUANTITY

We now have most of the mathematical apparatus necessary for finding the possible values of any dynamical quantity, $F(X, Y)$. We seek a transformation which will make $F(X, Y)$ a diagonal matrix, and *assume*, just as in the case of the energy, that the diagonal elements are the possible values of $F(X, Y)$. At the start, this matrix is numbered in the X scheme and it will be supposed diagonal in the A scheme of labeling. The variables X, Y are supposed to be known, and we seek a transformation function $S(X, A)$ which will carry all our matrices into the A scheme, by the use of equation (41) and the equations (42) to (46) which it implies. The next few pages are devoted to finding a differential equation for the transformation function $S(X, A)$. We shall state the result at once. If the reader desires he may omit the complicated proof in Secs. **14** and **15,** and pass at once to the discussion in succeeding sections.

It is found that the functions $S(X, A)$ are identical with the probability amplitudes used in the statistical interpretation of wave mechanics. The equation which they obey is a generalization of the wave equation, and may be stated in the form

$$F\left(X_r, \epsilon \frac{\partial}{\partial X_r}\right)S(X_r, A_r) = F(A_r)S(X_r, A_r). \tag{47}$$

$F(A_r)$ is a brief way of writing $F(X_r, Y_r)(A_1, A_2, \ldots A_n; A_1, A_2, \ldots A_n)$, which is allowable because F is diagonal in the A scheme, by hypothesis. Schrödinger's equation is a special case of equation (47), obtained as follows: Let $F \equiv H;\ X_r = q_r;\ Y_r = p_r;\ A_r = n_r h = h$ times the quantum number belonging to the rth degree of freedom; n_r is supposed continuous in the region of continuous energy values. Further, $F(A_r) = E(n_r)$. Thus we obtain,

$$H\left(q_r, \frac{h}{2\pi i} \frac{\partial}{\partial q_r}\right)S(q_r, n_r) = E(n_r)S(q_r, n_r). \tag{47a}$$

When there is only one degree of freedom and therefore only one quantum number n, this becomes

$$H\left(q, \frac{h}{2\pi i} \frac{\partial}{\partial q}\right)S_n(q) = E_n S_n(q). \tag{47b}$$

These equations are identical with that of Schrödinger. Of course, S depends on E, and so we may write $S_n(q) = S(q, E_n)$, but this is not desirable because the variables of S are supposed to be those which are used in labeling the matrix F in the old and new schemes. Strictly speaking, the quantities $n_r h$ are the labels to be used in the A scheme, in which H is diagonal. This discussion makes it clear that Schrödinger's ψ functions are the elements of the transformation matrix which enables one to transform any matrix from the scheme in which rows and columns are labeled according to values of q, to a scheme in which H is diagonal and the quantum numbers n_r (continuously variable) are the labels of the rows and columns.

In conclusion, it must be noted that equation (47) may not be valid when F is not expressible as a sum of powers of X_r and Y_r. Other equations of a still more general character must be used when we are dealing with mixed matrices, or when F is not algebraic.[1]

14. AUXILIARY RELATIONS FOR THE PROOF OF THE GENERAL WAVE EQUATION

We now consider the proof of equation (47). We shall require several transformation equations corresponding to the relations

$$S^{-1}f(X)S = f(A), f(X)S = Sf(A) \text{ and } S^{-1}f(X) = f(A)S^{-1},$$

where $f(X)$ and $f(A)$ indicate a matrix function $f(X_r, Y_r)$ expressed in the X and A schemes, respectively. They are as follows:

$$\iint S^{-1}(A'\xi_1)d\xi_1 f(\xi_1\xi_2)d\xi_2 S(\xi_2 A'') = f(A'A''), \tag{48}$$

$$\int f(X'\xi)d\xi S(\xi A'') = \int S(X'\alpha)d\alpha f(\alpha A'') \equiv f(X'A''), \tag{49}$$

$$\int S^{-1}(A'\xi)d\xi f(\xi X'') = \int f(A'\alpha)d\alpha S^{-1}(\alpha X'') \equiv f(A'X''). \tag{50}$$

We shall also need explicit formulas for the quantities Y_r, which are the momenta corresponding to the X_r. These variables must satisfy the relations

$$Y_rX_r - X_rY_r = \epsilon 1,$$
$$Y_rX_s - X_sY_r = 0,$$
$$X_rX_s - X_sX_r = 0,$$
$$Y_rY_s - Y_sY_r = 0. \tag{51}$$

The third of these is true because it was assumed (Sec. 12) that the X's commute among themselves. It is easily verified that the other three equations can be satisfied by writing

$$Y_r(X'X'') = \epsilon\delta(X_1' - X_1'') \cdots \delta(X'_{r-1} - X''_{r-1})\delta'(X_r' - X_r'')$$
$$\delta(X'_{r+1} - X''_{r+1}) \cdots \delta(X_n' - X_n''). \tag{52}$$

For a problem of one degree of freedom, equation (52) reduces to

$$Y(X'X'') = \epsilon\delta'(X' - X''). \tag{52a}$$

We shall confine our attention to proving that this value of Y satisfies the first equation of (51). Dirac's paper[2] may be consulted for the verification of the remaining relations. Remembering that $X(X'X'') = X'\delta(X' - X'')$, and using equation (52a), we have

$$(YX - XY)(X'X'') = \epsilon\int\{\delta'(X' - \xi)d\xi\xi\delta(\xi - X'') -$$
$$X'\delta(X' - \xi)d\xi\delta'(\xi - X'')\}. \tag{53}$$

We integrate the first term by parts so that it becomes

$$\epsilon\int\delta(X' - \xi)d\xi\frac{\partial}{\partial\xi}[\xi\delta(\xi - X'')].$$

[1] Dirac, *Proc. Roy. Soc.*, **114**, 243 (1927).
[2] *Loc. cit.*

On performing the differentiation indicated, and combining terms, equation (53) takes the form

$$\epsilon \int \{\delta(X' - \xi)\delta(\xi - X'') - (X' - \xi)\delta(X' - \xi)\delta'(\xi - X'')\}d\xi.$$

The first term yields the contribution

$$\epsilon\delta(X' - X'')$$

to the integral, in accordance with equation (37), and since this is the result we want, it only remains to prove that the second term contributes nothing to the integral. This is actually the case, because $(X' - \xi)$ $\delta(X' - \xi)$ is zero. The first factor vanishes if $\xi = X'$, and the second if ξ is not equal to X'. To sum up, the typical element of $YX - XY$ is $\epsilon\delta(X' - X'')$, which is to say, the matrix is equal to ϵ times the unit matrix.

15. PROOF OF THE GENERALIZED WAVE EQUATION

In order to obtain a proof of the generalized wave equation (47), we shall require some alternative expressions for the matrices X, Y, and $f(X, Y)$ when they are expressed in the mixed form, with X as the horizontal and A as the vertical label. These expressions will be obtained by using equation (52a). We begin by finding explicit formulas for $Y(X'A'')$ and $X(X'A'')$. By equations (49) and (52a) we have

$$Y(X'A'') = \int Y(X'\xi)d\xi S(\xi A'')$$
$$= \epsilon \int \delta'(X' - \xi)d\xi S(\xi A'').$$

By equation (36), therefore,

$$Y(X'A'') = \epsilon \frac{\partial S(X'A'')}{\partial X'}. \tag{54}$$

In n dimensions the proof is quite similar and yields the formula

$$Y_r(X'A'') = \epsilon \frac{\partial S(X'A'')}{\partial X_r'}. \tag{54a}$$

Remembering that $X(X'X'')$ is diagonal, we also find from equation (49) that

$$X(X'A'') = \int X'\delta(X' - \xi)d\xi S(\xi A'') = X'S(X'A''), \tag{55}$$

the generalization to n dimensions being

$$X_r(X'A'') = X_r'S(X'A''). \tag{55a}$$

In similar fashion we can show that

$$F(X_r)(X'A'') = \int F(X_r')\delta(X_r' - \xi)d\xi S(\xi A'') = F(X_r')S(X'A''). \tag{56}$$

Strictly speaking we should write $S(X_r'A_r'')$ in this relation, but this more cumbrous notation scarcely seems necessary.

However, when we have a function of both the X's and Y's the mixed representation of this function is of a different character. We suppose that this function $F(X_r, Y_r)$, is rational and integral in the quantities Y_r, a very necessary restriction.   We shall show that

$$F(X_r, Y_r)S(X'A'') = F\left(X_r', \epsilon \frac{\partial}{\partial X_r'}\right)S(X'A''),\qquad (57)$$

so that the elements of the matrix F in the (XA) scheme of labeling are given by the result of applying an operator to the function $S(X'A'')$. To prove this theorem we only need to show that if the theorem is true for any two functions f_1 and f_2, it is true for their sum and their product. (We know it is true for any X and Y, by equations (54a) and (55a), so we can show it is true for X_rY_s, X_r^2, etc., and can then pass to other functions step by step.)   The case of the sum is obvious.   As to the product, we have,

$$f_1(X_r, Y_r)f_2(X_r, Y_r)(X'A'')$$
$$= \iint f_1(X_r, Y_r)(X'\alpha)d\alpha\, S^{-1}(\alpha\xi)d\xi f_2(X_r, Y_r)(\xi A'')$$
$$= \iint f_1\left(X_r', \epsilon \frac{\partial}{\partial X_r'}\right)S(X'\alpha)d\alpha S^{-1}(\alpha\xi)d\xi f_2\left(\xi_r, \epsilon \frac{\partial}{\partial \xi_r}\right)S(\xi A''),\qquad (58)$$

and by the definition of a matrix product, this is the same as

$$f_1\left(X_r', \epsilon \frac{\partial}{\partial X_r'}\right)f_2\left(X_r', \epsilon \frac{\partial}{\partial X_r'}\right)S(X_r'A_r'').$$

This is the result desired.   In similar fashion we may show that

$$F(X_r, Y_r)S^{-1}(A'X'') = F\left(X_r'', \epsilon \frac{\partial}{\partial X_r''}\right)S^{-1}(A'X'').\qquad (59)$$

Let us now examine equation (57).   By equation (49), the left member is equal to

$$\int S(X'\alpha)d\alpha F(\alpha A'').$$

If we now require that F shall be diagonal in the $A - A$ scheme, we can show that equation (57) reduces to the generalized Schrödinger equation; for, when F is diagonal, the above integral takes the form

$$\int S(X'\alpha)d\alpha F(\alpha) \delta(\alpha - A'').$$

The integrand vanishes except when $\alpha = A''$, and the integral is equal to

$$\int S(X'A'')F(A'')\delta(\alpha - A'')d\alpha = S(X'A'')F(A'').\qquad (60)$$

Further, equation (57) holds true for every value of the X_r and the A_r. Therefore, we may omit the primes and double primes, which, up to the present, have emphasized the fact that we were attending to a particular matrix element, standing in the place for which each X_r takes the numerical value X_r', and A_r takes the value A_r'.   This means we are at liberty to deal with the function $S(X_r, A_r)$ instead of a special value of that function, $S(X_r'A_r')$.   Therefore, taking account of equation (60), equation (57) may be rewritten in the form

$$F\left(X_r, \; \epsilon\,\frac{\partial}{\partial X_r}\right)S(X_r, \; A_r) = F(A_r)S(X_r, \; A_r)$$

and this agrees with the generalized Schrödinger equation (47).

We have not yet proved that the transformation function $S(X_r, A_r)$ has the same meaning as the probability amplitude of Sec. **3**.   It seems best to postpone this proof until we have studied special cases of equation (47).

16. THE FREE MOTION OF A PARTICLE

We now proceed to illustrate the use of the generalized wave equation. First, we take up the train of thought begun in Sec. **6**, and find the transformation function $S(q_0, q)$ which applies to the motion of a free particle, following a treatment by Heisenberg.[1]   The solution of the problem is begun by writing down the energy function in terms of q numbers, which are nothing more than continuous matrices.   We have $H = p^2/2m$, and the equations of motion are

$$m\dot{q} = p, \; \dot{p} = 0. \tag{61}$$

The solution is

$$q = \frac{1}{m}p_0 t + q_0; p = p_0, \tag{62}$$

where p_0 and q_0 denote the momentum and the position at time $t = 0$. The time is treated as an ordinary number.   On forming the value of $pq - qp$, it is found to be identical with $p_0 q_0 - q_0 p_0$, so that the problem will be solved if we can find continuous matrices, q_0 and p_0, which obey the quantum condition.   But in order to write down the possible values for q_0, we must arrange the system of labeling so that q_0 is a diagonal matrix, and then apply the interpretative procedure outlined in Sec. **13**. Now, p_0 cannot be diagonal in this scheme of labeling, for if it were it would commute with q_0, and the quantum condition would not be obeyed. We see from equation (62) that q is not diagonal since it is equal to a matrix which does not enjoy this property.   Therefore, if we wish to obtain the possible values of q at the time t, we must transform all our matrices into a scheme of labeling in which q is diagonal, so that the interpretation process can be applied to it.   However, our line of advance will be somewhat different.   We know from experience that q can take all possible positive and negative values and shall not trouble ourselves to rediscover this fact by carrying through the process indicated.   Our real interest lies in the probability function $S(\eta, q)$ of Sec. **6**, which gives the distribution of an aggregate of particles in the one-dimensional q space, corresponding to an arbitrary distribution $S(\eta, q_0)$, η being any

[1] *Z. Physik*, **43**, 172 (1927).

parameter which is held constant during the motion. As in Sec. **5,** we take the original distribution to be a Gaussian error curve, that is,

$$S(\eta, q_0)S^*(\eta, q_0) = c \exp\left[-\frac{(q_0 - \bar{q}_0)^2}{q_1{}^2}\right], \tag{63}$$

and find the distribution curve at time t by equation (25), namely,

$$S(\eta, q) = \int S(\eta\ q_0)dq_0 S(q_0\ q).$$

The problem is to find $S(q_0, q)$, and this is identical with the typical element of the transformation matrix which carries us from the scheme in which q_0 is diagonal to the scheme in which q is diagonal. To get this function we apply equation (47), with the following values for the general symbols appearing therein:

X is simply q_0, and F is q itself, while A is also q.

This shows that Y is p_0, and when F is expressed in terms of q_0 and p_0 it takes the form $F(X,\ Y) = \dfrac{1}{m}p_0 t + q_0$. Therefore, the operator $F\left(X, \epsilon\dfrac{\partial}{\partial X}\right)$ is $\dfrac{\epsilon t}{m}\dfrac{\partial}{\partial q_0} + q_0$, and equation (47) takes the form

$$\frac{\epsilon t}{m}\frac{\partial S(q_0, q)}{\partial q_0} + q_0 S(q_0, q) = q S(q_0, q). \tag{64}$$

In this equation t is treated as a constant. It has the solution

$$S(q_0, q) = c \exp\left(\frac{m}{\epsilon t}\int(q - q_0)dq_0\right), \tag{65}$$

where c is a constant of integration. Substituting this in equation (25), and using equation (20), we have

$$S(\eta, q) = c\int \exp\left\{\frac{m}{\epsilon t}\left[q_0\left(q - \frac{t\bar{p}_0}{m}\right) - \frac{q_0{}^2}{2}\right] - \frac{(\bar{q}_0 - q_0)^2}{2q_1{}^2}\right\}dq_0.$$

To evaluate this integral we write

$$\beta = \frac{ht}{2\pi m q_1{}^2}, \tag{66}$$

and then the exponent takes the form,

$$-\frac{1}{2q_1{}^2}\left\{q_0{}^2\left(1 + \frac{i}{\beta}\right) - 2q_0\left[\bar{q}_0 + \frac{i}{\beta}\left(q - \frac{t\bar{p}_0}{m}\right)\right] + \bar{q}_0{}^2\right\}.$$

The term in $\bar{q}_0{}^2$ can be absorbed into the constant factor, and then the integration shows that

$$S(\eta, q) = c \exp\left[-\frac{\left(q - \dfrac{t\bar{p}_0}{m} - i\beta\bar{q}_0\right)^2\left(1 - \dfrac{i}{\beta}\right)}{2q_1{}^2(1 + \beta^2)}\right]. \tag{67}$$

From this we calculate the probability distribution,

$$S(\eta, q)S^*(\eta, q) = c \exp\left[-\frac{\left(q - \dfrac{t\overline{p_0}}{m} - \overline{q_0}\right)^2}{q_1{}^2(1 + \beta^2)} \right]. \qquad (68)$$

This formula shows that we are dealing with a Gaussian distribution of the representative points of the particles, symmetrical around the position $\dfrac{\overline{p_0}t}{m} + \overline{q_0}$, which would be the position actually occupied by each point if the motion were treated by classical methods. The spread of the distribution is greater than that of the original one in the ratio $1 + \beta^2$. These features are quite generally encountered in the problems of quantum mechanics. The center of gravity of the distribution obeys Newton's equation for the corresponding classical motion, and there is a progressive spread of the "packet" as time goes on.

Several other simple problems have been treated by Heisenberg[1] in quite similar fashion, and Kennard[2] has solved the problem of a particle in a homogeneous electric or magnetic field, as well as that of the harmonic oscillator. Darwin[3] has also studied a number of problems by this method. He treats the motion of a free electron in two and three dimensions, the motion of an electron in an atom, the Stern-Gerlach effect, and the motion of a spinning electron. Interesting mathematical methods for the solution of such problems are also developed in his paper. There are two later papers by Darwin[4] which deal with such problems from the standpoint of an improved system of wave equations introduced by Dirac.[5] Unfortunately, we cannot consider Dirac's equations here for reasons of space, although they open the way to the solution of many important problems. The exact form of the equations is still under discussion.[6]

17. THE MEANING OF THE TRANSFORMATION FUNCTION

In Sec. **13** we stated without proof that the transformation function $S(X, A)$ is identical with the probability amplitude for X when A is held constant. We now demonstrate the identity of these functions, using a method due to Dirac.[7] Consider a system having an energy function which does not involve the time, and let a perturbation depending on the time be applied, so that the new characteristic functions will involve

[1] *Loc. cit.*

[2] *Z. Physik*, **44**, 326 (1927).

[3] *Proc. Roy. Soc.*, **117**, 258 (1927).

[4] *Proc. Roy. Soc.*, **118**, 654 and **120**, 621 (1928).

[5] *Proc. Roy. Soc.*, **117**, 610 and **118**, 351 (1928).

[6] Eddington, *Proc., Roy. Soc.*, **122**, 358 (1929); Temple, *ibid.* **122**, 352 (1929).

[7] *Proc. Roy. Soc.*, **113**, 621 (1927).

the time. To find the transition probabilities induced by the perturbation, we may follow Born's method (Chap. XV, Sec. **23**). We first obtain the unperturbed ψ functions, let us say $\psi(E_0, q)$ and the perturbed functions $\psi(E, q)$.

If we expand the new wave functions in terms of the old ones we have

$$\psi(E, q) = \int c(E, E_0) dE_0 \psi(E_0, q), \tag{69}$$

where the coefficients $c(E, E_0)$ are also functions of the time. It is then assumed that $|c(E, E_0)|^2$ is a measure of the probability that an atom in the state E_0 will pass to a state with energy lying between E and $E + dE$, due to the perturbation. More generally, it is not necessary that the energy should appear in the wave functions. They could contain any other convenient parameter for distinguishing the various functions. Now, the transformation functions obey the relation

$$S(q, E) = \int S(q\ E_0) dE_0 S(E_0\ E). \tag{70}$$

The formal similarity of this equation with the preceding one, and the fact that similar equations hold for all dynamical variables, suggests that we can identify $S(X, A)$ of the matrix theory with the probability amplitude $S(X, A)$. Now the only conditions which must be satisfied by the probability amplitudes are those outlined in Sec. **3**, and we can verify that all of these are obeyed by the transformation functions, which completes the proof.

18. CONNECTION OF THE CHARGE-DENSITY AND STATISTICAL INTERPRETATIONS OF THE WAVE FUNCTION

We see from Chap. XV, Sec. **15**, that if we write

$$\rho = \Psi \Psi^* \tag{71}$$

and

$$s_x = \left(\frac{h}{4\pi i m}\right)\left(\Psi^* \frac{\partial \Psi}{\partial x} - \Psi \frac{\partial \Psi^*}{\partial x}\right), \tag{72}$$

with similar equations for s_y and s_z, then these four quantities obey the equation of continuity,

$$\frac{\partial \rho}{\partial t} + \frac{\partial s_x}{\partial x} + \frac{\partial s_y}{\partial y} + \frac{\partial s_z}{\partial z} = 0. \tag{73}$$

We understand now that this equation expresses the conservation of probability, rather than the conservation of charge. In Chap. XV, Sec. **15**, we introduced a factor ϵ, the charge of the particle under consideration, so that $\int \rho dv$ was equal to ϵ. This factor is not included above, for ρdv represents the probability that the particle shall lie in the element dv; the integral of this quantity over all space must be equal to 1, which represents certainty, unless we wish to violate established custom. We may call ρ the *density of probability*. Ordinarily, its value at any point will alter in the course of time, and the vector s *represents the flow* *of probability density* through unit area perpendicular to its direction, in unit time. Equation (73) tells us that the probability in a closed region can increase only if there is a flow of probability s through the boundary of the region.

Now, instead of considering a single particle, let us deal with an aggregate of particles which do not influence each other appreciably, *e.g.*, a beam of atoms rather than one atom. Then ρ is a measure of the average number of particles in dv, provided that dv can contain a number of particles large enough for statistical treatment without violating any of the conditions of the physical problem. In such a problem the direction of s must be that of the mass motion of the particles, and the magnitude of s must be proportional to the number of particles crossing unit area normal to s in unit time. Therefore, if the particles are charged, we see that Schrödinger's s is a measure of the current density, and ρ is a measure of the charge density. The normalization of these quantities in Chap. XV, Sec. **15**, was carried out in such a way that s represents the average current due to the motion of a single particle. This convention is useful, and we shall use the quantities

$$\rho = -e\Psi\Psi^*, \quad s_x = -\left(\frac{eh}{4\pi im}\right)\left(\Psi^*\frac{\partial\Psi}{\partial x} - \Psi\frac{\partial\Psi^*}{\partial x}\right), \tag{74}$$

rather than those in equation (72). The minus sign is introduced because the charge of the electron is negative.

The above treatment refers to the one-electron problem, *i.e.*, a problem with three degrees of freedom, and the flow of probability is a flow in ordinary space. In the general case, the flow takes place in the space of q's. Schrödinger[1] showed, however, that we can obtain a sort of projection of this flow on the three-dimensional space in which the coordinates are those of the pth electron, as follows: If we form the integral,

$$\rho_p \equiv \int\Psi\Psi^* dx_1 \cdots dz_{p-1}dx_{p+1} \cdots dz_n, \tag{75}$$

in which only the coordinates of the pth electron are present, the others having disappeared in the process of integration, then ρ_p *is the probability that the coordinates of the pth electron shall lie in the element $dx_p dy_p dz_p$, while the coordinates of the others take any values whatsoever.* Similarly,

$$s_{x_p} \equiv \left(\frac{-eh}{4\pi im_p}\right)\int\int\left(\Psi^*\frac{\partial\Psi}{\partial x_p} - \Psi\frac{\partial\Psi^*}{\partial x_p}\right)dx_1 \cdots dz_{p-1}dx_{p+1} \cdots dx_n \tag{76}$$

is a measure of the flux of probability in the x_p direction. We should expect that the charge density and current density for the pth particle would obey an equation of continuity, and such is the case. We can easily verify that

$$\frac{\partial\rho_p}{\partial t} + \frac{\partial s_{x_p}}{\partial x_p} + \frac{\partial s_{y_p}}{\partial y_p} + \frac{\partial s_{z_p}}{\partial z_p} = 0. \tag{77}$$

[1] *Ann. Physik*, **81**, 109 (1926).

The statistical velocity v of a stream of electrons in the three-dimensional space, x_p, y_p, z_p, is defined by the equation

$$s_p = \rho_p v_p, \tag{76a}$$

or

$$s = \rho v, \tag{76b}$$

in the one-electron problem.

19. THE UNIDIRECTIONAL BEAM OF ELECTRONS; RADIAL CURRENT OF ELECTRONS[1]

We now apply these ideas to a beam of electrons moving in the direction of the positive x-axis. If T is the kinetic energy, and p the momentum, the wave equation is

$$\frac{d^2\psi}{dx^2} + GT\psi = 0,$$

with the solution

$$\psi = a \exp\left(\frac{2\pi i p x}{h}\right), \tag{78}$$

where a is a constant. The time factor is $\exp(-2\pi i E t)$ where $E = T + mc^2$, and need not be considered further.

By equation (74), we expect the charge density and the current density in the beam to be

$$\rho = -e\psi\psi^* = -e|a|^2.$$
$$s_x = \frac{-eh}{4\pi i m}\left(\psi^*\frac{\partial\psi}{\partial x} - \psi\frac{\partial\psi^*}{\partial x}\right) = \frac{-ep|a|^2}{m},$$
$$s_y = s_z = 0. \tag{79}$$

As we should expect, the current is parallel to the negative x-axis, since the charge of the electron is negative. From equation (76a) we obtain the statistical velocity of the charges, namely,

$$v_x = \frac{s_x}{\rho} = \frac{p}{m}. \tag{80}$$

It follows that

$$T = \frac{mv_x^2}{2}. \tag{81}$$

These results predict every feature of the statistical behavior of a unidirectional electron beam, provided we can overlook effects due to mutual repulsion. To consider these effects, we should have to write a wave equation containing the coordinates of all the electrons in the beam. We could no longer write $V = 0$, but should use the potential energy of the entire system.

[1] In connection with Secs. **18** to **21**, the reader should consult a general resumé on the subject of aperiodic motions in wave mechanics, by WENTZEL, *Physik, Z.*, **29**, 321 (1928).

The case of charges emitted from a spherical electrode with uniform velocity is similar. If we seek for a solution of the wave equation in polar coordinates which possesses spherical symmetry, then we may neglect all terms in $\Delta\psi$ which contain partial derivatives of ψ with respect to the angular coordinates. The result is

$$\frac{1}{r^2}\frac{\partial}{\partial r}\left(r^2\frac{\partial\psi}{\partial r}\right) + GT\psi = 0, \tag{82}$$

which has the solution

$$\psi = \frac{a\exp(2\pi ipr/h)}{r}. \tag{83}$$

We have

$$\rho = -e\psi\psi^* = \frac{-e|a|^2}{r^2}. \tag{84}$$

The radial current density is calculated from the formula

$$i_r = \frac{-eh}{4\pi im}\left(\psi^*\frac{\partial\psi}{\partial r} - \psi\frac{\partial\psi^*}{\partial r}\right) \tag{85}$$

and is found to be $-\dfrac{ep}{m}\dfrac{|a|^2}{r^2}$. By equation (76a), the velocity is $v_r = p/m$, and $T = mv_r^2/2$ Of course, the θ- and φ-components of current density are zero.

20. BORN'S THEORY OF COLLISIONS

The interaction of material particles can be treated by the methods of wave mechanics. The development of this subject began with a paper by Born[1] on the interaction of an electron with an atom. This dealt with the problem in general terms and showed that the main features of critical potential experiments are reproduced qualitatively by the theory. The existence of critical potentials is predicted, and it is shown that one can obtain the space distribution of electrons which have suffered collision. The probability of each type of collision as a function of the voltage, and the effective cross-section of the atom for electrons of any velocity can also be obtained. In practice, the computations are involved and we must usually content ourselves with a first approximation to the solution. However, this is not necessarily a disadvantage, for it often happens that the first approximation is good enough for all practical purposes. Born[2] has carried through the calculations for the hydrogen atom. No data on the angular distribution of electrons which have collided with hydrogen atoms are available for comparison, for obvious experimental reasons. Possibly Born's computations yield a first approximation to the behavior of simple atoms like those of the alkalies, but this is by no means certain. The best

[1] *Z. Physik*, **38**, 803 (1926); preliminary note, *ibid.* **37**, 863 (1926).
[2] "Nachrichten Ges. der Wissenschaften zu Göttingen," p. 147 (1926).

proofs of the validity of the theory come from its application by Wentzel[1] to the spatial distribution of photoelectrons and the scattering of alpha particles. In the case of alpha particles, he showed that the first approximation to the solution of the problem leads to precisely the classical distribution formula (Chap. II, Sec. **15**) which has been so well verified by the experiments of Rutherford and his colleagues.

Several approximation methods are now available for the solution of collision problems. For a discussion of these and detailed references to the literature the reader may consult Wentzel's[2] résumé. Here we shall describe a procedure which is essentially that of Born. Matters are simplified if we consider atoms, all of which are in a single quantum state. The generalization necessary when this is not true will be easily carried through by the reader. The argument is unchanged except that we must replace the wave function appropriate to a single state by one which includes a term for every state which is present. Let the undisturbed atom be in a state of energy E_n, the wave function being u_n, and let its potential energy be $V_0(x_1, y_1, \ldots z_n)$. Further, let the bombarding electron have the wave function $\exp 2\pi i p_{x_0} x_0/h \equiv e^{ikx_0}$, when it is far removed from the atom. When the bombarding electron is closely coupled with the atom let the additional potential energy due to their interaction be V_1. The function V_1 depends on the coordinates of both the bombarding electron and the atom. The total potential energy is $V = V_0 + V_1$, and the total energy of the system is $E = T + E_n$, where $T = p_{x_0}{}^2/2m$ and is the initial kinetic energy of the bombarding electron. If V_1 were zero (no interaction), the wave function for the whole system would be

$$\psi_0 = a u_n e^{ikx_0}, \tag{86}$$

a being the normalization factor for e^{ikx_0}. We suppose that u_n is already normalized. The wave equation to be satisfied when there is interaction is

$$\Delta\psi + G(E - V)\psi = 0. \tag{87}$$

The boundary conditions are these: at infinity the wave function shall behave like a plane de Broglie wave, in so far as its dependence on x_0, y_0, and z_0 is concerned, while it shall obey Schrödinger's boundary conditions for an isolated atom (Chap. XV, Sec. **6**) when considered as a function of $x_1, \ldots z_n$.

We solve the problem by successive approximations, writing

$$\psi = \psi_0 + \psi_1 + \psi_2 + \cdots . \tag{88}$$

ψ_1 may be supposed to contain the first power of some small parameter; ψ_2, the second power; and so on. The method of attack is exactly like that in Chap. XV, Sec. **23**. We substitute equation (88) in the wave

[1] *Z. Physik*, **40**, 574 and 590 (1926).

[2] *Physik. Z.*, **29**, 321 (1928).

equation and equate all the terms which contain the same power of the parameter to zero. In this way we arrive at the following equations:

$$\Delta\psi_0 + G(E - V_0)\psi_0 = 0$$
$$\Delta\psi_1 + G(E - V_0)\psi_1 = GV_1\psi_0$$
$$\cdot \cdot \cdot \cdot \cdot \cdot \cdot \cdot \cdot \cdot \cdot \cdot \cdot \cdot \cdot \cdot$$
$$\Delta\psi_k = G(E - V_0)\psi_k = GV_1\psi_{k-1}. \tag{89}$$

In solving these equations it is assumed that ψ_1, ψ_2 etc., all vanish for infinite values of all the coordinates, *including* x_0, y_0, and z_0. If these conditions are satisfied, then the boundary conditions for ψ itself will also be obeyed. Born pointed out that the convergence of this process is assured only when V_1 vanishes more rapidly than $1/r_0^2$ at infinity, r_0 being the distance from the origin to the point x_0, y_0, z_0. Therefore, the method is not suitable for the problem of scattering by an inverse square center of force or by an ionized atom. (See the next section, however, for a description of the way in which Wentzel overcame this difficulty, when applying the method to the scattering of alpha particles.) Assuming that V_1 does vanish more rapidly than $1/r_0^2$, the equations (89) are solved by developing each function ψ_r in a series of wave functions of the undisturbed atom. The development coefficients will depend only on x_0, y_0, and z_0. We have

$$\psi_r = \sum_m f_{rm}u_m + \int\!f_{rE}u_E dE. \tag{90}$$

We find that the development coefficients f_{rm} and f_{rE} obey the differential equations

$$\left.\begin{array}{l}\Delta_0 f_{rm} + k^2{}_{nm}f_{rm} = G\int V_1\psi_{r-1}u_m dx_1 \cdot\cdot\cdot dz_n \equiv \Phi_{rm}, \\ \Delta_0 f_{rE'} + k^2{}_{nE'}f_{rE'} = G\int V_1\psi_{r-1}u_{E'} dx_1 \cdot\cdot\cdot dz_n \equiv \Phi_{rE'}.\end{array}\right\} \tag{91}$$

The coefficients k_{nm} and k_{nE} have the significance,

$$\left.\begin{array}{l}k^2{}_{nm} = G(T + E_n - E_m), \\ k^2{}_{nE'} = G(T + E_n - E'),\end{array}\right\} \tag{92}$$

E' being a particular value of E in the continuous spectrum of energy values. In equation (91), we must note carefully the meaning of the symbol Δ_0; it indicates $\dfrac{\partial^2}{\partial x_0{}^2} + \dfrac{\partial^2}{\partial y_0{}^2} + \dfrac{\partial^2}{\partial z_0{}^2}$. On the right side of equation (91), the Φ's are functions only of x_0, y_0, z_0, for the coordinates of particles in the atom disappear on integration. The solution of equation (91) can be written down by standard methods of potential theory. Putting x', y', z' for the coordinates of a "point of integration," it is

$$f_{rm} = -\frac{1}{4\pi}\int\Phi_{rm}(x',\ y',\ z')\frac{\exp{(\pm ik_{nm}|r' - r_0|)}}{|r' - r_0|}dx'dy'dz', \tag{93}$$

with a similar expression for f_{rE}; r' and r_0 denote the vectors from the origin to the points x', y', z' and x_0, y_0, z_0, respectively, so that

$$|r' - r_0|^2 = (x' - x_0)^2 + (y' - y_0)^2 + (z' - z_0)^2. \tag{94}$$

When we have substituted the values of f_{rm} and f_{rE} into equation (90), and ψ_r in turn into equation (88), the solution is complete, and we may proceed to interpret the results. We shall confine our attention to the first approximation function ψ_1, although the reader must be warned that this is not justifiable in some cases. Ordinarily, we are interested only in the value which ψ assumes when r_0 is large, that is, when the bombarding electron has moved away to a considerable distance. Considering only large values of r_0, then, we can neglect r' in comparison with r_0 in the denominator when carrying out the integration of equation (93) to obtain the development coefficients, for all the important contributions to the integral arise from volume elements in the immediate neighborhood of the atom. Also, we can simplify $|r' - r_0|$ in the

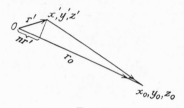

Fig. 6.

exponent. Figure 6 shows that for large values of r_0 this is approximately equal to $r_0 - r' \cos \alpha$, α being the angle between r' and r_0. But $r' \cos \alpha$ is equal to (nr'), the scalar product of r' and a unit vector n in the direction of r_0, so that

$$|r' - r_0| \cong r_0 - (nr').\tag{95}$$

Taking the factor $e^{ik_{nm}r_0}/r_0$ outside of the integral, writing out the value of Φ_{1m}, as given by equations (91) and (86), and remembering that $G = 8\pi^2 m_0/h^2$, we have

$$f_{1m} = \left(\frac{e^{ik_{mn}r_0}}{r_0}\right)\left(-\frac{2\pi m_0 a}{h^2}\right)\int V_1 \exp\left[ikx' - ik_{nm}(nr')\right]u_n u_m dv,$$

$$\equiv \left(\frac{e^{ik_{nm}r_0}}{r_0}\right)a_{nm},\tag{96}$$

where $dv = dx'dy'dz'dx_1 \cdots dz_n$. Finally, substituting equation (96) and the analogous formula for f_{1E} into equation (90), we get the value of ψ_1:

$$\psi_1 = \sum_m a_{nm}\frac{e^{ik_{nm}r_0}}{r_0}u_m + \int a_{nE}\frac{e^{ik_{nE}r_0}}{r_0}u_E dE.\tag{97}$$

Let us consider the meaning of a typical term in the summation of equation (97). Such a term is the wave function for the system composed of an undisturbed atom in the mth quantum state and an electron passing away from it radially with an energy which can be read out of the definition of k_{nm}. As we see from equation (92), this kinetic energy is $T - (E_m - E_n)$. This makes it possible to explain the principal qualitative facts in regard to collisions of electrons with atoms. If $n = m$, we have an elastic collision. The atom remains in the state n. If n is not m, we must distinguish two cases. In the first, T is less than $E_m - E_n$, and $k^2{}_{nm}$ is negative. This means that k_{nm} is imaginary and the exponent in equation (96) is negative, so that $\psi\psi^*$ drops off very rapidly as r_0 increases. Such exponentially decreasing contributions to the stream of deflected electrons will not be observed. The positive exponent is ruled out, since it would require very large charge density at large values of r_0. In the second case, T is greater than $E_m - E_n$, k_{nm} is real, and we have a stream of particles which have lost the energy $E_m - E_n$. This makes it clear that excitation must set in rather sharply when $T = E_m - E_n$.

The reader can carry through a similar argument for a typical term under the integral sign in equation (97). Such a term corresponds to an atom in one of the states for which E is greater than zero, the bombarding electron having the energy $T - (E - E_n)$.

The fraction of the electrons which undergo a certain type of inelastic collision and are deflected so as to pass through the arbitrary point x_0, y_0, z_0 is obtained very simply by using equation (85) to calculate the radial current density associated with each term of equation (85). It is apparent that we may use ψ_1 instead of $\psi_0 + \psi_1$ in equation (85). The term ψ_0 corresponds to the unidirectional stream of undeflected electrons. The result is found to be

$$i_r = \frac{h}{2\pi m_0 r_0{}^2}(\Sigma k_{nm}|a_{nm}|^2 + \int k_{nE}|a_{nE}|^2 dE), \qquad (98)$$

where it is to be understood that the sum includes only terms for which $E_m - E_n$ is less than T, and the integral, only terms for which $E - E_n$ is less than T. All terms which do not satisfy these conditions will be rapidly decreasing exponential functions of r_0. The conclusion is that $k_{nm}|a_{nm}|^2$ is a measure of the number of electrons which have lost energy $E_m - E_n$ and have been deflected in a direction specified by our choice of the point x_0, y_0, z_0. The dependence of a_{nm} and a_{nE} on the direction of the radius vector r_0 gives us the angular distribution of the scattered particles. To get the total number of electrons which have suffered a loss of energy $E_m - E_n$ and have been deflected in any direction whatsoever, we must evaluate $k_{nm}|a_{nm}|^2$, and then integrate over the entire sphere.

21. WENTZEL'S TREATMENT OF THE SCATTERING OF ALPHA PARTICLES

Because of its simplicity, the scattering of charged particles is chosen as an example of the above method.[1] If we think of the scattering center

[1] Wentzel, *Z. Physik*, **40**, 590 (1927).

as a bare nucleus, then V_0 of the preceding section is equal to zero, and all the potential energy of the system is represented by V_1, which is equal to $Z'Z''e^2/r$, if $Z'e$ and $Z''e$ are the charges on the two particles. However, we meet with divergent integrals if we attempt to use this form for V_1. Therefore, Wentzel replaced it by the assumption

$$V_1 = \frac{Z'Z''e^2}{r} \exp\left(-\frac{r}{R}\right),\tag{99}$$

where R is a distance of the order of magnitude of the atomic radius. In our final result it will appear only in a term which may be neglected, and, therefore, its value is of no importance. This assumption may be considered as an approximate way of taking account of the screening effect of the outer shells of electrons. It provides us with one of the simplest

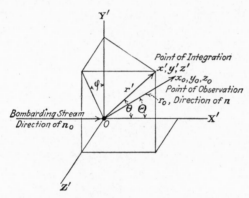

Fig. 7.

possible models of a neutral atom. We now proceed to evaluate equation (96). The wave function for a fixed scattering center is simply a constant multiplied by a time factor, and ψ_0 is equal to e^{ikx_0}, where $k^2 = GT$, T being the kinetic energy of the bombarding particle. The expansion of ψ_1 reduces to a single term, namely, $\psi_1 = f_{1E}$. This state of affairs is due to the assumed immobility of the scattering center, which has only a single energy state for the purposes of our problem. We have, therefore,

$$\psi_1 = \frac{e^{ikr_0}}{r_0}\left(-\frac{2\pi m_0 a}{h^2}\right)\int \frac{Z'Z''e^2}{r'} \exp\left[-\frac{r'}{R} + ikx' - ik(nr')\right]dv.\tag{100}$$

To carry out the integration we transform to polar coordinates ρ, θ, φ, with the axis $\theta = 0$ lying parallel to the bombarding stream, as shown in Fig. 7. Further, for the sake of easy comparison with Wentzel's results, we write $(n_0 r')$ for x', n_0 being a unit vector in the direction of the incident beam. Then $x' - (nr')$ becomes the scalar product of $n - n_0$ and r', which is equal to $|n - n_0| \rho \cos \theta$. The angle between the unit vectors n and n_0 is the angle of scattering, Θ, so $|n - n_0|$ is simply $2 \sin \Theta/2$. Thus equation (100) reduces to

$$\psi_1 = \frac{e^{ikr_0}}{r_0}\left(- \frac{2\pi m_0 a Z' Z'' e^2}{h^2} \right) \int_0^{2\pi} \int_0^\pi \int_0^\infty \exp\left[- \frac{\rho}{R} + 2ik \sin \frac{\Theta}{2} \rho \cos \theta \right]$$

$$\rho d\rho \sin \theta d\theta d\varphi = - \frac{e^{ikr_0}}{r_0} \frac{Z'Z''e^2}{T} \frac{1}{4 \sin^2 \dfrac{\Theta}{2} + \dfrac{1}{k^2R^2}}. \quad (101)$$

Now k is $2\pi/\lambda$, where λ is the wave length of the incident de Broglie waves, so kR is of the order of magnitude R/λ. For swift alpha particles, λ is small compared with R, and so the term containing R may be omitted from equation (101), except when very small scattering angles are under consideration. The ratio of the charge density in the scattered beam to that in the primary beam is proportional to

$$\frac{|\psi_1|^2}{|\psi_0|^2} = \frac{1}{r^2} \frac{(Z'Z''e^2)^2}{16T^2} \frac{1}{\sin^4 \dfrac{\Theta}{2}}. \quad (102)$$

This is the distribution derived by classical methods, which agrees with the results of Rutherford's experiments on the scattering of alpha particles by light atoms.

22. NEWTON'S EQUATIONS IN WAVE MECHANICS

Ehrenfest[1] has obtained a remarkable set of equations similar to Newton's law of motion, which governs the motion of the center of gravity of the wave group representing a particle. Since he stated these equations only for a single degree of freedom and did not give the derivation, Ruark[2] has written out the proof for any system which obeys the wave equation. For simplicity we consider a system with a single variable, such as a particle moving along the x-axis. The center of gravity of the probability distribution has the coordinate,

$$X = \frac{\int x \Psi \Psi^* dx}{\int \Psi \Psi^* dx} = \int x \Psi \Psi^* dx, \quad (103)$$

because the denominator is normalized and is equal to one. We define the momentum of the wave group as

$$P = \epsilon \int \Psi^* \frac{\partial \Psi}{\partial x} dx, \quad (104)$$

for when P is thus defined, we find by using the wave equation and carrying out a simple integration by parts that

$$m\dot{X} = P.$$

[1] *Z. Physik*, **45**, 455 (1927).
[2] *Phys. Rev.*, **31**, 533 (1928).

Now, we can show that the law of motion of the center of gravity is

$$m\ddot{X} = \dot{P} = \int \Psi\Psi^*\left(-\frac{\partial V}{\partial x}\right)dx. \qquad (105)$$

Differentiating equation (104) with respect to t, we have

$$\dot{P} = \left(\frac{h}{2\pi i}\right)\int\int\left(\frac{\partial \Psi^*}{\partial t}\frac{\partial \Psi}{\partial x} + \Psi^*\frac{\partial^2\Psi}{\partial x \partial t}\right)dx.$$

We replace $\partial\Psi^*/\partial t$ and $\partial^2\Psi/\partial x\partial t$, by their values obtained from the wave equation (65), Chap. XV, and $\dot{P}$ reduces to

$$\int \Psi\Psi^*\left(-\frac{\partial V}{\partial x}\right)dx - \frac{h^2}{8\pi^2}\int\left(\Delta\Psi^*\frac{\partial\Psi}{\partial x} - \Psi^*\frac{\partial\Delta\Psi}{\partial x}\right)dx.$$

On integrating the last term by parts, the second integral becomes

$$\int\left(\frac{\partial^2\Psi}{\partial x^2}\frac{\partial\Psi^*}{\partial x} + \frac{\partial\Psi}{\partial x}\frac{\partial^2\Psi^*}{\partial x^2}\right)dx.$$

The indefinite integral is $\dfrac{\partial\Psi}{\partial x}\dfrac{\partial\Psi^*}{\partial x}$; this vanishes at infinity by hypothesis, so the integral is zero, and equation (105) is verified. If we are dealing with a large-scale problem, in which the distances involved are very large compared with the effective width of the wave group, we can replace the right side of equation (105) by the value of $-\partial V/\partial x$ at the center of gravity, multiplied by $\int\Psi\Psi^*dx$. This integral is unity, and so we obtain the Newtonian equation of motion,

$$m\ddot{X} = -\frac{\partial V}{\partial x}.$$

If we deal with a system of particles instead of only one, we have for the pth particle

$$m_p\ddot{X}_p = \int \Psi\Psi^*\left(-\frac{\partial V}{\partial x_p}\right)dv, \qquad (105a)$$

there being similar equations for $\ddot{Y}_p$ and $\ddot{Z}_p$. The extension to still more general systems offers no difficulty. This makes the connection of wave and Newtonian mechanics very clear.[1]

---

[1] SCHRÖDINGER (*Naturwissenschaften*, **14**, 664 (1926)), suggested another type of connection between wave and ordinary mechanics. Using the linear oscillator as an example, he showed that we can obtain a solution of the wave equation for the oscillator which corresponds to a high and narrow peak, moving to and fro over a limited portion of the x-axis with simple harmonic motion. This solution is formed by taking an appropriate sum, $\Sigma c_n\Psi_n$, of a vast number of wave functions corresponding to high quantum numbers. Schrödinger found that the desired result is attained if we put $c_n = A^n/2^n n!$, A being any large positive number. HEISENBERG (*Z. Physik*, **43**, 172 (1927)) has pointed out that this method is not suited to furnish a connection between atomic and large-scale phenomena except in the case of the oscillator.

23. THE HYDRODYNAMIC INTERPRETATION

Since the probability density and the probability flux obey the hydrodynamical equation of continuity, it is natural to expect that changes in the distribution of $\Psi\Psi^*$ will be similar to the motion of a perfect liquid. Madelung[1] developed a hydrodynamical interpretation of wave mechanics on this basis. The situation has been treated as follows by Kennard.[2]   If we write

$$\Psi \equiv Re^{2\pi i\theta/h}, \tag{106}$$

the components of the probability flow, equation (72), can be rewritten in the form,

$$s_x = \frac{\rho}{m}\frac{\partial\theta}{\partial x}, \text{ etc.} \tag{107}$$

The analogous expression in the case of a perfect incompressible fluid flowing with velocity u would be $s_x = \rho u_x$, so that the velocity of an element of the field of probability may be taken as

$$u_x = \frac{1}{m}\frac{\partial\theta}{\partial x}, \text{ etc.,} \tag{108}$$

which shows that $-\theta/m$ is analogous to a velocity potential in hydrodynamics.   The law of motion of an element of probability is shown by Kennard to be

$$m_j\frac{du_j}{dt} = -\frac{\partial V}{\partial x_j} + \frac{h^2}{8\pi^2}\frac{\partial}{\partial x_j}\sum_{r=1}^{n}\frac{1}{m_r R}\frac{\partial^2 R}{\partial x_r^2}, \tag{109}$$

where now we are dealing with a system having n degrees of freedom. This shows that each element of the probability moves in the Cartesian space of each particle as that particle would move according to Newton's laws under the classical force plus a "quantum force" given by the term containing h in equation (109).   This point of view is often useful.

[1] *Z. Physik*, **40**, 322 (1927).
[2] *Phys. Rev.*, **31**, 876 (1928).

CHAPTER XIX

NON-HYDROGENIC ATOMS AND MOLECULES IN THE NEW MECHANICS

1. HEISENBERG'S THEORY OF THE TERM SYSTEMS OF HELIUM

There are two striking facts about the spectral terms of helium, which must be explained by any successful theory of this atom. The orthohelium and parhelium terms do not combine, and the interaction energy of two magnetic electrons is much too small to explain the difference between corresponding terms in these two systems. It was recognized by Heisenberg[1] that the cause of both these phenomena is a sort of resonance action between the two electrons, which would be described on an orbital theory by the statement that the two electrons interchange places, so that we can no longer speak of one electron as being more tightly bound than the other. In terms of the wave theory, this may be expressed by saying that the wave equation is symmetrical in the coordinates of the two electrons. Before entering on a study of the energy levels and spectral intensities of helium, we shall examine a much simpler problem of the same general type, considered by Heisenberg, namely, that of two coupled harmonic oscillators. We shall designate the coordinates of the oscillators by x_1 and x_2. If the coupling forces were absent, the energy of the system would be the sum of the energies of the two oscillators, separately. Such a system is degenerate, for if the quantum numbers of the oscillators take the values a_1 and a_2, respectively, we have the same total energy as though the quantum numbers were interchanged. This may be referred to as "exchange degeneracy." If the coupling forces give rise to a term $\lambda x_1 x_2$ in the energy, the Hamiltonian becomes

$$H = \frac{p_1^2}{2\mu} + \frac{\omega^2 \mu x_1^2}{2} + \frac{p_2^2}{2\mu} + \frac{\omega^2 \mu x_2^2}{2} + \lambda x_1 x_2, \tag{1}$$

μ being the mass and $\omega/2\pi$ the frequency which either oscillator would possess in the absence of the other. The usual method of solving vibration problems of this type is to seek for normal coordinates x_1' and x_2', in which the energy is a sum of squares, namely,

$$H = \frac{p_1'^2}{2\mu} + \frac{\omega_1^2 \mu x_1'^2}{2} + \frac{p_2'^2}{2\mu} + \frac{\omega_2^2 \mu x_2'^2}{2}. \tag{2}$$

[1] *Z. Physik*, **38**, 411 (1926).

In the present problem, the transformation which accomplishes this is,

$$x_1' = \frac{1}{2^{1/2}}(x_1 + x_2), \; x_2' = \frac{1}{2^{1/2}}(x_1 - x_2), \tag{3}$$

and

$$\omega_1^2 = \omega^2 + \lambda, \qquad \omega_2^2 = \omega^2 - \lambda. \tag{4}$$

H is obviously the sum of the energies of two fictitious oscillators of mass μ, with coordinates x_1' and x_2'. If only the first of these is excited, both of the actual oscillators move in the same phase, while if only the second is excited, they move in opposite phases. The quantized energy values may be represented in Fig. 1, which is an ordinary energy diagram. The quantum numbers of each term are written beneath the dot or cross which represents it. Now it is easy to show that the terms indicated by dots do not combine with those indicated by crosses. The electric dipole moment is proportional to $x_1 + x_2$, and so only the first fictitious oscillator possesses a moment. In transitions which give rise to radiation the quantum number of this oscillator must change by 1. Further, we would expect the quantum number of the second oscillator to remain unaltered, for it possesses no dipole moment. However, there are higher terms in the classical expression for the rate of radiation, proportional to homogeneous functions of x_1 and x_2 of the second and higher degrees. These functions must be symmetric in x_1 and x_2, since the two oscillators play similar parts in the radiation

Fig. 1.

process. On transforming such a function to the new variables, it will contain only even powers of x_2'. To illustrate this, suppose one of these symmetric functions were to contain the first power of x_2'. By equation (3), it would contain $x_1 - x_2$, and this is not symmetric, but antisymmetric in x_1 and x_2, changing sign when these two quantities are interchanged. In accordance with the correspondence principle, the absence of odd powers of x_2' in the expressions determining the radiation means that the quantum number n_2' can change only by zero or by an even integer in a transition. Therefore, we must expect weak lines corresponding to transitions from the first column to the third, from the second to the fourth, etc., in Fig. 1, but a change from one column to the adjoining one will not occur. Thus the term scheme is divided into two non-combining parts. As Heisenberg remarks, this rule is valid even in collision processes, since the probability of a transition due to collision is dependent on the perturbation due to the bombarding particle, and any such perturbation can be considered as producing a combination of dipole, quadrupole, and higher moments in the system.

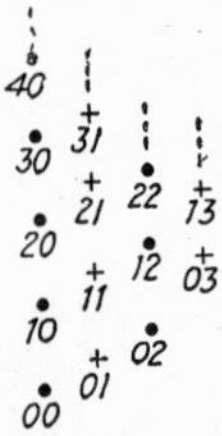

So far our remarks about the decomposition of the terms into two non-combining systems have been based on the older quantum theory, but they may be rigorously derived by means of the new mechanics, without

detailed knowledge of the wave functions.   Indeed, the results obtained
hold true for any two systems of precisely similar constitution which
are brought together, if the perturbation terms are symmetric in the
coordinates of the two systems. Heisenberg[1] outlined a proof which
depends on the matrix perturbation theory of Chap. XVII, Sec. **13**.
However, we shall present the corresponding proof in wave mechanics;
and shall begin by outlining perturbation theory.

2. SCHRÖDINGER'S PERTURBATION THEORY FOR DEGENERATE SYSTEMS[2]

A problem in wave mechanics is said to be "degenerate" when there
are several wave functions which belong to a single value of the energy.
Let there be α wave functions,

$$\varphi_{k1}, \varphi_{k2} \cdots \varphi_{k\alpha}, \tag{5}$$

belonging to the energy E_{0k}, and let us suppose they are normal and
orthogonal, not only among themselves, but with respect to all the other
wave functions.   When a suitable perturbation is applied to the system
we have α distinct wave functions, each one belonging to a distinct
value of the energy.   It is essential to know whether each one of these
functions can be considered as arising continuously out of one of the
functions of equation (5).   In general this will not be the case, and the
reason may be seen by looking at the question from the standpoint of
Bohr's theory.   Consider a hydrogen atom with inner number three,
for example, in the absence of an external field.   We may arbitrarily
choose a set of seven standard configurations of the atom, let us say the
seven positions which it could take up if a magnetic field were applied
along the X axis.   Each one corresponds to a wave function of the unperturbed system.   If a magnetic field directed along the Y-axis is applied
to the atom, it can take up any one of seven quantized positions in which
the component of angular momentum along the Y-axis is a multiple of
$h/2\pi$.   If the field is removed, the atom will be left in one of these positions, which will not agree with the standard configurations first considered.   However, each of the standard configurations can be made
to agree with one of the actual configurations, in which the atom is left
on removing the field, by a simple rotation.   In order to pass to a description in terms of wave mechanics, almost no change is necessary other
than to replace the words "configuration of the atom" by "wave function."   In view of what has been said, it is not very surprising to find
that when we are given any set of perturbed wave functions,

$$\psi_{k1}, \psi_{k2}, \ldots \psi_{k\alpha}, \tag{6}$$

---

[1] *Loc. cit.*   The proof is given in detail by BIRTWISTLE, "The New Quantum
Mechanics," p. 220.

[2] *Ann. Physik*, **80**, 437 (1926); also, "Abhandlungen," p. 85.

we can always find linear combinations of the φ's, namely,

$$\psi_{0k1} = \varphi_{k1}\beta_{11} + \varphi_{k2}\beta_{12} + \cdots + \varphi_{k\alpha}\beta_{1\alpha},$$
$$\psi_{0k2} = \varphi_{k1}\beta_{21} + \varphi_{k2}\beta_{22} + \cdots + \varphi_{k\alpha}\beta_{2\alpha}, \text{ etc.} \quad (7)$$

such that ψ_{k1} will pass continuously into ψ_{0k1}, ψ_{k2} into ψ_{0k2}, and so on, when the field is removed.

In equation (7), there is a restriction on the transformation coefficients β_{kh}. The original wave functions φ_{kh} were normalized and orthogonal, and the functions used in their stead should also have these properties. From equation (7),

$$\int \psi_{0kh}\psi^*_{0kh}\, dv = \sum_a \sum_b \beta_{ha}\beta_{h\,b} \int \varphi_{ka}\varphi^*_{kb} dv. \quad (8)$$

On the right, each integral is either one or zero, according as $a = b$, or $a \neq b$. Accordingly, the sum reduces to $\sum_a \beta_{ha}\beta_{h'\,a}$ and this must obey the relations

$$\sum_a \beta_{ha}\beta_{h'\,a} = \left\{ \begin{array}{l} 1 \text{ if } h = h' \\ 0 \text{ if } h \neq h' \end{array} \right\}, \quad (9)$$

in order that the unperturbed functions ψ_{0kh} may be normal and orthogonal. These relations are simply the condition that the transformation of equation (7) shall be orthogonal. The only way in which the perturbation theory for degenerate systems differs from that of Chap. XV, Sec. 22, is that the appropriate set of unperturbed characteristic functions must be found in the process of solving the perturbed wave equation. We take this equation in the form

$$\Delta\psi + C(E - V - \lambda F)\psi = 0, \quad C = \frac{8\pi^2}{h^2}, \quad (10)$$

just as in Chap. XV, Sec. 22. λF is the perturbation of the potential energy, λ being essentially proportional to the strength of the perturbing field. We proceed to solve this equation by assuming that the perturbed energy and the wave functions are given by

$$E_{kh} = E_{0k} + \lambda\epsilon_{kh},$$
$$\psi_{kh} = \psi_{0kh} + \lambda v_{kh} + \cdots, \quad (11)$$

formulas which are analogous to equation (119) of Chap. XV. We neglect powers of λ higher than the first, and obtain the equation for v_{kh}:

$$\Delta v_{kh} + C(E_{0k} - V)v_{kh} = C(F - \epsilon_{kh})\psi_{0kh}. \quad (12)$$

In Chap. XV we proved that the right member of the perturbed wave equation must be orthogonal to the corresponding solution of the unperturbed wave equation. In the present instance, the correct form of this theorem is that *the right member must be orthogonal to each of the α wave* *functions belonging to the original energy value* E_{0k}. This is expressed by the equations,

$$\int (F - \epsilon_{kh})\psi^*_{0kh}\varphi_{ki}dv = 0, \, i = 1, 2, \cdots \alpha. \tag{13}$$

If we substitute the value given in equation (7) for ψ_{0kh} the result is

$$\sum_a \beta_{ha}\int (F - \epsilon_{kh})\varphi_{ka}^*\varphi_{ki}dv = 0, \, i = 1, 2, \cdots \alpha. \tag{14}$$

Now ϵ_{kh} is a constant, and the integrals multiplying it are either zero or one, since the φ's were so chosen as to be normal and orthogonal. Now, let us write

$$\int F\varphi_{ka}^*\varphi_{ki}dv = F_{ai}, \tag{15}$$

and let us put ϵ in place of ϵ_{kh} and β_a in place of β_{ha}, since no misunderstanding will arise from so doing. Then the equations (14), written out in full, will take the form

$$\left. \begin{aligned} \beta_1(F_{11} - \epsilon) + \beta_2 F_{12} + \cdots + \beta_\alpha F_{1\alpha} &= 0, \\ \beta_1 F_{21} + \beta_2(F_{22} - \epsilon) + \cdots + \beta_\alpha F_{2\alpha} &= 0, \\ \cdots\cdots\cdots\cdots\cdots\cdots\cdots\cdots\cdots\cdots \\ \beta_1 F_{\alpha 1} + \beta_2 F_{\alpha 2} + \cdots + \beta_\alpha(F_{\alpha\alpha} - \epsilon) &= 0. \end{aligned} \right\} \tag{16}$$

Considering these relations as equations for the β's, they are homogeneous and of the first degree. In order that the β's may have values other than zero, the determinant of the coefficients must vanish, that is,

$$\begin{vmatrix} F_{11} - \epsilon & F_{12} & \ldots\ldots\ldots & F_{1\alpha} \\ F_{21} & F_{22} - \epsilon & \ldots\ldots & F_{2\alpha} \\ \cdots & \cdots\cdots\cdots\cdots\cdots\cdots & \cdots \\ F_{\alpha 1} & F_{\alpha 2} & \ldots\ldots\ldots & F_{\alpha\alpha} - \epsilon \end{vmatrix} = 0. \tag{17}$$

This is an algebraic equation of degree α, which serves to determine the α possible values, E_{kh}, arising from the characteristic value E_{0k} when it is split by applying the field, in accordance with equation (11). Having determined one of the roots of equation (17), we substitute it in equation (16), obtaining a system of consistent equations from which a set of ratios of the β's can be determined. The actual values of the constants β are then assigned with the aid of equation (9), giving us complete knowledge of the unperturbed wave function ψ_{0kh} to which ψ_{kh} will approximate when the field is removed and E_{kh} approaches E_{0k}. To find the perturbed wave function ψ_{kh}, we proceed just as we did in Chap. XV, Sec. **22**, with a few minor changes. In place of equation (123) of Chap. XV, we have

$$v_{kh} = \sum_j \sum_i v_{jhi}\varphi_{ji}. \tag{18}$$

The summation index j runs over all energy values of the unperturbed system; when k is given a definite value, i runs from 1 to α, so that we include all wave functions belonging to the energy value E_{0k}. Similarly, we expand the known function $(F - \epsilon_{kh})\psi_{0kh}$ appearing in equation (12) in the form

$$(F - \epsilon_{kh})\psi_{0kh} = \sum_k \sum_i C_{khi}\varphi_{ki}, \tag{19}$$

where

$$C_{khi} = \int (F - \epsilon_{kh})\psi_{0kh}\varphi_{hi}dv. \tag{20}$$

On using equations (18), (19), and (20) in the wave equation, the result is

$$\psi_{kh} = \psi_{0kh} + \lambda\sum_j{}' \sum_i \frac{C_{jhi}\varphi_{ji}}{E_k - E_j}. \tag{21}$$

The value $j = k$ is omitted in the first summation. Taking $h = 1$, 2, . . . α in succession, we obtain from equation (21) a set of α perturbed wave functions. This completes the solution of the problem.

3. THE ENERGY LEVELS OF HELIUM

The determination of the energy levels of helium is now only a matter of applying the theory of Sec. **2**. The wave equation is

$$\Delta\psi + G\left(E + \frac{Ze^2}{r_1} + \frac{Ze^2}{r_2} - \frac{e^2}{r_{12}}\right)\psi = 0, \tag{22}$$

where $G = mC = 8\pi^2 m/h^2$, x_1, y_1, and z_1 are the coordinates of the first electron and x_2, y_2, and z_2 those of the second, referred to the nucleus; r_1 and r_2 are the radii vectores of the two electrons and r_{12} the distance between them. Further, Δ has the significance

$$\Delta_1 + \Delta_2 \equiv \frac{\partial^2}{\partial x_1^2} + \frac{\partial^2}{\partial y_1^2} + \cdots + \frac{\partial^2}{\partial z_2^2}.^1$$

Approximate solutions of equation (22) can be obtained in several different ways, depending on the type of "unperturbed" motion which is chosen as a starting point. In making a qualitative study of the term system, it is convenient to follow a treatment given by Sommerfeld.[2] The unperturbed system is obtained by neglecting the term e^2/r_{12} in the potential energy, and thus it consists of a helium atom in which there is no interaction between the two electrons. The wave equation for the unperturbed system is

$$\Delta\psi + G\left(E_1 + E_2 + \frac{Ze^2}{r_1} + \frac{Ze^2}{r_2}\right)\psi = 0, \tag{23}$$

where E_1 and E_2 are the energies associated with the first and second electrons, respectively. Since the two electrons are independent, the wave

---

[1] Since the differentiations in $\Delta\psi$ are taken with respect to the actual coordinates instead of the quantities $m^{1/2}x_1$, $m^{1/2}x_2$, etc., we must use G in our computations wherever C appeared in Sec. **2**.

[2] "Supplement to Atombau," p. 267.

function for the atom is the product of two hydrogen wave functions. Let us suppose that these two functions are the ones appropriate to the nth and mth quantum states, respectively. Then their product may be written

$$\varphi_{(nm)} = \psi_n(x_1, y_1, z_1)\psi_m(x_2, y_2, z_2),$$

or

$$\varphi_{(nm)} = \psi_n(1)\psi_m(2). \tag{24}$$

We can readily verify this by substituting equation (24) in equation (23); for the resulting equation is found to be separable, and the equations for $\psi_n(1)$ and $\psi_m(2)$ are

$$\Delta_1\psi_n(1) + G\left(E_1 - A + \frac{Ze^2}{r_1}\right)\psi_n(1) = 0, \tag{25}$$

$$\Delta_2\psi_m(2) + G\left(E_2 + A + \frac{Ze^2}{r_2}\right)\psi_m(2) = 0, \tag{26}$$

where A is a constant introduced in the process of separating the variables. In accordance with Chap. XVI, Sec. **1**, we write

$$E_1 - A = -\frac{Rhc}{n^2}, \; E_2 + A = -\frac{Rhc}{m^2}. \tag{27}$$

Wherever the energy $-Rhc/n^2$ appears in the nth wave function of hydrogen, we must write $E_1 - A$ in $\psi_n(1)$, and $E_2 + A$ must replace $-Rhc/m^2$ in $\psi_m(2)$. However, the wave function

$$\varphi_{(mn)} = \psi_m(x_1, y_1, z_1)\psi_n(x_2, y_2, z_2),$$

or

$$\varphi_{(mn)} = \psi_m(1)\psi_n(2), \tag{24'}$$

is also a solution of equation (23), corresponding to the same total energy as equation (24). When using equation (24') we replace equation (27) by

$$E_1 - A = -\frac{Rhc}{m^2}, \; E_2 + A = -\frac{Rhc}{n^2}, \tag{27'}$$

with the understanding that A does not necessarily have the same value which it had in equation (27). Here we have a typical case of exchange degeneracy, except when both electrons are on equivalent orbits. When this occurs, $\varphi_{(nm)}$ is the same as $\varphi_{(m,n)}$, so there is only one wave function instead of two.

We are interested chiefly in states for which one of the quantum numbers is unity, and shall now restrict the discussion to such states. The energy levels may be numbered by giving the quantum number k of the second electron. In order to be in agreement with the notation of Sec. **2** we might write

$$\varphi_{k1} = \psi_1(1)\psi_k(2), \; \varphi_{k2} = \psi_k(1)\psi_1(2),$$

but even this notation is unnecessarily complicated. Since we shall speak only of the wave functions belonging to a given, although arbitrary.

value of k we may leave the subscript k out of all the formulas of Sec. 2. Accordingly, we put

$$\varphi_1 = \psi_1(1)\psi_k(2), \quad \varphi_2 = \psi_k(1)\psi_1(2), \tag{28}$$

and proceed to study the effect of the perturbing term e^2/r_{12}. In accord with equation (7), any linear combination of the wave functions φ_1 and φ_2 is also an acceptable wave function. We write a typical linear combination in the form

$$\psi_0 = \beta_1\varphi_1 + \beta_2\varphi_2, \tag{29}$$

and for a typical perturbed wave function, we write

$$\psi = \psi_0 + v. \tag{30}$$

If we put $\lambda = 1$ in (10), we have

$$F = \frac{e^2}{r_{12}}.$$

We calculate the quantities of equation (15), which are as follows:

$$\left.\begin{array}{l} F_{11} = \int \dfrac{e^2}{r_{12}}\varphi_1{}^*\varphi_1 dv, \ F_{12} = \int \dfrac{e^2}{r_{12}}\varphi_1{}^*\varphi_2 dv, \\[2mm] F_{21} = \int \dfrac{e^2}{r_{12}}\varphi_2{}^*\varphi_1 dv, \ F_{22} = \int \dfrac{e^2}{r_{12}}\varphi_2{}^*\varphi_2 dv. \end{array}\right\} \tag{31}$$

In equation (31), dv means $m^3 dx_1 dy_1 dz_1 dx_2 dy_2 dz_2$, and the integrations extend over all real values of the six coordinates. Further, the integrand of F_{11} is obtained from that of F_{22} by simply interchanging the coordinates of the two electrons. This shows that F_{11} is equal to F_{22}. It is convenient to arrange matters so that F_{12} is equal to F_{21}. If it turns out on integrating equation (31) that F_{12} is equal to $Re^{i\varphi}$, where R and φ are real, then we go back to equation (28) and redefine φ_2 as $e^{-i\varphi}$ times its original value. We shall assume that this has been done, so that F_{12} and F_{21} are real, and therefore equal. To find the perturbation of the energy, we need only form the equation (17),

$$\begin{vmatrix} F_{11} - \epsilon & F_{12} \\ F_{21} & F_{22} - \epsilon \end{vmatrix} = 0, \tag{32}$$

and in accordance with what we have just said this reduces to

$$(F_{11} - \epsilon)^2 = F^2{}_{12},$$

so that

$$\epsilon = F_{11} \pm F_{12}. \tag{33}$$

Let us choose the upper sign in this equation. Substituting the value of ϵ in the first equation of (16), we have,

$$\beta_1(-F_{12}) + \beta_2 F_{12} = 0,$$

or

$$\beta_1 = \beta_2.$$

Similarly, if we take the lower sign in equation (33) we get

$$\beta_1 = -\beta_2.$$

Therefore, the two unperturbed wave functions which are approached by the perturbed functions when e^2/r_{12} tends to zero are

$$\psi_{0s} = \beta_1(\varphi_1 + \varphi_2),$$

and

$$\psi_{0a} = \beta_1(\varphi_1 - \varphi_2).$$

The subscripts s and a indicate that one of these functions is symmetric and the other antisymmetric, in the coordinates of the two electrons. Since both functions must be normalized, we find that $\beta_1 = \dfrac{1}{2^{\frac{1}{2}}}$, and, therefore,

$$\psi_{0s} = \frac{1}{2^{\frac{1}{2}}}(\varphi_1 + \varphi_2), \tag{34}$$

$$\psi_{0a} = \frac{1}{2^{\frac{1}{2}}}(\varphi_1 - \varphi_2). \tag{35}$$

The term system is now seen to be of the kind depicted in Fig. 2. The normal state ($k = 1$) is single, but for any other value of k there are two states with energies differing by $2F_{12}$. The states which are symmetric in the positional coordinates are the parhelium terms, and the antisymmetric ones are the orthohelium terms. To show this, we need only note that for the normal state $\varphi_1 = \varphi_2$ and $\psi_{0a} = 0$. The absence of an antisymmetric function for the normal state explains the fact that there is no $1S$ state in the orthohelium system. The reason why each orthohelium term appears as a singlet rather than a triplet is that we have neglected the electron spin.

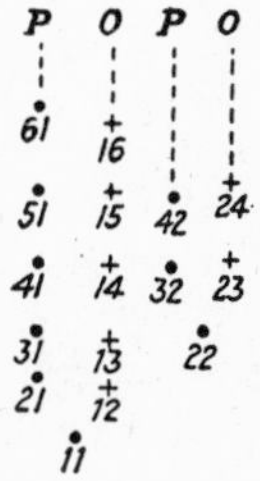

Fig. 2.

We can show, following Heisenberg,[1] that the parhelium and orthohelium terms do not combine. Consider a transition from a symmetric state (parhelium) with the wave function $\dfrac{1}{2^{\frac{1}{2}}}(\varphi_1 + \varphi_2)_n$ to an antisymmetric state (orthohelium) with the wave function $\dfrac{1}{2^{\frac{1}{2}}}(\varphi_1 - \varphi_2)_m$.

The intensity of the radiation is determined by the element $M(1, n; 1, m)$ in the matrix for the electric moment. Considering the x-component of the moment, we require the value of the integral,

$$J = \frac{e}{2}\int(x_1 + x_2)(\varphi_1 + \varphi_2)_n(\varphi_1 - \varphi_2)_m dv. \tag{36}$$

Obviously, the value of J is not altered if we interchange x_1 and x_2, y_1 and y_2, etc., leaving the functional form of the integrand unaltered. However, letting x_2 stand for x_2, y_2, z_2 and x_1 for x_1, y_1, z_1, we have

$$\varphi_1(x_2, x_1) - \varphi_2(x_2, x_1) = -[\varphi_1(x_1, x_2) - \varphi_2(x_1, x_2)]$$

[1] *Loc. cit.*

and so the value of J obtained by the interchange may be rewritten as

$$J = \frac{e}{2}\int(x_2 + x_1)(\varphi_2 + \varphi_1)_n[\varphi_2(x_1, x_2) - \varphi_1(x_1, x_2)]dv. \tag{37}$$

On adding equations (36) and (37) we have $2J = 0$, which proves our assertion. This result is not altered when we use $\psi_0 + v$ instead of ψ, and when higher approximations are taken into account.

We now consider the effect of electron spin on the term system, a problem which was also solved by Heisenberg.[1] First, let there be no interaction of the two electrons, and let them be placed in an external magnetic field. If m_1 and m_2 are the magnetic quantum numbers and $m = m_1 + m_2$, we have the following four cases;

Case	m_1	m_2	m	Wave function
I	$\frac{1}{2}$	$\frac{1}{2}$	1	$\psi_{\mathrm{I}} = \psi(\frac{1}{2})\psi(\frac{1}{2})$
II	$\frac{1}{2}$	$-\frac{1}{2}$	0	$\psi_{\mathrm{II}} = \psi(\frac{1}{2})\psi(-\frac{1}{2})$
III	$-\frac{1}{2}$	$\frac{1}{2}$	0	$\psi_{\mathrm{III}} = \psi(-\frac{1}{2})\psi(\frac{1}{2})$
IV	$-\frac{1}{2}$	$-\frac{1}{2}$	-1	$\psi_{\mathrm{IV}} = \psi(-\frac{1}{2})\psi(-\frac{1}{2})$

Each electron may take up one of two possible orientations and its wave function will be designated by $\psi(m_1)$ or $\psi(m_2)$, as the case may be. In the fifth column of the table we have the wave functions for the pair of electrons. The first and fourth states are not degenerate but the second and third have the same energy and may be derived, one from the other, by interchanging the two electrons. When we consider the interaction of the spins as a perturbation, two perturbed states of different energies and having different wave functions arise from cases II and III. The calculation of the energies is quite similar to that carried out above. The quantities F_{11}, etc., are evaluated, using the wave functions of the rotator in equation (15), and we have $\epsilon = F_{11} \pm F_{12}$, just as before. When the interaction term vanishes, the perturbed wave functions reduce to two functions, one of which is symmetric and the other antisymmetric in the quantum numbers m_1 and m_2, namely, $\psi_{\mathrm{II}} + \psi_{\mathrm{III}}$ and $\psi_{\mathrm{II}} - \psi_{\mathrm{III}}$. Thus we have three symmetric functions, ψ_{I}, $\psi_{\mathrm{II}} + \psi_{\mathrm{III}}$, and ψ_{IV} and one antisymmetric function, $\psi_{\mathrm{II}} - \psi_{\mathrm{III}}$. The symmetric functions correspond to triplet states, while the antisymmetric function represents a singlet state. The reader will readily verify the fact that the magnetic quantum numbers corresponding to these four wave functions are the correct ones for singlet and triplet terms.

We now obtain the wave functions for the entire system, neglecting the interaction between the spins and the translational motion. There are eight possibilities, as follows:

[1] *Z. Physik,* **39**, 499 (1926).

Symmetric Group	Antisymmetric Group
$(\varphi_1 + \varphi_2)\psi_{\text{I}}$	$(\varphi_1 - \varphi_2)\psi_{\text{I}}$
$(\varphi_1 + \varphi_2)(\psi_{\text{II}} + \psi_{\text{III}})$	$(\varphi_1 - \varphi_2)(\psi_{\text{II}} + \psi_{\text{III}})$
$(\varphi_1 + \varphi_2)\psi_{\text{IV}}$	$(\varphi_1 - \varphi_2)\psi_{\text{IV}}$
$(\varphi_1 - \varphi_2)(\psi_{\text{II}} - \psi_{\text{III}})$	$(\varphi_1 + \varphi_2)(\psi_{\text{II}} - \psi_{\text{III}})$

All of the states of the first group are said to be symmetric in the sense that an interchange of the two electrons leaves the magnitude and sign of the wave function unaltered. Similarly, all the states of the second group are antisymmetric. If the first group were realized in nature, all the parhelium terms, which have wave functions of the type $\varphi_1 + \varphi_2$, would be triplets, and the orthohelium terms would be singlets. In actuality, the reverse is true, and we must conclude that *only the antisymmetric terms occur.*

It is very interesting to see how the term system of helium can be predicted by considering the symmetry and other simple characteristics of the wave functions, without detailed knowledge of their form. Similar considerations were applied by Heisenberg[1] to the terms of other atoms and of molecules.

We shall not describe the detailed calculations which are necessary in order to determine the helium energy levels, but shall confine our attention to the methods of various investigators and the results which have been secured. Heisenberg[2] used a method, which is essentially that of Sec. **2,** to calculate the energy-differences of the orthohelium and parhelium terms $2P$, $3D$, and $4F$. The order of magnitude of the calculated differences is in agreement with the data. In view of the difficulty mentioned at the beginning of this section, such agreement must be considered encouraging. For the sake of a better approximation Heisenberg uses a model which differs somewhat from that considered above. It consists of a nucleus surrounded by a spherical shell of radius r_0, carrying a charge $-e$, so that an electron inside the shell will move under the force Ze^2/r^2, while outside it will experience the force $(Z - 1)e^2/r^2$. The divergence of this model from reality is removed by including terms in the perturbation energy to make the total potential energy the same as that given in equation (22). The function of the shell model is simply to enable us to make a start with wave functions which approximate to the truth more closely than the ones considered at the beginning of this section. Heisenberg's model is not suited for the calculation of the normal state. Likewise, Unsöld[3] showed that the use of equations (23), (24), etc., does not give a good approximation. Slater[4] attacked

---

[1] *Z. Physik*, **41**, 238 (1927).
[2] *Z. Physik*, **39**, 499 (1926).
[3] *Ann. Physik*, **82**, 355 (1927).
[4] *Proc. Nat. Acad. Sci.*, **13**, 423 (1927).

the problem in a somewhat different way. In his method, one of the electrons is held fast, while the other moves in the field of two fixed centers of force. The energy values depend on the distance between the two centers. The next step is to determine the motion of the second electron in a central field which is chosen on the basis of the results obtained in the problem of two centers. Finally, the Schrödinger perturbation method is applied to determine the interaction of both motions. Kellner[1] has used the approximation method of Ritz[2] in order to calculate the lowest term of helium and the lowest terms of the helium-like ions of lithium, beryllium, boron, and carbon. In the case of helium he was able to push the calculations to the fourth approximation before encountering serious difficulties. His value of 77.840 volts corresponds to a first ionization potential of 23.75 volts, which may be compared with the experimental value of 24.46 volts. The Ritz method has also been used by Finkelstein and Horowitz.[3]

Hylleraas[4] has greatly advanced the solution of this problem by adopting new variables, namely, the distances r_1 and r_2 from the nucleus to the two electrons, and the distance r_{12} between the electrons. When this is done, the successive approximations converge rapidly. Hylleraas' value of the ionization is less than 0.002 volts higher than the spectroscopic value, a result which shows beyond question that the wave-mechanical method of attack on this problem is essentially correct.

4. THE DIATOMIC MOLECULE

We shall now use the methods of wave mechanics to study the energy levels of a molecule consisting of two massive particles, m_1 and m_2, with coordinates x_1, y_1, z_1, and x_2, y_2, z_2, respectively. The potential energy is assumed to be a function only of their distance apart.

A beginning in the solution of this problem was made by Schrödinger[5] and it was solved in detail by E. Fues.[6] In accord with Chap. XV, Sec. 6 the wave equation is assumed to be

$$\frac{\Delta_1\psi}{m_1} + \frac{\Delta_2\psi}{m_2} + \frac{8\pi^2}{h^2}(E - V)\psi = 0, \tag{36}$$

where

$$\Delta_1\psi = \frac{\partial^2\psi}{\partial x_1^2} + \frac{\partial^2\psi}{\partial y_1^2} + \frac{\partial^2\psi}{\partial z_1^2} \quad \text{and} \quad \Delta_2\psi = \frac{\partial^2\psi}{\partial x_2^2} + \frac{\partial^2\psi}{\partial y_2^2} + \frac{\partial^2\psi}{\partial z_2^2}.$$

Let ξ, η, ζ be coordinates of the center of mass, defined by the relations $(m_1 + m_2)\xi = m_1 x_1 + m_2 x_2$, etc. and let x, y, z, be the coordinates of

[1] Z. Physik, **44**, 91 and 110 (1927).
[2] Details of the Ritz method are given in Courant-Hilbert.
[3] Z. Physik, **48**, 118 (1928).
[4] Z. Physik, **54**, 347 (1929) and earlier papers mentioned therein.
[5] "Abhandlungen," p. 51.
[6] Ann. Physik, **80**, 367 (1926).

m_2 referred to m_1, so that $x = x_2 - x_1$, etc.   By transformation, or by a direct application of the fundamental principles on which equation (36) is based, we find in these new coordinates that it becomes

$$\frac{1}{m_1 + m_2}\left(\frac{\partial^2\psi}{\partial\xi^2} + \frac{\partial^2\psi}{\partial\eta^2} + \frac{\partial^2\psi}{\partial\zeta^2}\right) + \frac{\Delta\psi}{\mu} + \frac{8\pi^2}{h^2}(E - V)\psi = 0. \qquad (37)$$

Here μ is the reduced mass, $\dfrac{m_1 m_2}{m_1 + m_2}$, and $\Delta\psi = \dfrac{\partial^2\psi}{\partial x^2} + \dfrac{\partial^2\psi}{\partial y^2} + \dfrac{\partial^2\psi}{\partial z^2}$.

This equation splits into two parts when we assume

$$\psi = f(x, y, z)g(\xi, \eta, \zeta),$$

and write

$$E = E_t + E_i.$$

E_t represents the translational energy of the molecule and E_i its internal energy.

The equation for g is

$$\frac{1}{m_1 + m_2}\left(\frac{\partial^2 g}{\partial\xi^2} + \frac{\partial^2 g}{\partial\eta^2} + \frac{\partial^2 g}{\partial\zeta^2}\right) + \frac{8\pi^2 E_t g}{h^2} = 0. \qquad (38)$$

We obtain exactly this equation if we consider free motion of a particle of mass $m_1 + m_2$.   The condition that g shall be finite through the whole of space, without being identically zero, can be satisfied whenever E_t is either positive or zero, but *cannot* be satisfied if E_t is negati e.   This means that the molecule can move with any velocity.   Further, the energy E which enters into the formula $E_n - E_m = h_\nu$ is seen to include the energy of translation of the whole molecule.

Let us now study the function f which describes the behavior of the molecule as seen by an observer moving with the molecule. f obeys the equation

$$\Delta f + G(E_i - V)f = 0. \qquad (39)$$

Since V depends only on r, the distance between the two masses, the equation is separable in polar coordinates r, θ, φ, exactly as in the case of the hydrogen atom or the two-dimensional rotator.   If we put

$$f = R(r)Y(\theta\varphi), \qquad (40)$$

then

$$Y = P_{jm}(\cos \theta)e^{im\varphi}, \qquad (41)$$

where $j = 0$ or a positive integer and m is always $\leq j$, so that f depends on θ and φ as described in Chap. XV, Sec. **8**.   The only change arises from the different form of the potential energy, occurring in the equation for R.   Before writing this equation we shall use another independent variable, related to r by the equation, $\rho = r/r_0$, in which r_0 is the equilibrium distance of the nuclei in the classical analogue of this problem, when the molecule is not rotating. Then, writing $I = \mu r_0^2$, we have

$$\frac{1}{\rho^2}\frac{d}{d\rho}\left(\rho^2\frac{dR}{d\rho}\right) + \left[\frac{8\pi^2 I}{h^2}(E_i - V) - \frac{j(j+1)}{\rho^2}\right]R = 0. \qquad (42)$$

We introduce a new dependent variable,

$$F = \rho R,$$

and then equation (42) becomes,

$$\frac{d^2F}{d\rho^2} + \left[\frac{8\pi^2 I}{h^2}(E_i - V) - \frac{j(j+1)}{\rho^2}\right]F = 0. \qquad (43)$$

Now a choice of the law of force must be made. Fues carries through the solution for two different laws:

(1) The potential energy function is supposed to be of the form used by Kratzer (Chap. XII, Sec. 4), namely,

$$V = C - (2\pi\nu_0)^2 I\left(\frac{1}{\rho} - \frac{1}{2\rho^2} + c_3(\rho - 1)^3 + c_4(\rho - 1)^4 + \cdots\right), \qquad (44)$$

where ν_0 is the frequency of vibration of the nuclei for zero amplitude. Kratzer constructed this function assuming that the molecule has a polar binding but since it is applicable only in the region where ρ differs only slightly from 1, it may be taken as an arbitrary potential energy function. We let the value of V for $\rho = 1$ be D, so that,

$$D = C - \tfrac{1}{2}(2\pi\nu_0)^2 I. \qquad (45)$$

(2) Expanding equation (44) in terms of $(\rho - 1)$, we secure

$$V = C - \tfrac{1}{2}(2\pi\nu_0)^2 I + \tfrac{1}{2}(2\pi\nu_0)^2 I((\rho - 1)^2 + c_3'(\rho - 1)^3 + $$
$$c_4'(\rho - 1)^4 + \cdots), \qquad (46)$$

where

$$c_3' = 2c_3 + 2 \text{ and } c_4' = 2c_4 - 3.$$

This is the most general form of the potential energy function for an anharmonic oscillator. In using this form for the potential energy, it is convenient to use $\xi = \rho - 1$ as the variable instead of ρ.

We proceed to solve equation (42) using the value of equation (44) for the potential energy. First, we must determine the meaning of the constant C. When the distance between the nuclei is very great, the force must approach zero. This means that at great distances the formula (44) is not valid. c_3 and c_4 are no longer constant, but must approach zero, and then $V_\infty = C$. Since we choose arbitrarily to make $V_\infty = 0$, $C = 0$, and from the value of C given by equation (45) we get

$$D = -(2\pi\nu_0)^2\frac{I}{2}. \qquad (47)$$

Now we introduce the abbreviations

$$A = \frac{8\pi^2 I(E_i + D)}{h^2}, \quad u = \frac{h}{4\pi^2 \nu_0 I}, \quad F'' = \frac{d^2F}{d\rho^2}, \tag{48}$$

and equation (42) becomes

$$F'' + \left[A + \frac{2}{u^2}\left(-\frac{1}{2} + \frac{1}{\rho} - \frac{1}{2\rho^2} + c_3(\rho - 1)^3 + c_4(\rho - 1)^4 + \cdots \right) \right.$$
$$\left. - \frac{j(j + 1)}{\rho^2} \right] F = 0. \tag{49}$$

The problem is now to determine the values of A for which R (that is, F/ρ), remains finite, single-valued, and continuous throughout space. The problem must be solved by perturbation methods, and Fues adopted the procedure of Schrödinger (Chap. XV, Sec. 22). The terms containing c_3 and c_4 are considered as perturbation terms and are omitted in obtaining an approximate solution. The characteristic functions thus obtained are of the form,

$$F = \rho^a e^{-b\rho} L_{k+n}^k(2b\rho). \tag{50}$$

In this equation n is a positive integer or zero,

$$a = \frac{1}{2} \pm \frac{1}{u}\left[1 + u^2\left(j + \frac{1}{2}\right)^2 \right]^{\frac{1}{2}},$$

$$b = \left(\frac{1}{u^2} - A \right)^{\frac{1}{2}},$$

$$k = \frac{2}{u}\left[1 + u^2\left(j + \frac{1}{2}\right)^2 \right]^{\frac{1}{2}}, \tag{51}$$

and L_{k+n}^k denotes the polynomial given in Chap. XVI, Sec. **2**, in connection with the theory of the hydrogen atom. In the present problem k is not an integer, as the corresponding parameter $2l + 1$ was for hydrogen.

The discrete energy levels are given by

$$E = E_t - D + h\nu_0\left(n + \frac{1}{2}\right) + \frac{h^2}{8\pi^2 I}\left(j + \frac{1}{2}\right)^2. \tag{52}$$

This is the ordinary band spectrum formula, with half-quantum numbers for both rotation and oscillation, in agreement with experiment. This spectrum corresponds to certain negative values of $A - \frac{1}{u^2}$, i.e., positive values of b. In addition, there is a continuous spectrum of characteristic values, which occurs when $A - \frac{1}{u^2} > 0$, so that the exponent in $e^{-b\rho}$ becomes imaginary. By equations (47) and (48) this reduces to $E_i > 0$, or $E - E_t > 0$. This result shows the existence of unquantized states in which the molecule must be considered as dissociated. For example, if two swiftly moving atoms pass by each other without uniting, we are dealing with states of the kind considered here. Since

E_i may change in such an encounter, this means that a continuous spectrum is emitted in such processes.

The computation of higher approximations is lengthy, and we shall simply give the result obtained by Fues. It is,

$$E = E_t - D - \frac{(2\pi\nu_0)^2 I}{2}\left(\frac{7}{4}c_3 + \frac{7}{8}c_3{}^2 + \frac{3}{4}c_4\right)$$

$$+ h\nu_0\left(n + \frac{1}{2}\right)\left[1 - \frac{3u^2}{2}(1 + 2c_3)\left(j + \frac{1}{2}\right)^2\right]$$

$$+ \frac{h^2(j + \frac{1}{2})^2}{8\pi^2 I}\left[1 - u^2\left(j + \frac{1}{2}\right)^2\right]$$

$$- \frac{h^2\left(n + \frac{1}{2}\right)^2}{8\pi^2 I}\left(3 + 15c_3 + \frac{15}{2}c_3{}^2 + 3c_4\right). \qquad (53)$$

This is essentially the formula of Kratzer, Chap. XII, except that half-quantum numbers occur instead of integers. The assumptions made in Fues' calculations are such that the result is valid only for quantum numbers which are not too great, just as was the case in deriving Kratzer's formula.[1]

As mentioned above, Fues' result obtained by using the value of equation (46) for the potential energy gives energy levels identical with the above (except for slight differences in the small correction terms containing u^2). But this identity holds true only for the discrete spectrum. When equation (46) is used and terms in c_3 and c_4 are taken into account, there is no continuous spectrum of characteristic values, in disagreement with fact. This point is important, for it indicates that the wave functions appropriate to the first form for V (generalized Laguerre polynomials) should be used in preference to those of the second form of V (Hermite polynomials) in calculating band spectrum intensities.

The selection rules for m and j are the same as those for m and l of the hydrogen atom, respectively, since the functions $P_{jm}(\cos\theta)$ and $e^{im\varphi}$ are the same for both. In Chap. XVI, Sec. 6, it was shown that these selection rules are: $\Delta j = \pm 1$ and $\Delta m = \pm 1$. Fues showed that the vibrational quantum number may change by $\pm 1, \pm 2, \cdots$, and that the values of the Einstein probabilities are

$$h\nu(n', j'; n'', j'')g_{j'}, A(n', j'; n'', j'') = P_0{}^2\left(\frac{u}{2}\right)^{\Delta n}\frac{n'!}{n''!}j\frac{[2\pi\nu(n', j'; n'', j'')]^4}{3c^3}$$

where $\Delta n = n' - n''$, j is the larger of j' and j'', and P_0 is the permanent electric moment. Since u is a small number of the order of 10^{-2}, the

[1] As stated in Chap. XII, Sec. 9, the formula (53) holds very well even for values of the vibrational quantum number only slightly less than that for which the molecule dissociates. Morse (Washington Meeting of the Am. Phys. Soc., 1929) derived an empirical law which gives this formula exactly with no higher terms. (See footnote Chap. XIII, Sec. 7 and CONDON and MORSE, "Quantum Mechanics," McGraw-Hill Book Company, Inc., New York (1929).

intensity factor is greatest for the rotational bands and decreases rapidly as Δn takes the values 0, 1, 2, . . . However, since we must multiply this factor by ν^4 to secure relative energies emitted and since ν for the first vibration band of HCl, for example, is ten to one hundred times the frequencies of the rotation band, we see that the fundamental rotation vibration band will be more intense than the rotation band; it will also be more intense than any higher harmonic rotation vibration band in agreement with experiment.

5. ROTATION SPECTRUM OF A MOLECULE HAVING AN AXIS OF SYMMETRY

In this section, our problem is to calculate the rotational energy levels of a molecule having a single axis of symmetry, neglecting the effects due to internal vibration.[1] We write down the kinetic energy, and form the wave equation from it by the procedure of Chap. XV, Sec. 20. Just as in the classical band spectrum theory of Chap. XII, Sec. 24, the molecule is represented by a top with two principal moments of inertia equal to A and the third equal to C, and the problem is treated in terms of the Eulerian angles θ, φ, χ. The result is

$$\frac{1}{\sin \theta}\frac{\partial}{\partial \theta}\left(\sin \theta\frac{\partial \psi}{\partial \theta}\right) + \frac{1}{\sin^2 \theta}\frac{\partial^2 \psi}{\partial \chi^2} + \left(\frac{A}{C} + \cot^2 \theta\right)\frac{\partial^2 \psi}{\partial \varphi^2}$$
$$- \frac{2 \cos \theta}{\sin^2 \theta}\frac{\partial^2 \psi}{\partial \varphi \partial \chi} + \frac{8\pi^2 A}{h^2}(E - V)\psi = 0. \quad (54)$$

The undisturbed top has no potential energy, so we set $V = 0$. This equation will be separated by the substitution,

$$\psi = \Theta(\theta) \exp (i\lambda\varphi + im\chi),$$

where λ and m must be integers in order that ψ be an acceptable function. Substituting in equation (54) gives the differential equation for Θ,

$$\frac{d^2\Theta}{d\theta^2} + \frac{\cos \theta}{\sin \theta}\frac{d\Theta}{d\theta} - \frac{(m - \lambda \cos \theta)^2}{\sin^2 \theta}\Theta + (j(j + 1) - \lambda^2)\Theta = 0 \quad (55)$$

where

$$j(j + 1) - \lambda^2 = \frac{8\pi^2 A E}{h^2} - \frac{A}{C}\lambda^2. \quad (56)$$

For convenience we introduce a new independent variable,

$$t = \tfrac{1}{2}(1 - \cos \theta)$$

and a new dependent variable,

$$X = t^{-d/2}(1 - t)^{-s/2}\Theta, \quad (57)$$

where

$$s = |\lambda + m| \text{ and } d = |\lambda - m|. \quad (58)$$

[1] DENNISON, *Phys. Rev.*, **28**, 318 (1926); REICHE, *Z. Physik*, **39**, 444 (1926); REICHE and RADEMACHER, *Z. Physik*, **41**, 453 (1927); KRONIG and RABI, *Phys. Rev.*, **29**, 262 (1927); MANNEBACK, *Phys. Zeit.*, **28**, 72 (1927). We follow the treatment of Reiche.

This change of variables brings the equation (55) to the form of the hypergeometric equation,

$$t(1 - t)\frac{d^2X}{dt^2} + [\gamma - (\alpha + \beta + 1)t]\frac{dX}{dt} - \alpha\beta X = 0, \qquad (59)$$

where

$$\gamma = 1 + d, \alpha = \frac{d + s}{2} + j + 1, \text{ and } \beta = \frac{d + s}{2} - j. \qquad (60)$$

It follows from the definition of d and s that $\gamma - 1 = d \geqslant 0$, and that $\alpha + \beta - \gamma = s \geqslant 0$, and that these quantities take only integral values. The only solution of the hypergeometric equation which makes Θ an acceptable function in the region $0 \leqslant t \leqslant 1$, that is, in the region $0 \leqslant \theta \leqslant \pi$, is the hypergeometric series,

$$X = F(\alpha, \beta, \gamma, t) = 1 + \frac{\alpha\beta}{\gamma}t + \frac{\alpha(\alpha + 1)\beta(\beta + 1)}{2!\gamma(\gamma + 1)}t^2 + \cdots \qquad (61)$$

and then only if either α or β is equal to a negative integer or zero; in this case the series will terminate and be finite for all values of t in the required interval.

Since α and β enter symmetrically into both the differential equation and its solution, it makes no difference which one is submitted to the restriction that it shall be negative or zero; so we take

$$\alpha = -p, p = 0, 1, 2, \cdots.$$

Then from equation (60),

$$\beta = p + d + s + 1,$$

$$j(j + 1) = \left(\frac{d + s}{2} + p\right)\left(\frac{d + s}{2} + p + 1\right),$$

$$j = \frac{d + s}{2} + p, \qquad (62)$$

and thus j is a positive integral number or zero. $\frac{d + s}{2}$ is equal to the greater of the two numbers $|\lambda|$ and $|m|$ and thus j is equal to the larger of these plus p. Solving equation (56) for the energy we have,

$$E_{j,\lambda,m} = \frac{h^2}{8\pi^2}\left[\frac{j(j + 1)}{A} + \left(\frac{1}{C} - \frac{1}{A}\right)\lambda^2\right]. \qquad (63)$$

This energy formula differs from that of classical theory (Chap. XII, Sec. 24) only through the occurrence of $j(j + 1)$ in place of j^2. The magnetic quantum number does not appear in the energy formula, since the system is degenerate in the absence of an external field.

The wave function is, therefore,

$$\psi = \Theta(\theta) \exp(i\lambda\varphi + im\chi)$$
$$= Nt^{d/2}(1 - t)^{s/2}F(-p, 1 + d + s + p, 1 + d, t)$$
$$\exp(i\lambda\varphi + im\chi), \qquad (64)$$

where N is a normalization factor. The element of volume in the coordinate space in which $ds^2 = 2Tdt^2$ is,

$$AC^{1/2} \sin \theta d\theta d\varphi d\chi \text{ or } AC^{1/2}2dtd\varphi d\chi,$$

and we choose N in such a way that

$$\int_0^{2\pi} \int_0^{2\pi} \int_0^1 \psi\psi^* A C^{1/2}2dtd\varphi d\chi = 1.$$

Integrating over φ and χ gives,

$$8\pi^2 N^2 A C^{1/2} \int_0^1 \Theta^2 dt = 1,$$

where Θ as a function of t can be secured from equation (64). Carrying out this integration and solving for N^2, we have,

$$N^2 = \frac{(1 + d + s + 2p)(d + s + p)!(d + p)!}{8\pi^2 A C^{1/2}p!(d!)^2(s + p)!}. \tag{65}$$

The particular hypergeometric series which we use in this case is known as the "Jacobian polynomial" which is,

$$F(-p, 1 + d + s + p, 1 + d, t) = F(\alpha, \beta, \gamma, t)$$

$$= \sum_{r=0}^{p} (-1)^r C_r{}^p \frac{(d + s + p + r)!d!}{(d + s + p)!(d + r)!} \cdot t^r, \tag{61A}$$

where

$$C_r{}^p = \frac{p(p - 1)(p - 2) \cdots (p - (r - 1))}{r!}, \text{ and } C_0{}^p = 1.$$

By comparing this with equation (61), it will be seen that the two are identical for the particular values of α, β, and γ appropriate to our problem and this shows that the series terminates at $r = p$. The preceding equations give us all the material needed for writing out the value of ψ for any combination of quantum numbers.

Example: Let $j = 4$, $\lambda = 2$, $m = 1$. We have then $d = \lambda - m = 1$, $s = \lambda + m = 3$, $p = j - \dfrac{d + s}{2} = 2$. Then,

$$F = 1 - 7t + 28/3 t^2,$$
$$\Theta = t^{1/2}(1 - t)^{3/2}F,$$
$$N = \frac{81}{4\pi^2 A C^{1/2}},$$

$$\psi_{j\lambda m} = \psi_{421} = \frac{1}{2\pi}\left(\frac{1}{AC^{1/2}}\right)^{1/2} 9t^{1/2}(1 - t)^{3/2}\left(1 - 7t + \frac{28}{3}t^2\right) \exp (i2\varphi + i\chi).$$

Changing the sign of λ does not change the energy, but changes the wave function to

$$\psi_{j-\lambda m} = \psi_{4-21} = \frac{1}{2\pi}\left(\frac{1}{AC^{1/2}}\right)^{1/2} 30t^{1/2}(1 - t)^{3/2}\left(1 - \frac{7}{2}t + \frac{14}{5}t^2\right) \exp (-i2\varphi + i\chi).$$

The probabilities of transition can be calculated in the usual way by forming the matrix elements for the electric moment. If the molecule has a permanent electric moment with components $P_{x'}$, $P_{y'}$, $P_{z'}$ or, if the transition includes an electronic-vibrational transition with these components of electric moment relative to the moving system of coordinates, the matrix elements of the components of electric moment parallel to the fixed X, Y, Z axes are proportional to

$$P_x(j'\lambda'm'; j''\lambda''m'') = \int P_x(P_{x'}, P_{y'}, P_{z'}, \theta, \varphi, \chi), \, \psi_{j'\lambda'm}{}^* \, \psi_{j''\lambda''m''} dv,$$

and two similar equations for P_y and P_z. $P_x(P_{x'}, P_{y'}, P_{z'}, \theta, \varphi, \chi)$ is given by equation (95) in Sec. 9 by substituting electric moments for coordinates in that equation, and dv equals the generalized element of volume, $AC^{½} \sin \theta d\theta d\varphi d\chi$. This has been done by Reiche and Rademacher[1] and Kronig and Rabi,[1] but we shall merely give the results as calculated by Dennison[2] using matrix mechanics. These amplitudes are especially important for they give the relative intensity of the rotational lines not only of the symmetric top molecule, but also of the diatomic molecule, since the latter differs from the former only in having a small moment of inertia about the figure axis. The permitted transitions are those for the following possible changes in the quantum numbers:

$$\Delta j = \pm 1, 0; \, \Delta \lambda = \pm 1, 0; \, \Delta m = \pm 1, 0;$$

there are thus twenty-seven possible types of transitions with λ and m taking the values,

$$-j \le \lambda \le j \text{ and } -j \le m \le j.$$

Since the energy does not depend on m nor on the sign of λ, many of these transitions will give identical frequencies in the absence of an external field and thus the intensities will be proportional to the sum of the squares of the amplitudes over all possible values of m and $\pm \lambda$. The results of the calculation for the field-free lines are as follows:

$g_{j'}A(\lambda', j'; \lambda'', j'')$	$j' - j''$	$\lambda' - \lambda''$
$\dfrac{c2(2j + 1)\lambda^2}{j(j + 1)}$	0	0
$\dfrac{c2(j^2 - \lambda^2)}{j}$	± 1	0
$\dfrac{c(2j + 1)(j + \lambda)(j - \lambda + 1)}{j(j + 1)}$	0	± 1
$\dfrac{c(j + \lambda)(j + \lambda - 1)}{j}$	± 1	± 1
$\dfrac{c(j - \lambda)(j - \lambda + 1)}{j}$	± 1	∓ 1.

(66)

j and λ in these formulas refer always to the larger of j' and j'' or λ' and λ'' and in the last two formulas the two upper or two lower signs of Δj and $\Delta \lambda$ are to be taken together. $g_{j'}$ is the quantum weight of the initial state and c is a constant multiplied by ν^4.

[1] *Loc. cit.*

[2] *Phys. Rev.*, **28**, 318 (1926).

The relative intensities of the lines of case a diatomic molecules are also given by these formulas by replacing λ by ι. They do not include the further restrictions required by the symmetry properties of the complete wave functions which will be discussed in Sec. **9**. The amplitudes are not changed appreciably by the λ-type doubling so that these formulas apply without change to the singlet system of levels and it will be found that they agree exactly with the formulas derived from the sum rules of Chap. XX, Sec. **8**.

6. STARK EFFECT AND ZEEMAN EFFECT OF THE ROTATIONAL SPECTRUM

The heavy symmetric top considered in Sec. **5** is doubly degenerate. Since m may take all the values $-j, \cdots 0, \cdots j$, there are $2j + 1$ wave functions which have the same energy for any particular values of j and λ. It is also possible to change the sign of λ without changing the energy of the molecule, so that altogether there are $2(2j + 1)$ wave functions for each energy state. These will give different values for the energy, only if the proper perturbing fields are present. The degeneracy in m is removed by an electric or magnetic field. An illustration of the removal of the degeneracy in λ will not be given, but a very similar case in the theory of diatomic molecules having $\lambda > 0$ will be discussed in Sec. **9**.

Reiche[1] has investigated the first-order Stark effect, while Manneback[2] has calculated both the first- and second-order terms. The model used by Reiche consists of an electric (or magnetic) dipole attached to the symmetrical molecule discussed above, with its moment μ directed along the axis of figure. This introduces a potential energy term,

$$V = -\mu F \cos \theta,$$

in equation (54) if the field is applied along the axis $\theta = 0$. The perturbation of the energy is calculated by Schrödinger's perturbation method for degenerate systems (see Sec. **2**). The term in F, giving the first-order Stark effect, is found to be

$$\Delta_1 E = -\frac{\mu F \lambda m}{j(j + 1)} \tag{67}$$

by the aid of formulas developed by Rademacher. In the special case $j = 0$, there is no change of energy proportional to F. Reiche[3] had previously solved this problem in terms of the Bohr theory. The present result differs from the older one only through the presence of $j(j + 1)$ in place of j^2. It is worth noting that the shifts predicted by equation (67) could easily be observed in the visible spectrum provided that

[1] *Z. Physik*, **39**, 444 (1926).

[2] *Physik, Z.*, **28**, 72 (1927).

[3] *Ann. Physik*, **58**, 668 (1919).

rotational and electronic energies are additive and that the model used is adequate. If $\mu \cong 10^{-18}$, then at 5,000 Å., the splitting in a field of 5,000 volts per centimeter would be of the order of 0.1 Å. for the transition from the state $j = m = \lambda = 1$ to the state $j = m = \lambda = 0$. This splitting is independent of the moments of inertia of the molecule, and serves as a direct measure of its electric moment.

The term in F^2 was obtained by Manneback both in wave and in ordinary dynamics. If $j \neq 0$, the result of the calculation by wave mechanics is

$$\Delta_2 E = \frac{\mu^2 F^2}{h^2/8\pi^2 A} \cdot 4[\Phi(j, m, \lambda) - \Phi(j + 1, m, \lambda)], \qquad (68)$$

where

$$\Phi(j, m, \lambda) = \frac{(j^2 - m^2)(j^2 - \lambda^2)}{(2j - 1)(2j)^3(2j + 1)}.$$

If $j = 0$, then,

$$\Delta_2 E = -\frac{1}{6} \frac{\mu^2 F^2}{h^2/8\pi^2 A}.$$

The result by ordinary mechanics when $j \neq 0$ is,

$$\Delta_2 E = \frac{\mu^2 F^2}{h^2/8\pi^2 A} \cdot \frac{1}{8j^2} \left[1 - 3\frac{m^2 + \lambda^2}{j^2} + 5\left(\frac{m\lambda}{j^2}\right)^2 \right]. \qquad (69)$$

Equation (68) merges into this when j is large compared with one, as it should. A knowledge of both $\Delta_1 E$ and $\Delta_2 E$ is necessary in order to calculate the dielectric constant of a dipole gas.

The theory of the Zeeman effect of diatomic molecules is similar to that of the Stark effect and has been given by Kemble,[1] Kemble, Mulliken, and Crawford[2] and by Kronig[3]; it is necessary to include a potential energy term in the wave equation for the symmetric top,

$$V = (\lambda + 2\sigma)\mu H \cos \theta, \quad \mu = \frac{eh}{4\pi mc},$$

where $(\lambda + 2\sigma)\mu$ represents the magnetic moment assumed to be in the direction of the line of nuclei and θ is taken as the angle between the direction of the external field and the line of nuclei. These assumptions apply to the case a molecule only. The additional term in the energy is

$$\Delta E = \frac{(\lambda + 2\sigma)\mu m H}{j(j + 1)}, \quad -j \leqslant m \leqslant j. \qquad (67A)$$

This formula predicts $2j + 1$ levels for a given value of j and that these levels become closer together as we go to higher values of j. It is difficult to test this theory because of the many closely spaced lines of band spectra

---

[1] "Molecular Spectra," Chap. VII, Sec. 6.   Old theory.

[2] *Phys. Rev.*, **30**, 438 (1927).

[3] *Phys. Rev.*, **31**, 195 (1928); *Z. Physik.* **45**, 557 (1926).

and because the closely spaced levels at large j values are difficult to separate. It is therefore necessary to calculate the intensities as well and thus predict the *centers of gravity* for the Zeeman patterns for large values of j.

The most detailed experimental study of the effect is that on the Ångström CO bands ($^1\Sigma \to {}^1\Pi$) by Kemble, Mulliken, and Crawford.[1] This work includes the Zeeman effect of a number of P-, Q-, and R-lines of these bands. The experiments confirmed the theory on three points: the separation of the outside components is proportional to the field strength and agrees quantitatively with the predicted values; the fine structure observed was that predicted by theory; and in low fields the intensities agreed with the values calculated by Kronig.[2] In higher fields the intensities of components displaced symmetrically on each side of the original line are not equal. In the Q-branch lines the lower frequency parallel components are more intense than the higher frequency components and this asymmetry decreases with increasing running number of the line. Kronig showed that this was to be expected due to a change in intensity with increasing field strength. The data on this point for lines of other branches is not conclusive.

7. THE HYDROGEN MOLECULE ION

The hydrogen molecule ion presents a three-body problem which can be solved by the separation of variables providing we assume that the protons are stationary. This problem was solved by Pauli[3] and Niessen[4] using the old quantum mechanics, but no agreement with the experimental values was secured. The problem has been attacked, using wave mechanics, by a number of authors;[5] Burrau used the separation of variables method, while the others used different perturbation methods.

The hydrogen molecule ion has nine degrees of freedom, and it is therefore necessary to specify nine coordinates. Three of these will fix the position of the center of mass of the system, three the motion of the protons relative to the center of mass, and three the position of the electron relative to the protons. The first three coordinates

---

[1] *Loc. cit.* and CRAWFORD, *Phys. Rev.*, **33**, 339 (1929). See also the work of HULTHÉN ("Dissertation," Lund (1923)) on the ZnH, CdH, and HgH bands and of WATSON and PERKINS (*Phys. Rev.*, **30**, 592 (1927)) on AgH, AlH, ZnH, and MgH bands.

[2] *Loc. cit.*

[3] *Ann. Physik*, **68**, 177 (1922).

[4] Diss. Utrecht (1922); *Ann. Physik*, **70**, 129 (1923).

[5] BURRAU, *Kgl. Danske Videnskabernes Selskab.* Medd, VII, 14 (1927); WANG, *Phys. Rev.*, **31**, 579 (1928); FINKELSTEIN and HOROWITZ, *Z. Physik*, **48**, 118 (1928); CONDON, *Proc. Nat. Acad. Sci.*, **13**, 466 (1927); PAULING, *Chem. Rev.*, **5**, 190 (1928); GUILLEMIN and ZENER, *Proc. Nat. Acad. Sci.*, **15**, 314 (1929); WILSON, *Proc. Roy. Soc.*, **118**, 617 (1928).

may be neglected immediately because the wave equation including all these coordinates will split into two parts, one of which will describe the motion of the center of mass and will be of exactly the same form as that of a free massive point moving with uniform velocity (Sec. **4**), while the other will describe the internal wave function and fix the internal energy. The second set of three coordinates, which fix the distance between the protons and the direction of the line joining them in space may be neglected for the moment because we do not intend to consider the rotation of the nuclei. We shall fix the distance between the protons later by applying the condition that the energy of the molecule must be a minimum. This last is approximately equivalent to quantizing the vibration of the nuclei in a zero vibrational state. This method is permissible for Born and Oppenheimer[1] have shown that the first approximation to the solution of the structure of molecules is secured by solving the problem of the electron motion relative to the nuclei considered as stationary.

The Schrödinger equation for the electron relative to two nuclei each of charge $+e$, fixed an arbitrary distance apart, is,

$$\frac{\partial^2 \psi}{\partial x^2} + \frac{\partial^2 \psi}{\partial y^2} + \frac{\partial^2 \psi}{\partial z^2} + G\left(E + \frac{e^2}{r_1} + \frac{e^2}{r_2} - \frac{e^2}{R} \right) = 0, \qquad (70)$$

where x, y, and z are the coordinates of the electron relative to axes fixed to the line of nuclei, r_1 and r_2 are the distances of the electron from the first and second nuclei, respectively, R is the distance between the nuclei and $G = 8\pi^2 m/h^2$. We introduce the elliptic coordinates

$$\xi = \frac{r_1 + r_2}{R}, \qquad \eta = \frac{r_1 - r_2}{R}, \qquad (71)$$

and take as the third coordinate the azimuth φ about the line of nuclei. The potential energy of the electron is then

$$V = -\frac{e^2}{r_1} - \frac{e^2}{r_2} = -\frac{4e^2\xi}{R(\xi^2 - \eta^2)} \qquad (72)$$

and the transformation equations for x, y, and z are,

$$z = \frac{R}{2}\xi\eta, \quad x = \frac{R}{2}(\xi^2 - 1)(1 - \eta^2) \cos \varphi, \quad y = \frac{R}{2}(\xi^2 - 1)(1 - \eta^2) \sin \varphi.$$

In the new variables the wave equation becomes,

$$\frac{\partial}{\partial \xi}\left\{ (\xi^2 - 1)\frac{\partial \psi}{\partial \xi} \right\} + \frac{\partial}{\partial \eta}\left\{ (1 - \eta^2)\frac{\partial \psi}{\partial \eta} \right\} + \left\{ \frac{1}{\xi^2 - 1} + \frac{1}{1 - \eta^2} \right\}\frac{\partial^2 \psi}{\partial \varphi^2}$$
$$+ G\left[\left(E - \frac{e^2}{R} \right)\frac{R^2(\xi^2 - \eta^2)}{4} + e^2 R\xi \right]\psi = 0. \quad (73)$$

[1] *Ann. Physik*, **84**, 457 (1927); See Condon and Morse, "Quantum Mechanics," McGraw-Hill Book Company, Inc. (1929), for a presentation of this work.

ψ is to be an acceptable function throughout space, that is, for all values of the variables satisfying the relations,

$$1 \leqslant \xi \leqslant \infty, \quad -1 \leqslant \eta \leqslant 1, \quad 0 \leqslant \varphi \leqslant 2\pi. \tag{74}$$

This equation is separated if we set,

$$\psi = X(\xi)Y(\eta) \exp (i\lambda\varphi), \lambda = 0, 1, \cdots$$

and the equations of X and Y are then,

$$\frac{d}{d\xi}\left\{(\xi^2 - 1)\frac{dX}{d\xi}\right\} + \left\{Ge^2R\xi + G\left(E - \frac{e^2}{R}\right)\frac{R^2}{4}\xi^2 + \frac{\lambda^2}{1 - \xi^2} + A\right\}X$$
$$= 0, \tag{75}$$

and

$$\frac{d}{d\eta}\left\{(\eta^2 - 1)\frac{dY}{d\eta}\right\} + \left\{G\left(E - \frac{e^2}{R}\right)\frac{R^2}{4}\eta^2 + \frac{\lambda^2}{1 - \eta^2} + A\right\}Y = 0. \tag{76}$$

A is the constant introduced in separating the variables. It is convenient to introduce the constants,

$$\gamma = G\left(E - \frac{e^2}{R}\right)\frac{R^2}{4} \text{ and } \epsilon = Ge^2R = \frac{2R}{a_0}, \tag{77}$$

where a_0 is the radius of the first Bohr orbit of hydrogen.

In solving equations (75) and (76) for the case of the normal state, Burrau adopted the following method: There will be no nodes in the wave function of the normal state of the ion and, therefore, λ may be set equal to zero and further we know the wave function will be positive at all points. New dependent variables $\sigma_\xi = -\dfrac{1}{X}\dfrac{dX}{d\xi}$ and $\sigma_\eta = -\dfrac{1}{Y}\dfrac{dY}{d\eta}$ are first introduced, which reduce the equations to the form,

$$\frac{d\sigma_\xi}{d\xi} = \sigma_\xi{}^2 - \frac{\gamma\xi^2 - 2(\epsilon - \sigma_\xi)\xi - A}{\xi^2 - 1}, \tag{78}$$

and

$$\frac{d\sigma_\eta}{d\eta} = \sigma_\eta{}^2 + \frac{\gamma\eta^2 + 2\sigma_\eta\eta - A}{1 - \eta^2}. \tag{79}$$

There are three arbitrary constants in these equations, γ, ϵ, and A. Equation (79) is used to secure the relation between γ and A, and then equation (78) to secure the relation between γ and ϵ. In addition, we use the condition that the energy as a function of R must be a minimum to fix the values of γ, ϵ, and A.

When $\eta = \pm 1$, the denominator of equation (79) becomes zero and thus if $d\sigma_\eta/d\eta$ is to remain finite, the numerator must also become zero. This fixes the values of σ_η at these two limits as,

$$\sigma_\eta(1) = \tfrac{1}{2}(A - \gamma) \text{ and } \sigma_\eta(-1) = -\tfrac{1}{2}(A - \gamma). \tag{80}$$

Moreover equation (79) requires that $\sigma_\eta(+\eta) = -\sigma_\eta(-\eta)$ since it is invariant to a change of sign of both σ_η and η, that is, σ_η has opposite signs on the two sides of the plane $\eta = 0$ and it must therefore be zero at this plane. σ_η is therefore expanded as an *odd* power series near $\eta = 0$ and in another power series near $\eta = 1$. Both series converge fairly rapidly at $\eta = \frac{1}{2}$ and the values of A and γ which make the two series converge to the same value at this value of η are determined by trial. In this way, pairs of values of A and γ are secured which give A as a function of γ.

Similarly σ_ξ is expanded in an ascending power series in $(\xi - 1)$ and in an inverse power series in ξ. Knowing A as a function of γ from the previous calculations, these series permit a calculation of γ as a function of ϵ, that is, the distance between the nuclei, and for each value of γ it is possible to calculate the energy from equation (77). In this way a plot of energy against internuclear distance can be made and the energy and internuclear distance for the minimum of this curve are the values of these quantities for the normal vibrationless state of $H_2{}^+$. The minimum value of E was found to be 16.29 $\pm$ 0.03 volts. From the shape of the curve of E plotted against R in the region of the minimum, Burrau found that the vibration frequency of the nuclei was about 2,250 cm.$^{-1}$, which gives for the nuclear vibration energy in the lowest state, $\frac{1}{2}h\nu = 0.14$ volts and thus the observable ionization energy of $H_2{}^+$ is calculated to be 16.15 $\pm$ 0.03 volts.[1]

The energy of dissociation of the hydrogen molecule is approximately 4.38 volts,[2] and this, together with the calculated value for the energy of the hydrogen molecule ion gives 15.31 for the ionizing potential of the hydrogen molecule. The observed values for this ionizing potential lie at about 16 volts. The discrepancy is probably due to the fact that the experimentally determined ionizing potential of the molecule is not that for the removal of an electron from the hydrogen molecule in its lowest state to form the hydrogen molecule ion in its lowest state. Some vibrational energy is probably given to the nuclei of the hydrogen molecule ion at the same time that the electron is removed (see Chap. XIII, Sec. 7). Birge (*loc. cit.*) secures 2,247 cm.$^{-1}$ for the value of ν_0 from band spectra, which corresponds to 0.277 volts. The agreement between the calculated and observed values is as good as can be expected.

Figure 3 shows a plot of the energy of the normal hydrogen molecule ion as a function of the distance between the nuclei as given by Burrau, and Fig. 4 shows the plot of the value of ψ^2 in an arbitrary median plane.

Unsöld, Pauling, Finkelstein and Horowitz, and Guillemin and Zener have applied perturbation methods to solve the problem of the hydrogen molecule ion, and have secured values which are in approximate agree-

---

[1] Burrau gave 16.22 volts due to an error in calculation; see Birge, *Proc. Nat. Acad.*, **14**, 12 (1928).

[2] Witmer, *Proc. Nat. Acad. Sci.*, **12**, 238 (1926); Dieke and Hopfield, *Z. Physik*, **40**, 299 (1926).

ment with those of Burrau.   The method of Guillemin and Zener is especially interesting, since it gives the wave function as well as the characteristic energy values.[1]

Though the wave functions for the hydrogen molecule ion in all its states have not been calculated, it is possible to see where the nodes

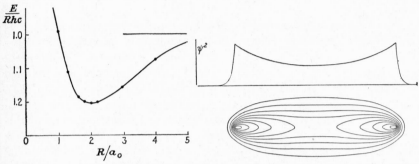

Fig. 3.—The energy of H_2^+ as a func-   Fig. 4.—The charge density for H_2^+.   (*After*
tion of R.   (*After Burrau*.)   *Burrau*.)

of these functions will appear, and to see how they will change as the two nuclei are brought infinitely close together to form a united He^+ ion.   The quantum number λ gives the number of nodal planes passing through the line of nuclei corresponding to constant φ, and as the two nuclei are brought close together these nodal planes become the meridian

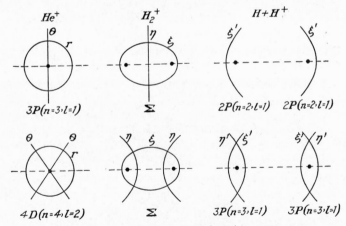

Fig. 5.—The nodes of He^+, H_2^+, and H.

nodal planes of the united atom, and λ becomes equal to the atomic quantum number m.   There can be no change in the number of these nodes in this process.   The nodes corresponding to constant ξ are ellipsoids of revolution and become the radial nodes of the united atom,

[1] See Condon and Morse, "Quantum Mechanics," McGraw-Hill Book Company, Inc. (1929) for a review of these perturbation methods.

while the nodes for constant η, which are hyperboloids of revolution, become the latitudinal nodes. Thus the ellipsoids become spheres, the hyperboloids cones and the planes remain planes. The numbers of ellipsoidal and hyperbolic nodes may be designated by n_ξ and n_η, respectively. The left side of Fig. 5 illustrates this change for the cases $n_\xi = 1$, $n_\eta = 1$, $\lambda = 0$, and $n_\xi = 1$, $n_\eta = 2$, $\lambda = 0$.

These diagrams represent only the nodes in an arbitrary plane through the line of nuclei and if rotated about this line the lines will generate the nodal surfaces. The l quantum number of the united atom is equal to $m + n_\eta(= \lambda + n_\eta)$ and the total quantum number is $n = n_\xi + n_\eta + \lambda + 1$.

It is also of interest to consider the changes in the nodal planes and thus the quantum numbers as the nuclei are separated to a great distance. This separation results in two identical wave functions, one about each nucleus, characteristic of the hydrogen atom in one of its steady states if the problem is solved using parabolic coordinates, say ξ', η', and φ. Since the wave function of the hydrogen molecule ion is normalized so that the total negative charge is that of one electron, each of these separated wave functions will be normalized so that the total charge is only one-half the electronic charge. This means that the electron remains near one nucleus for a time, then passes to the other for a time and then back again, etc., so that on the average it spends one-half the time on each. When separated a short distance the probability of such a "jump" is very small. Thus the hydrogen molecule ion separates into one atom and a proton, but the probability of the electron going with one nucleus is equal to its probability of going with the other. The nodes of constant φ and of constant ξ, *i.e.*, λ and n_ξ, will not change in this process of separation; λ becomes the m quantum number and n_ξ becomes $n_{\xi'}$, a quantum number conjugate to a parabolic coordinate of the hydrogen atom. On the other hand, there is a reduction of the number of nodes of constant η except in the case that this number is zero. If n_η is odd, one of the nodes is the median plane perpendicular to the line of nuclei and as the nuclei are separated, this node disappears; the nodes on one side of this plane become nodes in a parabolic coordinate of the one atomic wave function and those on the other side, nodes of the second atomic wave function. If n_η is even, no node is lost, but half of the nodes go to each atomic wave function. Thus the number of parabolic nodes, $n_{\eta'}$ in each atomic wave function is $\frac{1}{2}(n_\eta - 1)$, if n_η is odd, or $\frac{1}{2}n_\eta$, if n_η is even. This decrease in the quantum number when a molecule separates into atoms is called "demotion" of the quantum number and the increase in the number of nodes in the reverse process, that is, the formation of a molecule from atoms or ions, is called "promotion" of the quantum number. These changes for H_2^+ are illustrated at the right in Fig. 5 and a little study of these diagrams and the possible nodes will convince the reader that the changes must occur in this way. Following the rules of this and the preceding paragraph, it is possible to correlate the energy levels of H_2^+ with the levels of the hydrogen atom in an electric field and these in turn with the field-free levels,[1] and also with the terms of He^+. This is given in Fig. 6. This correlation between the H_2^+ and the $H + H^+$ levels was given by Hund.[2]

Two levels of H_2^+ approach each Stark effect level of the hydrogen atom: one of these has even n_η and the other odd n_η. If the coordinate

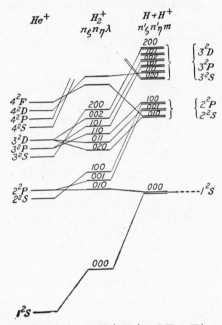

FIG. 6.—Correlation of He^+, H_2^+ and $H + H^+$ states.

of the electron is changed from η to $-\eta$, $Y(\eta)$ changes sign if n_η is odd, but does not change sign if n_η is even. Thus

$$Y(\eta) = \beta Y(-\eta), \tag{81}$$

where β equals 1 if n_η is even, and -1, if n_η is odd. Considering the reverse process, the two atomic wave functions can interact in two ways in one of which a node is formed between them (antisymmetric) and in the other of which no such node is formed (symmetric). This will be illustrated further by the hydrogen molecule in the following section. All the levels of H_2^+ given in the figure may not be stable; in particular the antisymmetric states will probably be unstable, since promotion always occurs with a consequent increase in energy when these are formed

[1] See KRAMERS, *Z. Physik*, **3**, 199 (1920).

[2] *Z. Physik*, **40**, 742 (1927).

from H and H^+. In more complicated molecules these relations are not so simple due to the interaction of the electrons in such molecules. If this interaction could be neglected, the wave equation could be separated in elliptical coordinates and all the arguments in this section in regard to demotion and promotion of quantum numbers could be used. To a first approximation this is true for many molecules, and the formation of more complex molecules from atoms has been discussed in this way (Sec. **8**).

8. THE STRUCTURE OF THE HYDROGEN MOLECULE

Heitler and London[1] solved the problem of the hydrogen molecule by applying the perturbation theory of wave mechanics. The wave equation is

$$\Delta_1\psi + \Delta_2\psi + G\left\{E - \left(\frac{e^2}{R} + \frac{e^2}{r_{12}} - \frac{e^2}{r_{a1}} - \frac{e^2}{r_{a2}} - \frac{e^2}{r_{b1}} - \frac{e^2}{r_{b2}}\right)\right\}\psi = 0,$$

$$\Delta_1 = \frac{\partial^2}{\partial x_1^2} + \frac{\partial^2}{\partial y_1^2} + \frac{\partial^2}{\partial z_1^2}, \Delta_2 = \frac{\partial^2}{\partial x_2^2} + \frac{\partial^2}{\partial y_2^2} + \frac{\partial^2}{\partial z_2^2}, G = \frac{8\pi^2 m}{h^2}, \quad (82)$$

where $x_1, y_1, z_1, x_2, y_2, z_2$, are the coordinates of electrons 1 and 2, R is the distance between the nuclei, r_{12} that between the electrons and r_{a1}, r_{a2}, r_{b1}, and r_{b2} the distances between electrons, 1 and 2, and nuclei, a and b, as indicated by the subscripts. The zero order approximate solution is secured by suitable combinations between the wave functions of the separate unperturbed hydrogen atoms in the lowest energy states. Two arrangements of electrons and nuclei are possible: (1) electron 1 may be on nucleus a and electron 2, on nucleus b; this gives

$$\psi_1{}^a = \frac{1}{\sqrt{\pi}}\left(\frac{1}{a_0}\right)^{3/2} \exp\left(-\frac{r_{a1}}{a_0}\right), \text{ and } \psi_2{}^b = \frac{1}{\sqrt{\pi}}\left(\frac{1}{a_0}\right)^{3/2} \exp\left(-\frac{r_{b2}}{a_0}\right) \quad (83)$$

for the unperturbed atomic wave functions; (2) electron 1 may be on nucleus b and electron 2 on nucleus a and thus the unperturbed function may be as readily,

$$\psi_2{}^a = \frac{1}{\sqrt{\pi}}\left(\frac{1}{a_0}\right)^{3/2} \exp\left(-\frac{r_{a2}}{a_0}\right), \text{ and } \psi_1{}^b = \frac{1}{\sqrt{\pi}}\left(\frac{1}{a_0}\right)^{3/2} \exp\left(-\frac{r_{b1}}{a_0}\right). \quad (84)$$

When the atoms are a great distance apart and the arrangement of electrons and nuclei is that given in (1),

$$\frac{e^2}{R} + \frac{e^2}{r_{12}} - \frac{e^2}{r_{a2}} - \frac{e^2}{r_{b1}}$$

becomes negligible and the product $\psi_1{}^a\psi_2{}^b$ is a solution of equation (82); but when the arrangement is that given in (2),

$$\frac{e^2}{R} + \frac{e^2}{r_{12}} - \frac{e^2}{r_{a1}} - \frac{e^2}{r_{b2}}$$

[1] *Z. Physik*, **44**, 455 (1927).

becomes negligible and $\psi_2{}^a\psi_1{}^b$ is a solution of equation (82). The energy in both these cases is $2E_0$ where E_0 is the energy of one hydrogen atom in its normal state. This is a case of double exchange degeneracy, for either the nuclei or electrons can be interchanged. The most general solutions of equation (82) when the nuclei are widely separated are therefore linear combinations of the two wave functions $\psi_1{}^a\psi_2{}^b$ and $\psi_2{}^a\psi_1{}^b$, namely,

$$\psi_{I0} = \beta_{11}\psi_1{}^a\psi_2{}^b + \beta_{12}\psi_2{}^a\psi_1{}^b, \; \psi_{II0} = \beta_{21}\psi_1{}^a\psi_2{}^b + \beta_{22}\psi_2{}^a\psi_1{}^b. \quad (85)$$

We require that ψ_{I0} and ψ_{II0} shall be normal and orthogonal, namely, that $\int \psi_{I0}\psi_{I0}{}^*dv$, and $\int \psi_{II0}\psi_{II0}{}^*dv$ shall equal 1 and that $\int \psi_{I0}\psi_{II0}{}^*dv$ shall be zero. These give three relations between the coefficients,

$$\beta^2{}_{11} + \beta^2{}_{12} + 2\beta_{11}\beta_{12}S = 1, \; \beta^2{}_{21} + \beta^2{}_{22} + 2\beta_{21}\beta_{12}S = 1, \quad (86)$$

and

$$\beta_{11}\beta_{21} + \beta_{12}\beta_{22} + (\beta_{11}\beta_{22} + \beta_{12}\beta_{21})S = 0,$$

where

$$S = \int \psi_1{}^a\psi_2{}^b\psi_2{}^a\psi_1{}^b dv.$$

The subsequent application of the perturbation theory of Sec. 2 shows that $\beta_{11}' = \beta_{12}$ and $\beta_{21} = -\beta_{22}$ and therefore the two unperturbed normal and orthogonal wave functions are

$$\psi_{I0} = (2 + 2S)^{-\frac{1}{2}}(\psi_1{}^a\psi_2{}^b + \psi_2{}^a\psi_1{}^b),$$

and

$$\psi_{II0} = (2 - 2S)^{-\frac{1}{2}}(\psi_1{}^a\psi_2{}^b - \psi_2{}^a\psi_1{}^b). \quad (87)$$

The first is symmetric in both the nuclei and electrons for an interchange of either does not change its sign, while the second is antisymmetric in both the nuclei and electrons since an interchange of either would change its sign. These symmetric and antisymmetric wave functions are similar to those of $H_2{}^+$ except that only single exchange degeneracy is present in the latter case, that is, only the nuclei can be exchanged.

We next assume two solutions of the perturbed wave equation (82),

$$\psi_I = \psi_{I0} + v_I, \; \psi_{II} = \psi_{II0} + v_{II}, \quad (88)$$

and assume that the corresponding characteristic energy values are,

$$E_I = 2E_0 + \epsilon_I, \; E_{II} = 2E_0 + \epsilon_{II}, \quad (89)$$

respectively. Substituting these in equation (82) and remembering that

$$\Delta\psi_1{}^a + G\left(E_0 + \frac{e^2}{r_{i1}}\right)\psi_1{}^a = 0$$

and that there are three similar relations for $\psi_2{}^b$, $\psi_1{}^b$, and $\psi_2{}^a$, equations for v_I and v_{II} are secured. These are

$$(2 \pm 2S)^{-\frac{1}{2}}\{\Delta + G(2E_0 - A - B - C)\}v_I(\text{or } v_{II}) = G\{(A - \epsilon_I,(\text{or } \epsilon_{II}))$$
$$(\psi_1{}^a\psi_2{}^b \pm \psi_2{}^a\psi_1{}^b) \pm B\psi_2{}^a\psi_1{}^b + C\psi_1{}^a\psi_2{}^b\}, \quad (90)$$

where the positive sign gives the equation for v_I and ϵ_I and the negative for v_II and ϵ_II, respectively, and

$$A = \frac{e^2}{r_{12}} + \frac{e^2}{R}, \; B = -\frac{e^2}{r_{a1}} - \frac{e^2}{r_{b2}}, \text{ and } C = -\frac{e^2}{r_{b1}} - \frac{e^2}{r_{a2}}.$$

The quantities on the right of equations (90) are called their "inhomogeneities" and each must be orthogonal to both ψ_{10} and $\psi_{\mathrm{II}0}$. The inhomogeneity of the equation for v_I is orthogonal to $\psi_{\mathrm{II}0}$ and that for v_II to ψ_{10}, if $\beta_{11} = \beta_{12}$ and $\beta_{21} = -\beta_{22}$ and so we derive these relations previously used in securing the normal and orthogonal forms of ψ_{10} and $\psi_{\mathrm{II}0}$. The conditions that the inhomogeneity of the equation for v_I shall also be orthogonal to ψ_{10} and that for v_II shall also be orthogonal to $\psi_{\mathrm{II}0}$ give two equations for ϵ_I and ϵ_II. These are,

$$\epsilon_\mathrm{I} = \frac{E_1 + E_2}{1 + S}, \text{ and } \epsilon_\mathrm{II} = \frac{E_1 - E_2}{1 - S}, \tag{91}$$

where

$$E_1 = \tfrac{1}{2}\int[A(\psi_1{}^a\psi_2{}^b)^2 + A(\psi_2{}^a\psi_1{}^b)^2 + B(\psi_2{}^a\psi_1{}^b)^2 + C(\psi_1{}^a\psi_2{}^b)^2]dv, \tag{92a}$$
$$E_2 = \tfrac{1}{2}\int(2A + B + C)\psi_1{}^a\psi_2{}^b\psi_2{}^a\psi_1{}^b dv. \tag{92b}$$

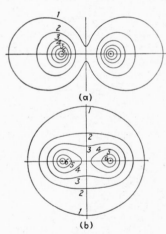

(a)

(b)

Fig. 7.—The charge density for H₂. (*After London.*) a. Elastic reflection. b. Stable molecule.

These integrals have been evaluated as functions of R by Heitler and London[1] and by Sugiura.[2] E_1 is the mean value of the potential energy of the system and is similar to such a mean energy taken in the classical way; as a function of R it has a slight minimum and would lead to a slight attraction of the two atoms. E_2 has no classical analogue, and is due to the resonance phenomenon, that is, to the two electrons exchanging places; it decreases rapidly with decreasing R and causes strong attraction in the symmetric case and strong repulsion in the antisymmetric case. ϵ_I and ϵ_II have been plotted in Fig. 15 of Chap. XIII; they are the $1\,^1\Sigma$ and lower $2\,^3\Sigma$ states, respectively.

The values of ϵ_I and ϵ_II can now be substituted in equation (90) and the wave equations solved by the method described in Sec. 2. The electron charge densities are then equal to $\psi_\mathrm{I}\psi_\mathrm{I}{}^*$ and $\psi_\mathrm{II}\psi_\mathrm{II}{}^*$. These have been calculated by London[3] and are illustrated in Fig. 7 for an arbitrary plane through the line of nuclei. In the antisymmetric case,

[1] *Loc. cit.*

[2] *Z. Physik,* **45**, 484 (1927).

[3] *Z. Physik,* **46**, 476 (1928).

a node forms at the median plane and following the reasoning of the preceding section would give a $2P$ state of the united helium atom.

Kemble and Zener[1] have applied the method used by Heitler and London to the interaction of a normal hydrogen atom and a hydrogen atom in its 2, 0 and 2, 1 states. They find sixteen possible wave functions. Though the computations are too involved to report here, one important point in regard to attraction and repulsion between atoms must be mentioned. In the case of the excited states of H_2, the unperturbed wave functions may have two types of symmetry: they may be symmetric or antisymmetric in the electrons, just as in the case of the neutral helium atom (Sec. 3); or they may be symmetric or antisymmetric in the nuclei. The solutions symmetric in the electron coordinates exclusive of the spin give the singlet levels, while the antisymmetric solutions give the triplet levels just as in the case of helium and for the same reasons. *This antisymmetry does not lead to the formation of a node at the median plane perpendicular to the line of nuclei and thus no promotion of the electron quantum numbers occurs.* Both antisymmetric (triplet) and symmetric (singlet) states of H_2 for which the energy decreases as R decreases can occur and the triplet states are the more stable. *Antisymmetry in the nuclei, i.e.,* a change in sign of the wave function when the nuclei are interchanged, *leads to the formation of a node at the median plane and thus to the promotion of the electron quantum numbers and strong repulsion.* Symmetry in the nuclei is thus more important than symmetry or antisymmetry in the electrons in determining whether two hydrogen atoms will attract or repel each other. These symmetric properties will be further discussed in Sec. **9,** where the rotation and vibration of nuclei and their spins will be included.

The second-order approximation in the solution of the wave equation will take account of the polarization forces between atoms and probably will lead to a slight attraction at large distances, that is, to the Van der Waals attraction between atoms and molecules, even in the case of the antisymmetric solution. This will be of importance in the case of readily deformable atoms.

9. THE SYMMETRY PROPERTIES OF DIATOMIC MOLECULES

In the preceding sections we have considered the symmetry properties of the wave functions of H_2 and $H_2{}^+$ assuming that the nuclei are stationary. In this section we shall discuss the problem for molecules containing many electrons and having like or unlike nuclei which are assumed to be rotating in three dimensions, and vibrating relative to each other. The facts presented are due principally to Hund,[2] Kronig,[3] and Wigner and

[1] *Phys. Rev.*, **33**, 512 (1929).

[2] *Z. Physik*, **42**, 93 (1927).

[3] *Z. Physik*, **46**, 814; **50**, 347 (1928).

Witmer;[1] we shall follow the general mathematical method of Kronig.

The Cartesian coordinates of the electrons of the molecule with reference to fixed axes will be taken as x_1, y_1, z_1, . . . x_n, y_n, z_n . . . and those of the nuclei as X_1, Y_1, Z_1, X_2, Y_2, and Z_2. The potential energy obviously does not depend on the position or orientation of the molecule in space. By introducing the reduced mass, $\mu = \dfrac{M_1 M_2}{M_1 + M_2}$ and fixing the position of one nucleus relative to the other by the coordinates X, Y, Z, where $X = X_1 - X_2$, $Y = Y_1 - Y_2$, $Z = Z_1 - Z_2$, the translation of the center of mass is eliminated from the problem in the usual way. The coordinates of the nuclei are given by the equations,

$$X_1 = X\frac{M_2}{M_1 + M_2}, \; X_2 = -X\frac{M_1}{M_1 + M_2};$$

similar relations hold for the Y- and Z-coordinates. The wave equation for the internal degrees of freedom is then

$$\left\{ \frac{1}{m}\sum_n \Delta_n + \frac{1}{\mu}\Delta_N + \frac{8\pi^2}{h^2}(E - V) \right\}\psi = 0, \tag{93}$$

where Δ_n is the Laplacian operator for the nth electron and equals $\dfrac{\partial^2}{\partial x_n^2} + \dfrac{\partial^2}{\partial y_n^2} + \dfrac{\partial^2}{\partial z_n^2}$, Δ_N equals $\dfrac{\partial^2}{\partial X^2} + \dfrac{\partial^2}{\partial Y^2} + \dfrac{\partial^2}{\partial Z^2}$, and E is the Eigenwert. Three other coordinates can be eliminated from the potential energy by referring the electrons to a frame of coordinates X', Y', Z', described relative to the fixed axes by the Eulerian angles θ, φ, and χ. Without loss of generality we take the Z'-axis as the line of nuclei so that $X' = 0$, $Y' = 0$, and $Z' = R$, the distance between the nuclei, and the X'-axis so that the first electron lies in the $Z'X'$ plane and has its x_1' coordinate greater than zero; the coordinates of the first electron in the X', Y', Z' system are therefore x_1', 0, z_1'. The Eulerian angles are then defined as in Chap. XII, Fig. 30. (χ is used instead of ψ to avoid confusion with the symbol for the wave function.) To secure the wave equation in the new coordinates it is only necessary to transform equation (93) from the coordinates, x_1, y_1, z_1, . . . x_n, y_n, z_n, . . . X, Y, and Z to the coordinates x_1', z_1', . . . x_n', y_n', z_n', . . . R, θ, φ and χ.

The potential energy may be regarded as consisting of three terms, the potential energy of electrons and nuclei, the mutual potential energy of the electrons and the mutual potential energy of the nuclei; these may be designated V_{EN}, V_{EE} and V_{NN} respectively. The first of these is,

$$V_{EN} = -\sum_n \left\{ \frac{Z_1 e^2}{r_{n1}} + \frac{Z_2 e^2}{r_{n2}} \right\},$$

[1] Z. Physik, **51**, 859 (1928).

where r_{n1} and r_{n2} are the distances of the nth electron from the first and second nuclei, respectively, and are given by the relations,

$$r_{n1} = \left[x_n'^2 + y_n'^2 + \left(z_n' - R \frac{M_2}{M_1 + M_2} \right)^2 \right]^{1/2},$$

and

$$r_{n2} = \left[x_n'^2 + y_n'^2 + \left(z_n' + R \frac{M_1}{M_1 + M_2} \right)^2 \right]^{1/2}.$$

This potential energy function has the important property to be used in the following discussion that *it is unchanged by a change of signs of all the z''s, if, and only if, both the charges and masses of the nuclei are the same:* it does not change in any case if the signs of all the x''s or y''s are changed.   The second term is

$$V_{EE} = \frac{1}{2} \sum_n \sum_m \frac{e^2}{r_{nm}},$$

where r_{nm} is the distance between the nth and mth electrons and is

$$r_{nm} = [(x_n' - x_m')^2 + (y_n' - y_m')^2 + (z_n' - z_m')^2]^{1/2}.$$

This term does not change if the signs of all the x''s or y''s or z''s are changed.   Finally,

$$V_{NN} = \frac{Z_1 Z_2 e^2}{R}.$$

Thus

$$V = V(x_1', z_1', \; \cdots \; x_n', y_n', z_n', \; \cdots \; R), \tag{94}$$

and is unchanged by a change of sign of any of these variables except the z''s, and it is unchanged by a change of sign of all the z''s, if, and only if, the charges and masses of the nuclei are the same.

The Laplacian operator for the electrons and nuclei can be calculated in the new coordinates by means of the transformation equations,

$$x = x'(\cos \varphi \cos \chi - \cos \theta \sin \varphi \sin \chi)$$
$$- y'(\sin \varphi \cos \chi + \cos \theta \cos \varphi \sin \chi) + z' \sin \theta \sin \chi,$$
$$y = x'(\cos \varphi \sin \chi + \cos \theta \sin \varphi \cos \chi)$$
$$- y'(\sin \varphi \sin \chi - \cos \theta \cos \varphi \cos \chi) - z' \sin \theta \cos \chi,$$
$$z = x' \sin \theta \sin \varphi + y' \sin \theta \cos \varphi + z' \cos \theta. \tag{95}$$

In these equations x, y, z, and x', y', z' may represent the coordinates of the electrons in the fixed and moving coordinates respectively or x, y, z, and z' may represent X, Y, Z and Z' of the nuclei; X', Y', and y_1' equal zero and do not appear in these equations, so that there are as many equations as either new or old coordinates.   This is an involved calculation which will not be given here.   The resulting equation may be written,

$$(H_0 + H_1 + H_2 - E)\psi = 0, \tag{96}$$

where

$$H_0 = \frac{h^2}{8\pi^2}\left\{\frac{1}{m}\Delta(x', y', z', \varphi, R) + \frac{1}{\mu}\Delta(R)\right\} + V(x', y', z', R), \quad (96a)$$

$$H_1 = \frac{h^2}{8\pi^2}\frac{1}{\mu R^2}\Delta(\theta, \varphi, \chi), \quad (96b)$$

$$H_2 = \frac{h^2}{8\pi^2}\frac{1}{\mu R^2}\Delta(x', y', z', \theta, \varphi, \chi). \quad (96c)$$

H_0 is the Hamiltonian operator for the case of non-rotating nuclei in the coordinates x', y', z', φ, and R, H_1 is the operator for the rotation of the nuclei, H_2 is the "cross product" operator which includes the Coriolis and centrifugal forces, and E is the Eigenwert. $\Delta(x', y', z', \varphi, R)$ is an operator, which contains the x''s, y''s, z''s and first and second partial derivatives with respect to them, the first and second partial derivatives with respect to φ but not φ itself, and R but no partial derivatives with respect to it; it is invariant to a simultaneous change in sign of φ and all the y''s with the other variables unchanged, and also to a change in sign of all the z''s with the other variables unchanged. The change in sign of φ and the y''s is equivalent to reversing the sign of "rotation" of the electrons, the change in sign of the y''s being necessary in order that the electrons "rotate" in the same order so that there is no change except in the sign of "rotation." $\Delta(R)$ is the differential operator for the vibration of the nuclei and equals $\dfrac{\partial^2}{\partial R^2} + \dfrac{2}{R}\dfrac{\partial}{\partial R}$. $\Delta(\theta, \varphi, \chi)$ is the differential operator of equation (54) with the term containing A/C omitted.

If we neglect H_2, we can assume two solutions of equation (96), i.e.,

$$\psi_1 = f_\lambda(x', y', z', R)\Theta_{j\lambda m}\exp i(\lambda\varphi + m\chi), \quad (97a)$$
$$\psi_2 = f_{-\lambda}(x', y', z', R)\Theta_{j-\lambda m}\exp i(-\lambda\varphi + m\chi), \quad (97b)$$

where f_λ and $f_{-\lambda}$ are functions of the coordinates indicated and the electronic, vibrational and rotational quantum numbers; $\Theta_{j\lambda m}(\theta)$ $\exp i(\lambda\varphi + m\chi)$ is the function of θ, φ, j, λ and m given in equation (64); and $\Theta_{j-\lambda m}(\theta)$ $\exp i(-\lambda\varphi + m\chi)$ is the same function with the sign of λ changed. Substituting equations (97a) and (97b) in equation (96) and neglecting H_2, we find that f_λ and $f_{-\lambda}$ satisfy the equations,

$$\left\{\frac{1}{m}\Delta(x', y', z', \pm\lambda, R) + \frac{1}{\mu}\Delta(R) + \frac{8\pi^2}{h^2}\left[E - \frac{h^2}{8\pi^2\mu R^2}(j(j+1) - \lambda^2) - \right.\right.$$

$$\left.\left. V(x', y', z', R)\right]\right\}\cdot f_{\pm\lambda}(x', y', z', R) = 0, \quad (98)$$

and that $\Theta_{j\lambda m}(\theta)$ and $\Theta_{j-\lambda m}(\theta)$ satisfy the equations,

$$\{\Delta(\theta, \pm\lambda, m) + j(j+1) - \lambda^2\}\cdot\Theta_{j\pm\lambda m}(\theta) = 0. \quad (99)$$

In these equations, (98) and (99), $\Delta(x', y', z', \lambda, R)$ and $\Delta(\theta, \lambda, m)$ are respectively the operators $\Delta(x', y', z', \varphi, R)$ and $\Delta(\theta, \varphi, \chi)$ with $\partial/\partial\varphi$,

$\partial^2/\partial\varphi^2$, $\partial/\partial\chi$, and $\partial^2/\partial\chi^2$ replaced by $i\lambda$, $-\lambda^2$, im, and $-m^2$, respectively, and $\Delta(x', y', z', -\lambda, R)$ and $\Delta(\theta, -\lambda, m)$ are these operators with the sign of λ changed. $j(j+1) - \lambda^2$ is a separation constant and is the Eigenwert of equation (99). We take as the unperturbed wave functions two linear orthogonal combinations of the solutions, ψ_1 and ψ_2, namely,

$$\psi_I = \beta_I[f_\lambda(x', y', z', R)\Theta_{j\lambda m}(\theta) \exp i(\lambda\varphi + m\chi) + f_{-\lambda}(x', y', z', R)$$
$$\Theta_{j-\lambda m}(\theta) \exp i(-\lambda\varphi + m\chi)], \quad (100a)$$

and

$$\psi_{II} = \beta_{II}[f_\lambda(x', y', z', R)\Theta_{j\lambda m}(\theta) \exp i(\lambda\varphi + m\chi) - f_{-\lambda}(x', y', z', R)$$
$$\Theta_{j-\lambda m}(\theta) \exp i(-\lambda\varphi + m\chi)]; \quad (100b)$$

the β_I and β_{II} are normalizing constants. The energy values for ψ_I and ψ_{II} are equal, if the Coriolis and centrifugal forces are neglected, but this degeneracy is removed when these are included. The inclusion of H_2 in the wave equation is now taken care of by the usual perturbation methods (Sec. 2); the characteristic energies of ψ_I and ψ_{II} are no longer the same, if $\lambda \neq 0$, and this causes the appearance of the λ-type doubling.[1] Each of these functions still has the $(2j+1)$-fold space degeneracy which can be removed by a perturbing external electric or magnetic field.

There are two transformations of coordinates for which the wave equation (96) is invariant and therefore for which the functions ψ_I and ψ_{II} either remain unchanged or change only their signs. The first applies only to molecules with like nuclei and the transformation consists only in interchanging the nuclei. This transformation can be defined by the equations,

$$\bar{x} = x', \bar{y} = -y', \bar{z} = -z', \bar{R} = R,$$
$$\bar{\theta} = \pi - \theta, \bar{\varphi} = \pi - \varphi, \bar{\chi} = \pi + \chi. \quad (101)$$

By following the transformation by means of Fig. 30, Chap. XII, or by substituting in equation (95) the reader can easily verify for himself that the effect is only to interchange the nuclei and leave every electron at its original position. *A wave function is said to be antisymmetric or symmetric in the nuclei, if it, respectively, does or does not change its sign in this transformation.* The differential operator of equation (98) is invariant to this transformation and the potential energy is also invariant, if the nuclei have equal charges and masses and, therefore, in this case,

$$f_\lambda(x', y', z', R) = \beta f_\lambda(x', y', -z', R), \beta = \pm 1. \quad (102)$$

If $\beta = +1$, the median plane, $z_1 = z_2 = \cdots z_n = 0$, is not a node, while if $\beta = -1$, this plane is a node.

In addition we have the relation,

$$f_{-\lambda}(x', y', z', R) = f_\lambda(x', -y', z', R), \quad (103a)$$

[1] See Kronig, *loc. cit.*; Van Vleck, *Phys. Rev.*, **33**, 467 (1929); Mulliken, *Phys. Rev.*, **33**, 507 (1929).

which can be proven as follows. Substituting $-y'$ for y' in equation (98), using the positive sign for λ throughout and remembering that

$$\Delta(x', -y', z', -\lambda, R) = \Delta(x', y', z', \lambda, R),$$

or

$$\Delta(x', y', z', -\lambda, R) = \Delta(x', -y', z', \lambda, R),$$

and also that

$$V(x', -y', z', R) = V(x', y', z', R),$$

we obtain the equation,

$$\left\{ \frac{1}{m}\Delta(x', y', z', -\lambda, R) + \frac{1}{\mu}\Delta(R) + \frac{8\pi^2}{h^2}\left[E - \frac{h^2}{8\pi^2\mu R^2}(j(j+1) - \lambda^2) - \right.\right.$$
$$\left.\left. V(x', y', z', R) \right] \right\} \cdot f_\lambda(x', -y', z', R) = 0.$$

The operator of this equation is that of equation (98) using $-\lambda$ and thus $f_\lambda(x', -y', z', R)$ can differ from $f_{-\lambda}(x', y', z', R)$ only by an arbitrary constant factor which can be chosen as 1 so that equation (103a) follows. In the special case that $\lambda = 0$, this arbitrary constant must be either $+1$, or -1, so that

$$f_0(x', y', z', R) = \pm f_0(x', -y', z', R), \tag{103b}$$

for otherwise there would be two functions ψ_I and ψ_II for only one characteristic energy value. Either ψ_I or ψ_II is zero, if the negative or positive sign, respectively, of equation (103b) applies. Further

$$\exp i\lambda(\pi - \varphi) = (-1)^\lambda \exp i\lambda\varphi, \tag{104a}$$
$$\exp im(\pi + \chi) = (-1)^m \exp im\chi, \tag{104b}$$

which can readily be seen and

$$\Theta_{j\lambda m}(\pi - \theta) = (-1)^{j-\lambda-m}\Theta_{j-\lambda m}(\theta), \tag{104c}$$

which is easily proven to be true by direct substitution of $\pi - \theta$ for θ and $-\lambda$ for λ in the expression for Θ from Sec. **5**. It is now evident that ψ_I is symmetric or antisymmetric in the nuclei, if

$$\beta(-1)^j = 1 \text{ or } -1, \text{ respectively}, \tag{105}$$

and ψ_II is symmetric or antisymmetric in the nuclei, if

$$\beta(-1)^{j+1} = 1 \text{ or } -1, \text{ respectively}. \tag{106}$$

Thus, as j increases, the levels are alternately symmetric and antisymmetric in the case of either ψ_I or ψ_II and for a λ-type doublet ($\lambda \neq 0$) with a given value of j, one of the levels is symmetric and the other antisymmetric. These results were first derived by Hund.[1]

In addition to being invariant to the transformation equations (101) the wave equation (96) is invariant to another transformation of coordinates regardless of whether the nuclei are like or unlike. This transformation is defined by the equations,

$$\bar{x} = x', \bar{y} = -y', \bar{z} = z', \overline{R} = R,$$
$$\bar{\theta} = \pi - \theta, \bar{\varphi} = 2\pi - \varphi, \bar{\chi} = \pi + \chi, \tag{107}$$

[1] *Loc. cit.*

and the reader can readily verify, as before, that this transformation amounts to a reflection of all electrons and nuclei in the origin of coordinates, *i.e.*, the center of mass. Wigner and Witmer[1] have designated the wave functions which do or do not change sign in this transformation as negative or positive respectively. Using the same methods as before, we find that ψ_I is negative or positive, if

$$(-1)^{j-\lambda} = -1 \text{ or } +1, \text{ respectively,} \tag{108}$$

and ψ_{II} is negative or positive, if

$$(-1)^{j-\lambda+1} = -1 \text{ or } +1, \text{ respectively.} \tag{109}$$

To secure the possible types of energy levels it is only necessary to give β and the quantum numbers their possible values and substitute these in equations (105), (106), (108), and (109). In particular, if

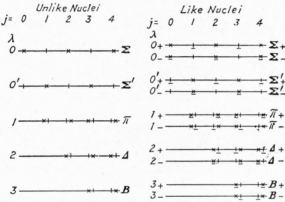

FIG. 8.—The terms antisymmetric in the nuclei are underlined, while symmetric terms are not. Positive and negative terms are indicated by $\times$ and $|$, respectively. The subscripts $+$ and $-$ at the right refer to the sign of β.

$\lambda = 0$, either ψ_I or ψ_{II} is zero, depending on whether the $+$ or $-$ sign of equation (103b), respectively, is to be used and either equations (106) and (109), or equations (105) and (108) give the possible types of levels. If ψ_I is not zero, the rotational levels with even j are the positive levels and if ψ_{II} is not zero, the rotational levels with even j are negative levels. These two types of states have been called the 0 and 0′ states or the Σ and Σ' states, respectively, by Wigner and Witmer. The possible types of levels are shown in Fig. 8.

In the case of molecules with like nuclei, the interchange of the nuclei does not change the positions of the electrons, so that x, y, and z and thus the components of the electric moment, $P_x = \Sigma ex$, $P_y = \Sigma ey$, and $P_z = \Sigma ez$ do not change sign in the transformation of equation (101) and therefore, taking P_x as an example,

$$\int P_x \psi_n{}^* \psi_m dv, \tag{110}$$

[1] *Z. Physik*, **51**, 859 (1928).

is zero unless ψ_n and ψ_m are either both symmetric or both antisymmetric in the nuclei. Otherwise, if the product of ψ_n and ψ_m is positive in one element of volume, there is another element of volume in which the product is equal in magnitude, but opposite in sign to the product in the first element of volume and when the integration is extended over all space the result will be zero. Thus only symmetric states combine with symmetric states and antisymmetric states with antisymmetric states with the emission of light. Further this rule should hold in collision processes. Any perturbing potential due for example to collisions with other molecules or the walls of the vessels must be symmetric with respect to an interchange of the nuclei. Letting P be this perturbing potential, the integral $\int P\psi_n{}^*\psi_m dv$ will be zero unless ψ_n and ψ_m are either both symmetric or both antisymmetric in the nuclei. This conclusion is also in agreement with the experimental facts (Chap. XII, Sec. **22**).

The integral of equation (110) is zero, if the two wave functions are either both positive or both negative. x, y, and z and therefore P_x, P_y, and P_z change sign in the transformation of equation (107). It is necessary, therefore, that either ψ_n or ψ_m of equation (110), but not both, shall change sign in this transformation, if the integral over all space is to be greater than zero. Thus negative terms combine with positive terms or *vice versa*. This rule is obeyed very well by known band systems. The Q_{1A1B} and Q_{2A2B} branches of OH described in Chap. XII, Sec. **21** are exceptions to this rule perhaps due to its breakdown by the electric fields present in a discharge tube.

So far, we have considered the case of singlet systems only, that is, the resultant spin of the electrons is assumed to be zero. If the electron spin is not zero, it is necessary to differentiate between Hund's cases a and b (Chap. XII, Sec. **16**). (We shall not discuss Hund's other cases, since these occur rather seldom.) In case b the electron spin is oriented relative to the k, which replaces the j of the preceding paragraphs. The spin does not change the symmetry properties of the molecule nor the rules governing the intercombinations of symmetric and antisymmetric, or positive and negative states. The effect is to split each of the levels shown in Fig. 8 into a multiplet; if $s = \frac{1}{2}$, each level splits into two of like symmetrical properties which have the same k, but j's differing by one, and if $s = 1$, into three of like symmetry properties with the same k value, etc. This splitting is due to the small coupling energy between the magnetic moment of the electron and that due to the rotation of the molecule.

Σ states belong to case b, but, if $\lambda \neq 0$, the states may belong to either case b already discussed or to case a. The correlation of case a and case b states, when $s = \frac{1}{2}$, has been given in Chap. XII, Sec. **16** and Fig. 20. Hund[1] and Van Vleck[2] have carried through this correlation

[1] *Loc. cit.*

[2] *Phys. Rev.*, **33**, 467 (1929).

of the case a doublets for both normal and inverted doublet levels. If we imagine a coupling force between s and λ which decreases to zero and then changes sign, it is possible to carry the normal doublets over into the inverted doublets adiabatically. Throughout this change, the symmetry properties relative to both the transformations of equations (101) and (107) do not change; the terms remain symmetric or antisymmetric, positive or negative, and the selection rules applying to combinations between these types of terms are exactly as stated above.

10. THE ROTATIONAL STATES OF H_2 AND He_2

The electrons of H_2 in its normal state are symmetric in the electron coordinates and antisymmetric in the electron spins so that the electron wave function is antisymmetric in the electrons including the spin just as in the case of the normal helium atom. The normal non-rotating hydrogen molecule is symmetric in the nuclei since there is no "hyperbolic" node and thus β of equation (102) is equal to 1; also λ is zero and the character of the rotational states shows that the positive sign of equation (103b) must be used, *i.e.*, the state is a Σ state and not a Σ' state. Therefore according to equation (105) the rotational states are symmetric, if $j = 0, 2, 4, \cdots$ and antisymmetric, if $j = 1, 3, 5, \cdots$. In addition, it is necessary to consider the proton spins, whose wave functions are entirely similar to those for the electron spins considered in Sec. 3; there are three symmetric and one antisymmetric nuclear spin functions with energies which are very nearly equal. *We have the rule that only the wave functions completely antisymmetric in the protons including the spins occur in nature.* The ψ's for $j = 0, 2, 4, \cdots$ must be multiplied by the antisymmetric spin function and the ψ's for $j = 1, 3, 5, \cdots$ by the three symmetric spin functions to secure wave functions which are completely antisymmetric in the nuclei. Thus the levels with odd j will have three times the probability of those with even j so that the *a priori* probabilities of the states are $2j + 1$, if $j = 0, 2, 4, \cdots$ and $3(2j + 1)$, if $j = 1, 3, 5, \cdots$. These *a priori* probabilities of the steady states are in agreement with the heat capacity of hydrogen (Chap. XII, Sec. 22).

A similar application of the rules for symmetric and antisymmetric levels and for positive and negative levels to the higher states of the H_2 molecule gives exactly the arrangement of levels illustrated, for example, in Chap. XII, Fig. 28. Since the symmetric levels have only one-third the probability of the antisymmetric levels both in the initial and final electronic states, the intensities of the lines emitted in transitions between them are less than those of lines due to combinations between the antisymmetric states. This accounts for the alternating intensities of these bands. Similar alternating intensities observed in other molecules with like nuclei are due to the presence of nuclear spins. Kronig[1]

[1] *Naturwis.* **16**, 335 (1928).

concludes that the nitrogen nucleus has 1 unit of spin from the fact that the relative *a priori* probabilities of the two sets of states are in the ratio of 1 to 2. The intensity data on chlorine (Cl^{35}-Cl^{35}) show that the relative *a priori* probabilities are approximately 1.4:1, while the Cl^{37}-Cl^{35} bands do not show alternating intensities.[1] Fluorine[2] probably has alternate levels with *a priori* probabilities of $(2j + 1)$ and $3(2j + 1)$. If so, the F nucleus has a spin of $\frac{1}{2}$ unit.

That the helium nucleus has no spin, is proved by the entire absence of one set of rotational levels of He_2. Without knowing more about the nuclear wave function, we cannot say whether it is the states with wave functions symmetric in the nuclei or antisymmetric in the nuclei which are present. Alternate lines of the bands of the O_2 molecule consisting of two atoms of mass 16 are also entirely absent, but all the lines are present in the bands of the O_2 molecule consisting of one atom of mass 16 and another of mass 17.[3] In this case the nuclei have the same charges, and different masses, and thus the potential energy of equation (94) changes with the change in sign of the z'''s and the wave function changes in other ways than sign in the transformation of equation (101). For this reason all states of the O_{16}-O_{17} molecule exist in nature.

[1] ELLIOTT, *Proc. Roy. Soc.* **123**, 629 (1929).
[2] GALE and MONK, *Phys. Rev.*, **33**, 114 (1929).
[3] GIAUQUE and JOHNSTON, *J. A. C. S.*, **51**, 1436 (1929).

CHAPTER XX

SPECTRAL INTENSITIES

PART I. INTENSITIES IN LINE SPECTRA

1. INTRODUCTORY

The study of the relative intensities of spectral lines entered on a new stage of development in 1924, and interest in the subject has grown very rapidly since that time. It had been known for many years that the ratio of intensities of the D-lines of sodium is $2:1$ under conditions where they are not self-reversed. In 1923 and 1924, Dorgelo[1] measured the intensities of a number of lines, mostly in the spectra of metals of the first and second groups, using the methods of photographic photometry, and showed conclusively that the intensities of lines belonging to the same multiplet often stand in the ratio of simple integers. Since that time the subject has been actively investigated by Ornstein and Burger and their colleagues at the University of Utrecht, and by a number of other investigators as well. Formulas have been obtained which give the relative intensities of the lines in a normal multiplet as a function of the initial and final quantum numbers of the emitting atom. Further it has been shown that integral intensity ratios are encountered in Zeeman patterns, and formulas which accurately represent these intensities are known. Duane and Siegbahn and others have studied intensity laws in X-ray line spectra, with the result that in a general way the intensities follow the theoretical formulas developed for optical line spectra.

Before describing experimental results, it will be well to study the factors on which the intensity of a spectral line depends. Consider an assembly of N atoms of which N_1 are in the lowest quantum state, N_2 in the second, etc., and let A_{nm} and B_{nm} be the probabilities of spontaneous and forced transitions, respectively, from the nth to the mth state, ρ being the density of radiation per unit interval of frequency at the frequency ν. The increase of the energy of the radiation field in time Δt, due to transitions from n to m, is *assumed* to be

$$\Delta E_{nm} = [A_{nm} + B_{nm}\rho]N_n h\nu\Delta t. \tag{1}$$

Similarly, the loss of energy due to absorption processes in which an atom passes from m to n is assumed to be

$$-\Delta E_{mn} = B_{mn}\rho N_m h\nu\Delta t.\,[2] \tag{2}$$

[1] *Z. Physik*, **13**, 206 (1923); **22**, 170 (1924).

[2] These assumptions were recently called in question by Schrödinger on the basis of the expression for the average x-coordinate of an electron given in equation (82) of

In the infra-red region the second term in equation (1) may be comparable with the first, but in the visible and ultra-violet regions, the second term is negligible, under the conditions usually encountered in terrestrial sources. However, this term cannot be neglected when we deal with sources at the high temperatures encountered in astrophysics. In the remainder of this chapter we shall suppose that the $B\rho$ term can be neglected. The quantities (1) and (2) are proportional to the measured intensities of emission and absorption lines, provided that self-reversal does not occur, and so we are chiefly interested in the relative values of $A_{nm}N_{n}h\nu$, or of $B_{mn}\rho N_{m}h\nu$. Now the value of ρ depends on the conditions of the experiment, and as we showed in Chap. III, Sec. **4**,

$$\frac{A_{nm}}{B_{nm}} = \frac{8\pi h\nu^3}{c^3}; \quad \frac{g_n}{g_m} = \frac{B_{mn}}{B_{nm}}, \tag{3}$$

where g_n and g_m are the statistical weights of the levels n and m, respectively. By using these relations, absorption measurements can be connected with measurements of intensities in emission. Only a small fraction of the lines in any spectrum can be studied in absorption, and we shall be mainly occupied with the relative values of $A_{nm}N_{n}h\nu$ for various spectral lines. Now, in accordance with equation (30) of Chap. VI and Chap. XVII, Sec. **10**, we have

$$A_{nm}h\nu = \frac{(2\pi\nu)^4}{3c^3}P^2(nm), \tag{4}$$

where $P^2(nm)$ is the nm element of the matrix representing the square of the electric moment. In order to arrive at relative experimental values of $P^2(nm)$ for comparison with the results of theory, the factor ν^4 must be taken into account. In the case of narrow multiplets this correction may be omitted. It is quite customarily used in discussing results for

---

Chap. XVI, Sec. **15**. On multiplying this expression by the electronic charge we have a quantity which Schrödinger interpreted as the electric moment corresponding to the ψ distribution there considered. If this interpretation were correct then the intensity of the radiation emitted in transitions from the nth to the mth state would be proportional to $c_n c_n{}^* c_m c_m{}^*$. On the statistical interpretation $c_n c_n{}^*$ is proportional to the population of the nth state, and $c_m c_m{}^*$ to that of the mth state, so the intensity should be proportional to the product of these populations. When this hypothesis was put forth there was no clear cut experiment which could decide the question. Ordinarily, the number of atoms removed from the lowest state by excitation processes is only a small fraction of the total number and so the population of the lower state may be treated as constant.

If this interpretation were correct, the relative intensity of two lines arising from the same higher level should change if we alter the relative populations of the lower levels; furthermore, the change in the relative intensities should be the same as that of the relative populations. This has been subjected to experimental test by GAVIOLA, (*Nature*, **122,** 772 (1928)), using a fluorescence method. His work shows conclusively that the population of the final state has no influence on the intensity of a spectral line.

lines which are widely separated, although it is known that this correction is not always valid (Sec. 3).   In what follows, we shall ordinarily assume that the ν^4 correction has been made.   It remains to consider the relative populations of the initial levels.   There are two especially simple cases in which the populations are definitely known.   First, if the atoms are in thermal equilibrium, we have

$$\frac{N_n}{N_m} = \frac{g_n \exp{(-E_n/kT)}}{g_m \exp{(-E_m/kT)}}.$$ (5)

This case is realized when we are dealing with furnace spectra of atoms and with the rotational states of molecules.   Second, if the excitation is sufficiently chaotic, as in the case of certain arcs and sparks where atoms in all states and electrons having a wide range of velocities are present, we have,

$$\frac{N_n}{N_m} = \frac{g_n}{g_m}.$$ (6)

Ordinarily, an attempt is made to arrange the experimental conditions so that equation (6) is satisfied, and, if this is the case, the intensity is determined by the product

$$I_{nm} = g_n A_{nm} h\nu,$$ (7)

that is,

$$I_{nm} \propto g_n \nu^4 P^2(nm).$$ (7a)

2. THE SUM RULE OF H. C. BURGER AND DORGELO

The following rule was proposed by H. C. Burger and Dorgelo[1] for the case of narrow multiplets:

The sum of the intensities of all lines of a multiplet which come from a given initial level is proportional to the quantum weight of that level; and the sum of the intensities of all lines of a multiplet which end on a given final level is proportional to the weight of that level.

Let us apply the second part of this rule to the sodium D-lines.   Here there is only one line arising from each of the initial levels $2^2P_{1/2}$ and $2^2P_{3/2}$, and the rule states that the ratio of their intensities must be the ratio of the weights of these states.   The weight of a state of quantum number j is $2j + 1$, and so the intensity ratio should be 2:4, which agrees with experiment.   Similarly, the first part of the sum rule applies to the sharp series doublets of the alkalies, and predicts that their intensities will also be in the ratio 2:4.   Measurements by Dorgelo on the carbon arc spectra of these metals show that the predictions of the sum rule are well verified for certain sharp series doublets.   Some typical data are given below.   Where several values of the intensity ratios are given, they correspond to different sets of experiments.

[1] *Z. Physik*, **23**, 258 (1924).

Element	Lines	Classification	Observed intensity ratio
Na	6,160–6,154	2^2P-3^2S	100:49
	6,160–6,154	2^2P-3^2S	100:50
K	5,802–5,782	2^2P-5^2S	100:49–54
	5,802–5,782	2^2P-5^2S	100:48–52
	5,802–5,782	2^2P-5^2S	100:52–55
K	5,339–5,323	2^2P-6^2S	100:47

It would appear from these data that the intensity ratio of a subordinate series doublet or triplet is independent of the initial level. Further, it is well recognized that the intensity ratio is 2:1 for the first principal series doublets of the alkalis. However, several investigators have found deviations from the predicted ratio for the higher members of these principal series. Recently, the whole subject has been reinvestigated by Sambursky.[1] His results refer to the four elements Na, K, Rb, and Cs. The data for Rb and Cs cover a larger number of lines than those for Na and K. They show that the ratio has the value two for the first series member, in agreement with previous work, rises to a maximum of 25 at the doublet 1^2S-6^2P in the case of cesium and to the value 5 for 1^2S-6^2P in the case of rubidium. After this it falls again. It appears, then, that the sum rule must be considered as an approximation even in the simple cases considered here. In the sections which follow, we shall encounter other instances in which it is not valid, but on the whole it is a useful guide. Its range of validity is somewhat similar to that of Landé's g formula, that is, it applies chiefly to normal multiplet spectra.

Dorgelo has found that the sum rule is approximately obeyed by the sharp series triplets of Mg, Ca, Zn, and Cd. For these triplets the intensities should be in the ratios 5:3:1. Further, the theoretical ratios 8:6:4 and 10:8:6 are verified for certain triplets in the sextet and octet systems of manganese.

Taylor[2] has examined the potassium doublet $1S$-$3D$, which contains the forbidden line $1^2S_{1/2}$-$3^2D_{3/2}$, using several different sources. In a carbon arc which was packed with a mixture of carbon and potassium carbonate, the ratio of intensities at low carbonate concentrations approximated to $3/2$, in good agreement with the sum rule. He made further experiments on the way in which the intensity of the forbidden lines increases with rising current and vapor density. He states that the results are in accord with the hypothesis that the forbidden lines are brought out by the action of ionic electric fields. However, the evidence for this is purely qualitative.

[1] *Z. Physik*, **49**, 731 (1928).
[2] *Phil. Mag.*, **5**, 166 (1928).

The real usefulness of the rule is better shown when we consider the composite doublets of the diffuse series.   Table 1 refers to these doublets. The final levels are marked at the left and the initial levels at the top, while a letter to represent the intensity of each line is inserted at the appropriate place in the body of the table.

TABLE 1

	$2^2D_{5/2}$	$2^2D_{3/2}$	
$2^2P_{3/2}$........	a	b	4
$2^2P_{1/2}$........	0	c	2
	6	4	

Since the transition $2^2P_{1/2}$-$2^2D_{5/2}$ is forbidden, we write zero for the intensity of this line.   To find the intensities of the other three lines we have the following conditions: The sum of the lines coming from $2^2D_{5/2}$ is to the sum of the lines coming from $2^2D_{3/2}$ as 6 is to 4, or

$$\frac{a}{b+c} = \frac{6}{4},$$

and likewise,

$$\frac{a+b}{c} = \frac{4}{2}$$

so that $a/c = 9/5$, $b/c = 1/5$.   Since the scale on which our results are expressed is immaterial, we take $a = 9$, $b = 1$, and $c = 5$.   This result was subjected to experimental test by Dorgelo.[1]   The means of his values for the cesium lines 6,212, 6,217, and 6,010 are in the ratios 9: 1.17: 5.05.

In cases where the sum rule is obeyed, we can draw certain conclusions as to the transition probabilities.   Considering an emission process, let j and j' be the inner numbers of the initial and final states, respectively. The sum of the intensities of the three lines emitted in transitions from j to $j + 1$, j, and $j - 1$ is proportional to g_j, according to the sum rule. If A is the factor of proportionality, we have

$$g_j A_{j,j-1} + g_j A_{j,j} + g_j A_{j,j+1} = g_j A.$$

or

$$\sum_{j\,=\,j+1,j,j-1} A_{j,j'} = A;\qquad(8)$$

and similarly, the second part of the rule leads to the relation,

$$\sum_{j\,=\,j'+1,j,j'-1} g_{j'} A_{j,j'} = g_{j'} A',\qquad(9)$$

A' being independent of j'.   This equation may be rewritten in the form,

$$\sum_{j\,=\,j'+1,j',j'-1} B_{j,j'} = B,\qquad(10)$$

where B is independent of j', by making use of the relation,

$$A_{j,j'} = \frac{8\pi h \nu^3}{c^3} B_{j,j'}.\qquad(11)$$

[1] *Physik. Z.*, **26**, 756 (1925).

3. INTENSITY RATIOS IN NORMAL MULTIPLETS

In general, the sum rule does not suffice to give us the intensity ratios of the lines in a normal multiplet. Before the discovery of the new mechanics, the correct formulas for multiplet intensities were found with the aid of the correspondence principle, by Kronig,[1] Russell,[2] and Sommerfeld and Hönl.[3] The model used by these investigators was the simple vector model considered in Chap. VI, Sec. 6 and in Chap. X. A charge characterized by the quantum numbers l and s moves in a plane orbit with frequency ω_l, and the normal to the orbital plane precesses around the resultant j of l and s, with frequency ω_j. The direction of j may be taken as the z-axis, and for our present purpose the orbit may be supposed circular, as seen by an observer rotating with the orbital plane. We resolve the circular motion into a linear oscillation parallel to the z-axis and two circular oscillations in opposite senses in the xy plane. The amplitudes of these oscillations are obtained by calculations of the kind employed in our study of the Zeeman effect on the basis of the classical theory (Chap. V, Sec. 10). We shall briefly recapitulate the results, adapting the notation to the present problem. First, consider the motion parallel to the z-axis. If C is the amplitude of the circular motion in the orbital plane, and θ is the angle between l εnd j, the amplitude of the oscillation parallel to the z-axis is $C \sin \theta$ and its frequency is ω_l. Since ω_j does not occur in the frequency of this oscillation, the corresponding transitions should obey the rules $\Delta l = \pm 1$, $\Delta j = 0$. In similar fashion we find that the frequencies $\omega_l \pm \omega_j$ and $-\omega_l \pm \omega_j$ are present in the motion in the xy plane. The corresponding transitions obey the selection rules $\Delta l = \pm 1$, $\Delta j = \pm 1$. The intensities I_{+1}, I_0, and I_{-1} of the harmonics corresponding to the various transitions are proportional to the entries in the following table:

$$
\begin{array}{lll}
 & \Delta l = +1 & \Delta l = -1 \\
\Delta j = +1 & I_{+1} \propto \frac{1}{2}(1 + \cos \theta)^2 & I_{+1} \propto \frac{1}{2}(1 - \cos \theta)^2 \\
\Delta j = 0 & I_0 \propto \sin^2 \theta & I_0 \propto \sin^2 \theta \\
\Delta j = -1 & I_{-1} \propto \frac{1}{2}(1 - \cos \theta)^2 & I_{-1} \propto \frac{1}{2}(1 + \cos \theta)^2 \quad (12)
\end{array}
$$

A simple sum rule is obeyed by these amplitudes. For given values of Δl, and of l and s, the sum of the intensities belonging to the three possible values of Δj is independent of θ. Now,

$$
\cos \theta = \frac{l^2 + j^2 - s^2}{2jl}, \tag{13}
$$

and so this sum is independent of j, and the above mentioned sum rule is simply the sum rule of Burger and Dorgelo. Consider now a spectral line emitted in a transition from l to $l + \Delta l$, j to $j + \Delta j$. By virtue

[1] Z. Physik, **31**, 885 (1925); **33**, 261 (1925).

[2] Proc. Nat. Acad. Sci., **11**, 314 and 322 (1925).

[3] Sitzber. der Preusz. Akad. der Wissenschaften, p. 141 (1925); see also HÖNL, Ann. Physik, **79**, 273 (1926).

of the correspondence principle for intensities (Chap. VI, Sec. **4**), we expect the intensity of this line to be roughly proportional to the corresponding entry in the above tabulation, using the value of cos θ given in equation (13). Of course, there is no justification for using the value of cos θ for the initial state rather than that for the final state, and the efforts of investigators in this field were devoted to discovering the appropriate modification of this procedure. Several guiding principles were available, such as the sum rule and the requirement that the true laws must yield zero intensity for certain lines, *e.g.*, for transitions between states for both of which $j = 0$. The formulas thus found have now been confirmed by the methods of matrix and wave mechanics. These formulas are rather involved, and can best be expressed, following Sommerfeld and Hönl, by adopting the abbreviations

$$P(j) \equiv (j + l)(j + l + 1) - s(s + 1)$$
$$Q(j) \equiv s(s + 1) - (j - l)(j - l + 1)$$
$$R(j) \equiv j(j + 1) + l(l + 1) - s(s + 1). \tag{14}$$

Then the products of the weight factor g for the initial state and the transition probability for a transition to the final state, are proportional to the quantities in the body of the following table:

	$l - 1 - l$	$l \to l$	$l \to l - 1$
$j - 1 \to j$	$\dfrac{P(j)P(j-1)}{4jl}$	$\dfrac{(2l+1)P(j)Q(j-1)}{4jl(l+1)}$	$\dfrac{Q(j)Q(j-1)}{4jl}$
$j \to j$	$\dfrac{(2j+1)P(j)Q(j)}{4j(j+1)l}$	$\dfrac{(2l+1)(2j+1)R^2(j)}{4jl(l+1)(j+1)}$	$\dfrac{(2j+1)P(j)Q(j)}{4j(j+1)l}$
$j \to j - 1$	$\dfrac{Q(j)Q(j-1)}{4jl}$	$\dfrac{(2l+1)P(j)Q(j-1)}{4jl(l+1)}$	$\dfrac{P(j)P(j-1)}{4jl}$

$$\Delta j = \begin{cases} +1. \quad I_{+1} = g_{j-1}A(j-1, l; j, l \pm 1) = \dfrac{cQ(j)Q(j-1)}{4jl}, \\[2mm] 0. \quad I_0 = g_j A(j, l; j, l \pm 1) = \dfrac{c(2j+1)P(j)Q(j)}{4j(j+1)l}, \\[2mm] -1. \quad L_1 = g_j A(j, l; j-1, l \pm 1) = \dfrac{cP(j)P(j-1)}{4jl} \end{cases} \tag{15}$$

$\Delta l = 0:$

$$\Delta j = \begin{cases} +1. \quad I_{+1} = g_{j-1}A(j-1, l; j, l) = \dfrac{c(2l+1)P(j)Q(j-1)}{(l+1) \cdot 4jl} \\[2mm] 0. \quad I_0 = g_j A(j, l; j, l) = \dfrac{c(2l+1)(2j+1)R^2(j)}{4l(l+1)j(j+1)}. \\[2mm] -1. \quad L_1 = g_j A(j, l; j-1, l) = \dfrac{c(2l+1)P(j)Q(j-1)}{(l+1) \cdot 4jl} \end{cases}$$

A considerable amount of material is now available for testing these formulas. Frerichs[1] has made measurements on multiplets of Ca, Cr, and Fe; van Milaan[2] has studied a number of multiplets of elements in the transition region of the first long period, and G. R. Harrison[3]

[1] *Z. Physik*, **31**, 305 (1925); *Ann. Physik*, **81**, 807 (1926).
[2] *Z. Physik*, **34**, 921 (1925); and **38**, 427 (1926); dissertation, Utrecht, 1926.
[3] *J. O. S. A.* and *R. S. I.*, **17**, 389 (1928).

has measured more than thirty multiplets of TiI and TiII. All these authors demonstrated that the theoretical intensity ratios cannot usually be obtained unless precautions are taken to subordinate the effects of self-reversal. Harrison applied corrections to his data to eliminate intensity reductions due to this cause. His correction is based on the assumption that the amount of self-reversal in a line belonging to a narrow multiplet is proportional to its intensity. To give a better idea of the type of data obtained we reproduce the measurements of Frerichs for a quintet DD' multiplet of chromium, in Table 2. The wave length of each line is given in the body of the table with the calculated intensity below, as well as the average measured intensity, in parentheses. The intensity of the strongest line is arbitrarily set equal to 100.

TABLE 2

j		$^5D'$				
		4	3	2	1	0
^5D	4	3,919.3 100(100)	3,941.6 20.0(24.5)			
	3	3,886.9 20.0(23)	3,908.9 46.0(46)	3,928.8 26.7(32)		
	2		3,883.4 26.7(36.5)	3,903.1 16.7 (about 19.5)	3,921.2 23.3(21)	
	1			3,885.4 23.3(<27)	3,903.3 3.3 (about 3)	3,916.4 13.3(13.7)
	0				3,894.2 13.3(13.7)	

The line 3,885.4 is assigned the value < 27, because a faint line is superposed on it; in the case of 3,903.1 and 3,903.3, only the sum of their intensities was measured. As far as agreement with the formulas is concerned, this multiplet is neither very bad nor very good. Much closer agreements are encountered in the data of Harrison. The extent to which the intensity formulas are verified may be judged from the following summary given by Harrison:

Of all the multiplets measured in TiI, 58 per cent were found to obey the intensity formulas to well within 5 per cent, and evidence was obtained in favorable cases which indicated that exact agreement could be expected when line separations were small. In TiII, 62 per cent of the multiplets measured were normal. In TiI, of the 42 per cent abnormal multiplets, 71 per cent of the lines were normal, while 16 per cent were abnormally weak and 13 per cent abnormally strong. For the ionized atom, of the 38 per cent abnormal multiplets, 61 per cent of the lines were normal, while 21 per cent were abnormally weak, and 18 per cent abnormally strong.   Of all the lines measured, 86 per cent appeared to obey the intensity formulas, while 7.6 per cent were too weak and 6.4 per cent were too strong.

Harrison further states that in agreement with the results of Frerichs for selected multiplets of elements in the iron group, no certain correlation was found in titanium between departure from the intensity formulas and from Landé's interval rule.   When intercombination lines occur, the intensity rules considered in this section must be modified, and some departures from the intensity formulas can be explained on this basis. Another cause of departure, encountered in the case of wide multiplets, is the insufficiency of the ν^4 correction.   While Ornstein, Eymers, and Coelingh[1] found that this correction brings the sharp and subordinate series lines of the barium spark spectrum into exact agreement with the intensity formulas, it is far from valid for the sharp series resonance lines of thallium, at 5,350 and 3,776 Å., according to measurements of Ornstein and H. C. Burger.[2]   In still other cases, neither of these causes can be invoked, and it must be concluded that the intensity formulas are not suitable to describe the facts.

4. INTENSITY RATIOS OF RELATED MULTIPLETS; INTERCOMBINATION LINES

Consider all the lines which are emitted in a transition from n', l' to n'', l''.   These lines belong to systems of different multiplicities. They form several ordinary multiplets, and include a number of inter-combinations as well.   We shall refer to such an aggregate of lines as a group of related multiplets.   An extension of the sum rule which enables us to obtain a certain amount of information about the relative intensities of lines in related multiplets was proposed by Ornstein and H. C. Burger.[3] By way of example, we consider a group of multiplets of ionized oxygen studied by van Wijk.[4]   The initial states are ^2P and ^4P and the final states are of the same character.   In Table 3, we give the wave lengths of all the lines which arise from the combinations of these levels, and which do not violate the selection principles.   The wave lengths are accompanied by arbitrary symbols, used by van Wijk to identify the lines.   In such an array, according to Ornstein and Burger, *after applying the ν^4 correction the sum of the intensities of all lines arising from a given initial level is proportional to its weight, and the sum of the intensities of all lines involving a given final level is proportional to its weight.*   In the example under consideration, there are no intercombination lines,

[1] *Z. Physik*, **40**, 403 (1927).

[2] Reported by ORNSTEIN, *Physik, Z.*, **28**, 688 (1927).

[3] *Z. Physik*, **40**, 403 (1926).

[4] *Z. Physik*, **47**, 622 (1928).

TABLE 3

		Final Levels			
		$^2P_{\frac{1}{2}}$	$^2P_{\frac{3}{2}}$	$^4P_{\frac{1}{2}}$	$^4P_{\frac{3}{2}}$	$^4P_{\frac{5}{2}}$

Initial levels		$^2P_{\frac{1}{2}}$	$^2P_{\frac{3}{2}}$	$^4P_{\frac{1}{2}}$	$^4P_{\frac{3}{2}}$	$^4P_{\frac{5}{2}}$
	$^2P_{\frac{1}{2}}$	3,954, d_1	3,983, d_2			
	$^2P_{\frac{3}{2}}$	3,945, d_3	3,973, d_4			
	$^4P_{\frac{1}{2}}$			4,326, q_1	4,346, q_2	
	$^4P_{\frac{3}{2}}$			4,317, q_3	4,337, q_4	4,367, q_5
	$^4P_{\frac{5}{2}}$				4,320, q_6	4,349, q_7

and this rule reduces to a statement of the sum rules for the doublet multiplet and the quartet multiplet, separately, together with additional relations which predict the relative intensities of the two multiplets. That is, the sum of the intensities in the first two columns, forming the doublet multiplet, should be proportional to the sum of the weights of $^2P_{\frac{1}{2}}$, and $^2P_{\frac{3}{2}}$, while the sum of the intensities of lines in the quartet multiplet should be proportional to the sum of the weights of $^4P_{\frac{1}{2}}$, $^4P_{\frac{3}{2}}$, and $^4P_{\frac{5}{2}}$. As a matter of fact, the intensity rules of Sec. 3 are fairly well obeyed within each multiplet, and the ratio of the total intensities of the multiplets, after applying the ν^4 correction, was found to be 1.9 when the source was at 50 cm. pressure, and 2.1 when it was at 18 cm. The situation is more complicated when the intensity of the intercombination lines is appreciable, for in this case the intensity rules of Sec. 3 cannot be expected to hold within the individual multiplets. Ornstein and Burger have studied the diffuse series of mercury, where the intercombination lines occur with considerable intensity. Application of the extended sum rule to the group of four lines near 3,650 (2^3P-3^3D and 2^3P-3^1D) gave a result in excellent agreement with experiment. However, in the case of certain helium lines, definite failure of the rule was observed. Pauli[1] suggested on theoretical grounds that for triplet and singlet terms the ratio of intercombination lines to ordinary lines should be proportional to $(\delta\nu/\Delta\nu)^2$, where $\delta\nu$ is the total separation of the outside terms of the triplet, and $\Delta\nu$ is the distance of the singlet term from the center of gravity of the triplet. This rule was tested by Ornstein and Burger for the first four diffuse series groups of mercury, with excellent results. However, the rule was not verified in another case which they studied.

We now consider another type of generalization of the intensity rules. Kronig[2] has given formulas for the relative intensities of the three multiplets emitted in the transitions l to $l + 1$, l to l, and l to $l - 1$,

[1] Geiger-Scheel Handbuch der Physik, Vol. 23, p. 255.

[2] Z. Physik, **33**, 261 (1925).

when the azimuthal number of only one electron undergoes a change, the quantum numbers of the others being unaltered. The formulas are complicated and we shall not reproduce them here. In general, they predict that the intensities of multiplets belonging to a triad should be in the ratios of small integers. Harrison[1] has tested these formulas by measuring the relative intensities of titanium multiplets. By way of example, we consider a triad of multiplets arising in transitions from the configuration $3d^34p$ to the configuration $3d^34s$, and designated by Harrison as Nos. 128, 172, and 209. They are of the types $^5F\text{-}^5G$, $^5F\text{-}^5F'$, and $^5F\text{-}^5D$. The wave-number separations are so large that we must consider not only the ν^4 correction but also the Boltzmann factor, $e^{-h\nu/kT}$, of equation (5), in order to arrive at the squared amplitudes which occur in the intensity formulas. The effective temperature of the source must be known in order to obtain the Boltzmann factor. Harrison found that a temperature of about 10,000°K. gave the best agreement between theory and experiment for a number of multiplets. Assuming this value of the temperature, the relative squared amplitudes for the three multiplets under consideration were found to be

$$89, 70, \text{ and } 48$$

while the values required by Kronig's formulas are,

$$90, 70, \text{ and } 50.$$

Indeed, these formulas are confirmed, at least qualitatively, in six of the eight cases studied in which they apply, regardless of the assumed temperature of the source.

5. INTENSITIES OF ZEEMAN-EFFECT COMPONENTS

The classical theory of intensities in the Zeeman effect, based on the correspondence principle, is very similar to that in Sec. 3. We consider an orbit which precesses around the lines of force with the velocity of the Larmor precession, and find the amplitudes of the various harmonics in the motion. The intensities of the transitions corresponding to these harmonics are indicated in the table, in which θ is the angle between the lines of force and the normal to the orbit.

$\Delta j =$	$+1$	0	-1
$\Delta m = +1$	$\frac{1}{4}(1 + \cos\theta)^2$	$\frac{1}{2}\sin^2\theta$	$\frac{1}{4}(1 - \cos\theta)^2$
0	$\frac{1}{2}\sin^2\theta$	$\cos^2\theta$	$\frac{1}{2}\sin^2\theta$
-1	$\frac{1}{4}(1 - \cos\theta)^2$	$\frac{1}{2}\sin^2\theta$	$\frac{1}{4}(1 + \cos\theta)^2$ (16)

[1] *J. O. S. A.* and *R. S. I.*, **18**, 287 (1929).

If we write $\cos \theta = m/j$, where m is the magnetic quantum number for the initial state, these formulas give us intensity values which should be a rough measure of the actual intensities. Ornstein and Burger[1] proposed the following sum rule for the transition probabilities in the Zeeman effect. *Fixing our attention on a single multiplet line for which the initial inner quantum number is j, we consider all the transitions from a magnetic energy level with quantum number m. The sum of the probabilities for all these transitions is the same for all choices of m; and, similarly, the sum of the probabilities of all transitions ending on a magnetic level m, j, is the same for all choices of m.* That is,

$$A(m, j; m + 1, j') + A(m, j; m, j') + A(m, j; m - 1, j') = C(j, j'), \quad (17)$$

$$A(m + 1, j; m, j') + A(m, j; m, j') + A(m - 1, j; m, j') = D(j, j'). \quad (18)$$

In these equations $C(j, j')$, and $D(j, j')$ are independent of m, and j' can take any one of the values $j + 1$, j, or $j - 1$. We can show by summing over all values of m that

$$(2j + 1)C(j', j) = (2j' + 1)D(j, j'). \quad (19)$$

Hönl,[2] and Kronig and Goudsmit[3] solved the problem of obtaining exact expressions for the Zeeman-effect intensities by utilizing the following considerations. The expressions (16) suggest that the correct expressions should be quadratic functions of m. If this is assumed and if it is also required that the sum rule shall be valid and the Zeeman pattern as a whole shall be unpolarized, we have just enough equations to determine the intensity formulas. The results are as follows:

$\Delta j = +1$:

$$\left. \begin{array}{l} A(m, j; m + 1, j + 1) = \dfrac{C(j, j + 1)}{2(j + 1)(2j + 3)}(j + m + 2)(j + m + 1), \\[2mm] A(m, j; m, j + 1) = \dfrac{C(j, j + 1)}{(j + 1)(2j + 3)}((j + 1)^2 - m^2), \\[2mm] A(m, j; m - 1, j + 1) = \dfrac{C(j, j + 1)}{2(j + 1)(2j + 3)}(j - m + 2)(j - m + 1). \end{array} \right\} \quad (20)$$

$\Delta j = 0$:

$$\left. \begin{array}{l} A(m, j; m + 1, j) = \dfrac{C(j, j)}{2j(j + 1)}(j - m)(j + m + 1), \\[2mm] A(m, j; m, j) = \dfrac{C(j, j)}{j(j + 1)}m^2, \\[2mm] A(m, j; m - 1, j) = \dfrac{C(j, j)}{2j(j + 1)}(j + m)(j - m + 1). \end{array} \right\} \quad (21)$$

[1] *Z. Physik*, **29**, 241 (1924).

[2] *Z. Physik*, **31**, 340 (1925).

[3] *Naturwis.*, **13**, 90 (1925); also Kronig, *Z. Physik*, **31**, 885 (1925).

$\Delta j = -1$:

$$A(m, j; m + 1, j - 1) = \frac{C(j, j - 1)}{2j(2j - 1)}(j - m)(j - m + 1)$$

$$A(m, j; m, j - 1) = \frac{C(j, j - 1)}{j(2j - 1)}(j^2 - m^2)$$

$$A(m, j; m - 1, j - 1) = \frac{C(j, j - 1)}{2j(2j - 1)}(j + m)(j + m - 1). \tag{22}$$

The dependence of these formulas on m has been verified by Heisenberg and Jordan[1] using matrix methods. The details of the computation will not be given here, since they have been conveniently summarized by Birtwistle.[2] The formulas have now been well confirmed for a number of lines in low fields. Ornstein, Burger, and van Geel[3] studied the first sharp triplet of zinc, and van Geel[4] extended the observations to systems of other multiplicities. His results for the triplet $2^3P - 2^3S$ of magnesium are typical of the type of agreement which is obtained. The theoretical and measured intensities for the components of these three lines are given in the following list. Parallel components are enclosed in parentheses; the calculated intensity is written above the experimental value in each case. The results for the three lines are expressed on the same scale and the total intensities of the lines are in the ratios required by the sum rule.

5,167 Å.:
    2   (4)   2
    23   (46)   23

5,172 Å.:
    3   3   (6)   (6)   3   3
    38   34   (75)   (71)   38   33

5,183 Å.:
    1   3   6   (6)   (8)   (6)   6   3   1
    ?   37   76   (75)   (100)   (72)   76   37   ?

Van Geel[5] has found that the intensity formulas hold true for the Zeeman effect of the intercombination line $2^3P_2 - 3^1D_2$ of mercury, at 3,663.28 Å. Further he has studied the intensities in the partial Paschen-Back effect of the first diffuse triplet of magnesium,[6] comparing the results with a theory worked out by Kramers, and independently by Miss Mensing.[7]

6. INTENSITIES IN THE SPECTRUM OF HYDROGEN

The data presented up to this point are not suited for a test of the new mechanics, for deviations from the formulas might be blamed on the insufficiency of the model. A definite test can be made by studying intensity relations in the spectra of hydrogenic atoms.

[1] Z. Physik, **37**, 263 (1926).
[2] "The New Quantum Mechanics," Chap. XV.
[3] Z. Physik, **32**, 681 (1925).
[4] Z. Physik, **33**, 836 (1925).
[5] Z. Physik, **47**, 615 (1928).
[6] Z. Physik, **39**, 877 (1926).
[7] Z. Physik, **39**, 24 (1926).

Numerous investigations of the Zeeman effect of hydrogen have shown that under suitable conditions of excitation the normal triplet is unpolarized and the two perpendicular components are of approximately equal intensities. Since this result is predicted by the classical theory, the correspondence principle, and the new mechanics as well, it is not adapted for distinguishing between these theories. However, the Stark-effect intensities are well suited for this purpose. The first estimates of intensities in the hydrogen Stark-effect patterns were made by Stark himself.[1] Kramers[2] compared these estimates with values calculated by the correspondence principle, obtaining a fair agreement, in general, although there were some striking discrepancies. The Stark-effect intensities of the first four Balmer lines have been computed on the new mechanics by Schrödinger[3] and by Epstein,[4] with results which are not in agreement. The method used by both these authors is to calculate the components of the polarization matrix in the way explained in Chap. XV, Sec. **17**. The mathematical details of the two treatments are quite different. Schrödinger uses the wave functions given in equation (50) of Chap. XVI, while Epstein uses expressions involving hypergeometric functions. In both cases, the unperturbed wave functions are employed. It is stated by Sommerfeld[5] that W. Zimmermann[6] has reconsidered the problem, using wave functions which contain the first power of the field strength. His computations indicate a slight asymmetry of the intensity pattern, but this is too small to be observed at the field strengths used in the laboratory; aside from this, Zimmermann's results agree with those of Schrödinger. Tests of the theoretical intensities have been made by Foster and Chalk[7] and by Mark and Wierl.[8] Foster and Chalk used the Lo Surdo method while Mark and Wierl employed the light from a beam of canal rays, subjected to strong fields in the space behind the cathode of a discharge tube. The auxiliary field could be applied either parallel or perpendicular to the direction of the beam. By filling the space behind the cathode with nitrogen at low pressure, Mark and Wierl obtained patterns due only to the atoms in the canal-ray beam, while light coming from atoms at rest was obtained by filling this space with hydrogen and using nitrogen canal rays. Most of Foster's results are in strikingly good agreement with those of Schrödinger. With a few exceptions the same is true of the results obtained by Mark and Wierl when studying the parallel com-

[1] *Ann. Physik*, **48**, 193 (1915).
[2] *Det Kgl. Danske Vidensk. Selsk. Skr.*, **3**, 287 (1919).
[3] *Ann. Physik*, **80**, 437 (1926).
[4] *Phys. Rev.*, **28**, 695 (1926).
[5] "Wellenmechanische Ergänzungsband," p. 193.
[6] Unpublished.
[7] *Proc. Roy. Soc.*, **123**, 108 (1929).
[8] *Naturwissenschaften* **16**, 725 (1928); *Z. Physik*, **53**, 526 (1929).

ponents of Hα, Hβ, and Hγ from moving atoms, with the field perpendicular to the direction of motion. However, they showed conclusively that in the type of tube which they employed, the theory does not apply to the perpendicular components, as obtained from moving atoms which are excited by collisions, from resting atoms, or from moving atoms which are emitting spontaneously in a high vacuum (Abkling-leuchten). This is well shown by the parallel components of Hβ, which lie at eight and ten times the quantum unit of frequency difference (Chap. V, Sec. **13**). Schrödinger's value for the ratio of their intensities is 1.06, while Foster and Chalk obtain 1.04. Mark and Wierl get 1.10 for the light emitted by moving atoms due to collisions, with the field perpendicular to the beam, and 0.85 for the light from atoms at rest. They suggest that some of these discrepancies may be due to the Stark-Lunelund effect, that is, the polarization of the light emitted by a beam of moving atoms in the absence of a field. It is perhaps natural to expect that the theoretical ratios will be more closely approximated under the conditions encountered in the discharge itself than in a beam of canal rays. As emphasized earlier in this chapter, the populations of the upper states will be in the ratios of their statistical weights only if the excitation is sufficiently chaotic. Further experiments will be required to elucidate the matter.

It is of interest to consider the theoretical decrease of intensity along the spectral series of hydrogen. The relative intensities of the first four Balmer lines were obtained by Schrödinger, by summing the intensities of the Stark-effect components. He also gives explicit formulas for the intensities of the Lyman and the Balmer series, communicated to him by Pauli. They are as follows, n being the total quantum number for the initial orbit:

$$\text{Lyman series: } I(n, 1) = \frac{2^7(n-1)^{2n-1}}{n(n+1)^{2n+1}} \tag{23}$$

$$\text{Balmer series: } I(n, 2) = \frac{2^7(n-2)^{2n-3}}{n(n+2)^{2n+3}}(15n^4 - 32n^2 + 16). \tag{24}$$

We shall not give the derivation, as it is carried through by Sommerfeld.[1] The results have been extended to the Paschen series by Sugiura.[2] It is well known that the relative intensities of the Balmer lines are very sensitive to changes in the source, and data obtained in the laboratory are not likely to check the computed intensities, except by accident. It would seem that measurements on stellar spectra would afford the best opportunity for a decisive test. Bongers[3] has measured the Balmer series and found that his results are represented by

$$\frac{I}{\nu^4} = \frac{c(n - n_0)^3}{n^{12}}, \tag{25}$$

---

[1] Wellenmechanische Ergänzungsband, p. 94.

[2] *Jour. de Phys.* (6), **8**, 113 (1927); *Z. Physik*, **44**, 190 (1927).

[3] Dissertation, Utrecht, (1927).

where n and n_0 are the quantum numbers of the initial and final states, respectively. This is in striking contradiction to the $1/n^3$ relation required by equation (24) for large values of n.

In order to obtain approximate expressions for the intensity distribution in the series of the alkali atoms, one may evaluate the intensities for the various fine structure components of hydrogen. These partial series have been calculated by Kupper,[1] the results being in good agreement with data of Trumpy.[2] However, Miss Bleeker[3] has measured the subordinate series of K, Rb, and Cs, and has found it possible to represent her results by the formula

$$I = \frac{c(n - n_0)^4}{n^{12}}. \tag{26}$$

Her formula is also well obeyed by several subordinate series of mercury.

There are two factors, the temperature and density, which may ordinarily be neglected in considering the intensities of the higher series members, but which are of importance in considering the conditions in the stars. Under equilibrium conditions the number of hydrogen atoms in the states of total quantum number n is

$$N_n \propto 2n^2 \exp\left[\frac{Rhc}{kT}\left(\frac{1}{n^2} - 1\right)\right], \tag{27}$$

where $2n^2$ is the a priori probability of these states and the exponential is the Boltzmann factor. Since $2n^2$ approaches ∞ as n becomes large and the exponential factor remains finite, the number of atoms in the higher quantum states becomes very large and in fact all the atoms should be in the infinite quantum state. Urey[4] and Fermi[5] suggested that a certain amount of space is excluded due to the "volume" occupied by the atoms and that this volume increases with the quantum number in such a way that the number of atoms in the nth state approaches zero as n becomes infinitely large. The volume of an atom is not easily defined or approximated, but this effect is certainly present. Density of the gas does not explain the deviation of Bonger's formula from the theoretical formula and it appears that this effect can only be of importance in stellar spectra.[6]

7. INTENSITIES OF X-RAY EMISSION LINES

The intensities of X-ray lines emitted by a solid target bombarded by electrons of a given energy depend on many factors beside the proba-

[1] *Ann. Physik*, **86**, 511 (1928).
[2] *Z. Physik*, **42**, 327 and **44**, 575 (1927).
[3] *Z. Phys. Chem.*, **120**, 63 (1926).
[4] *Astrophys. J.*, **49**, 1 (1924).
[5] *Z. Physik*, **26**, 54 (1924).
[6] For an elegant treatment of this subject see Fowler, "Statistical Mechanics," Chap. 14. Cambridge Press (1929).

bilities of transition and it is often very difficult to correct for these extraneous factors in order to estimate the probabilities as calculated from theory. Both the absolute and relative intensities change with the voltage on the X-ray tube; absorption in the target is especially important for the longer wave lengths; and in many cases it is difficult to separate all the lines of a multiplet so that the intensities can be estimated separately. Considering the many difficulties in interpreting the experimental results, the agreement with the theory for the intensity of multiplets presented in the preceding sections is as close as could be expected in some cases, but in others there appears to be definite disagreement between theory and experiment. We shall discuss the relative intensities of lines of the same multiplet for the most part.

Sommerfeld[1] pointed out the essential similarity of the X-ray doublets and the optical doublets and showed that the experimental facts then available were in approximate agreement with the rules of Dorgelo and Burger and in particular that the intensities of the $K\alpha_1$ and $K\alpha_2$ lines were approximately in the ratio of $2:1$ and that the $L\alpha_1$ and $L\alpha_2$ lines had approximately the relative intensities $9:1$ as required by these rules. Duane and Siegbahn[2] and their coworkers early investigated relative intensities in the K-series lines. The $K\alpha_1$ and $K\alpha_2$ and the $K\beta_1$ and $K\beta_3$ lines are two doublets of the $^2P - {}^2S$ type and in accordance with the theory of Secs. 2 and 3 should have relative intensities of $2:1$ in both cases. Duane and Stenström found a ratio of $2:1$ for the $K\alpha_1$ and $K\alpha_2$ lines of tungsten and Duane and Patterson a ratio of $1.93:1$ for these lines of molybdenum, while Allison and Armstrong secured a ratio of $2.1:1$ in the fourth order and $2:1$ in the fifth order for the $K\beta_1$ and $K\beta_2$ lines of molybdenum. Siegbahn and Za'ček secured for the intensity ratios of the $K\alpha_1$ and $K\alpha_2$ lines of Cu, Zn, and Fe, $100:51.2$, $100:50$, and $100:49.9$, respectively. These doublets are emitted in transitions from the same excited level, namely the K level, to the L_{II} and L_{III}, or the M_{II} and M_{III}, so that the relative intensities should measure the relative values of the A_{nm} coefficients for these transitions. Moreover, the coefficient of absorption of the target for these wave lengths will be small, since they lie on the long wave-length side of the K-absorption limit and far to the short wave-length side of the L-absorption limits. This makes the agreement with theory especially satisfactory.

The most complete investigations of intensities of the L-series lines are those of Allison and Armstrong,[3] Allison[4] and Jönsson,[5] who have

[1] *Ann. Physik,* **76,** 284 (1925).

[2] See Lindh, *Phys. Zeit.,* **28,** 95 (1927) for detailed references to the earlier literature.

[3] *Phys. Rev.,* **26,** 714 (1925).

[4] *Phys. Rev.,* **30,** 245 (1927); **32,** 1 (1928).

[5] *Z. Physik,* **46,** 383 (1927).

investigated lines of tungsten, thorium, uranium, silver, palladium, rhodium, molybdenum, and a few other elements. The results of these measurements for a number of X-ray multiplets are given in the following table:

Lines	$\gamma_3:\gamma_2$	$\beta_3:\beta_4$	$\gamma_5:\beta_6$	$\eta:l$	$\beta_1:\alpha_1:\alpha_2$
Transitions	$L_I \to N_{II,III}$	$L_I \to M_{II,III}$	$L_{II,III} \to N_I$	$L_{II,III} \to M_I$	$L_{II,III} \to M_{IV,V}$
Relative intensity, theory:...	100:50	100:50	50:100	50:100	56:100:11
Relative intensity, observed:					
Ag[1]	....	100:61	......	55:100	59:100:12
Pd[1]	......	100:64	......	60:100	59:100:12
Rh[1]	......	100:65	......	......	61:100:13
Mo[1]	......	100:70	......	......	62:100:13
W[1]	100:74	100:60	36:100	46:100	48:100:11
Th[2]	......	......	(0:1.4)	50:100	62:100:12
U[2]	100:107	100:98	(0:1.6)	46:100	49:100:11

[1] JÖNSSON, loc. cit.; ALLISON and ARMSTRONG'S data on tungsten are in approximate agreement with those of Jönsson.
[2] ALLISON, loc. cit.

These examples show the character of the agreement between theory and experiment; in the case of the β_1, α_1, and α_2 lines which form a $^2P \to {}^2D$ triplet, the agreement is very satisfactory; on the other hand, the experimental and theoretical intensity ratios of the γ_3 and γ_2, and of the β_3 and β_4 lines do not agree nearly so well; there is a consistent trend toward greater intensity of the weaker component until in U the theoretically weaker line has actually become the stronger of the two.

Wentzel[1] has calculated the relative intensities of the different X-ray lines with different values of n and l for the initial and final states using quantum mechanics. Allison and Jönsson have found only approximate agreement between their data and the theoretical predictions.

PART II. INTENSITIES IN BAND SPECTRA

8. THE SUM RULE APPLIED TO BAND SPECTRA

In the case of atomic spectra it was possible to neglect the exponential Boltzmann factor in considering intensities of lines, because under the usual conditions of excitation the populations of atoms in different states are proportional to the quantum weight. In the case of band spectra this is not true and the exponential factor of equation (5) must be retained. For this reason the sum rule of Burger and Dorgelo as stated in Sec. 2 does not apply to the relative intensities of band-spectrum lines. The intensity of a band line is proportional to the Einstein probability constant and the number of molecules in the initial state

$$I \propto -\frac{dE}{dt} = h\nu(nm)A_{nm}g_n \exp\left(-\frac{E_n}{kT}\right).\tag{28}$$

[1] Naturwiss., 14, 621 (1926).

It is usual to call $A_{nm}g_n$ the intensity factor, and using the customary symbols we shall write it $A(j', j'')(2j' + 1)$ for the transition from the j' to the j'' state, since $2j' + 1$ is the weight of the j' rotational state. The question arises as to whether an "effective temperature" can be assigned to a discharge which is not in equilibrium and whose temperature is therefore not defined. This will be discussed in Sec. **11**, where it is shown that experimental data are consistent with the inclusion of the exponential factor in equation (28).

The sum rule as applied to band spectra is:

The sum of the intensity factors, $A(j', j'')(2j' + 1)$, over all values of j'' permitted by the selection rules with j' constant, is proportional to the quantum weight of the j' state and the sum of these factors over all permitted values of j' holding j'' constant is proportional to the weight of the j'' state. This statement is evidently equivalent to that of Sec. **2**.

Fowler[1] and Dieke[2] first applied these rules to molecular spectra. Their application can be illustrated by the

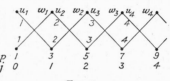

Fig. 1.

intensities of a $^1\Sigma \rightarrow {}^1\Sigma$ band. We represent $A(j', j'')(2j' + 1)$ for the lines of the P branch by $u_1, u_2, \ldots u_j \ldots$ and for those of the R branch by $w_1, w_2 \ldots w_j \ldots$ The transitions are shown in the diagram, Fig. 1. Then the sum rule requires that

$$u_1 = g_0 c, \; w_1 + u_2 = g_1 c, \; w_2 + u_3 = g_2 c, \; \cdots,$$
$$w_1 = g_0 c, \; u_1 + w_2 = g_1 c, \; u_2 + w_3 = g_2 c, \; \cdots,$$

or

$$u_1 = w_1 = g_0 c, \; u_2 = w_2 = (g_1 - g_0)c, \; \cdots.$$

Since $g_j = 2j + 1$, we have

$$u_1 = w_1 = c, \; u_2 = w_2 = 2c, \; \cdots;$$

then

$$(2j + 1)A(j, j - 1) = cj \text{ and } (2j - 1)A(j - 1, j) = cj, \qquad (29)$$

where j is the larger of j' and j'' in all cases.

This makes the lines symmetrically placed relative to the missing line equal in intensity except for the exponential factor of equation (28). This factor gives an R-branch line a slightly greater intensity in absorption and less intensity in emission than the P-branch line of the same running number; this can be easily seen by considering the diagram and the relative values of the energies of the initial states for the two lines in the cases of absorption and emission, respectively. The constant c is $P_0{}^2(2\pi\nu)^4/3c^3h\nu$, where P_0 is the electric moment due to the changes in electronic or vibrational quantum numbers in the case of electronic

[1] *Phil. Mag.*, **49**, 1272 (1925).

[2] *Z. Physik*, **33**, 161 (1925).

or vibration rotation bands or to a permanent electric moment of the molecule in the case of pure rotation bands.

9. THE INTENSITY FACTORS FOR CASE a MOLECULES[1]

Just as in the case of complex atomic multiplets the sum rule does not suffice to fix the relative intensities, it also cannot fix the relative intensities in more complex bands than those of the $^1\Sigma - {}^1\Sigma$ type. It is necessary to derive these relative intensities from a more extensive theory of the emitting molecule. The model which we use is the customary gyroscopic model having, in general, a resultant angular momentum about the line of nuclei equal to $\iota(= \lambda + \sigma)$ in quantum units. The relative intensities for case a were derived by London and Hönl[2] using a modification of the method of Sommerfeld and Hönl described in Sec. **3**. Since these relative intensities have been derived by applying matrix and wave mechanics to the heavy symmetric top as described in Chap. XIX, Sec. **5**, we shall not give the older calculations. To write down the relative intensities for the molecules of the case a type, it is only necessary to note that a diatomic molecule is a symmetric top with a small moment of inertia about the figure axis. The dependence of the wave function on θ, φ, and χ will be the same whether they fix the position of the rotating nuclei in the first case or the rotating electrons in the second, though the dependence of the energy on λ in the one case and ι in the other is quite different. The ι is equal to the sum of λ and σ; it appears from experimental data that $\Delta\iota = \Delta\lambda$, that is, σ does not reverse its direction relative to λ in a permitted transition, and that it is ι rather than λ which must be used in equation (66) of Chap. XIX to secure the proper A's.

The intensity factors in the symbols appropriate to this problem are:

$g_{j'}A(\iota', j'; \iota'', j'')$	$j' - j''$	$\iota' - \iota''$
$\dfrac{c2(2j + 1)\iota^2}{j(j + 1)}$	0	0
$\dfrac{c2(j^2 - \iota^2)}{j}$	± 1	0
$\dfrac{c(2j + 1)(j + \iota)(j - \iota + 1)}{j(j + 1)}$	0	± 1
$\dfrac{c(j + \iota)(j + \iota - 1)}{j}$	± 1	± 1
$\dfrac{c(j - \iota)(j - \iota + 1)}{j}$	∓ 1	± 1 (30)

where the j and ι occurring in these formulas are the larger of the initial and final values of these quantum numbers. The reader can easily verify

---

[1] See Chap. XII, Sec. **15** and Fig. 19 for the model interpretation of this case.

[2] Z. Physik, **33**, 803 (1925).

the fact that these intensity factors are in agreement with the sum rule of Sec. **8**; this is also evident in the case of the special examples given below.

To illustrate the theoretical intensities expected for this type of molecule, we shall use transitions of the $^1\Pi \to {}^1\Sigma$ and $^2\Pi \to {}^2\Pi$ types; the intensity factors are given in the following tables for these two cases:

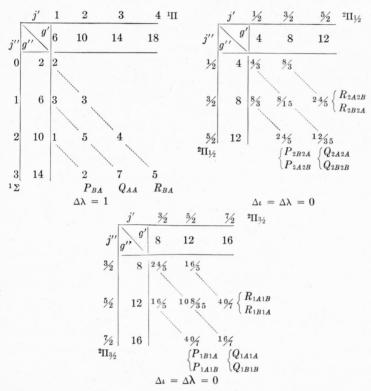

The weights are doubled ($g_j = 2(2j + 1)$) in this table and the intensity factors, equations (30), are so normalized that the sum rule gives the doubled quantum weight. We do this because corresponding to each value of j there are two states, if $\lambda \neq 0$, one positive and one negative, in the sense of Chap. XIX, Sec. **9**, *i.e.*, A and B states each of which has a weight of $2j + 1$. The branches, in the symbols used in Chap. XII, are given at the ends of the diagonals. In the case of the $^1\Pi \to {}^1\Sigma$ transition, the Q branch gains in intensity relative to the P and R branches as j increases, while the reverse is true in the case of the $^2\Pi \to {}^2\Pi$ transitions. This decrease in intensity of the Q branches in the latter case is very rapid. These Q branches are observed in the NO bands of Fig. 1, Chap. XII which are of this type, but decrease rapidly in intensity as j increases, in agreement with theory.

10. THE INTENSITY FACTORS FOR CASE b MOLECULES

The arguments used in deriving the intensity factors for these molecules can best be understood by considering the models of Chap. XII, Sec. **15**, and Fig. 19. Disregarding the s of case b for the moment, it is seen that the precession of ι about j in case a is entirely similar to the precession of λ about k in case b. Thus the amplitudes of the electric moment in case b, if k did not precess about j, should be the same as those of case a and are given by equation (30) with k and λ replacing j and ι, respectively. Since k precesses only very slowly about j, these amplitudes will not be appreciably changed by this precession.

On the other hand, the precession of k and s about j is entirely similar to the precession of l and s about j in atoms; k is the resultant of all "orbital" angular momenta of electrons and nuclei just as l is a similar resultant in the atomic case and s has the same significance in both. Thus, the relative intensities of all lines emitted for a certain value of Δk and different values of Δj are given by equations (15) for the atomic case, if we replace l by k in those formulas. Therefore, in order to secure the relative intensities for a given value of Δk, it is only necessary to multiply the appropriate factor of equations (30), with k and λ replacing j and ι in these formulas, by the appropriate factor of equations (15), with k replacing l of those formulas. The formulas so secured must be further multiplied by a normalizing factor. The loosely coupled s vector cannot change the total intensities for a given Δk appreciably. Therefore, the normalizing factor is secured by making the sum of all the intensities for a given Δk over all permitted values of Δj equal to the intensity required by the formulas for case a with k and λ replacing j and ι; or, what is the same thing, we require that the sum of the factors of equation (15) for a given Δk over all possible values of Δj multiplied by the normalizing factor shall equal 1. These normalizing factors have been secured by Mulliken[1] for doublet systems, i.e., $s = \frac{1}{2}$, and are:

$$\frac{1}{4k^2 - 1}, \text{ if } \Delta k = \pm 1,$$

and

$$\frac{1}{(2k + 1)^2}, \text{ if } \Delta k = 0. \tag{31}$$

To secure the correct intensity factor for any transition we have only to multiply the three appropriate factors from equations (15), (30), and (31).

Example.—We ask for the intensity factor for a $^PQ_{12}$ branch of a $^2\Pi \rightarrow {}^2\Sigma$ band for which $\Delta j = 0$, $\Delta k = -1$, and $\Delta \lambda = 1$. For this branch $j' = k' + \frac{1}{2}$, $j'' = k'' - \frac{1}{2}$ and, since $j' = j''$, $k'' = k' + 1$, and the k appearing in the formulas is equal to k''; therefore, we must substitute $j = k - \frac{1}{2}$ in the formulas. We multiply the first

[1] *Phys. Rev.*, **30**, 138 and 785 (1927).

factor of equation (31) by $(k - \lambda)(k - \lambda + 1)/k$, secured from equation (30) by substituting k and λ for j and ι, and by $(2j + 1)P(j)Q(j)/4j(j + 1)k$, secured from equation (15) by substituting k for l. Then substituting $j = k - \frac{1}{2}$ and simplifying we get,

$$g_jA(j, \lambda, k - 1; j, \lambda - 1, k) = c2\frac{(k + \lambda)(k + \lambda - 1)}{j(4k - 1)},$$

The results of these calculations are given in Table 4.

TABLE 4

Branch		Intensity factor $g_{j'}A(j', \lambda', k'; j'', \lambda'', k'')$	$j' - j''$	$\lambda' - \lambda''$	$k' - k''$
R_1	P_1	$\dfrac{c4(k + 1)(k^2 - \lambda^2)}{k(2k + 1)}$	± 1	0	± 1
R_2	P_2	$\dfrac{c4(k - 1)(k^2 - \lambda^2)}{k(2k - 1)}$	± 1	0	± 1
$^RQ_{21}$	$^PQ_{12}$	$\dfrac{c4(k^2 - \lambda^2)}{k(4k^2 - 1)}$	0	0	± 1
	Q_1	$\dfrac{c4\lambda^2(2k + 3)}{(k + 1)(2k + 1)}$	0	0	0
	Q_2	$\dfrac{c4\lambda^2(2k - 1)}{k(2k + 1)}$	0	0	0
$^QR_{12}$	$^QP_{21}$	$\dfrac{c4\lambda^2}{k(k + 1)(2k + 1)}$	± 1	0	0
R_1	P_1	$\dfrac{c2(k - \lambda)(k - \lambda + 1)(k + 1)}{k(2k + 1)}$	± 1	∓ 1	± 1
R_2	P_2	$\dfrac{c2(k - \lambda)(k - \lambda + 1)(k - 1)}{k(2k - 1)}$	± 1	∓ 1	± 1
$^RQ_{21}$	$^PQ_{12}$	$\dfrac{c2(k - \lambda)(k - \lambda + 1)}{k(4k^2 - 1)}$	0	∓ 1	± 1
P_1	R_1	$\dfrac{c2(k + \lambda)(k + \lambda - 1)(k + 1)}{k(2k + 1)}$	± 1	∓ 1	± 1
P_2	R_2	$\dfrac{c2(k + \lambda)(k + \lambda - 1)(k - 1)}{k(2k - 1)}$	± 1	∓ 1	± 1
$^RQ_{12}$	$^RQ_{21}$	$\dfrac{c2(k + \lambda)(k + \lambda - 1)}{k(4k^2 - 1)}$	0	∓ 1	± 1
	Q_1	$\dfrac{c2(k + \lambda)(k - \lambda + 1)(2k + 3)}{(k + 1)(2k + 1)}$	0	∓ 1	0
	Q_2	$\dfrac{c2(k + \lambda)(k - \lambda + 1)(2k - 1)}{k(2k + 1)}$	0	∓ 1	0
$^QP_{21}$	$^QR_{12}$	$\dfrac{c2(k + \lambda)(k - \lambda + 1)}{k(k + 1)(2k + 1)}$	$\left\{\begin{array}{c} -1 \\ +1 \end{array}\right.$	$\left.\begin{array}{c} \mp 1 \\ \mp 1 \end{array}\right\}$	0

In these formulas k and λ refer to the larger of the initial and final values of these quantum numbers, and the upper and lower signs to the branches given in the first and second columns, respectively. Each of the symbols of the first and second columns represent in general two branches; each P or R branch may be either an AB or a BA branch and each Q branch either an AA or a BB branch. All these branches will not be classified as one band for the change of λ is accompanied in general by a large change in the frequency emitted. For any given value of λ', the intensity factors given would be for three separate emission bands for which $\Delta\lambda = 0$, $+1$, and -1, respectively. There will be twenty possible branches in each of these bands, if $\lambda \neq 0$ for both electronic states. If $\lambda = 0$, for one state, this number is reduced to ten, since we assign the letter A to Σ states, and thus all branches designated by a symbol with a subscript B for this state do not appear. If $\lambda = 0$ in both states, there are only six branches with intensities given by the first three formulas. In this case, A states combine with A states in the P, R, and Q branches due to the fact that according to the theory of Chap. XIX, Sec. 9 the states are alternately symmetric and antisymmetric, positive and negative, and thus these transitions are possible.

We have now considered the intensities for case a and case b bands in which both states are either case a or case b. There is also the intermediate case in which one state belongs to case a and the other to case b or in which one state or the other is case a for small j and case b for large j. In such bands the intensities will not follow the formulas of this section and the preceding one exactly. Weak branches may appear representing the permitted transitions of both types. The CaH bands described in Chap. XII, Sec. 20 belong to the case b type, while the water bands of Chap. XII, Sec. 21 belong to the intermediate type. The intense branches of the water bands are those for $\Delta j = \Delta k = 0$, ± 1, which are permitted by the selection rules of case b and are equivalent to $\Delta j = 0$, ± 1 and $\Delta\iota = \Delta\lambda = -1$ when j is small so that these strong branches also obey the selection rules for case a.

11. TEMPERATURE AND THE INTENSITIES OF BAND SPECTRUM LINES

The selection rules and relative intensities discussed in Secs. **8**, **9**, and **10** are known to be qualitatively correct, but exact comparison between experiment and theory is not easily made because of the importance of the exponential factor in equations (5) and (28) and the difficulties of measuring precisely the intensities of lines so close together as are those of band spectra. Recently, Ornstein and van Wijk[1] and Kapuscinski and Eymers[2] have measured the intensities of the negative nitrogen bands (N_2^+) and of the mercury hydride bands, respectively, and find that it is possible to assign an "effective temperature" to the emitting gas and that the intensity factors derived above are in agreement with their data.

The N_2^+ bands studied are due to a $^2\Sigma \to {}^2\Sigma$ transition and, accordingly, the intensities are given by the first three factors of Table 4 with λ equal to zero. The band consists of six branches which group themselves

[1] Z. Physik, **49**, 315 (1928).
[2] Z. Physik, **54**, 246 (1929).

however into an R and a P branch each consisting of close triplets. The intensities of these close triplets added together is equal to $4ck$, where k is the larger of k' and k'', *i.e.*, $k = k'$ for the R branch and $k = k''$ for the P branch.[1] Then, according to Table 1, the intensities of these triplets will be

$$I_R(k) \propto A4ck' \exp\left(-\frac{h^2}{8\pi^2 I'}\frac{k'(k'+1)}{k_B T}\right),$$

and

$$I_P(k) \propto A4c(k'+1) \exp\left(-\frac{h^2}{8\pi^2 I'}\frac{k'(k'+1)}{k_B T}\right),$$

where A is a constant which is different for different values of k due to the alternation of intensities in the band. If then $(\log I_R)/k$ and $(\log I_P)/(k+1)$ are plotted against $k(k+1)$, straight lines should result. Two such lines are secured on one of which lie the points for even k and on the other the points for odd k. The two lines are parallel and their slope gives a value for the effective temperature. The separation of the lines along the axis of $(\log I_R)/k$ must be equal to $\log A(\text{even})/A(\text{odd})$ and this difference gives $A(\text{even})/A(\text{odd}) = 2$. Thus the quantum weights of the even levels are $2(2j+1)$ while those of the odd levels are $2j+1$.

The similar experiments on the HgH bands ($^2\Pi \to {}^2\Sigma$) do not give such an exact straight-line relation between the energy and log I divided by the intensity factor. In this case, the exponential factor of equation (28) is only approximately correct. The intensity factors agree with the predictions of the theory for the intermediate type between case a and case b.[2]

---

[1] See Chap. XII, Sec. **20** and Figs. 22 and 25 for a detailed description of this type of band.

[2] See HILL and VAN VLECK, *Phys. Rev.*, **32**, 250 (1928), for these intensity formulas.

CHAPTER XXI

DIFFRACTION OF ELECTRONS AND ATOMS BY CRYSTALS

1. INTRODUCTION

Davisson and Kunsman made the discovery that when electrons impinge on polycrystalline metal surfaces the fraction scattered at an angle θ with the normal to the surface does not decrease uniformly as θ increases. On the contrary, if the fraction scattered at the angle θ is plotted as a polar graph, the curve usually has several lobes or projections. A classical theory of the effect, outlined by Davisson and Kunsman, was based on the idea that a given electron might pass through the force-fields of the atoms in the crystal in a variety of ways. Its deflection would depend on the distance of closest approach to a nucleus and on many other factors, so that a definite test of the theory would lie beyond our present resources. The results seemed likely to remain unexplained, until Einstein[1] discussed de Broglie's matter waves, in 1924 and 1925. He emphasized the idea that if particles possess a wave-like character, diffraction phenomena should be associated with their motion, and the ordinary laws of motion will not be obeyed. Now we have seen (Chap. XV, Sec. 20) that the velocity of the waves associated with a free particle is E/mv, where E is the energy and mv the momentum. The frequency is E/h, and therefore, the wave length is

$$\lambda = \frac{h}{mv}. \tag{1}$$

Diffraction phenomena may be expected when one particle passes another within a distance of the order λ, or when it falls on a lattice structure with spacings somewhat greater than λ. In equation (1), the wave length is in centimeters, but if we agree to measure it in Ångström units, then for the electron we obtain

$$\lambda = \frac{12.2}{V^{1/2}} \text{ Ångströms}, \tag{2}$$

where V is the potential difference through which the electron must fall in order to attain the velocity v. This shows that moderate voltages correspond to wave lengths of the proper size for appreciable diffraction at a crystal grating. Elsasser[2] suggested that the results of Davisson

---

[1] *Sitz. Ber. d. Berliner Akademie* (1924) and (1925).
[2] *Naturwissenschaften*, **13**, 711, 1925; **16**, 720 (1928).

and Kunsman[1] might be explained as due to electron-diffraction. Today, we know this interpretation of the original experiments of Davisson and Kunsman is incorrect, but it furnishes a satisfactory explanation of a considerable body of data accumulated since April, 1925, when Davisson and Germer made a very significant discovery.[2] At that time they were investigating the distribution-in-angle of electrons scattered by a target of polycrystalline nickel, which has a face-centered cubic lattice. Due to an accident it became necessary to heat the target to high temperatures in vacuo. Distribution curves obtained after heating were radically different from earlier ones in that the lobes had increased in number and in prominence. This alteration proved to be due to a recrystallization of the target during the prolonged heating, such that its face was altered into a mosaic composed of about ten large single crystals. Systematic experiments were then undertaken, in which the area of the target bombarded was known to belong to a single crystal.

It will be useful to state the main results of this investigation, so that the reader may better understand the trend of the experimental work. In the words of Davisson and Germer, when the direction of bombardment is normal to the crystal face

. . . strong beams are found issuing from the crystal, but only when the speed of bombardment lies near one or another of a series of critical values, and then in directions quite unrelated to crystal transparency. The most striking characteristic of these beams is a one to one correspondence which the strongest of them bear to the Laue beams that would be found issuing from the same crystal if the incident beam were a beam of X-rays. Certain others appear to be analogues, not of Laue beams, but of optical diffraction beams from plane reflection gratings—the lines of these gratings being rows of atoms in the surface of the crystal. Because of these similarities between the scattering of electrons by the crystal and the scattering of waves by three- and two-dimensional gratings, a description of the occurrence and behavior of the electron diffraction beams in terms of the scattering of an equivalent wave radiation by the atoms of the crystal, and its subsequent interference, is not only possible, but most simple and natural. This involves the association of a wave length with the incident electron beam, and this wave length turns out to be in acceptable agreement with the value h/mv of the undulatory mechanics, Planck's action constant divided by the momentum of the electron.

Davisson and Germer have steadily continued their work, with results which confirm and extend this statement.

Further, G. P. Thomson has studied the diffraction of electrons by a large number of substances, using methods which are similar to the powder method and the Laue method of obtaining X-ray patterns. Electrons are accelerated by a voltage of the order of 15,000 to 60,000, and are caused to pass through a thin foil. Rings are obtained on a

[1] *Phys. Rev.*, **22**, 242 (1923).
[2] *Nature*, **119**, 558 (1927).

photographic plate placed some distance behind the foil, the radii being in striking agreement with those calculated on the hypothesis that the electrons behave like X-rays having the wave length h/mv. Similar experiments have been made by Rupp, using electrons of much lower voltages, and he has also found it possible to obtain electron spectra by allowing a homogeneous, well-defined beam of electrons to fall on a ruled grating. Further, Davisson and Germer, and also Rose, have detected beams which are analogous to the reflected X-ray beams obtained with a Bragg spectrometer. The reflection of atoms from crystals has been studied by Ellett and Olson and by T. H. Johnson, who obtain specularly reflected beams. We now describe these investigations in more detail.

2. DAVISSON AND GERMER'S APPARATUS

Figure 1 shows the metal parts of the electron-diffraction tube used by Davisson and Germer,[1] while Fig. 2 is a cross-sectional view. In

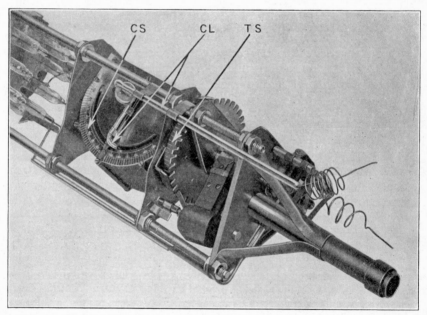

Fig. 1.—Electron diffraction apparatus of Davisson and Germer. The Scales TS and CS show respectively the azimuth of the target and the angular position of the collector. CL is the collector lead wire.

Fig. 2, F is the filament and G is a series of diaphragms, for producing a narrow beam of electrons. This beam falls normally on the target T, which can be rotated about an axis parallel to the beam. On the right, a weight hangs down from the axle carrying the target, so that it may be

[1] *Phys. Rev.*, **30**, 705 (1927); Germer, *J. Chem. Ed.*, **5**, 1041 (1928).

rotated by changing the orientation of the whole evacuated tube.   *C* is a double walled collector which receives diffracted electrons.   It is enclosed in a metal cylinder for protection from electrostatic effects, and is mounted on an arm which passes through a narrow slit in the wall of the cylinder. The arm may be rotated on an axis perpendicular to the plane of the diagram.   The angle between the incident beam and the scattered beam is called the "colatitude," and is denoted by θ, while the position of the axle carrying the target is specified by an azimuth φ.   Provisions are made for placing the collector at any desired potential.   Usually, the potentials are so chosen that only electrons which have suffered a small loss of velocity are recorded by the galvanometer.   The ratio of collector to bombarding current is of the order 10^{-4} under these conditions, so

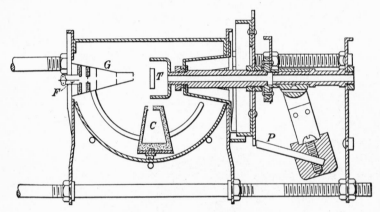

Fig. 2.—Cross-section of electron diffraction apparatus.

that by using bombarding currents of the order of 1 microampere, collector currents are obtained which are easily measurable with a sensitive galvanometer.

3. LAUE BEAMS OF ELECTRONS FROM A NICKEL CRYSTAL

We now describe the diffracted electron beams which are obtained when a beam impinges on the (111) face of a nickel crystal.   The geometry of the beams and the crystal will be easily understood from Fig. 3 where the cube is supposed to represent a crystal with its face cut parallel to the crystallographic axes.   One corner is then cut away, exposing a (111) face.   In Fig. 4, we are looking down on this face.   The atoms in the surface layer are indicated by the circles marked 1 and those in the second and third layers by the circles 2 and 3.   The fourth layer is identical with the first and so on.   The receiver is often set in one of the azimuths marked *A*, *B*, and *C*.   This being done, the collector is moved through the whole range of colatitudes permitted by the apparatus.   Let us suppose that the receiver is in the *A* azimuth and that the voltage of the bombarding electrons is chosen to be 36. If we plot the currents to the receiver in a polar graph, as a function of θ, we obtain

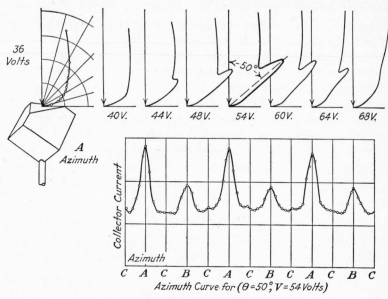

Fig. 3.—Above, curves showing development of diffraction beam in the *A*-azimuth. Below, variation of intensity with azimuth at colatitude 50°.

the curve shown at the left in Fig. 3.[1] On repeating the process with increasing voltages, a peak is developed on this curve at the position

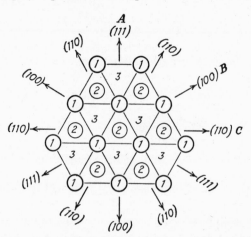

Fig. 4.—Arrangement of atoms in a (111) plane of nickel.

$\theta = 50°$. It reaches maximum development at 54 volts, and dies away again if we pass to higher voltages, as indicated in Fig. 3. By setting

[1] Davisson, *Bell System Tech. Jour.*, **7**, 90 (1928).

the receiver at $\theta = 50°$, and moving it in azimuth, a curve like that at the bottom of Fig. 3 is obtained. The peak thus outlined would be represented as a spur in a three-dimensional polar graph. The spur is repeated in each azimuth of the type A, as we should expect from the threefold symmetry of the crystal about the normal to the (111) face. The smaller maxima in the azimuth curve are due to another set of three spurs which reach their strongest development in colatitude 44° at 65 volts. The sharpness of some of these spurs and the precision with which they may be located will be appreciated from Fig. 5, which shows the variation with voltage of a set of beams occurring at $\theta = 55°$ in the A azimuths. These data are fairly typical; thorough exploration has resulted in the discovery of many such sets of spurs. When the first extended account of this work was published,[1] thirty such sets of beams had been found at bombarding potentials less than 370 volts. Six

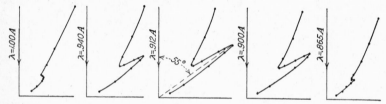

Fig. 5.—Variation with voltage of the second order spurs at $\theta = 55°$ in the A-azimuths.

of these were due to adsorbed gas and were not found when the crystal was thoroughly baked out. Concerning the others, Davisson and Germer say,

Of the twenty-four sets due to scattering by the gas-free crystal, twenty are associated with twenty sets of Laue beams that would issue from the crystal within the range of observation if the incident beam were a beam of heterogeneous X-rays, three that occur near grazing are accounted for as diffraction beams due to scattering from a single (111) layer of nickel atoms, and one set of low intensity has not been accounted for.

Eight sets which might be expected to occur were missing, but the intensities of all of these should be small, by analogy with X-ray diffraction patterns. A partial list of space-lattice beams is presented in Table 1.

We now consider the interpretation of a typical spur, for example the one discussed above. The voltage at which it is most pronounced corresponds to an electron wave length of 1.67 Å. If white X-rays were to fall on the crystal in the same direction as the incident electrons, a series of wave lengths would be selected for diffraction by the most heavily populated planes. In the azimuth A the wave length 2.87 Å. would be diffracted by (100) planes and would appear at colatitude 70°. Similarly there

[1] *Phys. Rev.*, **30**, 705 (1927).

TABLE 1

Azimuth	Voltage V	Wave length in vacuo, λ	Colatitude in degrees, θ	Order	Miller indices	Refractive index μ	Grating potential, E
	35 volts	(2.05) A	(72)	..	220		
	54	1.670	50	1	331	1.118	+13
	106	1.190	28	1	442	1.128	+11.5
	174	0.928	22	1	553	1.038	+13
111	181	0.910	55	2	551	1.036	+13
	248	0.778	44	2	662	1.036	+19
	258	0.763	<20	1	664	1.032	+15
	343	0.662	34	2	773	1.022	+15
	347	0.658	62	3	771	1.068	+48
	37	2.02	71	..	311		
100	65	1.520	44	1	422	1.123	+16.5
	126	1.093	28	1	533	1.047	+11
	143	1.024	56	1	531	0.979	− 7
110	170	0.940	46	1	642	1.075	+26
	188	0.894	43	1	642	1.024	+ 8

would be beams of wave length 1.49 Å. at 44° and 1.13 Å. at 33°. These X-ray beams would be expected to be quite prominent. Now, a set of electron beams having an equivalent wave length of 2.87 Å. would have a velocity below the limit which can be conveniently observed with the apparatus, but a set of beams with equivalent wave length 1.49 Å. arising from the (331) planes should be easily detected. No beams are found at the positions predicted by Bragg's law, and it is concluded that the beam having wave length 1.67 Å. is the one in question. Similar discrepancies between the position of X-ray beams and corresponding electron beams are found in practically all cases, and it is now understood that this is due to the fact that the equivalent wave length of an electron inside the crystal is not the same as its wave length in vacuo. It may be said that the crystal has a *refractive index* for electron waves, since the electron is accelerated as it approaches the crystal, due to the fact that the space inside is at a different average potential from the space outside. Leaving this for later consideration, we shall discuss the results in Table 1. It is important to realize that all these beams could be obtained from a surface grating having the same spacing (2.15 Å.) as the atoms in the (111) surface of the nickel crystal. The effect of the underlying layers of the crystal grating is to change the intensities of some of the beams which would be obtained from the first layer or to extinguish them due to interference between the contributions of the different layers. The presence of several layers also has the effect of limiting the wave lengths which can be diffracted to any one of a discrete set of wave lengths, just as in the case of X-rays. All these facts are clearly brought out by the following demonstration given by Davisson, which shows that the wave length of each electron beam can be calculated from the plane grating formula, using the diffraction angle which is actually observed *outside* the crystal. This is true regardless of the fact that the crystal possesses a refractive index greater than unity. In Fig. 6, let us suppose that radiation of wave length λ falls on a crystal at normal incidence. If the wave length inside the crystal is λ', then the index of refraction μ is equal to λ/λ'. Consider that portion of the beam which is diffracted by the planes shown in the

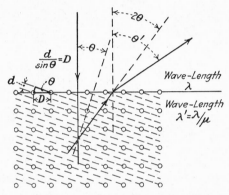

Fig. 6.—Diffraction by a crystal with refractive index differing from unity.

figure, the angle of incidence on these planes being θ. By Snell's law,

$$\frac{\lambda}{\lambda'} = \frac{\sin \theta'}{\sin 2\theta}. \tag{3}$$

If d is the interplanar spacing, and D the spacing of the surface rows then

$$d = D \sin \theta,$$

and by Bragg's law

$$n\lambda' = 2d \cos \theta = D \sin 2\theta.$$

Multiplying equation (3) by this equation we have

$$n\lambda = D \sin \theta' \tag{4}$$

which is the equation appropriate to a plane line grating of spacing D. Although the diffraction beams do *not* obey the simple Bragg condition $n\lambda = 2d \cos \theta$, they satisfy equation (4) very well. It should be remembered, however, that this formula cannot be applied indiscriminately. The only wave lengths which may occur in it are those allowed by the Bragg reflection condition. For example, beams occur at different voltages in the A and B azimuths because the plane gratings that make up the crystal are not piled exactly above one another. The lateral shifts of the gratings in these two azimuths are different. This means that the phase relations between the elementary beams emerging in the A azimuth are not identical with those in the B azimuth, so that the conditions for the production of a strong beam are satisfied at different voltages in these two cases.

The accuracy of measurement attained by Davisson and Germer in their first papers was such that calculated and observed values of the wave length might differ by 15 per cent. Later,[1] the apparatus was so improved that wave-length measurements based on diffraction beams and computed by equation (4) should not be in error by more than 1 per cent. This encouraging advance indicates that the method might be made sufficiently precise to be useful in the measurement of h.

4. G. P. THOMSON'S EXPERIMENTS

G. P. Thomson[2] has made extensive studies of the diffraction of electrons shot through foils of celluloid, gold, aluminum, and platinum. From de Broglie's law and the simple geometry of Thomson's apparatus one can see that the diameter D of any ring in the diffraction pattern obtained should vary inversely as the square root of the voltage applied to the tube. If the voltage V is high, it is necessary to take the relativity correction into account, and we then expect that the quantity $DV^{1/2}(1 + Ve/1,200 \ mc^2)$ will be constant. Thomson has improved the technique of this method so that the mean error of a set of observations is little more than 1 per cent. It can be shown that corrections due to the refractive index of the metal foil are negligible for voltages of the magnitude used in these experiments. A typical set of data referring to celluloid is given below:

V (volts)	D (centimeters)	$DV^{1/2}(1 + Ve/1,200 \ mc^2)$
50,000	0.85	195
42,500	0.90	189
36,000	1.00	193
30,500	1.05	186
23,200	1.25	193
21,000	1.30	190
16,800	1.47	191
16,100	1.48	189
11,500	1.62	175
9,800	1.86	185
......	....	Mean 189

The value of the spacing of the reflecting planes deduced from experiments of this kind is in good agreement with X-ray measurements, as the following tabulation (in Ångström units) will show:

[1] *Proc. Nat. Acad. Sci.*, **14**, 317 (1928).

[2] *Nature*, **122**, 279 (1928); *Proc. Roy. Soc.*, **117**, 600 (1928) and **119**, 651 (1928); *Phil. Mag.*, **6**, 939 (1928).

	Al	Au	Pt
Cathode rays....................	4.035	4.20	3.89
X-rays........................	4.043	4.064	3.913

In a rough way, the intensities of the rings parallel those to be expected in the case of the corresponding X-ray experiment. In some of Thomson's experiments the pattern resembles a Laue picture instead of a system of rings. As might be expected, such patterns are produced by the presence of large single crystals in the film.

Thomson has obtained the important result that the velocity of the diffracted electrons differs by less than 1 per cent from that of the incident beam. This indicates that the electron is to be considered as colliding with the crystal as a whole, and not with individual free electrons in the crystal. This is analogous to the well-known fact that diffracted X-ray beams do not show the Compton shift.

Thomson's experiments have been continued by Reid,[1] who worked with celluloid. While Thomson used a spark gap to measure the voltage of his electrons, Reid used the method of electrostatic deflection, obtaining results which agree within 1 per cent with those of Thomson. In experiments of this kind it is essential that the films should be thin enough to prevent blurring of the pattern by multiple scattering. The celluloid films are made by dissolving celluloid in amyl acetate and are of the order of 5×10^{-6} cm. thick.

5. RUPP'S DIFFRACTION EXPERIMENTS

Rupp[2] has extended the range of the foil method of studying electron diffraction to lower velocities, using voltages in the range from 120 to 320. He has obtained patterns from foils of the following metals, the most complete set of data being those for silver: Al, Pb, Ni, Cu, Ag, Au, Cr, Sn, and Zn. Of these, the first six are face-centered cubic, while Cr is body-centered cubic, Sn is tetragonal, and Zn hexagonal. The foils were about 10^{-6} cm. in thickness, and were prepared by the method of Müller in which the metal to be studied is evaporated on to the surface of a rock salt plate, which is then dissolved away. The apparatus is essentially a beta-ray spectrograph, which is placed in a magnetic field so that the paths of the electrons are circles. This has the advantage that electrons which lose any considerable portion of their velocity in passing through the film are deflected to one side and do not reach the central portion of the photographic plate.

In general agreement with Thomson, Rupp has demonstrated a general parallelism between the intensities of the various diffraction

[1] *Proc. Roy. Soc.*, **119**, 663 (1928).
[2] *Ann. Physik*, **85**, 981 (1928).

rings and the intensities of the corresponding rings in X-ray powder photographs for the same metals. More recently, he[1] has found it possible to obtain electron spectra by letting a homogeneous, well-defined beam of electrons fall on an optical grating having a constant of 8×10^{-4} cm; 150-volt and 70-volt electrons were used. The accuracy obtained in wave-length determinations was of the order of 2–3 per cent. In these experiments it was found to be essential to use a grating ruled on metal, perhaps because electrostatic charges would introduce difficulties if the grating material were an insulator.

6. KIKUCHI'S EXPERIMENTS ON DIFFRACTION PATTERNS OF SINGLE CRYSTALS

Kikuchi[2] has studied the diffraction patterns produced by a beam of electrons, homogeneous in velocity, which has passed through thin

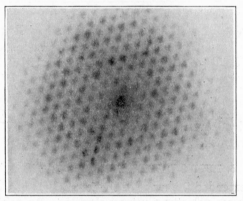

Fig. 7.—Diffraction pattern of a very thin mica sheet. (*After Kikuchi.*)

sheets of mica at nearly normal incidence. He has traced the interesting changes which occur as the thickness of the sheet increases. The thinnest sheets he used were not thick enough to produce interference colors. The pattern of such a sheet is shown in Fig. 7. According to Kikuchi, it is well explained by the assumption that the crystal behaves like a two-dimensional grating with a spacing of 5.17 Å. He states that his thinnest crystals contain only about 50 layers of unit cells (the grating space perpendicular to the cleavage plane being 20.4 Å.) and that the selective effect of the grating structure perpendicular to the plane of the sheet does not come into full play when the number of layers is so small. This seems surprising, but it must be remembered that the thickness of the sheets was estimated, not measured; Kikuchi states that it was probably of the order of 10^{-5} cm. or less.

[1] *Naturwiss.* **33**, 656 (1928); *Z. Physik,* **52**, 8 (1928).

[2] *Nature, and Proc. Imp. Acad. Japan,* **4**, 271, 275, 354 (1928).

When progressively thicker sheets are used, the pattern gradually alters, until it shows well-defined Laue spots produced by three-dimensional interference, as in Fig. 8. Straight dark lines accompanied by lighter lines on the side toward the center of the pattern can also be observed. Kikuchi states that these are the analogues of the lines employed by Rutherford and Andrade in their study of gamma-ray spectra.[1] The electron beam becomes divergent (though still homogeneous in velocity) in passing through the first portion of the sheet encountered, and then the electrons are in a condition to undergo Bragg reflection at planes of atoms nearly parallel to the direction of the original beam. The light lines are due to a local deficiency of electrons which have been diverted to the neighboring dark lines.

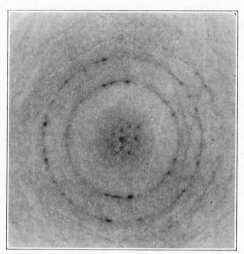

Fig. 8.—Diffraction pattern of a thick mica sheet. (*After Kikuchi.*)

7. THE REFLECTION OF ELECTRONS AT CRYSTAL SURFACES

Davisson and Germer[2] have studied the reflection of electrons from nickel with an arrangement essentially similar to a Bragg spectrometer. Setting the collector at the correct position for receiving a regularly reflected beam, they vary the voltage, and find that the intensity of reflection varies periodically. The maximum intensity is not obtained at voltages corresponding to the wave lengths which would be selectively reflected in the corresponding X-ray experiment, because the crystal behaves toward electrons as though it had a refractive index greater than unity. The following table gives a set of data for an experiment in which the angle of incidence was 10°:

[1] *Phil. Mag.*, **28**, 263 (1914).
[2] *Proc. Nat. Acad. Sci.*, **14**, 317 (1928); **14**, 619 (1928).

$V^{1/2}$	n	μ
(5.3)	2	(1.15)
8.0	3	1.14
11.4	4	1.07
14.7	5	1.04
18.1	6	1.02
21.2	7	1.01
24.2	8	1.01

The first column gives the values of $V^{1/2}$ at which the intensity of reflection passes through a maximum. The observations could not be extended much below $V^{1/2} = 8$ because the current of the incident beam becomes too small at low voltages. The first maximum at $V^{1/2} = 5.3$ was obtained by a modification of the usual procedure. The order of reflection n is given in the second column, while the third contains the index of refraction.[1] The formula used for determining the refractive index is a simple generalization of Bragg's law, and is as follows:

$$n\lambda = 2d(\mu^2 - \sin^2\theta)^{1/2}. \tag{5}$$

Putting in the value of λ and solving, we have

$$\mu = \left(\frac{150n^2}{4Vd^2} + \sin^2\theta\right)^{1/2}, \tag{6}$$

which enables one to obtain the refractive index as soon as the voltage of the incident electrons and the incidence-angle are given. The utility of interpreting electron diffraction experiments with the aid of a refractive index was pointed out by Eckart[2] and Bethe,[3] and the idea is now widely used. Let us examine the way in which the refractive index arises. It is due to the acceleration of the electron by forces of the crystal. If the potential drop through the crystal surface (the so-called "grating potential") is E volts, the wave length inside the crystal is smaller than that outside, in the ratio $V^{1/2}/(V + E)^{1/2}$ and we have

$$\mu = \left(1 + \frac{E}{V}\right)^{1/2}, \tag{7}$$

E being chosen positive. For each velocity, we can compute a value of E. Values for nickel are listed in the last column of Table 1. Those for several other metals have been determined by Rupp,[4] but Thomson[5]

[1] At first, Davisson and Germer favored another assignment of the beams, but now lend their support to the one given here. See also a note by Patterson, (*Nature*, **120**, 46 (1927)).

[2] *Proc. Nat. Acad. Sci.*, **12**, 460 (1927).

[3] *Naturwissenschaften*, **15**, 787 (1927); **16**, 333 (1928); *Ann. Physik*, **87**, 55 (1928).

[4] *Ann. Physik*, **85**, 981 (1928).

[5] *Phil. Mag.*, **6**, 939 (1928).

has pointed out an error in calculation which invalidates them.   This does not affect the value of Rupp's interesting experimental results.

At first it seems puzzling that E is not identical with the photoelectric threshold voltage of the crystal.   This may be explained by stating that the work required to remove a photoelectron is less than the potential drop across the surface, because conduction electrons are moving with a very considerable kinetic energy which aids them in escaping under the influence of light.   It must be remembered that the conduction electrons have an average kinetic energy much greater than $\frac{3}{2}kT$, for they obey the Fermi-Dirac statistics.[1]   The classical value $\frac{3}{2}kT$ does not account for the difference under consideration.   Since the refractive index is greater than unity, total reflection may occur for some electron beams, as suggested by Bethe.[2]   In Table 2, we give data pertaining to several beams which would strike the inner surface of the crystal at angles θ' so large that total reflection would occur.   If we call θ the angle of refraction, total reflection occurs when $\sin \theta$ as calculated by Snell's law is greater than unity.

TABLE 2

Azimuth	Order	Indices	Sin θ'	Sin θ, calculated	θ, observed
111	1	220	0.945	1.24	
	2	440	0.95	1.00	app. 90°
	3	551	1.00	1.02$_5$	
100	1	311	0.86	1.04	app. 90
	2	511	0.98$_5$	1.05	
	3	711	1.00	1.02$_5$	
110	1	420	0.98$_5$	1.06	
331	1	620	0.99$_5$	1.03	
210	1	640	0.96	0.99	app. 80

While this idea is not a cure-all for explaining missing beams, it has proved its utility in a number of instances.   Three beams in the table should be emitted nearly parallel to the crystal surface.   We should anticipate that such grazing beams will be both weak and broad, because fewer layers of the crystal are penetrated by the electron, and the resolving power of the crystal is, therefore, smaller.   As mentioned before, Davisson and Germer have listed several beams which they attribute to diffraction at the first layer of atoms.   Further, they have shown that if a small amount of gas is admitted to the apparatus it is possible to detect additional diffraction beams, due to the arrangement of these atoms in a space lattice, either on the surface or underneath the first

[1] Fermi, *Z. Physik*, **36**, 902 (1926); Dirac, *Proc. Roy. Soc.*, **112**, 661 (1926).
[2] *Loc. cit.*

layer of nickel atoms.   On heating the crystal, the so-called "gas beams" may be eliminated, which is excellent proof of this interpretation.

Rose[1] has studied the reflection of electrons by a single crystal of aluminium and comes to the conclusion that the results are consistent with the value unity for the refractive index.

Klemperer[2] has made the interesting suggestion that insulators may have a refractive index less than unity.   In support of this view, he discusses experiments made by Schmidt[3] and by others following him. In these experiments a beam of cathode rays was directed on the surface of a crystal and the dependence of the intensity of the reflected beam on the angle of incidence was studied.   When this angle is greater than a certain limiting value characteristic of the substance, and of the velocity of the incident electrons, the secondary beam is much diminished in intensity.   Klemperer considered this as evidence of a refractive index smaller than unity, due to the slowing up of electrons in the insulating material.   Rupp[4] suggested an alternative explanation, namely, that the piling up of electrostatic charge on the surface is responsible for the effect.   As the angle of incidence increases, the velocity being held constant, the component of velocity normal to the surface decreases, and eventually becomes so small that the bombarding electrons cannot penetrate to the surface.

8. REFLECTION OF ATOMS FROM CRYSTALS

T. H. Johnson[5] has found it possible to study the reflection of atomic hydrogen produced in a long discharge tube, at cleavage surfaces of calcite, sylvite, and rock salt, as well as natural faces of quartz.   The apparatus is complicated, and many experimental precautions must be taken in order to secure reproducible results.   The detector for the beam of reflected atoms is a glass plate smoked with white molybdenum trioxide, the surface of which is darkened wherever atomic hydrogen strikes it.   Arrangements were provided for heating the crystals, since, otherwise, a layer of adsorbed gas would interfere with crystal reflection; further, in the case of rock salt the surface is attacked by the atomic hydrogen.

Some of the hydrogen atoms are diffusely reflected, a phenomenon which Johnson interprets as due to adsorption followed by reevaporation. With the detecting plate at a distance of 1 cm. from the crystal, a specular beam superposed on the diffuse reflection can be recorded in 30 minutes. The intensity of this beam depends on the angle of incidence and on the temperature of the crystal.   In the case of rock salt at 400°C., the

[1] *Phil. Mag.*, **6,** 712 (1928).

[2] *Z. Physik*, **47,** 417 (1928).

[3] Dissertation, Berlin (1924).

[4] *Ann. Physik*, **85,** 981 (1928).

[5] *Jour. Franklin Inst.*, **206,** 301 (1928); *Abstract*, New York Meeting, Amer. Phys. Soc., Dec. 29, 1928.

intensity near grazing incidence is perhaps twice that at 30° and twenty times that 60° from grazing. At lower temperatures the diffuse background becomes less prominent, and it has been found possible to obtain a very large percentage of the reflected atoms in the specular beam, even at angles far from grazing. Johnson remarks that there should be interference maxima in directions other than that of the regularly reflected beam. He shows, however, that due to the Maxwell distribution of velocities, the wave lengths of the impinging atoms are distributed over a broad range, and the first order diffraction beam would be expected to extend over about 50°.

Ellett and Olson[1] have made similar experiments with unidirectional beams of cadmium and mercury atoms, striking a clean rock-salt surface. The reflected atoms produce a single spot about 0.8 mm. in diameter, while the glass receiving surface, cooled with liquid air, remains perfectly clear for several times the interval required to make the spot perfectly opaque. These spots were obtained with angles of incidence varying from 20 to 80°.

More recently,[2] they have shown that the atoms in the reflected beam all have the same velocity regardless of the temperature of the reflecting crystal. This demonstrates that we are dealing with a reflection which is analogous to the Bragg reflection of X-rays from a crystal. The data on specularly reflected cadmium atoms are as follows:

Angle of Incidence	Observed Velocity (Meters per Second)
22.5°	500
45	530
67.5	600

In a later paper Ellett, Olson, and Zahl[3] have given an equation which represents their data for cadmium. It is.

$$\frac{h}{mv} = 2d\left(2.26 - \frac{\varphi}{\frac{1}{2}mv^2} - \cos^2\theta\right)^{\frac{1}{2}}.$$

φ is the average potential energy of an electron when inside the crystal and m is the mass of a cadmium atom.

Ellett and Olson stated in their first paper that sodium is not reflected from a rock-salt surface. In view of the discovery that the reflected beam is analogous to a spectrum line obtained with the Bragg spectrometer, this observation can now be understood. It appears[4] that less than 1 per cent of the sodium atoms in the beam used by Ellett and Olson had a velocity such that they could satisfy the Bragg condition.

[1] *Phys. Rev.*, **31**, 643 (1928).

[2] *Science*, **68**, 89 (1928).

[3] *Phys. Rev.*, **34**, 493 (1929).

[4] Private communication from Dr. Ellett.

APPENDIX I

RELATIONS BETWEEN AVERAGE KINETIC AND POTENTIAL ENERGIES

The virial theorem of Clausius[1] states that for a system which is periodic or is in a steady state, the average kinetic energy over a long period of time is equal to $\frac{1}{2}$ the average value of the function $-\Sigma(Xx + Yy + Zz)$, which is called the "virial." We shall prove an extension of this theorem which holds true in relativity mechanics. Let the equations of motion of a particle in the system be

$$\frac{d(m\dot{x})}{dt} = X, \text{ etc.}$$

Then

$$xX = \frac{x\,d(m\dot{x})}{dt} = \frac{d(mx\dot{x})}{dt} - m\dot{x}^2.$$

We write down two similar equations for the y- and z-coordinates of each particle, and sum over all particles, obtaining

$$\Sigma(xX + yY + zZ) = \sum \frac{d}{dt}[m(x\dot{x} + y\dot{y} + z\dot{z})] - \Sigma mv^2. \tag{1}$$

Dividing by two, and averaging over a long time, the first term on the right disappears; for its average is simply the difference of its values at the end and at the beginning of the interval, divided by the interval. This difference is finite because we assume that the motion is periodic or that a state of kinetic equilibrium has been reached, so that neither the coordinates nor the velocities increase indefinitely with the time. Finally,

$$\left[\frac{\Sigma mv^2}{2} = -\frac{\Sigma(xX + yY + zZ)}{2} \right]. \tag{2}$$

Note that on the left side m is the actual mass of a moving particle, so the left member is not the average kinetic energy. However, it reduces to the average kinetic energy when relativity is neglected.

Interesting applications occur in the case of conservative systems, where $X = -\partial V/\partial x$, etc. If the potential V is a homogeneous function of the coordinates of degree n, then by Euler's theorem for such functions the virial equals $n\overline{V}$. In classical mechanics, equation (2) becomes

$$2\overline{T} = n\overline{V}. \tag{3}$$

Consider a system in which the force between two particles is along the line joining them and is proportional to the $(n-1)$th power of their distance apart. For the inverse square law, $n = -1$, and

$$2\overline{T} = -\overline{V} \tag{4}$$

so that the total energy is

$$E = -\overline{T} = \frac{\overline{V}}{2}. \tag{5}$$

A more general theorem is this: If the potential energy V is the sum of several functions, $V_1 + V_2 + \cdots$, which are homogeneous in the coordinates and of degrees n_1, n_2, etc., then the virial is

$$n_1\overline{V}_1 + n_2\overline{V}_2 + \cdots.$$

[1] See any edition of Jeans' "Kinetic Theory of Gases" for applications in statistical mechanics.

There are important cases in which the external forces depend on the velocities as well as the coordinates.   Consider an atom exposed to a uniform magnetic field. In order to make the illustration more widely applicable we suppose that a uniform electric field is also present.   Then, assuming the nucleus immovable, we have for each charge ϵ,

$$\frac{d(m\dot{x})}{dt} = X + \epsilon\left[E_x + \frac{1}{c}(\dot{y}H_z - \dot{z}H_y)\right], \text{ etc.}$$

Here X refers to all forces acting on the electron apart from those due to the electric and magnetic fields.   If these forces are due only to inverse square attractions and repulsions and have a potential V, then we show in the same manner as above that

$$\frac{\overline{\Sigma m v^2}}{2} = -\frac{\overline{V}}{2} + \frac{\overline{\mathbf{EM}}}{2} - \left(\frac{\epsilon}{2mc}\right)\overline{Hp}_H \qquad (6)$$

(For the electron $\epsilon = -4.77 \; 10^{-10}$, not $+4.77 \; 10^{-10}$.) M is the electric moment of the atom, and p_H the component of angular momentum in the direction of H while $\mathbf{EM}$ is the scalar product of the vector $\mathbf{E}$ and the electric moment.   If $\mathbf{E}$ is not present, the angle between H and p_H is constant.

Milne[1] has extended the theorem of the virial to systems subject to frictional forces proportional to velocities.   In many cases the existence of such forces prevents the existence of a steady state, but in cases where it does not, or in which the motion is periodic, such frictional forces contribute nothing to the virial and can be left out of account in computing the mean kinetic energy.

[1] *Phil. Mag.* **50,** 409 (1925).

APPENDIX II

QUANTUM INTEGRALS

1. Many integrals which arise in applying the quantum conditions can be evaluated by a "perturbation" method, starting from the value of

$$J_0 = \oint \left(A + \frac{2B}{r} + \frac{C}{r^2} \right)^{\frac{1}{2}} dr. \tag{1}$$

This integral arose in equation (18), Chap. V, and was evaluated there by direct methods with the result

$$J_0 = -2\pi i (C^{\frac{1}{2}} - BA^{-\frac{1}{2}}). \tag{2}$$

We now obtain this result by the use of complex integration (see Appendix VI, 4th edition of Sommerfeld). Considering r as a complex variable, we mark the branch

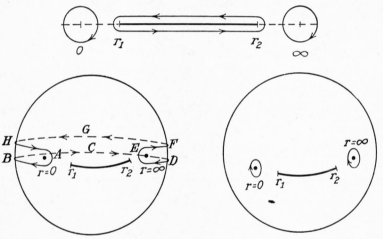

FIG. 1.

points r_1 and r_2 in the r plane (Fig. 1), representing the lower and upper limits of integration, respectively. The path of integration extends from r_1 to r_2, using the positive sign of the square root, and then from r_2 to r_1 using the negative sign of the square root. The path of integration may be deformed into a pair of infinitesimal circles passing around the poles of the integrand, at $r = 0$ and $r = \infty$. To see this it is convenient to represent the r plane on the surface of a sphere as in Fig. 1 and to stretch the path of integration like a rubber band until it assumes the position A-H. Bringing the portions BCD and EGH infinitesimally close to each other their contributions cancel and we are left with the circles HAB and DEF around the poles. At $r = 0$, J_0 can be expanded in the form

$$C^{\frac{1}{2}} \int \frac{dr}{r} \left(1 + \frac{B}{C} r + \cdots \right)$$

741

and the only term giving a finite contribution is the first one.   The residue obtained from this term is

$$-2\pi i C^{\frac{1}{2}},$$

where the minus sign appears because the direction of integration is clockwise. Using the transformation $s = 1/r$, J_0 takes the form

$$J_0 = -\int(A + 2Bs + Cs^2)^{\frac{1}{2}}ds, \tag{3}$$

and expanding in exactly similar fashion around $s = 0$, the contribution of the pole at $r = \infty$ is

$$2\pi i B A^{-\frac{1}{2}},$$

which completes the proof of equation (2).

2. We now evaluate

$$J_1 = \oint\left(A + \frac{2B}{r} + \frac{C}{r^2} + Dr\right)^{\frac{1}{2}}dr, \tag{4}$$

which occurs in the theory of the Stark effect (Chap. V, Sec. **12**). D is proportional to the electric field strength and is small compared to the other coefficients.   We expand the integrand in powers of Dr, retaining only the first power, the result being

$$\left(A + \frac{2B}{r} + \frac{C}{r^2} + Dr\right)^{\frac{1}{2}} = \left(A + \frac{2B}{r} + \frac{C}{r^2}\right)^{\frac{1}{2}} + \frac{Dr}{2}\left(A + \frac{2B}{r} + \frac{C}{r^2}\right)^{-\frac{1}{2}} + \cdots, \tag{5}$$

which shows that

$$J_1 = J_0 + \frac{D}{2}\oint r\left(A + \frac{2B}{r} + \frac{C}{r^2}\right)^{-\frac{1}{2}}dr + \cdots. \tag{6}$$

Since D is small, the positions of the branch points which persist when $D = 0$ are not much altered.   (In other words, the aphelion and perihelion distances of the electron are not much changed by the electric field.)   In evaluating each of the integrals in equation (6) we deform the path of integration as before until it consists of infinitesimal circles around the poles.   (In doing this, we are careful not to cross any of the branch points of J_1 or of the integral being evaluated.)   As to the second integral in equation (6), its only pole is at $r = \infty$, and the residue at infinity is such that we obtain

$$J_1 = J_0 + D\pi i A^{-\frac{1}{2}}\left(\frac{3B^2}{2A^2} - \frac{C}{2A}\right). \tag{7}$$

APPENDIX III

PHASE VELOCITY AND GROUP VELOCITY[1]

Consider a wave which is composed of a superposition of sinusoidal waves of various frequencies, a typical one being represented by $\cos 2\pi\nu\left(\dfrac{x}{u} - t\right)$. If u is the same for all frequencies, any modulation (*i.e.*, any rise or fall in the "envelope" of the curve representing the disturbance at a given instant) is transmitted with velocity u. The form of the wave group is not altered as it progresses, and if the energy of the waves depends essentially on their amplitudes the rate at which their energy is carried forward is the same as the velocity of a given phase of one of the component waves. But if the phase velocity u is a function of the frequency, the form of the group continually alters as it advances; the velocity of propagation of a signal, that is, a modulation, is not equal to u, and is called the "group velocity." Take the case of two cosine waves of equal amplitude with frequencies and velocities which differ by the small amounts $d\nu$ and du. The resultant is very like a cosine wave train with slowly varying amplitude, familiar from discussions of beats in books on sound. Its expression is

$$\cos 2\pi\nu\left(\frac{x}{u} - t\right) + \cos 2\pi(\nu + d\nu)\left(\frac{x}{u + du} - t\right)$$

$$\cong 2\cos 2\pi\nu\left(\frac{x}{u} - t\right)\cos\frac{1}{2}\left[\frac{x}{u}\left(\frac{d\nu}{\nu} - \frac{du}{u}\right) - t\frac{d\nu}{\nu}\right].$$

When $t = 0$ there is an amplitude 2 at $x = 0$. At a later time t_1, this peak will be at a point x_1 such that the argument of the last cosine term is zero, so the velocity g with which the peak or any other modulation of the train advances is given by

$$\frac{1}{g} = \frac{t_1}{x_1} = \frac{1}{u} - \frac{\nu}{u^2}\frac{du}{d\nu} = \frac{d(\nu/u)}{d\nu}. \tag{1}$$

Other useful formulations are

$$g = \frac{d\nu}{d(\nu/u)} = \frac{d(u/\lambda)}{d(1/\lambda)} = u - \lambda\frac{du}{d\lambda}. \tag{2}$$

These formulas hold approximately for waves of the more general type

$$y = \sum_i C_i \cos 2\pi\nu_i\left(\frac{x}{u_i} - t - \alpha_i\right), \tag{3}$$

where ν and u vary only *slightly* for the constituent wave trains. For the sake of a definite example suppose there is a maximum at the origin when $t = 0$. Let us refer to the argument of any cosine term in equation (3) as its phase. After a time Δt, *large* compared to $1/\nu$, the phase at a position Δx differs from its value at the origin when $t = 0$ by an amount $2\pi\nu\left(\dfrac{\Delta x}{u} - \Delta t\right)$. The phase change will be *nearly the same* for all the terms if Δx is so chosen that

$$d(\nu/u) \cdot \Delta x = d\nu \cdot \Delta t. \tag{4}$$

[1] See HAVELOCK, "The Propagation of Disturbances in Dispersive Media," Cambridge University Press (1914).

The *relative* change of phase of the terms in equation (3) is very small during a single period $1/\nu$ because of the above restriction on the variation of ν and u. Hence the combination of phases which gave rise to a maximum at the origin at time zero will be reproduced at a point within one wave length from the position Δx, at a time differing from Δt by less than one period. Thus $\Delta x / \Delta t$ is nearly the group velocity and equation (4) yields equation (2). Of course, it is possible so to choose the C's that our approximations do not hold. Wave groups of other types must be treated by special methods. It is often loosely stated that the velocity of transmission of energy is the group velocity, but since the latter is usually defined by kinematic relationships alone, this is not necessarily true. Frequently there is little sense in speaking of a group velocity. However, if we know the energy density ρ as a function of x, y, z, and t, it is easy to obtain an energy velocity g which may be defined as the group velocity. Its components satisfy a relation analogous to the equation of continuity in hydrodynamics:

$$\frac{\partial \rho}{\partial t} + \frac{\partial(\rho g_x)}{\partial x} + \frac{\partial(\rho g_y)}{\partial y} + \frac{\partial(\rho g_z)}{\partial z} = 0.$$

This does not determine g completely, and in general g will be a function of t as well as of the space coordinates, since it is not characteristic of the medium alone but depends also on the type of disturbance. The conventional character of the term "energy velocity" must be clearly appreciated. It is impossible to identify a given portion of energy at a later time, so g appears to be simply a convenient analogue of the velocity vector so useful in hydrodynamics.

APPENDIX IV

NORMAL ORTHOGONAL FUNCTIONS USED IN WAVE MECHANICS

1. THE SERIES EXPANSION OF AN ARBITRARY FUNCTION

To avoid repetition, we refer the reader to Chap. XV, Sec. 13 for the definition of normal orthogonal functions, and for a proof that the discrete solutions of Schrödinger's wave equation are orthogonal, provided we are dealing with a non-degenerate system. Similar proofs could be carried through for the more general wave equations introduced thereafter. Here we need more general definitions.

A set of functions of a single variable x is said to be normal and orthogonal in the interval A to B if

$$\int_A^B \psi_n \psi_m^* dx = 1 \text{ when } n = m$$
$$= 0 \text{ when } n \neq m. \tag{1}$$

In the discussion we shall omit the limits of integration wherever possible. The extension to functions of several variables is obvious. Nothing is said as to the behavior of the functions outside the range of integration. It is shown in Chap. XV, Sec. 21 that any function $f(x)$ which obeys certain restrictions can be expanded in a series of normal orthogonal functions

$$f(x) = \sum_k c_k \psi_k. \tag{2}$$

The ordinary Fourier series is a simple illustration of such an expansion. The whole subject becomes very clear if we approach it by setting ourselves the following problem:[1]

Suppose we are given a finite number of normal orthogonal functions ψ_1, ψ_2, etc. Let us try to approximate the function f by a linear combination of these functions, $\Sigma c_k \psi_k$, with constant coefficients c_k, in such a way that the mean square deviation is made as small as possible. That is. we seek the best fit by the method of least squares, arranging that

$$M = \int (f - \Sigma c_k \psi_k)^2 dx \tag{3}$$

shall be as small as possible. The conditions for this integral to be a minimum are

$$\frac{\partial M}{\partial c_1} = 0, \frac{\partial M}{\partial c_2} = 0, \text{ etc.} \tag{4}$$

By way of example, the first condition yields the equation

$$\int (f - \Sigma c_k \psi_k) \psi_1 dx = 0$$

and since the ψ's obey the conditions of equation (1), the result of the integration is

$$c_1 = \int f \psi_1 dx.$$

In general,

$$c_k = \int f \psi_k dx. \tag{5}$$

If any of the functions f or ψ_k were complex it would be in order to replace equation (3) by

$$M = \int (f - \Sigma c_k \psi_k)(f^* - \Sigma c_k^* \psi_k^*) dx,$$

and to generalize equation (4) correspondingly.

---

[1] The treatment of this problem follows that of COURANT-HILBERT, Vol. I, p. 35.

Since M is greater than or equal to zero, on expanding the expression for M and integrating term by term we have

$$0 \leq \int f^2 dx - 2\Sigma c_k \int f \psi_k dx + \Sigma c_k^2 = \int f^2 dx - \Sigma c_k^2.$$

The integral of f^2 is called the norm of f, and is written $N(f)$, so we have

$$\Sigma c_k^2 \leq N(f), \tag{6}$$

which is Bessel's inequality. It holds whatever be the number of functions used in the series for f.

Now let the number of functions in the set ψ_k approach infinity. If it is possible with their aid to approximate the function f as closely as we please then the set is said to be complete. The formula (5) for the development coefficients is unaltered and Bessel's inequality becomes the equation

$$\Sigma c_k^2 = N(f) \tag{7}$$

which is referred to as the "condition for completeness."

By similar methods it is easy to prove that for any two functions f and g, we have the relation

$$\int f g dx = \sum_k c_k d_k,$$

where the c's and d's are the development coefficients of f and g, respectively.

2. HOW TO CONSTRUCT A SYSTEM OF NORMAL ORTHOGONAL FUNCTIONS

If we are given a set of independent functions F_0, F_1, . . . , we can construct a set of normal orthogonal functions from them by straightforward application of the conditions of equation (1). The procedure is the following: We agree to write (ab) for $\int ab dx$. Let us pick out one of the functions F, say F_0, and form the function

$$\psi_0 = \frac{F_0}{[N(F_0)]^{1/2}}.$$

Then the norm of ψ_0 will be one, so that it is normalized correctly. If we define another function ψ_1' by the relation

$$\psi_1' = a_0 \psi_0 + a_1 F_1,$$

we may so choose the constants a_0 and a_1 that this function will be orthogonal to ψ_0. That is, we require that

$$\int \psi_1' \psi_0 dx = \int a_0 \psi_0^2 dx + \int a_1 F_1 \psi_0 dx = a_0 + a_1 (F_1 \psi_0) = 0.$$

This being done, we have in $\psi_1'/[N(\psi_1')]^{1/2}$ a function which is properly normalized and which is orthogonal to ψ_0. We continue this process, determining a function

$$\psi_2' = b_0 \psi_0 + b_1 \psi_1 + b_2 F_2,$$

in such a way that it is orthogonal to both ψ_0 and ψ_1, after which we normalize it, and so on. The formula for ψ_{n+1} is

$$\psi_{n+1} = \frac{1}{[N(F_{n+1})]^{1/2}} \left[F_{n+1} - \sum_1^n \psi_k(\psi_k F_{n+1}) \right]. \tag{8}$$

An interesting example is afforded by the Legendre polynomials. It is well known that any continuous function may be approximated throughout its course by a power series, as closely as we please. However, the functions in the sequence,

$$1, x, x^2, \ldots$$

are not orthogonal, whatever be the range of integration.   If we construct from them a set of polynomials which are normal and orthogonal in the interval -1 to $+1$, by the above process, we arrive at the functions

$$\varphi_n(x) = \left(\frac{2n+1}{2}\right)^{\frac{1}{2}} P_n(x) \tag{9}$$

where $P_n(x)$ is a Legendre polynomial, useful in the quantization of the rotator and of the hydrogen atom.   Other systems of polynomials often used in wave mechanics are obtained by orthogonalizing the system

$$p^{\frac{1}{2}}, \; xp^{\frac{1}{2}}, \; x^2 p^{\frac{1}{2}}, \; \ldots$$

where $p(x)$ is a so-called "weight function."[1]

We now summarize the more important properties of several systems of polynomials which are extensively required in problems of wave mechanics.

3. LEGENDRE POLYNOMIALS

These polynomials which are often called cylindrical harmonics, may be defined by the relation

$$P_n(x) = \frac{1}{2^n n!} \frac{d^n (x^2 - 1)^n}{dx^n}. \tag{10}$$

In physical problems x usually is the cosine of the angle θ between the z-axis and the radius vector, and we often find the Legendre functions written with $\cos\theta$ as the argument.   This explains why we normalize these functions over the interval -1 to $+1$.   These limits correspond to $\theta = \pi$ and $\theta = 0$, so that the integration covers all possible values of θ.

We have

$$
\begin{aligned}
P_0 &= 1, & P_4 &= {}^{35}\!/_8 x^4 - {}^{15}\!/_4 x^2 + {}^{3}\!/_8; \\
P_1 &= x, & P_5 &= {}^{63}\!/_8 x^5 - {}^{35}\!/_4 x^3 + {}^{15}\!/_8 x, \\
P_2 &= {}^{3}\!/_2 x^2 - {}^{1}\!/_2, & P_6 &= {}^{231}\!/_{16} x^6 - {}^{315}\!/_{16} x^4 + {}^{105}\!/_{16} x^2 - {}^{5}\!/_{16}, \\
P_3 &= {}^{5}\!/_2 x^3 - {}^{3}\!/_2 x, & P_7 &= {}^{429}\!/_{16} x^7 - {}^{693}\!/_{16} x^5 + {}^{315}\!/_{16} x^3 - {}^{35}\!/_{16} x.
\end{aligned} \tag{11}
$$

The recursion formula is

$$(n+1)P_{n+1} - (2n+1)xP_n + nP_{n-1} = 0. \tag{12}$$

The normalization factor for the P's may be obtained from equation (16), in the next section.

4. ASSOCIATED LEGENDRE POLYNOMIALS

These functions depend on two indices, n and m, and may be written either as $P_{n,m}(x)$ or as $P_n{}^m(x)$.   They may be defined by the relation

$$P_{n,m}(x) = (1 - x^2)^{m/2} \frac{d^m P_n(x)}{dx^m}, \; m \leqq n; \tag{13}$$

from which formula (38) in Chap. XV is derived.   If θ and φ are the polar angles, and if we write $x = \cos\theta$, the functions $P_{n,m}(x) \cos m\varphi$ and $P_{n,m}(x) \sin m\varphi$ are known as "tesseral harmonics."   Because of their utility in electrical problems, these harmonics are discussed in Jeans' "Electricity and Magnetism," Chap. VIII.   The following tabulation gives the values of the first few associated polynomials:

$P_{0,0} = 1$, $P_{1,0} = \cos\theta$, $P_{1,1} = \sin\theta$.

$P_{2,0} = \frac{1}{2}(3\cos^2\theta - 1)$, $P_{2,1} = 3\sin\theta\cos\theta$, $P_{2,2} = 3\sin^2\theta$.

$P_{3,0} = \frac{1}{2}(5\cos^3\theta - 3\cos\theta)$, $P_{3,1} = \frac{3}{2}\sin\theta(5\cos^2\theta - 1)$.

$P_{3,2} = 15\sin^2\theta\cos\theta$, $P_{3,3} = 15\sin^2\theta$.

$P_{4,0} = \frac{1}{8}(35\cos^4\theta - 30\cos^2\theta + 3)$, $P_{4,1} = \frac{5}{2}\sin\theta(7\cos^3\theta - 3\cos\theta)$,

$P_{4,2} = 15\frac{1}{2}\sin^2\theta(7\cos^2\theta - 1)$, $P_{4,3} = 105\sin^3\theta\cos\theta$,

$P_{4,4} = 105\sin^4\theta.$ $\tag{14}$

[1] For further information on this point the reader is referred to COURANT-HILBERT, Vol. 1, p. 72.

We have

$$\int_{-1}^{+1} P_{n,m}{}^2(x)dx = \frac{2}{2n+1}\frac{(n+m)!}{(n-m)!} \qquad (15)$$

so the corresponding normalized polynomials are

$$\left[\left(\frac{2n+1}{2}\right)\frac{(n-m)!}{(n+m)!}\right]^{\frac{1}{2}}P_{n,m}(x). \qquad (16)$$

Further,

$$\int_{-1}^{+1} P_{n,m}P_{q,m}dx = 0 \text{ when } q \neq n. \qquad (17)$$

5. JACOBIAN OR HYPERGEOMETRIC POLYNOMIALS

These polynomials occurred in the quantization of the polyatomic molecule. They are defined by

$$G_n(p, q, x) = \frac{x^{(1-q)}(1-x)^{q-p}}{q(q+1)\cdots(q+n-1)}\frac{d^n}{dx^n}[x^{q+n-1}(1-x)^{p+n-q}].$$

6. HERMITIAN POLYNOMIALS

In quantizing the oscillator we arrived at wave functions which are expressible in the form $e^{-v^2/2}H_n(v)$ where $H_n(v)$ is the nth Hermitian polynomial. It may be defined by the equation,

$$H_n(x) = (-1)^n e^{x^2}\frac{d^n e^{-x^2}}{dx^n}. \qquad (18)$$

From equation (18), we obtain the explicit formula

$$H_n(x) = (2x)^n - \frac{n(n-1)}{1!}(2x)^{n-2} + \frac{n(n-1)(n-2)(n-3)}{2!}(2x)^{n-4} + \cdots \qquad (19)$$

The values of the polynomials H_0 to H_5 are given in Chap. XV, Sec. 9. The recurrence formula of these polynomials is

$$H_{n+1} - 2xH_n + 2nH_{n-1} = 0, \qquad (20)$$

which proved very useful in obtaining the selection principle for the oscillator.

The Hermitian polynomials arise from the probem of finding functions to satisfy the normality condition

$$\int_{-\infty}^{+\infty} e^{-x^2}H_n(x)H_m(x)dx = 0; \ m \neq n; \ m \text{ and } n = 0, 1, 2, \cdots. \qquad (21)$$

The corresponding set of normalized functions is

$$\psi_n = \frac{H_n e^{-x^2/2}}{\pi^{\frac{1}{4}}(2^n n!)^{\frac{1}{2}}}, \ n = 0, 1, \cdots. \qquad (22)$$

7. THE FUNCTIONS $L_s{}^t$ OF THE HYDROGEN ATOM (GENERALIZED LAGUERRE POLYNOMIALS)

In Chap. XVI we saw that the ψ function of the hydrogen atom depends on the radius vector r through a factor

$$R(n, l) = x^l e^{-x/2}L_{n+l}^{2l+1}(x).$$

Here x is equal to $2r\left(-\frac{8\pi^2 mE}{h^2}\right)^{\frac{1}{2}}$ and the function L_{n+l}^{2l+1} is a polynomial which can be proved to be the $(2l+1)$ th derivative of the Laguerre polynomial $L_{n+l}(x)$, multiplied by $l!/(n+l)!$.

The Laguerre polynomials L_n are defined either by the conditions

$$\int_0^\infty e^{-x} L_s L_t dx = \begin{cases} 1 \text{ if } t = s \\ 0 \text{ if } t \neq s \end{cases}. \tag{23}$$

or, more simply, by the relation

$$L_s \equiv e^x \frac{d^s(x^s e^{-x})}{dx^s} = \sum_{p=0}^s (-1)^p C_p{}^s s(s-1) \cdots (p+1) x^p \tag{24}$$

$$\equiv (-1)^s \left(x^s - \frac{s^2}{1!} x^{s-1} + \frac{s^2(s-1)^2}{2!} x^{s-2} + \cdots + (-1)^s s! \right).$$

From this we find the first few polynomials to be

$$L_0 = 1, L_1 = 1 - x, L_2 = 2 - 4x + x^2, L_3 = 6 - 18x + 9x^2 - x^3. \tag{25}$$

The recursion formula of these polynomials is

$$L_{n+1} + (2n + 1 - x)L_n + n^2 L_{n-1} = 0. \tag{26}$$

The corresponding normalized functions are

$$\psi_n = e^{-x/2} \frac{L_n}{n!}, \ n = 0, 1, 2, \cdots. \tag{27}$$

To obtain the derivatives of the Laguerre polynomials, which occur in the theory of hydrogen, we use the second expression for L_s in equation (24). Differentiating t times, and writing $L_s{}^t$ for $d^t L_s / dx^t$, we have

$$L_s{}^t = s! \sum_{p=0}^{s-t} (-1)^{p+t} C^s{}_{s-t-p} \frac{x^p}{p!} \tag{28}$$

Some of these functions are listed in Chap. XVI. They are not themselves orthogonal, but the related set

$$x^l e^{-x/2} L_{n+l}^{2l+1}$$

which occur in the theory of hydrogen are found to enjoy this property over the range 0 to ∞.

Integrals of the type

$$\int_0^\infty x^p e^{-x} L_s{}^t(x) L_u{}^v(x) dx \tag{29}$$

have been treated by Schrödinger.[1] The more general integral

$$\int_0^\infty x^p e^{-(\alpha+\beta)x/2} L_s{}^t(\alpha x) L_u{}^v(\beta x) dx$$

can be evaluated in terms of the integrals of equation (29). The results are too lengthy to be quoted in detail. We encounter integrals of this kind in evaluating the intensities of the spectral lines of hydrogen.

[1] *Ann. Physik*, **80**, 437 (1926).

APPENDIX V

METHODS FOR DETERMINING CHARACTERISTIC ENERGY VALUES

The problem of finding the quantized energy values, for which ψ is finite, continuous, and single-valued, in other words, *acceptable*, is a broad one.

We must not expect that any single method will work in all cases. The method originally used by Schrödinger for the hydrogen atom was to obtain a very general expression for the part of ψ depending on r, in the form of a complex integral containing the constant E. A study of the properties of this integral then showed that it will not be an acceptable function except when E assumes the negative values given by the Balmer formula, or any positive value whatsoever. We now describe other methods which have much wider application. For simplicity we assume that the coordinates can be separated in the wave equation, so that we are confronted with an ordinary differential equation to determine a function F, of a single variable x, and that F must be finite, continuous, and single-valued over the range from minus infinity to plus infinity.

1. THE METHOD OF TERMINATING SERIES

A much used method, illustrated by our treatment of hydrogen, is to make a substitution of the type $F = IX$, where I vanishes at infinity, and is finite when x is finite, while X can be represented by a power series $\Sigma a_p x^p$ containing only positive integral powers. (Thus, in the H atom and in many other cases, F contains a factor $I = e^{-f(x)}x^s$ where $f(x)$ is positive for all physically allowable values of x, and s is a positive integer.) This solution will satisfy all requirements when x is finite, if the series terminates after a finite number of terms. Each coefficient a_p depends on the value of E, and of any other constants present in the original differential equation,

$$a_p = f(E, h, c \cdots). \tag{1}$$

To find the eigenwerte we must choose E-values which will make all the a's after a certain one vanish. Often it happens that the recursion formula for calculating later a's from earlier ones takes the simple form

$$a_{p+1} = c_p a_p, \tag{2}$$

where the coefficient c_p is a function of p, E, and universal constants. If E is so chosen that one of the c's vanishes, the series for X will terminate, e.g., if we choose E to make c_5 vanish, then $a_6 = 0$; therefore, $a_7 = 0$, and so on. Proceeding similarly with values of E which make other coefficients vanish, we obtain the complete set of eigenwerte. If the value of F remains finite or vanishes when $x \to \infty$ (due to the vanishing factor I), all requirements of the problem are met.

2. BECHERT'S METHOD

Bechert[1] has given a method which has the great advantage that the *eigenwerte are usually obtained without solving the wave equation*. It depends on a study of the way in which the solution behaves near singular points of the differential equation.

[1] *Ann. Physik*, **83**, 905 (1927).

i.e., points where its coefficients become either zero or infinite.   Two illustrations
will show the essential features of the method.

Harmonic Oscillator.—From Chap. XV, Sec. **9**, the equation for the oscillator is

$$\frac{d^2\psi}{dv^2} + (A - v^2)\psi = 0 \tag{3}$$

where $A = 2E/h\nu_0$.   This equation predicts a perfectly regular behavior for ψ
as long as the independent variable v is finite, but if v approaches $\pm \infty$, the behavior
of ψ must be examined in detail, because the coefficient of ψ becomes ∞.   Now when
v is very large, A can be neglected in comparison with v^2, and equation (3) reduces
to $\psi'' - v^2\psi = 0$.   Trying the solution $\psi = e^{\pm v^2/2}$, we get

$$\psi'' = (\pm 1 + v^2)$$

which is equal to $v^2\psi$, within a sufficient approximation for our purpose.   That is, ψ
behaves very nearly like $e^{\pm v^2/2}$ when v is large.   This is expressed by saying that
$e^{\pm v^2/2}$ is an asymptotic form for ψ when $v \to \infty$.   This gives us the hint that if we
make the substitution,

$$\psi = e^{-v^2/2}y,$$

then y will behave like a polynomial in the neighborhood of ∞.   The accurate
equation for y is

$$y'' - 2vy' + (A - 1)y = 0.$$

Let us use a new variable, $z = 1/v$, so that we can study the equation when z is very
small.   It becomes

$$z^4\frac{d^2y}{dz^2} + (2z^3 + 2z)\frac{dy}{dz} + \left(\frac{2E}{h\nu_0} - 1\right)y = 0.$$

Several terms may be neglected when z approaches zero, so that we have

$$2z\frac{dy}{dz} + \left(\frac{2E}{h\nu_0} - 1\right)y = 0,$$

in this region.   The integral of this is

$$y = cv^{(A-1)/2}.$$

To make this single-valued and to keep y finite when $v = 0$, we must have

$$\frac{A - 1}{2} = \frac{E}{h\nu_0} - \frac{1}{2} = \text{a positive integer, or zero;}$$

that is,

$$E_n = (n + \tfrac{1}{2})h\nu_0,$$

the energy values for the oscillator.

Briefly, the general procedure is this.   *Near singular points of the equation, certain
terms in the coefficients may be neglected.   The resulting equation is usually of simple
form and can be integrated immediately.   To make the solution single-valued, finite, and
continuous, E must be given definite values, the eigenwerte.*   The value of the method
arises from studying the solution only in a region where its behavior is especially
simple.

Another Illustration.—The differential equation of Legendre's polynomials is

$$(x^2 - 1)y'' + 2xy' + \lambda y = 0. \tag{4}$$

It is known[1] that solutions of this equation must be polynomials if they are to be finite
continuous, and single-valued in the interval -1 to $+1$.   We can determine λ so

---

[1] COURANT-HILBERT, p. 258, or the older editions of RIEMANN-WEBER's "Partielle
Differentialgeichungen."

that the solution will be a polynomial, by considering the state of affairs when $x = \infty$. We use the transformation $z = x^{-1}$, and study the behavior of the equation in the neighborhood of $z = 0$. It becomes

$$(z^{-2} - 1)\left(z^4 \frac{d^2y}{dz^2} + 2z^3 \frac{dy}{dz}\right) - 2z \frac{dy}{dz} + \lambda y = 0.$$

When z approaches zero this approximates the form,

$$z^2 \frac{d^2y}{dz^2} + \lambda y = 0.$$

Further in the region of large x (small z) the most important term in the polynomial solution of equation (4) is the highest power of x which it contains, say x^n. Substituting this in the last equation it takes the form

$$\lambda = -n(n + 1),\tag{5}$$

which gives the characteristic values of λ.

3. OTHER METHODS

Wentzel[1] has given a method which may be considered as a generalization of Sommerfeld's quantum conditions. It is both simple and convenient, but since its use involves the theory of functions we shall not discuss it here.

[1] *Z. Physik*, **38**, 515 (1926).

APPENDIX VI

APPLICATIONS OF THE CALCULUS OF VARIATIONS TO WAVE MECHANICS

In Chap. XV, Sec. 20, we met with the problem of making an integral of the form,

$$\int F dx dy dz dt, \tag{1}$$

assume an extreme value, where F is a function of the independent variables x, y, z, t, of the dependent variable u, and the first derivatives of u. We are given the form of the function F and the problem is to determine u in such a way as to make the integral a maximum or a minimum. (In what follows, we shall speak only of making it a minimum.) A problem of this kind generally has no meaning unless we agree to specify the values which u must take on the boundary of the region of integration, for otherwise we can choose values of u such that F will become infinite, thereby robbing the problem of its physical value and interest. It will suffice if we consider here the case where F depends on two independent variables x and y. The integral is taken over a two-dimensional region G in the xy plane, and values of u on the boundary are given. Our treatment is based on the very clear discussion given in Chap. IV of Courant and Hilbert's "Methoden der Mathematischen Physik." We write the integral in the form

$$I = \iint F(x, y, u, u_x, u_y) dx dy, \tag{2}$$

where

$$u_x = \frac{\partial u}{\partial x}, \text{ and } u_y = \frac{\partial u}{\partial y}.$$

Suppose now that U is the function which makes I assume its minimum value, and let $U + cv$ be another function which might be proposed as a possible form for u; c is a numerical parameter and v an arbitrary function of x and y. We may write

$$I(c) = \int F(x, y, U + cv, U_x + cv_x, U_y + cv_y) dx dy. \tag{3}$$

Because of the assumption that U is the function which makes I a minimum, we must have $dI/dc = 0$, when $c = 0$. Now by Taylor's theorem, since x and y are not changed $(dI/dc)_{c=0}$ is equal to

$$\left(\frac{\partial I}{\partial u}\right)_{u=U} v + \left(\frac{\partial I}{\partial u_x}\right)_{u=U} v_x + \left(\frac{\partial I}{\partial u_y}\right)_{u=U} v_y \tag{4}$$

and since differentiation with respect to c can be carried out under the integral sign this takes the form,

$$\iint \left(\frac{\partial F}{\partial U} v + \frac{\partial F}{\partial U_x} v_x + \frac{\partial F}{\partial U_y} v_y\right) dx dy = 0. \tag{5}$$

This is an equation which U must satisfy in order that I may be a minimum. For the validity of what follows, we must now assume that the boundary curve B has only a finite number of corners and that a line drawn parallel to either of the two coordinate axes will cut the curve in only a limited number of points. We consider the integration of the term $\frac{\partial F}{\partial U_x} \frac{\partial v}{\partial x}$ with respect to x. Integrating by parts, we have

$$\sum_i v(x_i') \frac{\partial F(x_i')}{\partial U_x} - \sum_i v(x_i'') \frac{\partial F(x_i'')}{\partial U_x} - \int v \frac{\partial}{\partial x}\left(\frac{\partial F}{\partial U_x}\right) dx,$$

where the significance of x'' and x' may be seen from the figure. Now integrating with respect to y the final result is

$$\iint \frac{\partial F}{\partial U_x}\frac{\partial v}{\partial x}dxdy = -\iint v\frac{\partial}{\partial x}\left(\frac{\partial F}{\partial U_x}\right)dxdy + \int_B v\frac{\partial F}{\partial U_x}\frac{dy}{ds}ds$$

where the boundary integral on the right is taken counterclockwise. The values of u are specified on the boundary and therefore v must vanish there, so that this integral is zero. We treat the third term of equation (5) similarly, and the condition for I to be a minimum reduces to

$$\iint v\left[\frac{\partial F}{\partial U} - \frac{\partial}{\partial x}\left(\frac{\partial F}{\partial U_x}\right) - \frac{\partial}{\partial y}\left(\frac{\partial F}{\partial U_y}\right)\right]dxdy = 0.$$

Since v is arbitrary, the factor in brackets must equal zero at every point of the region G. This gives us the Euler differential equation,

$$\frac{\partial F}{\partial U} - \frac{\partial}{\partial x}\left(\frac{\partial F}{\partial U_x}\right) - \frac{\partial}{\partial y}\left(\frac{\partial F}{\partial U_y}\right) = 0. \qquad (6)$$

This requires careful interpretation. In taking the partial derivative of $\partial F/\partial U_x$ with respect to x we must remember that this expression is a function of x in several

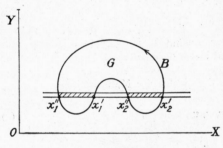

distinct ways. First, it may contain known functions of x; differentiation of these known functions will give rise to a term which we may write F_{U_xx}; second, it contains x implicitly through the presence of U, U_x, and U_y, all of which are themselves functions of x. Differentiation as to these intermediate variables will be indicated by the symbols F_{U_xU}, $F_{U_xU_x}$, and $F_{U_xU_y}$, respectively. We have, therefore,

$$\frac{\partial}{\partial x}\left(\frac{\partial F}{\partial U_x}\right) = F_{U_xx} + F_{U_xU}\frac{\partial U}{\partial x} + F_{U_xU_x}\frac{\partial U_x}{\partial y} + F_{U_xU_y}\frac{\partial U_y}{\partial x}.$$

The expression for the third term of equation (6) is similar. The problem is now reduced to finding a solution of equation (6) which will satisfy the boundary conditions. The extension to a larger number of variables is obvious.

By way of illustration, let us derive the relativistic wave equation by applying the variation principle proposed in Chap. XV, Sec. 20. It is assumed that the integral of equation (1) is to be made a minimum, where

$$F \equiv \left(\frac{\partial \Psi}{\partial x} - \frac{\epsilon}{c}\frac{A_x}{\mathbf{g}}\frac{\partial \Psi}{\partial t}\right)^2 + 2 \text{ similar terms in which } y \text{ and } z \text{ replace } x,$$

$$-\left(\frac{1}{c}\frac{\partial \Psi}{\partial t} - \frac{\epsilon}{c}\frac{\Phi}{\mathbf{g}}\frac{\partial \Psi}{\partial t}\right)^2 + \frac{m^2c^2}{\mathbf{g}^2}\left(\frac{\partial \Psi}{\partial t}\right)^2.$$

We write

$$\frac{\partial \Psi}{\partial x} = \Psi_x, \cdots \frac{\partial \Psi}{\partial t} = \Psi_t.$$

The Euler equation for Ψ is

$$\frac{\partial}{\partial x}\left(\frac{\partial F}{\partial \Psi_x}\right) + \cdots + \frac{\partial}{\partial t}\left(\frac{\partial F}{\partial \Psi_t}\right) - \frac{\partial F}{\partial \Psi} = 0.$$

Now

$$\frac{\partial F}{\partial \Psi_x} = 2\left(\frac{\partial \Psi}{\partial x} - \frac{\epsilon}{c}\cdot\frac{A_x}{\mathbf{g}}\cdot\frac{\partial \Psi}{\partial t}\right); \frac{\partial}{\partial x}\left(\frac{\partial F}{\partial \Psi_x}\right) = 2\left(\frac{\partial^2 \Psi}{\partial x^2} - \frac{\epsilon}{c}\frac{A_x}{\mathbf{g}}\frac{\partial^2 \Psi}{\partial x\partial t}\right).$$

Other terms are easily written by symmetry, and $\partial F/\partial \Psi = 0$. The result is equation (112) of Chap. XV.

APPENDIX VII

THE WAVE EQUATION IN CURVILINEAR COORDINATES

Some confusion may arise as to the proper form for Schrödinger's equation in curvilinear coordinates unless we pay careful attention to the definition of ψ in these coordinates. The whole subject has been clearly summarized by Podolsky[1] and parts of this section will follow his treatment. Since $\psi\psi^*$ has the significance of a probability, the value of ψ must be independent of the coordinate system used. In discussing the one-electron problem, we have used the relation $\int\psi\psi^*dv = 1$, where dv is an element of volume in a space where the coordinates x, y, z are equal to the actual Cartesian coordinates X, Y, Z of the electron multiplied by the square root of its mass. In these coordinates the wave equation is

$$\Delta\psi + \frac{8\pi^2}{h^2}(E - V)\psi = 0. \tag{1}$$

Then, on passing to polar coordinates which are related to x, y, and z by the usual transformation formulas, the normalization condition takes the form

$$\int\psi\psi^*r^2 \sin \theta dr d\varphi d\theta = 1. \tag{2}$$

The possibility of confusion arises from the fact that some authors use instead the function ψ_P which satisfies the relation

$$\int\psi_P\psi_P^*dr d\varphi d\theta = 1.$$

By comparison with equation (2), we see that

$$\psi_P = \psi(r^2 \sin \theta)^{1/2}.$$

Sometimes it is desirable to use ψ; at other times, our equations are simpler if written in terms of functions similar to ψ_P.

Another difficulty arises from the promulgation of false rules for obtaining the wave equations from the energy H. We shall have no trouble if we adhere to the variation principle in Chap. VX, Sec. 20 and to the wave equation derived from it. Now we have stated (Chap. XV, Sec. 10) that in Cartesian coordinates the wave equation can be derived from H by substituting

$$\frac{h}{2\pi i} \frac{\partial}{\partial x} \text{ for } p_x, \frac{h}{2\pi i} \frac{\partial}{\partial y} \text{ for } p_y, \text{ etc.}$$

If we express H in terms of other canonical variables p_r, q_r, write $\frac{h}{2\pi i} \frac{\partial}{\partial q_r}$ for p_r, and apply the resulting operator to a function F, we have a differential equation for F which is useful in Dirac's generalized wave theory (Chap. XVIII); but F is not ordinarily equal to ψ, for if we transform equation (1) into the coordinates q_r, we do not usually obtain the equation which defines F. The conclusion is, *we must not use the above process of substituting operators for momenta if we wish to obtain the equation for ψ in curvilinear coordinates. The correct process is to transform equation (1).*

To make our considerations quite general, we consider any system of coordinates $q_1 \ldots q_n$ in which the square of the element of arc is

$$ds^2 = \sum_j \sum_k g_{jk} dq_j dq_k. \tag{3}$$

[1] *Phys. Rev.*, **32**, 812 (1928).

We suppose, following Schrödinger, that each term contains a factor m, as mentioned above in the case of Cartesian coordinates, so that

$$ds^2 = 2T dt^2, \tag{4}$$

T being the kinetic energy. We define g to be the determinant formed from the elements g_{jk} drawn up in square array. Let g^{jk} equal $1/g$ multiplied by the cofactor of g_{jk} in this determinant. Then the appropriate generalization of equation (2) is

$$\int \psi \psi^* \sqrt{g}\, dq_1 \cdots dq_n = 1 \tag{5}$$

for the element of volume is $\sqrt{g}\, dq_1 \ldots dq_n$.[1] The general form for the wave equation (1) is

$$\frac{1}{\sqrt{g}}\sum_j \sum_k \frac{\partial}{\partial q_i}\left(\sqrt{g} g^{ik} \frac{\partial \psi}{\partial q_k}\right) + \frac{8\pi^2}{h^2}(E - V)\psi = 0. \tag{6}$$

If we wish to use the variable $W\left(= \dfrac{h}{2\pi i} \log \psi \right)$ in place of ψ, as we did in Chap. XV, Sec. 24, then equation (6) takes the form

$$\sum_j \sum_k g^{ik}\frac{\partial W}{\partial q_j}\frac{\partial W}{\partial q_k} + 2(V - E) = -\frac{h}{2\pi i}\sum_j \sum_k \frac{1}{\sqrt{g}}\frac{\partial}{\partial q_i}\left(\sqrt{g} g^{ik}\frac{\partial W}{\partial q_k}\right). \tag{6a}$$

The double sum on the left is simply the general form of $\operatorname{grad}^2 W$, while that on the right is ΔW; the whole equation reduces to the classical Hamilton-Jacobi equation if h approaches zero.

In spite of their complicated appearance the student will find that these equations usually lead to the wave equation with much less labor than that involved in direct transformation.

It is interesting to determine the form of $H(p, q)$ which will give equation (6) if we replace each p by the corresponding operator. Obviously, it is

$$H = \frac{1}{2\sqrt{g}}\sum_j \sum_k p_j \sqrt{g} g^{jk} p_k + V. \tag{7}$$

Podolsky[2] has also considered the differential equation for ψ_q, where

$$\int \psi_q \psi_q^* dq_1 \cdots dq_n = 1. \tag{8}$$

Comparison with equation (5) shows that

$$\psi_q = g^{1/4}\psi. \tag{9}$$

Using this relation in equation (6) we have

$$\frac{1}{2}\sum_j \sum_k g^{-1/4}\frac{h}{2\pi i}\frac{\partial}{\partial q_i}\left(g^{1/2} g^{ik}\frac{h}{2\pi i}\frac{\partial}{\partial q_k}g^{-1/4}\psi_q\right) + (V - E)\psi_q = 0. \tag{10}$$

By the method of substituting operators for momenta this can be derived from the function

$$H_q = \frac{1}{2}\sum_j \sum_k g^{-1/4} p_j g^{1/2} g^{jk} p_k g^{-1/4} + V. \tag{11}$$

The order of factors is important, of course, if we consider equations (7) and (11) as matrix equations.

[1] See Murnaghan's "Vector Analysis and the Theory of Relativity," The John Hopkins Press, Baltimore, for this and other geometrical formulas.

[2] *Loc. cit.*

APPENDIX VIII
USEFUL THEOREMS OF ELECTRODYNAMICS
1. MAXWELL'S EQUATIONS FOR FREE SPACE

We denote the components of the electric vector by E_x, E_y, and E_z, and those of the magnetic vector by H_x, H_y, and H_z. At any point the charge density is ρ and the velocity of the charge is **v**. For a space which is free of gross matter Maxwell's equations take the following form:

$$-\frac{1}{c}\frac{\partial H_x}{\partial t} = \frac{\partial E_z}{\partial y} - \frac{\partial E_y}{\partial z}, \tag{1}$$

(and two similar equations, obtained by cyclic permutation of x, y, and z);

$$\frac{\partial H_x}{\partial x} + \frac{\partial H_y}{\partial y} + \frac{\partial H_z}{\partial z} = 0; \tag{2}$$

$$\frac{1}{c}\left(4\pi\rho\dot{x} + \frac{\partial E_x}{\partial t}\right) = \frac{\partial H_z}{\partial y} - \frac{\partial H_y}{\partial z}, \tag{3}$$

(and two similar equations);

$$\frac{\partial E_x}{\partial x} + \frac{\partial E_y}{\partial y} + \frac{\partial E_z}{\partial z} = 4\pi\rho. \tag{4}$$

The magnetic vector potential obeys the relation

$$\mathbf{H} = \text{curl } \mathbf{A}, \text{ that is, } H_x = \frac{\partial A_z}{\partial y} - \frac{\partial A_y}{\partial z}, \text{ etc.} \tag{5}$$

(*Example.*—It can be shown by integrating equation (5) that one form for the vector potential of a uniform magnetic field directed along the z-axis is

$$A_x = -\frac{Hy}{2}, \; A_y = \frac{Hx}{2}, \; A_z = 0.) \tag{6}$$

When equation (5) holds true, we can show by using equation (1) that

$$E_x + \frac{1}{c}\frac{\partial A_x}{\partial t} = -\frac{\partial \Phi}{\partial x}, \text{ etc.} \tag{7}$$

The function Φ introduced in this manner is called the "electric potential," or the "scalar potential."

According to Lorentz, the force acting on a charge ϵ when it is exposed to an electric intensity **E** and a magnetic intensity **H** is $\epsilon\mathbf{F}$, where

$$\mathbf{F} = \mathbf{E} + \frac{1}{c}[\mathbf{vH}], \tag{8}$$

that is,

$$F_x = E_x + \frac{1}{c}(\dot{y}H_z - \dot{z}H_y), \text{ etc.} \tag{8a}$$

2. EQUATIONS OF MOTION OF A PARTICLE IN AN ELECTROMAGNETIC FIELD

The equations of motion of a particle of charge ϵ exposed to both electric and magnetic forces are

$$\frac{d}{dt}\left(\frac{m\dot{x}}{(1-\beta^2)^{1/2}}\right) = \epsilon\left(E_x + \frac{1}{c}[\mathbf{vH}]_x\right), \text{ etc.} \tag{9}$$

where m is the rest mass of the particle, and βc its velocity.

In case the term $-\dfrac{1}{c}\dfrac{\partial \mathbf{A}}{\partial t}$ in the electric vector $\mathbf{E}$ is equal to zero, the components of electric force are of the form $-\partial\Phi/\partial x$. The magnetic force $\dfrac{\epsilon}{c}[\mathbf{vH}]$ causes no change in the kinetic energy of the particle, because by definition, the vector $[\mathbf{vH}]$ is perpendicular to $\mathbf{v}$. Therefore, the energy equation takes the form

$$T + \epsilon\Phi = \text{constant}, \tag{10}$$

where T is the kinetic energy. The Lagrangian function, so useful in transforming the dynamical equations to other systems of coordinates is simply $T - \epsilon\Phi$; but in the general case where $\partial\mathbf{A}/\partial t$ is not zero, this expression is not correct. To determine the proper Lagrangian function, we try to throw equation (9) into the form

$$\frac{d}{dt}\frac{\partial L}{\partial \dot{x}} - \frac{\partial L}{\partial x} = 0,$$

and thus to determine the form of L by inspection. To do this, we replace $\mathbf{E}$ and $\mathbf{H}$ by their values in terms of the potentials. Then,

$$\frac{d}{dt}\left(\frac{m\dot{x}}{(1-\beta^2)^{1/2}}\right) = -\epsilon\frac{\partial\Phi}{\partial x} - \frac{\epsilon}{c}\frac{\partial A_x}{\partial t} + \frac{\epsilon}{c}\left[\dot{y}\left(\frac{\partial A_y}{\partial x} - \frac{\partial A_x}{\partial y}\right) - \dot{z}\left(\frac{\partial A_x}{\partial z} - \frac{\partial A_z}{\partial x}\right)\right]. \tag{11}$$

But

$$\frac{dA_x}{dt} = \frac{\partial A_x}{\partial x}\dot{x} + \frac{\partial A_x}{\partial y}\dot{y} + \frac{\partial A_x}{\partial z}\dot{z} + \frac{\partial A_x}{\partial t}.$$

We use the value of $\partial A_x/\partial t$ from this equation to eliminate it from equation (11), with the result

$$\frac{d}{dt}\left(\frac{m\dot{x}}{(1-\beta^2)^{1/2}} + \frac{\epsilon A_x}{c}\right) + \epsilon\frac{\partial\Phi}{\partial x} - \frac{\epsilon}{c}\left(\frac{\partial A_x}{\partial x}\dot{x} + \frac{\partial A_y}{\partial x}\dot{y} + \frac{\partial A_z}{\partial x}\dot{z}\right) = 0.$$

This suggests that we assume the relations

$$\frac{\partial L}{\partial \dot{x}} \equiv p_x = \frac{m\dot{x}}{(1-\beta^2)^{1/2}} + \frac{\epsilon A_x}{c}, \tag{12}$$

and

$$\frac{\partial L}{\partial x} = -\epsilon\frac{\partial\Phi}{\partial x} + \frac{\epsilon}{c}\left(\frac{\partial A_x}{\partial x}\dot{x} + \frac{\partial A_y}{\partial x}\dot{y} + \frac{\partial A_z}{\partial x}\dot{z}\right), \tag{13}$$

with similar equations for the other coordinates and momenta. By actual integration we find that these equations are consistent and that

$$L = mc^2(1 - (1-\beta^2)^{1/2}) - \epsilon\Phi + \frac{\epsilon}{c}\mathbf{Av}, \tag{14}$$

where $\mathbf{Av}$ denotes the scalar product of $\mathbf{A}$ and $\mathbf{v}$, that is,

$$A_x\dot{x} + A_y\dot{y} + A_z\dot{z}.$$

If other conservative forces not of electric origin are also acting, we must replace $\epsilon\Phi$ by the potential V, due to all the forces. The Hamiltonian function H is then obtained from the usual definition $H = \Sigma p\dot{q} - L$, where the p's are as defined in equation (12). We get

$$H = mc^2\left(\frac{1}{(1-\beta^2)^{1/2}} - 1\right) + V, \tag{15}$$

for the terms containing the A's conveniently disappear. However, this does not contain the p's, so we introduce them by eliminating β^2. Squaring and summing the three equations,

$$\frac{m\dot{x}}{(1-\beta^2)^{1/2}} = p_x - \frac{\epsilon A_x}{c}, \text{etc.,}$$

we have

$$\frac{\beta^2}{1-\beta^2} = \frac{1}{m^2c^2}\left[\left(p_x - \frac{\epsilon A_x}{c}\right)^2 + \left(p_y - \frac{\epsilon A_y}{c}\right)^2 + \left(p_z - \frac{\epsilon A_z}{c}\right)^2\right]. \tag{16}$$

Calling this quantity w^2 we find that

$$\frac{1}{(1 - \beta^2)} = 1 + w^2. \tag{17}$$

Therefore, H may be written

$$H = mc^2((1 + w^2)^{\frac{1}{2}} - 1) + V. \tag{18}$$

This is more conveniently expressed in the form

$$1 + w^2 = 1 + 2\frac{H - V}{mc^2} + \left(\frac{H - V}{mc^2}\right)^2,$$

that is

$$\left(p_x - \frac{\epsilon A_x}{c}\right)^2 + \left(p_y - \frac{\epsilon A_y}{c}\right)^2 + \left(p_z - \frac{\epsilon A_z}{c}\right)^2 = 2m(H - V) + \frac{(H - V)^2}{c^2}.$$

A more symmetrical form is obtained by using the total energy $\mathcal{E}$, which is the sum of H and the self-energy of the charge, mc^2. We have

$$\mathcal{E} = \frac{mc^2}{(1 - \beta^2)^{\frac{1}{2}}} + V,$$

whence

$$\left(\frac{\mathcal{E} - V}{c}\right)^2 = m^2c^2 + \frac{m^2v^2}{1 - \beta^2},$$

and using the value of $\dfrac{m^2v^2}{1 - \beta^2}$ from equation (16), we have

$$\sum_j \left(p_j - \frac{\epsilon}{c}A_j\right)^2 - \left(\frac{\mathcal{E} - V}{c}\right)^2 + m^2c^2 = 0, \tag{19}$$

where p_j stands for p_x, p_y, or p_z. The corresponding Hamilton-Jacobi equation is

$$\left(\frac{\partial W}{\partial x} - \frac{\epsilon}{c}A_x\right)^2 + \cdots - \frac{\left(\dfrac{\partial W}{\partial t} + V\right)^2}{c^2} + m^2c^2 = 0, \tag{20}$$

which is useful in deriving Schrödinger's wave equation.

3. LARMOR'S THEOREM[1]

This theorem describes the behavior of a system of particles, all having the same ratio of charge to mass (in sign as well as magnitude), in the presence of a constant uniform magnetic field **H**. It is supposed that in the absence of the field the particles move under the action of forces having a potential function which depends only on the coordinates. Then the theorem is, *the motion of the system is the same as it would be in the absence of the field, except that a uniform rotation around an axis parallel to the field is superposed, provided that effects proportional to the square and higher powers of* **H** *are neglected.*

A simple artifice enables us to apply the theorem to an atom even though the nucleus and the electrons have widely different e/m ratios; we assume the nucleus to be at rest and then to all intents and purposes it is excluded from the system. If we take the field **H** in the direction of the Z-axis, the equations of motion of an electron of charge $-e$ will be

$$\frac{d}{dt}(m\dot{x}) = -\frac{\partial V}{\partial x} - \frac{e}{c}\dot{y}H,$$

$$\frac{d}{dt}(m\dot{y}) = -\frac{\partial V}{\partial y} + \frac{e}{c}\dot{x}H,$$

$$\frac{d}{dt}(m\dot{z}) = -\frac{\partial V}{\partial z}. \tag{21}$$

---

[1] LARMOR's "Æther and Matter," p. 341; See BORN's "Atommechanik," pp. 240 and 270, and VAN VLECK's "Bulletin," p. 300.

We shall use the subscript i to distinguish the coordinates of the ith electron, and shall neglect the variation of mass with velocity. Introducing polar coordinates, the z-component of angular momentum of each electron is $mr^2 \sin^2 \theta \dot{\varphi}$. The angular momentum of the system is not constant, and in particular $p_z (\equiv p_\varphi)$ is variable. From equation (21),

$$\frac{d}{dt} \sum mr_i^2 \sin^2 \theta_i \dot{\varphi}_i = 2\pi m L \frac{d}{dt} \sum (x_i^2 + y_i^2) = \frac{d}{dt} \sum mr_i^2 \sin^2 \theta_i o^2$$

where

$$o = +\frac{eH}{2mc} = 2\pi L \qquad (22)$$

Since

$$\frac{d}{dt} \sum mr_i^2 \sin^2 \theta_i (\dot{\varphi}_i - o) = 0,$$

it is natural to use polar coordinates r, θ, χ, precessing about the z-axis with angular speed o. Then,

$$\dot{\chi}_i = \dot{\varphi}_i - o, \ \chi_i = \varphi_i - ot, \qquad (23)$$

and

$$\Sigma mr_i^2 \sin^2 \theta_i \dot{\chi}_i = p_\chi = \text{constant}.$$

If x', y', z' are Cartesian coordinates in the moving frame of reference,

$$\begin{aligned} x &= x' \cos ot - y' \sin ot, \\ y &= x' \sin ot + y' \cos ot. \end{aligned} \qquad (24)$$

To transform the equations of motion we note that

$$m\frac{d}{dt}(\dot{x} + 2oy) = -\frac{\partial V}{\partial x}, \ m\frac{d}{dt}(\dot{y} - 2ox) = -\frac{\partial V}{\partial y}.$$

From equation (24) we obtain

$$\frac{d}{dt}(\dot{x} + 2oy) = (\ddot{x}' + o^2 x') \cos ot - (\ddot{y}' + o^2 y) \sin ot$$

$$\frac{d}{dt}(\dot{y} - 2ox) = (\ddot{x}' + o^2 x') \sin ot + (\ddot{y}' + o^2 y') \cos ot.$$

By easy elimination of the terms containing ot, we find for each electron,

$$\begin{aligned} m\ddot{x}' &= -\frac{\partial V}{\partial x'} - mo^2 x', \\ m\ddot{y}' &= -\frac{\partial V}{\partial y'} - mo^2 y', \\ m\ddot{z}' &= -\frac{\partial V}{\partial z'}. \end{aligned} \qquad (25)$$

The motion of each electron may be accurately described as due to forces which have the potential

$$V + \tfrac{1}{2} mo^2 (x'^2 + y'^2).$$

Now V depends only on the relative positions of the particles and on their distances from the origin. None of these quantities are altered on passing to the moving system. In fact, $V(x', y', \text{etc.})$ involves the moving coordinates in precisely the same way as $V(x, y, \text{etc.})$ involves the resting coordinates. For a field of 10^4 gauss, and for the nth orbits of the hydrogen atom, $-\frac{\partial V}{\partial x'}$ exceeds $mo^2 x'$ by a factor of roughly $2.10^{11}/n^6$. Therefore, if we neglect the relatively insignificant terms in o^2 which are proportional to H^2, equations (25) predict that in the moving system the motions will be identical with those which would be performed in the absence of the field, which proves Larmor's theorem. For diatomic molecules the theorem holds true only in the very special case in which the nuclei remain permanently in a line parallel to the field.

It is worth noting that the Larmor precession of a negative charge is clockwise for an observer looking along the direction of the lines of force.

4. ENERGY, MOMENTUM, AND ENERGY FLOW IN THE ELECTROMAGNETIC FIELD

We are familiar with the idea that the energy of a system of charges, magnets, and currents may be considered as residing in the whole of space, the energy density at any point being

$$\frac{(KE^2 + \mu H^2)}{8\pi}, \tag{26}$$

K being the dielectric constant and μ the magnetic permeability. It is customary to think of the term containing E^2 as potential energy, and of the term in H^2 as kinetic energy. The time rate of change of the integral representing the total energy localized inside an arbitrary closed surface is composed of two terms. One of these represents the rate at which work is performed by the currents which flow inside the surface; the other can be written as a surface integral, and may be interpreted as the rate at which energy enters the volume under consideration. Suppose we write

$$S_x = \frac{c}{4\pi}(E_y H_z - E_z H_y), \text{ etc.} \tag{27}$$

or

$$\mathbf{S} = \frac{c}{4\pi}[\mathbf{EH}].$$

Then the quantities S_x, S_y, and S_z are the components of Poynting's vector, which represents the flow of energy across unit surface per unit of time, both in magnitude and in direction. The magnitude of the flow is

$$S = \frac{cEH \sin\theta}{4\pi} \tag{28}$$

where θ is the angle between the electric and the magnetic vectors.

The pressure due to radiation, and other effects which depend on the transfer of energy, are explained with perfect success if we assume that the momentum associated with an element of volume dv is

$$\frac{S dv}{c^2}. \tag{29}$$

5. RADIATION FROM A MOVING CHARGE

To obtain the rate of radiation of energy by a moving charge, we first determine the Poynting vector at every point of a surface surrounding it and then integrate the flow of energy over this surface.

To begin with, there will be no radiation from a charge moving with uniform velocity, for if we take our stand on a system of reference moving with the charge it will be at rest, and will possess zero magnetic field at every point in space. Therefore, the Poynting vector will everywhere be zero and the energy of the charge will be constant. Retransforming to the original system of coordinates, the intrinsic energy of the charge will still appear to be constant. Therefore, we pass at once to a study of an accelerated charge. For simplicity, we take the surface surrounding the charge to be a sphere with center at the origin and radius large compared with the wave length of the radiation. Let the charge be at the origin at time $t = -r/c$, where r is the radius of the sphere, and let its acceleration a be parallel to the Z-axis. The radiation which it emits while at the origin will reach any point P on the surface of the sphere when $t = 0$. Let the coordinates of P be r, θ, φ. The expressions for the field at P are given in Abraham's "Theorie der Elektrizitat," volume I, page 329. If r is so great that terms in higher powers of $1/r$ may be neglected in comparison with the term containing $1/r$ itself, then the electric and magnetic fields at P will have the magnitude

$$E = H = \frac{e \sin\theta \ a}{c^2 r}. \tag{30}$$

Further, **H** is tangent to the small circle, $\theta = $ constant, in Fig. 2, Chap. I, and **E** is tangent to the great circle $\varphi = $ constant, so that they are at right angles. The Poynting vector is, therefore,

$$S = \frac{c}{4\pi}(EH) = \frac{e^2 \sin^2 \theta \ a^2}{4\pi c^3 r^2}.$$

The instantaneous rate of flow of energy through the zone between θ and $\theta + d\theta$ is,

$$S \cdot 2\pi r^2 \sin \theta d\theta$$

and the rate at which the charge is losing energy is the integral of this expression;

$$\frac{a^2 e^2}{2c^3} \int_0^\pi \sin^3\theta \ d\theta = \frac{2e^2 a^2}{3c^3}. \tag{31}$$

We are now in a position to determine the radiation from a harmonic oscillator which obeys the equation of motion $z = A \cos 2\pi\nu t$. To be sure, the oscillator is at the origin only an infinitesimal fraction of the time, but if the amplitude A is very small compared with r and the velocity is small compared with c, then we can calculate the rate of radiation by the formulas above which apply to a charge at the origin, without introducing appreciable error. With this understanding, we write $a^2 = (2\pi\nu)^4 A^2 \cos^2 (2\pi\nu t)$. Substituting in equation (31) and averaging with respect to time we find that the mean rate of radiation is

$$-\frac{\overline{dE}}{dt} = \frac{(2\pi\nu)^4 e^2 A^2}{3c^3} = \frac{(2\pi)^4 e^2 A^2 c}{3\lambda^4}, \tag{32}$$

a formula which is the basis of all calculations of spectral intensities. If z is given by a sum of terms of the type $A_i \cos 2\pi\nu(t - \delta_i)$ where the ν's are quite arbitrary, so that the series is not in general a Fourier series, then the total radiation is simply a sum of terms of the type in equation (32); for in taking the time average of a^2 the integrals of cross-product terms such as $\cos 2\pi\nu_i(t - \delta_i) \cos 2\pi\nu_j(t - \delta_j)$ will be zero. Physically, this means that on the average the emission of light of one frequency is not influenced by the simultaneous emission of other frequencies.

6. THE RELATIVITY TRANSFORMATION

Let an observer move parallel to the x-axis with velocity $v = \beta c$, and let his x-axis be parallel to our own. If we distinguish quantities measured in his frame of reference by providing them with primes then the relation between his geometry and our own is found to be

$$x' = k(x - vt), \ y' = y, \ z' = z, \ t' = k\left(t - \frac{vx}{c^2}\right), \tag{33}$$

where

$$k = \frac{1}{(1 - \beta^2)^{1/2}}.$$

This is the Lorentz transformation, and the Maxwellian equations (1) to (4) are said to be invariant under this transformation. The type of invariance referred to will be made clear by the following considerations:

If f is any function of x, y, z, and t, we have

$$\frac{\partial f}{\partial x} = \frac{\partial f}{\partial x'}\frac{\partial x'}{\partial x} + \frac{\partial f}{\partial t'}\frac{\partial t'}{\partial x} = k\left(\frac{\partial f}{\partial x'} - \frac{v}{c^2}\frac{\partial f}{\partial t'}\right);$$

and similarly, we find

$$\frac{\partial f}{\partial y} = \frac{\partial f}{\partial y'}; \frac{\partial f}{\partial z} = \frac{\partial f}{\partial z'}; \frac{\partial f}{\partial t} = k\left(\frac{\partial f}{\partial t'} - v\frac{\partial f}{\partial x'}\right).$$

We use these relations to transform Maxwell's equation into the primed coordinates. It is then found that the transformed equations will take the *same form* as the original ones provided we write

$$
\begin{aligned}
H_x' &= H_x, & E_x' &= E_x, \\
H_y' &= k\left(H_y + \frac{v}{c}E_z\right), & E_y' &= k\left(E_y - \frac{v}{c}H_z\right), \\
H_z' &= k\left(H_z - \frac{v}{c}E_y\right), & E_z' &= k\left(E_z + \frac{v}{c}H_y\right).
\end{aligned}
\tag{34}
$$

The vectors $\mathbf{E}'$ and $\mathbf{H}'$ possess all the physical characteristics they should have in order that the moving observer may be justified in calling them the electric and magnetic intensities. This is insured by the fact that they are determined by Maxwell's equations in the primed coordinates. The formulas for $\mathbf{E}$ and $\mathbf{H}$ in terms of $\mathbf{E}'$ and $\mathbf{H}'$ are obtained if we change the sign of v and interchange the primed and unprimed coordinates in equation (34). A similar remark holds true for obtaining the unprimed coordinates in terms of the primed ones. From equation (33) we have

$$x = k(x' + vt'),\ y = y',\ z = z', t = k\left(t' + \frac{vx'}{c^2}\right).\tag{33a}$$

APPENDIX IX

PHYSICAL CONSTANTS AND CONVERSION TABLE

The following values of physical constants have been adopted in this book:[1]

c (velocity of light).................. $(2.99796 \pm 0.00004) \, 10^{10}$ cm. sec.$^{-1}$

h (Planck's constant)............... $(6.547 \pm 0.008) \, 10^{-27}$ erg. seconds

M_H (mass of H atom).............. $(1.6618 \pm 0.0017) \, 10^{-24}$ grams

$M = M_0/16$ (mass of atom of unit atomic weight).................. $(1.6490 \pm 0.0016) \, 10^{-24}$ grams

m_0 (mass of electron, spectroscopic).. $(9.035 \pm 0.010) \, 10^{-28}$ grams

m_0 (mass of electron, deflection)..... $(8.994 \pm 0.014) \, 10^{-28}$ grams

e/M_H............................ $(9,574.5 \pm 0.7)$ absolute em. units

M_H/m_0.......................... $1,839 \pm 1$ (spectroscopic) or $1,848 \pm 2$ (deflection)

a_0 (radius of first Bohr orbit of H)... $(0.5284_5 \pm 0.0004) \, 10^{-8}$ cm.

F (Faraday)...................... $96,494 \pm 5$ international coulomb per gram equivalent

$9,648.9 \pm 0.7$ absolute em. units per gram equivalent

e (electronic charge)............... $(4.770 \pm 0.005) \, 10^{-10}$ absolute es units

$(1.5911 \pm 0.0016) \, 10^{-20}$ absolute em units

e/m (spectroscopic)................. $(1.761 \pm 0.001) \, 10^7$ absolute em units per gram

$(5.279 \pm 0.003) \, 10^{17}$ absolute es units per gram

e/m (deflection).................... $(1.769 \pm 0.002) \, 10^7$ absolute em units per gram

$(5.303 \pm 0.006) \, 10^{17}$ abs. es units per gram

R_H (Rydberg constant of hydrogen).. $109,677.759 \pm 0.05$ cm.$^{-1}$

R_{He} (Rydberg constant of ionized helium)........................ $109,722.403 \pm 0.05$ cm.$^{-1}$

R (Rydberg constant for infinite mass) $109,737.42 \pm 0.06$ cm.$^{-1}$

Gram molecular volume, S.T.P....... $(22.4141 \pm 0.0008) \, 10^3$ cm.^{3} mole^{-1}

N (Avogadro's number)............ $F/e = (6.064 \pm 0.006) \, 10^{23}$ mole^{-1}

n (Loschmidt's number)............ $(2.705_6 \pm 0.003) \, 10^{19}$ cm.$^{-3}$ (at 0°C. atm)

R_0 (gas constant per mole)......... $(8.3136 \pm 0.0010) \, 10^7$ erg-deg.$^{-1}$ mole^{-1}

k (Boltzmann constant)............ $(1.3709 \pm 0.0014) \, 10^{-16}$ erg-deg.$^{-1}$

$c_2{}^1$ (second radiation constant)....... 1.4317 ± 0.0006 cm.-deg.

σ^1 (radiation constant)............. $\dfrac{2\pi^5 k^4}{15c^2 h^3} = (5.714 \pm 0.006) \, 10^{-5}$ erg cm.$^{-2}$ deg.$^{-4}$ sec.$^{-1}$

a^*................................ $\dfrac{4\sigma}{c} = (7.624 \pm 0.007) \, 10^{-15}$ erg cm.$^{-3} \cdot$ deg.$^{-4}$

d' (true grating constant of calcite at 20°C.)......................... $(3.0283 \pm 0.0010) \, 10^{-8}$ cm.

[1] These are the values given by BIRGE as the best values at present (*Phys. Rev. Supplement.* **1**, 1 (1929).)

* See Chap. III, Sec. **2**.

α (fine structure constant)........... $\dfrac{2\pi e^2}{hc} = (7.284 \pm 0.006)\ 10^{-3}$

$1/\alpha$.............................. 137.29 ± 0.11

α^2.............................. $(5.305 \pm 0.008)\ 10^{-5}$

h/e.............................. $(1.3725 \pm 0.0005)\ 10^{-17}\ \text{erg} \cdot \text{sec} \cdot \text{es}^{-1}$

$\beta = h/k$.......................... $(4.7757 \pm 0.0019)\ 10^{-11}\ \text{sec} \cdot \text{deg.}$

Band spectrum constant $= h/8\pi^2 c$ $(27.66 \pm 0.04)\ 10^{-40}$ gram cm.

Energy in calories per mole equivalent to one absolute volt-electron per molecule........................ $23{,}055 \pm 4$ cal. mole^{-1}

$\tfrac{3}{2}kT$ at 0°C...................... $(5.617_5 \pm 0.006)\ 10^{-14}$ erg

Wave length of the red Cd line in air at 15°C. 1 atm.................. 6,438.4696 I. A. (defines I. A. unit)

The following conversion factors are frequently used in considering atomic and molecular problems.

E = energy per molecule in ergs.

E' = energy per mole in 15° small calories.

$\tilde{\nu}$ = wave number = ν/c.

V = electron-volts.

In order to change from an energy expressed in one of these units to its equivalent expressed in any other unit, multiply the number expressed in the units as given at the top of the table by the number beneath it and opposite the symbol for the units desired. There is an uncertainty of at least one in the first inferior figure. The logarithms are given uniformly to five places though in most cases the use of these places is not justified by the precision with which the constant is known.

	E	E'	ν	$\tilde{\nu}$	V
E	1	$6.90_1 \times 10^{-17}$ $(0.83893{-}17)$	$6.54_7 \times 10^{-27}$ $(0.81604{-}27)$	$1.96_{28} \times 10^{-16}$ $(0.29288{-}16)$	$1.59_{11} \times 10^{-12}$ $(0.20170{-}12)$
E'	$1.44_9 \times 10^{16}$ (16.16107)	1	$9.48_6 \times 10^{-11}$ $(0.97709{-}11)$	2.84_4 (0.45393)	$2.305_5 \times 10^4$ (4.36277)
ν	$1.52_7 \times 10^{26}$ (26.18396)	$1.05_4 \times 10^{10}$ (10.02291)	1	$2.9979_6 \times 10^{10}$ (10.47683)	$2.430_3 \times 10^{14}$ (14.38566)
$\tilde{\nu}$	$5.09_5 \times 10^{15}$ (15.70712)	$3.51_6 \times 10^{-1}$ $(0.54607{-}1)$	$3.3356_0 \times 10^{-11}$ $(0.52317{-}11)$	1	$8.10_6 \times 10^3$ (3.90883)
V	$6.28_5 \times 10^{11}$ (11.79830)	$4.337_5 \times 10^{-5}$ $(0.63723{-}5)$	$4.11_{47} \times 10^{-15}$ $(0.61434{-}15)$	$1.233_6 \times 10^{-4}$ $(0.09117{-}4)$	1

SUBJECT INDEX

A

B

767

N

AUTHOR INDEX

A

Abegg, 4
Abraham, M., 157, 762
Aich, 488
Allen, H. S., 96, 167
Allison, 713
Ames, 618
Anderson, 483
Andrade, 16, 48, 52, 733
Andrews, 446
Angerer, 513
Anslow, 477
Aoyama, 269
Appleyard, 478
Armstrong, 713
Aronberg, 352
Aston, 32, 35, 37, 39, 42, 52

B

Babcock, 315
Back, 96, 147, 316, 321, 329, 332, 351, 709
Bäcklin, 266
Badger, 371
Bagley, 2
Balmer, 70
Baly, 342
Barkla, 222, 236, 244
Bartlett, 463
Barton, 462
Bates, J., 403, 509, 511
Batho, 82
Bauer, E., 86
Baxter, 482
Beams, 64, 83
Bechert, 334, 750
Beck, 44
Becker, 346
Becquerel, 19
Beeck, 488
Bergmann, 184
Berthoud, 17
Bestelmeyer, 26
Bethe, 734

Beutler, 504
Bevan, 185
Bichowsky, 96, 507
Bieler, 50
Biltz, 42
Bingham, R., 224
Birge, 377, 383, 390, 396, 399, 408, 417, 426, 447, 472, 513, 680, 764
Birtwistle, 16, 558, 600, 615, 709
Bjerrum, 374
Black, 466
Blackett, 21, 52, 475
Blake, 65
Bleeker (Miss), 712
Boeckner, 470
Bohr, 5, 14, 50, 65, 69, 89, 90, 124, 132, 139, 147, 155, 168, 171, 194, 202, 251, 252, 253, 270, 274, 283, 293, 294, 617, 620
Boltwood, 31
Boltzmann, 1, 490
Bongers, 711
Bonhoeffer, 434, 483, 511
Born, 117, 121, 153, 194, 197, 392, 399, 519, 544, 551, 553, 558, 585, 587, 593, 600, 603, 609, 622, 623, 629, 643, 646, 678, 759
Bothe, 51, 88, 622
Bowen, 206, 278, 350
Boyce, 461
Brackett, 70, 123
Bragg, W. H., 225, 229, 231, 269
Bragg, W. L., 225, 231, 269
Bramley, 556
Brasefield, 463
Bredig, 462
Breit, 84, 326, 336, 354, 359
Brickwedde, 84, 364
Bridgman, 489, 618
Brillouin, 17, 550, 551, 556, 568
Brode, 486
Bronk, 375, 383, 437,
Brönsted, 33, 291
Brüche, 486
Bucherer, 26

783